S0-ARK-485

Teacher's Manual

Food for Today

Eighth Edition

Helen Kowtaluk

Alice Orphanos Kopan, M.Ed., M.A., CFCS

New York, New York Columbus, Ohio Chicago, Illinois Peoria, Illinois Woodland Hills, California

Interior Design
DesignNet

Additional Interior Design
Gorman & Associates Inc.

Photo Credits
Corbis/Westlight
  Fotografia TM-11
Tim Fuller Photographers TM-9, TM-15
Joe Mallon Photography TM-12
Paul Rico Photography TM-5, TM-10

Brand Disclaimer

Publisher does not necessarily recommend or endorse any particular company or brand name product that may be discussed or pictured in this text. Brand name products are used because they are readily available, likely to be known to the reader, and their use may aid in the understanding of the text. Publisher recognizes other brand name or generic products may be substituted and work as well or better than those featured in the text.

Internet Disclaimer

The material in the ***Food for Today*** *Teacher Wraparound Edition* includes references to Internet Web sites that may provide information related to the text. Since these sites are not under the control of Glencoe/McGraw-Hill, the text publisher makes no representation concerning the content of the sites. Some sites could contain links to other sites that have inappropriate material. Teachers are strongly encouraged to preview Internet sites before referring students to them. Since sites may move, be discontinued, or be under construction, some of those listed may no longer be accessible.

The McGraw-Hill Companies

Send all inquiries to:
Glencoe/McGraw-Hill
3008 W. Willow Knolls Drive
Peoria, Illinois 61614-1083

ISBN 0-07-846292-4 (Student Edition)
ISBN 0-07-846297-5 (Teacher Wraparound Edition)
Printed in the United States of America
2 3 4 5 6 7 8 9 071 07 06 05 04 03

Contributing Writers

Linda R. Glosson, Ph.D., CFCS
Family & Consumer Sciences Teacher
Wylie High School
Wylie, Texas

Nanci M. Burkhart
Family & Consumer Sciences Teacher
Hueneme High School
Oxnard, California

Anna Sue Couch, Ed.D.
Professor
Family & Consumer Sciences Education
Texas Tech University
Lubbock, Texas

Brenda Barrington Mendiola, M.S., CFCS
Curriculum Director
Irion Co. ISD
Mertzon, Texas

Connie R. Sasse, M.Ed. CFCS
Family & Consumer Sciences Author
Overland Park, Kansas

Lynn E. Steil, M.S.
Science Teacher
Dowagiac Union Schools
Dowagiac, Michigan

The *Food for Today* Program

The ***Food for Today*** program provides the materials you need for secondary foods and nutrition courses. All components are introduced here and described in greater detail on the pages that follow.

- **Student Edition.** The foundation of the ***Food for Today*** program is the 720-page student edition. Besides the basics of nutrition, consumer skills, and food preparation, the text covers food science, global foods, safety, wellness, and more.
- **Teacher Wraparound Edition.** Complete lesson plans, including activities, projects, and supplemental information, are "wrapped" around the pages of the student edition in this resource for the teacher.
- **Student Workbook.** Chapter study guides in the workbook are divided into sections that correspond to those in the text. An activity is included for each of the 90 sections. The *Teacher Annotated Edition* of the *Student Workbook* has answers printed right on the pages.
- **Student Motivation Kit.** This collection of reproducible resources contains six individual booklets on special topics: *Skills for Making Food Choices, Foods Lab Resources, A Global Foods Tour, Reteaching Activities, Food Science Resources,* and *Enrichment Activities.*
- **Teacher Resource Guide.** The reproducible pages in this 288-page book include lesson plan organizers, chapter tests, section quizzes, and eight sample color transparencies with teaching suggestions.
- **Effective Instruction CD-ROM.** The CD-ROM contains three components to make teaching easier. With the **Exam***View*® *Test Generator,* you can create tests and quizzes. The lesson plans provided in Word for Windows® can be modified to suit your needs. PowerPoint® slides of the color transparencies enliven your class presentations.
- **Transparency Package.** These 56 ready-to-use color transparencies focus on key concepts. Each one corresponds to a section of the text.

Food for Today has long been recognized for its well-organized coverage of the content needed for foods and nutrition courses. As you explore and teach with ***Food for Today,*** you'll see many reasons why this text has become a classic in the field.

Flexible Organization

Food for Today is organized for easy use. The twenty-five chapters are divided among five units, with each chapter subdivided into sections. This arrangement offers you the flexibility to choose and sequence sections to fit your specific course.

UNIT 4
Foods for Meals and Snacks
Chapter 15 Convenience Foods
Chapter 16 Vegetables and Fruits
Chapter 17 Grains, Legumes, Nuts, and Seeds
Chapter 18 Dairy Foods and Eggs
Chapter 19 Meat, Poultry, Fish, and Shellfish
Chapter 20 Food Combinations
Chapter 21 Baking

Food for Today is divided into five units. Each unit opener lists the chapters contained in the unit.

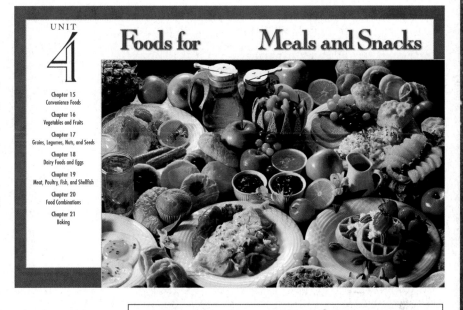

Motivating Visual Elements

Hundreds of photographs, illustrations, and charts give ***Food for Today*** eye appeal. Just as important, the visuals support text content with direct links to discussions. They show processes and provide examples. Visuals help students connect what they read with real life. Captions add to the value of visuals by expanding content and providing questions for discussion as well as activity ideas.

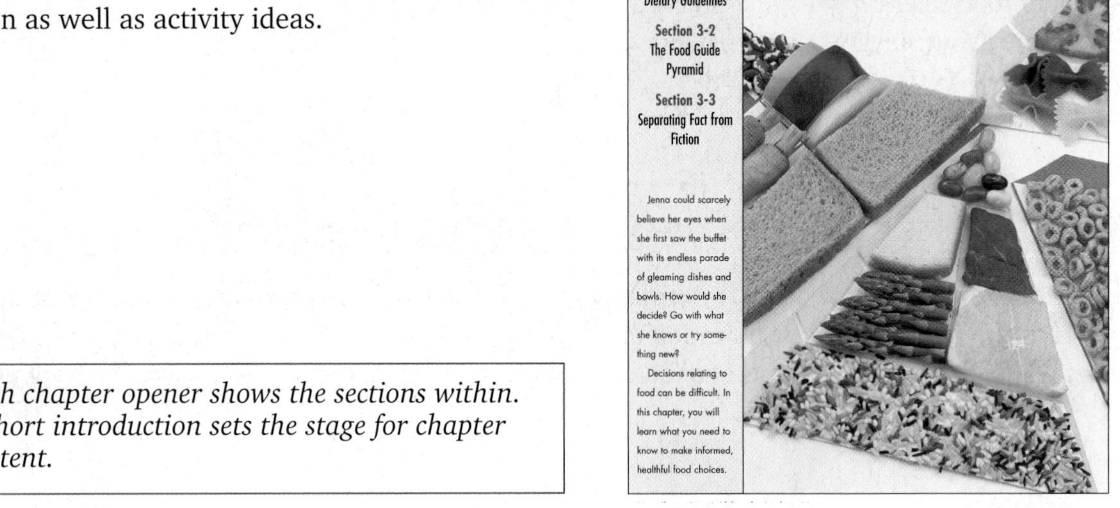

Each chapter opener shows the sections within. A short introduction sets the stage for chapter content.

Most sections are four to eight pages long. Openers list objectives and vocabulary terms. These terms are highlighted and defined in the text. At the end of the section, review questions and activities are supplied.

SECTION 1-1

Objectives

After studying this section, you should be able to:

- Describe the importance of nutrition and wellness.
- Explain how food helps meet physical and psychological needs.

Look for These Terms

nutrients

nutrition

wellness

psychological

Food and Health

If you were asked to identify the three things you need most to survive, how would you respond? Probably, one of your answers would be "food." Food is basic to life. When your body needs food, it lets you know. It registers as an empty feeling in your stomach. You know this feeling better as hunger.

Physical Needs

Food does more than stop hunger pangs. It supplies you with **nutrients**, chemicals from food that your body uses to carry out its functions. These chemicals are so important that they have given rise to a branch of science. That science, called **nutrition**, is the study of nutrients and how they are used by the body.

You have probably also seen or heard the term *nutrition* used in a more popular sense to refer to the effects of a person's food choices on his or her health. If your food choices provide all the nutrients you need in the right amounts, you are said to be practicing good nutrition.

Good nutrition has many benefits. When your body has needed nutrients, you not only feel and look your best, but you also grow and become strong. Your brain works as it should to maximize your thinking skills. In addition, you stay energetic and healthy, both now and later in life.

Strong Content

A glance through the ***Food for Today*** table of contents confirms that the text addresses the breadth of foods and nutrition. *Unit 1* provides a strong nutrition emphasis. *Unit 2* teaches students to work in the kitchen, using tools, recipes, and safe methods. Students explore consumer decisions in *Unit 3* as they learn about planning meals and shopping for food. *Unit 4* provides information on all types of foods, including preparation. In *Unit 5* students discover ethnic foods from around the world. Special career pages provide opportunities for students to learn about careers in food-related fields. Because this is only a glimpse at the ***Food for Today*** content, you'll need a closer look to see all that the text has to offer.

Special Features

Special features throughout ***Food for Today*** allow students to explore food science, get some practical advice, or learn more about staying healthy. Featured themes are easily recognized by the design of each feature box.

Safety Check

The ***Safety Check*** features allow safety information to stand out in the text. They draw attention to precautions that will help prevent accidents and foodborne illness.

The ***Q&A*** features present questions along with practical answers. These features extend the text, offering ideas that students can try themselves.

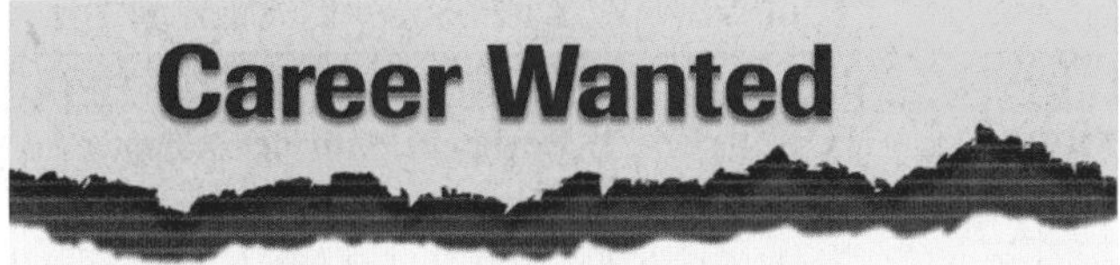

In the **Career Wanted** features at the end of each chapter, students meet people whose careers are food related. A career-connection activity links the work world to what students have learned. Experiences include interviews, job shadowing, and volunteering, as well as career investigation.

Recipe File

The **Recipe File** features contain recipes to use in the foods lab. Additional recipes are located in the *Foods Lab Resources* booklet in the *Student Motivation Kit.* Recipes have been chosen for their reasonable preparation times, appropriate skill level, and teen appeal. Ingredients are listed in metric and English. Clear, step-by-step directions and nutrition information are also provided. Questions at the end of each recipe connect text content to the recipe and can be used as a teaching tool before or after the lab.

The **Close-Up on Science** features show how food and nutrition topics relate to concepts in biology, chemistry, biochemistry, and physics.

Food Science ◆ LAB ◆

The **Food Science Lab** features are complete, self-contained mini-labs. Procedures and questions aim students toward meaningful conclusions.

For Your Health features suggest ways to incorporate nutrition and fitness in everyday living. The tips are followed by a brief activity or a set of critical thinking questions that reinforce the ideas.

Connecting Food and ...

The **Connecting** features integrate text content with other curriculum areas: health, mathematics, language arts, and social studies. A brief activity or a set of critical thinking questions completes each feature.

The **Infolink** features highlight important terms and phrases. A section reference points to an area of the text where more information can be found.

Chapter Review & Activities

To get the most from studying a chapter, students can use the Chapter Review & Activities. These two pages are located at the end of each chapter.

Chapter 3 Review & Activities

Summary

Section 3-1: Dietary Guidelines

- The Dietary Guidelines for Americans provide the following recommendations: Eat a variety of foods; maintain or improve your weight; choose an eating plan with plenty of grain products, vegetables and fruits; choose an eating plan low in fat, saturated fat, and cholesterol and moderate in sugars, salt, and sodium.

Section 3-2: The Food Guide Pyramid

- The Food Guide Pyramid, a tool to help you plan daily food choices, shows the approximate number of servings needed each day from each of the five food groups.
- The foods in the Food Guide Pyramid are grouped according to the nutrients they provide.
- Choosing nutrient-dense foods from the food groups will help you get the nutrients you need without excess calories.

Section 3-3: Separating Fact from Fiction

- Food-related skills, including critical thinking and communication, can help you identify information that may be misleading.
- It is important to stay informed about nutrition research, but use food-related skills to evaluate research findings.
- Advertisers use a variety of techniques to persuade you to buy their products.
- Be wary of food myths and fads, and know where to get accurate information about nutrition.

Checking Your Knowledge

1. What are the recommended limits for fat and saturated fat in an eating plan?
2. What are the benefits of choosing an eating plan with plenty of grain products, vegetables, and fruits?
3. Explain how the position of food groups in the Food Guide Pyramid diagram relates to the recommended number of servings of each.
4. Why does the Food Guide Pyramid give the recommended number of servings for each food group as a range instead of an exact number?
5. Briefly describe the main nutrients provided by each food group.
6. What problems are associated with excess sodium? Give three hints for cutting down on salt and sodium.
7. Why is it important to watch for follow-up reports on research findings?
8. Name three techniques used by advertisers to persuade you to buy their products.
9. What makes an infomercial misleading?
10. How can you tell whether the author of a book on nutrition is a reliable source of information on the subject?

Review & Activities Chapter 3

Thinking Critically

1. **Identifying Evidence.** A friend tells you that honey and molasses are better for you than white or brown sugar. How can you decide whether this is true?
2. **Recognizing Bias.** Suppose that you are reading a magazine or newspaper and happen upon a study on the effectiveness of vitamin C against colds. After reading the article, you discover that the study was financed by a company that makes vitamin C tablets. Why does this suggest a possible bias?

Working IN THE Lab

1. ***Taste Test.*** Heat three samples of a canned vegetable, such as green beans—one canned with salt and two canned without salt. Season one of the no-salt samples with a salt alternative, such as herbs or lemon juice. Compare the taste of the vegetables. Which do you prefer? Why?
2. ***Foods Lab.*** Compare the amount of fat in different types of ground beef. Weigh out ¼ pound (125 g) of regular ground beef and the same amount of ground round. Form each portion into a patty. Cook each patty in a separate skillet over medium-low heat until done (about five minutes on each side). After cooking, weigh each patty again. Pour the grease from each pan into a separate measuring cup. Which patty contained more fat? How might you use this information?

Reinforcing Key Skills

1. **Leadership.** As participants in a schoolwide health fair, your class is planning a presentation on the *Dietary Guidelines for Americans.* List the steps the planning group can take to heighten people's awareness of the guidelines and the Food Guide Pyramid.
2. **Management.** Eryka is writing a review of a recent nutrition study and has asked for your help in organizing her report. What questions would you suggest that Eryka ask herself about the study in order to evaluate it properly?

Making Decisions and Solving Problems

Your sister has learned that carrots are very nutritious. Therefore, she has stopped eating most other vegetables and eats large amounts of carrots at almost every meal. What would you tell your sister?

Making Connections

1. **Language Arts.** Find a newspaper or magazine article about a nutrition-related study. Identify the following information in the article: What was the purpose of the study? Who did the study and where? Who paid for it? What type of people or animals did the researchers study? How was the study carried out?
2. **Math.** Conduct a survey of classmates' eating habits by asking them to write down the number of servings of vegetables eaten the previous day. Calculate the class average. How does this average compare with the servings suggested in the Food Guide Pyramid?

- **Summary.** A recap of the main ideas in each section.
- **Checking Your Knowledge.** Questions that check students' recall of basic information in the chapter.
- **Working in the Lab.** Hands-on activities that include foods labs, food science labs, computer labs, demonstrations, and taste tests.
- **Thinking Critically.** Questions that call for critical thinking skills.
- **Reinforcing Key Skills.** Short situations for analysis, focused on directed thinking, management, communication, or leadership.
- **Making Decisions and Solving Problems.** Real-life situations that present students with content-related dilemmas and ask, "What would you do?"
- **Making Connections.** Activities that relate chapter content to mathematics, science, writing, language arts, social studies, health, and fine arts.

Appendices

Appendix A contains "Canada's Food Guide to Healthy Eating." This illustrated guide to food choices and serving sizes is recommended for people age four and over by Health Canada.

Appendix B is a chart of information on the caloric and nutrient content of commonly eaten foods.

Glossary and Index

The glossary, which begins on page 694, defines all vocabulary terms listed in the student edition at the beginning of each section. Section numbers follow the definitions to identify where terms are located.

A complete alphabetical index provides easy reference to text content. It begins on page 712.

Using the Teacher Wraparound Edition

The ***Food for Today*** *Teacher Wraparound Edition* (TWE) provides maximum teaching support in an easy-to-use format. Every page consists of a reduced-size student edition page surrounded by lesson plans that are filled with teaching activities and information. Later in the *Teacher's Manual* that you are now reading, you will find charts and other resources to use when planning lessons, implementing them, and assessing student learning.

Unit Opening Pages

Every unit of the TWE begins with the following items:

- **Introducing the Unit.** An activity that sparks interest in the unit while previewing selected concepts from the chapters.
- **Key to Ability Levels.** An explanation of the codes used with specific activities in the TWE. The activities are followed by one of three codes: L1, L2, or L3.
- **Unit Project.** A project for students to carry out while studying the unit. A follow-up to the project is suggested.
- **FCCLA Project Ideas.** Ideas that can be developed to fit Family, Career, and Community Leaders of America programs.

Chapter Opening Page

At the beginning of each chapter, the TWE provides the following items:

- **Advance Planning Guide.** Information about the materials and arrangements needed for labs and activities in the TWE.
- **Meeting Diverse Needs.** Activity ideas for meeting individual student needs.

Section Opening Page

Each section opening page contains a list of resources available in the ***Food for Today*** program. A quick glance tells you where to go to find study guides, activities, tests, and more.

The lesson plan for the section begins on this page. Lessons plans are organized throughout the section under the headers *Focus, Teach, Assess,* and *Close.*

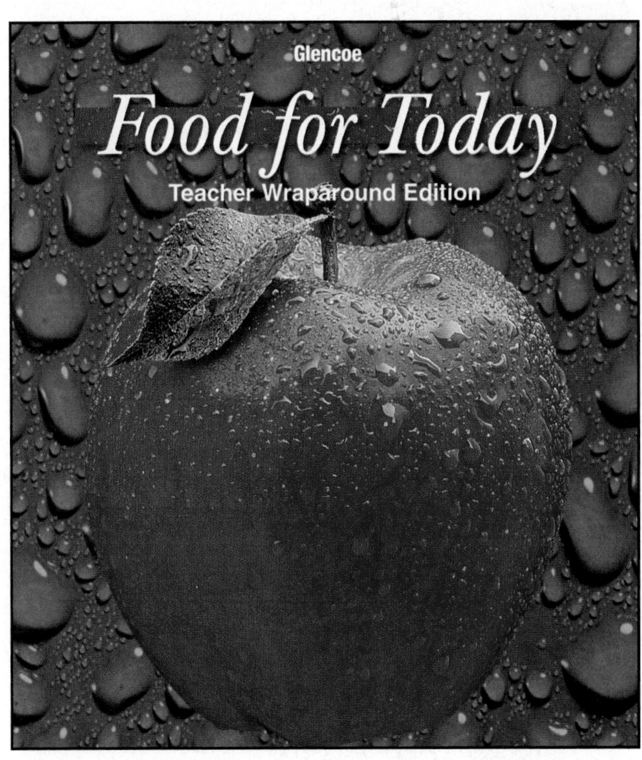

FOCUS

The section lesson plan begins with **FOCUS.** The following items are located here:

- **Motivators.** Ideas for short activities and discussions to get the section off to an interesting start.
- **Vocabulary Activity.** An activity related to Look for These Terms on the student page.
- **Study Skills.** Activity ideas that call for practicing such skills as guided reading, listening, and outlining.

TEACH

The core of every lesson plan is the **TEACH** portion. Many options for teacher-directed and independent activities and projects are provided. All reinforce section content. Look for these headings:

- **Basic Activities.** Activities that involve discussion, making comparisons, categorizing, or researching.
- **Leveled Activities.** Activities that offer different degrees of difficulty. Leveling codes L1, L2, and L3 are explained on unit opening pages.
- **Field Trip and Guest Speaker.** Suggestions for these events.
- **Demonstration Activities.** Ideas for teacher demonstrations.

In addition, many activities are highlighted in topical boxes. All of the items below and on the next page will help you add interest to your lessons.

FOOD SCIENCE

Activities, simple experiments, and additional information, all aimed at bringing more science content to a course.

Technology TIE-IN

Information that connects the text with past and present technology.

Reinforcing Key Skills

Real-life situations for evaluation. Based on directed thinking, management, communication, and leadership.

Interesting facts and statistics related to text topics.

HOME & COMMUNITY CONNECTION

Ways for students to take what they have learned into their home and community.

Extending Learning

Additional information related to text content and useful in class discussions.

VISUAL LEARNING

Discussion ideas to use with photos, illustrations, and charts.

RECIPE FILE

Four items in the TWE link to the Recipe File feature.

Preparation or cooking skill reinforced by each recipe.

Reference to coordinated materials in the *Foods Lab Resources* booklet.

Suggestions for guiding students in preparing the recipe safely and effectively.

Answers to ***Food for Thought***

Answers to questions in the feature.

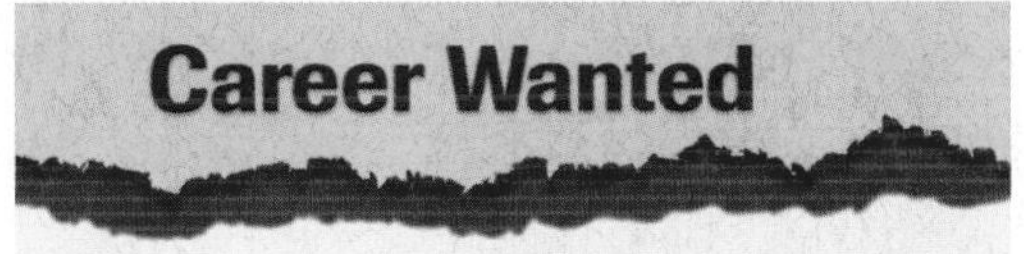

To use this feature on the student page, the following TWE materials are provided:

- **Thinking About the Career.** Discussion and activity suggestions.
- **Career-Building Opportunities.** Ways for students to explore careers.
- **For More Information.** Resources related to the career discussed.

Links to Features. These TWE boxes supply information, discussion ideas, and activities for text features.

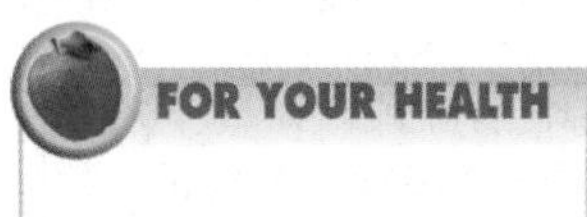

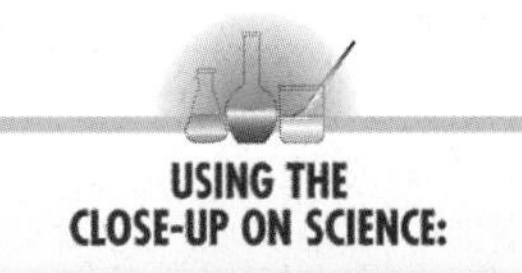

ASSESS

The **ASSESS** portion of a lesson plan is found on the last page of each section and also on the Chapter Review & Activities pages. The following items are provided:

- **Review.** Comprehension can be checked with the questions and activities on the student pages. Answers are supplied on the TWE pages.
- **Evaluation.** Options include an activity for evaluation as well as quizzes and tests. Quizzes and chapter tests are provided in the *Teacher Resource Guide,* or you can create you own with the **Exam***View*® *Test Generator* on the *Effective Instruction CD-ROM.*
- **Reteaching.** Activity ideas are offered. Another suggestion is the activity in the *Reteaching Activities* booklet in the *Student Motivation Kit.*

CLOSE

Lessons can be wrapped up with an activity or discussion idea under **CLOSE.** The lesson plan ends here, on the last page of each section.

Using the Student Workbook

The *Food for Today Student Workbook* reinforces understanding and application of text content. The workbook includes the following:

Study Guides

Every chapter has a study guide that helps students review and remember important chapter points. The study guide for each chapter is divided into sections that correspond to those in the text. Students can fill in the study guides as they read, and later use them for review.

Activities

An activity sheet for every section is included in the workbook. With these activities, students can work independently as they learn concepts and strengthen their thinking skills.

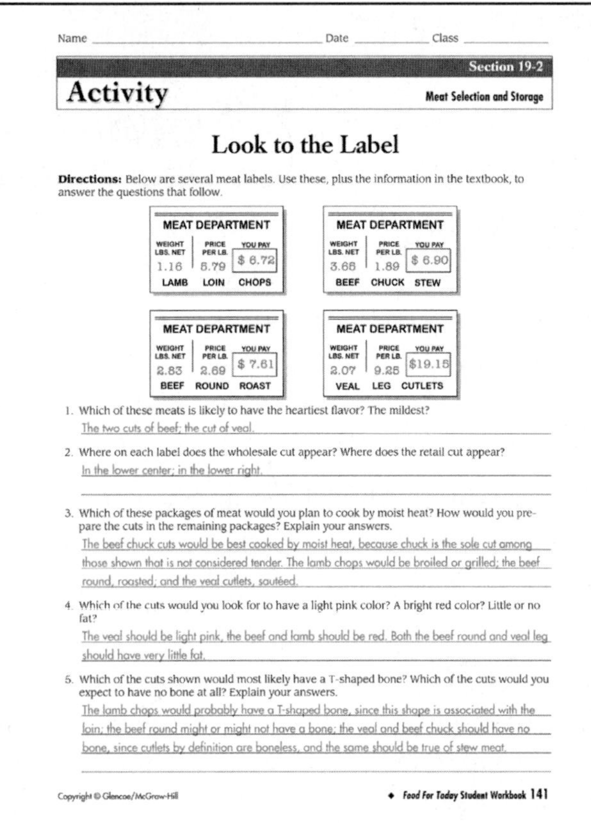

Name ______________ Date ________ Class ________

Section 19-2

Activity — Meat Selection and Storage

Look to the Label

Directions: Below are several meat labels. Use these, plus the information in the textbook, to answer the questions that follow.

1. Which of these meats is likely to have the heartiest flavor? The mildest?
   The two cuts of beef; the cut of veal.
2. Where on each label does the wholesale cut appear? Where does the retail cut appear?
   In the lower center; in the lower right.
3. Which of these packages of meat would you plan to cook by moist heat? How would you prepare the cuts in the remaining packages? Explain your answers.
   The beef chuck cuts would be best cooked by moist heat, because chuck is the sole cut among those shown that is not considered tender. The lamb chops would be broiled or grilled; the beef round, roasted; and the veal cutlets, sautéed.
4. Which of the cuts would you look for to have a light pink color? A bright red color? Little or no fat?
   The veal should be light pink, the beef and lamb should be red. Both the beef round and veal leg should have very little fat.
5. Which of the cuts shown would most likely have a T-shaped bone? Which of the cuts would you expect to have no bone at all? Explain your answers.
   The lamb chops would probably have a T-shaped bone, since this shape is associated with the loin; the beef round might or might not have a bone; the veal and beef chuck should have no bone, since cutlets by definition are boneless, and the same should be true of stew meat.

◆ *Food For Today Student Workbook* 141

Each page of the *Student Workbook* is perforated for easy removal. Answers are provided in the *Student Workbook Teacher Annotated Edition.*

Please note that the ***Food for Today*** *Student Workbook* is a consumable product to be used by only one student. Reproducing activity sheets is a violation of copyright law.

Using the Student Motivation Kit

The Student Motivation Kit contains six separate booklets, each with a specific purpose. A transportable file holds all six, providing convenient storage and mobility.

Skills for Making Food Choices

The activities in this booklet challenge students to use critical thinking and decision-making skills to solve problems. Real-life situations covering food and nutrition issues are evaluated.

A Global Foods Tour

Use this booklet to take students on an imaginary tour of 11 regions of the world to learn about foods and food customs. Students "visit" 25 ports of call. Maps, recipes, information, and activities are included.

Foods Lab Resources

These reproducible materials make foods labs effective:

- Recipes—including those from the student text.
- Activities for lab preparation and evaluation.
- Handouts for lab management.
- An answer key.

Reteaching Activities

These reproducible activities provide extra reinforcement to help students grasp key concepts. An answer key is provided.

Food Science Resources

With these reproducible experiments, students explore science, using foods and equipment found in a high school foods lab. No special equipment or hazardous chemicals are needed. Teaching guidelines and a planning chart are included.

Enrichment Activities

These activities challenge students to extend their learning. An answer key is provided.

Using the Teacher Resource Guide

The ***Food for Today*** *Teacher Resource Guide* provides valuable tools for teaching, including those described here.

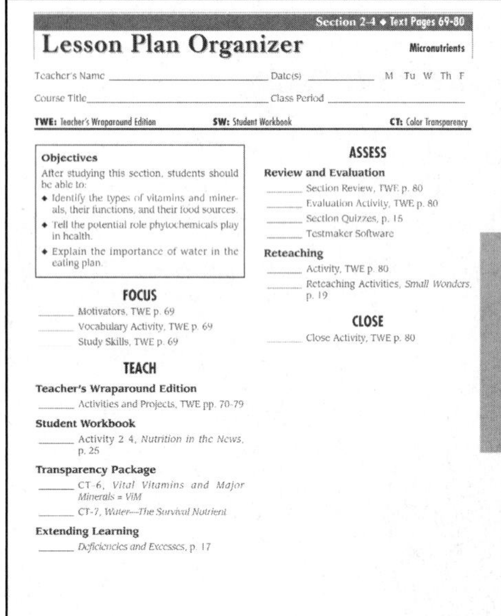

Section 2-4 ◆ Text Pages 69-80

Lesson Plan Organizer — Micronutrients

Teacher's Name ________ Date(s) ________ M Tu W Th F

Course Title ________ Class Period ________

TWE: Teacher's Wraparound Edition **SW:** Student Workbook **CT:** Color Transparency

Objectives
After studying this section, students should be able to:
- Identify the types of vitamins and minerals, their functions, and their food sources.
- Tell the potential role phytochemicals play in health.
- Explain the importance of water in the eating plan.

FOCUS
____ Motivators, TWE p. 69
____ Vocabulary Activity, TWE p. 69
____ Study Skills, TWE p. 69

TEACH
Teacher's Wraparound Edition
____ Activities and Projects, TWE pp. 70-79
Student Workbook
____ Activity 2-4, *Nutrition in the News*, p. 25
Transparency Package
____ CT-6, *Vital Vitamins and Major Minerals = VIM*
____ CT-7, *Water—The Survival Nutrient*
Extending Learning
____ *Deficiencies and Excesses*, p. 17

ASSESS
Review and Evaluation
____ Section Review, TWE p. 80
____ Evaluation Activity, TWE p. 80
____ Section Quizzes, p. 15
____ Testmaker Software
Reteaching
____ Activity, TWE p. 80
____ Reteaching Activities, *Small Wonders*, p. 19

CLOSE
____ Close Activity, TWE p. 80

Lesson Plan Organizers

These reproducible, checklist lesson plan organizers correlate teaching resources to each section of the text. The pages help you plan lessons and make full use of the ***Food for Today*** program.

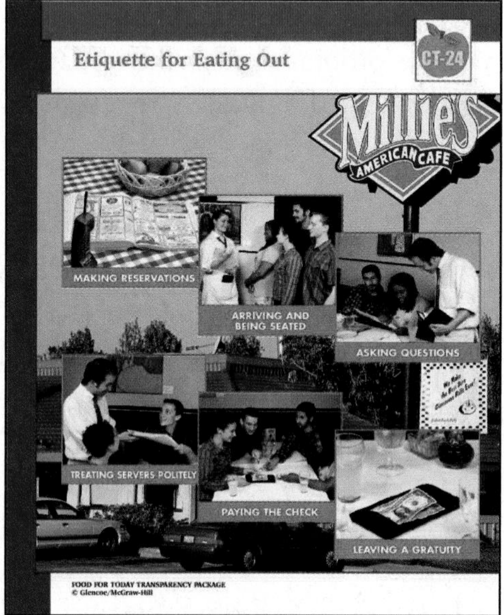

Sample Transparencies

Eight full-color transparencies show the quality and variety available in the full *Transparency Package* (sold separately). Teaching suggestions are included.

Testing Program

Reproducible quizzes correspond to every text section. Tests are provided for all chapters. Question types include matching, multiple choice, true/false, completion, short answer, and essay. Answer keys are provided.

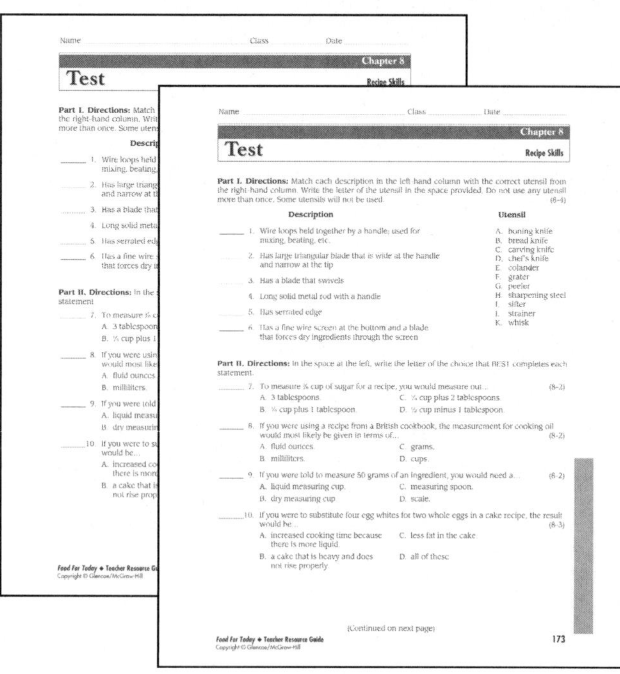

Name ________ Class ________ Date ________

Chapter 8

Test — Recipe Skills

Part I. Directions: Match each description in the left-hand column with the correct utensil from the right-hand column. Write the letter of the utensil in the space provided. Do not use any utensil more than once. Some utensils will not be used. (8-4)

Description
____ 1. Wire loops held together by a handle; used for mixing, beating, etc.
____ 2. Has large triangular blade that is wide at the handle and narrow at the tip
____ 3. Has a blade that swivels
____ 4. Long solid metal rod with a handle
____ 5. Has serrated edge
____ 6. Has a fine wire screen at the bottom and a blade that forces dry ingredients through the screen

Utensil
A. boning knife
B. bread knife
C. carving knife
D. chef's knife
E. colander
F. grater
G. peeler
H. sharpening steel
I. sifter
J. strainer
K. whisk

Part II. Directions: In the space at the left, write the letter of the choice that BEST completes each statement.

____ 7. To measure ⅜ cup of sugar for a recipe, you would measure out... (8-2)
A. 3 tablespoons. C. ¼ cup plus 2 tablespoons.
B. ¼ cup plus 1 tablespoon. D. ½ cup minus 1 tablespoon.

____ 8. If you were using a recipe from a British cookbook, the measurement for cooking oil would most likely be given in terms of... (8-2)
A. fluid ounces. C. grams.
B. milliliters. D. cups.

____ 9. If you were told to measure 50 grams of an ingredient, you would need a... (8-2)
A. liquid measuring cup. C. measuring spoon.
B. dry measuring cup. D. scale.

____ 10. If you were to substitute four egg whites for two whole eggs in a cake recipe, the result would be... (8-3)
A. increased cooking time because there is more liquid. C. less fat in the cake.
B. a cake that is heavy and does not rise properly. D. all of these.

(Continued on next page)

Food For Today ◆ Teacher Resource Guide
Copyright © Glencoe/McGraw-Hill
173

Using the Effective Instruction CD Rom

The CD-ROM makes teaching easier and learning more interesting. Lesson plans are provided in Word for Windows® so you can tailor them to fit your needs.

An interactive **Exam***View*® *Test Generator* can help you create quizzes and tests. Choose from hundreds of objective test items, or add questions of your own. You can arrange the items in any order to create multiple versions of the same test. Answers for all test items are included.

The CD-ROM also provides color transparencies as PowerPoint® slides. With these, you can create presentations that add impact and interest to your lessons.

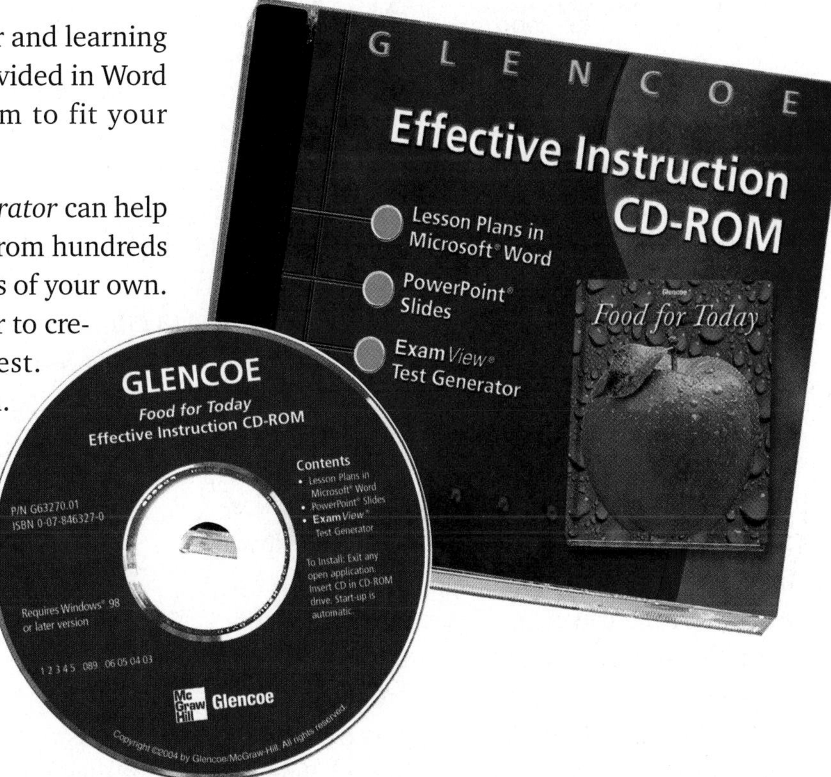

Using the Transparency Package

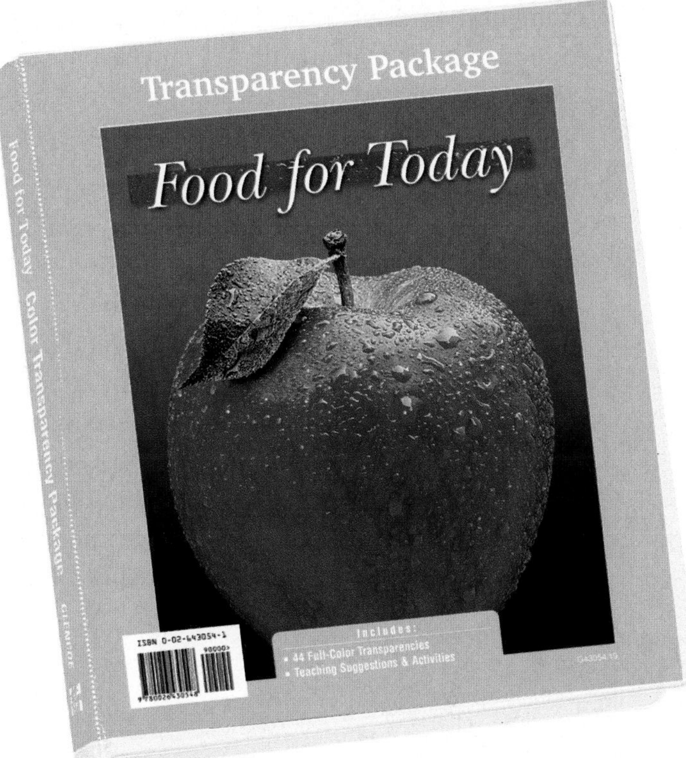

Color transparencies add visual appeal to lessons. The 56 ready-to-use color transparencies in this package bring key points to life, helping students "see" what is often difficult to understand just by reading.

You can use the transparencies in several ways. They are valuable visual tools for introducing topics, reinforcing concepts, and generating discussion. Each transparency is accompanied by teaching strategies and related activities.

Family & Consumer Sciences (FCS) National Standards

The eighth edition of ***Food for Today*** embraces the Family & Consumer Sciences (FCS) National Standards. These standards emphasize the importance of four fundamental processes as vehicles for obtaining, analyzing, and using content. These processes are directed thinking, resource management, communication, and leadership. Students are introduced to the skill areas in Section 1-5, "Skills for Food Choices," of the text. Students will apply their process skills in the "Reinforcing Key Skills" section of the Chapter Review & Activities.

- ***Directed Thinking.*** As a definition, thinking processes embrace complex, multifaceted activities of the mind. The process of thinking, as described in the FCS National Standards, emphasizes *directed thinking*—or the use of cognitive and metacognitive skills or strategies that increase the likelihood of desired outcomes. Related to the notion of critical thinking, the thinking process as defined is purposeful, reasonable, and goal-directed. Typical thinking process questions are: "What are the factors contributing to nutritional practices and wellness across the life span?" and "What impact do social influences have on food choices?"
- ***Communication.*** By exchanging thoughts, feelings, opinions, and information, a sender and receiver communicate. The skills involved in communication include speaking, listening, writing, and reading, as well as the interpretive processes of sensitivity, insight, and the ability to adjust communication to a specific audience. Typical communication process questions are: "How can we increase our understanding of factors that influence nutritional practices and wellness across the life span?" and "In what ways does the use of communication contribute to the impact of food choices on the global community?"
- ***Leadership.*** As a process, leadership encompasses all aspects of guiding and persuading individuals and groups to develop a purpose and commit to accomplishing that purpose. Leadership requires the use of various strategies to involve people in achieving a shared vision. Shared leadership encourages every group member to help make decisions and take action. Effective leaders are sensitive to the needs, thoughts, and feelings of others while demonstrating effective communication. Typical leadership process questions are: "What skills do we need to explore societal, governmental, and technological influences related to food choices and practices?" and "What steps can we take to heighten awareness of the need for sound nutritional practices across the life span?"
- ***Management.*** Management processes include setting goals, planning, implementing, evaluating, problem-solving, and decision-making. Management includes planning the steps to take and resources to use in meeting an objective, and carrying out the plan in an efficient and cost-effective way. Typical management process questions are: "What are the short- and long-term consequences of food technology on the global community?" and "What resources are needed to prepare nutritionally sound and aesthetically pleasing foods?"

FCS National Standards Correlations

The FCS National Standards are reinforced in ***Food for Today*** in the running content, special features, and in the section and chapter reviews.

Food for Today	*Nutrition and Wellness*	*Food Science, Dietetics, Nutrition*	*Food Production and Services*
Chapter 1: Exploring Food Choices	14.1, 14.2, 14.4, 14.5	9.1, 9.3, 9.5, 9.6	8.1, 8.2
Chapter 2: The Nutrients You Need	14.1, 14.2, 14.3, 14.4, 14.5	9.1, 9.6	8.2
Chapter 3: Guidelines for Good Nutrition	14.1, 14.2, 14.3,	9.1, 9.6	
Chapter 4: Planning Daily Food Choices	14.1, 14.2, 14.3, 14.4	9.1, 9.3, 9.6	8.1
Chapter 5: Food and Fitness	14.1, 14.2,14.4	9.2, 9.4, 9.6	8.4
Chapter 6: Special Topics in Nutrition	14.1, 14.2	9.1, 9.2, 9.4, 9.6	8.1
Chapter 7: Kitchen Principles	14.4, 14.5	9.2, 9.3	8.1, 8.2, 8.3
Chapter 8: Recipe Skills	14.3, 14.4, 14.5	9.1, 9.2, 9.3, 9.6	8.1, 8.3
Chapter 9: Cooking Methods	14.4, 14.5	9.1, 9.2, 9.6	8.1, 8.2
Chapter 10: Mealtime Customs	14.3, 14.4	9.1, 9.2, 9.6	8.2
Chapter 11: Planning Meals	14.1, 14.2, 14.4	9.1, 9.3, 9.6	8.1
Chapter 12: Shopping for Food	14.1, 14.4, 14.5	9.1, 9.2	8.1
Chapter 13: The Food Supply	14.4, 14.5	9.1, 9.3, 9.5, 9.6	8.1, 8.2, 8.6
Chapter 14: Buying for the Kitchen	14.4, 14.5	9.2	8.1, 8.7
Chapter 15: Convenience Foods	14.1, 14.5	9.3, 9.5, 9.6	8.1, 8.4, 8.5
Chapter 16: Vegetables and Fruits	14.1, 14.2, 14.4, 14.5	9.1, 9.2, 9.3, 9.6	8.1, 8.2
Chapter 17: Grains, Legumes, Nuts, and Seeds	14.1, 14.2, 14.3	9.1, 9.3, 9.6	8.1, 8.5
Chapter 18: Dairy Foods and Eggs	14.2, 14.3, 14.5	9.1, 9.2, 9.3, 9.6	8.1
Chapter 19: Meat, Poultry, Fish, and Shellfish	14.1, 14.2, 14.4	9.1, 9.2, 9.3, 9.6	8.1, 8.6
Chapter 20: Food Combinations	14.1, 14.3, 14.2	9.1, 9.2, 9.3, 9.6	8.2, 8.6
Chapter 21: Baking	14.1, 14.2, 14.4	9.1, 9.2, 9.5, 9.6	8.1
Chapter 22: Foods of the World	14.1, 14.2	9.1, 9.3	8.1
Chapter 23: Foods of the U.S. and Canada	14.1, 14.2	9.1, 9.3	8.1
Chapter 24: Special Topics in Food	14.1, 14.2, 14.4	9.1, 9.2, 9.6	8.1
Chapter 25: Careers in Food and Nutrition	14.4, 14.5	9.1	8.1

Meeting Individual Needs and Learning Styles

One of your greatest challenges as a teacher is to provide a positive learning environment for all students in your classroom. Because each student has his or her own unique set of abilities, perceptions, and needs, the learning styles and physical abilities of your students may vary widely.

Gardner's Theory of Multiple Intelligences		
TYPE	**DESCRIPTION**	**LIKES TO...**
Verbal/Linguistic Learner	Intelligence is related to words and language, written and spoken.	read, write, tell stories, play word games, and tell jokes and riddles.
Logical/Mathematical Learner	Intelligence deals with inductive and deductive thinking and reasoning, numbers, and abstractions.	perform experiments, solve puzzles, work with numbers, ask questions, and explore patterns and relationships.
Visual/Spatial Learner	Intelligence relies on the sense of sight and being able to visualize an object, including the ability to create mental images.	draw, build, design, and create things, daydream, do jigsaw puzzles and mazes, watch videos, look at photos, and draw maps and charts.
Bodily/Kinesthetic Learner	Intelligence is related to physical movement and the brain's motor cortex, which controls bodily movements.	learn by hands-on methods, demonstrate skill in crafts, tinker, perform, display physical endurance, and challenge self physically.
Musical/Rhythmic Learner	Intelligence is based on recognition of tonal patterns, including various environmental sounds, and on a sensitivity to rhythm and beats.	sing and hum, listen to music, play an instrument, move body when music is playing, and make up songs.
Interpersonal Learner	Intelligence operates primarily through person-to-person relationships and communication.	have lots of friends, talk to people, join groups, play cooperative games, solve problems as part of a group, and volunteer to help when others need it.
Intrapersonal Learner	Intelligence is related to inner states of being, self-reflection, metacognition, and awareness of spiritual realities.	work alone, pursue own interests, daydream, keep a personal diary or journal, and think about starting own business.
Naturalistic Learner	Intelligence has to do with observing, understanding, and organizing patterns in the natural environment.	spend time outdoors and work with plants, animals, and other parts of the natural environment; good at identifying plants and animals and at hearing and seeing connections to nature.

IS GOOD AT...	LEARNS BEST BY...	FAMOUS LEARNERS
memorizing names, dates, places, and trivia; spelling; using descriptive language; and creating imaginary worlds.	saying, hearing, and seeing words.	Maya Angelou-poet Abraham Lincoln-16th U.S. President Jerry Seinfeld-comedian Mary Hatwood Futrell-international teacher, leader, orator
math, reasoning, logic, problem solving, computing numbers, moving from concrete to abstract, thinking conceptually.	categorizing, classifying, and working with patterns and relationships.	Stephen Hawking-physicist Albert Einstein-theoretical physicist Marilyn Burns-math educator Alexa Canady-neurosurgeon
understanding the use of space and how to get around in it, thinking in three-dimensional terms, and imagining things in clear visual images.	visualizing, dreaming, using the mind's eye, and working with colors and pictures.	Pablo Picasso-artist Maria Martinez-a Pueblo potter famous for black-on-black ware pottery Faith Ringgold-painter, quilter, and writer I. M. Pei-architect
physical activities such as sports, dancing, acting, and crafts.	touching, moving, interacting with space, and processing knowledge through bodily sensations.	Marcel Marceau-mime Jackie Joyner-Kersey-olympic gold medalist in track and field Katherine Dunham-modern dancer Dr. Christian Bernard-cardiac surgeon
remembering melodies; keeping time; mimicking beat and rhythm; noticing pitches, rhythms, and background and environmental sounds.	rhythm, melody, and music.	Henry Mancini-composer Marian Anderson-contralto Midori-violinist Paul McCartney-singer, song writer, musician
understanding people and their feelings, leading others, organizing, communicating, manipulating, mediating conflicts.	sharing, comparing, relating, cooperating, and interviewing.	Jimmy Carter-39th U. S. President Eleanor Roosevelt-former First Lady Lee Iacocca-former president of Chrysler Corporation Mother Teresa-winner of Nobel Peace Prize
understanding self, focusing on feelings/dreams, following instincts, pursuing interests, and being original.	working alone, doing individualized projects, engaging in self-paced instruction.	Marva Collins-educator Maria Montessori-educator and physician Sigmund Freud-psychotherapist Anne Sexton-poet
measuring, charting, mapping, observing plants and animals, keeping journals, collecting, classifying, participating in outdoor activities.	visualizing, hands-on activities, bringing outdoors into the classroom, relating home/classroom to the natural world.	George Washington Carver-agricultural chemist Rachel Carson-scientific writer Charles Darwin-evolutionist John James Audobon-conservationist

Teaching Students with Special Needs

Students in your classroom may have learning disabilities or be physically or emotionally challenged, all of which may interfere with their ability to learn. Learning styles of your students can also vary. Some students may be visual learners; others may learn more effectively through hands-on activities. Others may work well independently, while still others benefit most when there is interaction with others. Finally, students come from different cultural backgrounds and some may have limited English proficiency.

Meeting Special Needs		
	DESCRIPTION	**SOURCES OF INFORMATION**
Limited Proficiency in English (LEP)	Certain students often speak English as a second language, or not at all. Customs and behavior of people in the majority culture may be confusing for some of these students. Cultural values may inhibit some students from full participation in the classroom.	*Teaching English as a Second Language* *Mainstreaming and the Minority Child*
Behaviorally Disordered	Children with behavior disorders deviate from standards or expectations of behavior and impair the functioning of others and themselves. These children may also be gifted or learning disabled.	*Exceptional Children* *Journal of Special Education*
Visually Impaired	Children who are visually disabled have partial or total loss of sight. Individuals with visual impairments are not significantly different from their sighted peers in ability range or personality. However, blindness may affect cognitive, motor, and social development.	*Journal of Visual Impairment and Blindness* *Education of Visually Handicapped* *American Foundation for the Blind*
Hearing Impaired	Children who are hearing impaired have partial or total loss of hearing. Individuals with hearing impairments are not significantly different from their peers in ability range or personality. However, the chronic condition of deafness may affect cognitive, motor, social, and speech development.	*American Annals of the Deaf* *Journal of Speech and Hearing Research* *Sign Language Studies*
Physically Challenged	Children who are physically disabled fall into two categories—those with orthopedic impairments (use of one or more limbs severely restricted) and those with other health impairments.	*The Source Book for the Disabled* *Teaching Exceptional Children*
Gifted	Although no formal definition exists, these students can be described as having above average ability, task commitment, and creativity. They rank in the top five percent of their classes. They usually finish work more quickly than other students, and are capable of divergent thinking.	*Journal for the Education of the Gifted Child* *Gifted Child Quarterly* *Gifted Creative/Talented*
Learning Disabled	All learning disabled students have a problem in one or more areas, such as academic learning, language, perception, social-emotional adjustment, memory, or ability to pay attention.	*Journal of Learning Disabilities* *Learning Disability Quarterly*

Rather than viewing these differences as impediments, the ***Food for Today*** *Teacher Wraparound Edition* enables teachers to see these differences as opportunities for sharing and enriching the entire classroom community. At the bottom of every chapter opener, you will find a box titled "Meeting Diverse Needs." This box contains activities that will help you make the most of special-needs situations. "Multiple Intelligences" draws upon the eight approaches to intelligence first theorized by educational theorist Howard Gardner of Harvard University (see chart on pages TM-18 and TM-19). Other activities have one of several variable heads, including "Celebrating Cultural Diversity," "Visually Impaired Students," "Hearing Impaired Students," and "Physically Challenged Students."

TIPS FOR INSTRUCTION
• Remember that students' ability to speak English does not reflect their academic ability. • Try to incorporate students' cultural experiences into instruction. The help of a bilingual aide may be effective. • Include information about different cultures in your curriculum to help build students' self-image. • Avoid cultural stereotypes. • Encourage students to share their cultures in the classroom.
• Work for long-term improvement; do not expect immediate success. • Talk with students about their strengths and weaknesses, and clearly outline objectives and tell how you will help them obtain their goals. • Structure schedules, rules, room arrangement, and safety for a conducive learning environment. • Model appropriate behavior for students and reinforce proper behavior. • Adjust group requirements for special needs.
• Modify assignments as needed to help students become independent. • Teach classmates how to serve as guides for students who are visually impaired; pair students so sighted peers can assist in cooperative learning work. • Tape lectures and reading assignments for students who are visually impaired. • Encourage all students to use their sense of touch; provide tactile models whenever possible. • Verbally describe people and events as they occur in the classroom. • Limit unnecessary noise in the classroom.
• Provide a favorable seating arrangement so students who are hearing-impaired can see speakers and read their lips (or interpreters can assist); avoid visual distractions. • Write out all instructions on paper on the board; overhead projectors enable you to maintain eye contact while writing. • Avoid standing with your back to the window or light source.
• With the student, determine when you should offer aid. • Help other students and adults understand physical disablilities. • Learn about special devices or procedures and whether any special necessary safety precautions are needed. • Allow students to participate in all activities, including field trips, special events, and projects.
• Emphasize concepts, theories, relationships, ideas, and generalizations. • Let students express themselves in a variety of ways, including drawing, creative writing, or acting. • Make arrangements for students to work on independent projects. • Utilize public services and resources, such as agencies providing free and inexpensive materials, community services and programs, and people in the community with specific expertise. • Make arrangements for students to take selected subjects early.
• Establish conditions and create an environment that leads to success. • Provide assistance and direction; clearly define rules, assignments, and duties. • Allow for pair interaction during class time; utilize peer helpers. • Practice skills frequently. • Distribute outlines of material presented in class. • Maintain student interest with games. • Allow extra time to complete tests and assignments.

Scope and Sequence

The following chart shows how major themes are woven throughout the ***Food for Today*** text. You will find it useful for planning your course, sequencing courses, emphasizing particular course themes, and correlating ***Food for Today*** to your curriculum.

Unit 1: Food, Nutrition, and You	
Nutrition and Health	Chapter 1: Exploring Food Choices Chapter 2: The Nutrients You Need Chapter 3: Guidelines for Good Nutrition Chapter 4: Planning Daily Food Choices Chapter 5: Food and Fitness Chapter 6: Special Topics in Nutrition
Consumer Information	Section 1-2: Influences on Food Choices Section 1-5: Skills for Food Choices Section 2-1: The Role of Nutrients Section 3-3: Separating Fact from Fiction Section 4-3: Eating Out
Management	Section 1-5: Skills for Food Choices Section 4-2: Positive Food Habits Section 5-2: Weight Management Section 6-2: Managing Health Conditions
Food Safety and Accident Prevention	Chapter 5: Nutrition for Sports and Fitness
Nutrition and Food Science	Section 1-4: Food, Science, and Technology Section 2-2: Carbohydrates, Fiber, and Proteins Section 2-3: Fats Section 2-4: Micronutrients Section 2-5: How Your Body Uses Food Section 5-4: Nutrition for Sports and Fitness
Food Preparation	
Social and Cultural Aspects	Section 1-2: Influences on Food Choices Section 1-3: Food and Culture Section 4-4: The Vegetarian Lifestyle Section 6-1: Food and the Life Span
Trends and Technology	Section 1-2: Influences on Food Choices Section 1-4: Food, Science, and Technology
Unit 2: Workspace, Tools, and Techniques	
Nutrition and Health	Section 7-4: Storing Food Section 8-3: Changing a Recipe
Consumer Information	Section 7-4: Storing Food Section 7-5: Conserving Natural Resources Section 9-1: Equipment for Cooking

Unit 2: Workspace, Tools, and Techniques (cont'd)	
Management	Section 7-5: Conserving Natural Resources Section 8-5: Time Management and Teamwork Section 10-1: Serving Family Meals
Food Safety and Accident Prevention	Section 7-2: Preventing Kitchen Accidents Section 7-3: Keeping Food Safe to Eat
Nutrition and Food Science	Section 7-3: Keeping Food Safe to Eat Section 8-3: Changing a Recipe Section 9-2: Heat and Cooking
Food Preparation	Chapter 8: Recipe Skills Chapter 9: Cooking Methods
Social and Cultural Aspects	Section 10-1: Serving Family Meals Section 10-2: Mealtime Etiquette
Trends and Technology	Section 7-5: Conserving Natural Resources Section 8-3: Changing a Recipe Section 9-1: Equipment for Cooking
Unit 3: Consumer Decisions	
Nutrition and Health	Section 11-1: Basic Meal Planning Section 11-2: Challenges in Meal Planning Section 12-2: Food Labels Section 13-2: A Safe Food Supply Section 13-3: The Global Food Supply
Consumer Information	Chapter 11: Planning Meals Chapter 12: Shopping for Food Chapter 13: The Food Supply Chapter 14: Buying for the Kitchen
Management	Section 11-1: Basic Meal Planning Section 11-2: Challenges in Meal Planning Section 11-3: Food Costs and Budgeting Section 12-1: Before You Shop Section 14-2: Choosing Kitchen Equipment
Food Safety and Accident Prevention	Section 12-3: In the Supermarket Section 13-2: A Safe Food Supply Section 14-2: Choosing Kitchen Equipment
Nutrition and Food Science	Section 13-2: A Safe Food Supply
Food Preparation	
Social and Cultural Aspects	Section 11-2: Challenges in Meal Planning Section 13-3: The Global Food Supply
Trends and Technology	Section 11-2: Challenges in Meal Planning Section 13-2: A Safe Food Supply Section 14-2: Choosing Kitchen Equipment Section 14-3: Designing a Kitchen

Scope and Sequence *(continued)*

Unit 4: Foods for Meals and Snacks	
Nutrition and Health	Section 15-1: Choosing Convenience Foods Section 16-1: Choosing Vegetables and Fruits Section 17-1: Choosing Grain and Grain Products Section 17-3: Legumes, Nuts, and Seeds Section 18-1: Choosing Dairy Foods Section 18-3: Egg Basics Section 19-1: Looking at Meat, Poultry, Fish, and Shellfish Section 20-1: Sandwiches, Snacks, and Packed Lunches Section 20-2: Salads and Dressings Section 20-3: Soups and Sauces Section 20-4: Casseroles and Other Combinations Section 21-1: Ingredients and Techniques for Baking Section 21-2: Quick Breads Section 21-3: Yeast Breads and Rolls Section 21-4: Cakes, Cookies, and Pies
Consumer Information	Section 15-1: Choosing Convenience Foods Section 16-1: Choosing Vegetables and Fruits Section 17-1: Choosing Grain and Grain Products Section 17-3: Legumes, Nuts, and Seeds Section 18-1: Choosing Dairy Foods Section 18-3: Egg Basics Section 19-1: Looking at Meat, Poultry, Fish, and Shellfish Section 19-2: Meat Selection and Storage Section 19-3: Poultry Selection and Storage Section 19-4: Fish, and Shellfish Selection and Storage
Management	Section 15-2: Cooking with Convenience Foods Section 21-3: Yeast Breads and Rolls
Food Safety and Accident Prevention	Section 15-1: Choosing Convenience Foods Section 16-1: Choosing Vegetables and Fruits Section 17-1: Choosing Grain and Grain Products Section 17-3: Legumes, Nuts, and Seeds Section 18-1: Choosing Dairy Foods Section 18-3: Egg Basics Section 19-1: Looking at Meat, Poultry, Fish, and Shellfish Section 19-2: Meat Selection and Storage Section 19-3: Poultry Selection and Storage Section 19-4: Fish and Shellfish Selection and Storage Section 20-1: Sandwiches, Snacks, and Packed Lunches

Unit 4: Foods for Meals and Snacks (cont'd)	
Nutrition and Food Science	Section 16-2: Preparing Raw Vegetables and Fruits Section 17-1: Choosing Grain and Grain Products Section 18-1: Choosing Dairy Foods Section 18-3: Egg Basics Section 19-1: Looking at Meat, Poultry, Fish, and Shellfish Section 20-2: Salads and Dressings Section 21-1: Ingredients and Techniques for Baking
Food Preparation	Section 15-2: Cooking with Convenience Foods Section 16-2: Preparing Raw Vegetables and Fruits Section 16-3: Cooking Vegetables and Fruits Section 17-2: Preparing Grain and Grain Products Section 17-3: Legumes, Nuts, and Seeds Section 18-2: Preparing Dairy Foods Section 18-3: Egg Basics Section 18-4: Using Eggs in Recipes Section 19-5: Preparing Meat, Poultry, Fish, and Shellfish Chapter 20: Food Combinations Chapter 21: Baking
Social and Cultural Aspects	Section 16-1: Choosing Vegetables and Fruits Section 17-1: Choosing Grain and Grain Products
Trends and Technology	Section 15-1: Choosing Convenience Foods Section 15-2: Cooking with Convenience Foods Section 21-3: Yeast Breads and Rolls
Unit 5: Expanding Your Horizons	
Nutrition and Health	Section 24-2: Entertaining Section 25-1: Career Opportunities Section 25-2: The Successful Worker
Consumer Information	Section 24-2: Beverages Section 24-4: Outdoor Meals
Management	Section 24-4: Outdoor Meals Section 24-5: Preserving Food at Home
Food Safety and Accident Prevention	Section 24-4: Outdoor Meals Section 24-5: Preserving Food at Home Section 25-1: Career Opportunities
Nutrition and Food Science	Chapter 24: Special Topics in Food
Food Preparation	Chapter 24: Special Topics in Food
Social and Cultural Aspects	Chapter 22: Foods of the World Chapter 23: Foods of the U. S. and Canada
Trends and Technology	Section 25-1: Career Opportunities

Suggested Course Outlines

The chart on pages TM-26 through TM-29 shows how ***Food for Today*** can be adapted for use in a variety of courses. Suggested course outlines are given for eight different types of courses:

- 18-week Foods and Nutrition course.
- 36-week Foods and Nutrition course.
- 18-week Advanced Foods and Nutrition course.
- 36-week Advanced Foods and Nutrition course.
- 18-week course with Food Science emphasis.
- 18-week course with Sports Nutrition emphasis.

To use the chart, find the heading for the desired type of course. Read down the column to see the suggested number of days to spend on each section of ***Food for Today.*** These outlines can easily be adapted to meet your particular needs.

Block Scheduling

In most high schools in the United States, the typical school day is made up of six, seven, or eight class periods of 40 to 50 minutes that meet 180 days a year. In "block scheduling," class sessions are scheduled for longer periods of time over fewer days. For example, a school day of block scheduling might consist of four blocks of 90-minute sessions that run for 90 days, or half a conventional school year.

The ***Food for Today*** *Teacher Wraparound Edition* has been designed with both the conventional and block-scheduling approaches to teaching in mind. In the text accompanying each of the five unit-opening spreads, you will find useful suggestions for managing the text in a block-scheduling fashion. You can further facilitate the teaching of key concepts by using the "InfoLinks" (described on page TM-7) to cover selected ideas and concepts in the program.

	Food for Today	*Foods and Nutrition 18 Weeks*	*Foods and Nutrition 36 Weeks*	*Advanced Foods and Nutrition 18 Weeks*	*Advanced Foods and Nutrition 36 Weeks*	*Food Science Emphasis 18 Weeks*	*Sports Nutrition 18 Weeks*	*Your Course*
Chapter 1	Section 1-1 Food and Health	1	1	2	2		2	
	Section 1-2 Influences on Food Choices	1	1	2	4		2	
	Section 1-3 Food and Culture	1	1		4			
	Section 1-4 Food, Science, and Technology	1	2	2	4	3		
	Section 1-5 Skills for Food Choices	1	2		3	1		
Chapter 2	Section 2-1 The Role of Nutrients	1	2	2		2	2	
	Section 2-2 Carbohydrates, Fiber, and Proteins	1	2	2		2	2	
	Section 2-3 Fats	1	2	2		2	2	
	Section 2-4 Micronutrients	1	2	2		2	2	
	Section 2-5 How Your Body Uses Food	1	2	2		2	2	
Chapter 3	Section 3-1 Dietary Guidelines	1	2	1		1	2	
	Section 3-2 The Food Guide Pyramid	1	2	1		2	2	
	Section 3-3 Separating Fact from Fiction	1	2	2	2	2	2	

Chapter	*Food for Today*	Foods and Nutrition 18 Weeks	Foods and Nutrition 36 Weeks	Advanced Foods and Nutrition 18 Weeks	Advanced Foods and Nutrition 36 Weeks	Food Science Emphasis 18 Weeks	Sports Nutrition 18 Weeks	Your Course
Chapter 4	Section 4-1 Daily Meals and Snacks	1	2		2		2	
	Section 4-2 Positive Food Habits	1	2		2		2	
	Section 4-3 Eating Out	1	2		2		1	
	Section 4-4 The Vegetarian Lifestyle	1	2	1	3		1	
Chapter 5	Section 5-1 Maintaining a Healthful Weight	1	2				2	
	Section 5-2 Weight Management	1	2				2	
	Section 5-3 Keeping Active	1	2				2	
	Section 5-4 Nutrition for Sports and Fitness	1	2	3		2	2	
Chapter 6	Section 6-1 Food and the Life Span	1	2		3	2	2	
	Section 6-2 Managing Health Conditions	1	2	3	1	2	2	
	Section 6-3 Eating Disorders	1	2	3	1	2	2	
Chapter 7	Section 7-1 Introduction to the Kitchen	1	1		1	1	1	
	Section 7-2 Preventing Kitchen Accidents	1	2		2	2	1	
	Section 7-3 Keeping Food Safe to Eat	1	2		3	2	1	
	Section 7-4 Storing Food	1	2		3	1	1	
	Section 7-5 Conserving Natural Resources	1	2	2	3	2		
Chapter 8	Section 8-1 Recipe Basics	1	1		2	2	1	
	Section 8-2 Measuring Ingredients	1	2		2	2	1	
	Section 8-3 Changing a Recipe	1	2	3	3	2	1	
	Section 8-4 Preparation Tasks	1	2		2	2	1	
	Section 8-5 Time Management and Teamwork	1	2		2	2	1	
Chapter 9	Section 9-1 Equipment for Cooking	1	2		1	1	1	
	Section 9-2 Heat and Cooking	1	1		1	2	1	
	Section 9-3 Conventional Cooking Techniques	2	2			2	1	
	Section 9-4 Microwave Cooking Techniques	1	2			2	1	
Ch. 10	Section 10-1 Serving Family Meals	1	2					
	Section 10-2 Mealtime Etiquette	1	2		2			

	Food for Today	***Foods and Nutrition 18 Weeks***	***Foods and Nutrition 36 Weeks***	***Advanced Foods and Nutrition 18 Weeks***	***Advanced Foods and Nutrition 36 Weeks***	***Food Science Emphasis 18 Weeks***	***Sports Nutrition 18 Weeks***	***Your Course***
Chapter 11	Section 11-1 Basic Meal Planning	1	2		1	1	2	
	Section 11-2 Challenges in Meal Planning	1	2	3	1		2	
	Section 11-3 Food Costs and Budgeting	1	2	3	4			
Ch. 12	Section 12-1 Before You Shop	1	2		2			
	Section 12-2 Food Labels	1	2		2		1	
	Section 12-3 In the Supermarket	1	2		2			
Chapter 13	Section 13-1 Where Does Food Come From?	1	2	2	4	2		
	Section 13-2 A Safe Food Supply	1	2	2	3	2		
	Section 13-3 The Global Food Supply	1	2	2	4	1		
Chapter 14	Section 14-1 Consumer Skills	1	2		2			
	Section 14-2 Choosing Kitchen Equipment	1	2		1			
	Section 14-3 Designing a Kitchen	1	2	3				
Ch. 15	Section 15-1 Choosing Convenience Foods	1	2		2		1	
	Section 15-2 Cooking with Convenience Foods	2	2		3	1	2	
Chapter 16	Section 16-1 Choosing Vegetables and Fruits	2	2		2		1	
	Section 16-2 Preparing Raw Vegetables and Fruits	2	2		3	2	1	
	Section 16-3 Cooking Vegetables and Fruits	2	3		2	2	2	
Chapter 17	Section 17-1 Choosing Grain and Grain Products	1	2		3	1	1	
	Section 17-2 Preparing Grain and Grain Products	1	2		4	2	2	
	Section 17-3 Legumes, Nuts, and Seeds	2	3		4	1	1	
Chapter 18	Section 18-1 Choosing Dairy Foods	1	2		1/2	1	1	
	Section 18-2 Preparing Dairy Foods	2	3		2	2	2	
	Section 18-3 Egg Basics	1	2		1	1	1	
	Section 18-4 Using Eggs in Recipes	2	3		2	2	1	

Chapter	Food for Today	Foods and Nutrition 18 Weeks	Foods and Nutrition 36 Weeks	Advanced Foods and Nutrition 18 Weeks	Advanced Foods and Nutrition 36 Weeks	Food Science Emphasis 18 Weeks	Sports Nutrition 18 Weeks	Your Course
Chapter 19	Section 19-1 Looking at Meat, Poultry, Fish, and Shellfish	1	2		1	1	1	
	Section 19-2 Meat Selection and Storage	1	2			1	1	
	Section 19-3 Poultry Selection and Storage	1	2			1	1	
	Section 19-4 Fish and Shellfish Selection and Storage	1	2		3	1	1	
	Section 19-5 Preparing Meat, Poultry, Fish, and Shellfish	2	3		4	2	2	
Chapter 20	Section 20-1 Sandwiches, Snacks, and Packed Lunches	1	2	2	2		2	
	Section 20-2 Salads and Dressings	1	2	2	2	2	2	
	Section 20-3 Soups and Sauces		2	2	2	2	2	
	Section 20-4 Casseroles and Other Combinations		2	2	2		2	
Chapter 21	Section 21-1 Ingredients and Techniques for Baking	2	2		3	1		
	Section 21-2 Quick Breads	2	2	1	1	2		
	Section 21-3 Yeast Breads and Rolls		2	3	1	2		
	Section 21-4 Cakes, Cookies, and Pies		3	3	1/2			
Chapter 22	Section 22-1 Latin America	1	2	3	5			
	Section 22-2 Africa and the Middle East	1	2	3	4			
	Section 22-3 Europe	1	2	3	3			
	Section 22-4 Asia and the Pacific	1	2	3	5			
Ch. 23	Section 23-1 Regional Foods of the East, Midwest, and South	1	2		3			
	Section 23-2 Regional Foods of the West and Canada	1	2		4			
Chapter 24	Section 24-1 Creative Techniques		2	2	3			
	Section 24-2 Beverages		2	2	3			
	Section 24-3 Entertaining		2	2	3			
	Section 24-4 Outdoor Meals		2	2	3			
	Section 24-5 Preserving Food at Home		2	2	3			
Ch. 25	Section 25-1 Career Opportunities		2	2	4	1	1	
	Section 25-2 The Successful Worker		3	2	2	1	1	
	Totals	90	180	90	180	90	90	

Internet Disclaimer

The material in the ***Food for Today*** *Teacher Wraparound Edition* includes references to Internet Web sites that may provide information related to the text. Since these sites are not under the control of Glencoe/McGraw-Hill, the text publisher makes no representation concerning the content of the sites. Some sites could contain links to other sites that have inappropriate material. Teachers are strongly encouraged to preview Internet sites before referring students to them. Since sites may move, be discontinued, or be under construction, some of those listed may no longer be accessible.

Agencies and Organizations

American Association for the Advancement of Science
1200 New York Ave., NW
Washington, DC 20005
www.aaas.org

American Association of Family and Consumer Sciences
1555 King St.
Alexandria, VA 22314
www.aafcs.org

American Bakers Association
1350 I St., NW, Suite 1290
Washington, DC 20005-3300
www.americanbakers.org

American Cancer Society
www.cancer.org

American College of Sports Medicine
P.O. Box 1440
Indianapolis, IN 46206-1440
www.acsm.org

American Culinary Federation
10 San Bartola Dr.
St. Augustine, FL 32086
www.acfchefs.org

American Dietetic Association
National Center for Nutrition and Dietetics
216 W. Jackson Blvd.
Chicago, IL 60606-6995
www.eatright.org

American Egg Board
1460 Renaissance Dr.
Park Ridge, IL 60068
www.aeb.org

American Frozen Food Institute
2000 Corporate Ridge, Suite 1000
McLean, VA 22102
www.affi.com

American Heart Association
7272 Greenville Ave.
Dallas, TX 75231
www.americanheart.org

American Seafood Institute (ASI)
25 Fairway Circle
Hope Valley, RI 02832
www.seafoodrus.org

American Society of Agronomy
677 S. Segoe Rd.
Madison, WI 53711
www.agronomy.org

Dairy Management Inc. (DMI)
10255 West Higgins Rd., Suite 900
Rosemont, IL 60018-5616
www.dairyinfo.com

Food and Drug Administration (FDA)
Center for Food Safety and Applied Nutrition (CFSAN)
U.S. Food and Drug Administration
5100 Paint Branch Pkwy.
College Park, MD 20740-3835
www.cfsan.fda.gov

Food and Drug Administration (FDA)
Consumer Information Office
5600 Fishers Ln.
Rockville, MD 20857
www.fda.gov

Food Marketing Institute
655 15th St., NW
Washington, DC 20005
www.fmi.org

International Association of Culinary Professionals
304 W. Liberty St., Suite 201
Louisville, KY 40202
www.iacp.com

International Food Information Council Foundation
1100 Connecticut Ave., NW, Suite 430
Washington, DC 20036
www.ific.org

Institute of Food Technologists
525 W. Van Buren, Suite 1000
Chicago, IL 60607
www.ift.org

National Confectioners Association
Chocolate Manufacturers Association
8320 Old Courthouse Rd., Suite 300
Vienna, VA 22181
www.candy.usa.org

National Council Against Health Fraud
119 Foster St.
Peabody, MA 01960
www.ncahf.org

National Eating Disorders Association
603 Stewart St., Suite 803
Seattle, WA 98101
www.NationalEatingDisorders.org

The National Health Council
1730 M St., NW
Washington, DC 20036
www.nhcouncil.org

National Food Processors Association
1350 I St., NW, Suite 300
Washington, DC 20005-3305
www.nfpa-food.org

National Restaurant Association
1200 17th St., NW
Washington, DC 20036-3097
www.restaurant.org

North American Meat Processors Association (NAMP)
1910 Association Dr.
Reston, VA 20191
www.namp.com

Produce Marketing Association
1500 Casho Mill Rd.
P.O. Box 6036
Newark, DE 19714-6036
www.pma.com

Society for Nutrition Education
9202 N. Meridian St., Suite 200
Indianapolis, IN 46260
www.sne.org

The Sugar Association
1101 15th St., NW, Suite 600
Washington, DC 20005
www.sugar.org

U.S. Department of Agriculture (USDA)
Food Safety and Inspection Service
1400 Independence Ave., SW, Room 2932-S
Washington, DC 20250-3700
www.fsis.usda.gov

U. S. Environmental Protection Agency (EPA)
Public Information Center
1650 Arch St.
Philadelphia, PA 19103-2029

EPA Headquarters
Ariel Rios Building
1200 Pennsylvania Ave., NW
Washington, DC 20460
www.epa.gov

Wheat Foods Council
10841 S. Crossroads Dr., Suite 105
Parker, CO 80138
www.wheatfoods.org

World Health Organization (WHO)
www.who.int/en

Periodicals

Consumer Reports
Consumers Union of the U.S., Inc.
101 Truman Ave.
Yonkers, NY 10703

Consumer Reports on Health
Consumers Union of the U.S., Inc.
P.O. Box 56356
Boulder, CO 80322-6356
www.consumerreports.org

FDA Consumer
Superintendent of Documents
P.O. Box 371954
Pittsburgh, PA 15250-7954
www.fda.gov/fdac

Mayo Clinic Health Letter
Subscription Services
P.O. Box 53889
Boulder, CO 80322-3889
www.mayo.edu

Nutrition Action Health Letter
1875 Connecticut Ave., NW
Washington, DC 20009
www.cspinet.org/nah/index.htm

University of California at Berkley Wellness Letter
Health Letter Associates
P.O. Box 420148
Palm Coast, FL 32142
www.berkleywellness.com

Web Sites

www.chocolateandcocoa.org
Chocolate and cocoa information

www.culinary.net
Family Features Editorial Syndicate
Recipes, food and nutrition information, and gateway to food associations and companies

www.fightbac.org
Partnership for Food Safety and Applied Nutrition
FIGHT BAC! Fighting the problem of foodborne illness

www.foodsafety.gov
FDA Center for Food Safety and Applied Nutrition
Gateway to government food safety information

www.popcorn.org
Information about popcorn, including recipes and history

Food for Today

Eighth Edition

Helen Kowtaluk

Alice Orphanos Kopan, M.Ed., M.A., CFCS

New York, New York Columbus, Ohio Chicago, Illinois Peoria, Illinois Woodland Hills, California

Front Cover Photo
FPG International/Denis Scott

Back Cover Photo
Corbis/Westlight
Japack

Interior Design
MKR Design, Inc.

Safety Notice

The reader is expressly advised to consider and use all safety precautions described in this book or that might also be indicated by undertaking the activities described herein. In addition, common sense should be exercised to help avoid all potential hazards and, in particular, to take relevant safety precautions concerning any known or likely hazards involved in food preparation, or in use of the procedures described in the Title, such as the risk of knife cuts or burns.

Publisher and Authors assume no responsibility for the activities of the reader or for the subject matter experts who prepared this book. Publisher and Authors make no representation or warranties of any kind, including but not limited to, the warranties of fitness for particular purpose or merchantability, nor for any implied warranties related thereto, or otherwise. Publisher and Authors will not be liable for damages of any type, including any consequential, special or exemplary damages resulting, in whole or in part, from reader's use or reliance upon the information, instructions, warnings or other matter contained in this book.

Brand Disclaimer

Publisher does not necessarily recommend or endorse any particular company or brand name product that may be discussed or pictured in this text. Brand name products are used because they are readily available, likely to be known to the reader, and their use may aid in the understanding of the text. Publisher recognizes that other brand name or generic products may be substituted and work as well or better than those featured in the text.

The McGraw-Hill Companies

Send all inquiries to:
Glencoe/McGraw-Hill
3008 W. Willow Knolls Drive
Peoria, Illinois 61614-1083

ISBN 0-07-846292-4 (Student Edition)
ISBN 0-07-846297-5 (Teacher Wraparound Edition)
Printed in the United States of America
2 3 4 5 6 7 8 9 071 07 06 05 04 03

CONTENTS IN BRIEF

Nutrition Consultant

Elizabeth Shipley Moses, M.S., R.D., C.D.E.
Clinical Nutritionist
Falls Church, Virginia

Technical Reviewers

Sherri Hoyt, R.D., L.D.
Outpatient/Clinical Dietitian
Missouri Baptist Medical Center
St. Louis, Missouri

Tamara S. Vitale, M.S., R.D.
Clinical Assistant Professor
Utah State University
Logan, Utah

Contributors

Gwen Bagaas
Middle School Educator
Jamestown Public Schools
Jamestown, New York

Brenda Barrington Mendiola, M.S.
Curriculum Director
Irion Co. ISD
Mertzon, Texas

Elise Zwicky
Writer/Editor
Pekin, Illinois

Teacher Reviewers

Linda Brown
Family and Consumer Sciences Teacher CTE Dept. Chair
Wake County Public Schools
Sanderson High School
Raleigh, North Carolina

Regina Chaney
Family and Consumer Sciences Teacher
Hazen Public Schools
Hazen, Arkansas

Gayle Dickinson, M.S.
Family and Consumer Sciences Dept. Chair
Lake Station Community Schools
Lake Station, Indiana

Lanell Early, M.S.
Culinary and Foods Technology Instructor
West Point Career & Technology Center
West Point, Mississippi

Mary H. Koch, NBCT, CFCS
Family and Consumer Sciences Teacher
Kewaskum High School
Kewaskum, Wisconsin

Sheila B. Kratzer, M.Ed.
High School Counselor
Calcasieu Parish School Board
Sulphur High School
Sulphur, Louisiana

Joyce P. Littlejohn
Family and Consumer Sciences Teacher
Duval County Public Schools
Samuel Wolfson Senior High
Jacksonville, Florida

Ann Roeger Marin
Food Production, Management & Services Instructor
Garland ISO
Garland, Texas

LaVoy Myers, M.Ed.
Retired Family and Consumer Sciences Teacher
Pocatello, Idaho

Diann Pilgrim, M.A.T.
Teacher-Coordinator
Birmingham City Schools
Birmingham, Alabama

Kadee Przysiecki-Poiry, NBCT
Family and Consumer Sciences Teacher
Rossford High School
Rossford, Ohio

Connie Toole
Family and Consumer Sciences Teacher
School Counselor
Jeff Davis High School
Hazlehurst, Georgia

CONTENTS

Unit 1: Food, Nutrition, and You

Chapter 3: Guidelines for Good Nutrition 88

Chapter 4: Planning Daily Food Choices 110

Chapter 5: Food and Fitness 136

Chapter 6: Special Topics in Nutrition 160

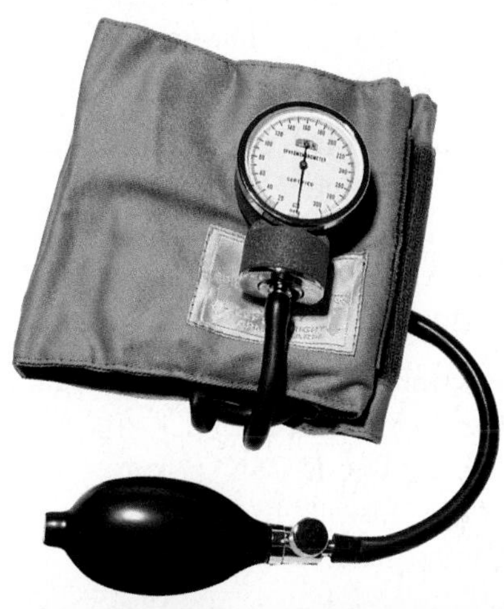

Unit 2: Workspace, Tools, and Techniques

Chapter 7: Kitchen Principles 186

Chapter 8: Recipe Skills 224

Chapter 9: Cooking Methods 260

Chapter 10: Mealtime Customs 296

Unit 3: Consumer Decisions

Chapter 11: Planning Meals 312

Chapter 12: Shopping for Food 334

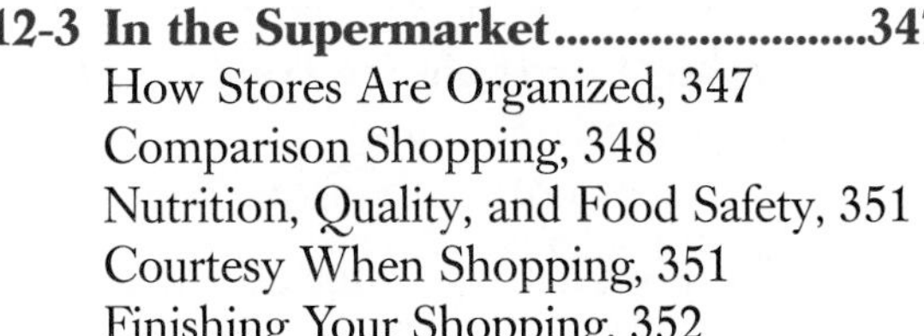

Chapter 13: The Food Supply 356

Chapter 14: Buying for the Kitchen 376

Unit 4: Foods for Meals and Snacks

Chapter 15: Convenience Foods 400

Chapter 16: Vegetables and Fruits 416

Chapter 17: Grains, Legumes, Nuts, and Seeds 438

Chapter 18: Dairy Foods and Eggs 462

Broguiere's
"Milk So Fresh . . .
The Cow Doesn't
Know It's Missing"

Chapter 19: Meat, Poultry, Fish, and Shellfish 490

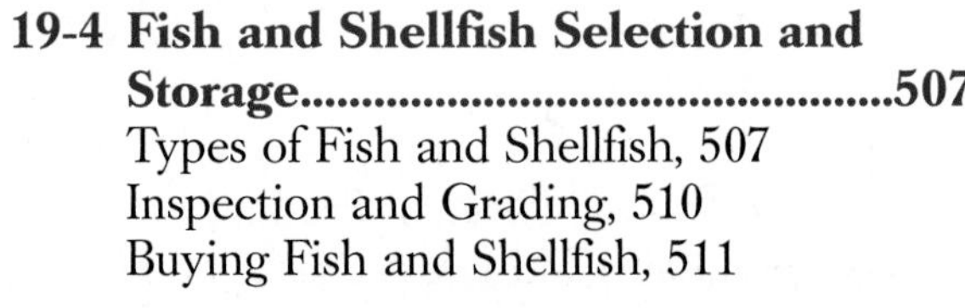

ALL NATURAL
LOUISE'S GARDEN
NO PRESERVATIVES
Louise's Garden
FAT FREE
Balsamic Vinaigrette
NET WT. 12 FL. OZ
No-Oil Dressin
LIME & CILANTRO
12 FL OZ/354 ML

ORGANICALLY PRODUCED BREAD FLOUR
ARROWHEAD MILLS
PREMIUM QUALITY
STONE GROUND
WHOLE WHEAT FLOUR
PYREX
METRIC

Unit 5: Expanding Your Horizons

Chapter 22: Foods of the World 592

Chapter 23: Foods of the U.S. and Canada 626

Chapter 24: Special Topics in Food 646

Chapter 25: Careers in Food and Nutrition 678

Career Wanted

Recipe File

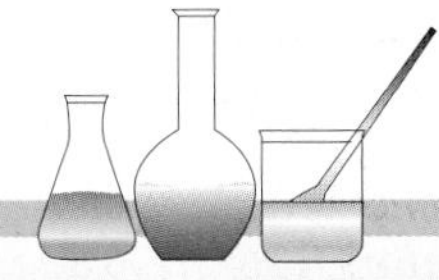

CLOSE-UP ON SCIENCE

Food Science ◆ LAB ◆

Connecting Food and ...

Health:

Math:

Language Arts:

Social Studies:

FOR YOUR HEALTH

Charts and Highlighted Topics

PHOTO CREDITS

Unit Openers
Paul Rico Photography

Chapter Openers
Tim Fuller Photographers

Section Openers, Contents
Joe Mallon Photography

Career Features
Roger B. Bean 181
Corbis
Nathan Benn 107
Ed Eckstein 257
Richard T. Nowitz 85, 487
Bob Rowan/Progressive Images 643
Corbis/Stock Market/Ariel Skelley 133
Corbis/Westlight
Brent Bear 435
Ril Premium 413
Paul A. Souders 525
David Frazier Photolibrary 347, 413
Getty/Don Smetzer 373
Joe Mallon Photography 49, 157, 221, 293, 307, 330, 353, 395, 459, 555, 587, 623, 675, 691

Text Credits
Articulate Graphics 127
Comstock 24, 30, 359, 636R
Corbis/Bettmann 42, 106, 156, 431B
Corbis/Westlight
Adamsmith Productions 164
Australian Picture Library/ John Carnemolla 153T, 456R
Cradoc Bagshaw 630
D. Baswick 469
Brent Bear 607
Steve Chenn 57
Jay Dickman 639L
Randy Faris 638T
Fotografia 165
Lois Frank 573B, 670B
Owen Franken 578B
Philip Gould 635L
J. Habel 628T
Richard Hamilton Smith 498T
D. & J Heaton 611R
R. W. Jones 33
Catherine Karnow 628B
Robert Landau 336
Warren Morgan 150
Chuck O'Rear 37, 217, 613R, 638B, 682
Douglas Peebles 638M
Jim Richardson 358
Bill Ross 41
Steve Smith 167, 595
Nik Wheeler 599B
Mike Yamashita 617T

David Frazier 594B

Tim Fuller Photographers 25, 34L, 34R, 43, 45, 54L, 78, 90, 94, 104, 117L, 117R, 118, 132, 139, 145, 149, 163, 173, 174, 177, 179, 186, 188, 191T, 194, 204, 207, 209, 218L, 218R, 233T, 264, 265, 268, 269, 270, 277, 283, 287, 288, 303, 304, 312, 314, 316, 323, 324, 328, 340, 343L, 343R, 351, 359, 367, 383B, 385, 389, 400, 404L, 404, 408, 409, 420L, 421, 428B, 430, 440T, 440B, 441, 447B, 452T, 465, 470, 473, 483B, 500, 505, 514, 521, 522, 531, 532, 545, 549, 552, 563, 568T, 571, 581R, 585, 593B, 594T, 608T, 608B, 609, 611RT, 611LT, 617B, 620B, 649, 661, 674, 680, 686,

Ann Garvin 275, 581L

Getty/Bill Losh 55
Tony Stone Images 600
Neil Gunderson 370
David Joel 39L
Bob Krist 610L
Mark Lewis 620T
Yves Marcoux 639R
Frank Oberle 361
Richard Passmore 35R
Jim Pickerell 363
Alan Sacks 366
Kevin Schafer 611L
Rene Sheret 103
Hugh Sitton 369
James Strachan 618
Erik Svenson 35L
J.M. Truchet 619T
Robert Torrez 54R

Health Connection 127

Joe Mallon Photography 40, 60, 61T, 61B, 65, 70, 74, 102, 112B, 121B, 123, 124, 142, 153B, 155, 191B, 192L, 192R, 195, 201, 212, 213, 220, 229, 231, 233B, 237, 243R, 246, 248, 262L, 262R, 281, 298L, 298R, 305, 329T, 329B, 339, 342L, 342R, 342B, 345, 346, 348, 35OL, 350R, 379, 380T, 423, 425T, 426, 431T, 442, 445, 452B, 456L, 471B, 483T, 486, 543, 544, 550, 553, 559B, 561, 562, 569, 576, 596, 610R, 612, 619B, 635R, 648, 655, 656, 657, 664, 688T

Kevin May 545

mkw Creative 226, 252, 253T, 253B, 378, 662, 687

Morgan-Cain & Associates 29, 243T, 243B, 272, 327, 362, 364T, 380B, 407, 499T, 499B, 501, 511, 681

Morgan-Cain & Associates/ David Ashby 504, 665

Morgan-Cain & Associates/ Carol Barber 58, 67, 144, 203, 263, 273, 280, 285, 365, 384, 390, 392, 493, 495, 498B, 667, 672, 673,

Photo Edit/Bill Akron 595

Mary Moye-Rowley 82, 234, 235, 244, 245, 247, 317, 352, 425B, 439B, 475B, 492T, 507B, 517, 538, 564, 568B, 570L, 570R, 574, 579, 583, 653, 665, 667, 672, 673

National Pork Council 546

Paul Rico Photography 39R, 46, 83, 91, 100, 112T, 114, 121T, 128, 138, 162, 169, 170, 200, 202, 238, 255, 271, 275, 278, 279, 289, 300, 315L, 315R, 322, 338, 386, 394, 402L, 402R, 403R, 406, 418, 420R, 432, 446, 449, 454, 455, 463B, 464, 472, 477, 479T, 479B, 485, 492B, 502, 506, 509, 515, 519, 520, 530, 536, 539, 540, 548B, 560, 565, 566, 580, 601, 602, 604, 613L, 629, 631L, 631M, 631R, 636L, 651, 669, 679B, 683, 688B, 690

Solar Cooking Org. 371

Stock Food
Douglas Johns Studio 544
Len Mastri Photog. 383, 393

Superstock/Yagi Studio 356

Dana White 94, 181, 205, 214, 254

UNIT 1

Food, Nutrition, and You

INTRODUCING UNIT 1

Before class begins, set up two large tables. On one, place an apple, some grains of corn, a bonnet, a garden trowel, and a cast-iron pot (or other symbols of pioneer cooking methods). On the other table, arrange a basket of tropical fruits, a packaged dinner, canned goods, packages of snacks, a sugary cereal, and a can of diet soda. Ask half the students to be seated at the pioneer table, and half at the other table. Ask the "pioneers" to discuss how they would provide food for their families, both in summer and in winter. How would they keep food from spoiling? Ask the "modern" table to discuss and list how they choose what to eat. How do they pick safe and nutritious food faced with so many choices? Compare the pioneer food system with the risks and responsibilities of choosing nutritious foods today.

UNIT 1

Food,

KEY TO ABILITY LEVELS Each section of the text contains skill-building activities. Each activity has been labeled for use with students of various learning styles and abilities.

L1 **Level 1** activities are basic activities and should be within the range of all students.

L2 **Level 2** activities are average activities and should be within the range of students working at average and above-average levels.

L3 **Level 3** activities are challenging activities designed for the ability range of above-average students.

Nutrition, and You

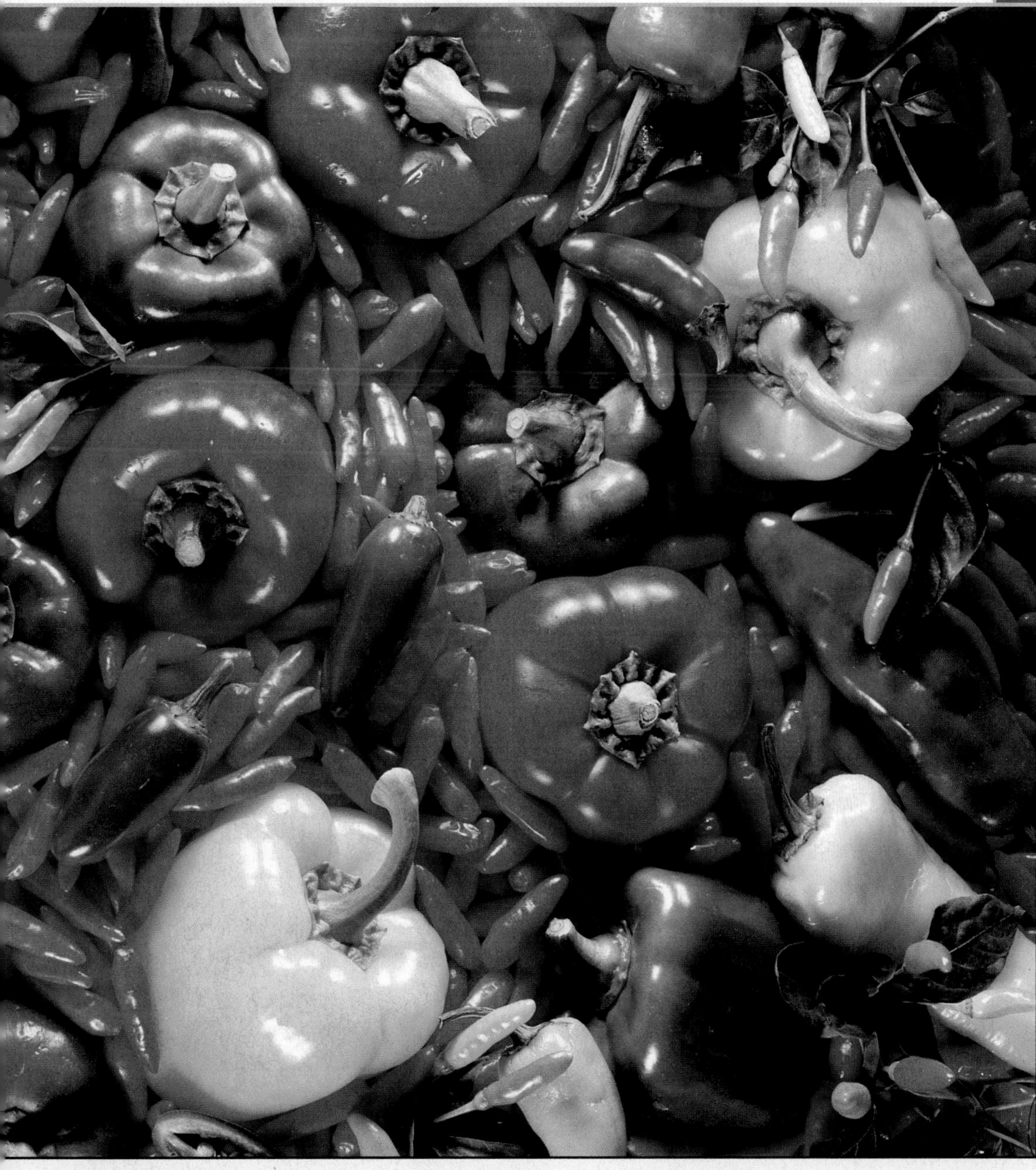

UNIT 1 PROJECT

On the board, write the words *nutrition* and *nutrient*. Ask students to define both words. Note that in this unit, they will be taking a very close look at both terms, their interrelationship, and other terms to which the two relate. In preparation for unit study, have students form small groups to develop a Nutrition Awareness Day. Plans for the day are to include graphics, fact sheets, videotaped interviews, and any other modes of expression that students are able to use. Encourage groups to add and expand the ideas for this project as they come up during the course of study.

As the end of unit study approaches, set aside a class period for Nutrition Awareness Day. Students are to invite members of other classes and the school administration to attend.

PROJECT FOLLOWUP

To assess the success of their Nutrition Awareness Day, students are to jointly develop a questionnaire to be filled out by visitors as they leave the room. Among the types of information students are to probe are the usefulness of the displays and the effects they are likely to have on each individual's future eating habits.

FCCLA Projects

Families First. Students plan and implement an event aimed at improving family members' health and interest in healthful food choices. One example is a family picnic that includes active games and a meal of nutritious foods.

Focus on Children. Students plan and help guide a preschoolers' field trip to a produce farm, farmer's market, or dairy processing plant. Students develop and carry out follow-up activities to help children remember the experience and to reinforce concepts.

CHAPTER

1

Exploring Food Choices

Advance Planning Guide ☑

- Bring to class samples of food items that are likely to be unfamiliar to students.
- Bring to class copies of health magazines with articles emphasizing wellness.
- Arrange for a representative from a local food bank or other community service agency to visit the class.
- Find case studies describing ways in which social pressures influence food choices.
- Videotape several television food commercials.
- Bring to class magazines containing pictures of foods associated with different cultural groups or regions.
- Prepare a list of ethnic foods.
- Bring to class small cubes of cheese or other small food items, and several pairs of chopsticks.
- Arrange for a representative of a local historical society to speak to students.
- Bring in a variety of science textbooks.
- Purchase a small bag each of baked potato crisps and potato chips made with synthetic fat.
- Invite a buyer or other representative from a supermarket to address the class.
- Bring to class an assortment of kitchen appliance catalogs.
- Find or create a scenario involving problem solving and food preparation.

CHAPTER

1

Have you ever noticed what an important role food plays in people's lives? In this chapter, you will find out.

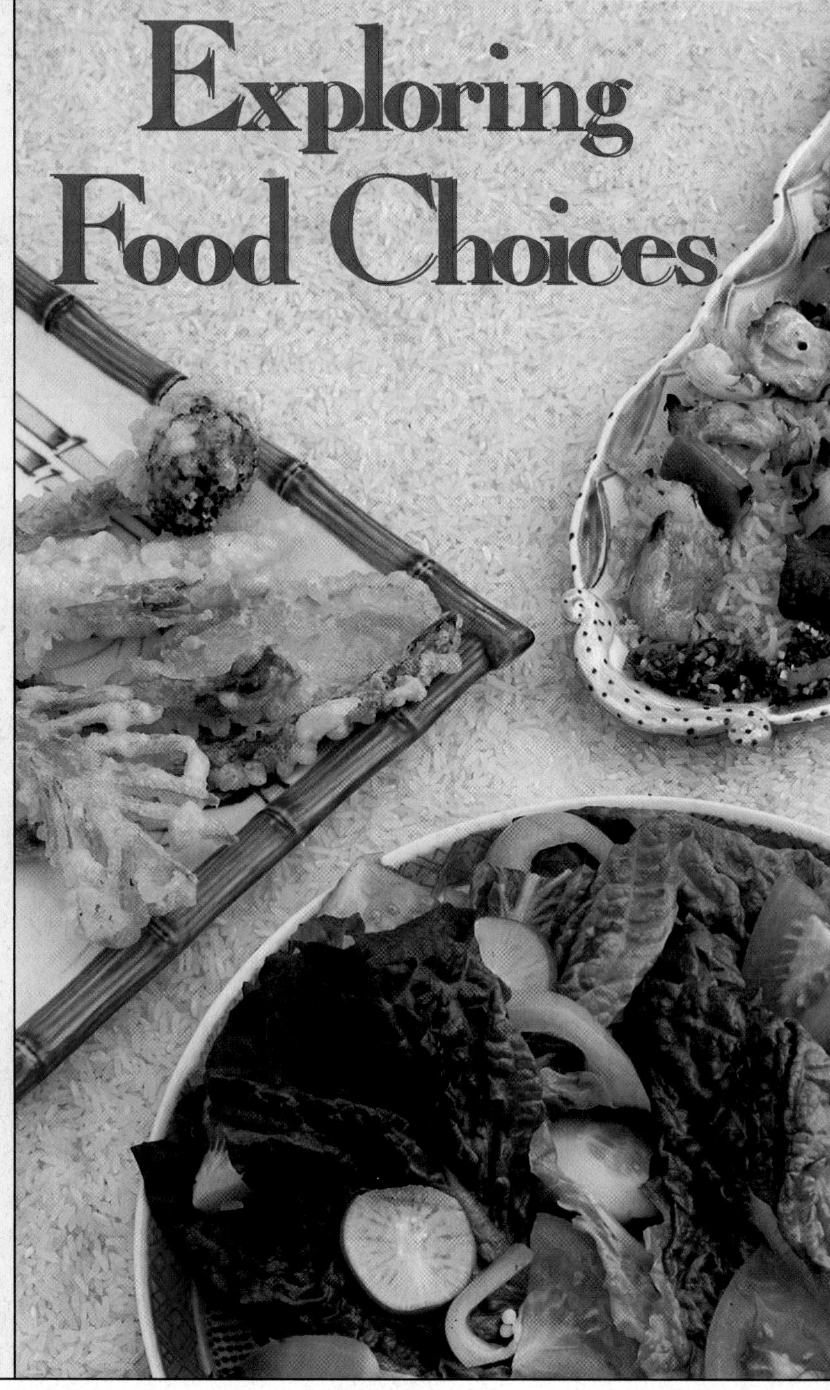

MEETING DIVERSE NEEDS

Celebrating Cultural Diversity. If there are students in the class who have lived in other countries, have them head a panel discussion in which they describe and compare the food customs of other cultures. Ask a volunteer to keep "minutes" of the discussion and later post these in a classroom resource section for reference during the study of Chapter 1.

SECTION 1-1

Food and Health

Objectives

After studying this section, you should be able to:

- Describe the importance of nutrition and wellness.
- Explain how food helps meet physical and psychological needs.

Look for These Terms

nutrients

nutrition

wellness

psychological

If you were asked to identify the three things you need most to survive, how would you respond? Probably, one of your answers would be "food." Food is basic to life. When your body needs food, it lets you know. It registers as an empty feeling in your stomach. You know this feeling better as hunger.

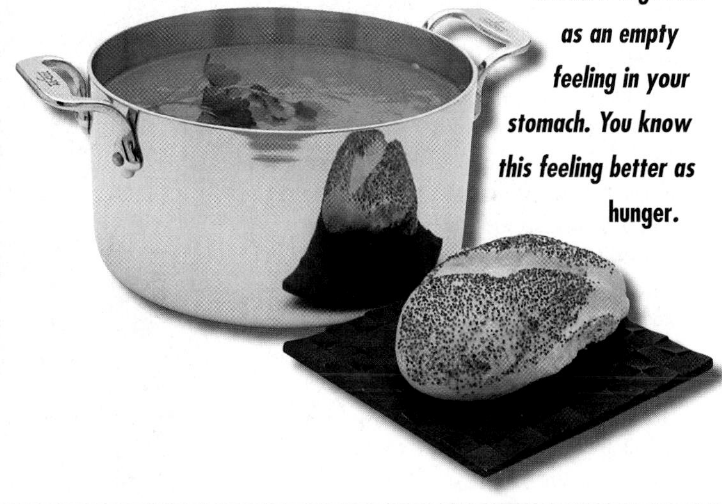

Physical Needs

Food does more than stop hunger pangs. It supplies you with **nutrients**, chemicals from food that your body uses to carry out its functions. These chemicals are so important that they have given rise to a branch of science. That science, called **nutrition**, is the study of nutrients and how they are used by the body.

You have probably also seen or heard the term *nutrition* used in a more popular sense to refer to the effects of a person's food choices on his or her health. If your food choices provide all the nutrients you need in the right amounts, you are said to be practicing good nutrition.

Good nutrition has many benefits. When your body has needed nutrients, you not only feel and look your best, but you also grow and become strong. Your brain works as it should to maximize your thinking skills. In addition, you stay energetic and healthy, both now and later in life.

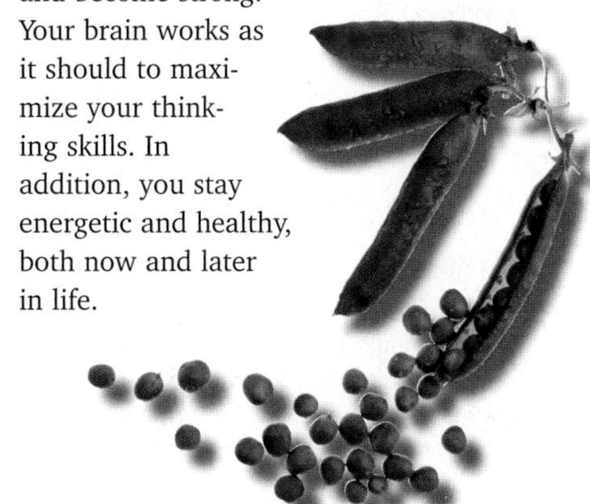

SECTION 1-1

Food and Health

FOCUS

MOTIVATORS

- Bring samples of two or three unfamiliar foods to class and ask volunteers to taste them. Have students explain why they like or dislike the foods.
- On the chalkboard, write the question: Why do we eat? Have students brainstorm as many possible answers as they can.

VOCABULARY ACTIVITY

Write the word *wellness* on the board. Ask how many students have heard or seen this word before. Invite volunteers to provide definitions of the word. Point out that students will be returning to this term again and again during their study of food and nutrition.

STUDY SKILLS

- **Listening.** Invite a group of volunteers to prepare an oral reading of the section.
- Have students read the section and complete the appropriate part of the Chapter 1 Study Guide in the *Student Workbook.*

Section 1-1 Resources

◆ **Student Workbook,** pp. 11, 14

◆ **Teacher Resource Guide**

Lesson Plan 1-1 Organizer

Section 1-1 Quiz

◆ **Effective Instruction CD-ROM**

Exam*View*® *Test Generator*

PowerPoint® Slide #1

◆ **Transparency Package,** CT-1

◆ **Student Motivation Kit**

Reteaching Activities, p. 9

Enrichment Activities

A Global Foods Tour, p. 12

Food Science Resources, pp. 36–39

TEACH

- *Physical Needs (text pages 23-25)*

Journal Activity

Introduce students to the idea of keeping a Wellness Journal throughout the course. Suggest that they set aside a special notebook or folder for this purpose. Explain that they will use the journal to write about personal ideas and experiences. Emphasize that the journal is private. Have them start their journal by listing several ways of practicing wellness.

Writing a Paragraph

Provide students with articles from health magazines emphasizing wellness. Ask students to read the articles, and then write a paragraph describing what wellness means to them. How does their definition compare with that in the articles? L1

FOR YOUR HEALTH

Direct students' attention to the "For Your Health" feature on this page. Invite students to self-administer the questionnaire. Without revealing individual responses to the questions, ask the class as a whole to discuss specific ways in which students can implement behaviors that promote wellness. For example, how might they ensure that they get plenty of rest? How might they go about learning stress management techniques?

FOR YOUR HEALTH

All's Well That Starts Well

Wellness is affected by many decisions you make. Do your decisions promote wellness? To find out, privately answer the following statements "true" or "false" on a separate sheet of paper. Be honest with yourself.

- I eat at least three regular meals each day, beginning with breakfast.
- I have a varied eating plan that includes plenty of fruits, vegetables, and whole grains.
- I drink at least six to eight cups of water every day.
- I get between seven and eight hours of sleep each night.
- I exercise at least 20 to 30 minutes three to four times a week.
- I take safety precautions, such as wearing a seat belt and using protective sporting gear.
- I avoid harmful substances, such as tobacco, alcohol, and other drugs.
- I ask for help when I need it.
- I know where to turn for current and reliable health and nutrition information.
- I can manage stress.
- I get along well with others.
- If I have a problem, I try to work it out.

If you answered "true" to eight or more statements, your health and wellness levels are high. Seven or fewer "true" answers means you should look closely at your wellness plan.

Following Up

- During this course, you'll be asked to write in your Wellness Journal. Begin your journal by listing any items above that you answered as "false." Look for ways to change those responses in the weeks ahead.

◆ **Getting the most out of life depends on feeling your best. What daily routines or habits promote your wellness?**

Wellness

Good nutrition is part of a bigger health picture known as wellness. **Wellness** is a philosophy that encourages people to take responsibility for their own health. Wellness is reflected in both your attitudes and your behaviors. Wellness decisions that influence your health include the following:

- ◆ The food choices you make.
- ◆ The amount of physical activity you get.
- ◆ How you manage your feelings and emotions.
- ◆ How you handle certain social situations.

Technology TIE-IN

Point out that technology is a double-edged sword. To prove this point, ask students to give examples of modern technology that have both improved and detracted from the quality of life. Suggest that the automobile is a prime example, noting that it made it easier for people to get from place to place, while simultaneously replacing more healthful modes of transportation (such as walking) for many people.

By developing habits that promote wellness, you have a better chance of staying healthy and happy throughout your life.

Practicing wellness doesn't guarantee you will never get sick or feel upset. It will, however, help you achieve the highest level of health you possibly can.

Psychological Needs

Besides keeping you physically healthy, food also helps you meet certain psychological needs. **Psychological** (sy-kuh-LAH-jih-kul) means having to do with the mind and emotions. To have good mental and emotional health, a person needs a sense of security, belonging, and enjoyment. Food can help people fulfill each of these psychological needs.

Security

From the moment an infant is born, security is critical. Security is the feeling of safety and well-being, of freedom from harm and want.

Infants first learn to feel secure when they are fed, cared for, and loved. Continuing to have an adequate amount of food to eat helps people build a lasting sense of security. Over time, this feeling enables them to reach out freely to others, to develop, and to explore the world.

Belonging

People's social nature shows as they interact. Whether a quiet evening at home or a lively night out at a party or football game, spending time with others brings a sense of belonging. People need to bond with each other and feel accepted. Food helps promote such bonds.

Food is part of many social events, including weddings and parties. Certain foods are linked to sporting events. Meetings often include food. Even when a friend comes to your house, you probably offer something to eat or drink. Why is it that very few social occasions omit food?

Food makes people feel welcome and at ease. By appeasing hunger, it brings comfort. Food can be a focus of conversation and activity. As a social custom, food adapts to any occasion. Certain foods link to traditions. Certainly, food is a basic part of socializing for many reasons.

◆ **Involving the whole family in food preparation is not only fun but provides opportunities for passing on family traditions. Write a short paragraph about one family food tradition practiced in your home or in the home of a relative.**

- *Psychological Needs (text pages 25-26)*

Discussion Activity

Discuss the role of food in helping to create a sense of belonging to a family or social group. Ask students to come up with and share personal anecdotes that reveal this concept.

Creating Posters

Identify and define the psychological needs that people have. Have students work in groups to identify ways food meets the needs for security, a sense of belonging, and personal enjoyment. Have groups develop posters around these themes, using clippings from magazines or computer clip-art. Display the posters as a bridge to further discussion. L1

Guest Speaker

Invite a representative from a local food bank or other community service agency to talk to students about the effect of food on a person's feelings of security—especially for people who do not know where their next meal may be coming from. As a class, participate in a food drive or other community outreach effort to provide food for people in need. Ask each student to write briefly in his or her Wellness Journal about the experience and what he or she learned from it.

Extending Learning

Psychological Needs—Psychologist Abraham Maslow developed a theory regarding basic human needs. It states that people have several levels of needs. The higher levels build on the lower ones.

The basic physical needs must be met first. Next comes the need for security and safety, followed by the need for love and belonging. The fourth level is the need for self-esteem, self-worth, and confidence. Self-actualization, the highest need, is the level of self-fulfillment and creative growth.

ASSESS

REVIEW

- Ask students to summarize the main ideas in this section.
- Have students complete the Section Review. (Answers appear below.)

EVALUATION

- Have interested students work together to prepare and stage a short, original skit that demonstrates the ways food affects people physically and psychologically.
- Have students take the quiz for Section 1-1. (Use the quiz in the *Teacher Resource Guide,* or construct your own with the **ExamView®** *Test Generator* on the *Effective Instruction CD-ROM.*)

RETEACHING

- Have students make lists of ways in which food satisfies various needs. Students are to leave out a key word in each list entry, then work with a partner at completing each others' lists.
- Refer to the *Reteaching Activities* booklet for the Section 1-1 activity sheet.

CLOSE

Have students draw two large overlapping circles, labeling one *physical,* the other *psychological.* Students are to complete their diagrams by showing ways that food meets one, the other, or both of these types of needs.

Because food is a necessity, families must make food plans and preparations every day. By working together as they shop, fix meals, and clean up and by sharing mealtimes, family members strengthen their bonds.

Enjoyment

What are your favorite foods? Does the thought of hot pizza or fresh-baked cookies make your mouth water? When giving pleasure, food has emotional impact. It satisfies the senses and makes you feel good.

Pleasure comes as much from creating food as from eating it. Turning an assortment of ingredients into a delicious dish to enjoy can be quite satisfying. Sharing the dish with others makes enjoyment even greater.

The human need for food is obviously complex. In so many ways, food contributes to what you are and what you will become. That's why you'll benefit from this course as you learn about good nutrition and making wise food choices.

Q ***I often eat when I'm not really hungry. Why am I doing that and how can I stop?***

A People sometimes turn to food for emotional reasons, which can lead to unhealthful weight gain and other physical problems. While food adds enjoyment to life, eating should not fulfill emotional needs that are better met in other ways. Pay attention to your thoughts and feelings when you eat. Do you feel stressed or bored? Is something troubling you? Are you turning to food just for comfort? Once you recognize causes, you can deal with them, whether that means exercising to relieve stress, finding a new interest to stop boredom, or seeking help with a problem.

Section 1-1 Review & Activities

1. What is nutrition? Identify two health benefits of good nutrition.
2. How does food help fulfill a need for security?
3. How does food help fulfill a need for enjoyment?
4. **Synthesizing.** How might a flood or other natural disaster threaten food supplies? How would this affect people's sense of security? How might the people react?
5. **Analyzing.** Do you think physical and psychological needs for food could ever conflict? Explain.
6. **Applying.** List foods you might serve at each of the following events: a school team victory party, a surprise birthday party for a friend, a wedding anniversary celebration for an adult couple. How do these foods help meet various needs?

Answers to Section 1-1 Review & Activities

1. The study of nutrients and how they are used by the body. See page 23.
2. Having enough to eat brings a feeling of well-being and freedom from want. Starts at birth and helps throughout life.
3. Food gives pleasure in eating, preparing, and sharing. It satisfies the senses and gives a good feeling.
4. It may destroy crops and cut off supply routes, threatening sense of security. People might become angry or feel helpless.
5. Yes. Possible answer: Overeating because of boredom or anxiety can lead to obesity and related physical problems.
6. Answers will vary.

SECTION 1-2

Objectives

After studying this section, you should be able to:

- Identify social influences on food choices.
- Describe how food choices are influenced by available resources and technology.
- Identify personal influences on food choices.

Look for These Terms

culture
media
resources
technology
lifestyle

Influences on Food Choices

Tom loves parmesan cheese, but his sister Abby can't stand the smell. Which foods do you like or dislike? More important, where do these preferences come from? Even though you may not be aware of them, many influences are at work when you make food choices.

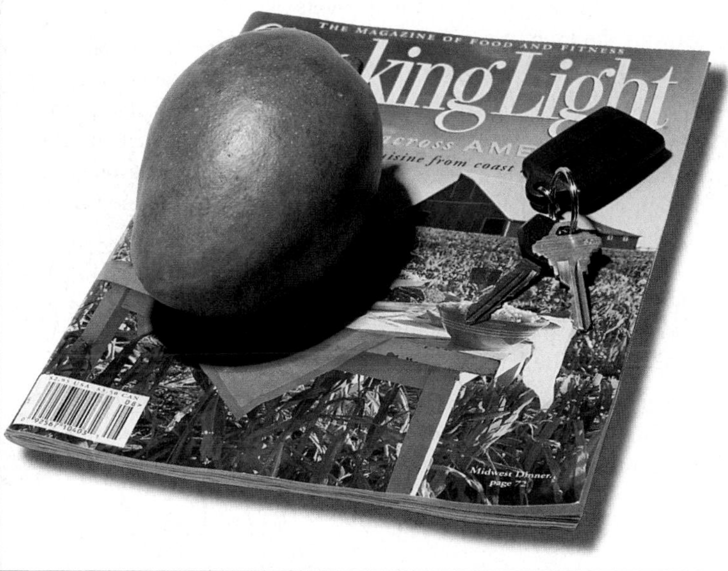

Social Influences

Although you are an individual, you are also a member of various social groups. Many of your preferences begin with the influence of culture, family, friends, and the media.

Culture

Culture refers to the shared customs, traditions, and beliefs of a large group of people, such as a nation, race, or religious group. These customs are part of what defines a group's unique identity.

Food customs are one aspect of culture. Every culture has its own traditional ways of preparing, serving, and eating foods. Some of these customs are one of a kind. The Mexican dish pollo con mole poblano, for instance, combines chicken with chocolate. Other customs are dictated by geography. The hot climate throughout much of southeastern Asia is ideal for growing rice, which is why rice is a staple starch in most southeast Asian cuisine.

Modern trends that have "shrunk" the world —high-speed transportation and communication, for instance—have made it possible for people to share and experience the foods of

Section 1-2 Resources

◆ **Student Workbook**, pp. 11, 15
◆ **Teacher Resource Guide**
Lesson Plan 1-2 Organizer
Section 1-2 Quiz
◆ **Effective Instruction CD-ROM**
Exam*View*® *Test Generator*

◆ **Student Motivation Kit**
Reteaching Activities, p. 10
Enrichment Activities
A Global Foods Tour, p. 157
Skills for Making Food Choices, pp. 7–8

SECTION 1-2
Influences on Food Choices

FOCUS

MOTIVATORS

- Ask students to describe one of their family's favorite foods and explain why it is special. (For example, it might be a recipe handed down through generations of the family or one associated with a particular cultural tradition.)
- Have students make up associative lists by dividing a page of their Wellness Journal into two columns. On one side, they are to note events (e.g., the movies, a baseball game). On the other, they are to note foods associated with each event (e.g., popcorn, hot dogs).

VOCABULARY ACTIVITY

Direct students to the vocabulary terms. Explain that one of the terms is an irregular plural (a plural form that does not take a final *-s*). Have students find and define all the words in a dictionary, noting the irregular plural (*media*) with its singular (*medium*).

STUDY SKILLS

- **Guided Reading.** Have students look at the headings within Section 1-2 to preview the concepts that will be discussed.
- Have students read the section and complete the appropriate part of the Chapter 1 Study Guide in the *Student Workbook*.

TEACH

- *Social Influences (text pages 27-28)*

Discussion Activity

Ask students to explain the term *culture.* Proceed to a discussion of examples of cultural traditions that influence food choices. (You may include items from the lists students developed during the second Motivator activity for this section.)

Comparison Activity

Invite students who have lived in another region of the country to present a brief oral report describing the differences and similarities in food customs they have found between that region and the one they currently reside in. Be sure to include differences as might apply only to terminology (for example, *flapjacks* versus *griddle cakes* versus *pancakes*).

Case Studies

Provide students with case studies describing ways in which social pressures can influence food choices. Have students write and share brief analyses of the cases they have been assigned. Where applicable, encourage students to provide additional examples from their own experiences (for example, they were induced by peer pressure to go out to eat just to be sociable when they were not all that hungry). L2

many cultures. Most cities in this country have Chinese and Italian restaurants. What foods from other cultures have you tried?

Family

Families probably have the single greatest influence on food choices. When you were very young, family members chose food for you. As you grew, you learned food habits by following the examples of family members. Many of their food preferences and eating patterns likely became yours as well.

Families sometimes develop special food traditions. One family often enjoys pancakes for Saturday night meals. Another never serves pork chops without applesauce. A family's food customs may reflect cultural background. For instance, the Masinelli family always serves two main dishes at Thanksgiving—turkey and lasagna.

People tend to feel comfortable with familiar foods. You might think you dislike foods that were never served at home. Part of the adventure of eating, however, is finding foods you enjoy by trying something new.

Friends

Along with growth and greater independence comes the influence of friends. Because eating is a social experience, time with friends often includes food. When you are together, your friends influence what and where you eat, and vice versa.

If your friends have different cultural backgrounds, you might learn to enjoy the foods they commonly eat. What foods have you learned to like due to a friendship?

The Media

In this information age, daily messages come from television, radio, movies, newspapers, magazines, advertisements, and the Internet. These sources, known collectively as the media, are a major influence on food choices. News reports shape decisions to eat—or not eat—a certain food. Magazines make people aware of new food trends.

Advertising has an especially powerful influence on people. Have you ever bought a particular cereal or snack food because a TV commercial made it sound so good? You might even choose the food without noticing the influence.

To make wise food choices, you need to understand the media's effect. After analyzing messages, you can manage your responses.

Q **My friends and I often eat together, but they choose food I don't want. What can I do?**

A Peer pressure is the desire to be like others in your circle of friends. This pressure increases during the teen years and influences decisions about actions, clothing, and even foods. One teen has friends who often eat high-calorie foods with little nutritional value. The pressure to join them is strong. How can you manage in similar situations? Going against the group isn't easy, but health should be your priority. Show confidence in your actions. Don't be judgmental, but quietly order different foods or add a touch of humor. True friends will respect your decisions. They may even learn from the example you set.

HOME & COMMUNITY CONNECTION

Have students research social events in their family or community that revolve around food. Possibilities include family picnics, company picnics, founder's day celebrations, and ethnic street fairs. If it can be arranged, students with access to video cameras might be asked to videotape one such event, interviewing people present with regard to the origin of the event and associated food customs. Play the videotapes for the whole class.

Connecting Food and Math

Food Advertising and Your Health

Each year, advertisers spend millions of dollars to sell food products. What types of foods are advertised the most? Study the pie chart below. Use the data in the chart to answer the questions that follow.

Think About It

1. Which food category gets the least advertising? Why do you think this is so?
2. Approximately how much more is spent on desserts, snacks, and soft drinks than on all the other categories combined?

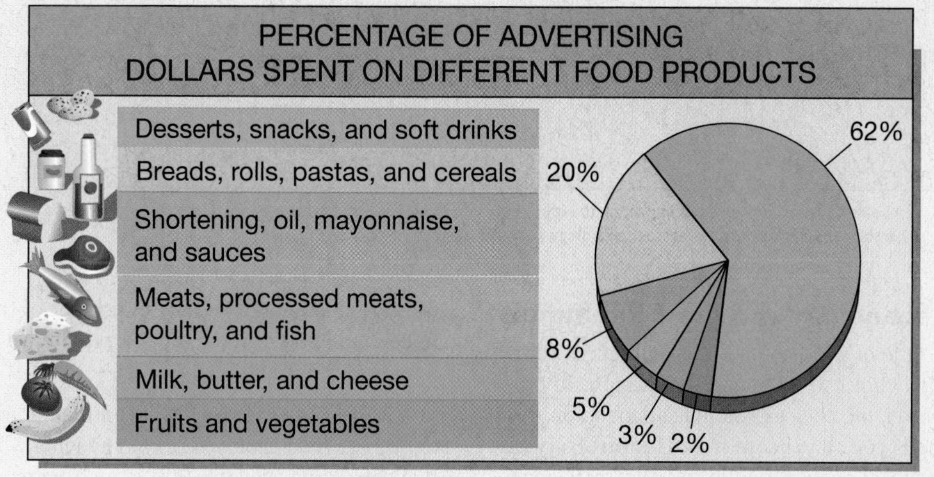

Available Resources

Your choice of foods depends a great deal on the resources that are available to you. **Resources** are objects and qualities that can help you reach a goal. For example, this textbook is a resource that helps you learn about food and nutrition.

Many resources are involved in obtaining the food you need. Money is an obvious one. Time, knowledge, abilities, equipment, and a place to buy food are also important.

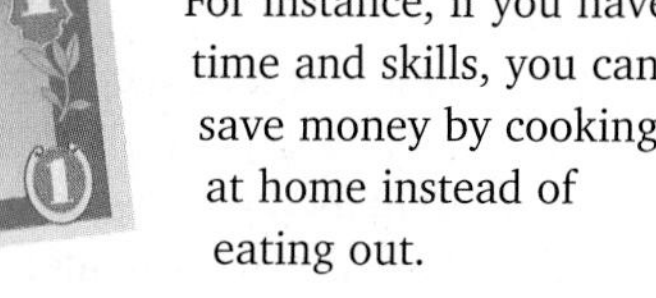

People's food choices differ because their resources differ. No one has an endless supply of all the resources, but everyone has some. You can often substitute one resource for another that is in short supply. For instance, if you have time and skills, you can save money by cooking at home instead of eating out.

FOOD SCIENCE

Food Processing

The science of food processing allows highly developed countries such as the United States to create high-tech methods of preserving food. This increases the variety and amount of food available. Examples of high-tech preservation techniques include freeze-drying, irradiation, and controlled-atmosphere packaging.

- *Available Resources*
- *Personal Influences*
  (text pages 29-31)

Discussion Activity

Discuss with students the concept of substituting resources. Emphasize that when some resources are in short supply, wise use of other resources may suffice in meeting specific goals. Ask students to give examples of various situations in which this happens. (If you lack the money to buy a birthday gift, you might call upon the resources of time and skill to make one of your own.)

Out-of-Class Project

Have students interview a parent or other adult in the household to discuss how time and other resources influence food choice and food preparation at home. Invite students to share and compare the results of their interviews, retaining especially useful ideas in a classroom resource folder. L1

USING CONNECTING FOOD AND MATH

Make sure students are able to read and interpret a pie chart by asking pertinent questions—for example, What percentage of advertising dollars is spent in a typical year on desserts, snacks, and soft drinks? (62 percent).

Answers to "Think About It"

1. Fruits and vegetables. Answers will vary.
2. Twenty-four percent (62 percent minus the sum of all the other percentages, or 38).

TEACH cont.

- *Available Resources*
- *Personal Influences (text pages 29-31)*

Discussion Activity

Ask students to explain why it is important to recognize the effect of moods on food *choices.* (Some food choices determined by moods may be unwise; by recognizing the influence of moods, you may be able to curb unhealthy impulses.)

Research Activity

Have students use print or online resources to investigate ways in which technology has influenced our food supply, as well as cutting-edge discussions of ways in which technology is likely to influence our food choices in the future. Have students report their findings to the class.

Forecast Activity

Have students write a short prediction of what their lifestyles might be like in five years and how their food habits might change as a result. Set aside time for students to share and compare forecasts.

Videotape Viewing

Prior to class, make videotapes of several television food commercials for different products. Ask students to write reviews of the ads to determine the methods advertisers use to persuade people to buy their products, as well as their effectiveness. Does the ad appeal to viewers' emotions? Their values? Their priorities? Allow time for students to share reviews.

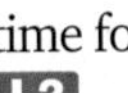

◆ **Technology has had an enormous impact on the foods available to us. Look up the term *agriculture* in an encyclopedia or other resource. Explain how changes in technology have increased the availability of foods to enjoy.**

Technology and the Food Supply

One of the resources that influences your food choices is the basic food supply. In other words, the choices you make depend on the foods you can choose from. **Technology**, the practical application of scientific knowledge, influences the food supply and, therefore, your choices.

Suppose you could step into a time machine that could whisk you 300 years into the past. What would your food choices be like? In this world of long ago, almost everything you ate would be grown by your family or your neighbors. In warm weather, food would be plentiful, but spoilage would be a problem. In cold weather, the challenge would be to make food last until the next harvest.

Today, modern technology has greatly increased the options available to you. Planes and trucks bring food from around the world to your local market. You can also take a frozen, already-prepared main dish out of the freezer and pop it in the microwave. In just minutes it's hot and ready to eat.

Advances in technology will continue to add to people's food choices. Can you imagine what foods might be available 300 years from now?

Personal Influences

Your lifestyle, values, priorities, and emotions also influence your choice of foods. They are part of the reason that your food choices are uniquely your own.

Your Lifestyle

Lifestyle refers to a person's typical way of life. Your lifestyle includes how you spend your time and what is most important to you. Lifestyle has a strong influence on what and where you eat, how and where you shop, and how you prepare food.

Reinforcing Key Skills

Present the following problem to student groups. Allow time for them to discuss and compare their responses.

Communication—Because lifestyle is often a function of the culture in which we live, people from other cultures may approach food choices in an entirely different manner from our own. Present this scenario to students: Three students from other countries are visiting your school. You have been asked to help them learn about traditions and customs in the United States. The visitors are from India, Mexico, and Japan. How do you approach this task?

A teen's lifestyle commonly revolves around school, family, friends, leisure activities, and possibly, a part-time job. A busy lifestyle can affect your food choices. For instance, you may buy a snack from a vending machine just because the food is available, easy to carry, and easy to eat quickly.

Values and Priorities

Not everyone spends time or money in the same way. People make choices based on their personal values and priorities.

Food choices also depend on personal values and priorities. Some people enjoy the time they spend preparing meals. Others would rather spend the time on another activity, such as a hobby or a sport.

It's not always easy to juggle your priorities. Time, money, health, enjoyment—all are important to most people. As you continue to study food, you will learn ways to meet the challenge of a busy lifestyle.

Your Emotions

Emotions and mood can influence food choices. Some people rely on certain foods to make them feel better when they are sad or depressed. They may choose different foods if they are happy or when they are celebrating an event.

Food often carries strong associations—both pleasant and unpleasant. For instance, Jarod can still remember being forced to eat spinach as a child. He does not like spinach to this day. On the other hand, Tonya loves spinach. It reminds her of meals at her grandmother's house and the associated feelings of comfort and security.

As you can see, even a decision as seemingly simple as what to have for lunch is influenced by many factors. Your background, your lifestyle today, and the world around you all play a part in your food choices.

Section 1-2 Review & Activities

1. What is culture? How does it relate to food choices?
2. What is a resource? Name five resources that are involved in obtaining food.
3. What is a lifestyle? Give an example of how a particular lifestyle can influence a person's choice of foods.
4. **Analyzing.** Think about ways in which your family has influenced your personal food choices. Identify one or two of your family's food traditions, and explain where they came from and why your family observes them.
5. **Extending.** Imagine that you are an inventor in the next century. Describe a new food product or kitchen appliance you would like to invent. Tell how it would affect people's food choices.
6. **Applying.** Find three food advertisements in magazines. Tell whether each makes you want to buy the product. Explain your reactions.

Answers to Section 1-2 Review & Activities

1. See the definition on page 27; culture helps shape food preferences.
2. An object or quality that can help you reach a goal; any five: money, time, knowledge, abilities, equipment, a place to buy food.
3. A person's typical way of life; possible answer: a person with a hectic lifestyle may have little time to eat and may hastily choose foods that fail to promote wellness.
4. Answers will vary.
5. Answers will vary. Encourage students to be creative.
6. Answers will vary. Remind students to support their answers.

ASSESS

REVIEW

- Ask students to summarize the main ideas in this section.
- Have students complete the Section Review. (Answers appear below.)

EVALUATION

- Have students prepare a presentation on the role of social influences and resources on food choices. Invite visitors to the classroom to take part in this educational presentation.
- Have students take the quiz for Section 1-2. (Use the quiz in the *Teacher Resource Guide,* or construct your own with the **Exam***View*® *Test Generator* on the *Effective Instruction CD-ROM.*)

RETEACHING

- Have small groups of students copy the main heads from the section on to sheets of paper. Each student is to think of two good questions for each main heading. Students are then to swap papers and attempt to answer the questions they have received.
- Refer to the *Reteaching Activities* booklet for the Section 1-2 activity sheet.

CLOSE

Ask students to identify all the influences on their personal eating habits on a page in their Wellness Journals. Next to each influence they should write a private symbol indicating whether that particular influence is positive or negative. They should then work at eliminating or changing all negative influences.

SECTION
1-3
Food and Culture

FOCUS

MOTIVATORS

- Have students extend the associative lists in their Wellness Journal by adding holidays (for example, Thanksgiving, Easter) and foods associated with that day (turkey, ham).
- Provide students with magazines and ask them to find pictures of foods associated with different cultural groups or regions around the world. Have students use the pictures to create posters, identifying the foods pictured and the culture or region with which they are associated. Have students present their posters to the class.

VOCABULARY ACTIVITY

Pronounce the term listed under "Look for This Term." Ask a volunteer to find the term in the section and read aloud its definition.

STUDY SKILLS

- **Outlining.** Have students read the section and outline it by copying the headers on paper and leaving space after each one. Students are to write a sentence in their own words, summarizing the content under each header.
- Have students read the section and complete the appropriate part of the Chapter 1 Study Guide in the *Student Workbook.*

SECTION
1-3

Objectives

After studying this section, you should be able to:

- Identify three aspects of culture.
- Give examples of cultural food customs.
- Explain how food customs have evolved throughout history.

Look for This Term

ethnic group

Food and Culture

Eric, Cyrise, and Amber were having lunch in the food court at the mall. Each went to a different food stand. Eric returned with wonton soup and stir-fried chicken. Cyrise chose a burrito, while Amber decided on shish kebab and pita bread.

Understanding Culture

The foods Eric, Cyrise, and Amber chose were all made from basic ingredients, such as grains, vegetables, and meat or poultry. However, each dish was distinctly different. Each represented the food customs of a different culture.

As noted in the previous section, *culture* refers to the shared customs, traditions, and beliefs of a group of people. What, however, constitutes "a group of people"? This question has several possible answers:

- **Geography.** People who live in a particular region or part of the world may be said to make up a cultural group.
- **Heritage.** A common heritage, or past, is another defining feature of a cultural group. Native Americans, descendants of the first people to live in the Americas, are one such group. Some people now living in the United States were born or have ancestral roots in other cultures. A cultural group based on common heritage is often called an **ethnic group**.
- **Religion.** Religion is another basis for defining cultural groups. Members of a particular faith usually have a common set of beliefs and follow specific practices.

Blending Cultures

If you were to take a survey of students in your school, you would probably find many cultures represented. Some students might trace their cultural roots to Ireland, others to Korea, still others to Venezuela. As such a mix reveals, the United States is a society of many cultures. Many people view this cultural richness as a great strength. People within the society are free to share and explore the customs of all the different cultures.

Section 1-3 Resources

◆ **Student Workbook,** pp. 12, 16
◆ **Teacher Resource Guide**
Lesson Plan 1-3 Organizer
Section 1-3 Quiz
◆ **Effective Instruction CD-ROM**
Exam*View*® *Test Generator*

◆ **Student Motivation Kit**
Reteaching Activities, p. 11
Enrichment Activities
A Global Foods Tour, p. 11

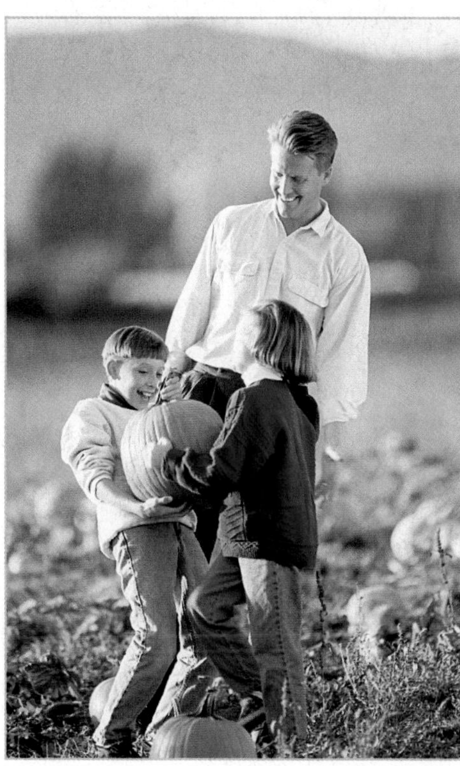

◆ **Food-related celebrations are common in this country. One town's annual pumpkin festival offers everything from pumpkin ice cream to pumpkin chili. Name a food custom associated with each of the four seasons.**

Understanding Cultural Food Customs

Food is essential in the everyday life of individuals and families. It can also play an important role in celebrations and ceremonies. It is not surprising that food customs are often a focal point in cultural traditions.

INFOLINK

For more on regional foods of the United States and Canada, see Chapter 23.

Examples of Food Customs

Food customs usually involve certain kinds of food, but that's just the beginning. They also include how food is prepared, how it is served, and how it is eaten.

Unique Foods

The foods chosen by Eric, Cyrise, and Amber have their roots in different parts of the world. For instance, wonton soup is a dish that originated in China. Wontons are dumplings filled with minced vegetables and meat. Shish kebab, chunks of meat threaded on a skewer, originated in the Middle East. So did pita bread, a distinctive flat bread that forms a pocket.

Within a nation, there may also be distinct regional food traditions. In the United States, well-known regional foods include cornbread and grits from the South, chili and barbecue from Texas, sourdough bread from San Francisco, and clam chowder from New England. Although these foods are now available all over the United States, each was developed in a particular section of the country.

Dietary Laws

Religious beliefs often include dietary laws, or rules about what foods may be eaten. For example, Jews who follow a kosher diet do not eat meat and dairy products in the same meal. Hindus do not eat beef because they consider cattle sacred animals. Muslims eat no pork.

TEACH

- *Understanding Culture*
- *Understanding Cultural Food Customs (text pages 32-36)*

Discussion Activity

Have several students volunteer to lead a discussion of different types of cultural groups, such as ethnic groups and religious groups, and the effects their heritage has on their food choices.

Visual Display Activity

Refer students to the paragraph with the heading "Blending Cultures" on p. 32. Note that the United States has been called a cultural melting pot. Have students working in groups investigate the ethnic distribution of cultural groups who migrated to this country in the late 18th and early 19th centuries. Groups are then to create a picture illustrating this rich diversity. Pictures are to include food and festivals in which food plays an important role.

Research

Provide a list of ethnic foods. Ask students to research at least one food and report on its origin and any customs that may be associated with it. L1

DID You Know?

- Hot dogs and hamburgers—those most "American" of foods—are both of German origin?

Extending Learning

Cultural Boundaries—To help students better understand the distinction between culture and nation, point out that foods know no political boundaries. Amplify on this point by noting that in the Dolomites, located along Italy's German border, Italians eat foods with German-sounding names such as *speck* (SHPEK), a robust wurst-like sausage. Another food that originated in this area, *gnocchi* (NYO-kee), a pasta, consists of small potato dumplings similar to *knockerl,* eaten across the border in Germany.

- *Understanding Cultural Food Customs (text pages 33-36)*

Discussion Activity

Ask students to identify differences in mealtime etiquette in different parts of the world. Ask: Are there differences among the regions of the United States?

Demonstration

If there are students in the class of Asian descent and/or who are especially adept at using chopsticks, have them conduct a chopstick clinic. They are to demonstrate the proper use of this dining utensil, beginning with hand placement and proceeding to the grasping of foods. Provide each student in the class with a set of chopsticks and small bits of food (such as cubes of cheese) so that they may practice the technique.

Book Review

Refer students to the portion of the text on this page that discusses dietary laws and religions and their effect on people's food choices. Help interested students locate copies of *Rules for Physical Health,* by 13th-century physician and rabbinical scholar Moses Maimonides. In the book Maimonides accounts for various dietary customs practiced among Jews and why they are advocated. Have reviewers share their printed reviews in class. L2

◆ **Food customs affect not only what is eaten, but how foods are served. With what cultures do you associate the eating utensils in these two pictures? In what ways have lines between the customs of these cultures been blurred?**

Cultural Etiquette

Social customs for serving and eating food also vary depending on the culture. Not all cultures use forks, knives, and spoons for eating. In China, Japan, and Korea, chopsticks are the traditional eating utensils. In some countries, such as India, Afghanistan, Algeria, and Morocco, it is considered proper to eat many foods using the fingers. In some nations of Africa, food is scooped up with a flat bread called *injera.*

Special Occasions

Some food customs relate to holidays, festivals, and religious observances. To celebrate the Chinese New Year, Judy Chen helps her mother make New Year's dumplings. The small, smooth, round dumplings are made of rice powder and water and are filled with a sweet soybean paste. Their shape symbolizes good fortune. For Easter, Poles and Ukrainians color eggs in complex designs. In Italy, a popular Easter food is a ring-shaped coffee cake with colored eggs tucked into the top.

Sometimes food itself is the theme for a festival. Harvest festivals have been common since ancient times. In the United States, Thanksgiving is the official harvest festival. Many communities also have their own festivals to celebrate the harvest of locally grown foods.

Not all holiday customs involve special foods. On Yom Kippur, the Jewish faith observes the Day of Atonement by fasting. Catholics refrain from eating meat on certain church holy days. During Ramadan, a month-long religious observance, Muslims do not eat or drink during the daylight hours.

Extending Learning

Nutrition—The prohibition against eating pork, common among followers of the Jewish and Islamic religions, arose long ago and relates to early outbreaks of disease purportedly spread by these animals. Students might be encouraged to investigate the spread of trichinosis, a foodborne illness, well into the late 20th century caused by eating pork that had not been sufficiently heated. Discuss other food health trends that have arisen in recent decades related to contamination by microbial organisms in meats.

How Food Customs Evolve

The many cultural groups dispersed throughout the world have many varied ways of preparing, serving, and eating food. None of these food customs can be considered better than any other. Different customs arise naturally as a result of different circumstances. For instance, you may be used to eating left-overs for lunch or dinner. In Japan, this would be considered unusual, even strange. This cultural difference can be understood if you realize that most Japanese do not have large refrigerators for food storage. Food is purchased fresh to be eaten that day. Dining on leftovers would be viewed as eating "old" food.

Food Customs Throughout History

A journey through history can help you understand food customs. In the distant past, cultural groups were limited in their food choices to items they could raise or gather locally. How these foods were cooked often depended on the types and amount of fuel available. For example, in many Asian countries, cooking fuel was scarce. To conserve fuel, food was cut into small pieces that would cook quickly.

Economic conditions in some cultures led to food distinctions along social class lines. The rich, who could afford the finest foods, dined on elegant fare prepared by top chefs. The rest of the people ate simple meals—typically, soup made from whatever food was available, accompanied by coarse, dark bread made from ground whole grains.

◆ **The status of regional dishes sometimes changes. Bouillabaisse, an elegant fish stew served in the south of France, began as a "peasant" dish consisting of leftover fish sold at day's end to local housewives. Investigate the origins of a dish from another culture that you have sampled.**

FOOD SCIENCE

Preservation

Sometimes political or economic conditions may necessitate a change in food customs or preparation techniques. For example, when the United States entered World War I, a method was needed to preserve food for armies at the front. For the first time, the United States began dehydrating foods on a large scale. This provided a lightweight, compact, long-lasting food source for the armed forces.

Today, dehydration is a major method of food preservation. Techniques have been improved, so the taste and texture of the foods are retained better than before.

- *Understanding Cultural Food Customs (text pages 33-36)*

Discussion Activity

Discuss with students why different customs arise in different countries and regions. Ask: What effect has high-speed travel had on food customs and preferences?

Making a Map

Have students make maps tracing the development and spread of specific food customs. Students should be instructed to use different colors and lines with occasional arrow heads to show the path foods took. Display the maps, and conclude with a discussion of this phenomenon. Ask: What may have prompted cultures to adopt unfamiliar foods? **L2**

VISUAL LEARNING ***Using the Photographs***

Have students study the photographs on this page. Make sure they understand what each depicts. Ask a volunteer to read aloud the caption. Note that one food considered a luxury in our own society was once fed to servants of the rich. Ask students to guess what that food might be. After allowing ample time for guessing, hold up a picture of a cooked lobster. Note that lobsters used to wash up on shores along the East Coast and were there for the taking.

TEACH cont.

- *A World of Food Choices (text page 36)*

Guest Speaker

Invite a representative of a local historical society to discuss food customs in your area 100, 200, and possibly even 1000 years ago. Each student is to prepare three good questions to ask.

Television Viewing

Students are to watch a cooking show on television and identify the cultural origins of the foods demonstrated. Students are to take notes as they watch, listing and then bringing to class their lists of special equipment (such as woks) and techniques (for example, stir-frying) that were used to prepare the food. Allow class time for students to compare and share lists. **L2**

Analyzing Restaurant Menus

Provide students with local restaurant menus and have students identify examples of regional, ethnic, and international food choices on the menus. Discuss the wide variety of foods available in the United States. **L1**

Small Group Project

Divide the class into small groups. Each group is to develop a timeline that traces the use of a certain food staple (such as wheat, rice, or corn) throughout known history. Timelines should show new technologies that influenced changes in the ways foods are used.

These and other food traditions were passed down from one generation to the next. Additionally, changes occurred along the way. Explorers took some of their own foods with them on their journeys and brought back strange foods from distant lands. Invading armies often brought new food customs with them.

European explorers who reached the Western Hemisphere found an abundance of foods eaten by the Native Americans. The explorers brought back samples and seeds of foods that were not found in Europe, such as dry beans, corn, tomatoes, potatoes, sweet potatoes, and cassava, a type of root. Over the centuries, some of these foods became popular in the Eastern Hemisphere.

As food customs traveled around the world, they were often changed because of unavailable ingredients or personal tastes. Sometimes a new dish resulted. For example, chop suey is an American invention based on the Chinese style of cooking.

A World of Food Choices

Today, the world is becoming "smaller." People and foods can be flown thousands of miles in a few hours. Satellite links and the Internet allow instant communication between people in remote corners of the globe. As a result, food customs are shared the world over. Foods grown halfway around the world are sold in your supermarket. Television programs and Internet sites can show you scenes of other countries and tell you how to prepare dishes from foreign lands.

It is no surprise, therefore, that ethnic and international foods are now an everyday part of American life. Supermarkets routinely stock a wide variety of ethnic foods, and many restaurants include an assortment on their menus. You probably enjoy many such foods, from tacos to pasta, without thinking of them as being unusual. They have become as familiar to Americans as steak and potatoes.

Connecting Food and Social Studies

Family Food Traditions

Traditions create bonds that unite members of busy families. As traditions are repeated, families look forward to them as signs of stability and continuation.

Many family traditions involve food and holidays. A favorite bread, pastry, cookie, or candy might be enjoyed every year for a celebration. A family might share an individual thanks or poem before a special meal. Maybe tradition says that Grandpa mashes the potatoes at an annual gathering. A family member could choose the menu for his or her birthday party. Family members might take turns making a table centerpiece, or a decoration that is worn but valued might reappear every year.

Long-held traditions link generations. Traditions can also bring families a sense of pride and identity with cultural heritage.

Think About It

1. The best traditions are said to be simple ones. Why do you think that's true?
2. Imagine that as a parent with a family of your own, you want to start a holiday tradition. Suggest three ideas that you would like to try.

Extending Learning

Origins of Foods

- *Sandwich.* In the 18th century, the Earl of Sandwich would not leave a card game to eat. He had his servant bring him slices of roast beef between pieces of bread. The food took his name.
- *Ice Cream Sundae.* At one time, laws prohibited the sale of sodas on Sunday. A clever clerk omitted the carbonated beverage, placed the ice cream in a dish, and poured sauce over it. This new confection could be served legally on Sunday.

◆ **Evidence that the world is "shrinking" may be seen in the American fast food restaurant chains cropping up in other cultures. What foods from Japan, China, or another Asian culture have you sampled?**

This variety is one of the benefits of living in a society of many cultures. Consider the mingling of international flavors in this meal: chicken vindaloo and rice (India), steamed snow peas and water chestnuts (China), and a dessert of guava shells and cream cheese (Mexico).

Flavors from around the world are being combined in recipes. Rachel makes pizza with chili-seasoned ground meat and tops it with grated sharp cheese and salsa—a spicy, Mexican, fresh-tomato sauce. American fast-food chains featuring fried chicken and hamburgers have sprung up around the globe. Such global diversity enriches everyone's life. No matter where people go, they can find foods they enjoy and experience the adventure of new flavors.

Section 1-3 Review & Activities

1. What are three aspects of culture?
2. Name four categories of cultural food customs. Give an example of each.
3. What often happens when food customs are introduced into new areas? Why?
4. **Evaluating.** Do you think members of a culture should retain some distinct food customs? Why or why not?
5. **Applying.** List some of your own or your family's favorite foods. Indicate the cultures that are represented.
6. **Analyzing.** How do you think the following might impact eating patterns of the future: blending of cultures; increased availability of varied foods; and changing economies?

ASSESS

REVIEW

- Ask students to summarize the main ideas in this section.
- Have students complete the Section Review. (Answers appear below.)

EVALUATION

- Have students write a short essay describing the concepts presented in the section.
- Have students take the quiz for Section 1-3. (Use the quiz in the *Teacher Resource Guide,* or construct your own with the **Exam***View®* *Test Generator* on the *Effective Instruction CD-ROM.*)

RETEACHING

- Ask pairs of students to view the photographs in the section without looking at the captions. Based on the section content, partners are to develop captions of their own that capture an important generalization.
- Refer to the *Reteaching Activities* booklet for the Section 1-3 activity sheet.

CLOSE

Refer to the posters students made for the second Motivator in this section. Discuss the similarities among the basic foods eaten by different cultures.

Answers to Section 1-3 Review & Activities

1. Geography, heritage, and religion.
2. Unique foods (wonton soup); dietary laws (not eating pork); etiquette (using chopsticks as opposed to a knife and fork); special occasions (Easter).
3. They evolve; either original ingredients are not available or the item is altered to conform to local tastes.
4. Answers will vary. Retaining some customs promotes cultural identity, adding interest to meals and life.
5. Answers will vary.
6. In general, such trends may dilute traditional patterns and foods; new ones may develop.

SECTION 1-4

Food, Science, and Technology

FOCUS

MOTIVATORS

- Ask students to recall from science classes examples of ways science relates to food (such as the effect of heat of food, the relationships between nutrition and health, or how bacteria cause spoilage). Define the term *food science* and explain the relationship between science, nutrition, and food preparation.
- Ask students to compare foods available and meal preparation in the 19th century and today. How has technology influenced the way in which foods are produced, processed, packaged, and shipped?

VOCABULARY ACTIVITY

Write the word *ergonomics* on the board. Point out that *erg,* a scientific measure of work, is from the Greek *ergon,* which means work. The suffix *-nomics* means "principles of." Have students use this information to discuss the meaning of ergonomics and then find the term and the definition in the section.

STUDY SKILLS

- **Listening.** Invite one or two students to prepare an oral reading of the section.
- Have students read the section and complete the appropriate part of the Chapter 1 Study Guide in the *Student Workbook.*

SECTION 1-4

Food, Science, and Technology

Objectives

After studying this section, you should be able to:

- Explain how science is related to nutrition and food preparation.
- Discuss the impact of food-related technology in the food industry and in the home.

Look for These Terms

food science

ergonomics

Stacey wandered down the supermarket aisles trying to decide on food for her party Saturday night. Finally, she chose a few old favorites as well as several new items that looked good, including fat-free cookies, mini-pizzas made for the microwave, and red, tomato-flavored tortilla chips.

It never occurred to Stacey that science and technology were responsible for the wide variety of foods that made her choices so difficult. Science and technology have had a tremendous impact on food, from the kinds of food available to the ways in which food is prepared.

Scientific Aspects of Food

The science of nutrition has links to a number of other basic sciences, including chemistry, biology, physics, and a recently developed science known as *ergonomics* (err-guh-NAHM-iks). Here is a brief look at these relationships.

Nutritional Research

The foundation of any scientific inquiry is research. The science of nutrition is no exception. So far, nutritional research has uncovered about 40 nutrients. No one knows how many other nutrients remain to be discovered. Once nutrients are discovered, scientists continue to investigate the role they play in health.

One promising direction of nutritional research in recent years has been into the realm of nutrient chemicals that occur naturally in plants. Research so far has offered hope that this class of nutrients may reduce the risk of certain forms of cancer and other potentially life-threatening diseases.

Section 1-4 Resources

- ◆ **Student Workbook,** pp. 12, 17
- ◆ **Teacher Resource Guide**
  - Lesson Plan 1-4 Organizer
  - Section 1-4 Quiz
- ◆ **Effective Instruction CD-ROM**
  - **Exam*View*®** *Test Generator*
  - PowerPoint® Slide #2
- ◆ **Transparency Package,** CT-2
- ◆ **Student Motivation Kit**
  - Reteaching Activities, p. 12
  - Enrichment Activities

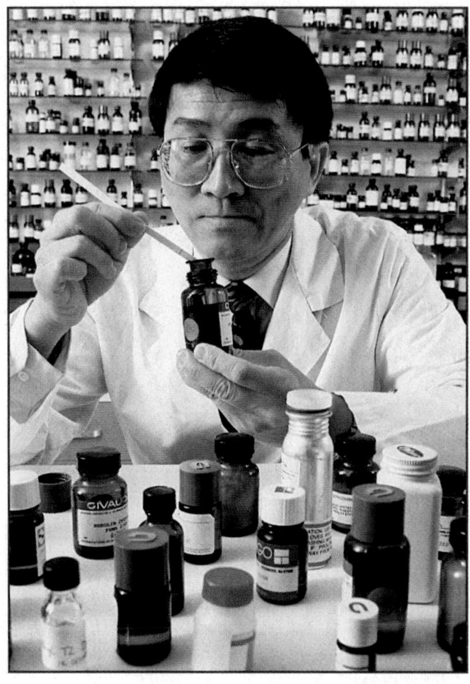

◆ **Food technologists help develop new foods and improve existing ones by relying on knowledge of food, nutrition, science, and technology. This technologist is testing flavors in a food research laboratory. Investigate olestra, a synthetic form of fat being used in some fried-food products. What information is available regarding the healthfulness of this product?**

The Science of Food Preparation

Moira's friend Keisha is a whiz in the kitchen. Inspired by Keisha's example, Moira tried making a cheese soufflé, an airy blend of eggs and cheese. She followed Keisha's recipe exactly—well, almost exactly—but the soufflé didn't turn out right. "I guess I just don't have Keisha's magic touch," Moira decided.

What makes the difference between a light, fluffy soufflé and a hard, flat one? The answer isn't found in magic but in science.

Food preparation is governed by natural laws. When certain foods are heated, chilled, mixed, or manipulated in other ways, they undergo chemical and physical changes. In fact, a recipe might legitimately be compared to a chemistry experiment. If you change the conditions of the experiment, the results are likely to change. In the same way, even a slight change in a recipe can cause the final product to turn out differently.

A knowledge of **food science**—the scientific study of food and its preparation—can help you understand why certain instructions in a recipe are important. If something doesn't turn out right, food science can help you understand why so that you'll be able to keep the problem from happening again.

◆ **Creating delicious tempting foods is not the result of kitchen "secrets" but hard science. In your Wellness Journal, keep a running list of science tips you learn from your reading. Refer back to these from time to time.**

TEACH

• *Scientific Aspects of Food (text pages 38-40)*

Textbook Review

Provide small groups of students with a variety of science textbooks covering such disciplines as chemistry, physics, and biology. Have them find examples of ways in which science is directly related to food. On the chalkboard, list the related sciences and the examples identified. L2

Inference Activity

Provide students with newspaper articles or other articles written for a lay audience that address some aspect of nutrition research. Students are to look for all and any relationships between nutrition and health implied in the articles.

Research Activity

Have students carry out their own food science research by selecting a nutrient and writing a paper that explains its function in the body, the foods that provide it, and any cautions surrounding its overuse. Students are to include recommendations on ways of getting adequate amounts and a bibliography.

FOOD SCIENCE

Lifestyle Disease and Eating Habits

Food scientists continue an ongoing search for links between eating habits and lifestyle diseases—particularly cancer and heart disease, two leading causes of death among Americans. Typical of this research is the relatively recent discovery of a purported connection between phytochemicals in plant foods and reduction in lifestyle disease as well as contributory factors such as blood pressure and cholesterol levels. Ask students to review current popular literature to find other dietary claims for reduction in the risk of cancer and heart disease. Are the claims well substantiated?

- *Scientific Aspects of Food (text pages 38-40)*

Discussion Activity

Ask students to brainstorm a list of tools and equipment used in the modern kitchen that were unavailable to earlier generations of cooks.

Redesigning a Kitchen

Have students work in groups to research and apply the principles of ergonomics to the redesign of a kitchen, kitchen appliances, food preparation equipment and tools, or food preparation tasks. Have groups plan and present the results of their efforts to the class in a multimedia format of their choice. L2

USING THE Food Science LAB

Acquaint students with this first of a number of lab-type features they will encounter throughout *Food for Today.* To reinforce the importance of rigorous scientific method when doing a lab activity, you may wish to demonstrate this first activity yourself, first gathering the materials you will need.

Answers to Conclusions

1. If the activity was carried out appropriately, the egg whites that were permitted to reach room temperature will have achieved the greatest volume.
2. Students would know to separate the whites and allow them to reach room temperature well in advance.

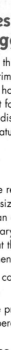

Food Science ◆ LAB ◆

How Does Temperature Affect Egg Whites?

Throughout this program, you will perform experiments in food science. You will learn how different factors affect different foods. In this experiment you will discover what effect, if any, temperature has on beaten egg whites.

Procedure

1. Place three refrigerated egg whites in a quart-size glass mixing bowl that is clean and free of grease. With a rotary beater or electric mixer, beat the whites until they form peaks that bend over slightly when the beaters are lifted out of the whites.
2. Scoop the contents into a clean measuring cup and record the results.
3. Repeat the procedure with three egg whites that have been at room temperature for 30 minutes.

Conclusions

- Which egg whites produced the greatest volume?
- How might this information help you if you were preparing meringue for a pie or a cake that called for beaten egg whites?

Ergonomics

Have you ever experienced a headache or eye strain after staring at a computer screen for a long period? If so, you understand the need for ergonomics. **Ergonomics** is the study of ways to make tools and equipment easier and more comfortable to use. In addition to computer hardware, ergonomicists have developed types of seating that cause less wear and tear on the muscles, bones, and joints than conventional chairs.

Ergonomics has played a key role in the design of kitchens, appliances, and food preparation equipment. Cookware and kitchen tools are ergonomically designed to make food preparation easier and faster.

Work simplification, an important part of ergonomics, means looking for the fastest and easiest method for getting a job done. Using work simplification in the kitchen or foods lab can save time and energy, as you will discover.

Technology TIE-IN

Note that a technological advance of the late twentieth century has led to a health problem, which has benefited from the science of ergonomics. That problem is *repetitive task syndrome*—a debilitating problem associated with the use of computer keyboards and mouses. The field of ergonomics has provided several solutions to this problem, including:

- the introduction of the "ergonomic" keyboard and mouse.
- the development of wrist pads and elevated mouse pads for computer users.

Technology and Food

Through technology, new or improved products and processes are developed. Examples can be found in the food industry and in the home.

The Food Industry

Technology plays a major role in how foods are produced, processed, packaged, and shipped. For instance:

- Food processing plants are using computers and robots to help control the quality of their products.
- New forms of packaging have been developed to keep food safe longer. In some cases, special packaging methods allow foods that traditionally require refrigeration to be stored at room temperature.
- Food scientists continue to develop new fat and sugar substitutes and new ways to use them in foods.
- Scientists are using a technique called genetic engineering to improve and refine foods.

In later chapters, you will learn more about the food industry and the products that have been developed as a result of technology.

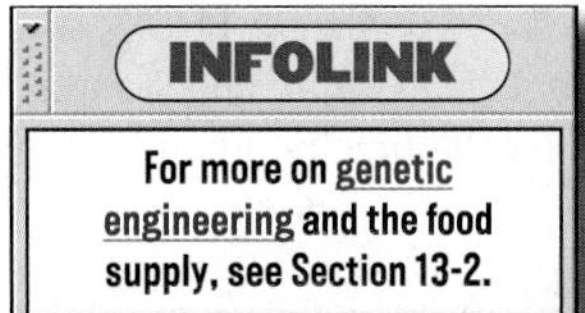

INFOLINK
For more on genetic engineering and the food supply, see Section 13-2.

◆ **Hydroponic farming—the growing of crops without soil—is still a relatively new industry.** Learn more about other cutting-edge areas of technology. Share your findings with classmates in a brief report.

- ***Technology and Food (text pages 41-43)***

Packaging Timeline

In the front of the class, display a "juice box," an aluminum can, and a resealable bag. Working in pairs or small groups, students are to research the history of one of the three types of packaging. They are to use online resources or may speak with representatives of the companies that produce these products. They are to present their findings in the form of an illustrated time line showing (1) when the packaging was developed, (2) when it was first released for consumer use, (3) what form of packaging it replaced. **L1**

Taste Test

Provide students with small samples of potato snack products for a taste test. One is to be potato chips made with a fat substitute, the other baked potato crisps. Conceal the packages in which the products were purchased. Place the potato chips on a plate and label them Sample A, labeling the other product Sample B. Ask students to independently record their reactions to the two products. What words were used to describe each product? Did any students prefer the baked product? Reveal the identities of both products, noting their nutrient contents.

Extending Learning

Genetic Engineering—Genes are present in the chromosomes of all plants and animals. Usually, many genes are present on each chromosome. Scientists often use a technique known as "gene splicing" (substituting one gene or set of genes for another) to achieve the desired characteristics. Genetic engineering holds promise for helping improve the quality and quantity of available food.

Discussion Activity

Ask students to describe the benefits of using genetic engineering to develop food products. Are there any disadvantages to using genetic engineering? If so, discuss them.

TEACH cont.

- *Technology and Food (text pages 41-43)*
- *Food for Tomorrow (text page 43)*

Guest Speaker

Invite a buyer or other representative from a supermarket to address the class on the difficulties of maintaining produce quality during shipping and display in the supermarket. How might improved "keeping qualities" impact stores and consumers?

Price Comparisons

Provide students with kitchen appliance catalogs, and have students compare the prices and features of basic and "high-tech" models of common kitchen appliances such as refrigerators and ranges. What conclusions can students draw based on their findings? How can this information be used to guide their own purchases of such appliances in the future? L1

Kitchen Safety Inspection

Point out that kitchen appliances are now so commonplace that many people forget the most elementary safety precautions. Have students learn about appliance safety, and then perform a safety inspection of the classroom foods lab and their home kitchens. They should report any problems at home to an adult in charge. Have them write about their findings in their Wellness Journals. L2

Safety Check

Learning to use new technology can be exciting, but don't forget about safety. Always read the instructions before using an appliance or other device for the first time.

The Home

Do you have a microwave oven in your home? Today, 90 percent of U.S. households do. These devices, which cook many foods in a fraction of the time required by conventional ovens, are one of many examples of how technology has benefited the home. Another standard fixture in many home kitchens nowadays is the food processor, which has made chopping, dicing, and similar preparation tasks easier than ever.

Technology has led not only to the development of new kitchen tools but also to the updating of older ones. Both major appliances—such as ranges, refrigerators, and dishwashers—and small appliances have become increasingly more reliable and easier to use while using less energy. Many of today's appliances contain a "brain" in the form of a computer chip. Some even alert the user when repair is needed.

New technology does have its drawbacks. Appliances with advanced features are more costly than basic models. In some cases, the advanced features may add to the difficulty and cost of repairs. Learning to use new features and controls can be time-consuming.

◆ **This picture shows what the earliest microwave ovens looked like. In addition to changes in size, what other differences can you see between this and microwaves now?**

Technology TIE-IN Direct students' attention to the photographs on pp. 42 and 43. Note that a common denominator among the two photos is size. Observe that if the photo of the computer were from the same period as the microwave oven, it would be even larger than the oven. Ask students to brainstorm other examples of products and innovations that have "shrunk" increasingly over the years thanks to technological advances. Ask: Can a device become *too* small? Have students defend their answers.

Personal Computers

Personal computers are proving helpful in the planning of meals. Some people use computers to store recipes, plan menus, and prepare shopping lists. A computer can also help you keep track of food spending and supplies. Software and Internet sites are available to evaluate both individual foods and entire meals for their nutritional content.

◆ Information on the Internet can help you make nutritious food choices. Be sure that the sources are reliable organizations and experts.

Applying Knowledge and Skills

Throughout this course, you'll expand your knowledge about foods, nutrition, and the impacts of science and technology. You'll gain skills than enable you to make healthful food choices and to prepare nutritious foods in tasty ways. You will be able to apply what you learn every day in the future as you aim to live a healthy life.

How else might you apply knowledge and skills from this course? You could have opportunities in the business world. Many careers today are food-related. From chef, to restaurant employee, to dietitian, to food scientist, many workers use the kind of information you are about to study. In the weeks ahead, think about how your new knowledge and skills might be used in business. If you enjoy what you're learning, you might like a related career as well.

Section 1-4 Review & Activities

1. How is a recipe like a chemistry experiment?
2. What does *ergonomically sound* mean when applied to a kitchen tool?
3. Give an example of two recent technological advances in the food industry.
4. **Applying.** Using ads from the newspaper or a home-shopper catalogue, compare the price and features of a basic model and a high-tech model of a common kitchen appliance, such as a toaster. Present your conclusions in a brief report.
5. **Comparing and Contrasting.** Name one advantage and one disadvantage of using a personal computer to help with meal planning.
6. **Analyzing.** Explain how you think knowledge of food science would be useful in a career as a chef.

ASSESS

REVIEW

- Ask students to summarize the main ideas in this section.
- Have students complete the Section Review. (Answers appear below.)

EVALUATION

- Have students write a short essay titled "Technology and Its Boundaries." In it, they should discuss advances they learned about as well as inherent dangers in technology when taken too far.
- Have students take the quiz for Section 1-4. (Use the quiz in the *Teacher Resource Guide,* or construct your own with the **Exam***View®* *Test Generator* on the *Effective Instruction CD-ROM.*)

RETEACHING

- Ask each student to give two examples of how food science and technology affect his or her daily life. Examples include packaging innovations that allow perishable foods to be stored at room temperature, and microwave technology that reduces cooking time and increases food choices.
- Refer to the *Reteaching Activities* booklet for the Section 1-4 activity sheet.

CLOSE

Have students create side-by-side dioramas of the modern kitchen and the kitchen of long ago. Students should draw on section content.

Answers to Section 1-4 Review & Activities

1. Changes in conditions or ingredients can lead to differing results.
2. It has been designed with ease of use and comfort in mind.
3. See the bulleted list on page 41.
4. Answers will vary.
5. Possible advantage: Helps ensure the nutritional soundness of food selections. Possible disadvantage: Removes the human element in meal planning.
6. Answers will vary.

SECTION

1-5

Skills for Food Choices

FOCUS

MOTIVATORS

- Ask students to identify the resources involved in providing family meals. List the resources on the chalkboard. Ask students to identify tasks involved in management. List the tasks on the chalkboard. How is managing family meals similar to managing a business?
- Divide the class into groups. Ask students to pretend they are in charge of family meals for the next week. Have them list the decisions that must be made in planning and preparing family meals. In what order do these decisions occur? Compare the lists compiled by different groups.

VOCABULARY ACTIVITY

Pronounce the two terms listed under "Look for These Terms." Have students find the terms and their definitions in the section.

STUDY SKILLS

- **Guided Reading.** Have students look at the headings within Section 1-5 to preview the concepts that will be discussed.
- Have students read the section and complete the appropriate part of the Chapter 1 Study Guide in the *Student Workbook.*

SECTION 1-5

Skills for Food Choices

Life is filled with choices, many of which involve food. No matter what the decision is, every food choice becomes easier when you have a grasp of four related skills. These are thinking, communication, leadership, and management.

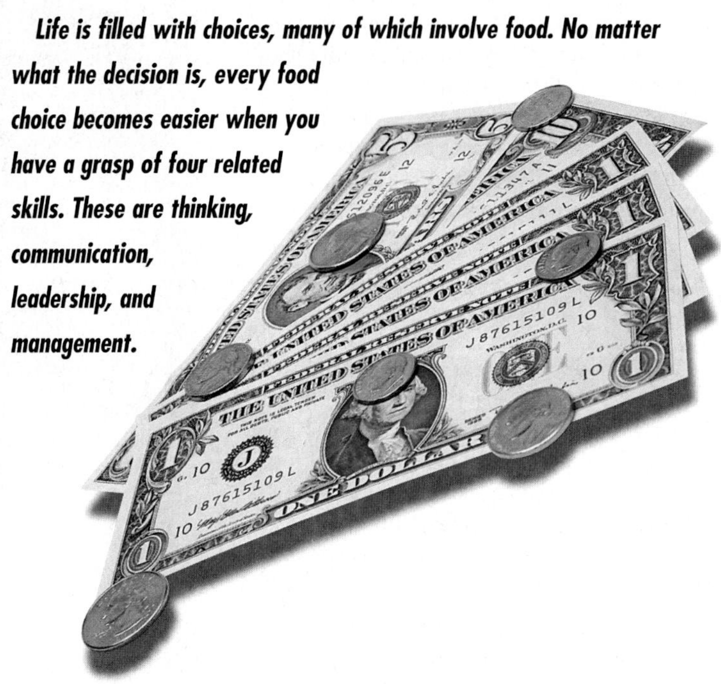

Objectives

After studying this section, you should be able to:

- Identify skills related to the food choices you make.
- Give examples of how management techniques relate to the study of food and nutrition.
- Explain the steps in the decision-making process.

Look for These Terms

critical thinking

management

Thinking

Most of the thinking you do each day is an automatic process that begins the instant you wake up. It is this type of thought that enables you to carry out routine tasks, such as finding your way to school. Yet, there is another type of thought, unique to humans, known as directed thinking. Directed thinking is using higher-level reasoning skills in a deliberate and purposeful way to arrive at a desired outcome.

One especially important aspect of directed thinking is **critical thinking**, which involves examination of printed and spoken language in order to gain insights into meanings and interpretations. When you read between the lines of a health claim for a food product that sounds too good to be true, you are using critical thinking.

In a society in which you are confronted with many food choices, critical thinking can be a valuable skill. It can help you, for example, recognize and resist negative influences on your overall pattern of food choices.

Communication

Critical thinking is tied closely to a second skill that can guide healthful food decisions—communication. Communication is the sending and receiving of thoughts, feelings, opinions, and information. Communication is made up of a number of subskills, including speaking, listening, writing, and reading. An effective

Section 1-5 Resources

- ◆ **Student Workbook,** pp. 13, 18
- ◆ **Teacher Resource Guide**
  - Lesson Plan 1-5 Organizer
  - Section 1-5 Quiz
  - Chapter 1 Test
- ◆ **Effective Instruction CD-ROM**
  - **Exam***View*® *Test Generator*
  - PowerPoint® Slide #3
- ◆ **Transparency Package,** CT-3
- ◆ **Student Motivation Kit**
  - Reteaching Activities, p. 13
  - Enrichment Activities

communicator is able to process and evaluate advertisements and other media messages concerning foods. He or she is then able to react to the information in an appropriate fashion.

Leadership

Do you think of yourself as a leader or as a follower? As a food-related skill, leadership may be defined as helping those around you develop positive food goals and attitudes. Leadership skills may be targeted at groups as small as a family and as large as a community, a nation, or the world. On its most immediate level, leadership might mean setting a good example for younger brothers or sisters by making healthful food choices at home. On a broader level, a leader might be a concerned citizen who alerts government officials about pollution or other practices that pose a risk to the food supply.

◆ **Thinking skills help you evaluate products and make healthful choices. Communication skills allow you to compare ideas with others. With leadership skills, you can help others make healthful choices. What skills might be in use here?**

Connecting Food and Language Arts

Nonverbal Communication

According to an old saying, "Actions speak louder than words." This means that your nonverbal communication skills can be as important as your verbal skills. Nonverbal communication takes place without words. Facial expressions, especially, offer quick clues to what you're thinking and feeling. How might this link to foods?

Think About It

- Suppose you have been invited to a friend's home for dinner. You take a bite of a dish that is unfamiliar to you, and you think it tastes terrible. What do you do?

TEACH

- *Thinking*
- *Communication*
- *Leadership*
  (text pages 44-45)

Discussion Activity

Ask students to review the different types of thinking. Ask: What type of thought is involved in picking out clothing to wear for the day? In deciding whether a certain food promotes good health?

Food Journal Activity

Have students keep a food journal over a 24-hour period to identify all the decisions they made about food. Have students share and compare examples with classmates.

Nonverbal Communication Activity

Point out that not all communication takes place through words. To help students grasp this point, write the sentence "Would you please hand me that pencil?" on the chalkboard. Instruct several volunteers to read the sentence, each one emphasizing a different word. As they speak, other students are to indicate the emotion the sentence conveys (e.g., anger, confusion). Invite students to observe people communicating over the next 24 hours and to make notes about the many non-verbal ways in which people communicate. Review some of these in the next class session (body language, facial expressions, hand gestures).

Extending Learning

Leadership—Having positive role models to look to for leadership is important to wellness. The Search Institute, a non-profit group in Minneapolis, Minnesota, has found that when certain "protective factors" are present in a teen's life, the amount of risk-taking behavior decreases, and the chances for growing up healthy, caring, and responsible increase. Among these factors the institute isolates are the support and encouragement of people in your life, positive role models, and positive values.

TEACH cont.

- *Management (text page 46)*

Discussion Activity

Have students discuss the various resources that need to be managed to prepare foods wisely and efficiently (time, energy, food, equipment, knowledge, abilities).

Case Study

Have students work in pairs or small groups to apply management skills to a situation which requires decisions about food (for example, deciding what to serve at a party). Set aside time for groups to discuss their findings. L1

Making a Preparation Schedule

Have students work in groups to plan a schedule for preparing a simple meal. Provide recipes for the meal and give the serving time. Have students compare the groups' schedules as a bridge to a dialogue on problems that arose and possible ways to improve this process. L2

COMPUTER ACTIVITY
Using Scheduling Software

If the classroom computer or another computer in the school has scheduling software, demonstrate the program. Have students determine whether this software could be used to manage money, time, or other resources mentioned in the section.

Management

Management refers to specific techniques that help you use resources wisely. Among the many ways in which management techniques play a role in sound food choices are the following:

- **Managing your time.** Helps you accomplish what you really need and want to do within given time constraints. An effective manager is able to find time in even the busiest of schedules to ensure getting the nutrients his or her body needs.
- **Managing your money.** Enables you to meet financial goals and get the most value for your dollar. An example of money management is comparison shopping—examining the cost of similar food items to see which offers the best value.
- **Record-keeping.** Helps you make plans and evaluate how well you use your resources. For instance, keeping a record of the foods you eat for a few days can help you make better food choices.
- **Organizing.** Arranging items in an orderly and logical way. For example, organizing a shopping list by grouping similar items together cuts down on shopping time.

With practice, the decision-making process will become automatic. Think about a difficult decision you have made or might be faced with in the future. Use the steps in the decision-making model to help you make your decision.

Reinforcing Key Skills

Present the following problem to student groups. Allow time for them to discuss and compare their responses.

Management—You arrive home late following an afterschool club meeting and find a note reminding you it is your turn to cook. Recipe books have been opened to the appropriate pages, and the refrigerator and pantry have all the ingredients you need. When you compute the time needed for assembly and preparation, you find you cannot possibly manage in the allotted time. What do you do? How can you prevent the same scenario from occurring again in the future?

Making Decisions

What might the four skills just described have in common? Each involves decision making. Think about the food decisions you make. Choosing which peanut butter to buy is a minor decision. Choosing the food you'll take on a two-week wilderness camping trip, however, has greater impact.

Some people give little thought to high-impact decisions. They may even put off a decision until it's too late to make one effectively. Important decisions deserve attention.

Steps in Decision Making

With practice, making decisions becomes easier. Try this seven-step process on a decision you are facing:

1. ***Identify the decision to be made and your goals.*** What do you want the result to be? Suppose you are cooking for a party. Your goals might be finding something easy to fix and easy to keep hot or cold, and something most people will like.
2. ***Consider your resources.*** What do you have available that could help you in this situation? A resource for finding recipes is a cookbook. An electric slow cooker is a resource for keeping food hot at the party.
3. ***Identify your options.*** Be creative and open to new ideas. As you think of solutions that might work, make a list.
4. ***Consider each option.*** Imagine the results of each possible choice. If you need to, gather more information. Then list the advantages and disadvantages of each option. How well would each meet the goals you originally set?

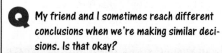

My friend and I sometimes reach different conclusions when we're making similar decisions. Is that okay?

A As long as you're satisfied with the options chosen, differences don't matter. Since you and your friend are individuals, what's right for one might not be right for the other. For example, suppose you and a friend want to improve what you eat for lunch. You might decide to start packing a lunch in order to eat more nutritiously. If that's not convenient for your friend, he or she might decide to buy cafeteria lunches instead. Because the decision-making process is flexible, it works well for anyone. What counts is completing each step.

5. ***Choose the best option.*** Often there is no perfect solution. Weigh and compare options; then choose the one that seems best. What if none of the choices is acceptable? Try going back to step 3 to see whether an option has been overlooked.
6. ***Carry out your decision.*** Make a plan based on your choice. If you decide to make mini-pizzas for the party, plan when and how you will make them. Then put your plan into action.
7. ***Evaluate the result.*** How did your decision turn out? If it worked well, take pride in what you accomplished. If it didn't, don't be discouraged. Accept that you did your best; then try to learn from the experience.

- *Making Decisions (text pages 47-48)*

Discussion Activity

Have students list the steps in the decision-making process. Ask whether these steps could be followed in any order. Why or why not?

Problem-Solving Activity

Divide the class into small "think tank" groups. Present each with the same problem related to food preparation. Challenge groups to use the seven decision-making steps to solve the problem. Discuss and compare the solutions proposed by the different groups.

Group Skit

Observe that the seven-step decision-making process can be applied not only to food decisions but to life decisions. Invite groups of students with aptitudes for acting and/or writing to compose and stage short one-act plays in which a teen uses the decision-making process to resist peer pressure to make an unhealthful food choice. Other members of the class are to be an attentive audience and write reviews of the production, noting what it taught them. L2

Extending Learning

Careers in Food and Nutrition— Students can be encouraged to contact:

- National Association of Trade and Technical Schools, P.O. Box 10429, Dept. BL, Rockville, MD 20850
- The Educational Foundation of the National Restaurant Association, 20 N. Wacker Dr., Ste. 2620, Chicago, IL 60606
- Council on Hotel, Restaurant, and Institutional Education, 311 First St. NW, Washington, DC 20001

ASSESS

REVIEW

- Ask students to summarize the main ideas in this section.
- Have students complete the Section Review (Answers appear below.)

EVALUATION

- Have students prepare a bulletin board display that highlights the seven steps of the decision-making process.
- Have students take the quiz for Section 1-5. (Use the quiz in the *Teacher Resource Guide,* or construct your own with the **Exam***View*® *Test Generator* on the *Effective Instruction CD-ROM.*)

RETEACHING

- Make up a simple food preparation problem similar to the one in the section. Set up a station in the classroom for each step of the decision-making process. Each should illustrate how the step can be applied to the problem. Have students visit each station and summarize what they find there.
- Refer to the *Reteaching Activities* booklet for the Section 1-5 activity sheet.

CLOSE

Review with students their response to the Motivator activities for this section on p. 44. Conduct a round-table discussion on how their ideas have changed, if at all.

Decision Making and Food Choices

Whether the points in a ballgame or the votes in an election, everything counts toward a win. The same applies to little food decisions that seem insignificant. Decisions about what to eat for lunch or what to have for a snack, for example, seem minor until you realize that together they help point you toward a lifetime of good or poor health.

Food decisions can become habits. Regularly skipping breakfast is a habit that can be broken. So is eating a candy bar for lunch every day. At first, change is difficult, but eventually the new habit takes over. With positive change, health is promoted rather than threatened.

Career Decisions

One of the most important decisions you will ever make is how to earn your living as an adult. Too often, people decide on a line of work without really knowing much about it. They are unaware of many other possible careers, any one of which might prove even more satisfying to them.

You might be surprised at the wide range of careers that relate to food and nutrition. This textbook will help you explore many of the possibilities. At the end of each chapter, you will find a career feature that focuses on a particular worker and his or her job. The final chapter will provide more in-depth information to help you think about and prepare for a career.

Section 1-5 Review & Activities

1. What four skills are associated with food choices?
2. Name three management techniques. Tell how each relates to food and nutrition.
3. Identify the seven steps in the decision-making process.
4. **Applying.** Take action, real or imagined, to express your opinion on a food-related issue. You could write a letter, send an electronic message, or create an informative Power-Point presentation. Sample topics are: healthful food choices in restaurants; the global food supply; dwindling farm land; and school lunches.
5. **Applying.** Jorge has noticed that some of his basketball teammates don't follow the coach's rules, including those for eating nutritiously. This may be contributing to many game losses. How can Jorge be a leader without alienating his friends?
6. **Applying.** Imagine that your class has been asked to cook a meal for a local senior citizen's group. Identify at least three decisions that would have to be made. Choose one and explain how you would use the decision-making process in this situation.

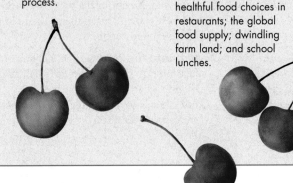

Answers to Section 1-5 Review & Activities

1. Critical thinking, communication, leadership, and management.
2. Any three: Managing time (ensuring that nutrient needs are met even with demanding schedule); managing money (getting the most value for food dollar); record-keeping (planning and evaluating use of resources); organizing (cutting wasted time).
3. See page 47.
4. Answers will vary.
5. Might set an example; point out link to nutrition subtly or with humor.
6. Decisions may include date for meal, menu, division of duties. Explanations will vary.

Career Wanted

Test Kitchen Worker

Education and Training

- Postsecondary training in food production or dietetics
- On-the-job training in laboratory production

Qualities

- Analytical skills
- Creativity
- Problem-solving skills
- Ability to work with others

"The proof really *is* in the pudding."

Mei Chin

Q. How did you get started as a test kitchen worker, Mei?

A. In high school I loved my job as a short-order cook, and I enjoyed food science. I started looking into jobs that combined both interests. My counselor suggested foods and nutrition courses at the community college, and the counselor there helped me find this job.

Q. What do you test foods for?

A. Anything that affects quality. If the manufacturer wants to change the packaging, we make sure it keeps the food just as fresh. We test "lite" versions of products to make sure that changing ingredients doesn't affect texture. We have equipment that measures qualities like toughness and flakiness.

Q. Is it more individual work or teamwork?

A. It's both. We may do separate tasks, but it's a coordinated effort. I might run a nutritional analysis while someone else weighs a food sample for the next test. We all work under the direction of the food scientist who leads the project.

Related Career Opportunities

Entry Level
- Fry cook
- Caterer's assistant

Technical Level
- Lab technologist
- Dietitian
- Baker

Professional Level
- Food technologist
- Executive chef
- Market analyst

Making Career Connections

TESTING SIMULATION. Learn how blind taste tests are conducted and set one up in class. Have classmates evaluate different brands or regular and modified versions of a food (fat-free and low-sodium, for example). Create a list of qualities to judge, such as texture, flavor, aroma, saltiness, etc. Compile and discuss the results.

Career Wanted

Test Kitchen Worker

Thinking About the Career

Direct students' attention to the experiences Mei Chin had leading up to her job as a test kitchen worker. Ask about part-time jobs held by current class members that might be gateways to higher-level positions. Encourage students who currently work to speak with their employers about the possibilities of advancement as well as lateral or upward moves into related fields. Have them report their findings to the class.

Career-Building Opportunities

Ask students to find out about one of the other careers listed in "Related Career Opportunities." Students may use online or print resources or may contact a local employment agency. Instruct students to put their findings in the form of a Help Wanted ad to be posted on a classroom food career bulletin board.

For More Information

For additional information about careers as test kitchen workers, encourage students to contact individual food manufacturers, as well as the following resources:

- Association of Professional Consultants
  www.consultapc.org
- Small Business Administration
  www.sba.gov
- U.S. Food and Drug Administration
  5600 Fishers Lane
  Rockville, MD 20857–0001
  www.fda.gov

REVIEW

- Have students complete the Chapter Review. (Answers appear below.)

EVALUATION

- Divide the class into two teams. Each team should brainstorm questions about Chapter 1. Then allow the teams to take turns asking each other the questions they listed. At the end of the questioning period, the team with the most correct answers wins.
- Have students take the test for Chapter 1. (Use the chapter test in the *Teacher Resource Guide,* or construct your own with the **ExamView®** *Test Generator* on the *Effective Instruction CD-ROM.*)

ANSWERS

Checking Your Knowledge

1. Scientific meaning: the study of nutrients and how they are used by the body; popular meaning: how a person's food choices affect his or her health.
2. Possible answer: When a friend comes over to your house, you offer something to eat or drink.
3. Communication sources, including television, radio, the movies, newspapers, magazines, advertisements, and the Internet; possible answer: news reports may shape your decision to eat a certain food; magazines may make you aware of new food trends; advertising attempts to make foods sound enticing.
4. Any three: Money, time, knowledge, abilities, equipment, and a place to buy food.
5. Possible answer: Having access to foods from various cultures may add variety to a person's eating plan.

Chapter 1 Review & Activities

Summary

Section 1-1: Food and Health

- Good nutrition is an important part of physical health and wellness.
- Food can contribute to psychological health by providing security, a sense of belonging, and enjoyment.

Section 1-4: Food, Science, and Technology

- The science of nutrition is linked to other sciences, including chemistry and ergonomics.
- Food science is the scientific study of food and its preparation.
- New technology is changing the way food is produced and processed, as well as the way people plan and prepare meals.

Section 1-2: Influences on Food Choices

- Social influences on food choices include culture, family, friends, and the media.
- Food choices also depend on available resources.
- Technology has increased the options available.
- Factors affecting personal food choices include lifestyle, values and priorities, and emotions.

Section 1-5: Skills for Food Choices

- Four skills related to food choices are thinking, communication, leadership, and management.
- The decision-making process can help in many situations.

Section 1-3: Food and Culture

- Different cultures have distinct food customs.
- Many food customs that originated in the distant past have changed and mingled with others along the way.
- With technology, the world has shrunk, increasing the sharing of cultural customs relating to food.

Checking Your Knowledge

1. Give two meanings of the word *nutrition*.
2. How can food provide a sense of belonging?
3. Define *media.* How does the media affect food choices?
4. Identify three resources that might affect food choices.
5. How does living in a society relate to food customs?
6. How did geography affect food customs in the past? Why does it have less influence today?
7. What do natural laws of science have to do with food preparation?
8. Name two results of technology that have streamlined food preparation and cooking in the home.
9. How is critical thinking different from the thought processes used in daydreaming?
10. What should you do if a decision doesn't turn out as you expected?

Working IN THE Lab

1. ***Taste Test.*** Wearing a blindfold, taste food samples prepared by your teacher. Describe the aroma, texture, and flavor. Try to identify the food. Discuss how the senses contribute to the enjoyment of food. What role do they play in making food choices?
2. ***Food Preparation.*** Prepare popcorn in the microwave oven, on the range, and in a popcorn popper. Compare the methods for time, cost, and taste. What are the advantages and disadvantages of each method? Which would you be more likely to choose in the future?

Thinking Critically

1. **Recognizing Values.** Mark and Ina's family and consumer sciences class is holding its annual international dinner. As in years past, each person is asked to bring a homemade dish. Mark plans to make a delicious Spanish soup of white beans, collard greens, fresh garlic, and sausage. Ina has decided to look through the cookbooks and computer files in the classroom library and see which dish would take the least time and effort to make. What values and priorities are reflected by each approach to the task of preparing food?
2. **Recognizing Fallacies in Logic.** Angelina is thumbing through a magazine and comes upon an article proclaiming that the microwave oven has changed daily life. Without reading even the opening paragraph, Angelina flips ahead to the next feature in the magazine, mumbling under her breath that this is just another underhanded effort to sell appliances and, in so doing, cater to the magazine's advertisers. Explain what, if anything, is wrong with the position Angelina has taken.

Reinforcing Key Skills

1. **Directed Thinking.** Rory is watching TV when a commercial comes on for a candy bar that claims to provide all the nutrients your body needs in a given day. State whether or not you would advise Rory to buy the product. Explain your advice.
2. **Communication.** Ella and Sean have volunteered to bake cakes for a charity bake sale. As they work, Ella notices that Sean is spending a lot of time on the phone with friends. She is beginning to fear that the two will miss their deadline, which is in two days. What would you advise Ella to do?

Making Decisions and Solving Problems

You are helping your family shop for a new microwave oven. A basic model, which is in your price range, looks easy to use. However, you think your family would like some of the special features found in higher-priced models. How would you help your family decide which oven to buy?

Making Connections

1. **Social Studies.** Using cookbooks, food magazines, or online sources, learn about three foods eaten in the United States that originated in other cultures. Prepare a map that shows the place of origin of each food and the route it took to reach this country. Use a different colored line for each food. Be sure to include a legend indicating what the colors represent.
2. **Economics.** Interview a local supermarket manager or other community merchant to investigate the role management skills play in his or her job. Prepare by drafting questions regarding each of the management techniques detailed in the chapter. Learn what other management skills are used in business. Share your findings in the form of a tape-recorded interview or a brief oral report.

ANSWERS cont.

6. People were limited to foods grown and gathered locally; today high-speed transportation makes it possible to enjoy foods from all over the world.
7. They govern physical and chemical changes that occur when foods are heated, chilled, and so forth.
8. Possible answer: Microwave ovens and food processors.
9. Critical thinking involves examination of printed and spoken language in order to gain insights into meanings and interpretations. Higher-level reasoning skills are used that are not used in daydreaming.
10. Try not to be discouraged. Accept that you did your best; then try to learn from the experience.

Thinking Critically

1. Mark's values might be seen to include pride in self-accomplishment, and his priorities might be seen to include an interest in cooking. Inferences about Ina's values cannot be ascertained from the information provided, although her priorities seem not to gravitate toward cooking.
2. As far as Angelina knows, the article may go on to present information on how this technological wonder has altered life for the *worse*. The problem with Angelina's position is that it is only partly informed, and it demonstrates the importance of reading past headlines and opening sentences.

CHAPTER

2

The Nutrients You Need

Advance Planning Guide ☑

- Bring to class an assortment of magazines and books featuring dietary information.
- Print out Internet articles on dietary information.
- Bring in magazines that include pictures of people who are malnourished.
- Arrange necessary permissions for a field trip to a supermarket or farmer's market.
- Bring in a variety of Nutrition Facts panels from food packages.
- Bring to class an assortment of pictures of foods that contain cholesterol.
- Arrange for a local registered dietitian, possibly affiliated with the American Heart Association, to speak to the class.
- Bring to class line drawings of the human digestive system.
- Bring in articles about folate and its preventive role in disease.
- Arrange for a physical education instructor or a school coach to demonstrate safe techniques and provide suggestions for weight-training activities for teens.
- Obtain articles about the role of garlic in promoting health.
- Bring to class a marble and long narrow balloon.

CHAPTER 2

The Nutrients You Need

You may know the saying "You are what you eat." As you'll soon find out, there is much truth in those words. In this chapter, you'll learn about the many nutrients your body needs.

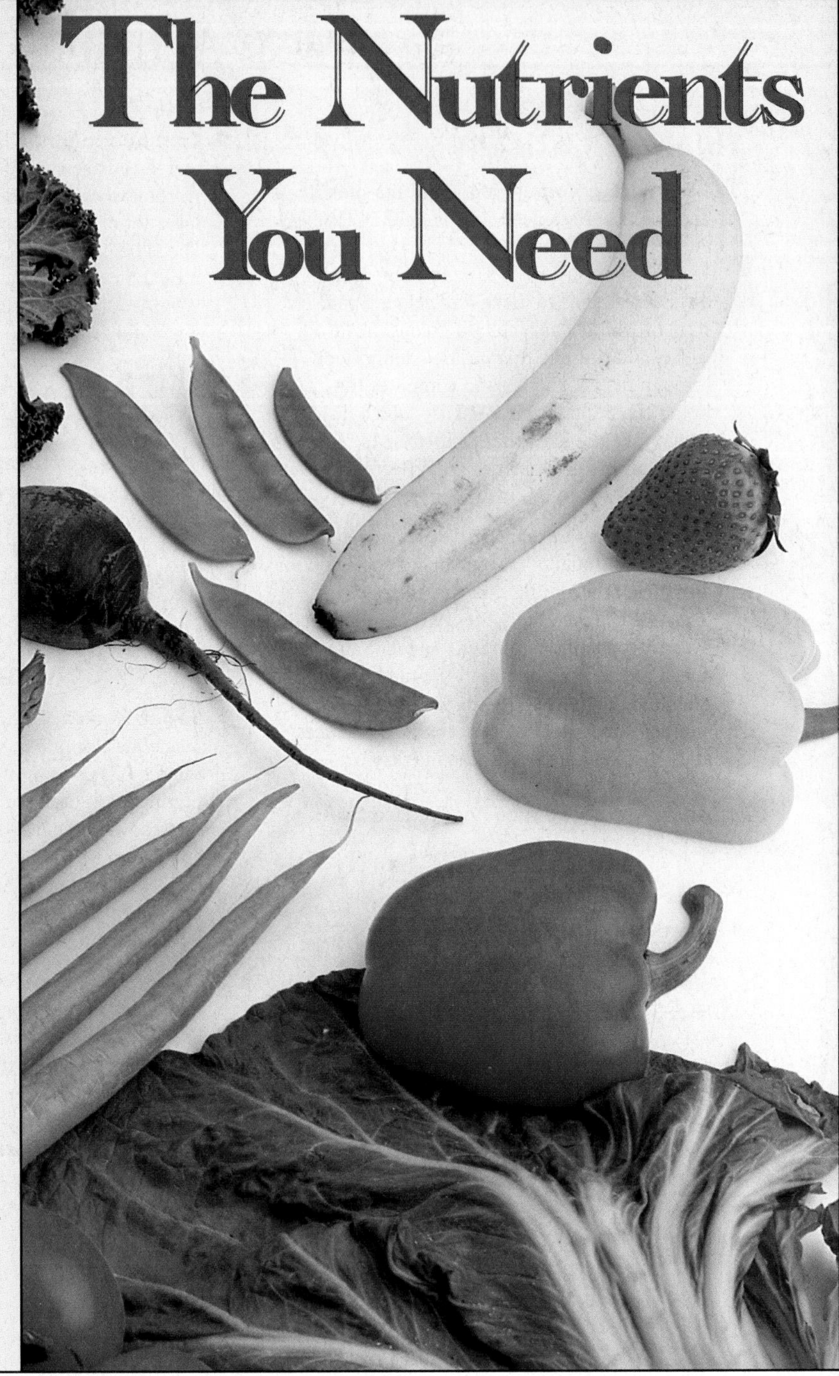

MEETING DIVERSE NEEDS

Musical/Rhythmic Learners. If there are students in the class with musical abilities, invite them to compose (or adapt) and perform a song on nutrient needs. The song should include the key ideas introduced in the chapter. Introduce the performance by explaining to the class that they will now be hearing the "anthem" for this chapter and, ideally, for their lives.

SECTION 2-1

The Role of Nutrients

Objectives

After studying this section, you should be able to:

- Name the six major types of nutrients.
- Explain the purposes of DRIs, RDAs, and AIs.
- Give guidelines regarding calorie needs and calorie sources.

Look for These Terms

carbohydrates
dietary fiber
fats
proteins
vitamins
minerals
nutrient deficiency
malnutrition
DRIs
RDAs
AIs
calorie

If you have ever looked under the hood of a car, you know that its engine is made up of many interconnected parts and systems. The human body is organized in a similar way. Just as a car needs gasoline to run, the body also needs its own type of fuel. Like a car, the body requires regular care and maintenance to work efficiently.

The Six Main Nutrients

The nutrients your body needs to keep you healthy are divided into six major types. Although you will learn more about each type later, they are introduced here.

- **Carbohydrates** (kar-boh-HY-drayts) are the body's main source of energy. One unique and important form of this major nutrient is **dietary fiber**, a mixture of plant materials that is not broken down in the digestive system. All forms of carbohydrates, except fiber, provide energy.
- **Fats** are a concentrated source of energy. You need fats in moderate amounts to perform important functions in your body, including transporting nutrients.

SECTION 2-1

The Role of Nutrients

FOCUS

MOTIVATORS

- On the chalkboard, use X's and O's to represent the lineups of two soccer teams. Discuss the positions of different players. Ask students what might happen if a position were left vacant. Add the names of nutrients to one of the teams. Identify these as the "players" in the wellness game. Explain that nutrients act as a team in your body.
- Ask students to share information they know about calories. Where do calories come from? Why do people have varying caloric needs? Why does an individual's calorie needs vary from day to day?

VOCABULARY ACTIVITY

Direct students' attention to the list "Look for These Terms," and in particular to the acronyms in the list. Ask what other such terms they are familiar with (e.g., FBI, U.S.). Explain that these are just a few of the acronyms they will encounter in this program.

STUDY SKILLS

- **Outlining.** Have students read the section and outline it by copying the headers on paper and leaving space after each one. Students are to write a sentence in their own words, summarizing the content under each header.
- Have students read the section and complete the appropriate part of the Chapter 2 Study Guide in the *Student Workbook.*

Section 2-1 Resources

◆ **Student Workbook,** pp. 19, 22
◆ **Teacher Resource Guide**
Lesson Plan 2-1 Organizer
Section 2-1 Quiz
◆ **Effective Instruction CD-ROM**
Exam*View*® *Test Generator*
PowerPoint® Slide #4
◆ **Transparency Package,** CT-4
◆ **Student Motivation Kit**
Reteaching Activities, p. 14
Enrichment Activities

TEACH

- *The Six Main Nutrients (text pages 53-55)*

Discussion Activity

Discuss with students specific food sources for each of the six major nutrients. Emphasize that individuals require varying amounts of each of these nutrients and discuss how activity level affects overall needs. Expand the discussion to how obesity or other health conditions affect the dietary recommendations for each major nutrient.

Research Activity

Have students investigate the most recent scientific research to determine the most common vitamin or mineral deficiency in America. Direct the students to reputable sources of information in this regard, including online government-sponsored sites geared to teens that you have prescreened. Have students report their findings to class.

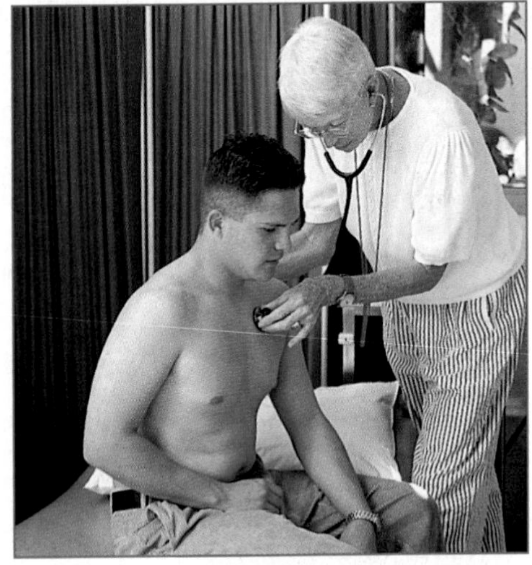

◆ **Good nutrition is essential for good health. What are other benefits of good nutrition?**

- **Proteins** are nutrients that help build, repair, and maintain body tissues. Proteins are also a source of energy.
- **Vitamins** are chemicals that help regulate many vital body processes and aid other nutrients in doing their jobs. Your body requires only small amounts of vitamins.
- **Minerals** are nonliving substances that help the body work properly and, in some cases, become part of body tissues, such as bone. Like vitamins, minerals are needed in only small amounts.
- **Water** is a nutrient because it is essential to life. It makes up most of your body weight too.

Benefits of Good Nutrition

Like team members, nutrients work together. Because each has a special role, no nutrient can be substituted for another. Therefore, health suffers when nutrients are missing from a diet. On the other hand, if you regularly get all the necessary nutrients, you benefit from the positive effects.

- **Growth, development, and function.** Thousands of chemical processes in your body depend on nutrients to work. To grow and development properly and to keep your body functioning well, you need foods with these nutrients.
- **Fitness.** Without enough nutritional gas, your motor runs down. Good nutrition not only keeps you going, it keeps you going strong. Some people are so used to operating at a low level that they don't realize what feeling good is like.
- **Job performance.** Whether at work or school, you need to give your best. Thinking skills, alertness, attitude, and stamina can peak with good nutrition. In turn, grades and work benefit.

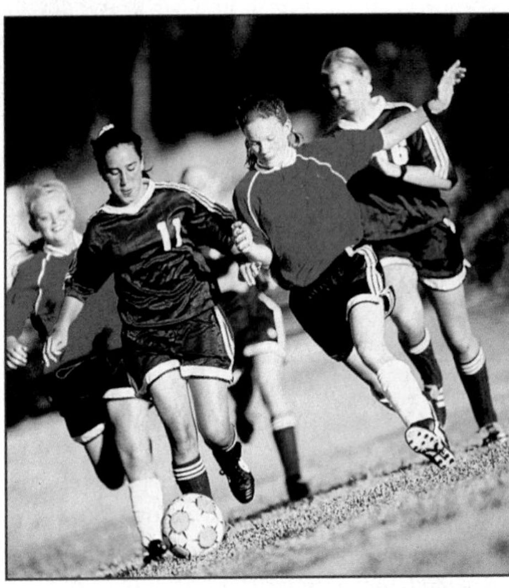

◆ **Just as a team relies on each member, your body relies on all the vital nutrients in the food you eat to function smoothly. Use the table "Nutritive Value of Foods" in Appendix B at the back of this book to analyze a food you regularly eat. Identify nutrients it contains.**

Extending Learning

Malnutrition—Approximately one eighth of the world's population suffers from malnutrition. Although population growth has slowed in the industrialized nations, it has accelerated in developing countries, where human demand often overtaxes life support systems. Tropical forests are dwindling and soils are eroding. With the demise of these natural resources, food and fuel diminish and malnutrition follows.

- **Appearance.** Shiny hair, bright eyes, and smooth, clear skin all link to nutrition. If you want a healthy "glow," nutrients are at least part of the answer.
- **Risk of illness.** Fewer colds, flu, and other illnesses occur when you eat nutritious foods regularly.
- **Long-term health.** The body has an amazing capacity to keep on working despite how it is treated, but continual mistreatment affects health. You may know people who changed their eating habits after developing a serious illness. A better way to help preserve the quality of life, and even life itself, is to develop good eating habits early. Although no foods are "bad," a balanced eating plan increases your chances for long-term health.

Serious Health Problems

Poor nutrition over a prolonged period can lead to **malnutrition** and serious health problems. Getting too little or too much of a nutrient can cause malnutrition. Any person can become malnourished due to a poor diet or a medical condition.

A nutrient shortage, called a **nutrient deficiency**, produces many possible symptoms depending on the nutrient. Examples are skin rashes, depression, hair loss, bleeding gums, and night blindness. As a specific example, a lack of vitamin D can keep children's bones from growing properly. Their bones become weak, and the children develop bowed legs. A lack of vitamin D in adults can cause brittle bones, which break easily. Muscle weakness and spasms are other results. Nutrient excesses cause problems too. A few symptoms are yellowing skin, a rapid heart rate, and low blood pressure.

◆ **The benefits of good nutrition are many. What does it mean to say that these teens are "the picture of good health?"**

In some developing countries of the world, chronic malnutrition is a serious problem. Bad weather, inadequate transportation, and political and economic difficulties are causes. Anywhere that poverty exists, however, even in some parts of the United States, malnutrition is possible.

How Much Do You Need?

Everybody needs the same nutrients, although not necessarily in the same amounts. Females require more iron than males. Athletes and others who are physically active need more of most nutrients than inactive people. Older adults require less of many nutrients.

Scientists have developed a series of standards for assessing nutrient needs among people of different age and gender groups. These standards have different names but are known under the general label "Dietary Reference Intakes," or **DRIs**.

Two examples of DRIs are Recommended Dietary Allowances (RDAs) and Adequate Intakes (AIs). **RDAs** are the amounts of a

- *The Six Main Nutrients*
- *Benefits of Good Nutrition*
- *Serious Health Problems (text pages 53-55)*

Nutrient Mapping

Have students create a cognitive map of types of nutrients. Have them 1) write the word "nutrients" in a circle in the center of a sheet of paper; 2) draw satellites around the center circle and label them with the names of the six major types of nutrients; 3) draw lines from each nutrient to connect with listed functions of that nutrient. L1

Interpretive Activity

Set up a display of magazines, books, or Internet articles featuring dietary information. Include some that recommend single foods or food groups and some that exclude foods or food groups. Ask students to select one and explain whether it supports the rule that nutrients work together as a team.

Observation Activity

Provide students with magazines that include pictures of people who are malnourished. Ask students to identify physical characteristics resulting from malnutrition. Have students locate on a map the countries mentioned in the stories.

Reinforcing Key Skills

Present the following problems to student groups. Allow time for them to discuss and compare their responses.

Leadership—Instead of drinking protein- and carbohydrate-rich milk, your brother takes a calcium supplement, noting the advice on the bottle "Equals 1 glass of milk." How do you respond?

Communication—Your best friend said, "I'm trying to eat more healthfully, so I'm going to follow the seven-day grapefruit diet. I eat just grapefruit for seven days." How do you respond?

TEACH cont.

- *How Much Do You Need? (text page 55-56)*

Discussion Activity

Ask students to explain why, of the more than 40 nutrients known, many do not have RDA values. Discuss why researchers must determine critical facts such as the amount of the nutrient used by the body, how it is used, and what the effects of an "overdose" of the nutrient are before scientists can recommend amounts. How do established RDAs and AIs have an impact of food selection? What's the difference between percent Daily Values and the RDAs?

Product Comparison

Have students obtain a variety of breakfast cereal nutrition labels showing percent Daily Values for a variety of nutrients. Have students (or groups of students) make graphs showing the percent Daily Values for key nutrients. Compare the graphs for various cereals. L1

Research Activity

Have students research Recommended Daily Allowances guidelines. Direct the students to reputable sources of information in this regard, including online government-sponsored sites, geared to teens, that you have prescreened. How have these guidelines changed through the years? Why have they changed?

nutrient needed by 98 percent of the people in a given age and gender group. When a lack of scientific information makes it impossible to establish the RDA for a particular nutrient, approximate nutrient measures, or **AIs**, are set instead. Both RDAs and AIs are used to determine average individual needs.

The DRIs, including RDAs and AIs, are updated periodically as new information becomes available. They are used by dietitians, nutritionists, and other health professionals. DRIs are an important tool in shaping U.S. nutrition policy and for developing educational programs. They are also used by the food industry for product development.

The U.S. Food and Drug Administration (FDA) has used the DRIs as the basis for another set of guidelines. These are known as Daily Values (DVs) and are used in nutrition labeling.

Most nutrients are needed in relatively small amounts. It's easier to measure them using the metric system, the system of measurement used by scientists. The metric system includes small units of measure, such as the milligram (mg). For example, female teens need 15 milligrams (mg) of iron each day. That's equivalent to about 0.0005 ounce—about the size of a single dry bean.

Energy from Nutrients

Running, walking, sitting, and even reading this sentence all require energy. Your body gets this energy from carbohydrates, as well as protein and fats. The energy is measured in units called *kilocalories* (KIL-oh-KAL-uh-reez). A kilocalorie—or **calorie**—is the amount of energy needed to raise the temperature of 1 kilogram (a little more than 4 cups) of water 1 degree Celsius. In the metric system, energy is measured in kilojoules (KJ).

Dietary Reference Intakes (DRIs) for Selected Vitamins and Minerals*

Vitamins	Males Age 14-18	Females Age 14-18	Minerals	Males Age 14-18	Females Age 14-18
Folate (μg)	**400**	**400**	Calcium (mg)	1,300	1,300
Niacin (mg)	**16**	**14**	Iodine (μg)	**150**	**150**
Riboflavin (B2) (mg)	**1.3**	**1.0**	Iron (mg)	**11**	**15**
Thiamin (B1) (mg)	**1.2**	**1.0**	Magnesium (mg)	**410**	**360**
Vitamin A (μg RE**)	**900**	**700**	Manganese (mg)	2.2	1.6
Vitamin C (mg)	**75**	**65**	Molybdenum (μg)	**43**	**43**
Vitamin D (μg)	5	5	Phosphorus (mg)	**1,250**	**1,250**
Vitamin E (mg)	**15**	**15**	Zinc (mg)	**11**	**9**

* The numbers shown include RDAs (in bold type) and AIs.
** RE = retinol equivalent; μg = microgram; mg = milligram.

HOME & COMMUNITY CONNECTION

Ask students to research their AI for calcium. Then, using food labels, have them add the % daily value for calcium they obtain in one typical breakfast or other meal at home. Have students compare the % daily value they obtained in one meal to established AIs for their age and gender. Encourage students to discuss their findings with an adult in the house, including any healthful changes that should be made in food purchases.

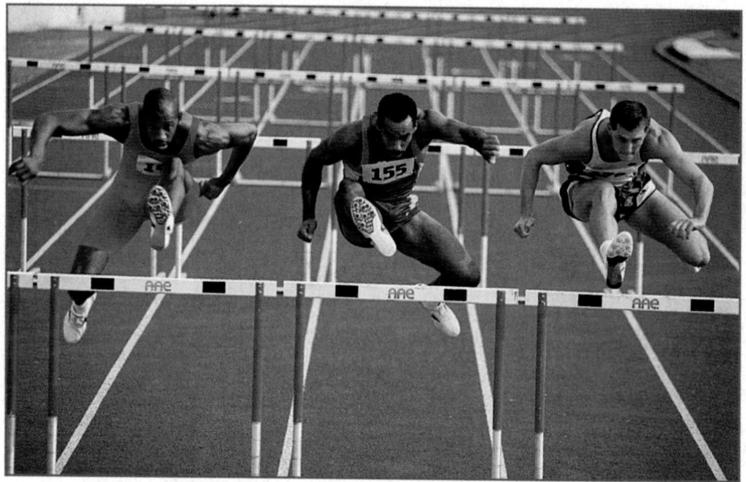

◆ Vigorous activity, such as running or swimming, uses large amounts of energy. Speak with a physical education teacher or athletic trainer in your school about the calorie requirements of athletes. Share your findings with the class.

Your Energy Needs

The number of calories your body needs for energy in a given day depends on a number of factors. These include your activity level, age, weight, and gender. If you are still growing, the number is affected by increased energy demands for building muscles and bones.

The U.S. Department of Agriculture recommends the following calorie intakes:

- 2,800 calories for teen males, many active men, and some very active women.
- 2,200 calories for most children, teen females, active women, and many inactive men. Women who are pregnant or breastfeeding may need more.
- 1,600 calories for many inactive women and most older adults.

Keep in mind that these calorie levels vary with the amount of physical activity in your life. For instance, teens who spend most of their leisure time in front of the computer or TV will need to adjust their caloric intake if they take up hockey or soccer.

Recommended Sources of Calories

Scientists have determined that carbohydrates and proteins in their purest forms each provide 4 calories per gram, whereas fat provides 9 calories per gram. Notice that fat has more than twice the number of calories per gram as either of the other energy-producing nutrients.

Health experts recommend that you get less than 30 percent of the calories you take in from fat, approximately 60 percent from carbohydrates, and at least 10 percent from protein. This ratio provides the healthiest balance of the three nutrients.

For instance, Julie, who needs about 2,200 calories a day, should get less than 660 of those calories from fat ($2{,}200 \times 0.3 = 660$). How many grams of fat will supply 660 calories? Since there are 9 calories in 1 gram of fat, divide 660 by 9. The answer is about 73 grams. If Julie eats a cheeseburger and dessert for lunch, totaling about 47 grams of fat, she will need to eat low-fat choices the rest of the day to stay under 73 grams of fat.

- *Energy from Nutrients (text pages 56-58)*

Discussion Activity

Have students discuss the relationship between caloric intake, exercise, and weight gain or loss. Ask students to discuss how the recommended daily percentages of the different sources of energy (carbohydrates, proteins, fats) may be the same or different based on caloric intake, exercise, and weight.

Demonstration

On the chalkboard, show the difference between calories and kilocalories (1000 calories = 1 kilocalorie) and ask students to do some simple equations using this conversion factor.

Computer Analysis

Have students track their food and beverage intake for three days, using computer software to analyze their own eating plans. Have them check the percentages of calories from carbohydrates, proteins, and fats. What adjustments, if any, are needed for a balanced eating plan? L2

FOOD SCIENCE — Measuring Kilocalories

An instrument called a calorimeter is used to calculate the energy content provided by foods. A measured amount of food is placed in the calorimeter chamber and burned. Scientists calculate how much heat is given off in the process. The results tell them how many kilocalories the food provides. Discuss with students reasons why knowing kilocalories provided by foods can be important for your health.

ASSESS

REVIEW

- Ask students to summarize the main ideas in this section.
- Have students complete the Section Review. (Answers appear below.)

EVALUATION

- Ask students to write a brief summary of the nutrition topics discussed in this section. In the summary, have students include how the information is useful for their daily eating.
- Have students take the quiz for Section 2-1. (Use the quiz in the *Teacher Resource Guide,* or construct your own with the **Exam***View*® *Test Generator* on the *Effective Instruction CD-ROM.*)

RETEACHING

- Have students read about the importance of nutrients in a selected reference. Then ask them to list four important points made about nutrition. Analyze how these points compare with points made in this chapter.
- Refer to the *Reteaching Activities* booklet for the Section 2-1 activity sheet.

CLOSE

Hold a class discussion on the nutrients people need. Include in the discussion nutrients of which Americans, in general, may get too much or too little. Also apply section information to popular fad diets, such as high-protein, low-carbohydrate diets, which may provide insufficient nutrients.

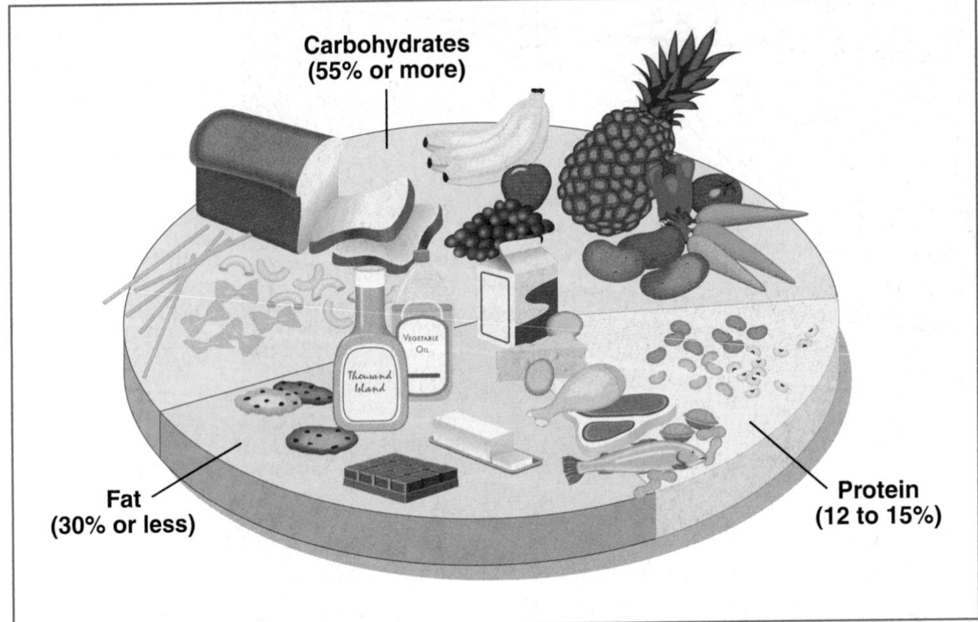

◆ **It is not just the number of calories you take in that is important but the sources of those calories. This drawing shows the recommended percentages for the healthiest balance of carbohydrates, protein, and fat. What percentage of your daily food intake should include fruits, vegetables, and grains?**

Section 2-1 Review & Activities

1. What are the six major types of nutrients? What are the main functions of each?
2. What are DRIs? How are they used by professionals or industry?
3. Which nutrients supply your body with energy? How is food energy measured?
4. **Comparing and Contrasting.** Juan is a moderately active 15-year-old male. His mother, Inez, is a very active 40-year-old. What calorie levels are suggested for each? How are they the same? How are they different?
5. **Analyzing.** Some fad diets recommend levels of fewer than 1,000 calories per day. Why is such an approach unhealthful for reaching a healthy weight?
6. **Applying.** Use the information in this section to determine your approximate calorie needs. Make a list of the days of the week you exercise or play sports. Which day(s) of the week will you need the most calories? Which day(s) will you need the fewest calories? Why?

Answers to Section 2-1 Review & Activities

1. Carbohydrates (energy), fats (energy), proteins (build/repair body), vitamins (body functions), minerals (body functions), and water (essential to life).
2. Dietary Reference Intakes—standards for accessing nutrient needs for different age and gender groups; shape U.S. nutrition policy, develop educational programs and food products.
3. Carbohydrates (except fiber), proteins, and fats; calories.
4. Both need approximately 2800 calories per day. Their needs will vary depending on many factors, including activity level.
5. 1000 calories is far lower than recommended for children, teens, and adults. Too few calories will cause a lack of energy; and nutrient deficiencies could result in poor health.
6. Answers will vary.

SECTION
2-2

Objectives

After studying this section, you should be able to:

- Name sources of simple and complex carbohydrates.
- Explain why soluble and insoluble fibers are important.
- Distinguish between complete and incomplete proteins.

Look for These Terms

insoluble fiber

soluble fiber

refined sugars

amino acids

complete proteins

incomplete proteins

Carbohydrates, Fiber, and Proteins

As you read in Section 2-1, for good health you need six basic nutrients, plus fiber. Read on to learn more about these, beginning with carbohydrates, fiber, and proteins.

Carbohydrates

The body's main source of energy is carbohydrates. You may know them as starches and sugars. They are found mainly in foods from plant sources, such as fruits, vegetables, grain products, and dry beans and peas. For good health, eat a variety of these foods every day. Generally, they are the least expensive form of energy you can buy.

If you don't eat enough carbohydrates, your body will use the other energy-producing nutrients for energy. When it does this, however, it keeps those nutrients from doing their specialized jobs.

Depending on their source, carbohydrates fall into one of two categories—complex and simple carbohydrates.

Complex Carbohydrates

Complex carbohydrates are broken down into two subcategories: starches and dietary fiber. Both are found in dry beans, peas, and lentils; vegetables, such as potatoes and corn; and grain products, such as rice, pasta, and breads. Foods high in starch are usually good

Section 2-2 Resources

◆ **Student Workbook**, pp. 19, 23
◆ **Teacher Resource Guide**
Lesson Plan 2-2 Organizer
Section 2-2 Quiz
◆ **Effective Instruction CD-ROM**
Exam*View*® *Test Generator*

◆ **Student Motivation Kit**
Reteaching Activities, pp. 15-16
Enrichment Activities
Food Science Resources, pp. 46–49, 116–120

SECTION
2-2

Carbohydrates, Fiber, and Proteins

FOCUS

MOTIVATORS

- Have students bring to class news or magazine articles about the importance of carbohydrates, dietary fiber, and protein in one's eating plan. Discuss positive or negative reasons these nutrients are newsworthy.
- Ask students to identify foods that have been the mainstay of the human eating plan throughout history (grains, fruits, vegetables, meat, fish, poultry, eggs, legumes, and nuts). Ask: What foods are available today that have not been mainstays? Are these additions healthful?

VOCABULARY ACTIVITY

Ask students to define the meaning of the prefix *in-* as in the term *insoluble* and *incomplete*. What relationship do these words have to their counterparts without *in-*?

STUDY SKILLS

- **Guided Reading.** Have students look at the headings within Section 2-2 to preview the concepts that will be discussed.
- Have students read the section and complete the appropriate part of the Chapter 2 Study Guide in the *Student Workbook.*

TEACH

• *Carbohydrates (text pages 59-61)*

Discussion Activity

Ask students to name sources of carbohydrates. Discuss the difference in the types of carbohydrates within each named source.

Field Trip

Plan a field trip to the bulk-grain section of a supermarket or farmer's market. Have students identify the visual characteristic of grains that are high in fiber. Compare high fiber grains (whole grains) to refined, processed grains.

Categorizing Activity

Have students compare the calories and nutritional content of natural and processed carbohydrate foods. Is there an overall connection related to calorie content and fiber content?

Poster Project

Have students work in groups to make posters illustrating the chemical makeup of sugars, starches, and fiber. Use the posters to explain the differences in simple and complex carbohydrates. L2

Creating a Chart

Have students create charts listing foods that are high in soluble and insoluble fiber. Allow time for students to discuss the importance of getting plenty of fiber in their eating plans. L1

◆ Grain products, dry beans and peas, and fruits and vegetables are important sources of carbohydrates. Explain the process in which starches and sugars provide energy for the body.

sources of proteins, vitamins, minerals, and dietary fiber.

Dietary Fiber

As noted in Section 2-1, dietary fiber is the only form of carbohydrate that does not provide energy. It consists of nondigestible plant materials. This complex carbohydrate is found only in foods from plant sources, such as fruits, vegetables, grain products, and dry beans and peas.

There are two kinds of fiber, insoluble and soluble. Most fiber-containing foods provide both.

Insoluble Fiber

Insoluble fiber is fiber that will not dissolve in water. Insoluble fiber absorbs water, much like a sponge does, and contributes bulk. It helps food move through the large intestine at a normal rate. It promotes regular bowel movements and helps prevent constipation. This type of fiber appears to lower the risk of colon cancer. You can find it mainly in fruit and vegetable skins and in whole wheat or wheat bran products.

Soluble Fiber

Soluble fiber is fiber that dissolves in water. Soluble fiber increases the thickness of the stomach contents. Studies show that it may reduce blood cholesterol levels. You can find soluble fiber in fruits, vegetables, dry beans, peas, lentils, and oat products.

How Much Fiber?

How much fiber do you consume? If you are like most other Americans, you get only about half the recommended fiber intake. The American Dietetic Association recommends 20 to 35 grams of dietary fiber a day for adults. To compute your daily fiber needs during the growth years, which include adolescence, add 5 to your age. For instance, a 14-year-old needs 19 grams of fiber daily (14 + 5).

To get enough fiber, eat a wide variety of plant foods every day. Bean burritos, chili with beans, vegetable stir-fry dishes, and vegetable pizza are all excellent choices. Increase fiber gradually, and be sure to drink plenty of fluids to avoid digestive upset.

Extending Learning

Cellulose—Point out that carbohydrates meet many human needs in addition to nutrition:

- We use cellulose, one of the most common carbohydrates, to make clothing (of cotton, rayon, and linen).
- We use cellulose, in the form of wood, to build homes.

Thus, carbohydrates meet the most basic human needs: food, clothing, and shelter.

Simple Carbohydrates

Simple carbohydrates, or sugars, are a natural part of many foods. These sugars include *fructose* (FROOK-tohs), found in fruits; *maltose* (MALL-tohs), found in grain products; and *lactose* (LACK-tohs), found in dairy products. Most foods that contain these sugars also provide other nutrients, such as proteins, vitamins, and minerals.

Refined sugars are sugars that are extracted from plants and used as a sweetener. The most widely used refined sugar is *sucrose* (SOOK-rohs), or table sugar. Sucrose comes from plants such as sugar cane or sugar beets. Other refined sugars include corn syrup, honey, maple syrup, molasses, and brown sugar. Refined sugars do not supply nutrients other than simple carbohydrates. Eating large amounts of sweetened foods can lead to excess weight, which can contribute to health problems.

Proteins

When it comes to the energy they provide, complex and simple carbohydrates and proteins are all created equal. However, unlike their sweet and starchy counterparts, proteins have unique building roles in the body. They are used mainly to help the body grow and repair worn-out or damaged parts. About one-fifth of your body's total weight is protein. Your hair, eyes, skin, muscles, and bones are made of proteins. The proteins you eat help maintain them in good condition.

◆ **Good sources of protein include animal foods, which are called complete proteins, and plant foods, such as the ones pictured. Describe a meatless meal that would provide the protein your body needs.**

• *Carbohydrates (text pages 59-61)*

Checklists

Ask students to develop a checklist of guidelines for choosing a healthful cereal. Guidelines should include fiber and sugar content. Allow time for students to share and compare their checklists. L1

Comparison

Have students list their ten favorite carbohydrate-rich foods. Is the carbohydrate mostly simple or complex? L1

COMPUTER ACTIVITY
Using Nutrition Software

Using a nutrition software program, have students compare the calories and nutrients provided by one teaspoon white sugar, brown sugar, honey, and molasses. Discuss the findings in class.

Research Activity

Provide articles from the Internet, magazines, and books that discuss the intake and use of sugar. Ask students to read an article and make a list of its most important points. Discuss with students if sugar seems to be negatively viewed and how to put negative views into the total eating plan perspective.

VISUAL LEARNING *Using the Photograph*

Have students look at the photo that shows sources of protein. How many of these foods do students include regularly in their eating plans? Have a discussion about increasing the variety of food sources they use each day.

Extending Learning

Lactose—A carbohydrate naturally found in milk is lactose, a simple carbohydrate. Although most people think of sugar as a sweet food, lactose is not sweet. It is found in varying amounts in dairy foods; milk is high in lactose and hard cheese is low. About 75% of adults worldwide do not produce adequate amounts of an enzyme to digest lactose. Dairy-free substitutes and lactose-reduced dairy products are available for people who are lactose intolerant.

TEACH cont.

- *Proteins*
  (text pages 61-63)

Discussion Activity

Ask students to list the many functions protein performs in the body. Discuss what happens if we obtain too much or too little protein. Ask students to explain why nine amino acids are called *essential*. How can people make sure they get enough of them?

USING CONNECTING FOOD AND MATH

In class, brainstorm a one-day "typical" meal plan for a teenage male or female. Using a food values reference book, record the amount of protein provided by the "typical" meal plan. Ask the students how the protein content of the "typical" plan compares to their own protein needs.

Connecting Food and Math

How Much Protein Should You Eat?

To meet the demands of a more active lifestyle and the growth spurt associated with the teen years, your body needs more protein now than it may later in life. How much protein do you need? This formula will help you find out:

1. **Multiply your ideal body weight in pounds by one of the following numbers.** If you are between the ages of 11 and 14 and do light activity, use the number 0.45. If you are between the ages of 15 and 18, use the number 0.40. If you are between the ages of 11 and 18 and are very active—for example, if you participate in a sport—use the number 0.55.
2. **Write the calculated number in your Wellness Journal.** This is your recommended daily allowance of protein expressed in grams.

Note: Nutritionists recommend that no more than a third of your protein come from animal sources, which are higher in fat than vegetable sources of protein.

Proteins also regulate important body processes. For instance, they play a major role in fighting disease because parts of the immune system are proteins.

Proteins can do their job only if you consume enough carbohydrates and fats for your energy needs. If not, the body uses proteins for energy instead of for building and repairing.

Proteins are found in all foods from animal sources, including meat, poultry, fish, eggs, and dairy products. They are also found in foods from plant sources, especially dry beans and peas, peanuts, vegetables, and grain products.

Although protein is essential, nutrition experts agree that too much can be harmful. First, excess amounts are broken down and stored by the body as fat. Second, high-protein intake can stress the kidneys as the body works to break down the extra protein and remove the byproducts.

Complete and Incomplete Proteins

Proteins are made of chains of chemical building blocks called **amino** (uh-MEE-noh) **acids**. Just as letters of the alphabet are arranged to make countless different words,

Should I eat more meat to get stronger?

A Some people associate protein with strength and meat with protein. As a result, they hope to build muscles and strength by eating extra meat. Don't forget that eggs, milk, grains, legumes, and vegetables also supply protein—plus many other nutrients the body needs. You do need protein to build muscle cells, as well as all other cells, but focusing on many nutrient sources is more healthful then overemphasizing one.

HOME & COMMUNITY CONNECTION

Ask students to interview a parent or other adult at home about the most common protein sources that are available in home meals. Have students record at least ten sources. Then have students provide suggestions for one protein-rich food source that's not on the list and suggests ways that the new food can be incorporated into home meals. In class, have students compare protein sources commonly consumed. Are there more animal than protein sources mentioned? Why or why not?

these chemical substances that make up body proteins can also be arranged in numerous ways. Your body can make all but 9 of the 22 known amino acids. These nine are called *essential amino acids* because they must come from foods you eat.

Complete proteins—proteins that supply all nine essential amino acids—include meat, poultry, fish, eggs, dairy products, and soy products. Except for soybeans, all foods from plant sources supply **incomplete proteins**, proteins lacking one or more essential amino acids. Although such foods by themselves fail to deliver all the essential amino acids, it is possible to obtain them all by eating a variety of foods and enough calories throughout the day. This is especially important for people who follow a vegetarian eating plan.

Most Americans get the largest amount of their protein from animal sources. Health experts, however, recommend that people get more of their protein from plant sources. Why? Plant sources generally have less fat, and low-fat choices are recommended. You will learn more about fats in the next section.

INFOLINK

For more information on specific nutrient needs in a vegetarian eating plan, see Section 4-4.

CLOSE-UP ON SCIENCE: BIOCHEMISTRY

Amino Acids and Body Proteins

In the body, specialized particles in the cells called ribosomes (Reye-buh-SOHMS) assemble individual amino acids into specific types of protein. Ribosomes can work overtime to create those proteins in greatest demand at certain times of life or in certain situations. Suppose you cut yourself with a knife. Ribosomes may combine some of the amino acids eaten in peanut butter with others in multigrain bread to help repair the injured skin, replace lost blood, and fight infection at the wound.

Section 2-2 Review & Activities

1. List three foods that supply simple carbohydrates and six foods that supply complex carbohydrates.
2. Why is it important to obtain both soluble and insoluble fiber?
3. What is the difference between complete and incomplete proteins?
4. **Synthesizing.** Studies show that most Americans eat less fiber than is needed for good health. Identify some possible reasons this would be true.
5. **Analyzing.** Suppose someone said "Cutting out carbohydrates is a good way to lose weight." What would your response be?
6. **Applying.** Think of the last meal you ate. Which foods supplied carbohydrates? Fiber? Proteins? What types of carbohydrates, fiber, and proteins were they?

Answers to Section 2-2 Review & Activities

1. Simple carbohydrates: fruit, milk, grain products. Complex: dry beans and peas, potatoes, corn, rice, pasta, whole-grain breads.
2. The two types of fiber perform different tasks: Insoluble fiber helps foods move through the digestive system, and soluble fiber helps lower cholesterol levels.
3. Complete proteins provide all the amino acids the body needs to build protein; incomplete do not.
4. Answers will vary.
5. Simple carbohydrates eaten as refined sugars may be cut; complex carbohydrates are needed for health and energy.
6. Answers will vary.

ASSESS

REVIEW

- Ask students to summarize the main ideas in this section
- Have students complete the Section Review. (Answers appear below.)

EVALUATION

- Have students make a list in their Wellness Journal of ways of using the information covered in this section to incorporate healthier changes, especially more fiber, in their own and their family's eating plans. Encourage students to follow up with a description of their family's reaction to new foods. What long-term changes in eating habits at home may result?
- Have students take the quiz for Section 2-2. (Use the quiz in the *Teacher Resource Guide,* or construct your own with the **Exam***View*® *Test Generator* on the *Effective Instruction CD-ROM.*)

RETEACHING

- Have students create posters to demonstrate one of the following: Types of Protein, Simple and Complex Carbohydrates, or Soluble and Insoluble Fiber.
- Refer to the *Reteaching Activities* booklet for the Section 2-2 activity sheet.

CLOSE

Lead a discussion on getting the proper balance of carbohydrates, including fiber, and proteins in your eating plan. As a class, develop a one-day meal plan demonstrating proper balance.

SECTION

2-3

Fats

FOCUS

MOTIVATORS

- Ask students to identify sources of fat in foods. Which of these sources are solid at room temperature? Which are liquid? Was it more difficult to give examples of solid or of liquid fats? What does this tell you about judging the amount of fat in food?
- Discuss reasons people may be concerned about the amount of cholesterol they consume. What are some reasons why teens may be concerned?

VOCABULARY ACTIVITY

Direct students' attention to the list "Look for These Terms." Pronounce aloud the word *polyunsaturated.* Ask a volunteer to investigate the meaning of the prefix *poly-* (many). Have students identify three other words that use the prefix *poly-*.

STUDY SKILLS

- **Listening.** Invite a group of volunteers each to prepare an oral reading of a page of text from the section, while others follow along silently.
- Have students read the section and complete the appropriate part of the Chapter 2 Study Guide in the *Student Workbook.*

SECTION

2-3

Objectives

After studying this section, you should be able to:

- Describe the functions and sources of fats.
- Discuss the effects of cholesterol and fatty acids on health.
- Identify three basic types of fatty acids.

Look for These Terms

cholesterol

LDL

HDL

saturated fatty acids

polyunsaturated fatty acids

monounsaturated fatty acids

hydrogenation

Fats

"Eat Less Fat!" "New Study Links Disease with Excess Saturated Fat!" Headlines like these seem to be everywhere these days. So, it seems, are fat-free and low-fat foods.

Although reducing fat in your eating plan is sound advice for most people, fat is not always the villain you may have been led to believe. In fact, as you will see, you can't live without some fat.

Functions and Sources of Fats

Fats—or, more specifically, substances called *essential fatty acids,* found mainly in vegetable oils—are an essential nutrient with several important functions. Fats promote healthy skin and normal cell growth, and carry vitamins A, D, E, and K to wherever they are needed. In addition, fats stored in the body provide a reserve supply of energy and act as a cushion to protect your heart, liver, and other vital organs.

From a sensory standpoint, fats add flavor to food. Because they move through the digestive system slowly, they help you feel full longer.

What, then, is the problem with fat? Studies show that most Americans eat too much fat—and the wrong kinds. Doing so can increase the risk of illness such as heart disease and cancer. It can also create a health risk by contributing to overweight or obesity. Remember, fats have twice as many calories per gram as carbohydrates or proteins.

Section 2-3 Resources

◆ **Student Workbook,** pp. 20, 24
◆ **Teacher Resource Guide**
Lesson Plan 2-3 Organizer
Section 2-3 Quiz
◆ **Effective Instruction CD-ROM**
Exam*View*® *Test Generator*
PowerPoint® Slide #5
◆ **Transparency Package,** CT-5
◆ **Student Motivation Kit**
Reteaching Activities, pp. 17–18
Enrichment Activities
Food Science Resources, pp. 43–45, 59–61

◆ **Some of the foods shown here are obvious sources of fat. Which of the foods pictured do you regularly eat? List other foods that you eat that may contain hidden fat.**

Although fats cannot, nor should not, be eliminated from one's eating plan completely, it is important to limit their use. One way of accomplishing this is to eat more complex carbohydrates. Another is to choose low-fat foods. Foods high in fat include butter, margarine, oils, cream, sour cream, salad dressing, fried foods, some baked goods, and chocolate. Moderate to large amounts of fat are also found in some cuts of meat, nuts and seeds, peanut butter, egg yolks, whole milk, and some cheeses.

 ***Is avoiding fat completely the best approach for healthful eating?***

 No. Your body has an essential need for some fat. A good guideline is to follow a low-fat eating plan (less than 30 percent of total calories from fat).

Cholesterol, Fats, and Health

"Is cholesterol the very same thing as fat?" "Do I need any cholesterol, or can I eliminate it from my eating plan?" Questions like these about cholesterol are common. You may have asked some yourself.

What Is Cholesterol?

Cholesterol (kuh-LES-tuhr-ol) is not fat. Rather, it is a fatlike substance present in all body cells that is needed for many essential body processes. It contributes to the digestion of fat and the skin's production of vitamin D. Adults manufacture all the cholesterol they need, mostly in the liver. Infants' and children's bodies, on the other hand, don't produce enough cholesterol. So they need it in their eating plans.

TEACH

- *Functions and Sources of Fats (text pages 64-65)*

Discussion Activity

Ask students which substances in fats the human body needs. Without essential fatty acids, the transportation within the body of which vitamins would be affected? On the board, ask a few volunteers to list, under each fat-soluble vitamin heading, a good source of each vitamin.

Presentation Project

Have a small group of volunteers work together to develop an oral presentation comparing the effects of eating too much fat to too little fat. They are to explain why some people may eat too much fat and how this problem can be avoided. Allow time for a question-and-answer session. 

Label Analysis

Display a Nutrition Facts panel from a food package to acquaint students with this device. Have students select a food they regularly eat and to examine the Nutrition Facts panel to determine how much fat the food contains. What percentage of the total product does the fat represent? Discuss hidden fats and the role they may play in giving false impressions about which foods are actually high in fat. L2

Extending Learning

Essential Fatty Acids—The two essential fatty acids are linolenic acid and linoleic acid. They are called "essential" fatty acids because the body cannot manufacture them. They must be supplied by food a person eats. These two fatty acids are both polyunsaturated fatty acids. They are found in the natural oils of plants and fish. The body needs them for its basic functions, including production of various hormones. Deficiencies of these fatty acids are unlikely since the body readily stores them.

- *Cholesterol, Fats, and Health (text pages 65-68)*

Discussion Activity

Discuss what cholesterol is, its functions, and how it's transported. Ask students to explain what LDLs and HDLs are and the differences between them. Draw a diagram on the board of HDL and LDL transportation using trucks, packages, and a highway to depict the transportation in the bloodstream.

Cholesterol Analysis

Provide students with pictures of foods that contain cholesterol. Have students work independently to find the cholesterol per serving of each food. They are then to organize the foods pictured in terms of the amount of cholesterol they contain. What conclusions can they draw? L1

Taste Test

1. Provide six bowls of cream cheese mixtures: (1) regular, (2) light or reduced fat, (3) fat free, (4) regular blended with salsa, (5) light or reduced fat blended with salsa, and (6) fat free blended with salsa. Number the bowls 1 through 6.
2. Students will label a piece of paper 1 through 6.
3. Provide each student with tasting spoons or bite-size pieces of a plain bagel.
4. Students will then taste each of the six cream cheese mixtures and determine which mixture matches which fat/ cream cheese category.
5. Ask students to share findings. What were the characteristics of the higher fat product? Did adding salsa make the fat free cheese more appealing?

A certain amount of cholesterol circulates in the blood. It does not float through the bloodstream on its own, but in chemical "packages" called lipoproteins (LIH-poh-PROH-teenz). There are two major kinds of lipoproteins, LDL and HDL.

- **LDL**, which stands for "low-density lipoprotein," is a chemical that takes cholesterol from the liver to wherever it is needed in the body. However, if too much LDL cholesterol is circulating, the excess amounts of cholesterol can build up in artery walls. This buildup increases the risk of heart disease or stroke. Thus, LDL cholesterol has come to be called "bad" cholesterol.
- **HDL** stands for "high-density lipoprotein" and refers to a chemical that picks up excess cholesterol and takes it back to the liver, keeping it from causing harm. For this reason, HDL cholesterol has come to be known as "good" cholesterol.

Medical tests can determine the amounts of total cholesterol, LDL cholesterol, and HDL cholesterol in the bloodstream. The risk of heart disease may increase if LDL and total cholesterol levels are too high and if the HDL level is too low.

Making wise food choices can help reduce the amount of harmful cholesterol in the bloodstream. As you will see, both cholesterol and fat in foods may affect blood cholesterol levels. The good news is that cholesterol can't make you fat since it doesn't provide energy.

Cholesterol in Foods

Did you also know that all animals have the ability to manufacture cholesterol? This means that if you eat any animal product, including meat, poultry, and fish, you will likely be consuming some cholesterol. Other foods high in cholesterol are egg yolks, liver and other organ meats, and some shellfish. Eating less of these foods may help reduce blood levels of LDL cholesterol.

Saturated and Unsaturated Fats

For most people, the amounts and types of fats eaten have a greater effect on blood cholesterol levels than does the amount of cholesterol eaten.

The fats found in food, such as butter, chicken fat, or corn oil, are made up of different combinations of *fatty acids.* There are three basic kinds of fatty acids. Each has a different effect on cholesterol levels. All fats include all three kinds of fatty acids, but in varying amounts.

- **Saturated** (SAT-chur-ay-ted) **fatty acids** are fats that appear to raise the level of LDL ("bad") cholesterol in the bloodstream. Foods relatively high in saturated fatty acids include meat, poultry skin, whole-milk dairy products, and the tropical oils—coconut oil, palm oil, and palm kernel oil.
- **Polyunsaturated** (PAH-lee-un-SAT-chur-ay-ted) **fatty acids** are fats that seem to help lower cholesterol levels. Many vegetable oils, such as corn oil, soybean oil, and safflower oil, are high in polyunsaturated fatty acids.
- **Monounsaturated** (MAH-no-un-SAT-chur-ay-ted) **fatty acids** are fats that appear to lower LDL ("bad") cholesterol levels and may help raise levels of HDL. Foods relatively high in monounsaturated fatty acids include olives, olive oil, avocados, peanuts, peanut oil, and canola oil.

A simple rule of thumb is that fats that are solid at room temperature, such as butter, are made up mainly of saturated fatty acids.

Reinforcing Key Skills

Present the following problems to student groups. Allow time for them to discuss and compare their responses.

Critical Thinking—Pete has a high cholesterol level and is overweight. He eats at a "fast food" restaurant for dinner five nights a week. What "fast food" choices can Pete make that are lower in fat, specifically saturated fat?

Communication—Your next door neighbor Brianna is 6 months old. Her mother has high cholesterol, so she is eliminating cholesterol from Brianna's meals. What advice might you give Brianna's mother?

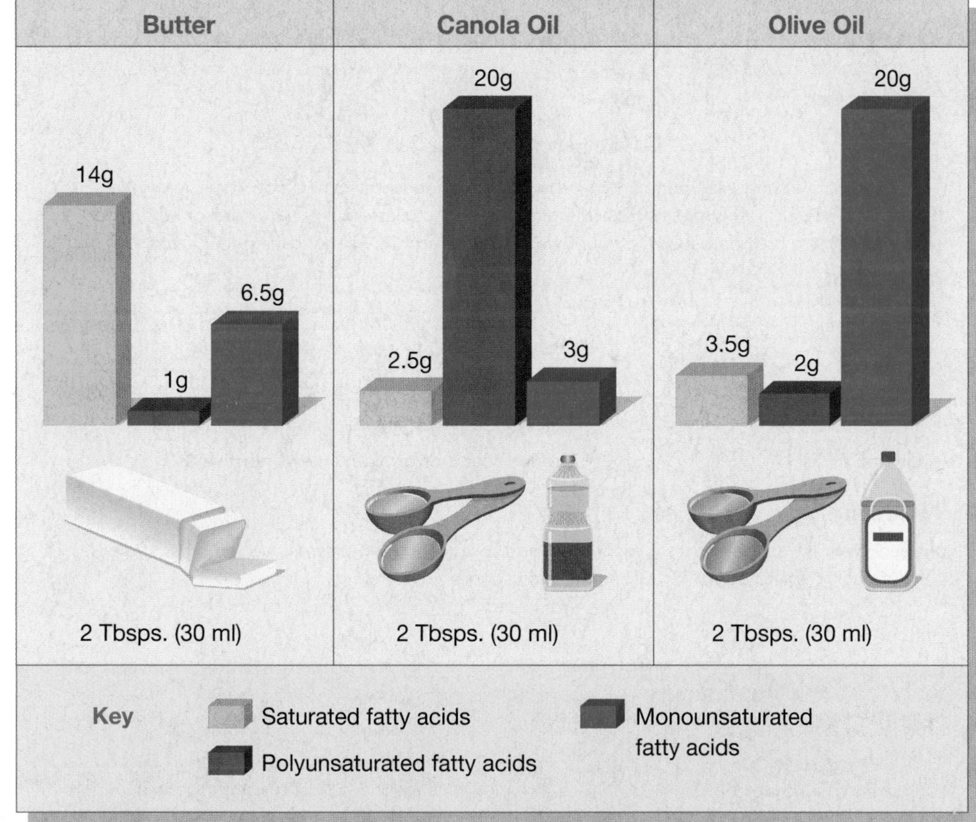

◆ **Butter, canola oil, and olive oil each contain all three types of fatty acids. Identify the type of fat that is highest in each of the following: polyunsaturated fatty acids, saturated fatty acids, and monounsaturated fatty acids.**

Fats that are liquid at room temperature, such as corn oil and olive oil, are composed primarily of unsaturated fatty acids. For better health, people choose unsaturated fats rather than saturated. They also limit the total amount of fat eaten.

Trans Fats

Trans fats are another type of fat to avoid. Most trans fats are produced when food processors turn liquid fats into solids to lengthen a product's shelf life. They do this through **hydrogenation** (hy-DRAH-juh-NAY-shun), a process that adds missing hydrogen atoms to unsaturated fat. The product gains a firmer texture, but also the unhealthful properties of saturated fat.

Since trans fats increase cholesterol production, they should be avoided. Any food label that lists ingredients that are "hydrogenated" or "partially hydrogenated" points to the possible presence of trans fats.

- *Cholesterol, Fats, and Health (text pages 65-68)*

Discussion Activity

Discuss the difference between saturated and unsaturated fats. How do these fats compare to hydrogenated fats? Discuss the process of hydrogenation. What does hydrogenation do to liquid fatty acids? Why might such a procedure be performed?

Classification Activity

Display samples of various types of fats. Have students categorize the fats as saturated or unsaturated.

COMPUTER ACTIVITY

Creating a Pamphlet

Invite students to create pamphlets that summarize, in a lively text format, tips on cutting down the amount of total fat, saturated fat, and cholesterol in one's eating plan. The booklet may be run off on the classroom or home computer, using either word-processing or desktop publishing booklets with original or computer art. Have students speak to their doctor or public health clinic director about leaving copies of the booklet available as an educational service for their clients.

Guest Speaker

Invite a local registered dietitian (possibly affiliated with the American Heart Association) to come to class to speak with the students about the latest research on cholesterol, fats, and health. Have students prepare one question each to potentially ask the dietitian.

FOOD SCIENCE

Chemical Structure of Fats

Fats are sometimes called triglycerides. This refers to their structure: three fatty acids attached to a glycerol molecule.

Fatty acids are made up of the elements carbon, oxygen, and hydrogen. These elements are arranged differently for the various types of fatty acids. Unsaturated fatty acids have some hydrogen missing from their chemical structure. Depending on the number of hydrogen atoms that are missing, they are either monounsaturated (one missing) or polyunsaturated (more than one missing). Saturated fatty acids contain all the possible hydrogen atoms.

ASSESS

REVIEW

- Ask students to summarize the main ideas in this section.
- Have students complete the Section Review. (Answers appear below.)

EVALUATION

- Have students write a short essay describing the concepts presented in this section. To conclude the essay, students should list three of their own recommendations for Americans related to cholesterol, fats, and health. *(Example: To reduce saturated fat in your eating plan, switch from butter to canola oil for sautéing.)*
- Have students take the quiz for Section 2-3. (Use the quiz in the *Teacher Resource Guide,* or construct your own with the **Exam***View*® *Test Generator* on the *Effective Instruction CD-ROM.*)

RETEACHING

- Ask one student to portray a husband or wife eating a breakfast of fried eggs, bacon, buttered toast, and coffee with cream. Let another student portray a spouse who understands the risks of an eating plan high in fats, cholesterol, and calories.
- Refer to the *Reteaching Activities* booklet for the Section 2-3 activity sheet.

CLOSE

Ask students to develop a bulletin board display that shows positive and negative eating habits with respect to fat. The display may consist of pictures, including technical art, and article headlines.

FOR YOUR HEALTH

Reducing Saturated Fat

For years, consumers cut back on cholesterol, hoping to lower their blood cholesterol levels. However, research now suggests that saturated fat—not cholesterol—is the cause of high blood cholesterol. Here are some ways to cut down on saturated fat, without cutting the flavor.

Instead of . . .	Try . . .
• Butter	• Fruit spread or tub margarine (for spreading) • Olive oil or canola oil (for frying and stir-frying) • Applesauce or mashed bananas or prunes (for baking)
• Whole milk	• Buttermilk, fat-free milk, or flavored fat-free milk
• Ground chuck	• Ground round or ground turkey breast meat

Following Up

- Speak with the school nurse, a local physician, or other health professional on other strategies for reducing saturated fat in your eating plan. Share your findings with the class.

Section 2-3 Review & Activities

1. Name two functions of fat. List six foods high in fat.
2. What is cholesterol? Why is LDL cholesterol called "bad" cholesterol?
3. Name three types of fatty acids. Which is considered least healthy? Why? Where is it mainly found?
4. **Evaluating.** Suppose you are shopping for peanut butter. One brand claims "No Cholesterol" in large letters on the label. The kind you usually buy makes no such claim. Would you switch brands? Why or why not?
5. **Comparing and Contrasting.** Is switching from butter to olive oil a good approach for weight loss? Why or why not?
6. **Applying.** Design a magazine ad encouraging people to cut down on fat and cholesterol. Include at least five facts from this section, and point out one common misconception.

68 **Chapter 2 ◆ The Nutrients You Need**

Answers to Section 2-3 Review & Activities

1. To provide essential fatty acids and carry vitamins A, D, E, and K throughout the body. Examples will vary.
2. A fatlike substance that is manufactured by the liver and is present in all body cells. LDL can build up in the artery walls, increasing the risk of heart disease or stroke.
3. Saturated, monounsaturated, polyunsaturated; saturated; because it raises the LDL level in the bloodstream; in poultry skin, some meats, whole milk, tropical oils.
4. Answers will vary.
5. No. Both have about the same number of calories.
6. Answers will vary.

SECTION
2-4

Objectives

After studying this section, you should be able to:

- Identify the types of vitamins and minerals, their functions, and their food sources.
- Tell the potential role phytochemicals play in health.
- Explain the importance of water in the eating plan.

Look for These Terms

antioxidants
water-soluble vitamins
fat-soluble vitamins
major minerals
electrolytes
trace minerals
osteoporosis
phytochemicals

Micronutrients

You have probably heard the expression "Good things come in small packages." This expression certainly applies to vitamins and minerals. Although they are among the six key nutrients and are essential for good health, your body requires only the tiniest amounts of them. These micronutrients, along with water and a class of substances called phytochemicals (fy-toh-KEM-ih-kuhls), complete your body's nutrient team.

Vitamins

Vitamins help keep your body's tissues healthy and its many systems working properly. They also help carbohydrates, fats, and proteins do their work.

Scientists are still learning about the functions of vitamins. One relatively recent discovery is that some vitamins have antioxidant (an-tee-OKS-ih-dunt) properties.

Antioxidants are substances that protect body cells and the immune system from harmful chemicals in the air, certain foods, and tobacco smoke. Other recent studies suggest that some vitamins may protect against illnesses such as heart disease and cancer. More research is needed, however, before scientists can say for certain what specific roles all the vitamins have in the body.

Section 2-4 Resources

◆ **Student Workbook,** pp. 20, 25
◆ **Teacher Resource Guide**
Lesson Plan 2-4 Organizer
Section 2-4 Quiz
◆ **Effective Instruction CD-ROM**
Exam*View*® *Test Generator*
PowerPoint® Slides #6, 7
◆ **Transparency Package,** CT-6, 7
◆ **Student Motivation Kit**
Reteaching Activities, p. 19
Enrichment Activities
Food Science Resources, pp. 66–68, 108–109

SECTION
2-4
Micronutrients

FOCUS

MOTIVATORS

- Provide students with this riddle: *What nutrients are essential for life but provide no calories?* Through inquiry, help students to recognize that the answer is vitamins, minerals, and water.
- Write the term "nutritional insurance" on the chalkboard. After ascertaining that no such thing exists, point out that many people regard vitamin and mineral supplements in this fashion. Discuss the dangers in this type of faulty reasoning.

VOCABULARY ACTIVITY

Direct students' attention to the list "Look for These Terms." Pronounce aloud the word *phytochemicals*. Ask a volunteer to investigate the meaning of *phyto-* (a plant). Ask students to provide their own definition for *phytochemicals*.

STUDY SKILLS

- **Outlining.** Have students read the section and outline it by copying the headers on paper and leaving space after each one. Students are to write a sentence in their own words, summarizing the content under each header.
- Have students read the section and complete the appropriate part of the Chapter 2 Study Guide in the *Student Workbook*.

TEACH

- *Vitamins (text pages 69-72)*

Discussion Activity

Discuss why vitamins are necessary. With what functions do they help? What is the main difference between fat-soluble and water-soluble vitamins?

List Activity

Have students compile companion lists of (1) their favorite food sources of each vitamin and (2) vitamins for which they have few favorite food sources. Ask students to pool their resources and to note foods they hadn't previously thought of eating that help them avoid a deficiency of the vitamins on their "B" list.

Counseling

Have students do a 24-hour food recall, listing everything they ate yesterday. Have students use a computer nutrition software program to determine whether their one-day eating plan was lacking in any vitamins and then print out a report. Have students team up in class, switch printed reports, and counsel each other on what foods can be added to their eating plans to eliminate any vitamin-deficient areas. If there are no deficiencies, students can counsel each other on how to obtain a variety of sources of vitamins. L3

Types of Vitamins

So far, scientists have identified 13 different vitamins, only one of which—vitamin D—is manufactured by the body. The rest must be derived from food.

Vitamins are classified into two groups:

- **Water-soluble vitamins** are vitamins that dissolve in water and thus pass easily into the bloodstream in the process of digestion. Water-soluble vitamins include vitamin C and the eight B vitamins.
- **Fat-soluble vitamins** are vitamins that are absorbed and transported by fat. They include vitamins A, D, E, and K.

The charts on pages 71-73 list the functions and food sources of these nutrients.

If you eat more fat-soluble vitamins than you need, they will be stored in the body's fat and in the liver. Your body can draw on these stores when needed. In contrast, water-soluble vitamins remain in your body for only a short time. Therefore, you need them on a daily basis.

Vitamin Sources

Some vitamins can be found in a wide range of foods. Others are limited to just a few food sources. To be sure you are getting the vitamins your body needs, remember the following tips:

- Eat plenty of fruits and vegetables every day. These plants are the only naturally occurring source of vitamin C. In particular, eat plenty of dark green vegetables (such as broccoli and spinach) and deep yellow-orange fruits and vegetables (such as carrots, sweet potatoes, and cantaloupe). These foods can help meet your need for vitamin A.
- Drink milk. Fortified milk is one of the best sources of vitamin D. The body can also make some vitamin D through the action of sunlight on the skin. That's why it's also called the "sunshine vitamin." If you don't drink fortified milk, be sure to get enough vitamin D from other sources.
- When you eat bread or pasta, choose enriched, whole-grain products. These are excellent sources of folate, an important vitamin that builds red blood cells. Other sources include green leafy vegetables, dry beans, and some fruits.

Foods high in vitamins usually contain substantial amounts of other nutrients as well. Use the table on pages 71 and 72 to identify foods in this picture that are high in vitamin C. Which contain B vitamins?

FOOD SCIENCE: Discovery of Vitamins

When vitamins were first discovered, they were given letter names: vitamin A, vitamin B, and so on. Later, scientists were able to analyze the chemical makeup of the vitamins. For example, vitamin C is ascorbic acid. Today, many vitamins are still commonly referred to by their letter names. Others are known by their chemical names, such as riboflavin and niacin.

Water-Soluble Vitamins

Vitamin/Functions	*Food Sources*
Thiamin (Vitamin B_1) • Helps turn carbohydrates into energy • Needed for muscle coordination and a healthy nervous system	• Enriched and whole-grain breads and cereals • Dry beans and peas • Lean pork • Liver
Riboflavin (Vitamin B_2) • Helps your body release energy from carbohydrates, fats, and proteins	• Enriched breads and cereals • Milk and other dairy products • Green leafy vegetables • Eggs • Meat, poultry, fish
Niacin (Vitamin B_3) • Helps your body release energy from carbohydrates, fats, and proteins • Needed for a healthy nervous system and mucous membranes	• Meat, poultry, fish • Enriched and whole-grain breads and cereals • Dry beans and peas • Peanuts, peanut butter
Vitamin B_6 • Helps your body use carbohydrates and proteins • Needed for a healthy nervous system • Helps your body make nonessential amino acids, which then make body cells	• Poultry, fish, pork • Dry beans and peas • Nuts • Whole grains • Some fruits and vegetables • Liver and kidneys
Folate (Folacin, Folic acid) • Teams with vitamin B_{12} to help build red blood cells and form genetic material • Helps prevent birth defects • Helps your body use proteins • May help protect against heart disease	• Green leafy vegetables • Dry beans and peas • Fruits • Enriched and whole-grain breads
Vitamin B_{12} • Helps your body use carbohydrates, fats, and proteins • Teams with folate to help build red blood cells and form genetic material • Needed for a healthy nervous system	• Found naturally in animal foods, such as meat, poultry, fish, shellfish, eggs, and dairy products • Some fortified food • Some nutritional yeasts

- *Vitamins (text pages 69-72)*

Discussion Activity

Ask students to list vitamins that affect the nervous system. What foods supply these vitamins? What could result over time if someone consistently did not obtain these vitamins in adequate amounts?

Checklists

Have students develop a checklist of 10 guidelines for obtaining all the vitamins needed from foods. Have the students use the checklist to examine a family member's eating habits. The checklist can be posted on the refrigerator at home to help all family members obtain adequate vitamins from foods. L1

Deciphering Misinformation

Ask students to bring to class one article from a newspaper, magazine, or Internet source that inappropriately promotes vitamins. Have each student share the misinformation with the class and discuss why it's inappropriate. For instance, some nutrient advertisements claim that vitamin C can cure a common cold. On what fact might this claim be based? Why should people not depend on vitamin C to cure a cold? L1

Extending Learning

Vitamin A—For centuries, "dry eye," which resulted in blindness, was a common affliction of malnourished children. In the early 1900s, Dr. Mori, a Japanese physician, cured the disease with cod-liver oil and chicken livers. During WWI, Dr. E. V. McCollum used butter to clear up the condition. Danish physician, C. E. Block, read of Dr. McCollum's results and cured the disease with butter or whole milk. The substance in butterfat was identified as vitamin A, the first individual vitamin discovered. Cod-liver oil was the richest source of vitamin A.

- *Vitamins (text pages 69-72)*

Illustration Activity

Provide students with line drawings of the human digestive system. Have students use colored pencils to represent fat- and water-soluble vitamins. Use a blue pencil to show that extra amounts of water-soluble vitamins are eliminated in urine. Use a red pencil to show that extra amounts of fat-soluble vitamins are stored in the body's fat and in the liver. Discuss how these facts can help you know how often each type of vitamin must be included in the eating plan and the effects of consuming too much.

Discussion Activity

If someone ate only plant-based foods, what vitamin would likely be lacking in one's eating plan. How can a vegetarian who doesn't eat any animal products obtain adequate amounts of vitamin B_{12}? Discuss how supplements can be beneficial in some cases.

Reading Activity

Provide students with articles about folate and its preventive role in (1) neural tube defects and (2) heart disease. Have students read the articles and then summarize them for the class.

Water-Soluble Vitamins (cont'd)

Vitamin/Functions	*Food Sources*
Pantothenic acid • Helps the body release energy from carbohydrates, fats, and proteins • Helps the body produce cholesterol • Needed for a healthy nervous system • Promotes normal growth and development	• Meat, poultry, fish • Eggs • Dry beans and peas • Whole-grain breads and cereals • Milk • Some fruits and vegetables
Biotin • Helps your body use carbohydrates, fats, and proteins	• Green leafy vegetables • Whole-grain breads and cereals • Liver • Egg yolks
Vitamin C (Ascorbic Acid) • Helps maintain healthy capillaries, bones, skin, and teeth • Helps your body heal wounds and resist infections • Aids in absorption of iron • Helps form collagen, which gives structure to bones, cartilage, muscle, and blood vessels • Works as an antioxidant	• Fruits—citrus fruits (orange, grapefruit, tangerine), cantaloupe, guava, kiwi, mango, papaya, strawberries • Vegetables—bell peppers, broccoli, cabbage, kale, plantains, potatoes, tomatoes

Minerals

Like vitamins, minerals are vital for good health. Most minerals become a part of your body, such as your teeth and bones. Others are used to make substances that your body needs.

Types of Minerals

Minerals can be divided into three groups:

- **Major minerals** are minerals needed in relatively large amounts. These include calcium, phosphorus, and magnesium.
- **Electrolytes** (ee-LEK-troh-lyts) are specific major minerals that work together to maintain the body's fluid balance. These include potassium, sodium, and chloride.
- **Trace minerals** are minerals needed in very small amounts, but they are just as important as other nutrients. They include iron, copper, zinc, iodine, and selenium. Scientists continue to research trace minerals and their functions.

Reinforcing Key Skills

Present the following problems to student groups. Allow time for them to discuss and compare their responses.

Directed Thinking—Explain that although vitamin D is not commonly found in foods, exposure of skin to sunlight produces vitamin D. Ask students: In what areas of the United States is a deficiency of vitamin D most likely?

Communication—Imagine overhearing this part of a phone conversation: "I don't get colds, so I don't need to get much vitamin C."

Safety Check

Since fat-soluble vitamins are stored in the body's tissues, an excess buildup of them is possible, leading to toxic or other damaging effects. An overdose of vitamin A, for example, can cause nerve and liver damage, bone and joint pain, vomiting, and abnormal bone growth. People who take vitamin supplements are advised to use caution.

Meeting Your Mineral Needs

Though your need for some minerals is small, getting the right amount is important to your health. For example, getting too much or too little iodine can cause thyroid problems. The thyroid gland, located in the neck, produces substances needed for growth and development. For certain individuals, getting too much sodium, or too little potassium, may be linked to high blood pressure.

Fat-Soluble Vitamins

Vitamin/Functions	*Food Sources*
Vitamin A • Helps protect you from infections • Helps form and maintain healthy skin, hair, mucous membranes, bones, and teeth • Helps you see normally at night • Works as an antioxidant	• Dairy products • Liver • Egg yolks • Foods high in beta carotene (see phytochemicals, p. 78)
Vitamin D • Helps your body use calcium and phosphorus • Helps your body build strong and healthy bones and teeth	• Fortified dairy products • Egg yolks • Higher-fat fish—salmon and mackerel • Fortified breakfast cereals and margarine
Vitamin E • Works as an antioxidant	• Nuts and seeds • Green leafy vegetables • Wheat germ • Vegetable oils
Vitamin K • Necessary for blood to clot normally	• Green leafy vegetables • Fruits and other vegetables • Dairy products • Egg yolks • Wheat bran and wheat germ

- *Minerals (text pages 72-77)*

Discussion Activity

Discuss osteoporosis and its causes. What can people do to build strong bones and help prevent the development of osteoporosis?

Field Trip

Take the class to the school gym. Invite the physical education instructor or a school coach to demonstrate safe techniques and suggestions for weight-training activities that can strengthen bones. Discuss how eating is only one part of a healthy lifestyle.

Product Comparison

Provide small groups of students with Nutrition Facts panels from each of several cans of foods representing food groups. Have groups work at systematically comparing the % Daily Values for calcium and iron. After groups have shared and compared their finding, ask: What differences, if any, can you find between foods representing different food groups? How can knowing the calcium or iron content of foods help in planning a healthy eating plan? L3

Reinforcing Key Skills

Present the following problems to student groups. Allow time for them to discuss and compare their responses.

Communication—For health reasons, your school wants to eliminate chocolate milk and keep only regular milk for lunch service. What would your feedback be to the school?

Leadership—You notice your younger sister is drinking soda with most meals and seldom drinks milk. What might you say to her?

TEACH cont.

- *Minerals (text pages 72-77)*

Discussion Activity

Discuss the function of iron in the body. What are some dietary sources of iron? If a teenage girl doesn't eat red meat, how would you suggest she meet her iron needs?

Research Activity

Have students investigate the most recent scientific claims regarding the role of sodium in affecting blood pressure. Direct the students to reputable sources of information in this regard, including online government-sponsored sites, geared to teens, that you have prescreened. Have students report their findings to class.

Lab Experience

Have selected students cover a bowl with plastic wrap. Have them pretend their bowl was filled with popcorn; salt the "food" as though it was a real bowl full of popcorn. Have each student measure how much salt was added. (Current health recommendations: less than 2400 mg sodium/day; 1 teaspoon salt=2300 mg sodium) What conclusions can the class draw about the amount of added salt in one's eating plan? L1

Getting the right balance of minerals is not difficult. The key is to eat a wide variety of foods. However, you may need to pay special attention to whether you are getting enough calcium and iron—two major minerals especially important for teens.

Calcium and Strong Bones

As noted in the chart on page 75, calcium has several important functions. One of these is to maintain bone strength. Lack of calcium throughout life is one of the factors that can lead to **osteoporosis** (AH-stee-oh-puh-ROH-sis). This is a condition in which the bones become porous, making them weak and fragile. As a result, posture may become stooped and bones can break easily. Osteoporosis affects over 25 million Americans, both men and women. The condition is most common in women. It is estimated that up to 50 percent of women over age 45 and 90 percent of women over age 75 have osteoporosis.

You can lessen your risk of osteoporosis, but you need to start now. Bone mass builds up during childhood, the teen years, and young adulthood. The more you do to build strong, healthy bones now, the less likely you will be to develop osteoporosis when you are older.

Here are some "bone-building" tips you can follow:

- Eat plenty of calcium-rich foods. These include dairy products, dry beans and peas, and dark green, leafy vegetables.
- Follow other basic guidelines for healthy eating. Remember, nutrients work in teams. Like best friends on a team, vitamin D and many other nutrients work together with calcium.
- Play a sport, take part in some other vigorous activity, or exercise regularly. Weight-bearing exercise, such as walking or jogging, and weight training help build and maintain strong bones.
- Avoid tobacco products, alcohol, and excess caffeine (found in coffee, tea, and soft drinks). All may contribute to osteoporosis.

Weight-resistance training, which includes the activity shown here, helps build and maintain strong bones. Name two foods you can eat that aid in this process. Identify the nutrient contained in these foods.

Extending Learning

Potassium—It is rare to have a potassium deficiency and also rare to suffer harmful effects from consuming too much potassium. Healthy people excrete excess potassium. However, people with kidney problems may not be able to excrete excess amounts. In such cases, too much potassium may contribute to heart problems. These people may be counseled to decrease their intake of potassium-containing foods and to avoid the use of salt substitutes. Many salt substitutes replace sodium with potassium.

Iron and Red Blood Cells

Iron is essential for making hemoglobin (HEE-muh-gloh-buhn), a substance in your red blood cells that carries oxygen to all the cells in your body. If you don't get enough iron, your blood may not be able to carry enough oxygen to your cells. The resulting condition is called *iron-deficiency anemia* (uh-NEE-mee-uh). People with anemia are often tired, weak, short of breath, and pale.

Where can you find iron? Some sources are lean red meat, dry beans and peas, dried fruits, grain products, and dark green, leafy vegetables. Eating foods rich in vitamin C at the same time as foods rich in iron helps the body absorb more of the iron from plant foods. Interestingly, the iron content of foods cooked in an iron skillet gets a boost. Researchers disagree, however, on how much iron can be absorbed from this source.

Major Minerals

Mineral/Functions	*Food Sources*
Calcium	
• Helps build bone and maintain bone strength • Helps prevent osteoporosis • Helps regulate blood clotting, nerve activity, and other body processes • Needed for muscle contraction, including the heart	• Dairy products • Canned fish with edible bones • Dry beans, peas, and lentils • Dark green, leafy vegetables—broccoli, spinach, and turnip greens • Tofu made with calcium sulfate • Calcium-fortified orange juice and soy milk
Phosphorus	
• Works with calcium to build strong bones and teeth • Helps release energy from carbohydrates, fats, and proteins • Helps build body cells and tissues	• Meat, poultry, fish • Eggs • Nuts • Dry beans and peas • Dairy products • Grain products
Magnesium	
• Helps build bones and make proteins • Helps nerves and muscles work normally	• Whole-grain products • Green vegetables • Dry beans and peas • Nuts and seeds

• *Minerals*
(text pages 72-77)

Reading Activity

Provide students with articles on iron and iron-deficiency anemia. Have students read the articles and then summarize them for the class.

Dietary Analysis

Have students do a 24-hour dietary recall, listing everything they ate yesterday. Ask students to circle foods that are good sources of iron. Ask students to place a star next to foods that are rich in vitamin C that were consumed at the same time as iron-rich foods. Point out the nutrient teamwork between vitamin C and iron.

Menu Planning

As a class, have students plan three lunch menus that incorporate foods that are high in iron. Students will then develop and send a proposal to the food service director of the school system requesting their menu suggestions be incorporated into their school lunches. The proposal needs to include the menus and the reason the menus are suggested. **L2**

Reinforcing Key Skills

Present the following problems to student groups. Allow time for them to discuss and compare their responses.

Creativity—Ask students to develop lists of ten ways for non-milk drinkers to increase their calcium consumption. Would their suggestions differ for people of different age groups?

Communication—Knowing that salt is an acquired taste, what would you suggest to a person who loves salty food and tasty food but has been advised to eat less sodium?

- *Minerals (text pages 72-77)*

VISUAL LEARNING

Using Charts Have students refer to the chart on page 77 to identify good sources of zinc. Have students make a list of zinc-rich foods they consume regularly. Discuss the importance of zinc, especially for the elderly.

Discussion Activity

Ask students to name minerals that are supplied by dry beans and peas. Why are these food choices a healthy part of one's eating plan?

DID You Know?

- Researchers have discovered a connection between zinc and the sense of smell. When one 40-year-old individual who had lacked a sense of smell from the age of 4 was given 500 mg of zinc every day for one month, he was able to smell an unpeeled banana 12 feet away.
- Overdoses of zinc can cause severe abdominal cramps.

Electrolytes

Mineral/Functions	*Food Sources*
Sodium • Helps maintain the fluid balance in your body • Helps with muscle and nerve action • Helps regulate blood pressure	• Table salt • Processed foods
Chloride • Helps maintain the fluid balance in your body • Helps transmit nerve signals	• Table salt
Potassium • Helps maintain the fluid balance in your body • Helps maintain the heartbeat • Helps with muscle and nerve action • Helps maintain normal blood pressure	• Fruits—bananas and oranges • Vegetables • Meat, poultry, fish • Dry beans and peas • Dairy products

Trace Minerals

Mineral/Functions	*Food Sources*
Iron • Helps carry oxygen in the blood • Helps your cells use oxygen	• Meat, fish, shellfish • Egg yolks • Dark green, leafy vegetables • Dry beans and peas • Enriched or whole-grain products • Dried fruits
Iodine • Responsible for your body's use of energy	• Saltwater fish • Iodized salt
Copper • Helps iron make red blood cells • Helps keep your bones, blood vessels, and nerves healthy • Helps your heart work properly	• Whole-grain products • Seafood • Organ meats • Dry beans and peas • Nuts and seeds

Extending Learning

Electrolytes—When you perspire, you lose sodium, chloride, and other electrolytes, as well as a significant amount of water. Loss of water and electrolytes can result in muscle cramps and dehydration. Several electrolyte replacement products are now on the market to help people replace water and minerals rapidly. The human body can only sweat about one liter per hour, and it can keep up that rate for no more than a few hours. If water and essential minerals are not replaced, heat exhaustion or heat stroke may occur.

Trace Minerals (cont'd)

Mineral/Functions	*Food Sources*
Zinc • Helps your body make proteins, heal wounds, and form blood • Helps in growth and maintenance of all tissues • Helps your body use carbohydrates, fats, and proteins • Affects the senses of taste and smell • Helps your body use vitamin A	• Meat, liver, poultry, fish, shellfish • Dairy products • Dry beans and peas, peanuts • Whole-grain breads and cereals • Eggs • Miso (fermented soybean paste)
Selenium • Helps your heart work properly • Works as an antioxidant	• Whole-grain breads and cereals • Vegetables (amount varies with content in soil) • Meat, organ meats, fish, shellfish
Fluoride • Helps strengthen teeth and prevent cavities	• In many communities, small amounts are added to the water supply to help improve dental health.

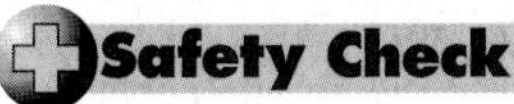

Rich in many vitamins and minerals, eggs can be a valuable contribution to a healthful eating plan. However, if eggs aren't handled properly, a food-borne organism called salmonella can grow. Don't keep eggs and egg-rich foods between 40 and 140° F (4 and 60° C) ("the temperature danger zone") for more than two hours.

Phytochemicals

If you look up *phytochemical* in a dictionary, you will find that this word (from the Greek *phyton,* or "plant") was coined over 150 years ago. It was only in the last decade that an important scientific discovery—the presence of disease-fighting nutrients in plant foods—gave a new meaning to the term **phytochemical**.

Current estimates suggest that every plant has at least 50 to 100 different phytochemicals. So far, most of the research has concentrated on identifying and classifying these substances, though early studies hint that many may play important roles in reducing the risks of cancer and other diseases. Some phytochemicals, like vitamins, are antioxidants.

One of the best-known phytochemicals is beta carotene (bay-tuh KAR-uh-teen), a substance that gives fruits and vegetables their bright yellow-orange and dark green colors. Beta carotene is an antioxidant believed to prevent certain kinds of cancer. The body uses beta carotene to produce vitamin A.

The following table lists just a few of the phytochemicals being studied.

• *Minerals*
(text pages 72-77)

Discussion Activity

Ask students to list minerals that help the heart work properly. These are critical minerals; yet with the exception of calcium and potassium, they are rarely mentioned in articles about health and nutrition. Ask students why this might be so.

Discussion Activity

Ask students to name minerals that are supplied by dry beans and peas. Aside from the protein they contain, why are these food choices part of a healthful eating plan? Discuss how to incorporate them in eating plans.

Research Activity

Ask students to research the problems caused by deficiency or overconsumption of one of these minerals: calcium, phosphorus, magnesium, chlorine, potassium, sodium, iron, iodine, or zinc. Have the students write a short report on their findings.

Ask students to determine where the source of most of their drinking water comes from in their community. (Municipal tap water, well water, bottled water.) Then have them determine whether their drinking water source provides fluoride. Research for the students some phone numbers or websites that might help them find the answer. What conclusions can students draw about their water supply and additional need for fluoride?

- *Phytochemicals (text pages 77-78)*

Discussion Activity

Phytochemicals are said to be the vitamin and minerals of the 21st century. Ask students what their projections are for phytochemicals.

Finding Recipes

Have students look for recipes that provide two or more of the phytochemicals listed in the chart on this page. Ask students to name the phytochemicals provided in the recipe, their food sources, and their potential health benefit. L1

Research Activity

Provide articles from the Internet, magazines, newspapers, and books that discuss garlic's relationship to health. Ask students to read an article and make a list of the most important points. Discuss with students how to put this information into perspective.

Supermarket Survey

Have students visit one supermarket and record the forms of soy available, such as soy milk, tofu, soyu flour, tempeh, miso, and soybean oil. Permit time for them to discuss and compare their findings. L1

Phytochemicals

Phytochemical	*Food Source*	*Potential Health Benefits*
Beta carotene	• Yellow and orange fruits and vegetables • Dark green vegetables	• May play role in slowing the progression of cancer
Allyl sulfides	• Onions, garlic, leeks, chives, shallots	• May play role in cancer prevention • May play role in lowering blood pressure and cholesterol
Indoles	• Cabbage, broccoli, kale, cauliflower	• May play role in cancer prevention
Saponins	• Soybeans, dry beans, peas • Most vegetables	• May prevent cancer cells from multiplying
Lutein	• Kale, spinach, collards, mustard greens, romaine lettuce	• May protect against blindness
Phytosterol	• Soybeans and some soy products • Nuts and whole-grain products • Many vegetable oils	• May play role in cancer prevention • May lower cholesterol

Water

Often called the "forgotten nutrient," water is actually the one most critical to survival. People can live for weeks without food, but only for a few days without water. Why is that?

Water exists in all body cells. In fact, about 50 to 60 percent of your body is water. After helping break foods down into nutrients, water carries the nutrients to the cells that need them. In the cells, water participates in chemical reactions that break the nutrients down into usable forms. As you can see, food isn't much use to the body without water.

Because of water, your joints stay lubricated, your skin soft, and your mind alert. Water filters out impurities and gets rid of waste products. Water also helps keep the body temperature normal. Think of what happens when you get too warm. Perspiration evaporates into the air and cools your body. Knowing all this may make you

◆ Health experts suggest drinking water rather than soft drinks. Beverages with caffeine tend to remove water from the body and may keep water from entering body cells.

Extending Learning

Soybeans (and Soyfoods)—Soybeans are a good source of saponins and phytosterols. They are also rich in other phytochemicals: Daidzein and genistein (isoflavonoids); flavonoids; coumarins; terpenes; and more. As a good source of phytochemicals, soybeans and soyfoods may play key roles in disease prevention. The oil from soy provides essential fatty acids, from which omega-3s are derived. Soyfoods include tofu, tempeh, miso, and soy milk. Tofu and tempeh are made from the beans and grains; soy milk is make from pureed soybeans and water.

want to run to the nearest water fountain. That isn't a bad idea considering how much water your body needs.

How Much Is Enough?

On average, the body uses about 2 to 3 quarts (2 to 3 L) of water a day. If lost fluid isn't replaced, a person can become dehydrated. Health experts recommend drinking about 8 cups (2 L) of water daily. During strenuous physical activity or in hot weather, when you perspire heavily, you need even more. A good rule of thumb is to drink 1 cup (250 mL) of water for every ½ pound (250 g) of weight lost. Weighing before and after an exercise event helps you gauge what you need.

Eight cups of water may seem like a lot, but other liquids, such as milk, fruit juice, and soup, contribute to your supply. Most fresh fruits and vegetables also contain large amounts of water. Watermelon, for example, is over 90 percent water. As a reminder to drink water, you could carry a sipper bottle. If you like, add flavor with a little fresh lemon juice.

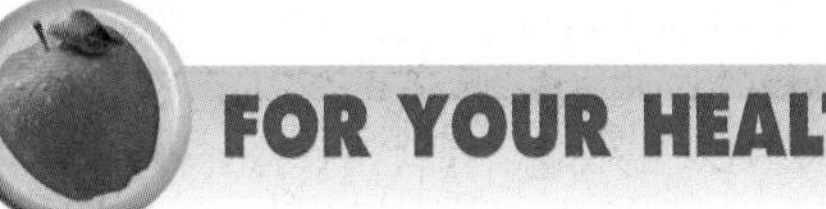

Dehydration

Thirst doesn't just mean you need water; it warns of dehydration. By the time you feel thirsty, you have already lost a significant amount of water. That's why you need to drink water regularly, not just when you're thirsty.

Signs of dehydration are both physical and mental. Subtle signs include dry lips, muscle or joint soreness, crankiness, and lightheadedness. Dehydration can lead to headaches, dizziness, nausea, and vomiting. Muscle fatigue, which can become chronic, is also possible. A water deficit in the body slows blood circulation, reducing the ability to concentrate. Extreme dehydration can produce seizures, brain damage, and even death.

Following Up

- Keep a food and beverage log over several days. Total the approximate amount of water you get from all sources. Is it enough? Do you need to make changes?

Water Issues

Much has been written about water quality. Are water supplies safe? Should you drink bottled water? What about fluoride? The answers are not always clear. Where you live can affect your decisions.

Most municipal systems do a good job of processing water, as regulated by the Environmental Protection Agency (EPA). Some people wonder, however, about the lengthy, aging pipes that water travels through. Of course, not all people drink water from municipal systems. In either case, anyone who has concerns about quality can have water tested.

The Food and Drug Administration (FDA) regulates bottled water. This water is generally drawn from protected sources and may have further treatment to remove impurities. Everyday use of bottled water can be expensive, so most people weigh costs against concerns.

Many communities add fluoride to water. Fluoride has greatly reduced tooth decay over the years and is also linked to strong bone development. Although some people wonder about possible harmful effects, the American Medical Association, the National Institute of Dental Health, and the National Cancer Institute all endorse fluoridation of drinking water. Fluoride toothpastes, tablets, and treatments are available for those who want them.

- *Water*
  (text pages 78-80)

Discussion Activity

Discuss the many roles water plays in the body. Why can people live much longer without food than without water? Why is water so critical?

Calculation Activity

Ask students to calculate the amount of water the body uses in one week, one month, and one year, based on an average water loss figure of 2-5 quarts (2-3 liters) per day.

Research Activity

Have students find out the water content of their top five favorite foods and list their findings in a chart. Have students compare charted findings.

See lab on page 80. Explain that food professionals often use methods other than those used by the general public to achieve more precise results. Using a nutrition software program or nutrition composition book, make a list of the water content of 10 commonly consumed foods. Ask how knowing the water content of foods may be useful. Ask students to brainstorm another 10 foods with high water contents. Compare their results to the published data.

Extending Learning

Designer Water—Fitness enthusiasts have many kinds of sports drinks to choose from. Now, so-called designer water—offering various minerals, vitamins, and other additives—has been introduced. Designer water may be more healthful than other sports drinks because it contains fewer calories. However, the additives it offers are readily available in fruits and vegetables, so Americans may be better off saving their money and drinking tap water.

ASSESS

REVIEW

- Ask students to summarize the main ideas in this section.
- Have students complete the Section Review. (Answers appear below.)

EVALUATION

- Have students describe what they have learned in this section in a short written essay. In the essay, have them conclude with three healthful changes they will try to make to their own eating plans based on the information learned in this section.
- Have students take the quiz for Section 2-4. (Use the quiz in the *Teacher Resource Guide,* or construct your own with the **Exam** *View*® *Test Generator* on the *Effective Instruction CD-ROM.*)

RETEACHING

- Have students develop a quiz game (e.g. Nutrition Jeopardy or Wheel of Nutrition) to review important facts about vitamins, minerals, phytochemicals, and water.
- Refer to the *Reteaching Activities* booklet for the Section 2-4 activity sheet.

CLOSE

Lead a discussion on the importance of eating a variety of healthful foods every day to provide the body with vitamins, minerals, phytochemicals, and water. With the students, plan a one-day meal plan, including beverages, that provides adequate amounts of micronutrients, phytochemicals, and water studied in this section.

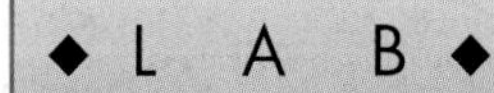

Food Science ◆ LAB ◆

How Much Water Is in Food?

Meeting daily fluid needs can seem challenging to many people. However, many foods contain a lot of water. Which foods have the most? You are about to find out.

Procedure

1. Weigh a raw potato, apple, and carrot, and record the weight of each.
2. Place one of the foods in a food processor, and process until it is a liquidy mash. Pour and scrape the food into a strainer, forcing out as much liquid as possible. Weigh the liquid, and measure it.
3. Calculate the percentage of water by comparing the liquid weight with the original weight.
4. Repeat with each of the remaining foods.

Conclusions

- ◆ Which food had the highest water content? Which had the lowest?
- ◆ Do you think it is possible to meet at least half (4 cups; 4 L) of your water needs through solid food? Explain.
- ◆ Repeat the experiment using a slice of bread. Predict the percentage that is water. Was your prediction right?

Section 2-4 Review & Activities

1. Which vitamins are fat-soluble? Water-soluble? Why is this distinction important?
2. Why do you need calcium? Iron? What foods provide these nutrients?
3. How much water do you need to drink each day to replenish your body's water supply?
4. Define *phytochemical.* Explain the potential role of phytochemicals in good health.
5. **Evaluating.** Why are trace minerals just as important as other minerals, even though they are needed in such small amounts?
6. **Comparing and Contrasting.** Cereal A is high in fiber (7 grams per serving) with 75 percent of seven vitamins and minerals. Cereal B is low in fiber (1 gram per serving) with 100 percent of the same seven vitamins and minerals. Which would you choose? Why?
7. **Applying.** Use the information from this section to create a vitamin and mineral checklist. Armed with your checklist, determine which vitamin and mineral needs can be met by the foods available in your home. Discuss your findings with an adult in your home.

Answers to Section 2-4 Review & Activities

1. A, D, E, K. C and the B vitamins. Fat-soluble vitamins can be stored by the body, but water-soluble vitamins can't.
2. Calcium: To build strong bones, help regulate body functions, and aid in muscle contraction. Iron: To help carry and use oxygen. See charts on pp. 75-76.
3. Eight cups (2 L).
4. Plant chemicals. May slow cancer, lower cholesterol and blood pressure, and protect against blindness.
5. Answers will vary. Students should realize all nutrients are vital.
6. Answers will vary.
7. Answers will vary.

SECTION
2-5

How Your Body Uses Food

While you are reading this page, your body is busily working—inhaling oxygen from the air and exhaling waste products. Your heart is busy, too. In the time it takes to read this paragraph, about 100 million of your body cells will die and new ones will take their place. If you ate in the last several hours, your digestive system is breaking down the food into nutrients.

Objectives

After studying this section, you should be able to:

- Outline the process of digestion.
- Explain how nutrients are absorbed, transported, and stored.
- Tell how the body uses food to produce energy.

Look for These Terms

digestion
esophagus
peristalsis
glucose
glycogen
oxidation
basal metabolism

Digestion

The process of breaking down food into usable nutrients is known as **digestion**. It takes place in the digestive system, a long, hollow tube that extends from the mouth through the entire body. Here is what happens to food on its journey through the digestive system.

The Mouth

The digestive process starts before you even begin to eat the food. Just smelling and seeing food, or even thinking about it, can start saliva flowing in your mouth. Saliva is the first of many digestive juices that act on food to break it down chemically.

Food is also broken down physically as your teeth grind it into tiny pieces. Chewing food well is important. It mixes the food with saliva and makes it easier to swallow and digest. Solid food should be chewed until it is the consistency of applesauce.

SECTION
2-5
How Your Body Uses Food

FOCUS

MOTIVATORS

- Present a large illustration of the human digestive system. Ask students to list the parts of the body involved in digestion, beginning with where this process starts. They may be surprised to find that the mouth is the starting point.
- Have students think about what they have eaten today. Then briefly describe how this food is still at work in the body.

VOCABULARY ACTIVITY

Direct students' attention to the list "Look for These Terms." Pronounce aloud the word *esophagus*. Ask a volunteer to investigate the meaning of the root *-phag-* (to eat or pertaining to ingestion).

STUDY SKILLS

- **Guided Reading.** Have students look at the headings within Section 2-5 to preview the concepts that will be discussed.
- Have students read the section and complete the appropriate part of the Chapter 2 Study Guide in the *Student Workbook*.

Section 2-5 Resources

◆ **Student Workbook,** pp. 21, 26
◆ **Teacher Resource Guide**
Lesson Plan 2-5 Organizer
Section 2-5 Quiz
Chapter 2 Test
◆ **Effective Instruction CD-ROM**
Exam*View*® *Test Generator*
◆ **Student Motivation Kit**
Reteaching Activities, p. 20
Enrichment Activities
Food Science Resources, pp. 40–42
Skills for Making Food Choices, pp. 9–10

TEACH

- *Digestion (text pages 81-83)*

Discussion Activity

Ask students to describe the two ways in which the mouth participates in the digestive process. Discuss the ways in which the stomach breaks food down.

Demonstration

Bring to class a marble and long narrow balloon. With scissors, cut off the closed end of the balloon. Demonstrate the action of peristalsis by squeezing the marble through the balloon. Ask students to explain what peristalsis is and its purpose in digestion.

Food Comparison

Have students prepare a timeline that compares the amount of time needed to digest different types of food. Display the timelines, and discuss the various findings. L2

Research Activity

Have students use print or online resources to research the different enzymes and digestive aids produced by the body and write a one page summary of their findings.

◆ **Each part of the digestive tract has a specific role in breaking food down into nutrients. In what body organ does digestion begin?**

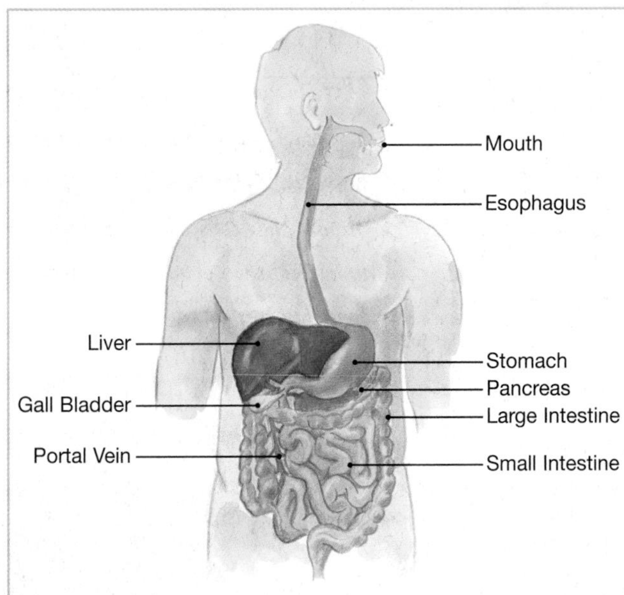

The Esophagus

Once the food is swallowed, it passes into the **esophagus** (ih-SOFF-uh-gus), a long tube connecting the mouth to the stomach. The muscles of the esophagus contract and relax, creating a series of wavelike movements that force the food into the stomach. This muscular action is called **peristalsis** (PEHR-uh-STAHL-suhs).

The Stomach

The stomach, the next stop on the digestive journey, is the widest part of the digestive system. It is a muscular pouch located on the left side of your body inside the rib cage. On the average, your stomach can hold about 4 cups (1 L) of food.

The walls of the stomach manufacture gastric juices—a combination of acid and enzymes that helps in the chemical breakdown of the food. In addition, the stomach breaks food down physically through peristalsis. The food is churned until it turns into a thick liquid called chyme (KIME).

Different kinds of food take different amounts of time to break down and leave the stomach. Think of your stomach as a holding tank. Carbohydrates take the shortest amount of time, usually one to two hours. Proteins take longer, about three to five hours. Fats take the longest time to digest, up to seven hours. That is why a food with fat will keep you from feeling hungry for a longer time.

The Small Intestine

From the stomach, chyme is released into the small intestine a little at a time. The small intestine is a long, winding tube between the stomach and the large intestine. Here, the chyme is acted on by three types of digestive juices:

- Bile, a substance that helps your body digest and absorb fats. Bile is produced in the liver and stored in the gall bladder until needed.
- Pancreatic (pan-kree-AT-ik) juice, which contains enzymes that help break down carbohydrates, proteins, and fats. It is produced by the pancreas (PAN-kree-us), a gland connected to the small intestine.
- Intestinal juice, produced in the small intestine. This digestive fluid works with the others to break down food.

When fully broken down, carbohydrates are turned into a simple sugar called glucose (GLOO-kohs). **Glucose** is the body's basic

Reinforcing Key Skills

Present the following problems to student groups. Allow time for them to discuss and compare their responses.

Management—Ask students how knowing the length of time carbohydrates, proteins, and fats stay in the stomach could aid an athlete in deciding what and when to eat before a competitive event.

Communication—Someone at a party shares with the crowd misinformation he or she heard that glucose is harmful to the body. How might you set the facts straight without making the speaker feel foolish?

fuel supply. Fats are changed into fatty acids. Proteins are broken down into amino acids. Vitamins, minerals, and water do not need to be broken down—they're ready for action just as they are. They can be used by your body in the same form in which they occur in food.

Using the Nutrients

Once food has been broken down into nutrients, digestion is complete. However, your body still has work to do. It must absorb the nutrients and take them to where they can be used or stored.

Absorption

After digestion, the nutrients are absorbed into the bloodstream. Most absorption takes place in your small intestine. The lining of the small intestine is arranged in folds. It is lined with billions of tiny fingerlike projections, called villi (VIL-eye). The villi increase the surface area of the intestine so that more nutrients can be absorbed.

After absorption, some waste mineral, including fiber, is left in the small intestine. This waste material is moved into the large intestine, also called the colon. The colon removes water, potassium, and sodium from the waste. The remainder is stored as a semi-solid in the rectum (REK-tum), or lower part of the intestine, until it is eliminated.

Processing and Storing Nutrients

After the nutrients are absorbed by the villi of the small intestine, they are carried through a blood vessel, called the portal vein, to the liver. One of the liver's many jobs is to turn nutrients into forms the body can use. For instance, it converts amino acids into different kinds of proteins. Then the proteins are carried by the blood to wherever they are needed.

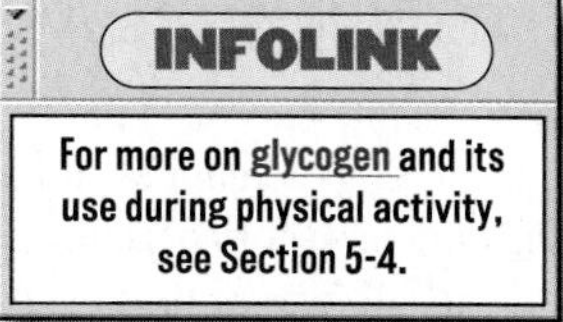

INFOLINK
For more on glycogen and its use during physical activity, see Section 5-4.

Some nutrients, if not needed immediately, can be stored for future use. Extra glucose, for example, is converted by the liver into **glycogen** (GLY-kuh-juhn), a storage form of glucose. Glycogen is stored in the liver and the muscles. If there is more glucose than can be stored as glycogen, the rest is converted to body fat. Fats are then deposited throughout the body as an energy reserve. Excess fatty acids and amino acids are also converted to body fat.

Minerals are stored in various ways. For instance, iron is stored in the liver and in bone marrow. Fat-soluble vitamins are stored mainly in the liver and in body fat.

Some nutrients, including most water-soluble vitamins, are not stored for long periods. If not needed, they are removed from the body with wastes.

◆ **Even when you are asleep your body continues to work and renew itself. Name the type of energy your body uses during periods of rest.**

- *Using the Nutrients (text page 83)*
- *How Nutrients Are Used (text page 84)*

Discussion Activity

Have students discuss the role the teeth play in digestion. Why is it important for food to be broken into small pieces before it is swallowed?

Discussion Activity

Have students discuss what would happen if gravity rather than peristaltic waves directed food from the mouth to the stomach.

Discussion Activity

Ask students to explain the difference between digestion and absorption. What role does the liver play in using nutrients?

Creating Models

Have students create *models* to illustrate the absorption of nutrients. Have students explain their models to the class. Use the models to create a display on how the body uses food. Place the display in the school library or donate it to an elementary school in your district. L1

Discussion Activity

Discuss why the body stores fat. How is the ability both helpful and harmful?

FOOD SCIENCE

Sphincter Muscles

A small muscular valve, called a sphincter (SFINK-turr), is located where the esophagus meets the stomach. It works like a one-way gate, letting the food into the stomach but keeping it from being forced back into the esophagus. Another sphincter is located between the stomach and the small intestine.

ASSESS

REVIEW

- Ask students to summarize the main ideas in this section.
- Have students complete the Section Review. (Answers appear below.)

EVALUATION

- Ask students to prepare a skit that explains the processes of food digestion and absorption.
- Have students take the quiz for Section 2-5. (Use the quiz in the *Teacher Resource Guide,* or construct your own with the **ExamView**® *Test Generator* on the *Effective Instruction CD-ROM.*)

RETEACHING

- Have students develop a lesson plan for teaching grade school students about digestion. They may use skits, games, or videotapes.
- Refer to the *Reteaching Activities* booklet for the Section 2-5 activity sheet.

CLOSE

Draw a diagram (similar to the illustration on page 82) of the body with all parts of the digestive tract. Have student volunteers label each part of the digestive tract. Lead a class discussion on digestion and the importance of eating the right balance of foods to aid the digestive process.

How Nutrients Are Used

Nutrients and oxygen are carried throughout the bloodstream to individual cells, where they are used for specialized purposes. As you may recall, one of these is to provide energy. This is done by combining glucose with water. Such a process in which fuel is combined with oxygen to produce energy is known as **oxidation** (AHKS-ih-day-shuhn). Another example of oxidation is a log burning in a fireplace. The fuel in that case is wood. To keep burning, the wood must have oxygen from the air. Energy is produced as light and heat.

In your body, the fuel is glucose. When glucose reaches the cells, it is combined with oxygen. The result is energy as heat and power for the cells.

Your body uses energy for two basic purposes:

- *Automatic processes,* such as breathing, digesting food, and creating new cells. Even when you are resting or sleeping, your body is using minimal amounts of energy. This minimum amount of energy required to maintain the life processes in a living organism is called **basal metabolism** (BAY-zuhl muh-TAB-uh-lih-zuhm).
- *Physical activities,* such as work and exercise. The more active you are, the more energy you use. For instance, you would use more energy walking up a flight of stairs than riding in an elevator.

Generally, about two-thirds of the calories used by the body are for basal metabolism. However, this varies from person to person. It depends on factors such as age, body size, and body composition—the ratio of lean tissue to fat. The amount of energy used for basal metabolism is sometimes called the *basal metabolic rate,* or BMR.

As you can see, the human body is an amazing organism. Without even thinking about it, your body carries on thousands of complex processes every moment of your life.

Section 2-5 Review & Activities

1. How do nutrients get from the digestive system to the bloodstream?
2. Name two ways in which excess glucose can be stored.
3. What two substances combine to produce energy in the cells? What is the process called?
4. **Analyzing.** If someone had a portion of the small intestine removed because of a disease, what nutritional problems could result?
5. **Comparing and Contrasting.** On Monday, Ben's lunch provided 500 calories and was 90 percent fat, 10 percent protein. On Tuesday, lunch provided 600 calories and was 30 percent fat, 10 percent protein, 60 percent carbohydrate. Which meal do you think stayed in Ben's stomach longer? Why?
6. **Applying.** Sketch a design for a poster or bulletin board showing how food is broken down into nutrients and how nutrients travel through the body.

Answers to Section 2-5 Review & Activities

1. They are absorbed by the villi in the small intestine.
2. As glycogen in the liver and muscles; as body fat.
3. Glucose and oxygen; oxidation.
4. Answers will vary but may describe nutritional deficiencies due to malabsorption.
5. Monday's, due to high percentages of fat and protein, which take longer to digest.
6. Students may use a variety of approaches (example: a "road map" with signs to indicate the path taken by food and nutrients).

Career Wanted

Food Scientist

"If it's related to food, it's related to food science."

Reynaud Kelly

Education and Training
- Advanced degree in food science, biochemistry, or related field
- Research and laboratory skills

Qualities
- Detail oriented
- Analytical thinking skills
- Ability to work independently

Q. Reynaud, what projects have you been involved in recently?

A. Right now, I'm working on a vitamin mix for a dietary supplement that's designed for people with extra nutritional needs. I've also done research on fatty acids and helped develop flavors for food manufacturers.

Q. It sounds like science is involved in every aspect of food production.

A. People are surprised at just how involved we are. The food industry is very competitive. Food makers are looking for every edge. If we can show that a new method of freezing food preserves nutrients better, that can mean profits for the company making the technology and the food maker that buys it.

Q. What's the next "big thing" in food science?

A. I think we'll see more interest in nonfood items made from food products. We already have an ink made from soybeans, and a corn-based fuel called gasohol. That's not only good economics. There's a growing feeling that we can't afford to waste any of the world's resources.

Related Career Opportunities

Entry Level
- Food processing plant worker
- Health food store salesperson

Technical Level
- Quality assurance analyst
- Dietetic assistant
- Laboratory technologist

Professional Level
- Nutritionist
- Toxicologist
- Technical writer

Making Career Connections

CAREER EXPLORATION. Find out how food scientists have made a food such as table salt or milk more nutritious. What nutrients were involved? What processes were used to improve the food? With other students, compile findings into a video that explains how science helps make foods more nutritious and more available.

Career Wanted

Food Scientist

Thinking About the Career

Have students think of other questions they would like to ask Reynaud Kelly about being a food scientist. (Examples: Do you specialize in any particular type of food or food problem? How many hours a week do you work?)

Ask students to brainstorm a list of the ways food scientists can help people (provide better nutrition, produce better seeds, prevent illness, etc.).

Career-Building Opportunities

Most food scientists begin by working in a university, private industry, or nonprofit research foundation. Advancement depends on their education, experience, and quality of their job performance. Food scientists with experience and good job performance may become supervisors of major research programs or may specialize in a certain area of food science.

For More Information

For additional information about careers in food or agricultural science, encourage interested students to contact:

- American Society of Agronomy
  677 S. Segoe Rd.
  Madison, WI 53711
  www.agronomy.org
- Higher Education Programs
  USDA/CSREES/SERD
  1400 Independence Ave., SW
  Stop 2251
  Washington, DC 20250-2251
  www.reeusda.gov

REVIEW

- Have students complete the Chapter Review. (Answers appear below.)

EVALUATION

- Divide the class into two teams (A and B). Each team is to brainstorm questions about Chapter 2. Then allow the teams to take turns asking each other questions. At the end of the questioning period, the team with the most correct answers wins.
- Have the students take the test for Chapter 2. (Use the chapter test in the *Teacher Resource Guide,* or construct your own with the **Exam***View*® *Test Generator* on the *Effective Instruction CD-ROM.*)

ANSWERS

Checking Your Knowledge

1. RDAs and AIs. They are similar, except AIs are developed when there is lack of scientific evidence to firmly establish an RDA.
2. Carbohydrates: approximately 60%; proteins: at least 10%; fats: less than 30%.
3. Insoluble: fruit and vegetable skins, whole wheat and wheat bran products. Soluble: fruits, vegetables, dry beans, peas, and lentils; oat products. *Any two from each.*
4. Amino acids; they lack one or more essential amino acids.
5. LDLs (low-density lipoproteins) take cholesterol from the liver to wherever it is needed in the body; however, excess LDL cholesterol can build up in the arteries. HDLs (high-density lipoproteins) pick up excess cholesterol and take it back to the liver.
6. Corn oil: polyunsaturated; olive oil: monounsaturated; coconut oil: saturated.

Chapter 2 Review & Activities

Summary

Section 2-1: The Role of Nutrients

- The six major types of nutrients work as a team.
- Lack of or excess of certain nutrients can result in poor health.
- Recommended amounts have been set for some nutrients.
- The energy supplied by nutrients is measured in calories.

Section 2-2: Carbohydrates, Fiber, and Proteins

- Carbohydrates include complex and simple carbohydrates.
- Both soluble and insoluble fiber are important for good health.
- Complete protein can be obtained by eating animal foods or a wide variety of plant foods.

Section 2-3: Fats

- Fats perform several important jobs.
- Eating too much fat is linked with several health problems.
- The three types of fatty acids—saturated, polyunsaturated, and monounsaturated—appear to have different effects on blood cholesterol levels.
- Experts recommend that people limit their intake of total fat, saturated fat, and cholesterol.

Section 2-4: Micronutrients

- Each vitamin and mineral has specific functions and food sources.
- Some minerals are needed in large amounts and others in small amounts.
- Phytochemicals may prevent diseases.
- Every day you must replace the water lost by the body.

Section 2-5: How Your Body Uses Food

- Digestion is the process of breaking down food into usable nutrients.
- After digestion, nutrients are absorbed and put to use.
- Some nutrients can be stored if not needed right away.
- The bloodstream carries nutrients to all the cells in the body.
- Glucose and oxygen combine to produce energy for physical activities and basal metabolism.

Checking Your Knowledge

1. Name two examples of DRIs and explain how they differ.
2. What percentage of daily calories should come from carbohydrates? From proteins? From fats?
3. What are two types of dietary fiber? List two food sources for each type.
4. What are proteins made of? Why are plant proteins considered incomplete?
5. What is the difference between HDL and LDL cholesterol?
6. Which type of fatty acid is corn oil highest in? Olive oil? Coconut oil?
7. How does your body use beta carotene? In what foods is it found?
8. Which minerals are electrolytes? What do electrolytes do?
9. Name four digestive juices. In what part of the digestive system does each do its work?
10. What is basal metabolism?

Thinking Critically

1. **Determining Accuracy.** An advertisement claims that a special nutrient supplement will "meet all your daily nutrient needs." What is wrong with this claim?
2. **Comparing and Contrasting.** One frozen dinner boasts "only 300 calories per serving." The nutrition information shows that the dinner contains 20 grams of fat. A similar product lists 400 calories and contains 10 grams of fat. How do these foods differ? How do they reflect recommendations from nutritionists?

Working IN THE Lab

1. ***Taste Test.*** Taste samples of ripe fresh fruits provided by your teacher. Which do you think are highest in natural sugar?
2. ***Food Science.*** Rub a sample of butter or margarine on a piece of white paper. Label the spot left by the butter. Do the same with samples of ten different foods, such as cheese, a potato, an apple, and a cookie. Let the paper dry for 15 minutes. Which foods left a translucent spot that did not disappear? How do those spots compare with the spot left by the butter? What do you conclude?

Reinforcing Key Skills

1. **Communication.** Reanne, who has iron-deficiency anemia, has been instructed by her physician to cut back on red meat because of her high cholesterol. What solutions can you propose to Reanne?
2. **Management.** Veejay is overweight. He lives with his father in a tiny apartment without a kitchen. In the main room they have a microwave and a small refrigerator/freezer. They eat only microwaved frozen pizzas and "fast food." Within the constraints posed by his environment, what steps can Veejay take to improve his and his father's food choices?

Making Decisions and Solving Problems

Your uncle tells you he has decided to increase the fiber in his eating plan. Since he hasn't eaten much fiber before, he plans to eat twice the recommended amount for several days. He asks your opinion.

Making Connections

1. **Math.** Collect and bring to class three food labels that include nutrition information. Multiply the number of grams of saturated fat by 9 to find the number of saturated fat calories per serving. Divide that number by the total calories from fat. Then multiply by 100 to get the percentage of saturated fat compared with total fat. What does this percentage mean for heart health? Compare results with classmates. Hint: An easier way to calculate this percentage is by using grams instead of calories.
2. **Social Studies and Health.** In regions of the world where food is scarce, certain nutrient deficiencies are common. Using library resources, find information about three specific deficiency diseases. What are the symptoms? How can each disease be prevented? How can each be treated?

ANSWERS cont.

7. It uses beta carotene to produce vitamin A; in dark green and deep yellow-orange fruits and vegetables.
8. Potassium, sodium, and chloride; they work together to help maintain the body's fluid balance.
9. Any four: saliva (mouth); gastric juices (stomach); bile, pancreatic, and intestinal juices (large intestine).
10. The energy a person's body uses when resting or sleeping.

Thinking Critically

1. Answers will vary. Stress that supplements cannot entirely take the place of good eating habits.
2. 180 calories of the 300 in the first product are from fat; 90 of the 400 in the second, making it the healthier choice. If balanced properly, either can be included in a low-fat or low-calorie eating plan. There are no "bad" foods.

Reinforcing Key Skills

1. Encourage small portions of lean, red meat; good sources of vitamin C with meals to enhance iron absorption; and other foods containing iron—dry beans and peas, dried fruits, grain products, and dark green leafy vegetables. Also, prepare foods in an iron skillet when possible.
2. Take a study trip to a grocery store and discover the microwavable and ready-to-eat food choices available. Plan a one- or two-week menu, that can be routinely followed, utilizing a variety of food choices discovered on the study trip. Healthy "fast food" choices can be planned one or two times per week in the eating plan.

CHAPTER

3

Guidelines for Good Nutrition

Advance Planning Guide ☑

- Invite a registered dietitian or nutritionist to address the students.
- Buy an assortment of shelf-stable foods.
- Prepare a story about a teenager with poor eating habits.
- Purchase ten low-sugar or sugar-free food items.
- Bring in an illustration of the former "four food groups."
- Prepare a printed dinner menu based on the former four main food groups.
- Obtain copies of the school cafeteria's weekly menu.
- Obtain sample dinner meal plans from Canada or some other country.
- Prepare a list of combined foods, such as taco and tuna salad sandwich.
- Create menus for meals in which one of the food groups is missing.
- Bring to class articles and advertisements that represent misleading and confusing nutrition claims.
- Bring in a variety of nutrition books and articles.

CHAPTER 3

Guidelines for Good Nutrition

Section 3-1 Dietary Guidelines

Section 3-2 The Food Guide Pyramid

Section 3-3 Separating Fact from Fiction

Jenna could scarcely believe her eyes when she first saw the buffet with its endless parade of gleaming dishes and bowls. How would she decide? Go with what she knows or try something new?

Decisions relating to food can be difficult. In this chapter, you will learn what you need to know to make informed, healthful food choices.

MEETING DIVERSE NEEDS

Visually Impaired Students. If there are students within the class with visual impairments, create a "tactile" Food Guide Pyramid out of a stacked pyramid of shoeboxes and an assortment of shelf-stable food. For the "Bread, Cereal, Rice, Pasta Group," fill one box with cereal flakes, uncooked rice, and the like. Cut a hole in the top of each such prepared box, and invite students to reach in and "feel" what food group is represented.

SECTION 3-1

Dietary Guidelines

Objectives

After studying this section, you should be able to:

- Discuss what the *Dietary Guidelines for Americans* contributes to good health.
- Explain how each Dietary Guideline contributes to good health.
- Describe ways of reducing fats and sodium in your eating plan.

Look for These Terms

moderation

lifestyle diseases

Whether you are deciding what to have for breakfast or packing food supplies for a two-week camping trip, making food choices that promote good health is a difficult challenge. Just think of the thousands of foods and food products lining the shelves in your supermarket. How can you tell which items will give your body the nutrients it needs?

The Dietary Guidelines for Americans

AIM FOR FITNESS...
- ▲ Aim for a healthy weight.
- ▲ Be physically active each day.

BUILD A HEALTHY BASE...
- ■ Let the Pyramid guide your food choices.
- ■ Choose a variety of grains daily, especially whole grains.
- ■ Choose a variety of fruits and vegetables daily.
- ■ Keep food safe to eat.

CHOOSE SENSIBLY...
- ● Choose a diet that is low in saturated fat and cholesterol and moderate in total fat.
- ● Choose beverages and foods to moderate your intake of sugars.
- ● Choose and prepare foods with less salt.

The Dietary Guidelines for Americans

To help you make this decision, the U.S. Department of Agriculture (USDA) and the U.S. Department of Health and Human Services have published a helpful set of guidelines called the *Dietary Guidelines for Americans*.

The Dietary Guidelines listed in the chart above offer nine main recommendations, each of which will be explored in this section. Following these guidelines will help decrease your risk of eating-related illness now and in the future.

Aim for Fitness

Aim *for Fitness*

Aim for a Healthy Weight

Generally, a few extra pounds can't do much harm. Being truly overweight, however, poses a serious health risk. It may contribute to one or more **lifestyle diseases**—illnesses

Section 3-1 Resources

◆ **Student Workbook,** pp. 27, 29
◆ **Teacher Resource Guide**
Lesson Plan 3-1 Organizer
Section 3-1 Quiz
◆ **Effective Instruction CD-ROM**
Exam*View*® *Test Generator*
PowerPoint® Slide #8
◆ **Transparency Package,** CT-8

◆ **Student Motivation Kit**
Reteaching Activities, p. 21
Enrichment Activities
A Global Foods Tour, p. 10
Food Science Resources, pp. 43–45
Skills for Making Food Choices, pp. 11–12

SECTION 3-1

Dietary Guidelines

FOCUS

MOTIVATORS

- Create a bulletin board entitled, "You Can Solve the Dietary Puzzle by Following These Guidelines." Label large jigsaw puzzle pieces with the nine Dietary Guidelines for Americans. Discuss how each piece of the puzzle increases your chances of living a long and healthy life.
- Invite a registered dietitian to speak to the class on the *Dietary Guidelines for Americans.* Have him or her discuss practical ways teens can follow the guidelines. Have students develop questions to ask the dietitian.

VOCABULARY ACTIVITY

Ask students to define *moderation.* Ask them to identify situations in which *moderation* is a good idea. Ask how they think the concept of moderation relates to food choices. Ask how they think it relates to *lifestyle diseases.*

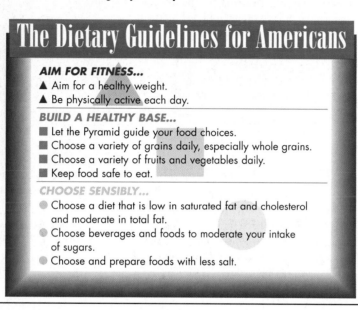

STUDY SKILLS

- **Guided Reading.** Have students look at the headings within Section 3-1 to preview the concepts that will be discussed.
- Have students read the section and complete the appropriate part of the Chapter 3 Study Guide in the *Student Workbook.*

TEACH

- *Dietary Guidelines for Americans (text pages 89-95)*

Problem-Solving Activity

Distribute a story to class about a fictional 14-year-old girl's eating habits that do not follow the Dietary Guidelines—too large portions, no variety, etc. Have each student circle all nutritional problems in the story. Then discuss identified problems in class.

Teenage Meal Analysis

Have students work in groups to analyze the "typical" American teenager's eating plan, based on their own experience. Have them develop a list of teen dietary guidelines. Have each group present its guidelines to class. **L1**

Research

Have students research the history of the Dietary Guidelines for Americans. Why were the Dietary Guidelines developed? Who developed them? How can the Dietary Guidelines help Americans improve their eating plans? Then, evaluate the current guidelines. With the students' research findings and evaluation, have them compile their results and write a letter to the Dietary Guidelines for Americans committee on suggestions for the next Guidelines update. **L2**

that relate to how a person lives and the choices he or she makes. These diseases include high blood pressure, heart disease, stroke, diabetes, and certain kinds of cancer.

Being too thin can also be a problem. It may mean that you are not eating enough to meet your body's energy and nutrient needs.

Maintaining a healthful weight is a balancing act. Food provides energy—the key is to balance the energy supplied by the food you eat with the energy your body uses.

INFOLINK
For more on strategies for maintaining a healthful weight, see Section 5-1.

Be Physically Active Each Day

Being physically active will help you balance that energy. Everyone can improve their health—and have fun—by including some moderate activity in their daily lives. Chapter 5 discusses ways to incorporate physical activity into your overall plan for health, maintain a healthy weight, how to stay active, and the importance of nutrition in sports and fitness.

Build a Healthy Base

BUILD a Healthy Base

Use the Pyramid

The Food Guide Pyramid is a tool that was developed to help you make daily food choices. It is not a rigid rule, but rather a flexible set of guidelines to help you build a healthy base in your eating plan. You will learn more about how to use the Food Guide Pyramid in Section 3-2.

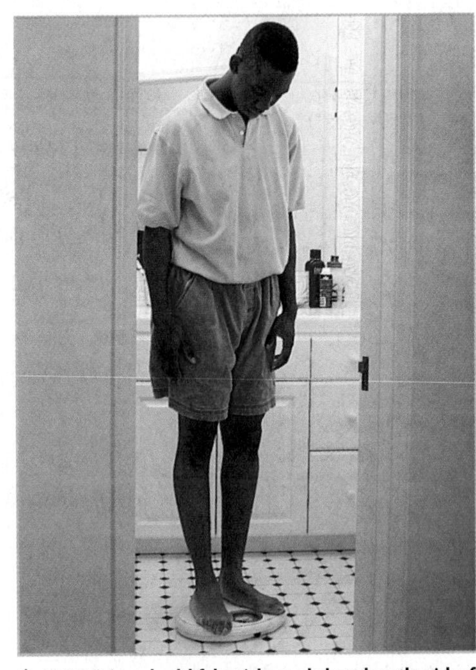

◆ Maintaining a healthful weight can help reduce the risk of lifestyle-related health problems such as high blood pressure. Analyze the statement "A person's eating patterns alone are not enough to ensure total health, even if the person is at an appropriate weight."

You may know the expression "Variety is the spice of life." When it comes to choosing the foods that make up your eating plan, variety is a good way of making sure you get all the nutrients your body needs. As you learned in Section 2-1, scientists have identified about 40 different nutrients. By eating a variety of foods, you can be sure you get all the nutrients you need, as well as some that have not yet been identified.

No single food can supply all nutrients in the amounts you need. Consider this: sweet potatoes are packed with vitamins A and C and fiber, but have no calcium or phosphorus.

Reinforcing Key Skills

Present the following problems to student groups. Allow time for them to discuss and compare their responses.

Critical Thinking—Ask students to hypothesize why it's difficult to determine exact healthy weight for individuals of the same age and gender.

Management—You're responsible for cooking for someone who always eats large portions of their favorite foods, but rarely eats fruits or vegetables.

Fat-free milk is a good source of calcium and phosphorus, but has no fiber and little vitamin C. As you can see, you need to eat a variety of foods for good health.

A concept that goes hand-in-hand with variety is **moderation**—avoiding extremes. Do you know someone who eats just a few favorite foods regularly and avoids other foods altogether? People who limit the variety of foods they eat are missing out on essential nutrients. By eating moderately sized servings of many different kinds of foods, you get a wider variety of nutrients for good health.

Keep in mind that there are no "bad" or "good" foods. Any food that supplies nutrients can be part of a healthful eating plan. The key is to balance your food choices so that, overall, they lead to good health. Variety and moderation can help you do just that.

Choose a Variety of Grains, Fruits, and Vegetables Daily

Most of the calories supplied by the food you eat should come from grain products, vegetables and fruits. They are considered the foundation of a healthful eating plan for several reasons:

- Grain products, vegetables, and fruits are key sources of carbohydrates your body needs for energy. Chapter 2 explains that carbohydrates should supply about 60 percent of your calories.
- Dietary fiber is found only in foods from plant sources. Because these foods contain different types of fiber, choose a variety of grains, especially whole-grain products, vegetables, and fruits to be sure you get the fiber your body needs.
- Grain products, vegetables, and fruits are excellent sources of many vitamins and minerals essential to health. Take another look at the vitamin and mineral charts in Section 2-4. Notice how many of the nutrients listed there are supplied by grain products, vegetables, and fruits. Some nutrients, such as vitamin C and beta carotene, are found only in fruits and vegetables.
- Most grain products, vegetables, and fruits are low in fat. Eating more of these foods can help you cut down on the amount of fat in your eating plan—as long as you don't add high-fat toppings, such as butter, sour cream, or rich sauces.

Get in the habit of eating more grain products, vegetables, and fruits. Think of them as central to your food choices rather than as extras to have "on the side." With so many flavorful choices available, you'll find it to be an enjoyable habit as well as a healthful one.

◆ **When planning meals, remember that you need more servings of grain products, vegetables, and fruits than you do of other foods. Explain why this is recommended.**

- *Dietary Guidelines for Americans (text pages 89-95)*

Discussion Activity

Discuss the reasons why grain products, vegetables, and fruits make a good foundation for daily food choices. Ask students to give examples of breakfast, lunch, or dinner menus that illustrate this Dietary Guideline.

Research Activity

Have students write a report on what the National Cancer Institute or American Cancer Society advises about eating grain products, vegetables, and fruits as a way to reduce the risk of cancer. Are there certain food choices that are highly recommended? If so, which ones and why? Have students compare the cancer recommendations to the Dietary Guidelines for Americans.

Finding Recipes

Have students look for recipes that are based on grains, fruits, or vegetables. Have students discuss one recipe they chose and how it can be incorporated into an eating plan that meets the Dietary Guidelines. L1

Extending Learning

Vegetable Variety—Point out to students that meeting the Dietary Guidelines for Americans should be easier today than just five or ten years ago due to the growing variety and availability of vegetables. While common vegetables that students eat may include potatoes, lettuce, and carrots, encourage students to expand their vegetable variety by choosing these choices: arugula, bok choy, celeriac, collard greens, fennel, jicama, plantain, and tomatillos. If possible, bring a sample of one or more of these vegetables for students to taste.

- *Dietary Guidelines for Americans (text pages 89-95)*

Group Project

Working in small groups, have students develop a list of ten foods that provide cholesterol and how to limit each choice in an eating plan. Allow time for student groups to compare lists. L1

Menu Analysis Activity

Provide a written high-fat meal plan to students. Ask each student to find all significant visible and invisible sources of fat in the menu. Discuss results in class, including how the high-fat choices may be less nutritionally dense. With students, create a new menu by substituting some high-fat choices with lower fat, more nutritionally dense choices.

Research Activity

Have students find and summarize an article on current research theories related to fat, saturated fat, and cholesterol. Ask students to report their findings to the class. Why are health experts concerned about high-fat diets?

Keep Food Safe to Eat

Keeping food safe to eat is a very important part of nutrition. It is free of harmful bacteria and contaminants that can make you sick.

There are four words to remember that will keep your food safe to eat: clean, separate, cook, and chill. You will learn more about these practices in Section 7-3.

Choose Sensibly

Choose a Diet That is Low in Saturated Fat and Cholesterol and Moderate in Total Fat

There are several reasons why the Dietary Guidelines encourage people to eat less fat and cholesterol. A high-fat eating plan is linked with various lifestyle diseases. Regularly choosing foods high in fat, saturated fat, and cholesterol can lead to overweight or other medical problems.

Health experts have suggested the following goals regarding fat in your daily food choices:

- **Saturated fat:** 10 percent or less of your calories. Remember, the highest proportions of saturated fatty acids are found in animal fats and in tropical oils, such as coconut, palm, and palm kernel oil.
- **Cholesterol:** Limit the amount of cholesterol eaten. Only foods from animal sources contain cholesterol. Since trans fats promote cholesterol production in the body, limit foods that are hydrogenized.
- **Total fat:** 30 percent or less of the calories you eat. Section 2-1 shows how to calculate the amount of fat that is equal to 30 percent of the day's total calories.

Visible and Invisible Fats

Studies show that on the average, Americans get 34 percent of calories from fat. Many people are unaware of how much fat is in the food they eat.

Some fat is called *visible fat* because it is easily seen. For example, you can see the butter on a baked potato or the layer of fat around a pork chop.

Suggestions for Lowering Fat

High-Fat Food	*Low-Fat Alternative*	*Fat Savings*
Whole milk (1 cup/250 mL)	Fat-free milk	8 grams less fat
Fried chicken (3 oz./84 g)	Baked chicken without skin	8 grams less fat
Regular salad dressing (1 Tbsp./15 mL)	Flavored vinegar, lemon juice, or fat-free dressing	9 grams less fat
Potato chips (1 oz./28 g)	Plain popcorn, air popped (1 cup/250 mL)	10 grams less fat
Premium ice cream (½ cup/125 mL)	Low-fat frozen yogurt	20 grams less fat
Cheddar cheese (1 oz./28 g)	Part-skim mozzarella	4 grams less fat
Sour cream on a baked potato (2 Tbsp./30 mL)	Plain nonfat yogurt Salsa	6 grams less fat

FOOD SCIENCE

Melted Fat When a visible fat melts, students may wonder whether the melting process changes saturated fats to unsaturated fats. The answer is "no." Just heating fat, such as butter, in a skillet doesn't change its chemical structure. As soon as the butter is cooled back down to room temperature, it becomes solid again. During this heating and cooling process, the structure never changes even though the appearance does. If possible, demonstrate this visual experiment to the class.

Making Invisible Fats Visible

Have you ever seen a magician make an object seem to suddenly appear? You are about to do something similar. This isn't an illusion. You are about to make the invisible fat in foods visible!

Procedure

1. Start with a clean, dry work surface. Place five or six potato chips on a paper towel, and fold the edges of the towel over the chips. Press lightly to crush the contents.
2. Open the towel. Dump the solid contents into a waste receptacle, and brush away any crumbs that remain. Return the towel to its place on the work surface next to a sticky note or other piece of paper that identifies the food used.
3. Repeat steps 1 and 2 for small amounts of each of the following foods: pretzels, apple, snack crackers, muffin, and air-popped unflavored popcorn.
4. Leave the paper towels undisturbed for 30 minutes. This will allow any water on the towels to evaporate. At the end of the 30 minutes, examine each paper towel by holding it up to a window or other light source. Any grease stains or other light spots show that the product contains some fat.

Conclusions

- ◆ Which foods produced stains? Which did not?
- ◆ Are any of the foods you used ones that you regularly eat?
- ◆ Were you surprised by any of your findings? If so, which?
- ◆ What changes in your eating habits might you consider making as a result of this experiment?

Much of the fat people eat, however, is *invisible fat*. It is part of the chemical composition of the food and cannot be seen. Foods such as whole milk, some cheeses, egg yolks, nuts, and avocados are loaded with invisible fat. So are fried foods and some baked goods.

Lowering Fat

Controlling the amount of fat in your eating plan can help reduce your risk of lifestyle diseases and other health problems. It also allows you to eat more food without increasing your total calories. Remember, a gram of fat has 9 calories, while a gram of protein or carbohydrates has only 4 calories.

It's easier than you might think to cut down on fat. One way is by substituting low-fat food choices for high-fat ones. As you progress through this program, you will learn other ways of reducing the fat in the foods you eat and the cooking you do.

Technology TIE-IN Food technologists have developed a variety of fat replacers. There are three main categories of fat replacers: (1) Carbohydrate-based, (2) Protein-based, and (3) Fat-based.

One example is olestra, a fat-based, calorie-free fat replacer. It's made from sugar and vegetable oils, but provides no calories since the body is not able to digest or absorb it. As technology advances, consumers can expect to find more and improved-tasting products that use fat replacers.

- *Dietary Guidelines for Americans (text pages 89-95)*

VISUAL LEARNING ***Using the "Suggestions for Lowering Fat" Chart***

Have students identify low-fat substitutions for seven common high-fat foods other than those on page 92. On large posterboard divided into high-fat and low-fat columns, have each student pick his or her best recommendation and record the food and its low-fat alternative in the appropriate columns. Discuss the students' results.

USING THE

Explain to students that food professionals use more precise methods than those used in class to achieve certain results. Demonstrate this by spreading 2 Tbsp. peanut butter in between two slices of fat-free bread. Have them repeat the activity with the sandwich. Discuss the results. Point out how scientists measure nutrient content of the entire edible portion of foods.

Recipe Modification

Have students research ways to modify favorite recipes to reduce sugar, salt, fat, and cholesterol. Suggest that students search cookbooks to compare regular and modified recipes. L2

TEACH cont.

- *Dietary Guidelines for Americans (text pages 89-95)*

Nutrient Identification Activity

Display 10 deceptively low-sugar or sugar-free food items in class, labeled 1–10. On a blank sheet of paper, have each student determine, just from the name of the product, whether the product has sugar. Discuss results in class, including how many were tricked by certain foods.

COMPUTER ACTIVITY

Creating a Pamphlet

Invite students to create pamphlets that provide, in a lively text format, tips (or checklist) on "How to Shake the Salt Habit." The booklets may be run off on the classroom or a home computer, using either word-processing or desktop publishing software. Students may illustrate their booklets. Have students speak with directors at public health centers, or their family doctor, about leaving booklets as a service to clients.

FOR YOUR HEALTH

Ask students to do a survey of their home kitchens and make a list of at least five food sources that each provide at least one of the sugars on the list on page 95. On the chalkboard, make 14 columns and a heading for each sugar. Under each heading, have students record a food source that contains each type of sugar.

Choose Beverages and Foods to Moderate Your Intake of Sugars

You expect to find sugar in foods such as candy, desserts, and baked goods. Did you know, though, that other foods—ketchup, salad dressing, and peanut butter, for example—may also contain refined sugar?

Like natural sugar, the refined sugars added to many foods provide energy. However, these sugars are limited in nutrients. The Dietary Guidelines recommend that most healthy people use only moderate amounts of these sugars. Very active people with high energy needs may be able to consume more, as long as they choose nutritious foods. People with low energy needs should use refined sugars in very small amounts.

Q *How can I cut down on sugar in my diet?*

A Most people eat far too much sugar. The added calories can lead to a weight gain, which can cause health problems. You can get the energy you need from fruits, milk, and other foods that have naturally occurring sugars as well as other nutrients. Limit desserts, snacks, and beverages that are high in sugar and lack other nutrients. Many 12-ounce soft drinks, for example, contain nine teaspoons of sugar, but little else. Read food labels. The more sugars listed and the higher they are on the list, the more added sugars the product contains. Choose unsweetened, high-fiber cereals and sweeten them with fruit. A sweet treat is enjoyable, but with wise choices you can manage your overall sugar intake.

Choose and Prepare Foods with Less Salt

Table salt contains sodium and chloride, both of which are essential nutrients. Most people, however, eat more salt and sodium than they need for good health. Salt is added to most foods and beverages during processing. Many foods also naturally contain sodium. Here are hints for limiting salt and sodium:

- Add little, if any, salt to food when cooking and at the table. When you must add salt, shake once—not twice.
- Choose salty snacks—chips, crackers, pretzels, and nuts—only occasionally.
- Go easy on processed foods. They generally have more sodium than fresh ones.
- Check labels for sodium content. Choose foods lower in sodium most of the time.

◆ **What makes an apple a good snack?**

FOOD SCIENCE

Cereal Experiment

Conduct a blind taste test of six to eight breakfast cereals with varying sugar contents. Ask students to rank them according to expected sugar content. Have students compare their perception of sweetness to the information on the box labels. How well do they correspond? Ask students to write a summary of their experiment and discuss their conclusions based on their findings.

FOR YOUR HEALTH

How Sweet It Is!

Because there are many different kinds of sugars, you may not be aware that a product you are buying has been sweetened. Examine the ingredients lists of products you buy. Any of the following terms that appear on the label will tell you that the product contains added sugar:

- Sucrose
- Raw sugar
- Dextrose
- Maltose
- Honey
- Corn sweetener
- High-fructose corn syrup
- Fruit juice concentrate
- Brown sugar
- Glucose
- Fructose
- Lactose
- Syrup
- Molasses

Following Up

1. Check the ingredients labels of three products you regularly eat. Which contain one of the sugars in the list above? Which contain more than one?
2. Three of Theo's favorite foods contain at least one form of sugar. Devise a strategy Theo could use to cut down on the amount of sugar in his eating plan.

Section 3-1 Review & Activities

1. Why is eating a variety of foods important to good health?
2. What is meant by the term *invisible fat*? Name three foods in which it is found.
3. List five examples of different sugars that may appear on food labels.
4. **Analyzing.** Which of the nine recommendations in the Dietary Guidelines do you think is hardest for most people to follow? Why?
5. **Evaluating.** Research the dietary guidelines of other countries. What are the similarities and differences?
6. **Applying.** Choose one Dietary Guideline. In your Wellness Journal, list five to ten suggestions for helping yourself and other people to follow it.

ASSESS

REVIEW

- Ask students to summarize the main ideas in this section.
- Have students complete the Section Review. (Answers appear below.)

EVALUATION

- Have students write a short essay on "Why I think it's important to follow the Dietary Guidelines for Americans."
- Have students take the quiz for Section 3-1. (Use the quiz in the *Teacher Resource Guide,* or construct your own with the **Exam***View*® *Test Generator* on the *Effective Instruction CD-ROM.*)

RETEACHING

- Have students write a "press release" announcing the Dietary Guidelines for Americans. Direct students to use the five "w's" and one "h" used by reporters: *what, who, why, where, when, and how.*
- Refer to the *Reteaching Activities* booklet for the Section 3-1 activity sheet.

CLOSE

Have students create posters recommending that people follow all nine Dietary Guidelines. Tell students to be creative and make the posters appealing as well as convincing. Discuss selected posters. Display all the posters around the school.

Answers to Section 3-1 Review & Activities

1. It ensures you get all the nutrients your body needs.
2. Fat that is part of the chemical composition of food. Examples will vary but may include whole milk, cheese, egg yolks, nuts, avocados, fried foods, and baked goods.
3. See list in "For Your Health" feature on this page.
4. Answers will vary. Ask students to provide reasons for their answers.
5. Answers will vary. Ask students to support their answers.
6. Answers will vary.

SECTION

3-2

The Food Guide Pyramid

FOCUS

MOTIVATORS

- If possible, bring an illustration of the former "four food groups," where half the suggested intake was from the dairy and meat groups. Develop a dinner menu based on these food groups and discuss why and how meals are different today.
- Referring to the Food Guide Pyramid, ask students to name foods that are high in calories and foods that are low in calories in each food group. Which of the high-calorie foods named are high in sugar? In fat? Explain how low- or moderate-calorie foods generally provide more important nutrients for the number of calories.

VOCABULARY ACTIVITY

Direct students attention to the compound word *nutrient-dense.* Have a volunteer define each part of the hyphenated term. Ask: How can this term be used when discussing the *Food Guide Pyramid*?

STUDY SKILLS

- **Listening.** Ask for volunteers to prepare an oral reading of each page of text from the section, while others follow along silently.
- Have students read the section and complete the appropriate part of the Chapter 3 Study Guide in the *Student Workbook.*

SECTION 3-2

Objectives

After studying this section, you should be able to:

- Describe the food groups in the Food Guide Pyramid.
- Give guidelines for using the Food Guide Pyramid to plan daily food choices.

Look for These Terms

Food Guide Pyramid

nutrient-dense

The Food Guide Pyramid

You probably know the expression "A picture is worth a thousand words." The authors of the* Dietary Guidelines for Americans *decided to follow the wisdom of these words. They included a graphic tool to help readers better understand the concepts summarized in Section 3-1.

Understanding the Pyramid

Who hasn't seen the **Food Guide Pyramid** printed on the back of cereal boxes, bread wrappers, and countless other food packages? Subtitled "A Guide to Daily Food Choices," this pyramid-shaped food grouping system is designed to help you choose a variety of foods in moderate amounts, including plenty of grains, vegetables, and fruits.

The Food Guide Pyramid includes five food groups:

- Bread, Cereal, Rice, and Pasta Group.
- Vegetable Group.
- Fruit Group.
- Milk, Yogurt, and Cheese Group.
- Meat, Poultry, Fish, Dry Beans, Eggs, and Nuts Group.

Using the Pyramid

Foods are arranged in the Food Guide Pyramid according to the recommended number of servings. The Bread, Cereal, Rice, and Pasta Group is at the base of the pyramid—and is the largest section—because you need more servings from this group than any of the others. Within each food group is a wide assortment of foods. They differ in nutrients and calories—both naturally occurring and according to preparation methods. Spinach, for example, has more vitamins and minerals than iceberg lettuce. French fries have more fat and calories than a plain baked potato. Peaches canned in syrup have more sugar and calories than fresh peaches.

In addition to the five food groups, the pyramid includes a section labeled "Fats, Oils, and Sweets." Foods in this category include

Section 3-2 Resources

- ◆ **Student Workbook,** pp. 27, 30
- ◆ **Teacher Resource Guide**
  Lesson Plan 3-2 Organizer
  Section 3-2 Quiz
- ◆ **Effective Instruction CD-ROM**
  Exam*View*® *Test Generator*
  PowerPoint® Slide #9
- ◆ **Transparency Package,** CT-9
- ◆ **Student Motivation Kit**
  Reteaching Activities, p. 22
  Enrichment Activities

salad dressings and oils, cream, butter, margarine, refined sugars, soft drinks, candies, and sweet desserts. These foods provide calories from fat and sugar, but few or no vitamins and minerals. Fats and sweets are placed at the small tip of the pyramid to show that they should be used sparingly.

On the pyramid diagram, you will notice small circles and triangles. These represent fats and added sugars. Notice that these symbols appear not only at the tip of the pyramid but also within the food groups. This is to show that fats and sugars can occur in some of the foods in each group.

Choosing Nutrient-Dense Foods

In general, the greater the number of servings in a particular group, the larger the space it is given in the pyramid. The most space is given to foods that are **nutrient-dense**, low or moderate in calories yet rich in important nutrients. As a rule, nutrient-dense foods are low in fats and added sugars and high in other nutrients, such as complex carbohydrates, fiber, proteins, vitamins, and minerals. Organizing the pyramid in this fashion is a way of helping you remember to eat more servings of grains, fruits, and vegetables than of any other foods.

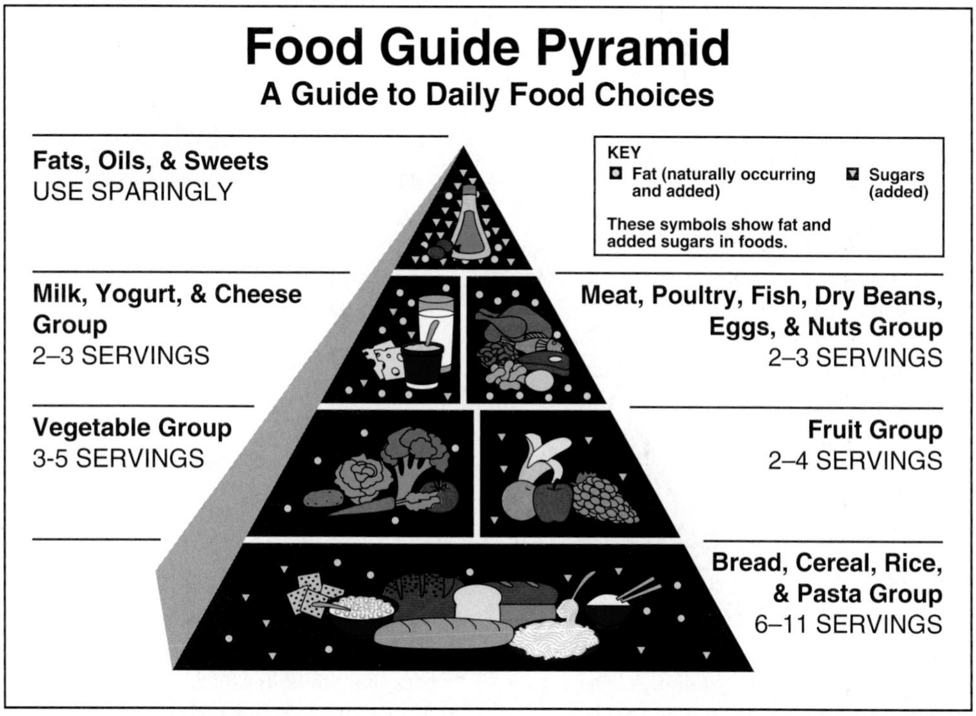

Food Guide Pyramid
A Guide to Daily Food Choices

KEY
▫ Fat (naturally occurring and added) ▾ Sugars (added)
These symbols show fat and added sugars in foods.

Fats, Oils, & Sweets USE SPARINGLY

Milk, Yogurt, & Cheese Group 2–3 SERVINGS

Meat, Poultry, Fish, Dry Beans, Eggs, & Nuts Group 2–3 SERVINGS

Vegetable Group 3-5 SERVINGS

Fruit Group 2–4 SERVINGS

Bread, Cereal, Rice, & Pasta Group 6–11 SERVINGS

◆ **The Food Guide Pyramid shows the types of foods you need and in which amounts in order to balance your daily food intake. Which three food groups have the highest number of recommended daily servings? Explain why.**

- *Understanding the Pyramid (text pages 96-101)*

Categorizing

Ask students each to draw a Food Guide Pyramid with its five food groups and fill each group with three specific favorite food choices. Using the fat and sugar symbols on the Pyramid, have students determine how the symbols apply to their food choices. Select a few volunteers to discuss their personal pyramids. L1

Food Guide History Activity

Have students trace the history of food guides in the United States. Ask students to write a report of their findings. In class, discuss what changes have been made in the food guides as health professionals learned more about the role of food in good health? Draw one or two of the previous food guide diagrams for comparison.

Class Discussion Activity

Have students study the Food Guide Pyramid. Discuss how the Pyramid graphically depicts the importance of each food group. Ask students to discuss how the pyramid graphic is a better educational tool than a wheel or circle graphic.

Extending Learning

Food Group Systems—There are many food grouping systems developed throughout the world, including many different systems within the United States. For instance, a German health newsletter outlines seven food groups.

The World Health Organization has developed various pyramids that depict different cultural eating habits. The Mediterranean Pyramid and the Asian Pyramid are two examples of systems that have been developed. The USDA Food Guide Pyramid has the most widespread use in the United States today.

TEACH

- *Using the Pyramid (text pages 96-101)*

Designing Educational Tools

Have students design an educational aid showing how the Food Guide Pyramid applies to older citizens. Have them present their project to a local senior citizens' center. L1

Demonstration

Discuss recommended servings for the Bread, Cereal, Rice, and Pasta Group. Why does the recommended number of servings vary? Ask students to discuss the meaning of "one serving" in this group. Bring a bagel; ask the class to determine how many servings it provides. Weigh it on a food scale. (The bagel may be 4+ servings.) Discuss how this information is useful for meal planning?

Publishing Activity

Ask each student to develop a list of 10 practical recommendations for increasing fruit and vegetable consumption. Have students combine their best recommendations. Nominate a student to write an article, such as "Twenty Tips to Increase Fruit and Vegetable Intake." Then help the students submit the article for publication, on behalf of the class, to the school newsletter or local paper.

The Food Groups

All five food groups are important to health. Each provides some, but not all, of the nutrients you need. One group cannot replace another. You need a variety of foods from the food groups each day.

Bread, Cereal, Rice, and Pasta Group

This group includes all kinds of grain products. They supply complex carbohydrates, fiber, vitamins, and minerals.

You need 6 to 11 servings from this group every day. Some examples of a serving are:

- 1 slice bread.
- 1 ounce (28 g) ready-to-eat cereal.
- ½ cup (125 mL) cooked cereal, rice, or pasta.

To get the fiber you need, choose as many whole-grain foods as you can, such as whole wheat bread and whole-grain cereals. This group includes many low-fat choices, but also some higher-fat ones, such as croissants and other baked goods.

Vegetable Group

Vegetables provide beta carotene, which your body uses to make vitamin A. They also supply vitamin C, folate (a B vitamin), and minerals such as magnesium and iron. They provide fiber and complex carbohydrates and are low in fat.

You should have three to five servings of vegetables daily. Each of the following counts as one serving:

- 1 cup (250 mL) raw leafy vegetables.
- ½ cup (125 mL) other vegetables, cooked or chopped raw.
- ¾ cup (175 mL) vegetable juice.

Different types of vegetables provide different nutrients. For variety, include dark green, leafy vegetables, such as kale; deep yellow-orange vegetables, such as sweet potatoes; starchy vegetables, including corn, peas, and potatoes; dry beans and peas; and others.

Fruit Group

Fruits provide important amounts of beta carotene, vitamin C, and potassium. Edible skins are good sources of fiber. Like vegetables, most fruits are low in fat and sodium.

You need two to four servings of fruit every day. One serving equals:

- 1 medium fruit, such as an apple, a banana, or an orange.
- ½ cup (125 mL) chopped raw, cooked, or canned fruit.
- ¾ cup (175 mL) fruit juice.

Be sure to have fruits rich in vitamin C regularly, such as citrus fruits, melons, and berries. Eat whole fresh fruits often for the fiber they provide. When choosing canned or frozen fruits, look for products without added sugar. Count only 100 percent fruit juices as a serving of fruit.

Reinforcing Key Skills

Present the following problems to student groups. Allow time for them to discuss and compare their responses.

Critical Thinking—Ask students what might happen to a person who regularly eats foods high in calories and low in nutrient density.

Communication—Imagine someone who is overweight and eats one 5-oz. plain bagel for a snack between each meal because they are fat-free and believes they count as one serving each.

Milk, Yogurt, and Cheese Group

Foods in this group are high in protein, vitamins, and minerals. They are also one of the best sources of calcium.

Most adults need two servings of milk products daily. Three servings are recommended for pregnant or breast-feeding women, teens, and young adults up to age 24. One serving equals:

- 1 cup (250 mL) milk or yogurt.
- 1½ ounces (42 g) natural cheese.
- 2 ounces (56 g) processed cheese.

Low-fat choices from this group include skim milk, nonfat yogurt, and nonfat dry milk. Go easy on high-fat cheese and ice cream. Remember, too, that some milk products, such as flavored yogurt, contain added sugar.

Meat, Poultry, Fish, Dry Beans, Eggs, and Nuts Group

This group is an important source of protein, vitamins, and minerals. Two to three daily servings are recommended.

- 2 to 3 ounces (56 to 85 g) of cooked lean meat, poultry, or fish equals one serving. This is about the size of an average hamburger or the amount of meat in half a medium chicken breast.
- Each of the following portions is the equivalent of 1 ounce (28 g) of meat: ½ cup (125 mL) cooked dry beans; one egg; or 2 tablespoons (30 mL) peanut butter.

The total of your daily servings should be the equivalent of 5 to 7 ounces (140 to 196 g) of cooked lean meat, poultry, or fish. For instance, you might eat an egg for breakfast, a cup of cooked dry beans in bean soup for lunch, and a lean hamburger for dinner. These foods would give you the equivalent of 6 ounces (168 g) of meat.

To limit the fat in your diet, select lean meats, fish, and poultry without skin. Have dry beans and peas often—they are high in fiber and low in fat. Go easy on eggs, nuts, and seeds. Eggs are high in cholesterol; nuts and seeds are high in fat.

Crossover Foods

Some foods in the Food Guide Pyramid have been identified by the authors of the guide as "crossover" foods. These foods, which include dry beans and other legumes, may be considered as belonging to more than one food group. For example, dry beans may be considered as one serving from either the Meat, Poultry, Fish, Dry Beans, Eggs, and Nuts Group or the Vegetable Group. Note that any crossover food can be used to satisfy a serving requirement from *either* group it is classified in, but not *both*.

How Many Servings for You?

You may have noticed that the Food Guide Pyramid does not give an exact number of servings for each group. Instead, it gives a range, such as three to five servings of vegetables. This is because people have different needs for calories and nutrients, depending on their age, gender, body size, and activity level.

- *Using the Pyramid (text pages 96-101)*

Contest Activity

Hold a contest: "How many types of dry beans can you name in 60 seconds?" Collect lists and provide a prize (i.e. bean bag) for the most correct answers.

Menu Evaluation

Distribute copies of the school cafeteria's weekly menu to students. Have them label each food according to the food group(s) represented: B = bread, etc.; V = vegetable; F = fruit; D = dairy; and M = meat, etc. Are meals nutritionally balanced? L1

Lab Experience

1. Provide students with ingredients for making a "Pyramid Pizza": ready-made pizza dough, tomato sauce, pineapple, mozzarella cheese, ham and almonds. (You can use another combination.)
2. Divide students into 3 or 4 groups to prepare and bake pizzas. Tell students each pizza will make 8 servings.
3. Have groups measure and record the amounts of each ingredient they use, and then calculate how many servings of each Pyramid group one slice of their pizza contains.
4. Enjoy the pizzas. L2

Extending Learning

Dairy, Calcium, and Teens—One of the key nutrients in dairy products is calcium. In the United States, dairy foods supply 75% of the food supply's calcium. Calcium needs vary depending on age and life-stage. The Adequate Intake (AI) level of calcium for teens is 1300 milligrams per day. One serving of milk provides about 300 milligrams of calcium. Therefore, teens need to be encouraged to consume three to four servings from the Milk, Yogurt, and Cheese group every day, not two to four servings.

- *Using the Food Pyramid (text pages 96-101)*

Food Record

Have students keep a record of the foods they eat for two days. Have them determine how many servings of each of the food groups they have eaten. Ask students to count the number of different foods they ate each day. Did their plan include variety and foods in each group? Ask them to make suggestions for improving their food intake. L2

Discussion Activity

Discuss serving ranges recommended in the Food Guide Pyramid for each food group. What people should eat servings near the top of the serving range? Near the bottom? Why?

Research Activity

Divide the class into groups. Provide each group with a sample dinner meal plan from another country. Ask students to find out what food groups make up each food, and how many servings of each food group are included in the meal.

Categorizing Activity

Provide students with a list of combined foods, such as taco and tuna salad sandwich. With an empty diagram of the Pyramid, have students write the name of the food in all the appropriate food groups represented.

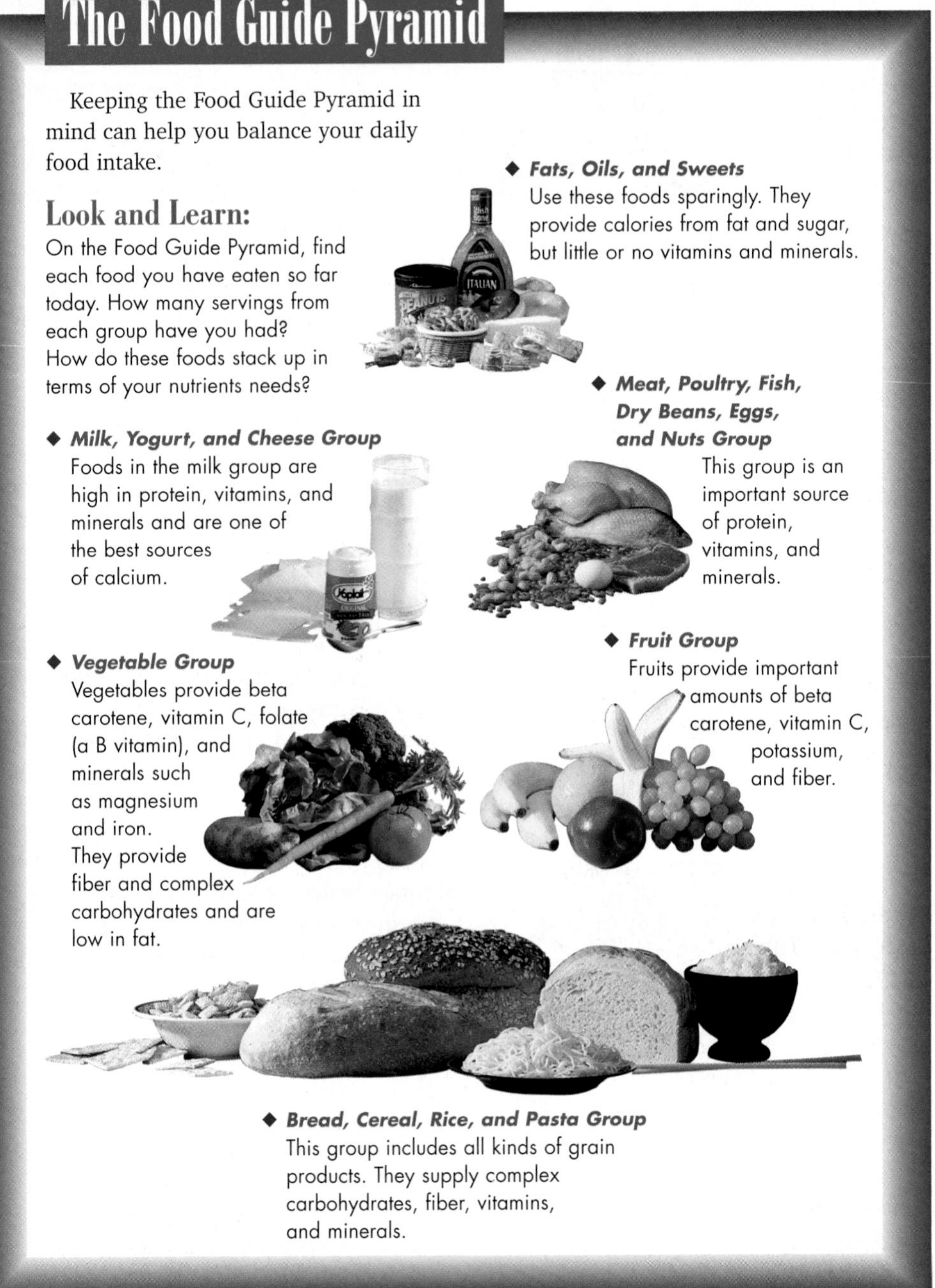

The Food Guide Pyramid

Keeping the Food Guide Pyramid in mind can help you balance your daily food intake.

Look and Learn:

On the Food Guide Pyramid, find each food you have eaten so far today. How many servings from each group have you had? How do these foods stack up in terms of your nutrients needs?

◆ ***Fats, Oils, and Sweets***
Use these foods sparingly. They provide calories from fat and sugar, but little or no vitamins and minerals.

◆ ***Milk, Yogurt, and Cheese Group***
Foods in the milk group are high in protein, vitamins, and minerals and are one of the best sources of calcium.

◆ ***Meat, Poultry, Fish, Dry Beans, Eggs, and Nuts Group***
This group is an important source of protein, vitamins, and minerals.

◆ ***Vegetable Group***
Vegetables provide beta carotene, vitamin C, folate (a B vitamin), and minerals such as magnesium and iron. They provide fiber and complex carbohydrates and are low in fat.

◆ ***Fruit Group***
Fruits provide important amounts of beta carotene, vitamin C, potassium, and fiber.

◆ ***Bread, Cereal, Rice, and Pasta Group***
This group includes all kinds of grain products. They supply complex carbohydrates, fiber, vitamins, and minerals.

Extending Learning

To What Food Group Do Potato Chips Belong?—Many snack foods are high in fat, yet they are vegetable- or grain-based. For instance, regular potato chips are made from potatoes, a vegetable. Although fried, potato chips fit within the Food Guide Pyramid Vegetable Group. Since potato chips are one of the higher fat choices in the Vegetable Group, they need to be consumed in moderation and balanced with lower-fat, nutritionally-dense Vegetable Group choices.

In general, most male teens need the highest number of servings from each food group. Most female teens need the middle number of servings (such as nine servings from the bread group). However, all teens need three servings from the milk group.

You may be used to eating amounts of food that are larger or smaller than what is considered a serving according to the Food Guide Pyramid. For example, if you eat 1 cup (250 mL) of cooked spaghetti, remember to count that as two servings, not one, from the Bread, Cereal, Rice and Pasta Group.

Some foods include ingredients from more than one food group. If you're eating tacos, you would have servings from the bread group (taco shell), meat group (meat or bean filling), milk group (cheese), and vegetable group (lettuce and tomatoes). Depending on the amounts of the different fillings, you might have full or half servings from the different groups.

The Food Guide Pyramid makes it easy to plan for good nutrition. It is a valuable tool for getting all the nutrients you need in the proper balance.

Section 3-2 Review & Activities

1. List the five food groups in the Food Guide Pyramid. Give the range of recommended daily servings for each group.
2. What does the term *nutrient-dense* mean? How does it relate to choosing foods from the pyramid?
3. For each food group, give two examples of serving sizes.
4. **Analyzing.** Do you feel the pyramid design is an effective way to get the desired nutrition message across? Why or why not?
5. **Extending.** Name two combination foods (other than tacos). List the food groups that are represented by the combination food's ingredients.
6. **Applying.** Make up a one-day menu that provides the recommended servings from the Food Guide Pyramid for a female teen.

Answers to Section 3-2 Review & Activities

1. See the Food Guide Pyramid on page 97.
2. Nutrient-dense means that a food is low or moderate in calories, yet rich in important nutrients. The Pyramid is based on grains, fruits, and vegetables—nutrient-dense foods.
3. Examples will vary but can be found on pages 98-99 of the text.
4. Answers will vary. Studies support its effectiveness. Ask students to support their answers.
5. Answers will vary. Two examples: Grilled Cheese (Bread/Milk), Spaghetti with Meatballs (Bread/Vegetable/Meat).
6. Answers will vary.

ASSESS

REVIEW

- Ask students to summarize the main ideas in this section.
- Have students complete the Section Review. (Answers appear below.)

EVALUATION

- Provide students with two or three basic recipes. Ask them to record the Food Guide Pyramid groups represented and the approximate number of servings represented for each food group by each recipe.
- Have students take the quiz for Section 3-2. (Use the quiz in the *Teacher Resource Guide,* or construct your own with the **Exam***View*® *Test Generator* on the *Effective Instruction CD-ROM.*)

RETEACHING

- Distribute menus for meals in which one of the food groups is missing. Ask students how they would change each menu to make it more nutritionally balanced.
- Refer to the *Reteaching Activities* booklet for the Section 3-2 activity sheet.

CLOSE

Lead a discussion about the Food Guide Pyramid and the choices that people can make within its guidelines to eat nutritiously. On the chalkboard, have students fill in a large diagram of the pyramid with one serving of one food per person, placed in the appropriate group (e.g. "¾ cup orange juice" written in the Fruit Group section.)

SECTION 3-3

Separating Fact from Fiction

FOCUS

MOTIVATORS

- Bring to class articles and advertisements that represent misleading nutrition claims. Ask students to look for clues in the articles that would help them separate fact from fiction.
- Ask students to share experiences of being fooled or misled by a nutrition claim. Then, have students read the section objectives. Discuss the purpose of studying the section.

VOCABULARY ACTIVITY

Refer students to the two terms listed under "Look for These Terms." Ask students which term can be used as an adjective, adverb, verb, and noun. Have a volunteer student look up various definitions of *bias* and determine which form of the term will be used in this section.

STUDY SKILLS

- **Outlining.** Have students read the section and outline it by copying the headers on paper and leaving space after each one. Students are to write a sentence in their own words, summarizing the content under each header.
- Have students read the section and complete the appropriate part of the Chapter 3 Study Guide in the *Student Workbook.*

SECTION 3-3

Separating Fact from Fiction

Objectives

After studying this section, you should be able to:

- Explain how to evaluate news reports, advertisements, and other information related to foods and nutrition.
- Identify the techniques advertisers use to sell products.
- Discuss how food myths originate.

Look for These Terms

bias

study design

"Now, with less sugar!" a TV ad for a soft drink promises. "Scientists Find That Fried Foods Are Good for You," announces the headline of a tabloid that catches your eye as you stand in the supermarket checkout line.

Each day, dozens of media messages about food and nutrition come your way. With this wealth of information, some of it conflicting, how can you tell what to believe and what to disregard?

Developing Consumer Skills

Part of the answer to the question above is mastering two of the food-consumer skills you learned about in Chapter 1. Those skills —critical thinking and communication—constitute a first step in learning how to separate fact from fiction. As a critical thinker, you learn to look for the "angle" in a given message. When you see an ad, for example, you are alert to the fact that advertisers have something to sell and, therefore, may not be the most reliable information sources.

As an effective communicator, you learn to consider the source of the information. You become able to discriminate between legitimate sources and popularizers.

◆ **Evaluating competing health claims and information is an important skill to learn. Make a list of different information sources—for example, scientific journal, newspaper tabloid, television program, etc. Rate each from 1 to 5 in terms of its credibility.**

Section 3-3 Resources

◆ **Student Workbook,** pp. 28, 32
◆ **Teacher Resource Guide**
Lesson Plan 3-3 Organizer
Section 3-3 Quiz
◆ **Effective Instruction CD-ROM**
Exam*View*® *Test Generator*
PowerPoint® Slide #10
◆ **Transparency Package,** CT-10
◆ **Student Motivation Kit**
Reteaching Activities, p. 23
Enrichment Activities

Going to the Source

How often do you read articles or hear news stories about food that contain phrases such as "a recent study shows" or "scientists have found"? On the surface, such reports seem believable enough. How can you tell whether to accept the information at face value? Here are some ways:

- Check the original source, when possible. Credible research is carried out by qualified scientists and recognized institutions. The results are then reported in scientific and professional journals. Be wary of the results of research attributed to unnamed sources.
- Be alert for bias on the part of the people who performed or reported on the study. A **bias** is a tendency to be swayed toward a particular conclusion. Which would you expect to be more objective, a study of the effectiveness of a food supplement paid for by the supplement's manufacturer or one carried out by an independent research facility?
- Read past the headlines. Headlines are designed to get your attention and may be misleading. Don't jump to a conclusion before you have read or heard the whole report.
- Consider the body of evidence. Is the report based on preliminary findings? If so, it may be too early to make any changes in your eating habits. Wait until more evidence has been gathered. Remember, too, that different scientists view study results differently and that it takes time to study and adequately test early findings. Be on the lookout for follow-up reports.
- Consider the **study design**, that is, the approach used by researchers to investigate a claim. Some studies, known as clinical trials, are performed on human subjects. Others are designed around animal subjects. Findings involving animals aren't always reliable.

◆ **Valid scientific studies are done by professional researchers under controlled conditions. Name two sources to which you can turn for reliable results of such studies.**

Evaluating Advertisements

Are there TV commercials you enjoy watching? Advertising can be informative and entertaining. At times, however, advertisements can be misleading. When it comes to food ads, the emphasis is seldom on real nutrition issues. Here are a few of the techniques advertisers use to persuade an unsuspecting public to buy their products:

- **Limited information.** Advertisements often give only the facts that will encourage you to buy, without telling the whole story.

TEACH

- *Developing Consumer Skills (text pages 102-106)*

Discussion Activity

Ask students to list techniques advertisers use to convince people to buy their products. Discuss questions people can ask themselves when they're evaluating an advertising or promotional campaign.

Debate

Have students form two groups for a debate. One group is to argue the benefits of a real or "make believe" product advertisement, such as how eliminating a food group from your eating plan is the key to permanent weight loss or a new chocolate bar that claims to replace your Fruit Group. The other group is to argue the opposing view. Have the teams stage a debate in front of an impartial jury of their peers. L1

Checklists

Ask students to develop a checklist of key signs they should look for when they are trying to determine whether a claim is true or false. Have students use their checklist to evaluate several advertisements that you have provided them. L1

Extending Learning

Advertising Techniques—Other advertising techniques include:

- *Repetition.* The same message is repeated many times in different media. This helps imprint the advertiser's name and message in the consumer's mind. Think of one of your favorite foods that is advertised regularly. Do you remember the advertising message?
- *Urgency.* Most advertisements try to motivate consumers to take action right away. For instance, the ad might say, "Buy now," "Limited time offer" or "Limited supply."

- *Developing Consumer Skills (text pages 102-106)*

Class Discussion Activity

Have students name ways, other than advertising, in which companies promote products. Discuss the following about the techniques: Do they give you the needed facts to make informed choices? Do they appeal to your emotions?

Evaluating Advertising

Have students collect advertisements for nutrition-related products. Ask students to evaluate the advertising techniques used to encourage a purchase. What facts are given? What needs or wants does the ad appeal to? What information is given about the people promoting the product? L2

Nutrition Claim Activity

Provide each student with a copy of an advertisement that makes confusing nutrition claims. Ask students how they would decide whether to believe the claims. Have students identify questionable claims. Repeat with a nutrition research article.

Finding Online Resources

Encourage students to find organizations on the Internet that fight against health fraud. Suggest that they conduct searches using key words such as "fraud" and "fraud and health claims." You may wish to supervise searches. Conclude by having researchers share their findings. L1

What the Terms Mean

Some words and phrases that turn up in reports of scientific studies are often misunderstood. Here are a few of them and what they really mean.

Term	Meaning
• Associated with	• Implies a connection between two things that can't be explained by mere coincidence; does not indicate that a cause-and-effect relationship has been established.
• Double the risk	• If the original risk is 1 in 1 million, double the risk translates to 1 in 500,000.
• Probability	• Refers to the likelihood of an event's taking place; is not the same thing as a certainty.
• Significant	• Also appearing sometimes as "statistically significant"; implies a probability of 95 percent or better.
• Survival	• Indicates the percentage of people with a specific disease or condition who are still alive after a given period; does not mean the same thing as a cure.

- **Positive images.** An ad may use images of things that people feel positively about, such as friendship or a good appearance. The advertiser's hope is that the consumer will associate these images and feelings with the product.
- **Celebrity endorsement.** Some ads show popular performers or athletes promoting the product. They don't tell you whether the person actually uses the product in real life.
- **Appeal to basic needs.** Advertisers may focus on ways the product meets a need for security or self-esteem. They try to convince you that the product will make you look or feel better.
- **Scare tactics.** Advertisers may play on people's fears of aging or developing a medical condition by claiming that their product can prevent or relieve the symptoms or provide essential nutrients.
- **False claims.** Ads may make claims that are not true, such as fast or guaranteed results. Remember, if a claim sounds too good to be true, it usually is.
- **Infomercials.** Infomercials are TV ads made to look like regular consumer programs or televised news reports. Unless you look carefully, you may believe you're watching something you are not!

Besides advertising, companies use other techniques to promote their products. A soft drink company may lend its name to a sports event or arrange to have its product shown in a movie. Coupons and eye-catching store displays encourage consumers to buy. Even product packages are a form of advertising.

Remember that the purpose of advertising is to get people to buy a product. Your goal is to get good nutrition at a fair price. Be sure your buying decisions are based on your own priorities, not the advertiser's.

FOOD SCIENCE

Reliability of Information

It's important to know how to read claims about new findings scientifically by considering the following questions:

- Who did the study and where? Who paid for it?
- Who were the subjects of the study? How many subjects were used?
- How was the study designed and carried out?
- Who is reporting on the study? What are his or her qualifications?
- Have other studies been done on the subject? How many? What did they show?

Food Myths

When Margaret has a cold, her mother gives her a mixture of hot tea and fruit juice flavored with cloves. Margaret's mother learned this remedy from her own mother. In reality, this mixture has no medicinal value. Its use as a cold remedy is nothing more than a food myth.

Where do food myths originate? Some, like Margaret's grandmother's "cure" for the common cold, are handed down through generations of the same family. Others are spread by word of mouth. When a food or nutrition myth becomes so widespread as to be embraced by a fairly large group, it becomes a fad. One weight-loss fad that was popular some years ago was the grapefruit diet. It was grounded in the myth that eating grapefruit at every meal could help a person shed pounds.

◆ **No product can guarantee good health or weight loss. Make your choices based on facts, not false promises. Which aspects of skills for food choices come into play when evaluating product labels?**

Connecting Food and Social Studies

Teen Consumerism

The purpose of advertising is to sell, and today's teens are a target market. Think about the kinds of promotions that have inspired you to try a new product. A recent marketing and lifestyle study revealed the following buying habits in response to various promotions:

	AGE		
Promotion	**12-15**	**16-17**	**18-19**
Free sample	48%	47%	38%
Coupon	35%	40%	42%
Contest/sweepstakes	26%	21%	19%
Free gift with purchase	25%	21%	20%
Cash rebate	11%	10%	11%
Frequent-buyer clubs	6%	8%	9%

Think About It

1. Which promotional technique appeals to the greatest percentage of teens? Which appeals to the fewest teens? How do your buying tendencies compare with those of other people in your age group?
2. Which technique would most inspire you to try a new food product? Explain your reasoning.

Reinforcing Key Skills

Present the following problems to student groups. Allow time for them to discuss and compare their responses.

Critical Thinking—Have students share current examples of widely-held nutrition beliefs. Do they think they are facts or myths? Why?

Communication—A friend's mother announced that she was following the new soup diet. She then started serving soup with every meal to help the entire family lose weight.

- *Developing Consumer Skills (text pages 102-106)*

USING CONNECTING FOOD AND SOCIAL STUDIES

Provide teen magazines to groups of students. Have them identify the promotional techniques used in each of the advertisements. Then, have them state whether they were interested in purchasing each product based on the promotion. Compare student responses to the percentages on this page.

Develop Advertisements

Provide a bunch of grapes, or other fruit, to each of four groups of students. Have each group develop a 60-second commercial promoting the health benefits of grapes. If possible, videotape the commercials. Evaluate the commercials. L1

Guest Speaker

Invite a registered dietitian or nutritionist to describe how health and nutrition research is conducted and reported. Ask the speaker to identify potential problems in conducting and reporting the results that create a need for caution when reading reports of research. If possible, have the speaker share a printed report of flawed nutrition research compare to a report of solid nutrition research. Have students summarize what they learned in a short report.

ASSESS

REVIEW

- Ask students to summarize the main ideas in this section.
- Have students complete the Section Review. (Answers appear below.)

EVALUATION

- Have students prepare a skit for an elementary school group demonstrating facts and fallacies about nutrition and how to tell the difference.
- Have students take the quiz for Section 3-3. (Use the quiz in the *Teacher Resource Guide,* or construct your own with the **Exam***View*® *Test Generator* on the *Effective Instruction CD-ROM.*)

RETEACHING

- Provide students with several short advertisements, some that are misleading and some that are not. Have students practice telling the difference.
- Refer to the *Reteaching Activities* booklet for the Section 3-3 activity sheet.

CLOSE

Hold a class debate on the virtues and drawbacks of advertising techniques. How far should advertisers be able to go legally? Have students research food myths that have existed in the United States and other countries in the past. Ask students to report their findings to the class.

As with news reports and advertisements, consumer skills can help you avoid becoming the victim of food myths or fads. When you are confronted with a food or nutrition "fact":

- Keep a healthy skepticism. Ask the individual who shares the information what his or her source is. Then investigate the source yourself.
- Seek a qualified opinion. Consult a registered dietitian, other qualified nutrition expert, or a health care professional.

Q ***What sources can I contact if I am suspicious about any nutrition information I have received or if I just want more facts?***

A You might contact any of the following: a local nutritionist or dietitian; your local health department; your food science teacher; a professional organization, such as the American Dietetics Association; or the nutrition department at a nearby university or college.

Remember, your health is your responsibility. Separating nutrition fact from fiction is an important part of exercising that responsibility.

◆ **The spreading of health myths and quackery began long ago. Name some products today that make great health claims.**

Section 3-3 Review & Activities

1. Why doesn't any one scientific study provide enough evidence from which to draw a conclusion?
2. Name two techniques advertisers use to sell food products.
3. Where do food myths originate?
4. **Analyzing.** Why do you think some people continue to believe false claims and myths when there is no evidence to support them?
5. **Extending.** "Scientists Say Miracle Vitamin Stops Aging." You have a friend who wants to start taking large doses of that vitamin. What advice would you give your friend?
6. **Applying.** Look for ads that you think are false or misleading, and bring them to class. Identify the misleading statements or techniques used in each.

Answers to Section 3-3 Review & Activities

1. Results must be verified by other researchers.
2. Any two: limited information, positive images, celebrity endorsement, appeal to basic needs, scare tactics, false claims, infomercials.
3. They are handed down through generations of the same family or spread by word of mouth.
4. Answers will vary, but students should realize that some people are always looking for an easier or faster way to good nutrition.
5. Answers will vary, but students should mention pointing out the unreliability of the source.
6. Ads will vary.

Career Wanted

Dietetic Technician

Education and Training
- Associate's degree in dietetic technology
- Completion of approved dietetic technician program

Qualities
- Communication skills
- Analytical skills
- Enjoy working with people
- Problem-solving skills

"You really are what you eat."

Jan Bradshaw

Q. How did you choose a career in dietetics, Jan?

A. Like a lot of teens, I was self-conscious about my looks. My teacher stressed that good looks are healthy looks, and good health comes from good nutrition. It was such a boost to know that I didn't have to starve myself to feel positive about myself. That lesson left an impact.

Q. How does a dietetic technician compare to a dietitian?

A. A dietetic technician is supervised by a dietitian. I work with a clinical dietitian in the hospital outpatient unit. I counsel her patients on how to eat right for their particular health condition—heart disease or diabetes, for example. We discuss each case, and I get her recommendations.

Q. Where do you see your career in five years?

A. With people living longer and looking to diet to improve quality of life, this field is growing. I think I'd like to be certified as an RD, a registered dietitian. For that I'd need to get my bachelor's degree, plus added coursework, and do a supervised internship. I enjoy teaching about nutrition, and as an RD, I could teach in colleges and medical centers.

Related Career Opportunities

Entry Level
- Dietary assistant
- Hospital kitchen worker

Technical Level
- Buyer for school lunch program
- Weight-management clinic nurse
- Hospice cook

Professional Level
- Professor of dietetics
- Sports nutritionist
- Food company consultant

Making Career Connections

JOB SHADOWING. Arrange to job shadow a dietetic technician or someone in a similar position for part of the day. How does he or she help develop individual eating plans? What tools and techniques that you've studied in Chapter 3 are used to explain nutrition concepts? Report your findings to the class.

Career Wanted

Dietetic Technician

Thinking About the Career

Have students think of other questions they would like to ask Jan Bradshaw about being a dietetic technician. (Examples: For what kinds of tasks do you use a computer? Do you need to take a national exam to become registered as a dietetic technician? Do you need continuing education to maintain your credentials?)

Ask students to list possible opportunities for dietetic technicians besides the clinical setting. (Examples: Teaching community healthy cooking classes, leading supermarket tours, or writing nutrition articles for a Web site.)

Career-Building Opportunities

Provide students with sample, detailed job descriptions for a dietitian and a dietetic technician. Have students compare the differences and determine what additional skills and educational requirements are needed for a dietetic technician to become a dietitian.

For More Information

For additional information about careers in dietetics or related fields, encourage students to contact:

- American Dietetic Association
  216 W. Jackson Blvd.
  Chicago, IL 60606-6995
  www.eatright.org
- Nutrition, Health, and Food Management Division
  American Association of Family and Consumer Sciences
  1555 King Street
  Alexandria, VA 22314
  www.aafcs.org

REVIEW

- Have students complete the Chapter Review. (Answers appear below.)

EVALUATION

- Divide the class into three groups. Assign each group one section of Chapter 3. Ask each group to write questions about its section. Then have groups take turns asking their questions to the other two groups.
- Have students take the test for Chapter 3. (Use the chapter test in the *Teacher Resource Guide,* or construct your own with the **Exam***View*® *Test Generator* on the *Effective Instruction CD-ROM.*)

ANSWERS

Checking Your Knowledge

1. Total fat: 30 percent; saturated fat: 10 percent.
2. They provide starches and fiber, proteins, vitamins, and minerals, yet many of them are low in fat.
3. Foods at the bottom of the Pyramid are those that have a higher number of recommended servings; number of recommended servings decreases toward the top of the Pyramid.
4. The actual number of servings required for individuals differs according to age, gender, body size, and activity level.
5. All food groups provide vitamins and minerals in varying amounts. Main nutrients include: Bread (carbohydrates, fiber, B-vitamins), Vegetable (carbohydrates, fiber, beta carotene, vitamin C, folate), Fruit (carbohydrates, fiber, beta carotene, vitamin C, potassium), Milk (protein, carbohydrates, calcium), Meat (protein, iron).

Chapter 3 Review & Activities

Summary

Section 3-1: Dietary Guidelines

- The Dietary Guidelines for Americans provide the following recommendations: Eat a variety of foods; maintain or improve your weight; choose an eating plan with plenty of grain products, vegetables and fruits; choose an eating plan low in fat, saturated fat, and cholesterol and moderate in sugars, salt, and sodium.

Section 3-2: The Food Guide Pyramid

- The Food Guide Pyramid, a tool to help you plan daily food choices, shows the approximate number of servings needed each day from each of the five food groups.
- The foods in the Food Guide Pyramid are grouped according to the nutrients they provide.
- Choosing nutrient-dense foods from the food groups will help you get the nutrients you need without excess calories.

Section 3-3: Separating Fact from Fiction

- Food-related skills, including critical thinking and communication, can help you identify information that may be misleading.
- It is important to stay informed about nutrition research, but use food-related skills to evaluate research findings.
- Advertisers use a variety of techniques to persuade you to buy their products.
- Be wary of food myths and fads, and know where to get accurate information about nutrition.

Checking Your Knowledge

1. What are the recommended limits for fat and saturated fat in an eating plan?
2. What are the benefits of choosing an eating plan with plenty of grain products, vegetables, and fruits?
3. Explain how the position of food groups in the Food Guide Pyramid diagram relates to the recommended number of servings of each.
4. Why does the Food Guide Pyramid give the recommended number of servings for each food group as a range instead of an exact number?
5. Briefly describe the main nutrients provided by each food group.
6. What problems are associated with excess sodium? Give three hints for cutting down on salt and sodium.
7. Why is it important to watch for follow-up reports on research findings?
8. Name three techniques used by advertisers to persuade you to buy their products.
9. What makes an infomercial misleading?
10. How can you tell whether the author of a book on nutrition is a reliable source of information on the subject?

Thinking Critically

1. **Identifying Evidence.** A friend tells you that honey and molasses are better for you than white or brown sugar. How can you decide whether this is true?
2. **Recognizing Bias.** Suppose that you are reading a magazine or newspaper and happen upon a study on the effectiveness of vitamin C against colds. After reading the article, you discover that the study was financed by a company that makes vitamin C tablets. Why does this suggest a possible bias?

Working IN THE Lab

1. ***Taste Test.*** Heat three samples of a canned vegetable, such as green beans—one canned with salt and two canned without salt. Season one of the no-salt samples with a salt alternative, such as herbs or lemon juice. Compare the taste of the vegetables. Which do you prefer? Why?
2. ***Foods Lab.*** Compare the amount of fat in different types of ground beef. Weigh out ¼ pound (125 g) of regular ground beef and the same amount of ground round. Form each portion into a patty. Cook each patty in a separate skillet over medium-low heat until done (about five minutes on each side). After cooking, weigh each patty again. Pour the grease from each pan into a separate measuring cup. Which patty contained more fat? How might you use this information?

Reinforcing Key Skills

1. **Leadership.** As participants in a schoolwide health fair, your class is planning a presentation on the *Dietary Guidelines for Americans.* List the steps the planning group can take to heighten people's awareness of the guidelines and the Food Guide Pyramid.
2. **Management.** Eryka is writing a review of a recent nutrition study and has asked for your help in organizing her report. What questions would you suggest that Eryka ask herself about the study in order to evaluate it properly?

Making Decisions and Solving Problems

Your sister has learned that carrots are very nutritious. Therefore, she has stopped eating most other vegetables and eats large amounts of carrots at almost every meal. What would you tell your sister?

Making Connections

1. **Language Arts.** Find a newspaper or magazine article about a nutrition-related study. Identify the following information in the article: What was the purpose of the study? Who did the study and where? Who paid for it? What type of people or animals did the researchers study? How was the study carried out?
2. **Math.** Conduct a survey of classmates' eating habits by asking them to write down the number of servings of vegetables eaten the previous day. Calculate the class average. How does this average compare with the servings suggested in the Food Guide Pyramid?

ANSWERS cont.

6. High blood pressure. Any three: add little or no salt to food when cooking and at the table; choose salted snacks only occasionally; go easy on processed foods; check labels for the amount of sodium in foods and choose those that are lower in sodium.
7. Different scientists may view the results differently, and it may take time for nutrition experts to study the research methods and findings.
8. Any three: limited information, positive images, celebrity endorsement, appeal to basic needs, scare tactics, false claims, infomercials.
9. People reading or viewing an infomercial may think they are seeing an informative news report, not a commercial.
10. By finding out more about the author and his or her qualifications; by contacting one or more of the authorities listed in Section 3-2.

Thinking Critically

1. Students should list sources they could refer to, such as those listed on page 106.
2. Students should realize that the company wants the study to show that vitamin C is effective against colds.

Reinforcing Key Skills

1. Steps will vary.
2. Ask these questions: Who did the study and where? Who paid for it? Who were the subjects of the study? How many subjects were used? How was the study designed and carried out? Who is reporting on the study? What are his or her qualifications? Have other studies been done on the subject? How many? What did they show?

CHAPTER 4 Planning Daily Food Choices

Advance Planning Guide ☑

- Locate or create a case study of a person who displays poor eating habits.
- Obtain restaurant menus.
- Obtain nutritional data from a local fast-food restaurant or on the Internet.
- Plan a trip to a local restaurant with a salad bar.
- Invite a local restaurant manager to speak to the class.
- Purchase the makings of a mini-salad or taco bar for a class demonstration.
- Purchase rice milk, soy milk, and cow's milk for a class tasting.
- Make sure the classroom library has an ample supply of cookbooks with options that could be used by vegetarians.
- Purchase ingredients for basic vegetarian recipes.
- Purchase ready-made pizza crusts and a variety of toppings suitable for vegetarians.
- Bring to class photographs of various foods.
- Purchase sheets of poster board.

CHAPTER 4

Planning Daily Food Choices

When it comes to eating, different families and individuals follow different patterns. In this chapter, you will learn about some of these patterns as well as reasons for the differences.

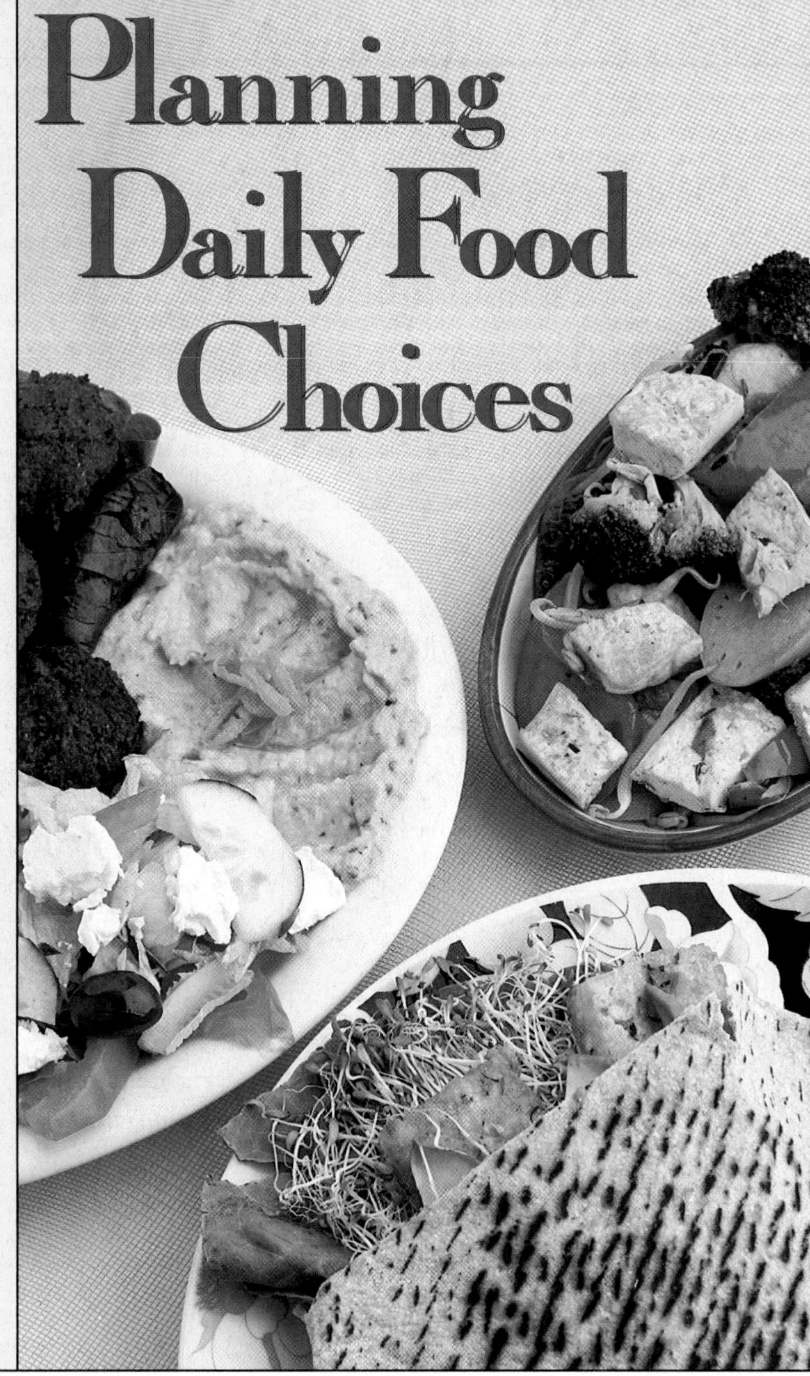

MEETING DIVERSE NEEDS

Naturalistic Learners. If there are students in the class with a green thumb, invite them to plan (and potentially plant) an edible garden. Suggest that the garden will be the sole source of snack food for a family of four this summer. Have the students share their plan with the class, identifying the seeds or seedlings selected and explaining why they were chosen (e.g. because of region of country or to provide variety of tastes, colors, textures, and nutrients).

SECTION 4-1

Daily Meals and Snacks

Objectives

After studying this section, you should be able to:

- Identify different eating patterns.
- Discuss how nutritional needs can be met through meals and snacks.

Look for These Terms

eating patterns

grazing

As an exchange student from Italy, Frederica was surprised by some of the "strange" eating customs she encountered on her visit to the United States. For instance, the family she was staying with had their big meal in the evening, instead of at noon, as she was used to doing at home.

Eating Patterns

Have you ever visited or studied the homeland of another culture? If so, you, like Frederica, may have been struck by differences in that culture's eating patterns. **Eating patterns** are food customs and habits, including when, what, and how much people eat. People have different schedules, so people often have different eating patterns. Some people eat the traditional three meals a day, while others prefer to eat five or six "mini-meals." Still others may follow different eating patterns from one day to the next.

Any eating pattern is acceptable as long as the food choices in it reflect sound nutritional practices. It is also important to eat regularly. If you try to go too long without food, your body won't have the fuel it needs. Studies show that people who skip meals make up for it by overeating later. Usually, meal skippers eat more in a day than they would if they chose to eat at regular intervals.

Traditional Meals

Despite the differences noted above, traditional eating patterns in many cultures—including Frederica's—revolve around three main meals. These are breakfast, the midday meal, and the evening meal.

SECTION 4-1

Daily Meals and Snacks

FOCUS

MOTIVATORS

- Ask students to list the times they usually eat during the day and the term they use to describe each meal or snack. How many students follow a traditional meal pattern of breakfast, midday meal, and evening meal? How many students usually eat their largest meal in the evening?
- If any students have ever lived in another country or have relatives who have done so, ask them to describe the meal patterns of that country. How similar are the meal patterns of the country described to meal patterns in the United States?

VOCABULARY ACTIVITY

Discuss with students the difference between formal and informal definitions. Ask a volunteer to investigate the formal and informal definition for *grazing* and identify which is used in this section.

STUDY SKILLS

- **Listening.** Ask for volunteers to prepare an oral reading of each page of text from the section, while others follow along silently.
- Have students read the section and complete the appropriate part of the Chapter 4 Study Guide in the *Student Workbook.*

Section 4-1 Resources

◆ **Student Workbook,** pp. 33, 35
◆ **Teacher Resource Guide**
Lesson Plan 4-1 Organizer
Section 4-1 Quiz
◆ **Effective Instruction CD-ROM**
Exam*View®* *Test Generator*
PowerPoint® Slide #11
◆ **Transparency Package,** CT-11
◆ **Student Motivation Kit**
Reteaching Activities, p. 24
Enrichment Activities
Food Science Resources, pp. 43–45
Skills for Making Food Choices, pp. 13–14

TEACH

- *Eating Patterns*
- *Traditional Meals (text pages 111-114)*

Discussion Activity

Ask students to describe factors that have an effect on the eating pattern a person develops. Ask students to list and describe traditional meals.

Research Activity

Ask students to research the importance of breakfast and write a formal report of the findings. How does it relate to school performance? To overall health? Discuss healthful breakfast choices. Discuss the reasons why some people tend to skip breakfast. How can this problem be overcome?

VISUAL LEARNING ***Using the Photograph***

Ask students to extend the information in the lower photograph on this page by developing a one-week breakfast planner, using foods and beverages (other than just those in the photograph) only one time each. Students might share their information in the form of a calendar on a poster board that indicates, under each day of the week, the name of each food and beverage and the food groups they represent.

◆ **Your daily schedule is one of the factors that influence your eating pattern. Name some others.**

Breakfast

Breakfast is the most important meal of the day. Why? When you first awaken after seven or eight hours of sleep, your body's fuel gauge reads "empty." Breakfast gives you energy to get your motor running. A good breakfast also helps you feel alert during the morning hours. If you skip breakfast, it's harder to concentrate on your schoolwork. Recent research reveals that students who eat breakfast get to school on time and do better scholastically than those who don't eat breakfast.

Not all breakfasts are equal, however. A breakfast consisting of a complex carbohydrate, protein, and fruit—for example, whole-grain cereal or a muffin, milk, and a banana—gives you more lasting energy than a doughnut and a soft drink. You may feel fine after eating the doughnut and soft

Connecting Food and Social Studies

Family Eating Patterns

In colonial America, extended families often lived and ate together. Food was raised on family farms and took long hours to prepare. Although many foods were available, little was known about nutrition, so health problems linked to foods were common.

The events that have shaped America since those early days have all continued to influence how, what, and when families eat. Industrialization made more foods readily available and took people away from farms and into cities, where they experienced new ways of living—and eating. Immigrants shared a wide range of different food tastes. Families of the 1930s struggled through the Depression, when 9 cents for a loaf of bread was costly. During the 1940s and 1950s, most mothers were not employed outside the home, making family meals their sole responsibility.

In more recent decades, the employment of women has increased, and technology has had a huge effect on food variety and availability. Busy schedules, restaurants, new nutrition data, and modern food processing methods have all had a strong influence on eating patterns. You may begin to wonder how these patterns will change in the future.

Think About It

1. Research and describe a specific time period in American history. Compare family eating patterns of that period to those of today.
2. Predict what you think family eating patterns will be like in the next twenty years. What will influence those patterns?

Extending Learning

Daily Meals—In the past, family members were expected to be prompt for meals, to eat together, and to eat whatever had been prepared. Mealtime gave family members a chance to communicate with each other. This helped maintain family stability. In today's society, the ritual of the family meal has often been replaced by a new ritual —quickly prepared, simple meals eaten when there's time. As a result, these families miss out on the important social benefits of meal sharing. Discuss some social benefits of meal sharing.

◆ **Eating breakfast makes a difference in how you feel all morning. Any of these nutritious choices can give your body fuel for a morning of activity. In your Wellness Journal, list other eye-opening morning meal possibilities you might like to try to add variety.**

drink, but you will probably experience a mid-morning letdown.

Some people skip breakfast because they are bored with standard breakfast fare. Any food, though, can be a breakfast food, as long as it provides some of the nutrients your body needs. Try having pizza, tacos, soup with crackers, or refried beans on toast for breakfast. Round out the menu with a serving of fruit and a glass of low-fat milk.

FOR YOUR HEALTH

Beating the Breakfast Blahs

Are you a breakfast skipper? If time is your problem, begin by getting up a few minutes earlier. Make a meal out of foods such as these:

- Low-fat flavored or plain yogurt, whole-grain muffin or bagel, and a banana.
- Peanut butter and jelly sandwich and low-fat milk.
- A breakfast drink made by blending low-fat milk or yogurt, juice, and fruit.

Following Up

1. Using the Food Guide Pyramid in Chapter 3 (page 97), plan a week of breakfasts. Each breakfast must include one or two servings from the grains group, one serving from the dairy group, and one serving from the fruit group.
2. Try the breakfasts. Rate each in terms of variety, originality, ease of preparation, and enjoyment. Keep a list in your Wellness Journal of breakfast ideas that you rate highly. Continually add new ones.

Midday and Evening Meals

Whether you call it lunch, brunch, or some other name, the midday meal gives you energy and nutrients to carry you through the rest of the day's activities. The evening meal is a good time to think about the food you've eaten for the day. It's your chance to fill in any food group servings that are lacking.

Dinner traditionally means the largest meal of the day. It may be eaten at midday or in the evening, depending on your personal preference and your schedule. In some cultures, including Federica's, people prefer to eat dinner at midday and a lighter meal, sometimes called supper, in the evening. The larger midday meal provides fuel for the day's activities. Some people find they sleep better if the evening meal is light.

The usual custom in American culture is to have a light meal, or lunch, at midday, saving the largest meal for the evening—a time when all or most family members can eat together. On weekends or special occasions, some individuals and families may follow a different pattern.

- *Traditional Meals (text pages 111-114)*

Group Project

Ask students to work in groups to plan nutritious and appealing lunch menus. Have students, as a class, select and later prepare the most nutritious and appealing lunch menu. L1

Research Activity

Have students research meal patterns in Spain, Greece, India, Japan, or China. Ask students to report their findings to the class by developing a typical one-day meal plan for the specific culture's meal pattern.

COMPUTER ACTIVITY
Nutrition Analysis

Invite students to plan a one-day traditional meal following a traditional pattern in America. Ask students to analyze the meal using a computer nutrition software program. How does the nutrition analysis compare to what we know about Americans' eating habits in general? How can the meal or meal pattern be changed to improve the healthfulness of the traditional American meal?

HOME & COMMUNITY CONNECTION

Ask students to interview the family member that cooks or provides most of the family's meals. With the family "cook," list the times served and specific meals that will be eaten for dinner for two days, such as tonight and tomorrow night. Ask students to list reason(s) why each time is chosen. Are there different patterns from one day to the next? Is this the largest meal of the day? Explain. Discuss answers in class, noting similarities and differences.

TEACH *cont.*

- *Snacks*
- *Grazing*
  (text pages 114-115)

Discussion Activity

Discuss the value of eating snacks between regular meals. Compare snacking to grazing. How do people's lifestyles contribute to the need to graze?

Packaged Food Analysis

Ask students to bring an empty package from a snack food item. Have them use the nutrition labels to determine the nutrients supplied by the foods. Have each student summarize the nutrition information and provide a suggestion to class on how the snack food item can be part of a healthy eating plan. **L3**

Public Service Announcement

Have students who are effective public speakers team with others who are effective researchers and writers to create a public service announcement on snacks that can be part of a student's healthful eating plan. The announcement should list snacking tips along with a list of snack suggestions, noting those that may be available at school. If it can be arranged with the administration, students should present their public service announcement over the school's public address, television, or computer system. **L2**

Dinner

No matter when it is eaten, a dinner usually focuses on a main dish, a grain product, vegetables, a beverage, and sometimes, dessert. With an increasing awareness of nutritional needs, more and more people are preparing main-dish meals that include smaller portions of meat, poultry, or fish, with the grain and vegetables mixed right in. Such a dinner might center on stir-fried chicken with broccoli and water chestnuts, served over rice. Accompanied by a tossed salad, low-fat milk, and a whole wheat roll, and followed by fruit for dessert, such a meal follows the *Dietary Guidelines for Americans.*

Snacks

If you enjoy between-meal snacks, here is good news: Snacking is not necessarily a bad habit. In fact, during the teen years, when your nutritional and caloric needs are at a high point as a result of rapid body growth, snacking can actually help you meet those needs.

Of course, what you choose to snack on can make all the difference. Many snack foods—such as candy, chips, granola, cookies, and other sweets—are high in fat, sugar, and calories.

For a nutritious snack, you can choose almost any nutrient-dense food. Try leftovers from the refrigerator, fresh fruits or vegetables, low-fat dairy products, or whole-grain breads and cereals.

Remember, too, to pay attention to the *timing* of your snacks. If you snack too close to mealtime, you may not be able to eat the nutritious foods included in the meal.

Grazing

Some people prefer eating five or more small meals throughout the day instead of three large ones. This eating pattern is sometimes called **grazing**. Some health experts view grazing as a healthful alternative to conventional meal patterns.

If grazing is your eating pattern, think about your food choices toward the end of the day. Are you lacking any servings from any of the food groups? If so, eat those foods so that you'll be sure to meet the daily recommendations. At the same time, check to be sure you are not eating too much. The day's total servings and calories should be the right amount for you, just as if you were eating three traditional meals.

◆ **Snacks can be part of a healthful eating plan when you select wisely. Using the table "Nutritive Value of Foods" in Appendix B at the back of this book, analyze two or three foods you regularly snack on. Which are low in fat and/or calories? Which are not?**

Technology TIE-IN Point out that the rise in the percentage of Americans who snack is partly related to the growth of technology. Prior to the television-age, less than half of Americans consumed at least one snack a day. Today 75 percent of men and women do, and the number is rising. Studies indicate that watching television tends to cause increased snacking—especially on high-calorie, high-fat snacks. Discuss reasons why television watching is related to increased snacking. How may computer use correlate to snacking?

As you have learned, eating patterns vary from person to person and day to day. In the end, *when* you eat is less important than *what* you eat. The eating pattern that helps you get the nutrients and calories you need is the one that's best for you. Identifying your eating pattern can help you plan for good nutrition.

Changing Eating Patterns

As families go through different stages of life their eating patterns change. The age of family members, their activities, and their health all influence eating decisions.

What do you think a typical eating pattern in a family with young children might be? While younger children are at home, families tend to eat meals together. Employed parents may include eating out in their routine. If family income is lower in these early years, eating out may be less frequent and more likely to include inexpensive family restaurants. Adults make most decisions about what children eat, aiming to promote health.

As families grow older, children become teens, who have opportunities to eat out on their own. Hungry teen appetities influence the amount of food purchased and prepared. Food costs increase, and busy schedules can mean that family members sometimes eat in shifts.

When children have grown and left the family home, eating patterns change again. Supermarket food costs may decrease. Some families at this stage, however, spend additional money eating out, a more affordable option with fewer people in the family.

As people age, eating patterns are still different. If aging family members are less active, they usually eat lighter meals, sometimes grazing. Health concerns may influence food choices.

Of course, all of these are just generalities. Circumstances create many variations in eating patterns for individuals and families. What different family eating patterns have you noticed?

Section 4-1 Review & Activities

1. Give three examples of different eating patterns.
2. Why is breakfast considered the most important meal of the day?
3. What kinds of snack foods can help you meet your nutrient needs?
4. Compare family eating patterns at different stages of life.
5. **Analyzing.** Think about this statement: "Snacking during the teen years has the potential to help as well as the potential to do harm." Write a short paragraph that explains your interpretation of the sentence.
6. **Comparing and Contrasting.** Divide a sheet of paper into two columns. In one column, list as many advantages of grazing as you can. In the second column, list as many disadvantages as you can.
7. **Applying.** In your Wellness Journal, make a list of 15 nutritious snack foods that require little preparation. Put a check mark by those you have already tried. Put a star by those you plan to try.

ASSESS

REVIEW

- Ask students to summarize the main ideas in this section.
- Have students complete the Section Review. (Answers appear below.)

EVALUATION

- Have students write a short essay about the topics discussed in this section.
- Have students take the quiz for Section 4-1. (Use the quiz in the *Teacher Resource Guide,* or construct your own with the **ExamView®** *Test Generator* on the *Effective Instruction CD-ROM.*)

RETEACHING

- Have students write down the types of foods included in the meals they eat most often at home, including the times meals are eaten. Ask them to identify food groups represented by the foods.
- Refer to the *Reteaching Activities* booklet for the Section 4-1 activity sheet.

CLOSE

Have students think of a favorite food product that can be purchased in a grocery store. Then have each student design a one-page advertisement for the food, including in the ad information on how to incorporate the food into a healthy eating plan. Display and discuss the advertisements.

Answers to Section 4-1 Review & Activities

1. Three meals a day; many minimeals; different eating patterns depending on daily schedules.
2. After many hours of sleep, your energy level is low. Breakfast provides energy for the day.
3. Nutrient-dense foods.
4. Answers will vary.
5. Paragraphs should include the following points: Snacking can help meet increased nutritional needs during the teen years. If, however, snack foods high in fat, sugar, and calories are chosen, snacking does more harm than good.
6. Answers will vary.
7. Answers will vary.

SECTION
4-2
Positive Food Habits

FOCUS

MOTIVATORS

- Ask students to make a list of their most and least healthy eating habits.
- Ask students to identify things they would need to know about their current eating habits before they can decide how to improve their least healthy eating habits.

VOCABULARY ACTIVITY

Pronounce the term listed under "Look for This Term." Have students find the term and its definition in the section.

STUDY SKILLS

- **Guided Reading.** Have students look at the headings within Section 4-2 to preview the concepts that will be discussed.
- Have students read the section and complete the appropriate part of the Chapter 4 Study Guide in the *Student Workbook*.

SECTION
4-2

Objectives

After studying this section, you should be able to:

- Analyze your current eating habits.
- Suggest practical ways to improve your eating habits.

Look for This Term

appetite

Positive Food Habits

If you are like most people, some of your eating habits are healthful, but others could stand improvement. The first step in improving your eating habits is to recognize the kinds of food choices you make now. Then you can keep your good habits and work on improving the poor ones.

Analyzing Your Current Habits

People sometimes aren't aware of how often and what they eat. Sometimes, they eat just to be sociable. Maybe you have found yourself making room for dessert at the end of a big meal. In such cases, you are eating not in response to hunger, but to appetite. **Appetite** is a desire, rather than a need, to eat.

Appetite is a learned, rather than an inborn, response. It is shaped by social influences, such as friends, as well as personal ones, such as emotions.

Keeping a Food Record

One way of becoming more aware of your habits is by keeping a food record. This is simply a list of all the foods you eat for a specific period of time—usually three consecutive days, including a weekend. A food record is not a test you have to pass. Rather, it is a way of letting you know the kind of food choices you are making now and how much you are eating.

INFOLINK
For more on social influences on your food choices, see Section 1-2.

Section 4-2 Resources

◆ **Student Workbook**, pp. 33, 36
◆ **Teacher Resource Guide**
Lesson Plan 4-2 Organizer
Section 4-2 Quiz
◆ **Effective Instruction CD-ROM**
Exam*View*® *Test Generator*
◆ **Student Motivation Kit**
Reteaching Activities, p. 25
Enrichment Activities

Whether you keep your food record in a diary, a personal journal, or just a page in your loose-leaf binder, it should include the following:

- The time you ate.
- The food eaten and the approximate amount.
- A brief description of the eating situation, including where you were, what you were doing, your mood, and any other information that could help you understand your food habits.

Reviewing Your Food Record

At the end of the allotted time, take a look at your food choices. For each day, count the number of servings you had from each group in the Food Guide Pyramid (page 97). Compare your totals with the recommended number of servings. Did you eat at least the minimum amount of servings? If not, which foods were you lacking? Were your food choices high or low in fats and added sugars?

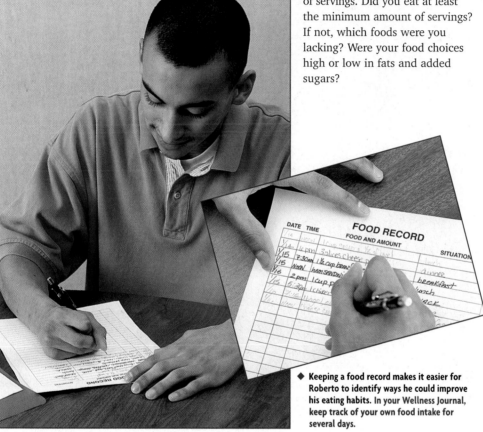

◆ **Keeping a food record makes it easier for Roberto to identify ways he could improve his eating habits. In your Wellness Journal, keep track of your own food intake for several days.**

- *Analyzing Your Current Habits (text pages 116-117)*

Food Journal

Have students keep a 3-day food record. Have them follow the text's guidelines. Have students analyze their current eating habits and count the number of Food Guide Pyramid servings represented. Which food groups were lacking? Were fats, oils, and sweets eaten too frequently? **L1**

TEACH

- *Improving Your Eating Habits (text pages 118-119)*

Nutrition Assessment Activity

Based on the food journal kept for the activity on page 117, have students write a nutrition assessment, providing recommendations to improve eating habits. Read three assessments anonymously to the class. Compare the assessments with "typical" teenagers' eating habits.

FOR YOUR HEALTH

Have students read the feature on page 119. Explain that food professionals use the Food Guide Pyramid servings as guidelines, based on averages. Amplify on this by showing students with 3 fruits: 1 large, 1 medium, 1 small. Note how it provides 3 servings. Emphasize the importance of knowing serving sizes for determining average daily servings.

Ask: Why is it important to repeat experiments?

Improving Your Eating Habits

Once you have identified any poor eating habits, think about why they occur. Did you tend to make poor food choices in certain situations, such as while watching TV or when you were unhappy? Were you responding to appetite rather than hunger?

Next, think about how you can correct any problems you isolated. Don't just tell yourself, "I'll eat better from now on." That promise is hard to keep because it isn't specific. Instead, decide on specific changes you can make.

Remember, eating is an enjoyable part of life. Don't take the pleasure out of it. You can make changes in your food habits and have fun doing it.

◆ **In settings like this one, it is possible to choose foods that are both satisfying and provide needed nutrients. Visit the food court of a mall near you, and make a list of the meal and snack possibilities that help you satisfy your nutrient needs.**

FOOD SCIENCE: Modifying Eating Habits

Have students use scientific journals and other references to research ways to change habits successfully. Have students report their findings to the class. Relate the suggestions to changing eating habits. As a class, develop guidelines for positive change.

Have students design an experiment to test the guidelines they have developed. Remind students that they must have both a control group and an experimental group. Have interested students try the experiment. Ask them to report the results to the class.

FOR YOUR HEALTH

What's a Healthful Portion?

When it comes to eating, a problem for many people is not just *what* they eat. Rather, it's *how much* they eat. Learning to identify healthful portions can be a first step in controlling the tendency to overeat.

To see how much you know about accurate healthful portions, try the following:

1. Consult the Food Guide Pyramid for suggested single servings of each of the following foods: apple, cooked rice, unsalted pretzels, cooked chopped meat (hamburger).
2. Spoon what you imagine to be a single serving of each of these foods onto separate paper plates. Measure out an accurate portion of each food onto a second set of plates. Record any differences between the two portions of each food.
3. After several days, repeat the entire experiment. Record your results.

Following Up

1. How close were you at estimating correct serving sizes? Did you become more skilled at judging correct amounts when you repeated the experiment?
2. Were the recommended serving sizes less or more of each food than you normally eat?
3. How can learning to estimate accurate healthful servings decrease your risk of having eating-related illnesses now and in the future?

Section 4-2 Review & Activities

1. What is appetite?
2. What is a food record? What is its purpose?
3. When keeping a food record, what information do you need to write down?
4. **Analyzing.** Keep a detailed food record of what you eat for three consecutive days, including a weekend. Note amounts eaten as well as information about the contents of multi-food dishes. Then use nutrition analysis software to analyze your diet during that time period. How does the number of servings you ate compare to recommendations in the Food Guide Pyramid? What does your analysis show about your nutrient intake? Was your eating for the three days typical of your eating pattern?
5. **Applying.** Use the food record and analysis you created in activity 4 to examine your current eating habits. Write a list of specific changes you intend to make, and put them into practice. Repeat your food analysis in a month. Which new eating behaviors have become habits? What changes need further effort? What new ideas for change do you have?
6. **Synthesizing.** How could you give encouragement to a friend who is working on new eating habits?

ASSESS

REVIEW

- Ask students to summarize the main ideas in this section.
- Have students complete the Section Review. (Answers appear below.)

EVALUATION

- Present a case study of a person who displays poor eating habits and ask students, acting as "student dietitians," to suggest specific improvements.
- Have students take the quiz for Section 4-2. (Use the quiz in the *Teacher Resource Guide,* or construct your own with the **ExamView**® *Test Generator* on the *Effective Instruction CD-ROM.*)

RETEACHING

- Place the title "Seven Good Eating Habits for Students" on a bulletin board. Have students decide on the habits. Decoratively write the habits on the bulletin board. Have students find and display pictures representing each habit.
- Refer to the *Reteaching Activities* booklet for the Section 4-2 activity sheet.

CLOSE

Lead a discussion on the importance of habits in our daily lives and how habits, in general, influence our eating habits. Have students brainstorm examples of habits that influence eating. Discuss how people who are overweight need to change food-related habits, not just foods.

Answers to Section 4-2 Review & Activities

1. A desire, rather than a need, to eat.
2. A list of all the foods you eat for a specific period of time—usually three consecutive days, including a weekend; it is a way of letting you know the kind of food choices you are making now and how much you are eating.
3. The time you ate; the food eaten and the approximate amount; a brief description of the eating situation.
4. Answers will vary.
5. Answers will vary.
6. Possible answer: You could explain how to maintain and review a food record.

SECTION
4-3
Eating Out

FOCUS

MOTIVATORS

- Ask students to identify foods they typically choose when they eat out. Which of these choices are high in fat? What nutritious choices are usually available?
- Distribute restaurant menus to the students. Have students select a meal they would probably order from the menu. Ask students to check their choices for foods that are high in fat. Discuss how eating out fits into overall daily food choices.

VOCABULARY ACTIVITY

Direct student's attention to the two terms under "Look for These Terms." Pronounce aloud the word *entrée*. Note the accent; discuss what this means in pronunciation of the word. Ask a volunteer to investigate and compare the various definitions of *entrée*.

STUDY SKILLS

- **Outlining.** Have students read the section and outline it by copying the headers on paper and leaving space after each one. Students are to write a sentence in their own words, summarizing the content under each header.
- Have students read the section and complete the appropriate part of the Chapter 4 Study Guide in the *Student Workbook*.

SECTION
4-3

Eating Out

"Let's eat out!" Each year Americans spend about 22 percent of their food dollar on restaurant meals, including meals eaten at fast-food chains. Another 22 percent is spent on take-out foods brought into the home.

Objectives

After studying this section, you should be able to:

- Give guidelines for making nutritious food choices when eating out or ordering ready-to-eat food.
- Explain how home meal replacements fit into overall food choices.

Look for These Terms

home meal replacement

entrée

Restaurants

There are three main types of restaurants. Each has its pros and cons with regard to food choices and nutrition.

- **Full-service restaurants.** These are restaurants that offer table service, meaning you sit at a table and a server takes your order. Nutrition varies, depending on the menu. Some restaurants offer a wide variety of choices. Others specialize in certain types of food, such as fish, steaks, or ethnic food.
- **Self-serve restaurants.** Examples are cafeterias and restaurants with buffets or food bars. Some self-serve restaurants, particularly those that advertise "all you can eat," allow you to return for second and third helpings. Such offers—which appeal to the appetite, not to hunger—are an invitation to overeat.
- **Fast-food restaurants.** These restaurants usually offer a limited range of foods, many of which are high in fat, sugar, and sodium. Some fast-food chains have added more healthful choices to their menus in recent years. You can now find broiled and roasted foods, salads, low-fat milk, and fruit juice.

Many factors enter into your choice of restaurant, such as the price of a meal and how quickly you want to be served. Nutrition should also be a consideration. Try to select a restaurant that you know offers healthful choices.

Section 4-3 Resources

◆ **Student Workbook,** pp. 34, 38
◆ **Teacher Resource Guide**
Lesson Plan 4-3 Organizer
Section 4-3 Quiz
◆ **Effective Instruction CD-ROM**
Exam*View*® *Test Generator*
PowerPoint® Slide #12
◆ **Transparency Package,** CT-12
◆ **Student Motivation Kit**
Reteaching Activities, p. 26
Enrichment Activities

◆ At full-service restaurants, you usually have many food options. How can you use this fact to your advantage to make healthful choices?

Meals to Go

As the pace of daily living speeds up, many people today are choosing to buy ready-to-eat meals to take home. These foods, which you may know better as take-out or carry-out meals, are known in the food service industry as **home meal replacements**.

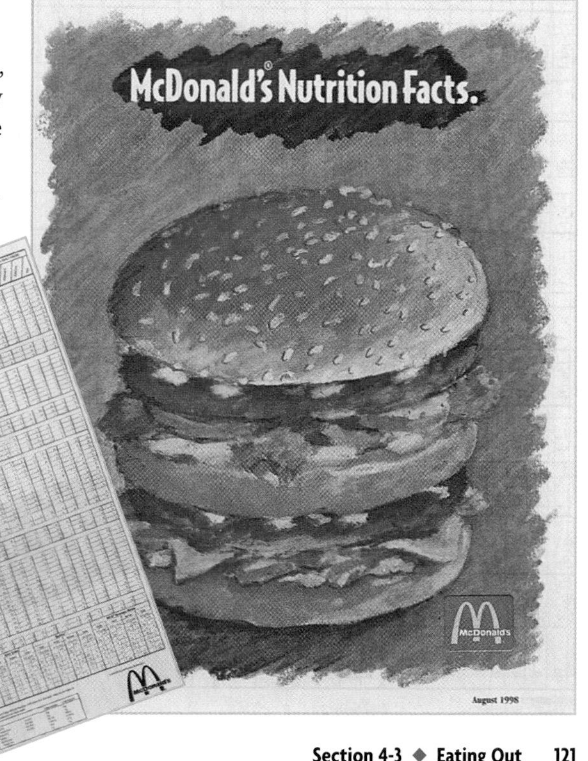

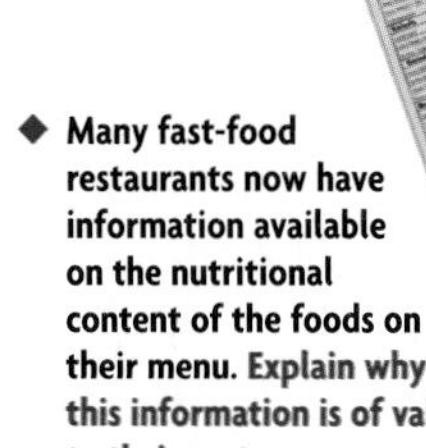

◆ Many fast-food restaurants now have information available on the nutritional content of the foods on their menu. Explain why this information is of value to their customers.

TEACH

- *Restaurants*
- *Meals to Go (text pages 120-122)*

Compare-and-Contrast Activity

Ask students to list three major types of restaurants and describe the advantages and disadvantages of each (from a nutritional point of view). Discuss factors that enter into the choice of a (1) restaurant and (2) home meal replacements from each of the three types of restaurants.

Making a Bar Graph

Provide students with full-size copies of nutritional data sheets like the one shown on this page. Have them isolate the makings of three high-calorie meals and three relatively low-calorie meals obtainable. Have students make bar graphs showing the fat and sodium content of the various meals. Invite students to display their graphs as a basis for further discussion. L3

Group Project Development

Ask students to pretend they are fast food restaurant chain owners. Have students work in groups to decide on a restaurant name, a nutritionally-balanced menu, and a promotional campaign. Each group should present its ideas to the class for feedback.  L1

FOOD SCIENCE

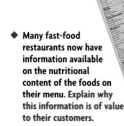

Menu Development Fast food restaurants have been around since the 1950s. The main goal was to provide quick food. Today, healthful food that tastes good is also a priority.

Many of the larger fast food restaurant chains employ nutrition experts and food scientists to help develop good-tasting foods that are nutritious and can be served quickly. Ask the manager of a local fast food restaurant how you can find out about the role food science plays in that restaurant chain's menu. Students may be directed to corporate headquarters. Share this information with the class.

- *Making Healthful Food Choices (text pages 122-125)*

Food Selection Activity

Distribute restaurant menus to students. Have them practice selecting nutritionally-dense foods. On the board, have students write all the words that indicate less healthful choices in their menus. Then, write words that indicate healthful choices.

Comparison Activity

Have students compare full meal and a la carte choices on restaurant menus. Ask students which is the most and least expensive and decide which option seems to make eating healthy easier.

Field Trip

Arrange a trip with students to a local restaurant with a salad bar. Ask students to make a list of the foods on the salad bar and analyze calorie and fat content of its choices. Have students plan a nutritious salad using salad bar foods available. Discuss how to include high-fat salad bar choices in a nutritious salad.

Skits

Ask students to identify what they could do if they are at a restaurant in which menu portions are too large. Have students work in pairs to write and present skits demonstrating acceptable ways to handle these situations. L1

Safety Check

According to the National Highway Traffic Safety Administration (NHTSA), nearly 6 percent of all fatal traffic accidents are caused by drivers handling food or beverages while at the wheel. Eating while driving is a major distraction. If you reach for a soft drink or hold food with one hand while you drive, you're asking for an accident to happen. Play it safe. Make your car a "no-food zone."

Home meal replacements may come from delicatessens, fast-food chains, or establishments that specialize in one kind of food, such as pizza. Another popular option is the meal centers found in some supermarkets. Resembling restaurant salad bars and buffets, these centers feature a wide variety of take-out foods, ranging from complete meals to sandwiches. Many meal centers offer fresh cut-up salad ingredients, soups, beverages, and desserts.

Today, many full-service restaurants have take-out menus. Still another recent innovation in some locales is the "meal taxi." Consisting of a fleet of cars operated by an independent food delivery service, the meal taxis will pick up food from any one of a number of participating restaurants and deliver it to your home.

Making Healthful Food Choices

The food choices you make when you eat out or bring food in are important ones. Whether you are dining at a fancy restaurant or having a pizza delivered, you need to count the food as part of your overall eating plan. The following paragraphs explain how.

Eating Out Healthfully

"Am I stuffed," Paul groaned as he and his friends emerged from a restaurant. "I don't think I'll ever eat again!"

Have you ever made a remark like that after eating out? It hints at one of two potential pitfalls associated with eating in restaurants —portion size. The other pitfall is the menu choices you make.

Ordering from the Menu

The meal that made Paul feel so full consisted of fried potato skins followed by batter-dipped chicken with mashed potatoes and gravy. Several words from this description—"fried," "batter-dipped," and "gravy"—are clues that foods are high in fat. Other such terms are

- Breaded
- Creamy
- In a cheese sauce (or *au gratin*)
- Scalloped
- Rich
- Crispy
- Parmigiana
- Tempura

When ordering from a menu, look for items described as "broiled," "baked," or "steamed." These terms identify foods that are usually relatively low in fat. When in doubt about how a dish is prepared or what ingredients it contains, ask your server. You might also ask whether your food can be prepared differently from how it is described—for example, broiled instead of fried.

Reinforcing Key Skills

Present the following problems to student groups. Allow time for them to discuss and compare their responses.

Management—Ask students to think of or create good-tasting, nutritious toppings for a pizza, salad, and pasta. Have students share their ideas, explaining why they are nutritious toppings. If possible, allow students to try one of their ideas.

Communication—Imagine being the manager at a full-service restaurant. Several health-conscious customers complain that there aren't any healthful entrées on the menu.

Be wary, too, of toppings, such as sauces, mayonnaise, salad dressings, and sour cream. Request either that your food be served without the topping or that the topping be served on the side so that you can use as little as you want. Still another option is to ask for a substitute—for example, a low-fat salad dressing or lemon juice in place of an oily, high-fat dressing, or a simple tomato sauce instead of a cream sauce on pasta.

You can watch your sodium intake by asking the kitchen to eliminate salt and sodium-based seasonings. One such seasoning, monosodium glutamate (mah-no-SO-dee-uhm GLUE-tuh-mate), or MSG, is used as a flavor enhancer, especially in Chinese foods.

Keep in mind that variety is one of the keys to good nutrition. If your choices are limited—as they usually are in a fast-food restaurant—you may come up short on other food groups needed for good health, such as fruits and vegetables. If so, make an extra effort to include those foods in other meals during the day.

How Big Is a Serving?

These are "official" serving sizes from the Food Guide Pyramid.

Look and Learn:
What other strategies can you think of for controlling portion size?

A(n) . . .
is as big as a serving of . . .

1 oz.

⅓ cup

1 cup

3 oz.

¼ cup

• *Making Healthful Food Choices (text pages 122-125)*

Discussion Activity

Ask students why it is important to consider the calories and nutrients provided by the entire day's food intake. Why is this especially important with today's busy lifestyles? If food choices are limited when you eat out, how might you compensate during the rest of the day?

Group Project

Have students work in groups to make a list of convenience foods available from each of these sources: vending machines, convenience stores, mall shops, and drive-through windows. Ask students to identify the healthful food choices available from each source. Using the foods available, have each group plan a healthful menu to share with the rest of the class.

TEACH cont.

- *Making Healthful Food Choices (text pages 122-125)*

Demonstration

Set up a mini-salad or taco bar in the classroom. Select two student volunteers: one to demonstrate an "ideal" main-course portion, the other an American's typical portion. Select two other students to dissect the meals, measuring or weighing each item. Provide students with calorie and fat (and other nutrients, if desired) contents for a serving of food bar items. Have the class calculate total calorie and fat content of each meal. Discuss findings.

Discussion Activity

Ask students to list advantages and disadvantages of eating a home-packed lunch compared to eating school cafeteria food. The list should contain nutrition, safety, convenience, and cost information.

Guest Speaker

Invite a local restaurant manager to speak to your class about healthy (including food safety) practices at their restaurant. This speaker might bring menus, an appropriately portioned plate of a healthy entrée, and sample tastings. Have students be prepared to ask the speaker questions.

Controlling Portions

Have you ever been served so much food in a restaurant that you were unable to finish? Many restaurants offer very large servings—sometimes two to three times what the Food Guide Pyramid recommends.

When it comes to eating in restaurants, remember that "less is more." There are several ways of accomplishing this:

- Build your meal around several appetizers instead of one large main dish, or **entrée** (AHN-tray)—the term used for main dishes on many restaurant menus.
- If you do opt for an entrée, do not eat the entire serving. Let your hunger, not your appetite, be your guide. Most restaurants will pack leftover food so that you can take it home.
- Make the salad bar your main course. Many full-service restaurants have salad bars, often with soup choices and breads. Choosing from the salad bar is a good way not only of controlling the amount of food you eat but also of getting servings of vegetables and fruits in your meal.

Another practical and healthful solution to controlling portion size and limiting fats, salt, and sugar in your eating plan is to prepare more meals at home. Save eating out for special occasions. This gives you a chance to splurge occasionally on higher-fat and higher-calorie foods without feeling guilty. Just be sure the rest of the time to follow the guidelines in the Food Guide Pyramid.

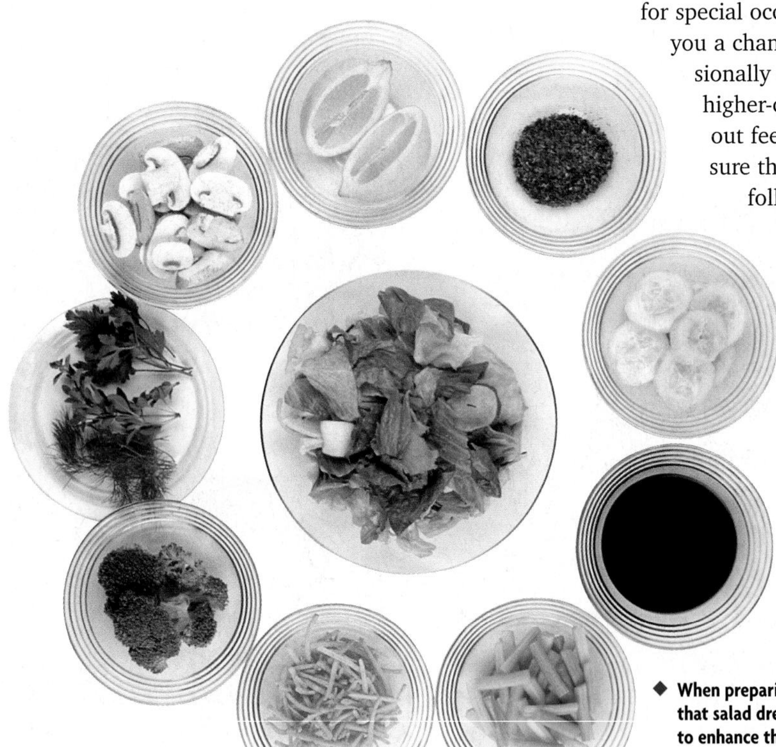

◆ **When preparing a salad, keep in mind that salad dressing isn't the only way to enhance the flavor.** Name some other low-fat, low-sodium possibilities for tossed salad.

Reinforcing Key Skills

Present the following problems to student groups. Allow time for them to discuss and compare their responses.

Management—Have students create a different meal for eating "on the go" for five school days. The meals must be nutritious and follow the Dietary Guidelines, but they must also be appealing and portable.

Communication—You order home-delivery of stir-fried chicken and vegetables for dinner from a local Chinese restaurant. The food is at room temperature when it arrives.

Food Safety

When you bring food home to eat or have it delivered, is it safe to eat? That question can be answered in one word: *temperature.* To avoid causing foodborne illness, hot food should be served hot and cold food should be cold. If food brought into the home is not going to be eaten right away, refrigerate it to prevent harmful bacteria from starting to grow. Heat it as necessary before serving. Many restaurants that deliver have special equipment that will keep hot food hot and cold food cold until it reaches your door.

Eating at School

Most schools have a cafeteria that serves lunch and sometimes breakfast as well. Usually, the cafeteria offers a complete meal that was planned with good nutrition in mind. Bringing food from home is also an option. You'll learn how to pack a nutritious lunch or snack in Chapter 20.

Q ***Can I eat healthfully from vending machines?***

A That depends on the machine, and on your choices. Some vending machines offer mostly sugary, high-sodium snack foods—not your best bet, nutritionally speaking. It may take added effort to find more healthful choices—dried fruit or cheese and crackers, for example, rather than candy bars and potato chips. Some machines offer more substantial foods, including soup and sandwiches. Learning which nutrients each ingredient supplies can help you choose wisely from these foods. Remember that a good diet needs a variety of nutritious foods. Turning to a vending machine occasionally shouldn't be a problem, but if you regularly choose it over a wholesome cafeteria lunch, you could be headed for health problems.

INFOLINK

For more on foodborne illness and keeping food safe to eat, see Section 7-3.

Section 4-3 Review & Activities

1. What does the term *home meal replacement* mean?
2. Give two suggestions for making healthful food choices from a restaurant menu.
3. Identify two ways of controlling portion size when you eat out.
4. **Analyzing.** Cal was delayed in traffic for nearly an hour on his way back from picking up food for the family's meal. Why should this be a concern?
5. **Applying.** Develop a lunch menu for a fast-food restaurant. Make sure the menu emphasizes foods low in fat, sugar, and sodium. Give names to these food items.

ASSESS

REVIEW

- Ask students to summarize the main ideas in this section.
- Have students complete the Section Review. (Answers appear below.)

EVALUATION

- Have students use a variety of actual menus, representing many different cuisines, to select nutritious meals.
- Have students take the quiz for Section 4-3. (Use the quiz in the *Teacher Resource Guide,* or construct your own with the **ExamView**® *Test Generator* on the *Effective Instruction CD-ROM.*)

RETEACHING

- Have students list their ten favorite restaurant dishes, preferably representing at least two of the three main types of restaurants. Help students determine how the dishes can be included in a healthful eating plan. Also help students determine whether minor preparation or portion size modifications can be made so the choices fit more easily into a healthy eating plan.
- Refer to the *Reteaching Activities* booklet for the Section 4-3 activity sheet.

CLOSE

Lead a class discussion on problems associated with eating out nutritiously and how those problems can be solved. As a class, develop a wallet-sized "tip card" that provides tips for eating out healthfully.

Answers to Section 4-3 Review & Activities

1. It is a ready-to-eat meal to take home.
2. Any two: Choose foods whose descriptions indicate they are lower in fat, ask for toppings to be served on the side, ask the kitchen to eliminate salt and sodium-based products.
3. Any two: Build your meal around several appetizers instead of one large main dish; do not eat the entire entrée; make the salad bar your main course.
4. The food may be at a temperature that promotes bacterial growth and, therefore, foodborne illness.
5. Answers will vary.

SECTION
4-4
The Vegetarian Lifestyle

FOCUS

MOTIVATORS

- Write *vegetarian* on the chalkboard. Discuss reasons why people follow vegetarian eating plans. Ask students to identify foods usually included in a vegetarian eating plan.
- Have students taste samples of rice milk, soy milk, and cow's milk. Ask students for their reactions. Discuss how milk from plants and other vegetarian foods help vegetarians meet specific nutrient needs. Compare Nutrition Facts panels for each of the three products. Identify other foods that help meet vegetarians' nutrient needs.

VOCABULARY ACTIVITY

Pronounce the terms listed under "Look for These Terms." Have students find the term *vegetarians* and its definition in the section. Then have three student volunteers investigate the combining form meanings of *lacto* and *ovo,* then *lacto-ovo,* and interpret the meanings as they relate to *vegetarians.*

STUDY SKILLS

- **Guided Reading.** Have students look at the headings within Section 4-4 to preview the concepts that will be discussed.
- Have students read the section and complete the appropriate part of the Chapter 4 Study Guide in the *Student Workbook.*

SECTION
4-4

Objectives

After studying this section, you should be able to:

- Identify foods eaten by different types of vegetarians.
- Discuss reasons why people choose to become vegetarians.
- Plan nutritious vegetarian meals.

Look for These Terms

vegetarians
vegans
lacto vegetarians
ovo vegetarians
lacto-ovo vegetarians

The Vegetarian Lifestyle

Inez and her friends were standing in the lunch line, trying to decide what to eat. After Jennie had made her choices, Inez looked at her tray and said, "What? No hamburger today?"

"No," said Jennie, "I'm thinking of becoming a vegetarian."

Vegetarianism

Vegetarians are people who do not eat meat, poultry, or fish. In addition, some vegetarians do not eat dairy foods or eggs.

A vegetarian eating plan can supply complete nutrition. However, as with any other way of eating, the food choices require some thought and planning. Before Jennie changes her way of eating, she would be wise to learn more about making vegetarian food choices.

Facts About Vegetarians

Some people are confused about what foods vegetarians eat. In fact, there are several kinds of vegetarians, depending on what foods they include in their eating plans:

- **Vegans** (VEE-guns or VEH-juns), also known as pure vegetarians, are people who eat only foods from plant sources, such as grain products, dry beans and peas, fruits, vegetables, nuts, and seeds.
- **Lacto vegetarians** are people who eat dairy products in addition to foods from plant sources.
- **Ovo vegetarians** are people who eat eggs in addition to foods from plant sources.
- **Lacto-ovo vegetarians** are people who eat foods from plant sources, dairy products, and eggs.

Section 4-4 Resources

◆ **Student Workbook,** pp. 34, 40
◆ **Teacher Resource Guide**
Lesson Plan 4-4 Organizer
Section 4-4 Quiz
Chapter 4 Test
◆ **Effective Instruction CD-ROM**
Exam*View*® *Test Generator*
PowerPoint® Slide #13
◆ **Transparency Package,** CT-13
◆ **Student Motivation Kit**
Reteaching Activities, p. 27
Enrichment Activities

People choose to become vegetarians for many reasons. Some people do so because they feel it is a healthier way of eating. Of course, it's not necessary to become a vegetarian in order to practice healthful eating habits. Still, studies show that well-chosen vegetarian eating plans are healthier than the average American eating pattern. For instance, most Americans eat too much protein and fat, whereas vegetarian eating plans can provide enough protein and be relatively low in fat.

Good Nutrition for Vegetarians

If they make wise food choices, vegetarians can usually get all the nutrients they need. As with any other eating patterns, the key to good vegetarian nutrition is variety. Although vegetarians choose to avoid some foods, they still have plenty of other foods from which to select.

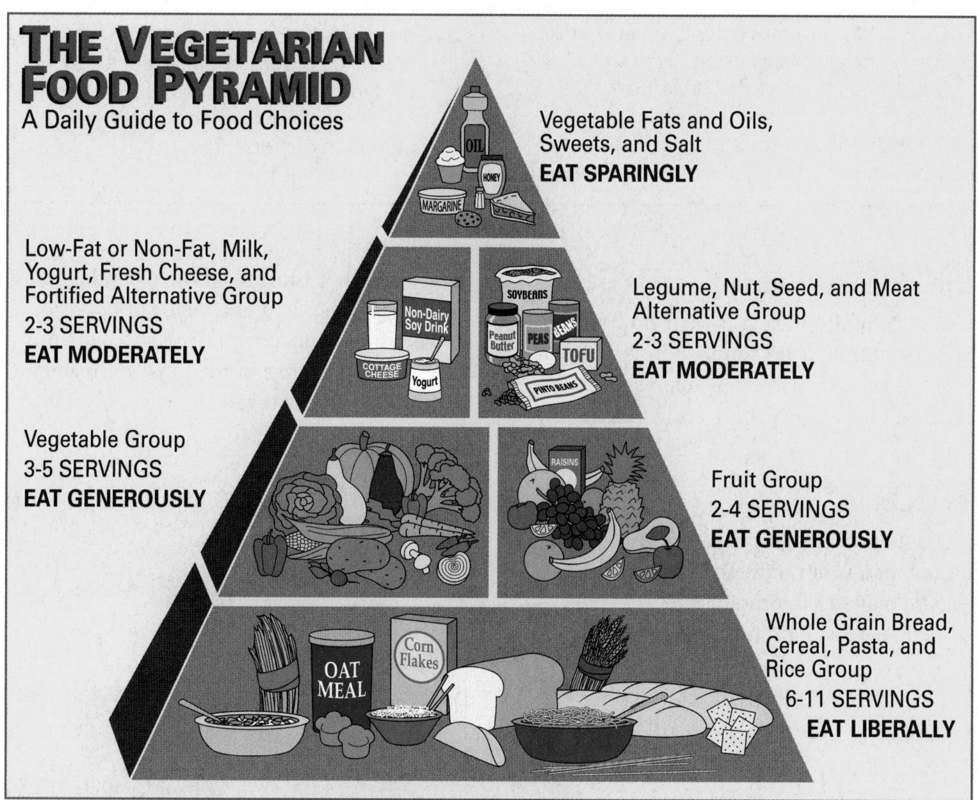

◆ **The Vegetarian Food Pyramid gives specifics for people who prefer a meatless eating plan. How does it compare to the Food Guide Pyramid?**

TEACH

- *Vegetarianism*
- *Facts About Vegetarians*
- *Good Nutrition for Vegetarians (text pages 126-131)*

Categorizing

On a sheet of paper, ask students to list the four basic types of vegetarians. Then, under each type, list the definitions, food choices, fat and protein contents, and pros and possible cons of each. Have students share and compare lists. L2

Guest Panel Activity

Invite a guest panel of students who represent different types of vegetarian eating plans to discuss the similarities and differences in what they eat. If preferred, the panel may be in "talk show" format. Students can provide the "host" a list of questions to ask about the vegetarian plans.

Meal Planning Activity

Ask students to research non-animal sources rich in iron and calcium. On the board, plan a one-day vegan meal plan with students, including as many of the iron- and calcium-rich sources as possible. Discuss how supplementation may be necessary for vegans to meet vitamins D and B_{12} needs. Ask students how these vitamin needs can be met through foods in other vegetarian eating plans.

Reinforcing Key Skills

Present the following problems to student groups. Allow time for them to discuss and compare their responses.

Management—Ask students to think about the effects that becoming a vegetarian would have, not only on their food choices, but also on their lifestyles and habits. What changes would they have to make? How would they deal with these changes in a healthful fashion?

Communication—Your friend Jill, who loves ice cream, nuts, and cheese, has decided to become a lacto-vegetarian to help better manage her weight.

TEACH cont.

- *Good Nutrition for Vegetarians (text pages 127-131)*

USING CONNECTING FOOD AND SOCIAL STUDIES

Have volunteers research and share their findings on vegetarianism in the United States today. Then have all students write an additional paragraph to "The Vegetarian View" which describes the growth of vegetarianism in the U.S. since 1908. Have several volunteer students read their paragraphs in class, inviting all students to pick out the best line or two from each paragraph. Then, with the class, write a consensus paragraph.

Adapting Recipes

Provide students with cookbooks. Have students look for recipes that vegetarians could use. Have students identify the recipes and determine which of the four vegetarian types could use the recipes. L2

Checklists

Have students develop a checklist of essential vitamins and minerals. Have students use their checklists to analyze typical vegetarian menus. Discuss which menus provide protein, fat, iron, calcium, and vitamins B_{12} and D. L2

DID You Know?

- In the 1960s, about 4 percent of the population considered themselves vegetarians. In the 1990s, the number jumped to 7 percent.

Connecting Food and Social Studies

The Vegetarian View

You may think of vegetarianism as a recent development, but in reality, it dates to antiquity. For over two millennia, vegetarianism has been a religious practice among certain Hindu and Buddhist sects, which consider all animal life to be sacred. Another religious group, the Trappist monks, embraced vegetarianism in 1666. More recently, the practice was adopted by Seventh-Day Adventists.

As a Western movement, vegetarianism got its start in Manchester, England, in 1809, among members of the Bible Christian Church. The first nonreligious practice of vegetarianism took place in 1847, when the Vegetarian Society was founded. In 1850, the movement spread to the United States, and in 1908, the International Vegetarian Union was founded.

Think About It

1. Some people become vegetarians because they are concerned about the world food supply and believe that eating meat contributes to the problem of world hunger. Learn about this view from outside resources. Summarize your findings in a brief report.
2. Other people become vegetarians for economic reasons. Compare the cost of a typical vegetarian meal with that of a nonvegetarian meal. Show your findings in a graph.

Specific Nutrients

It is helpful to take a look at how some specific nutrients are supplied in vegetarian food choices. Of particular interest are protein, fat, iron, calcium, and vitamins B_{12} and D.

Protein

Obtaining enough protein on a vegetarian eating plan is not difficult, even for vegans. As you may recall, proteins are made up of amino acids. Proteins from plant sources do not provide all the essential amino acids. However, eating a wide variety of foods from plants can provide complete protein over the course of the day—for example, dry beans or peas together with any grain products, nuts, or seeds.

◆ **Grain products, dry beans and peas, nuts and seeds, and vegetables are all sources of protein. Identify three other nutrients provided by these products.**

Extending Learning

Vegetarians—The emphasis on low-fat, low-cholesterol, and high-fiber eating plans has led many people to become "semi-vegetarians." These people eat mostly grains, vegetables, fruits, and dairy products. Occasionally, they may eat small amounts of meat, poultry, or fish.

Discuss with students possible reasons for the growth in vegetarianism.

Fat

Some people who become vegetarians are surprised to find themselves putting on weight. Often, this is because their eating plan centers on whole milk, cheese, or eggs, all of which are high in fat. Nuts and seeds are also high in fat.

The solution to this problem is to eat these nutritious, but high-fat, foods in moderation. Choose a meal plan that emphasizes grain products, fruits, and vegetables. These foods provide many important nutrients but are low in fat.

◆ **Because lacto vegetarians eat dairy products, they can get calcium from milk and other dairy foods. How can a vegan be sure to get enough calcium?**

Iron

As noted in Chapter 2, iron is essential in making hemoglobin, a substance in blood that carries oxygen to all body cells. This important mineral is found in many fruits, vegetables, and grain products, especially dry beans and peas and dried fruits. Since the iron in foods from plant sources is not easily absorbed, however, vegetarians run the risk of an iron shortage.

INFOLINK

For more on the many different varieties of grain products, see Sections 17-1 and 17-2.

Because vitamin C aids the body in its absorption of iron, a sensible solution is to eat foods rich in vitamin C together with foods high in iron. If vegetarians eat a wide variety of foods, including rich sources of vitamin C, they will probably meet their iron needs. Another way to get iron is by using cast-iron cookware.

Calcium

Getting enough calcium is of particular concern for vegans as well as others who do not drink milk. As you have learned, a good supply of calcium is essential for healthy bones and teeth.

Calcium needs can probably be met by eating good plant sources of the nutrient. These include dry beans and green, leafy vegetables, such as spinach, kale, and mustard greens.

Even so, it may be difficult for vegans to get enough calcium. They may be advised to drink fortified soy milk. Some health professionals recommend that vegans use calcium supplements.

Vitamins B_{12} and D

Another concern regarding vegan eating plans is vitamins B_{12} and D. Since Vitamin B_{12} is not found in foods from plant sources, the *Dietary Guidelines for Americans* recommends that vegans take supplements. Vegans may also need supplements of vitamin D, which is found mainly in fortified milk.

- ***Good Nutrition for Vegetarians (text pages 127-131)***

Recipe Analysis

Have students locate recipes for preparing vegetarian entrées. They are to collect the recipes into a multi-page document. Give each student a copy for discussion. Which recipes are appropriate for all types of vegetarian eating plans? Which recipes supply high-calcium foods? High-iron foods? **L1**

Supermarket Survey

Have students visit one supermarket and record the specialized vegetarian products available, such as veggie hot dogs, veggie burgers, and veggie deli meats. Permit time for them to discuss and compare their findings. **L1**

Taste Test

1. Divide the class into four groups.
2. Provide each group with ingredients and basic vegetarian recipes, each using one or more of the following: (1) soy milk, (2) tofu, (3) seitan, and (4) vegetable protein.
3. Ask students to discuss their recipe. How was the vegetarian ingredient used?
4. Ask students to evaluate the taste and appearance of the dishes.
5. Then, as a class, write a menu description for each recipe.

Reinforcing Key Skills

Present the following problems to student groups. Allow time for them to discuss and compare their responses.

Management—Present this situation to students: You are a vegan attending a dinner meeting with a large group of people at a local restaurant. This is an important meeting for you, since you will be asked to make a presentation. When you get to the restaurant, you discover that none of the foods on the menu are appropriate for a vegan. What do you do?

TEACH cont.

- *Good Nutrition for Vegetarians (text pages 127-131)*

Menu Planning

Have students plan and write out a one-day, well-balanced vegetarian eating plan. L1

Research Activity

Have interested students research vegetarianism in other countries. What types of recipes do they use? Do they follow the same guidelines as vegetarians in America? What are the differences? Invite these students to share their findings in oral reports, if possible with samples of recipes described.

Debate

Have students form two debate groups. One group is to argue vegetarian eating plan benefits, others the challenges. Each team should anticipate what the other team may debate. Have teams stage a debate in front of an impartial jury of their peers. L1

Lab Experience

Provide ready-made pizza crusts and a variety of toppings suitable for vegetarians. Have half the students create two different vegan pizzas, the other half, two different lacto-ovo vegetarian pizzas. Have students compare and critique vegetarian pizzas. If time allows, ask students to nominate one student in each group to draw pizza box covers for their creations. Each group should also name their pizzas. L2

◆ Vegetarians often eat pasta with a marinara sauce, which is simply pasta sauce without the meat. Vegetables can be added for extra nutrition and heartiness. Once they are used to the taste of a meatless pasta dish, even people who are not vegetarian enjoy marinara. They like having one additional way to reduce fat in their diet.

Planning Vegetarian Meals

Planning vegetarian meals can be easy. Just follow the basic guidelines for meal planning covered earlier in this chapter, but with some modifications, as follows:

- ◆ Substitute products made from soybeans and wheat for foods from animal sources. Many of these items, including soy milk, bean curd (or tofu), and seitan (SAY-tan) —a wheat-based meat substitute—can be found in supermarkets or health food stores.
- ◆ Get acquainted with the many varieties of grain products and dry beans and peas that are available. For instance, you might want to try such grains as millet, bulgur, and barley.
- ◆ Be sure to include good sources of vitamin C in your daily eating plan. Citrus fruits and melons are excellent sources.

Q *I've seen recipes for tofu burgers, tofu lasagna, and tofu shakes. Can I really get such different food tastes just from tofu?*

A In many ways, tofu is the "foundation food" of soy cookery. Tofu is made by curdling soymilk, the liquid pressed from grinding soaked, cooked soybeans. In recipes, tofu easily absorbs the flavors of other ingredients. Tofu textures range from firm, to soft, to silken, which increases its versatility. With these two qualities, tofu can be made to taste like meat in a sandwich or cream cheese in cheesecake. Sample different recipes and you'll probably find many dishes to enjoy.

FOOD SCIENCE

Analyzing Vegetarian Eating Plans

Have volunteers who are not currently vegetarians follow a vegetarian eating plan for a week. Students should keep a scientific log of what they eat each day and how they liked it. At the end of the week, they should analyze the nutritional value of the foods they ate. Have students create a written report of their experiment. The report should include their log, nutritional analysis, a statement of how they felt after eliminating meat, and explanations of problems they encountered, if any, while following the vegetarian eating plan.

- Use dark green, leafy vegetables, such as kale and mustard greens, liberally.

Vegetarian Recipes

Many vegetarian recipe books are available. They range from basic information on getting started with vegetarian foods to gourmet and ethnic recipes. Since vegetarian recipes are sometimes high in fat, choose them carefully. You can also adapt favorite nonvegetarian recipes, substituting ingredients such as seitan or bulgur for meat.

Many ethnic cuisines, such as Asian and Central and South American, are based on vegetarian foods. They can provide you with a wealth of menu ideas and recipes as well as introduce you to new foods.

Beans are a staple in the vegetarian diet. Which are the pinto beans, navy beans, and kidney beans in this photo? (See page 453 for help.) How might each be used in varied recipes?

Eating Out Vegetarian-Style

Because of customer demand, many restaurants have begun offering at least one vegetarian meal on their menu. Except for vegans, most vegetarians should have no problems making food choices when eating out. They can usually find meatless meals made with milk, eggs, or cheese. Some food choices might include baked potatoes with cheese toppings, pizza, meatless lasagna, bean soup, and omelets.

Since vegans eat no animal products, their choices are more limited. Many restaurants offer salad bars or a selection of salads on the menu, but for those who eat out frequently, the limited choices can be tiresome.

Here are some suggestions for vegans to consider when eating out:

- Read the menu descriptions carefully. Sometimes the ingredients for each selection are listed. If not, and an item sounds as though it might be suitable, ask the server what it contains.
- Tell the server that you are a vegetarian, and ask whether the chef would be willing to make up a plate of cooked vegetables.
- Ethnic restaurants, such as Chinese, East Indian, Mexican, and Middle Eastern, usually offer some vegan meals.
- If a restaurant does not offer any vegan meals except salads, talk to the manager. Restaurants are always looking for ways to attract new customers and may be receptive to your ideas.

- *Good Nutrition for Vegetarians (text pages 127-131)*

Problem Solving Activity

Have students work in groups to solve the following problems that occur in a vegetarian diet. How can a vegetarian reduce fat consumption? How can a vegetarian avoid an iron shortage? How can vegans avoid deficiencies of vitamins B_{12} and D?

Analyzing Menus

Provide students with restaurant menus. Have students select menu items for a meal to be eaten by a vegetarian. L1

Field Trip

Take a field trip to a suitable restaurant and have students choose nutritious vegetarian meals. Ask students to write a summary of what they chose, whether they liked it, and why.

ASSESS

REVIEW

- Ask students to summarize the main ideas in this section.
- Have students complete the Section Review. (Answers appear below.)

EVALUATION

- Have students divide sheets of paper into four columns and prepare a diagram of the types of vegetarians, including the capsule summaries of the challenges facing each in a largely "meat-driven" society.
- Have students take the quiz for Section 4-4. (Use the quiz in the *Teacher Resource Guide,* or construct your own with the **Exam***View*® *Test Generator* on the *Effective Instruction CD-ROM.*)

RETEACHING

- Display photographs of various foods and have students practice choosing foods that would be acceptable to different types of vegetarians.
- Refer to the *Reteaching Activities* booklet for the Section 4-4 activity sheet.

CLOSE

On each of four blank poster boards, draw empty Food Guide Pyramids. Label each drawing with one of the four types of vegetarian eating plans. Have students work jointly to fill in the appropriate food group sections with foods (drawings or words) that can be consumed for each of the representative eating plans.

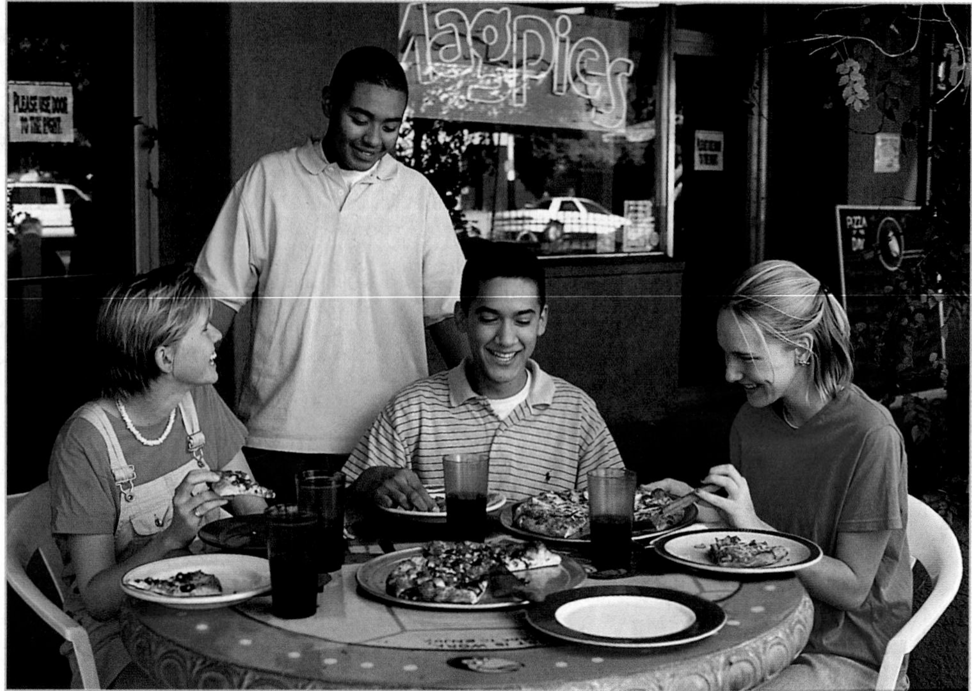

◆ **Vegetarians can find dishes that work for them in most restaurants today. Some restaurants have fewer offerings than others, but the number of selections available is generally increasing. The next time you're in a restaurant, note what dishes might be chosen by a vegetarian. Could a person make a meal by choosing a few side dishes? How would the cost compare to a regular meal?**

Section 4-4 Review & Activities

1. How are a vegan and a lacto-ovo vegetarian similar? How are they different?
2. What reason do the majority of people give for becoming vegetarians?
3. How can vegetarians be sure to get enough protein? Iron?
4. Give three guidelines for planning vegetarian meals.
5. **Evaluating.** Do you think restaurants should offer more choices for vegetarian customers? If they did, would nonvegetarian customers also benefit? Why or why not?
6. **Applying.** Plan one day's meals and snacks for a vegetarian. Explain the type of vegetarian the menu is for and why you chose those foods.
7. **Applying.** Locate a recipe for a meatless main dish that sounds good. Try making the recipe in your foods lab or for your family at home. Report on the results.

Answers to Section 4-4 Review & Activities

1. Neither eats meats; lacto-ovo vegetarian eats eggs and dairy products.
2. They feel it's more healthful.
3. Protein: Eat a wide variety of foods from plants; iron: Consume vitamin C sources and iron sources together.
4. Any three: substitute soybean and wheat foods for foods from animals; eat many varieties of grains, dry beans, and peas; include good sources of vitamin C; eat many dark green, leafy vegetables.
5. Answers will vary. Adding healthful choices benefits all customers.
6. Answers will vary.
7. Answers will vary.

Career Wanted

Food Web-Site Designer

"Each hit is a customer in the door."

Junilla Dawson

Education and Training
- Bachelor's degree in art, design, or communications
- Understanding of HTML
- Courses in computer sciences

Qualities
- Communication skills
- Creativity
- Problem-solving skills
- Eye for design

Q. What exactly does a Web designer do, Junilla?

A. Designing Web sites is like creating an interactive poster. I choose the words and images on each page, plus the links and other information. Then I write it all in HTML tags, the directions that computers understand for putting it all together. I also maintain and update the site.

Q. How do you decide what goes on a Web site?

A. I work with the site's sponsor. In foods and nutrition, it's usually health facts, recipes, and lots of great-looking foods. Once I understand the sponsor's goals, I work out technical issues: eye appeal, navigation, speed, and easy access.

Q. The explosion of the Internet must offer a lot of opportunities.

A. It does, but a lot of competition, too. I have to keep up with evolving technology to create an attractive site and also stay current on food issues. People take more responsibility for their health today, and they want information to make good choices.

Related Career Opportunities

Entry Level
- Computer salesperson
- Word processing specialist

Technical Level
- Graphic designer
- Computer support technician
- Junior screen print artist

Professional Level
- Software engineering manager
- Video producer
- Information systems analyst

Making Career Connections

WEB DESIGN. Design two Web pages based on chapter information. Talk with a Web designer to get ideas. How will you create an eye-catching, understandable format? Will you use animation? Will you tailor your pages to a certain group? What links will you include? Sketch your ideas and present them to the class.

Career Wanted

Food Web-Site Designer

Thinking About the Career

Have students interview a Web-site designer, preferably a food or nutrition designer. Among questions that students might ask are: How long have you been a designer? How did you get your job? What experience did you need? What college major do you suggest would provide me with the best chance of a career in Web-site designing? Describe your potential position's job title and career in ten years. Describe the differences between a Web-site designer's job now and what it may be like in ten years. Discuss results of students' interviews in class.

Career-Building Opportunities

Choose one of the "Technical Level" careers indicated in "Related Career Opportunities." Using help wanted ads and online resources, learn more about the requirements of the career. What are the requirements, such as degrees, previous job experience, or specific knowledge of computer programming?

For More Information

For additional information about careers in Web-site designing, encourage students to contact:
- National Web Design Association www.2webs.com/nwda/index.html

REVIEW

- Have students complete the Chapter Review. (Answers appear below.)

EVALUATION

- Ask students to plan three nutritious meals for an active teenager: one that can be prepared at home; one that could be chosen from a restaurant menu; and one for a person on a vegan diet.
- Have students take the test for Chapter 4. (Use the chapter test in the *Teacher Resource Guide,* or construct your own with the **ExamView®** *Test Generator* on the *Effective Instruction CD-ROM.*)

ANSWERS

Checking Your Knowledge

1. Possible answer: Eating three meals a day, eating many small meals.
2. It gives you energy to get you started, helps you feel alert during the morning, and helps you get to school on time and do better scholastically.
3. Eating five or more small meals throughout the day.
4. List all the food you eat for a specific period of time—usually three consecutive days, including a weekend; include the time you ate, the food eaten and the approximate amount, and a brief description of the eating situation.
5. A vague promise, such as "I'll eat better from now on," is hard to keep.
6. Any three: fried, batter-dipped, gravy, breaded, creamy, in a cheese sauce (or *au gratin*), scalloped, rich, crispy, parmigiana, tempura.
7. It can help you stop eating an entire large entrée when you are full.

Chapter 4 Review & Activities

Summary

Section 4-1: Daily Meals and Snacks

- People follow different eating patterns, from eating three meals a day to grazing.
- Be sure your daily food choices provide the right amount of calories and nutrients.
- Eat regularly, start the day with a nutritious breakfast, and choose snacks wisely.

Section 4-2: Positive Food Habits

- Keep a food record to identify your eating habits. Then you can evaluate your habits and decide whether you want to change them.
- Work at improving your eating habits gradually, and set specific, realistic goals.

Section 4-3: Eating Out

- All types of restaurants have pros and cons with regard to food choices and nutrition.
- Learning to identify the healthful choices on a restaurant menu and controlling portion size are important skills to develop.
- Wise food choices are also important when eating at school or eating on the go.

Section 4-4: The Vegetarian Lifestyle

- Some vegetarians eat only foods from plants, while others also eat dairy products or eggs.
- People become vegetarians for many reasons.
- The vegetarian way of eating can be healthful as long as sound food choices are made.
- To plan vegetarian meals, modify the basic guidelines for good nutrition.

Working IN THE Lab

1. ***Food Preparation.*** Using recipe books or magazines, find three ideas for quick and easy foods that would provide needed nutrients. As a group, prepare the foods in class for lunch. Working independently, evaluate the foods on the basis of cost, ease of preparation, and taste. Record your results in your Wellness Journal.
2. ***Taste Test.*** Taste samples of vegetarian dishes provided by your teacher. Judge them on taste and appearance.

Checking Your Knowledge

1. Describe two different eating patterns.
2. Why is breakfast such an important meal?
3. What is meant by the term *grazing*?
4. Briefly describe how to keep a food record.
5. When you are planning to improve your food habits, why is it important to decide on specific changes?
6. Name three clues that a food on a restaurant menu may be high in fat.
7. How can an awareness of appetite help you eat healthfully when eating out?
8. Name four types of vegetarians and the foods eaten by each.
9. Why do some vegetarians need to be careful about eating too much fat?
10. Why is calcium a concern for some vegetarians? Name two foods that can help meet their calcium needs.

Review & Activities Chapter 4

Thinking Critically

1. **Analyzing Behavior.** Alyssa was reviewing her food record. She noticed that when she ate alone or with her family, she usually made healthful food choices. However, her choices were less wise when she ate out with friends. Why might this be so?
2. **Predicting Consequences.** How might consumer complaints or suggestions affect menu items offered by a restaurant? What might happen if restaurant owners ignore consumer complaints and suggestions?
3. **Recognizing Stereotypes.** Suppose you and a friend are eating out. You hear a person at the next table asking if there are any vegetarian dishes on the menu. Your friend says, "How dumb. People who don't eat meat are weird." Is this a reasonable judgment? What can you say to help your friend better understand vegetarians and their way of eating?

Reinforcing Key Skills

1. **Management.** Kris has been invited to the home of a friend for the evening meal. Kris knows that her friend's family eats a light meal in the evening because they have their big meal at noon. Because of her hectic schedule, Kris was able to have only a sandwich and piece of fruit at lunchtime. How can she satisfy her nutritional needs and hunger while at her friend's home?
2. **Communication.** Harris's science club is having a year-end celebration in a local restaurant. Harris, who is very conscious of his nutrient needs, would like to ask how a certain dish is prepared. The server appears to be busy, however, taking orders from other people at the table. How can Harris satisfy his need for information without being a burden to other members of the club?

Making Decisions and Solving Problems

Your dad routinely fixes breakfast for the family. Most mornings he prepares eggs, bacon or sausage, and buttered biscuits, and serves whole milk. You appreciate his willingness to see that you have a hot breakfast each morning. However, you are concerned about the fat and cholesterol in the foods he prepares.

Making Connections

1. **Social Studies.** Using library resources, research the eating patterns in two other cultures. Present your findings to the class. Discuss why eating patterns vary from one culture to another.
2. **Health.** Visit two fast-food restaurants or consult a Web site that provides information about the number of calories, grams of fat, milligrams of cholesterol, and milligrams of sodium contained in their foods. Use this information to create a guide to fast-food dining in your area. Include the most healthful options on each of the menus.

ANSWERS cont.

8. Vegans—eat only foods from plant sources, such as grain products, dry beans and peas, fruits, vegetables, nuts, and seeds; lacto vegetarians—eat dairy products in addition to foods from plant sources; ovo vegetarians—eat eggs in addition to foods from plant sources; lacto-ovo vegetarians—eat foods from plant sources, dairy products, and eggs.
9. Their eating plan may center on whole milk, cheese, eggs, nuts, and seeds, all of which are high in fat.
10. It is a concern for vegans because they do not drink milk. Any two foods: dry beans and green leafy vegetables, such as spinach, kale, mustard greens.

Thinking Critically

1. Answers will vary. Students should recognize that friends are one of the primary social influences on eating, especially during the teen years.
2. Answers will vary. Students should recognize that most restaurants try to improve in response to suggestions from customers. Otherwise, they might lose business.
3. Answers will vary. Students should recognize that a well-balanced vegetarian meal is just as nutritious as any other well-balanced meal and that judging a person on the basis of personal habits is an example of faulty reasoning.

Reinforcing Key Skills

1. Possible answer: Kris could augment her eating plan with a late afternoon snack that is filling and rich in nutrients, such as hearty vegetable soup with crackers.
2. Possible answer: He might share his views on good nutrition with others at the table or politely suggest to the restaurant manager that he or she consider adding nutrition information to the menu.

CHAPTER 5

Food and Fitness

Advance Planning Guide ☑

- Draw or obtain outlines of five bodies, from underweight to obese.
- Arrange with a school health professional to conduct a private "body fat clinic."
- Prepare copies of nearly identical meal plans, one providing 2000 calories, the other 1900 calories.
- Bring to class a 5-lb plastic bag of shortening.
- Arrange for a registered dietitian to come to class as a guest speaker.
- Prepare or find sample case studies of different overweight adults with varying shapes and sizes.
- Create or locate a sample, three-day meal plan of a 13-year-old, 5'8", 120-pound (54 kg), inactive male.
- Obtain a copy of *Little House in the Big Woods* by Laura Ingalls Wilder.
- Arrange a field trip to a local fitness center.
- Invite a registered dietitian or sports nutritionist to class to speak to students about nutrition for athletes.
- Purchase several sports beverages and orange juice for a display.
- Find or create an 1800-to-2000 calorie, one-day eating plan.

CHAPTER 5

Food and Fitness

In addition to eating sensibly, one of the most important habits teens should develop is getting regular physical activity. In this chapter, you'll learn about the many benefits.

MEETING DIVERSE NEEDS

Physically Challenged Students. If there are students in the class who are physically challenged but mobile, ask them to explode myths about people with disabilities keeping active. Invite these students with lower-body limitations to demonstrate arm circles or upper-body rowing. Discuss types of fitness equipment available for the physically-challenged.

SECTION 5-1

Maintaining a Healthful Weight

Objectives

After studying this section, you should be able to:

- Explain why there is no one ideal body shape.
- Describe methods used to determine whether a person's weight is at a healthy level.

Look for These Terms

body mass index (BMI)
skinfold calipers
obese
waist-to-hip ratio

Although Alonza ate sensibly and was physically active, she was still unhappy with her body. Maybe you know someone like Alonza. Some people are dissatisfied with their body shape because they lack realistic goals.

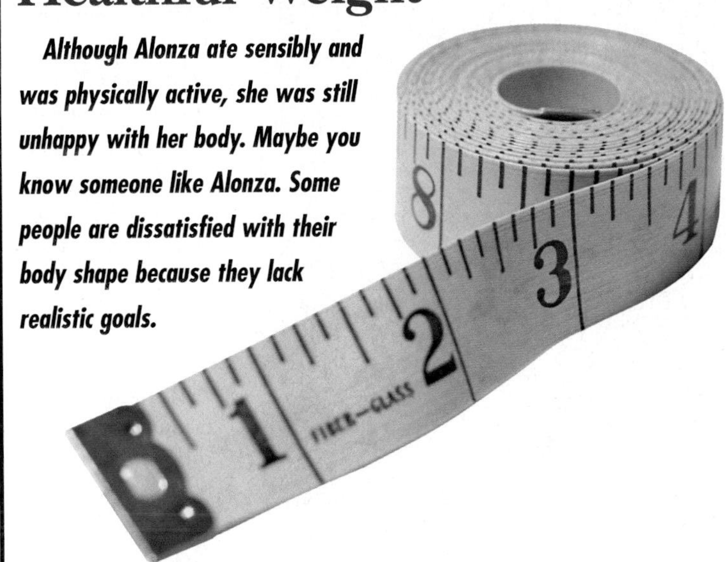

Unrealistic Images

If you had to name some relatives and friends who are very special to you, who would they be? If you're like most teens, you chose people because of their qualities, not the way they look. People come in all shapes and sizes, but they are most appreciated for other reasons.

When it comes to appearance, teens are often more critical of themselves than of others. Many teens compare themselves to television and magazine images that are far from typical. Some stars and models eat poorly to achieve a look. Some photos are even touched up to change appearances. Striving to look like media images can bring disappointment as well as health risks.

What Is a Healthy Weight?

Weight is on the mind of many teens who have concerns about their health and appearance. Some want to gain weight, and some want to lose. Deciding how many pounds to gain or lose is the question. After learning more about healthful weights, many teens discover that they are just fine the way they are.

INFOLINK
For more on lifestyle diseases and how to lessen their risk, see Section 3-1.

Section 5-1 Resources

◆ **Student Workbook**, pp. 41, 43
◆ **Teacher Resource Guide**
Lesson Plan 5-1 Organizer
Section 5-1 Quiz
◆ **Effective Instruction CD-ROM**
ExamView® *Test Generator*
◆ **Student Motivation Kit**
Reteaching Activities, p. 28
Enrichment Activities

SECTION 5-1

Maintaining a Healthful Weight

FOCUS

MOTIVATORS

- Show students photos of models from earlier decades when admired sizes and shapes were fuller. (Artwork from different eras offers additional perspectives.) Discuss with students how social attitudes about size and shape haven't always been the same.
- Ask students how they would decide whether a person is underweight, overweight, or a healthy weight for his or her body. On the chalkboard, list students' responses. Discuss advantages and disadvantages of using each suggestion.

VOCABULARY ACTIVITY

Direct students' attention to the list "Look for These Terms." Pronounce aloud all words. Instruct volunteers to find these words within the lesson and read aloud the definition of each.

STUDY SKILLS

- **Listening.** Invite volunteers to prepare an oral reading of each page of text from the section, while others follow along silently.
- Have students read the section and complete the appropriate part of the Chapter 5 Study Guide in the *Student Workbook*.

TEACH

- *Unrealistic Images*
- *What Is a Healthy Weight? (text pages 137-140)*

Writing Activity

Discuss sources of "ideal" body images. Ask students to name famous people who represent unrealistic "ideal" bodies. Identify the role of genes on these bodies. How do these role models influence their admirers? Then, encourage interested students to write a letter to the publisher of a magazine that promotes unhealthy weight.

Categorizing

Have students bring to class two photographs, from magazines or other sources—one picture depicting healthy weight and the other an unhealthy weight. In class, have students compile all photographs in appropriate categories. Allow time for students to discuss similarities and differences. L1

Calculations

Provide students with heights and weights of models. Have students calculate the models' BMI's. Ask students to discuss what BMI's below 20 indicate. L1

◆ **When you evaluate your weight, be realistic. Sometimes a visual impression isn't accurate. How can you determine what is the best weight for you?**

What is a healthy weight? The best weight for you is one that helps you stay healthy throughout life. It minimizes your risk of developing diseases and is based on knowledge about what is right for you.

Body Frame

Can two people of the same height have different, but appropriate, weights? They can because they have different skeletal structures, called frame. Every person inherits a body frame, often categorized as small, medium, or large. Obviously, a person with a large frame can carry more weight than someone who has a small frame.

You can estimate your frame size with this simple method. Wrap your thumb and index finger (next to the thumb) around your wrist. Your frame is small if they overlap, medium if they meet, and large if they don't meet.

Determining Healthful Weight

Health professionals use several methods to evaluate whether a person's weight is healthful. Three of these look at body mass index, body fat percentage, and waist-to-hip ratio.

Body Mass Index

Body mass index (BMI) uses a ratio of weight to height. You can compute your BMI by doing the following:

1. Record your weight in pounds.
2. Measure your height in inches.
3. Multiply your weight by 703; then divide that number by your height squared (your height times itself).

By locating your BMI in the chart on the next page, you can determine whether you are at risk for health problems related to weight.

Although it is more accurate than just your weight alone, the BMI is not a foolproof measurement of health or fitness. For example, a bodybuilder may have a BMI of 30 or higher. Athletes and other individuals with large muscle masses are not necessarily at risk even if they have high BMIs. In such cases, body fat measurements may be taken.

Reinforcing Key Skills

Present the following problems to student groups. Allow time for them to discuss and compare their responses.

Critical Thinking—A TV "talk" show features people who have lost 50 pounds or more. The host reports that these guests have all achieved their ideal weights. What is the danger in making such a statement on national television?

Critical Thinking—Two wrestlers on the school team are the same height, but one has a BMI of 24 and the other of 31. How do you explain the difference? Does either one have a problem? Explain your reasoning.

BMI	Risk for health problems related to your weight
20-24	Very low risk
25-29	Low risk
30-34	Moderate risk
35-39	High risk
40+	Very high risk

Body Fat Percentage

Instead of BMI, some health professionals prefer to check the amount of body fat a person has in relation to muscle. In many instances, this gives a truer picture of healthy weight than the BMI—or just the number on a scale. Measuring body fat percentage can show when extra pounds are from muscle, not fat.

You may have given yourself a "pinch test" to see how much body fat you have, like the teen in the photo. Health professionals do a similar, but more sophisticated, test using **skinfold calipers**, a device that pinches the skin to measure body fat. Healthy body fat percentages for nonathletes are approximately 15 to 19 percent for males, and 20 to 25 percent for females. Individuals with percentages above these ranges are said to be **obese** (oh-BEESE), a term that means having excess body fat. Many athletes have body percentages in the range of 5 to 12 percent for males, and 10 to 20 percent for females. Body fat percentages lower than these ranges may indicate an eating disorder, which you'll read about in Chapter 6.

Technology is providing new ways to determine body fat percentage. Scanning equipment can analyze body composition, even telling where fat is distributed within the body. As these procedures are refined, their cost will go down and availability increase.

Waist-to-Hip Ratio

Comparing the shapes of apples and pears to the shape of the human body gives another way to look at fat. To use this method, health professionals classify people as either an apple or a pear depending on their **waist-to-hip ratio**, a measure of how fat is distributed in the body.

◆ **Measuring the ratio of body fat to muscle gives a more reliable picture of a person's weight than the "pinch test" shown here. What is a desirable body fat-to-muscle ratio for females? For males?**

- ***What Is a Healthy Weight? (text pages 137-140)***

Discussion Activity

Ask students to explain why some health professionals use body-fat tests instead of relying strictly on weight to determine overweight.

Student Demonstrations

Have students research the impact of different clothing fashions and designs on the appearance of different body types. Have students stage a narrated fashion show based on research results. How can dressing positively contribute to self-esteem? **L1**

Body Fat Clinic Activity

Arrange with a school health professional to conduct a private "body fat clinic." Invite any students interested in receiving a skinfold test for body fat to participate. Assure all students that tests are to be conducted in a private setting and that results are to be kept strictly confidential. Ask the same students to calculate their BMIs using the formula on page 138. Have students report to the class whether the findings of the two tests varied and by how much. Conclude with a discussion of factors that might account for these differences.

FOOD SCIENCE

Energy Balance

Emphasize to students that one pound (0.45 kg) of body fat contains 3500 calories. This fact is the basis for scientific understanding of weight gain and loss. The energy balance between food eaten and energy expended in metabolism and activities results in weight gain, loss, or maintenance. So, to lose one pound in a week, an adult would need to expend an additional 500 calories per day.

ASSESS

REVIEW

- Ask students to summarize the main ideas in this section.
- Have students complete the Section Review. (Answers appear below.)

EVALUATION

- Provide students with a list of weights, heights, and waist and hip measurements of ten real (or imaginary) individuals. Have students calculate BMIs and waist-to-hip ration for all ten and determine which represent healthy weights. Re-emphasize the importance of the varying shapes and sizes (measurements) that all represent healthy weights.
- Have students take the quiz for Section 5-1. (Use the quiz in the *Teacher Resource Guide,* or construct your own with the **Exam***View*® *Test Generator* on the *Effective Instruction CD-ROM.*)

RETEACHING

- Have students write a short entry in their Wellness Journals describing their impression of healthy weight now and explaining why it has (or hasn't) changed based on what they learned in this section.
- Refer to the *Reteaching Activities* booklet for the Section 5-1 activity sheet.

CLOSE

Lead a class discussion on the "ideal" weight. Discuss why "ideal" differs with each individual. As a class, brainstorm a list of suggestions for how to devalue the unrealistic "ideal" image of underweight role models.

Adults with pearlike shapes carry most of their fat on the thighs and hips. Those with applelike shapes carry most of it over the abdomen. Research shows that "apples" may have greater risks of health problems than "pears." Apples, however, seem to be able to lose excess weight more easily than pears.

Adults can check body shape very easily: Stand relaxed and measure the waist without pulling in the stomach. Then measure the hips where they are largest. Dividing the waist measurement by the hip measurement gives the waist-to-hip ratio.

Adult women should have a ratio no higher than 0.80; adult men should have no higher than 0.95. Ratios above these limits may increase the risk of health problems, even if the BMI shows that weight is at a healthy level.

The Healthy Weight for You

As you can see, there's more to evaluating a person's weight than meets the eye. If you're wondering about your weight, comparing yourself to friends or a picture in a magazine isn't a good idea. Instead, talk to a health professional, who will use reliable methods to judge whether your weight is healthy for you.

No matter what your shape or size, following a sound weight management program is beneficial. The ideas in the next section can help you maintain a healthy weight for life.

Q ***Should I use weight-for-height tables to figure out the right weight for me?***

A Ideas about what weights are right for people have changed over the years. For this reason, you'll find weight-for-height tables with different recommended ranges, depending on who created the table and when. Appropriate weight should be based on more than just height. Age, gender, body frame, and amount of muscle all influence what a person can weigh and remain healthy. By using other methods of evaluating weight, you may get a better picture of what your weight should be.

Section 5-1 Review & Activities

1. Why are the physical images of celebrities not always what they seem to be?
2. Name three methods that health professionals may use to evaluate the healthfulness of a person's weight.
3. **Synthesizing.** What "ideal" body shape is shown in the media? Why do you think that images of the ideal body have such a powerful effect on people?
4. **Applying.** A teen who is 5'8" tall weighs 160 pounds. What is the teen's BMI? Does this weight pose any risk for health problems? Explain.
5. **Evaluating.** A teen who is 5'10" tall weighs 210 pounds. He is on the football team at school. What is his BMI? Is his weight a concern? Explain.

Answers to Section 5-1 Review & Activities

1. Celebrities may eat poorly, and photos may be retouched.
2. Body mass index, body fat percentage, and waist-to-hip ratio.
3. Answers will vary. The ideal shape is often that of an underweight individual. The media have projected thinness as the ideal. There is a psychological factor involved.
4. BMI is 24.3, just beyond very low risk range. Might consider percentage of body fat and other factors to evaluate risk.
5. BMI is 30.1. Weight may be due to higher than average muscle mass.

SECTION
5-2

Objectives

After studying this section, you should be able to:

- Recognize questionable weight-loss methods.
- Describe techniques for successful weight loss and weight gain.
- Give guidelines for maintaining a healthy weight.

Look for These Terms

overweight
fad diets
over-the-counter drugs
behavior modification
underweight

Weight Management

"Lose ten pounds in ten days." "Eat all you want and lose weight." "Gain muscle and lose fat without exercise." If claims like these sound too good to be true, it is because they generally are.

So what is a healthy approach to weight management? Whether you need to lose weight, gain weight, or maintain your current weight, you'll find tips in this section to help you achieve and manage a healthy weight throughout your lifetime.

Losing Excess Weight

Excess weight can be a health risk. Studies show that **overweight**—weighing more than 10 percent over the standard weight for one's height—is a risk factor in heart disease, diabetes, cancer, and high blood pressure. For many people, losing weight is a positive step toward better health. If you begin a weight management program now, it can lead to a lifetime of better health.

Evaluating Weight Management Methods

With so much attention focused on health and appearance, weight-loss methods are a big business. Everywhere you turn, you can find books, articles, and advertisements that claim to provide the answers to weight loss.

Some popular types of weight management methods include:

◆ **Weight management diets.** Eating plans that reduce calorie intake for weight loss.

◆ **Student Workbook,** pp. 41, 44
◆ **Teacher Resource Guide**
Lesson Plan 5-2 Organizer
Section 5-2 Quiz
◆ **Effective Instruction CD-ROM**
Exam*View*® *Test Generator*
PowerPoint® Slide #14
◆ **Transparency Package,** CT-14
◆ **Student Motivation Kit**
Reteaching Activities, pp. 29–30
Enrichment Activities
Skills for Making Food Choices, pp. 15–16

SECTION
5-2
Weight Management

FOCUS

MOTIVATORS

- Ask students to describe weight-loss methods with which they are familiar. Who recommends each method? How successful are these weight-loss methods in the short term? In the long term?
- Hand out nearly identical meal plans, one providing 2000 calories, the other 1900 calories. (For example, reduce butter on a baked potato from 1 Tbsp. to about 1 tsp.) Remind students that 1 pound of body fat is worth about 3,500 calories. Ask the class to calculate how many pounds a person could lose in a month (30 days) by making a similar 100-calorie reduction each day. *(0.86 pounds)* How many pounds could he or she lose in a year (365 days)? *(10.4 pounds)*

VOCABULARY ACTIVITY

Pronounce the terms listed under "Look for These Terms." Have students find the terms and their definitions in the section.

STUDY SKILLS

- **Guided Reading.** Have students look at the headings within Section 5-2 to preview the concepts that will be discussed.
- Have students read the section and complete the appropriate part of the Chapter 5 Study Guide in the *Student Workbook*.

TEACH

- *Losing Excess Weight (text pages 141-146)*

Research Writing

Assign students to write a research paper on one of four health conditions and its relationship to overweight: 1) heart disease, 2) diabetes, 3) cancer, or 4) high blood pressure. L1

Categorizing Activity

Ask students to list three popular methods of losing weight. As a class, brainstorm positive and negative aspects of each method. Discuss the positive role of a registered dietitian.

Debate

Divide class into groups. Provide each group with one diet or diet product (i.e. liquid meal replacement beverage, over-the-counter diet pills, or copy of a fad diet.) Have each group split into two sides: for and against. Allow time for students to plan for their debates. Stage the debates in front of the entire class. After each debate, allow time for discussion. L3

Demonstration

Bring in a five-pound plastic bag of shortening. Discuss the health consequence of the extra fat in our body. Have a student hold the "fat" in an outstretched hand—it will be difficult to hold for a long time.

- **Weight management centers.** Organizations that provide both an eating plan and psychological support.
- **Weight management products.** Pills, shakes, prepared meals, and more, all sold with the promise of helping people lose weight.

Some of the weight management methods that are promoted are based on sound nutrition principles. A counseling session with a dietitian who provides you with an individualized eating plan is an example of a sound weight management method. Many methods, however, are not based on sound nutrition. Some methods can even be dangerous to health.

Fad Diets and Other Dangers

Every now and then, a scheme comes along that promises quick and/or easy weight loss. The best known of these schemes are **fad diets**—popular weight-loss methods that ignore sound nutrition principles. Fad diets vary considerably but have one trait in common. They are risky.

Here are some other fad approaches to watch out for:

- Very low-calorie diets (800 calories or less per day). These may not provide enough energy or enough of the nutrients needed for good health.
- Eating plans based on a single food, such as grapefruit. As you know, your body needs a variety of foods every day.
- Fasting—going without food. This can be extremely damaging to your health.
- Diet pills. Some drugs can be obtained by prescription only and may play a small role in treating obesity. They're not for people with just a few pounds to lose. Alternatively, some **over-the-counter drugs**—drugs that can be obtained without a prescription—may contain herbs or other ingredients that could create serious health problems.
- Plans that promise quick weight loss (over 2 pounds, or 1 kg, per week).

Even a weight-loss plan that is acceptable for adults may pose problems for teens. During the teen years, growth and development continue, and nutrients are critical for these processes. A weight-loss plan might not allow a teen to get enough of the nutrients needed to become a healthy adult. For this reason, any teen who has concerns about being overweight should see a health professional before starting a weight-loss plan.

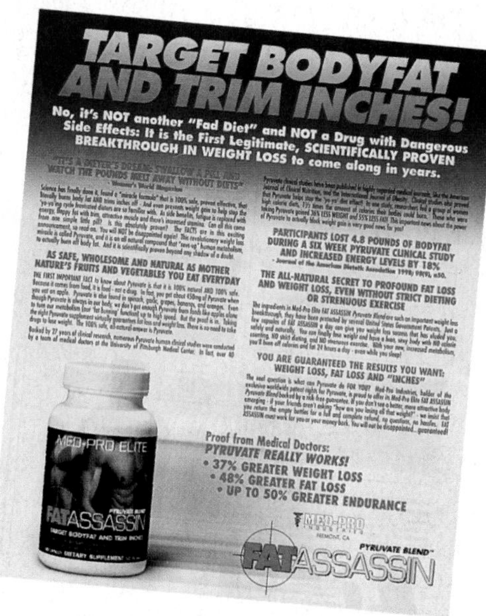

◆ **There are no magic ways to lose weight. The advertisements for diet pills, for example, don't tell you that they can cause serious health problems. Write a paragraph about a sensational advertisement for a weight-loss product you have seen. Identify why the promises will most likely prove false.**

Extending Learning

Herbal Weight Loss—Many over-the-counter weight-loss remedies contain herbs. These herbal preparations are not regulated like prescription drugs, and few are labeled with comprehensive ingredient information. Also, just because herbs are "natural" doesn't mean they're helpful. One herb, ephedra (ma huang), has been linked to 800 incidents of heart rate abnormalities and other side effects, including over a dozen deaths. Risks of taking herbal weight-loss preparations often outweigh benefits.

Ten Red Flags of Junk Science

If you want to follow a weight management program, check it out first. Compare statements or claims made by the program with any combination of these "red flags" to help determine if the program is a healthful plan.

1. Recommendations that promise a quick fix.
2. Warnings of danger from a single product or regimen.
3. Claims that sound too good to be true.
4. Simplistic conclusions drawn from a complex study.
5. Recommendations based on a single study.
6. Dramatic statements that are refuted by reputable scientific organizations.
7. Lists of "good" and "bad" foods.
8. Recommendations made to help sell a product.
9. Recommendations based on studies published without peer review.
10. Recommendations from studies that ignore differences among individuals or groups.

Source: Food and Nutrition Science Alliance (FANSA)

Disadvantages to Consider

Certain weight-loss methods, although not dangerous to health, have other disadvantages.

Some methods simply don't work and are frauds. For instance, some products that claim to suppress appetite may use too little of an ingredient to actually have an effect.

Cost is another consideration. Weight management centers and special diet products can be expensive. Think carefully about what you are getting for your money.

Some weight-loss plans offer very limited food choices. Favorite foods are denied and the diet becomes monotonous. As a result, people find it difficult to stay on the plan long enough to get the results they want. Imagine giving up your favorite food for a year or more. Could you do it?

Of those who do manage to lose weight by dieting, approximately 95 percent gain it back. The most likely reason is that weight-loss diets are seen as temporary ways of eating. Instead of learning to make healthful food choices, dieters often rely on printed menus or prepackaged meals. As soon as they have lost the weight, they tend to go back to their old eating habits.

What can I do to make my low-calorie, low-fat meals look more satisfying?

A Use small plates to help you moderate portion sizes. A full small plate of food will look much more appealing than a sparse large plate of food. In addition, don't forget to get a variety of food shapes, textures, and colors for more lively meals.

- *Losing Excess Weight (text pages 141-146)*

Guest Speaker

Invite a registered dietitian to speak to the class about weight management eating plans suggested to patients and how to best help patients maintain lost weight. Ask the speaker to expand on "Disadvantages to Consider."

Critical Thinking Activity

Have students list their three favorite foods. Then have students imagine what their eating plans would be like without those three foods. Have students share their thoughts in a class discussion. Emphasize the impracticality, monotony, and short-term nature of weight management approaches focused on specific food elimination.

Book Reviews

Provide small groups of students with a list of books to read (or skim) and critique. Suggested titles include:

- *The New Cabbage Soup Diet* by Margaret Danbrot
- *Dr. Atkins's New Diet Revolution* by Robert C. Atkins, M.D.
- *Sugar Busters!* By H. Leighton Steward (editor)
- *The New Beverly Hills Diet* by Judy Mazel and Michael Wyatt

Set aside class time for groups to give critiques. What common threads run through the critiques? What do these approaches have in common? Which of the "Ten Flags of Junk Science" does each book raise? L1

Reinforcing Key Skills

Present the following problem to student groups. Allow time for them to discuss and compare their responses.

Leadership—At a PTA meeting, there is disagreement on whether to continue offering white bread in school lunches because of a new diet report claiming white bread is a large culprit problem of overweight students. What do you say when you stand up to address the assembly?

TEACH cont.

- *Losing Excess Weight (text pages 141-146)*

Discussion Activity

Discuss the principle of behavior modification and its implications for losing weight. Ask students to explain why it is important for people to set specific, but reasonable, weight management goals. Discuss the importance for adults to lose no more than ½ to 1 pound per week.

Case Study Analysis Activity

Provide students with three sample case studies of different overweight adults with varying shapes and sizes. Have each student review the case studies and develop realistic goals for each one. As a class, develop consensus goals for each case study.

Role Play Activity

Choose six volunteer students. Three students will act as patients and three as dietitians. Assign the "patients" the following conditions: (1) healthy weight, (2) overweight, and (3) obesity. All are seeking advice from the "dietitian" on weight loss. Have students role-play the situation. If necessary, provide "dietitians" with sample questions. As a class, discuss reasons why it was important for each of these types to see the dietitian before beginning weight loss programs.

Successful Weight Management

If so many weight management methods don't work, what does work? The most successful way to lose and manage weight is through **behavior modification**, making gradual, permanent changes in eating and activity habits. That is the key to keeping weight at a healthy level throughout life.

Reasonable Goals

Setting specific goals for weight loss can be a motivator that provides a way to see progress. When goals are reasonable, they are more likely to be met.

A realistic attitude about body size and weight is essential. Trying to reach an unreasonable weight or clothing size just won't work.

A teen who has a large amount of weight to lose can divide the larger goal into a series of smaller ones. For instance, David needed to lose 40 pounds (18 kg), but he set his first goal at 10 pounds (4.5 kg). The smaller goal was easier to reach and gave him the encouragement he needed to stick with his program.

Weight loss takes time. Just as excess weight isn't gained overnight, it can't be lost that quickly either. Eating and exercise habits develop over a period of many years, so changing them can be a challenge. Health experts recommend losing no more than ½ to 1 pound (0.25 to 0.5 kg) per week. The more slowly weight is lost, the easier it is for the body to adjust. The lost weight is more likely to come from body fat—and to be maintained for a long time.

Increased Activity

Inactivity is one of the basic causes of overweight. Just increasing physical activity, even without cutting down on food, can result in a leaner body. Jogging ten miles a day, however, isn't the answer for those who are beginning an exercise program. Increasing daily activity in small ways is a better way to start. Choosing the stairs instead of the elevator burns extra calories. Walking the dog instead of watching it play is another simple way to get active. Like setting reasonable weight-loss goals, setting reasonable activity goals makes them easier to continue.

Calories Burned in Activities

Degree of activity	Calories per minute
Sitting or standing quietly	1 to 2 calories
Light activity: cleaning house, playing baseball	4 calories
Moderate activity: brisk walking, gardening, cycling, dancing, playing basketball	6 calories
Strenuous activity: jogging, playing football, swimming	9 to 10 calories
Very strenuous activity: running fast, playing racquetball, skiing	12 calories

◆ **Physical activity is a key to successful weight loss. In which of the activities above do you participate?**

Extending Learning

Inactivity and Weight—Many Americans lead a sedentary lifestyle—they get limited physical activity. Excess weight in teens is often caused by lack of exercise.

Studies show a direct relationship in adults, teens, and kids between weight and the number of hours spent watching television. The more hours people watch television, the more overweight they are. This can be due to commercial encouragement and consumption of high-calorie foods, plus burning fewer calories.

Q **When I try to lose weight, I get really hungry. What can I do?**

A Hunger is a natural response that drives the body to seek food. This response adapts to changes in the amount of food you eat, but not immediately. That's good news, because you know that feelings of hunger do lessen. Usually within a few days of cutting food intake, you feel full sooner since stomach capacity gradually decreases. Some foods satisfy hunger better than others, including protein, carbohydrates, and fiber. High-fat foods tend to leave you hungry and wanting to eat more. Exercise helps control hunger; it not only burns calories but also makes you want fewer of them. So—be patient. Hunger may not be a problem as long as you eat nutritiously while eating a little less.

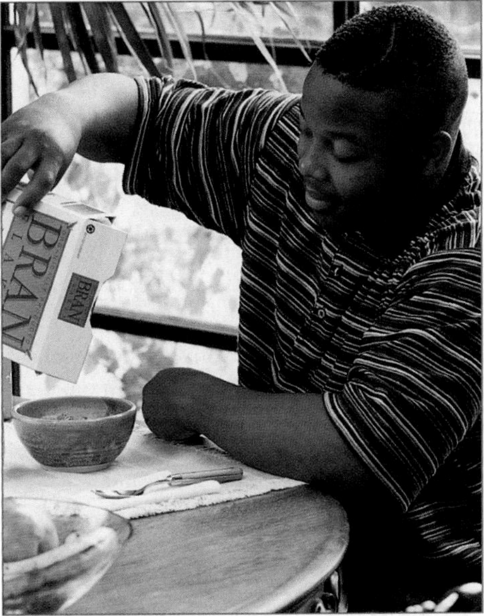

◆ **By eating sensibly, you can maintain a healthy weight. What other measures can a person take to achieve a healthy weight?**

One principle that people who need to lose weight should keep in mind is that the balance between energy in food and energy used for activities affects weight. When the body is active enough to use up the same number of calories taken in from food, weight stays at about the same level. If food provides more calories than are used up during activity, the extra calories are stored as fat, which causes a weight gain. When activities use more calories than are taken in from food, weight is lost.

In theory, the energy balance can change just by eating less. In reality, however, increasing the activity level is better. Why? Studies show that exercise not only burns calories during the activity but also increases metabolism for a short time afterward. In other words, the amount of energy used for basic body processes increases. Regular activity also helps ensure that lost weight comes from body fat, not muscle.

Whatever a person's level of physical activity is when starting a weight-loss plan, increasing that level is advisable. Without added physical activity, less weight is lost. Ideas for becoming more active are suggested in Section 5-3.

- *Losing Excess Weight (text pages 141-146)*

Demonstration

Ask for two student volunteers. Have one student measure the pulse of a second student. Then have this student run in place for 2 minutes. Repeat pulse measurements and record. When the student's pulse and respiration return to normal, have him or her put on a 25-pound (11 kg) backpack and run in place for another 2 minutes. Record the pulse rate again. Discuss the effects of exercise and extra weight on a person's pulse rate. Have the students draw conclusions.

Display

Ask students to bring to class one serving of any snack or dessert they eat regularly, along with a copy of its Nutrition Facts panel. Have students set up a display of their food portion with its Nutrition Facts panel. Allow time for students to study serving sizes versus calories and other nutrients provided by the servings. Discuss the display, especially any surprising findings. L1

Goal Setting Activity

Have each student plan one personal, measurable eating habit goal for next week. (For example: I will eat fruit instead of an empty-calorie dessert three times next week.) Have students plan a week's menu to help meet this personal goal. Follow-up with students the next week; discuss if goals were met.

Extending Learning

Positive Attitude and Weight Management—For successful weight management, it's just as important to improve your attitude as it is to set reasonable goals. Read the following negative attitude statements and ask students for a positive attitude replacement for each one: I can't do it; I'll never eat my favorite food again; I have to lose five pounds by this weekend.

- *Gaining Needed Weight*
- *Maintaining a Healthy Weight (text page 147)*

Menu Planning Activity

With students, brainstorm a list of at least twenty nutrient-dense foods or food ingredients. Have students suggest interesting ways to enjoy nutrient-dense choices in a meal plan to promote weight gain.

Critical Thinking

Provide students with a sample, three-day meal plan of a 13-year-old, 5'8", 120-pound (54 kg), inactive male. In groups, have students modify the meal plans to promote a healthy weight gain [approximately ½ pound (0.25 kg) per week]. Allow time for students to share meal plan results. L2

Problem Solving

Have students form brainstorming groups. One group is to identify obstacles to maintaining a healthy weight, while the other gives techniques (solutions) to maintaining a healthy weight. Then have groups combine lists to determine if there is a technique that can help with each obstacle. Discuss solutions to obstacles in class. L1

Class Challenge

Group students into pairs. Have each pair brainstorm lists of realistic, alternative activities to eating. The pair with the most activities wins. Discuss activity suggestions in class. L1

Eating Habits

Establishing new, more healthful eating habits also helps when trying to reach and maintain a healthy weight. A sensible eating plan is enjoyable and allows a reasonable number of calories each day. Dietitians can provide reliable eating plans.

Successful weight management depends partly on monitoring serving sizes. Too much food of any kind can result in weight gain.

Eating fewer calories from fat is also good advice. Remember that fat supplies more than twice as many calories per gram than carbohydrates and proteins do. Therefore, high-fat foods cause weight gain more easily than other foods. In addition, studies suggest that fats in food are turned into body fat more easily than are excess carbohydrates and proteins. This makes grains, fruits, vegetables, and other foods that are naturally low in fat a wise choice.

If too many calories are consumed, eating less fat still won't result in weight loss. Some low-fat foods are very high in calories. Portion sizes of low-fat and fat-free potato chips and brownies, for example, need to be controlled. Just because fat is removed during processing doesn't make such snacks healthful.

INFOLINK

For more specific information on serving sizes according to the Food Guide Pyramid, see Section 3-2.
For more on choosing nutrient-dense foods, see Section 3-2.

On any eating plan, nutrient-dense foods are a sensible choice. These foods supply the most nutrients for the least number of calories. Lean meats and fat-free or low-fat dairy products are wise choices as well.

By controlling portion sizes, eating less fat, and choosing nutrient-dense foods, most people who need to lose weight have plenty to eat without getting hungry, yet they still lose weight.

Serving Sizes

Some people know which foods are healthful, but they forget or have a difficult time determining what a healthy portion is. Here are some visual ways to estimate serving sizes.

Food portion	*Compare the size of one serving to . . .*
1 medium potato	Computer mouse
½ cup cooked rice	Cupcake
1 medium piece fruit	Tennis ball
½ cup fruit (chopped)	15 marbles
½ cup vegetables (chopped)	Standard lightbulb
3 oz. meat	Deck of cards
1½ oz. natural cheese	9-volt battery
½ cup or 1 scoop ice cream	Racquetball
1 tsp. butter	Tip of thumb to the first joint

Extending Learning

Muscle Weight—To lose a pound of body fat requires an expenditure of 3500 calories. The same can be applied in reverse; to gain a pound of body fat requires an excess of 3500 calories. However, when gaining weight the healthy goal is to gain more muscle than fat. In theory, it takes an excess of about 2500 calories, not 3500 calories, to support the gain of one pound of pure muscle. The rate of muscle building will vary from person to person. People with more "male" hormones tend to build muscle more easily.

Gaining Needed Weight

Overweight is a serious health problem. So is the flip side of the "weight coin." **Underweight** means weighing 10 percent or more below the standard weight for one's height. A person who is too thin has little body fat as an energy reserve and, possibly, less of the protective nutrients the body stores. This condition makes it harder for the person to fight off infection.

Gaining weight can be just as challenging as losing weight. If you're concerned about being too thin, discuss the matter with a physician. There may be a medical reason for an inability to put on weight.

Here are some hints to help you gain weight without adding fat to your food choices:

- Go for larger portions of nutrient-rich foods from the five food groups.
- Eat regular meals.
- Enjoy nutrient-dense snacks, including yogurt and fresh or dried fruit.
- Don't forget to stay active. Exercise can help assure weight gained is muscle, not fat.

Maintaining a Healthy Weight

Whether someone has lost or gained weight, or has always been a healthy weight, maintaining a healthy weight is the goal to meet for better health. Once you achieve a healthy weight, you should have no problem maintaining it as long as you continue to follow sound eating and activity habits. Still, if your weight starts to change, here are some suggestions:

- Keep a food record for a few days. Analyze the results to see if you are slipping into a poor eating pattern.
- Stay active. If you find your weight going up, increase your activity level.
- Keep a list of activities to do as alternatives to eating. If you find you're eating too much or too little because of stress, boredom, or some other reason, look to your list for healthful ways to cope with the situation. Try taking a hot bath, chatting with a friend, going for a walk, or simply brushing your teeth.

INFOLINK

For more on how to keep a food record, see Section 4-2.

Section 5-2 Review & Activities

1. What are the health risks associated with overweight? With underweight?
2. Name three signs that a weight-loss plan is unsafe.
3. What is behavior modification? How does it relate to weight loss?
4. **Analyzing.** Why are fad diets popular? What could be done to educate people how to determine when an eating plan may be a fad diet?
5. **Synthesizing.** Is it possible for someone to gain weight by eating a low-fat diet? Explain.
6. **Applying.** In newspapers and magazines, find ads for weight-loss methods. Evaluate them on the basis of the information you have read in this section.

Answers to Section 5-2 Review & Activities

1. Overweight: Heart disease, diabetes, cancer, and high blood pressure. Underweight: Little body fat and less protective nutrients the body stores.
2. *Any three:* Very low-calorie diets based on a single food; fasting; diet pills; promise of quick weight loss.
3. Gradual, long-term changes in eating and exercise habits; it's key to keeping weight at a healthy level throughout life.
4. Because they promise "miraculous" results; answers will vary.
5. Yes, too many calories from any source can result in weight gain—especially if someone is inactive.
6. Answers will vary.

ASSESS

REVIEW

- Ask students to summarize the main ideas in this section.
- Have students complete the Section Review. (Answers appear below.)

EVALUATION

- Have students prepare a plan for members of their household to maintain a healthy weight. Have students share at least one suggestion from their list.
- Have students take the quiz for Section 5-2. (Use the quiz in the *Teacher Resource Guide,* or construct your own with the **Exam***View*® *Test Generator* on the *Effective Instruction CD-ROM.*)

RETEACHING

- Working in pairs, students are to compile a list of high-calorie foods and drinks that total about 3500 calories. Emphasize that this is the amount of calories a person needs to decrease in order to lose 1 pound (0.45 kg).
- Refer to the *Reteaching Activities* booklet for the Section 5-2 activity sheet.

CLOSE

Discuss the importance of achieving and maintaining a weight that's healthy and realistic. To promote healthy weight in the classroom, have the class decide on one goal to promote activity in the classroom, such as starting class each day with five minutes of arm circles or toe touches.

SECTION
5-3
Keeping Active

FOCUS

MOTIVATORS

- Ask students to identify the types of activity they get regularly. If possible, have some students demonstrate activities. How much time per week is spent in each activity? Do students believe they should be more active?
- Ask students to brainstorm all the possible reasons why people should stay active. Record responses on the chalkboard.

VOCABULARY ACTIVITY

Refer students to the list under "Look for These Terms." Have them note the two different types of exercise listed. Then, have one student look up the definition for *aerobic*. Discuss what the prefix *an-* means. Then have students define *anaerobic* based on the findings.

STUDY SKILLS

- **Outlining.** Have students read the section and outline it by copying the headers on paper and leaving space after each one. Students are to write a sentence in their own words, summarizing the content under each header.
- Have students read the section and complete the appropriate part of the Chapter 5 Study Guide in the *Student Workbook*.

SECTION
5-3

Objectives

After studying this section, you should be able to:

- Explain the benefits of being active.
- Describe the basic types of exercise.
- Make a plan for an activity program.

Look for These Terms

lifestyle activities

aerobic exercise

anaerobic exercise

Keeping Active

Almost everywhere you look—at school and in your community—you can see people of all sizes and shapes participating in physical activity. Physical activity in all its many forms can provide real benefits for a healthy life.

Benefits of Activity

You know that staying active is important for weight management. Why else should you be active?

- ◆ It helps keep your body mobile. If your muscles are not used regularly, they tend to stiffen, and movement eventually becomes painful and difficult. Regular activity can keep your muscles strong and flexible throughout life.
- ◆ It helps improve psychological health. Regular activity can help you feel better by reducing stress and anxiety. Studies show that active people have a brighter outlook on life.

Types of Activity

You probably already do some physical activity as part of your daily routine, such as biking or playing basketball. Maybe you perform a regular chore at home, such as raking leaves or walking the dog. These are examples of **lifestyle activities**, forms of physical activity that are a normal part of your daily routine or recreation that promote good health throughout a lifetime.

A second type of activity is sports, which usually involve competition and are guided by a set of rules. When you think of sports, you may think of team sports such as football, basketball, and hockey, but other possibilities exist:

Section 5-3 Resources

◆ **Student Workbook,** pp. 42, 45
◆ **Teacher Resource Guide**
Lesson Plan 5-3 Organizer
Section 5-3 Quiz
◆ **Effective Instruction CD-ROM**
Exam*View*® *Test Generator*
PowerPoint® Slide #15
◆ **Transparency Package,** CT-15
◆ **Student Motivation Kit**
Reteaching Activities, pp. 31–32
Enrichment Activities

◆ Exercise includes more than running or lifting weights. Hobbies like gardening can reduce stress and increase physical activity. Make a list of leisure activities that you enjoy. Use online or print resources or consult the graphic on page 144 to determine how much energy the activities expend.

- **Individual sports.** Activities you can do by yourself, such as bicycling or golf. Many individual sports also are called lifetime sports because they are more likely than team sports to become part of a person's routine over a lifetime.
- **Partner sports.** Activities carried out with one other person. A benefit of partner sports is that they are easier to organize at a moment's notice than are group events, such as a softball game.
- **Nature sports.** Activities in which there is some interaction with one of the forces of nature, such as surfing, rock climbing, sailing, orienteering, and swimming. A benefit of nature sports is that they can be relaxing and can promote good mental health.

Safety Check

You may have heard the popular expression, "No pain, no gain." Despite what you may already believe, pain during exercise is a sign that something is not right. If you experience pain, you should modify or stop the exercise you are performing.

Types of Exercise

Virtually all activities work one or more muscle groups and, therefore, include some form of exercise. Some people, including teens, are beginning to rediscover so-called traditional exercises, such as doing crunches or working out with weights.

The many forms of exercise can be divided into two basic types. A well-rounded exercise program includes both.

- **Aerobic** (uh-ROH-buhk) **exercise** is vigorous activity in which oxygen is continuously taken in for a period of at least 20 minutes. During this time, the heart rate increases, sending more oxygen to the muscles to be used as energy to do more work. Aerobic exercises include walking, jogging, climbing stairs, bicycling, aerobic dancing, and swimming. A healthy goal is to do aerobic exercise a minimum of three days a week—and for at least 30 minutes total on each of those days.

TEACH

- *Benefits of Activity*
- *Types of Activity (text pages 148-149)*

Historical Comparison Activity

Read a passage from *Little House in the Big Woods* by Laura Ingalls Wilder (Chapter 11, "Harvest"). Point out that the need to "get exercise" is a modern phenomenon. Exercise was a basic part of our agrarian ancestors' lives.

Pyramid Activity

On the chalkboard, draw a "Physical Activity Pyramid," modeled after the Food Guide Pyramid. This graphic should contain six compartments labeled (from the bottom up): Lifestyle Physical Activity; Recreational Activity; Aerobic Exercise; Flexibility and Strength; Leisure Activities; Rest or Inactivity. Have students copy the graphic into their Wellness Journals. Alongside the pyramid, they are to list all forms of activity they perform in a typical week. They are then to complete their pyramids following a discussion of activities in the section.

Demonstration

Invite a physical education teacher to demonstrate exercises that improve flexibility, condition muscles, and strengthen the heart and lungs. Discuss how a person can judge the potential benefit of specific activities. What health and safety considerations should one take in selecting activities for an exercise program?

Extending Learning

Bone Benefits of Activity—How does activity help prevent osteoporosis? Bone is living, growing matter. Weight-bearing activity puts stress on bones. This increases the flow of blood and bone-building nutrients to the bone, which reduces bone loss and stimulates new bone growth.

Weight-bearing activities include walking, basketball, jogging, aerobic dancing, volleyball, racquet sports, and weight-lifting—even mowing the lawn.

- *Types of Exercise*
- *Getting the Activity Habit (text pages 149-151)*

USING CONNECTING FOOD AND HEALTH

To find true resting heart rate, have students take their pulse before they get out of bed the next morning. Then have students recalculate their target heart range the next day. That will be the range they should use during aerobic exercise.

Ask students to research Borg's Ratings of Perceived Exertion (RPE) Scale. Then have them write a brief report comparing RPE and target heart rate.

Cost Comparisons

Have student volunteers research and compute estimated costs associated with various types of exercise. Include expenses such as equipment, use of facilities, clothing, and transportation. Encourage students to share their findings as a bridge to a classwide discussion. Ask: Which activities are least and most expensive? Is there a correlation between cost and activity benefit? L2

Field Trip

Take a field trip to a local fitness center. Ask the trainer to discuss the roles of food and exercise in weight management and fitness. Have students be prepared to ask the trainer questions.

- **Anaerobic** (AN-uh-ROH-buhk) **exercise**, which builds flexibility and endurance, involves intense bursts of activity in which the muscles work so hard that they produce energy without using oxygen. Running the 100-meter dash is an example of an anaerobic activity. Resistance training, another form of anaerobic exercise, builds muscles by requiring them to resist a force. The more work the muscles do, the stronger they become. Resistance can be provided by weights, machines, or your own body weight. Anaerobic exercise should be done at least two times per week—and is especially helpful in combination with aerobic exercise.

Getting the Activity Habit

The first step in starting an exercise or activity program should be to have a medical checkup. Once you get a clean bill of health, you can start planning.

◆ **Getting exercise by doing physical activities that you can enjoy with friends is a way of increasing the likelihood of staying with the activity. Give other guidelines for choosing a physical activity that you will want to continue for the exercise benefits.**

Connecting Food and Health

Finding Your Target Heart Range

Just as eating within a certain fat range is good for the heart, so aerobic exercise needs to be done within a prescribed range for maximum cardiovascular benefit. This range, which differs from person to person, is your *target heart range.* To find your target heart range:

1. First find your *resting heart rate* by sitting quietly for 5 minutes. Then take your pulse by placing two fingers (but not your thumb!) on the side of your neck just under the jawbone.
2. Subtract your age from 220.
3. Subtract your *resting heart rate* (the result of step 1) from the number you arrived at in step 2.
4. Multiply the number you arrived at in step 3 twice—first by 0.85 and again by 0.6.
5. Add each of the numbers you got in step 4 to your *resting heart rate.*

The resulting totals represent your target heart range.

Think About It

1. Do you think your calorie needs will vary if you exercise for 30 minutes at a level below your target heart range? Why or why not?
2. During long bouts of exercise at the target heart range, the body uses glycogen for fuel. What food(s) should be eaten following exercise to replace this reserve fuel?

Extending Learning

Aerobic Exercise and the Heart— When performing weight training or other anaerobic exercise, where you work against a resistance, you gain muscle strength. That helps your arms and legs. Since your heart is a muscle, it needs to be strengthened too. It requires aerobic exercise to strengthen it. By jogging, cycling, inline skating, or performing another aerobic exercise, your heart pumps (beats) faster to get your blood to working muscles. By getting regular aerobic exercise, this repeated, increased workload helps make the heart stronger.

FOR YOUR HEALTH

Act Now!

You can easily work lifestyle physical activity into your everyday schedule. Here are some suggestions:

- Walk rather than ride to school.
- Get up to change the channel instead of using the remote.
- Play upbeat music while doing household chores.
- Plan social activities around physical ones. For example, turn a birthday party into a skating party.

Following Up

1. On the basis of the examples above, think of four ways in which you are currently inactive and four ways of becoming more active. Write your ideas in your Wellness Journal.
2. What would you tell an inactive person about the importance of regular lifestyle physical activity?

Are you already physically active? If not, there is no better time than now to start. Lifestyle activities taken up during the teen years are more likely to become lifelong habits than those acquired later in life. During the teen years, your energy level is also probably higher than it will be at any other period of your life.

What activity or sport should you choose? The possibilities are almost endless. Just be sure to pick something that holds your interest and that you can do—or at least learn to do —well. You're more likely to stick with an activity that you like doing and are good at. In addition, select an activity that fits in with your current lifestyle, including your schedule. If you already belong to several after-school clubs, don't try out for a team sport that holds its practices at the same time. Use the management and decision-making skills you learned about in Chapter 1 to help you make an informed choice.

The benefits of staying active are well worth the time spent. Like good nutrition, regular activity is a habit that gives a lifetime of physical and emotional rewards.

Section 5-3 Review & Activities

1. Name three benefits of exercise.
2. What are the two basic types of activity? Of exercise?
3. What are the steps for getting into the activity habit?
4. **Analyzing.** Why do you think people are advised to get a medical checkup before beginning a new program of physical activity or exercise?
5. **Evaluating.** What is your favorite form of activity or exercise? Which of the basic types does it involve?
6. **Applying.** Make a chart that outlines an exercise plan for the next week. Include at least three exercise sessions and at least two different forms of exercise. Be prepared to explain the benefits of your plan.

ASSESS

REVIEW

- Ask students to summarize the main ideas in this section.
- Have students complete the Section Review. (Answers appear below.)

EVALUATION

- Have students make a list in their Wellness Journal of ways to increase activity in each part of the Physical Activity Pyramid, except for the "Rest or Inactivity" section.
- Have students take the quiz for Section 5-3. (Use the quiz in the *Teacher Resource Guide,* or construct your own with the **Exam***View*® *Test Generator* on the *Effective Instruction CD-ROM.*)

RETEACHING

- Provide pictures of people exercising. Have students classify the exercises in the appropriate Physical Activity Pyramid sections.
- Refer to the *Reteaching Activities* booklet for the Section 5-3 activity sheet.

CLOSE

Lead a discussion on the different types of activity and how to determine the right exercise program for you. Have students develop a one-week exercise plan that includes at least five more daily minutes of activity, of choice, than they do at present.

Answers to Section 5-3 Review & Activities

1. Any three: Improved mobility, psychological health, physical health, fun.
2. Lifestyle activities and sports; aerobic and anaerobic exercise.
3. Have a medical checkup; plan to become physically active; choose an activity or sport.
4. People with underlying medical problems might harm themselves.
5. Answers will vary. Students should realize there are benefits to all forms of exercise.
6. Answers will vary. Emphasize that the plan needs to be realistic and enjoyable.

SECTION 5-4

Nutrition for Sports and Fitness

FOCUS

MOTIVATORS

- Bring to class sports magazines that include articles on how athletes' nutrient needs can be met. Do the articles perpetuate any common myths? Discuss the accuracy of the information provided in these articles.
- On the board, develop a one-day meal and beverage plan for a 16-year-old, moderately active, male student. Then, have students anticipate what it will be for a 16-year-old athlete, training for a marathon. Point out that the primary differences in an athlete's nutrient needs are the increased needs for energy and for water.

VOCABULARY ACTIVITY

Pronounce the terms listed under "Look for These Terms." Have one student find the definition of the prefix *de-*. Have another student define *hydration*. Ask the class to develop their own definition of *dehydration*.

STUDY SKILLS

- **Note Taking.** Have students read Section 5-4 independently. As they are reading the section, they are to take notes on the most important points.
- Have students read the section and complete the appropriate part of the Chapter 5 Study Guide in the *Student Workbook*.

SECTION 5-4

Nutrition for Sports and Fitness

Objectives

After studying this section, you should be able to:

- Explain how an athlete's nutrient needs can be met.
- Give suggestions for pregame meals.
- Point out the dangers of using anabolic steroids to build muscles.

Look for These Terms

dehydration

anabolic steroids

When you think of the word athlete, what comes to your mind? Maybe you picture a professional ballplayer. However, an athlete may also be a high school swimmer or a 50-year-old who enjoys her morning run. Regardless of the level of intensity involved, the performance of all athletes can benefit from good nutrition.

Nutrient Needs of Athletes

Eating right can't improve an athlete's skills—only practice can do that. An athlete's daily food choices, however, can make a difference between a good performance and a poor one.

Generally, an athlete's nutritional needs can be met by following the recommendations in the Food Guide Pyramid. However, the athlete does have two nutritional needs that far exceed those of the average person: the need for energy and the need for water.

Energy Needs

As noted earlier, during digestion, carbohydrates are broken down into the simple sugar glucose, which is used for energy. Extra carbohydrates are turned into a storage form of glucose known as glycogen, which is stored in the liver and muscles.

During vigorous and extended periods of exercise, the body uses glycogen for fuel. When the glycogen is used up, the athlete runs out of energy. Therefore, it's essential for athletes to eat plenty of carbohydrates to build up their glycogen stores.

During training and competition, athletes may need two or three times as much energy as the average person. Complex carbohydrates are the best choice for supplying this additional energy. "Carbohydrate loading," as this eating pattern is called, includes eating foods such as dry beans and peas, breads, cereal, pasta,

Section 5-4 Resources

◆ **Student Workbook,** pp. 42, 46
◆ **Teacher Resource Guide**
Lesson Plan 5-4 Organizer
Section 5-4 Quiz
Chapter 5 Test
◆ **Effective Instruction CD-ROM**
Exam *View® Test Generator*
PowerPoint® Slide #16
◆ **Transparency Package,** CT-16

◆ **Student Motivation Kit**
Reteaching Activities, p. 33
Enrichment Activities

◆ **Successful athletes know that performing their best requires good nutrition.** After reading this section, list two do's and don'ts for teen athletes in training.

rice, and potatoes. Similar to the nonathlete's calorie needs, about 60 percent of an athlete's calories should come from carbohydrates, about 25 percent from fat, and about 15 percent from protein. Individual needs vary. Note that health experts do not recommend carbohydrate loading for teen athletes.

◆ **Be sure to drink additional water whenever you exercise vigorously, even if you don't feel thirsty.** Why is drinking water important?

Liquid Needs

Athletes lose a great deal of water through perspiration—as much as 3 to 5 quarts (3 to 5 L) during a strenuous workout. If the water is not replaced right away, **dehydration** (dee-hy-DRAY-shun), or lack of adequate fluids in the body, can result. This condition can lead to serious health problems.

An athlete who is dehydrated may become weak and confused. The body can become overheated, especially when exercising in hot weather. Heat exhaustion or heat stroke can result. These are serious conditions requiring immediate medical attention.

To prevent dehydration, athletes should drink water before, during (about every 15 minutes), and after an event. They should drink water even if they do not feel thirsty. Thirst is a sign that dehydration has already begun.

TEACH

- *Nutrient Needs of Athletes (text pages 152-155)*

Discussion Activity

Ask students to brainstorm a list of foods high in complex carbohydrates. Discuss why athletes need at least 60 percent carbohydrates in their eating plans.

Guest Speaker

Invite a registered dietitian or sports nutritionist to class to speak to students about nutrition for athletes and how athletes should eat during training. If possible, invite the dietitian that consults for a nearby college sports team.

USING THE

Explain to students that food professionals often use methods other than those used by the general public or in the classroom to achieve certain reactions.

Relate the energy burned by the nuts to energy (fuel) for athletes. The heat given off by the nuts (or any other food) is what fuels the body during activity. The greater the need for energy (fuel) the more food needs to be consumed—up to 6000 calories a day by some athletes. Plan a 6000-calorie meal plan as if for a star football player in your area.

Extending Learning

Carbohydrate Loading—A combination of rest and extra carbohydrates to boost muscle storage of glycogen is the physiological goal of carbohydrate loading. Athletes will gradually decrease their training several days prior to an endurance event. Three days prior to the event, they will increase carbohydrates, mostly complex carbohydrates, to about 70 percent of their eating plans while maintaining the same caloric intake. This way the athletes will rest their muscles while boosting glycogen stores—and hopefully prevent extreme fatigue.

- *Nutrient Needs of Athletes (text pages 152-155)*

Supermarket Survey

Ask students to visit a local health food store or supplement section at a grocery store. Have students record the name, description, and Nutrition Facts panel information of a hi-protein supplement (powder mix, bar, or pill), marketed to athletes. Have students share findings in class. Discuss how athletes may be led to believe they need more protein. L1

Display Activity

Set up a display of several sports beverages marketed to the athlete, along with water and orange juice. Ask students to compare the nutrition labels. Discuss how the beverages compare to water, orange juice, and to each other. Discuss advantages and disadvantages of each for the athlete.

Applying Science

Have students examine online or print resources relating to physiology. Ask: Why do athletes need to consume more water than non-athletes? What are dehydration, heat stroke, and heat exhaustion and how are they a problem for athletes—and for non-athletes? Have students write a report of their findings. L2

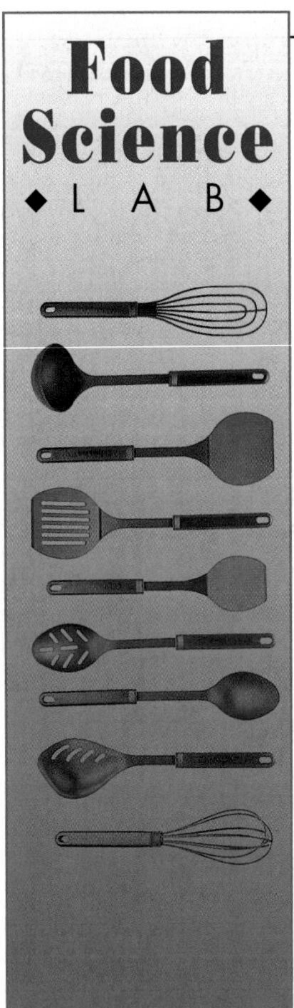

Calories to Burn

You know the expression "Seeing is believing." You are about to see the energy released when food is burned by your system.

Procedure

1. Press the eye of a needle into the narrow end of a cork. Mount a walnut on the point of the needle. Weigh the resulting construction.
2. Remove both ends of a large can and one end of a small can. Punch holes in the large can near the bottom and in the small can near the top (the open end).
3. Pour 100 mL of tap water into the small can. Measure the temperature of the water.
4. Insert a glass rod through the holes in the side of the small can. Use the rod to balance the small can within the large can.
5. Place the nut on a nonflammable surface and light it with a match. Immediately place the large can over the burning nut so that the water can is above the nut. Allow the nut to burn for two minutes or until the flame goes out.
6. Stir the water with the thermometer. Record the water's highest temperature. Weigh the nut/cork/needle construction again, and record the result.

Conclusions

- ◆ How much did the weight of the nut change?
- ◆ How much did the temperature change?
- ◆ Repeat the experiment using a different kind of nut. Do you arrive at a different result? Why or why not?

One good way to gauge the amount of water to drink is to weigh in before and after the event. Loss of water usually shows up as a loss in body weight. For each ½ pound (250 g) lost during exercise, athletes should drink 1 cup (250 mL) of fluid, just as they would do during exercise.

In addition to water, juices and fruit drinks can be used. However, because they are high in sugar, they can cause stomach cramps, diarrhea, and nausea. To cut down on sugar, dilute juices and fruit drinks with an equal amount of water.

Sports drinks are also available. They are valuable mainly to athletes involved in exercise lasting longer than 90 minutes.

Common Myths

Some athletes believe they need extra protein to build muscles. It's true that dietary protein is needed to build body protein. Remember, however, that most Americans eat far more protein than they need. An athlete's protein requirements can be met easily through normal eating. Excess protein does nothing to build up muscles—only physical training can do that.

Reinforcing Key Skills

Present the following problems to student groups. Allow time for them to discuss and compare their responses.

Communication—Ask students to explain how myths about athletic nutritional needs get started and why people tend to believe them. Compare myths about athletic nutritional needs to other common myths about food and nutrition. Ask students to discuss similarities and differences.

What about vitamin or mineral supplements? Almost all athletes who eat a wide variety of nutritious foods do not need vitamin or mineral supplements. The same is true of salt tablets. While some salt and potassium are lost through perspiration, these minerals can be easily replaced in well-chosen daily meals.

Timing of Meals

If you eat just before an athletic event, the digestive process competes with your muscles for energy. Instead, eat three to four hours before the event to allow time for proper digestion.

Follow these suggestions to get the most from your pre-event meal:

- Choose a meal that is low in fat and protein and high in complex carbohydrates. As you may recall, fat and protein take the longest to digest.
- Eat foods you enjoy and have eaten before. A pre-game meal is no time to experiment with a new food.
- Choose foods that you know you can digest easily.
- Have a reasonably sized meal (not too large) so that the stomach is relatively empty by event time.
- Drink large amounts of fluids with the meal.

After an athletic event or a hard workout, you need to refuel your body. In addition to replacing the water you have lost, be sure to eat nutritious food within one to four hours after the event—the sooner the better. Studies indicate that more carbohydrate (as glycogen) can be deposited in the muscles immediately after exercise than hours afterward.

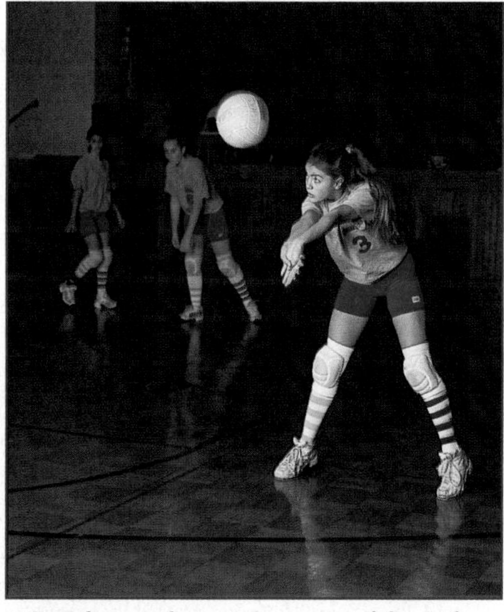

◆ **To perform your best, eat a pre-game meal three to four hours before the event starts.** Give two other pre-game tips for teen athletes.

Anabolic Steroids

All athletes want to perform well in sports and to have well-developed muscles. Many, however, are in a hurry to build up their muscles. Instead of depending on training alone, they mistakenly resort to taking **anabolic steroids** (AN-uh-bahl-ik STEHR-oydz), prescription medicines used to help build muscle strength in patients with chronic diseases. When used as an illegal drug, anabolic steroids can exact a terrible price on the user in terms of both health and behavior.

For more on the process of digestion, see Section 2-5.

- *Timing of Meals*
- *Anabolic Steroids (text pages 155-156)*

Guest Speaker

Invite a high school coach to discuss the timing of meals before and after athletic events. Ask them to share menus of pre-event meals and how fluid is replaced during the events.

Creative Writing

Have students write a poem, a song, or a news article describing the dangers of using anabolic steroids. Dangers may include both physical and psychological effects. Have volunteers read or perform their pieces aloud. 

Computer Research

Have students research, via the Internet, supplements, such as creatine, that are sometimes used by athletes. Have them research guidelines or statements issued by professional sports teams on the use of these products. What side-effects are associated with their use? Based on their research findings, have students develop a warning statement, for student athletes at their school, on the hazards of certain supplements. L2

Extending Learning

Ergogenic Aids—To potentially improve athletic performance, athletes have a choice of hundreds of ergogenic aids. "Ergogenic" implies a potential to increase performance by increasing work output. Ergogenic aids include amino acid supplements, creatine, co-enzyme Q-10, bee pollen, and more. Unfortunately, scientific research doesn't support the supposed performance-enhancing or muscle-building benefits. In fact, only continuous work of a muscle, such as in athletic training, builds muscle size or strength.

ASSESS

REVIEW

- Ask students to summarize the main ideas in this section.
- Have students complete the Section Review. (Answers appear below.)

EVALUATION

- Provide students with an 1800-to-2000 calorie, one-day eating plan. Ask students to adapt the menu for a student athlete of choice.
- Have students take the quiz for section 5-4. (Use the quiz in the *Teacher Resource Guide,* or construct your own with the **Exam***View*® *Test Generator* on the *Effective Instruction CD-ROM.*)

RETEACHING

- Have students list the hazards of steroid use. Then have them explain how to safely enhance athletic performance.
- Refer to the *Reteaching Activities* booklet for the Section 5-4 activity sheet.

CLOSE

Have students work as a team to develop a handbook on nutrition for athletes. Encourage students to print and distribute copies to members of school sports teams. What misconceptions were the booklets successful at correcting?

Steroids interfere with a person's ability to have children. In teens, they can impair bone growth. When taken over a period of time, they damage the liver, heart, and stomach, and can cause high blood pressure. Other physical side effects of steroid use can include fatigue, muscle cramps, and acne.

Remember that there are no quick fixes to improving athletic performance. Careful training and sound nutrition, practiced every day, are the surest ways to long-lasting top athletic performance.

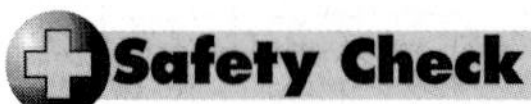

Safety Check

Creatine, an amino acid that is sold as a supplement, has grown in popularity among athletes hoping to improve performance. Although it's not an anabolic steroid, creatine is not without side effects or concerns. Taking the supplement may cause an electrolyte imbalance that can lead to dehydration and heat-related illness.

◆ **Canadian sprinter Ben Johnson was stripped of his Olympic medal, and eventually of the right to compete, for illegal use of steroids. Identify three physical risks and one psychological risk of using these dangerous drugs.**

Section 5-4 Review & Activities

1. How do the nutritional needs of athletes differ from those of nonathletes?
2. Give three suggestions for planning meals before an athletic event.
3. What are two negative side effects that can arise from the use of steroids?
4. **Synthesizing.** How could you persuade a friend of a teammate to avoid using anabolic steroids?
5. **Comparing and Contrasting.** Jill, an inactive student, and Mina, a swimmer, both weigh 120 pounds (54 kg). How do their protein needs differ?
6. **Applying.** Use the Food Guide Pyramid and recipe books to plan three meals for an athlete who is in training for a sport of your choice.

Answers to Section 5-4 Review & Activities

1. Athletes need more energy and more water.
2. Any three: See bulleted list on page 155.
3. Any two: Inability to have children; impaired bone growth; damage to liver, heart, and stomach; high blood pressure.
4. Educate about the side effects and illegal status; show a picture or article of an ex-anabolic steroid user who developed side effects.
5. Both need only the recommended amounts of protein for teens.
6. Answers will vary. The meals should meet all the guidelines of the Food Guide Pyramid.

Career Wanted

Athletic Trainer

Education and Training

- Degree in physical education, sports medicine, or physical therapy
- Training program supervised by certified trainer

Qualities

- Good physical condition
- Leadership skills
- Enjoy working with people

"Athletic training isn't just for athletes."

Jodi Chambers

Q. Jodi, you work at a health club. What are your responsibilities there?

A. I teach a number of exercise classes, from beginner to advanced. I also work one-on-one with club members to design personal fitness programs, based on each person's goals and abilities.

Q. What's the biggest challenge in your job?

A. So many people come to me just wanting to muscle up or lose weight. I try to help them see that total fitness and health is more than that. Nutrition, aerobic conditioning, and flexibility are included. In fact, some people with average bodies are in better overall health than people who look like world-class athletes.

Q. This may sound obvious, but does a person need to be an athlete to be an athletic trainer?

A. Well, you do have to be fit enough to lead the classes, but a good trainer also knows about anatomy and kinesiology, and even food science. I want to supply good information to help people take care of their bodies.

Related Career Opportunities

Entry Level
- Physical therapist aide
- Lifeguard
- Summer camp counselor

Technical Level
- Physical therapist assistant
- Recreation activity leader
- Water fitness instructor

Professional Level
- Physical therapist
- Physical education teacher
- Sports nutritionist

Making Career Connections

CAREER INTERVIEW. Interview a coach or physical education teacher, asking: What trends have you noticed in children's and teens' health and fitness? What are your goals for athletes or students? How do you encourage young people to be active? What do you advise about weight and nutrition? Compare interview results in class.

Career Wanted

Athletic Trainer

Thinking About the Career

Ask students to research the difference between a non-certified athletic trainer and certified athletic trainer. What is the difference between the jobs they perform? Then have students develop potential questions to ask Jodi Chambers about being an athletic trainer. (Examples: Where else would you consider working besides a health club? If you advanced your education, what degree would you like to obtain?)

Career-Building Opportunities

Using online resources, ask students to find out about meetings offered in their area or memberships offered by professional physical education, sports, or physical therapy associations that offer free or discounted services to students. Have students compile a list of the opportunities.

For More Information

For additional information about careers in physical fitness, encourage students to contact:

- American College of Sports Medicine
  P. O. Box 1440
  Indianapolis, IN 46206-1440
  www.acsm.org
- American Dietetic Association
  www.eatright.org
- American Physical Therapy Association
  1111 North Fairfax St.
  Alexandria, VA 22314-1488
  www.apta.org
- American Alliance for Health, Physical Education, Recreation, and Dance
  1900 Association Dr.
  Reston, VA 20191-1598
  www.aahperd.org
- National Association for Sport and Physical Education
  1900 Association Dr.
  Reston, VA 20191-1598
  www.aahperd.org/naspe

REVIEW

- Have students complete the Chapter Review. (Answers appear below.)

EVALUATION

- Provide students with descriptions of two or three hypothetical people who have different weight management needs. Have students describe the steps that each hypothetical person should take.
- Have students take the test for Chapter 5. (Use the chapter test in the *Teacher Resource Guide,* or construct your own with the **Exam***View*® *Test Generator* on the *Effective Instruction CD-ROM.*)

ANSWERS

Checking Your Knowledge

1. For muscular individuals, including many athletes, because muscle weighs more than fat.
2. People with apple-shaped figures seem to run more risk of some health problems than do those with pear-shaped figures.
3. ½ to 1 pound (250 to 500 g) per week; weight loss has a greater chance of being from fat and of being a long-term change.
4. Any three: Be realistic about body size and shape; divide large weight-loss tasks into smaller, more obtainable goals; allow time to reach goal; aim for weight loss of no more than ½ to 1 pound (250 to 500 g) per week.
5. Any two: Eat larger quantities of nutritious food; eat regular meals; eat healthful snacks between meals; include regular activity.
6. Both can help prevent injury.
7. Exercise during which your body requires more oxygen. Examples: walking, jogging, climbing stairs, bicycling, and swimming.
8. 60 percent.

Chapter 5 Review & Activities

Summary

Section 5-1: Maintaining a Healthful Weight

- It's best to accept your inherited body shape and focus on being fit and healthy.
- Three methods used to evaluate whether a person is at a healthy weight involve determining body mass index, body fat percentage, and waist-to-hip ratio.

Section 5-2: Weight Management

- A weight management program can help you achieve and maintain a healthy weight.
- Many popular weight-loss methods are ineffective, and some are dangerous to health.
- The best way to lose weight is through gradual, permanent changes in eating and exercise habits.

Section 5-3: Keeping Active

- Regular physical activity has many physical and psychological benefits.
- Activity takes the form of either lifestyle activities or sports.
- A fitness program that has a variety of enjoyable activities is more likely to be successful.

Section 5-4: Nutrition for Sports and Fitness

- Athletes should emphasize complex carbohydrates and drink plenty of fluids.
- Pre-event meals should be planned and timed carefully.
- Using unprescribed anabolic steroids is illegal and has dangerous side effects.

Working IN THE Lab

1. ***Foods Lab.*** Make a list of simple snacks that would be suitable for a person who is changing eating habits to lose weight. The snacks should be easy to prepare, low in fat and calories, and nutritious. Work in groups to prepare the snacks.
2. ***Food Preparation.*** Plan and prepare a pre-event meal for a group of athletes in your school. Prepare a handout giving facts about nutrition and athletic performance to give to each participant. Interview athletes after their performances to find out how they felt during the events.

Checking Your Knowledge

1. When can the body mass index be an inaccurate measurement of healthy weight?
2. In terms of health, what is the difference between having an apple-shaped figure and a pear-shaped figure?
3. What is an appropriate amount of weight for an adult to lose in one week? Why is this amount suggested as opposed to a higher amount?
4. List three guidelines for setting a reasonable weight-loss goal.
5. Give two suggestions for gaining weight healthfully.
6. Why are flexibility and strength exercises important?
7. What is meant by the term *aerobic exercise*? Give two examples.
8. About what percentage of an athlete's calories should come from carbohydrates?
9. What can happen if an athlete doesn't replace water lost through perspiration?
10. About how long before an athletic event should the pre-event meal be eaten? Why?

Thinking Critically

1. **Determining Credibility.** Suppose you are interested in losing weight. Several of your friends are following the plan described in a best-selling diet book. Before you decide whether to join them, what information would you want to know about the author? About the diet plan? How will you find the information? How will it influence your decision?
2. **Recognizing Bias.** Why do you think some children receive more encouragement to participate in exercise and sports than others do? How do you think such encouragement (or lack of it) affects children?
3. **Recognizing Fallacies.** A basketball coach recommends a special "power supplement," claiming it will improve performance. After using the supplement for a week, several members of the team say that it helped them shoot more accurately. Do you think they are right? Why or why not?

Reinforcing Key Skills

1. **Communication.** Romy has been instructed by her physician to lose weight. However, she says she already eats the minimum servings suggested by the Food Guide Pyramid. What solutions can you propose to Romy?
2. **Leadership.** Student athletes are often led to believe that taking anabolic steroids or certain supplements will give them a performance advantage. What steps can be taken to heighten the awareness of the dangers for student-athletes of taking these products?

Making Decisions and Solving Problems

You strain your leg muscle while jogging one day. The doctor tells you to try to stay off your feet for a few weeks. However, you want to continue with some type of exercise during that time.

Making Connections

1. **Math.** Find the waist-to-hip ratio (rounded to two decimal places) for each of the following adults: (a) female, waist 27 in., hips 36 in.; (b) female, waist 33 in., hips 40 in.; (c) female, waist 35 in., hips 45 in.; (d) male, waist 36 in., hips 35 in.; (e) male, waist 34 in., hips 36 in. Which of the ratios indicate a health risk?
2. **Language Arts.** Write an article for a newspaper, Web site, or newsletter on one of the following subjects: safe weight loss, planning an exercise program, or nutrition for athletes.

ANSWERS cont.

9. Dehydration can occur.
10. Three to four hours; to allow for proper digestion.

Thinking Critically

1. Answers will vary. Students should realize that not all people who write books about weight management are qualified to do so. They should look into the author's educational background and try to find out what health professionals think about the book. They may want to check the book's recommendations against the "Ten Red Flags of Junk Science."
2. Answers will vary. Family and community values, resources, and attitude toward sports may be factors. Children tend to follow whatever encouragement or discouragement they are given.
3. Answers will vary. Students should realize that medical studies have proved that supplements have no effect on athletic ability. Psychologically, these students may believe they are shooting more accurately.

Reinforcing Key Skills

1. Romy needs to include more exercise, especially aerobic exercise for its calorie-burning ability. She may need to be more aware of hidden fats in her food, too.
2. Answers will vary. To increase awareness, coaches, teachers, and parents need to be informed. They can help educate student-athletes. The media can have a positive effect. Also, having a local professional athlete visit the school to educate students about the dangers could be most effective.

Making Connections

1. (a) 0.75; (b) 0.83 (health risk); (c) 0.78; (d) 1.02 (health risk) (e) 0.94.
2. Articles will vary.

CHAPTER 6

Special Topics in Nutrition

Advance Planning Guide ☑

- Create or find a case study of a pregnant woman who is underweight and rarely drinks milk or eats vegetables.
- Invite an obstetrician, certified nurse midwife, or dietitian as a guest speaker.
- Ask a mother to bring her infant to class to demonstrate bottle-feeding.
- Prepare a list of 15 to 20 statements related to teens and food.
- Arrange a visit to a center for aging adults.
- Invite a local fitness instructor to visit the class.
- Obtain from hospitals, physicians, or dietitians copies of recommended eating plans for people who are ill or are recovering.
- Prepare packets of ten recipes, some of which should contain common allergens.
- Prepare a list of a dozen misconceptions related to stress, dietary supplements, and special eating plans.
- Bring to class pictures of individuals suffering from eating disorders.
- Invite a health care professional or counselor to discuss symptoms of eating disorders and sources of help.

CHAPTER 6

Special Topics in Nutrition

Since Ali was a toddler, people have been telling her that she had her mother's dimples. Like Ali, each of us is the sum of hereditary traits.

Although you cannot control your genetic makeup, you have total control over your behaviors and habits—including the food choices you make.

MEETING DIVERSE NEEDS

Physically Challenged Students. If there are students within the class who are wheelchair bound, ask them to teach a class to students on special food, nutrition, or health needs and challenges specific to physically-challenged individuals, young and old. The student "teachers" should be encouraged to use visual teaching methods.

SECTION
6-1

Food and the Life Span

Life is like a roller coaster—filled with unexpected twists, turns, dips, and steep summits. Just as a roller coaster never stays in the same place for long, so your life consists of a series of changes.

Objectives

After studying this section, you should be able to:

- Identify the varying nutritional needs for each stage of the life span.
- Explain how to encourage healthful eating habits for people in every stage of the life span.

Look for These Terms

life span
fetus
obstetrician
certified nurse midwife
colostrum
pediatrician

The Life Span

Scientists refer to this constant progression from one stage of development to the next as the **life span**. The human life span is made up essentially of five developmental stages, each with its own growth and nutritional needs. These stages are the prenatal period, infancy, childhood, adolescence, and adulthood.

Prenatal Period

Did you know that each of us begins life as a single cell? During the nine months of a normal pregnancy, this cell divides and multiplies millions of times, ultimately developing into a being able to survive in the outside world. Proper development during the prenatal period depends on the right nutrients. Yet, the **fetus** (FEE-tus)—or unborn baby—is powerless to control its nutrient needs. Responsibility for meeting these needs falls to the mother.

Nutrition During Pregnancy

A woman usually does not learn of her pregnancy until a month or more after she has become pregnant. Meanwhile, the food she has eaten has been the only nourishment

SECTION
6-1

Food and the Life Span

FOCUS

MOTIVATORS

- Have students work in groups to find magazine pictures of people representing different life span stages, as well as pictures of foods associated with each life cycle stage. Students are to use the pictures to create a bulletin board.
- List the stages of the life span across the top of the chalkboard. Discuss characteristics of each stage. Ask students to identify foods associated with each stage of the life span. Write the foods named under the appropriate life span stage.

VOCABULARY

Pronounce the terms listed under "Look for These Terms." Have students find the terms and their definitions in the section. Then, using the terms *obstetrician* and *pediatrician*, ask two volunteer students to determine (1) the branch of medicine in which each practices and (2) an adjective describing the type of care each provides.

STUDY SKILLS

- **Guided Reading.** Have students look at the headings within Section 6-1 to preview the concepts that will be discussed.
- Have students read the section and complete the appropriate part of the Chapter 6 Study Guide in the *Student Workbook*.

Section 6-1 Resources

◆ **Student Workbook,** pp. 47, 49
◆ **Teacher Resource Guide**
Lesson Plan 6-1 Organizer
Section 6-1 Quiz
◆ **Effective Instruction CD-ROM**
Exam*View*® *Test Generator*
PowerPoint® Slide #17
◆ **Transparency Package,** CT-17
◆ **Student Motivation Kit**
Reteaching Activities, pp. 34–35
Enrichment Activities

TEACH

- *The Life Span*
- *Prenatal Period (text pages 161-163)*

Discussion Activity

Ask students to describe the responsibilities of a pregnant woman regarding the nutrients provided to the fetus. Ask students to explain why it is important for expectant mothers to make healthy food choices.

Case Study Activity

Share with students a case study of a pregnant woman who is underweight and rarely drinks milk or eats vegetables. On the chalkboard, record a one-day meal plan that she typically follows. Ask students to determine why the woman and the fetus are both at nutritional risk. Ask them to provide recommendations to improve her chances of having a healthy, full-term baby of normal birth-weight.

Finding Recipes

Distribute cookbooks to students. Ask them to pick three recipes each that they believe would be nutritious choices for a pregnant woman to incorporate into her meal plan. Have students state why they chose each recipe. L2

for the unborn baby. Therefore, concern about good nutrition should begin before pregnancy. A healthy woman who has good eating habits before her pregnancy begins is more likely to have a safe pregnancy and a healthy baby. Poor eating habits can place the baby at risk for serious health problems.

Teen Pregnancy

Teen pregnancies are particularly at risk because teens need added nutrients for both themselves and the fetus. Poor eating habits can increase the risk of having a baby with a low birth weight (under 5½ pounds, or 2.5 kg) and also with physical or learning problems. Because most teens are not fully developed, they are also more likely to have difficult pregnancies.

Guidelines for Pregnant Women

A female who suspects she is pregnant should see a health professional as soon as possible. Most women see an **obstetrician** (ob-stuh-TRISH-un), a physician who specializes in pregnancy. Increasing numbers of females are opting for the services of a **certified nurse midwife**, an advanced practice nurse who, in addition to providing prenatal care, specializes in the delivery of healthy babies.

Whatever type of health professional is consulted, the expectant mother should follow recommendations for the kinds and amounts of food to be eaten. These generally include the following:

- Choose a variety of low-fat, nutrient-dense foods from the Food Guide Pyramid.
- Boost calories slightly to supply enough energy for both mother and fetus.
- Select at least two daily servings of high-protein foods, such as fish, poultry, meat, eggs, and dry beans.
- Have three to four servings of low-fat cheese or yogurt a day (about six servings for pregnant teens).
- Opt for foods high in iron, such as meat, poultry, fish, dry beans, and leafy, green vegetables. To help the body better absorb iron, supplement these choices with plenty of citrus fruits and other rich sources of vitamin C.
- Pick foods rich in folate, such as enriched breads and cereals, fruits, and dark green vegetables.
- Drink eight glasses of water daily, in addition to juices and milk.

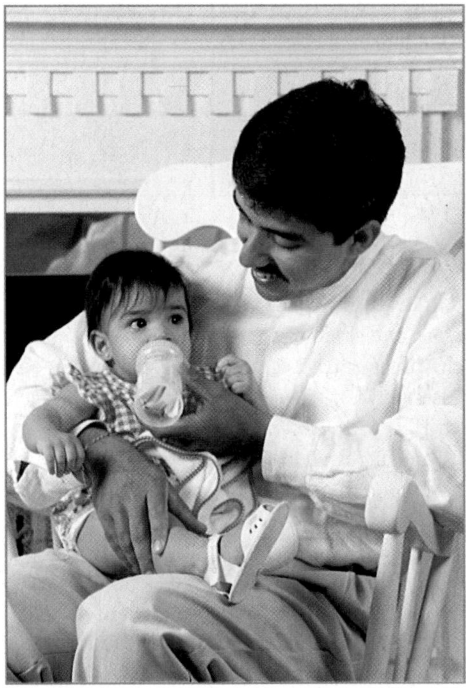

◆ **Eating right is essential throughout a person's life, but nutritional needs vary at different stages of the life cycle. Write a paragraph explaining why this is true.**

Extending Learning

Food Cravings—During pregnancy, some women have "cravings" for certain foods. Students may have heard of the "ice cream and pickles" craving—even though it's rare to have this particular craving. Increased hunger may begin to occur during or around the 13th week of pregnancy. That's when blood estrogen levels increase. Estrogen acts somewhat like an appetite stimulant. As long as eating desired foods do not replace nutritious choices or cause excess weight gain, it's usually fine for a pregnant woman to enjoy craved food.

◆ During pregnancy, six to eight glasses of liquid, including water, juices, and milk, are needed daily.

Pregnancy and Weight Gain

Females should expect to gain some weight during pregnancy. A healthy weight gain is usually 25 to 35 pounds (11 to 16 kg). A health professional may recommend a slightly different weight-gain range for underweight or overweight women. Women carrying twins may be advised to gain as much as 35 to 45 pounds (16 to 20 kg).

Pregnant women should not go on weight-loss programs. Limiting food deprives the fetus of much-needed nutrients and can seriously affect the baby's health. Those who have made nutritious food choices should return to their prepregnancy weight within a few months after childbirth.

Can a working parent take time off to care for a new baby?

A For good health, families need ways to balance work and home life. The Family and Medical Leave Act of 1993 (FMLA) was enacted for this reason. Through this federal legislation, certain employers are required to allow workers up to 12 weeks of unpaid leave per year to care for a newborn or a newly adopted or foster child. Workers may also take time to care for a seriously ill family member or recuperate from their own serious illness. A worker must have been employed by the company for at least 12 months and about 25 hours each week to be eligible. The law doesn't apply to very small companies.

Infancy

Good nutrition plays a critical role during the unparalleled growth and development of infancy. The harmful effects of poor nutrition during this stage can last a lifetime.

Feeding Newborns

There are two choices for feeding newborn infants—breast-feeding or bottle-feeding. Both provide all the nutrients the baby needs for the first four to six months.

Breast milk has the right amount and type of fat for a baby. The protein in breast milk is more easily digested and absorbed than the protein in cow's milk.

For the first three days after birth, the mother's breasts produce a special form of milk known as **colostrum** (kuh-LAH-strum). This is a thick, yellowish fluid that is rich in nutrients and antibodies, substances which protect the baby from infection. Later, the colostrum changes to true breast milk.

A woman who is breast-feeding should eat the same foods recommended during pregnancy and drink plenty of liquids. The right food choices will help her produce enough milk to keep the baby well fed and healthy. She should not restrict calories.

• *Prenatal Period (text pages 161-163)*

Guest Speaker

Invite an obstetrician, certified nurse midwife, or dietitian to speak on the dietary advice given to pregnant women. Ask the speaker to discuss neural tube defects, fetal alcohol syndrome, and potential dangers of dieting or using herbal remedies. Have students write a short summary of what they learn.

Posters

Assign each student a nutrient of particular concern for pregnant women, including iron, calcium, and folate. Have students make posters that suggest how the nutrient is important during pregnancy, what happens if a pregnant woman doesn't get enough of it, and what five or more foods (list or draw) are rich in the nutrient. Display posters in classroom. L1

Menu Planning Activity

Have students prepare a table that lists the amounts of calories and nutrients needed by pregnant women. Then, share with students a three-day meal plan of a non-pregnant woman. Assign student groups to adapt the meal plan (using a nutrition software program) to meet nutrient needs if the woman became pregnant.

Ask students to determine how to find a certified nurse midwife in your community and then record the approximate number of these health professionals in local practice. In class, review results of students' findings. Hold a discussion of the possible advantages and disadvantages of choosing a certified nurse midwife over an obstetrician.

TEACH cont.

- *Infancy (text pages 163-164)*

Demonstration

Invite a mother with her infant to demonstrate proper bottle-feeding and burping techniques for infants. Additionally, using a doll "baby," have students each practice proper feeding and burping techniques. Review with students why following these proper techniques are important.

Checklists

Have students develop a checklist of guidelines for adding solid food to a baby's eating plan, including foods to offer and month (age) to offer them. Have students who have an infant sibling or close relative or neighbor use their checklist with the infant's mother or father. L1

Videotape Segments

If students have access to a video camera, invite teams to create "how-to" videotape segments on one of the three issues noted in the Safety Check on this page. The segment should expand the information, using students' research of the selected issue. If it can be arranged, allow class time for groups to air their segments, inviting prospective parents from the community to attend. L2

Bottle-feeding infant formula can also provide good nutrition. Infant formula is usually made of a cow's milk base. Vegetable oils and carbohydrates are added to make it similar to breast milk. Other types of formula are also available. For infants allergic to cow's milk, formulas with a soybean base are often used.

Adding Solid Food

After the first four to six months, the baby will be ready for solid food. The child's **pediatrician**, a physician who cares for infants and children, can offer sound recommendations. A baby's first "solid" foods are actually strained foods that are easy to swallow and digest. They should be introduced one at a time. That way, if the baby has a reaction, the cause of the food allergy can be easily identified. The first solid food is usually iron-fortified rice cereal, followed by strained vegetables and fruits. More variety is added later.

During the last half of the first year, infants' eating skills improve. They can be given foods that need some chewing. They begin to learn to pick up some solid foods with their fingers. Healthful finger-food choices include pieces of fruit (without skins), cooked vegetables, cheese, and crackers. Babies also begin to use a spoon for self-feeding.

By the end of the first year, a baby usually can eat the same foods as the rest of the family, but in smaller amounts. Parents or caregivers should not try to limit the amount of fat eaten by children under age two. Babies and toddlers have high energy requirements and, thus, need more fat in their eating plans than do older children and adults.

Safety Check

- Cow's milk should not be given to infants because their digestive systems are not fully developed. After 12 months of age, toddlers can be offered about 2 cups (500 mL) of whole milk (in place of breast milk or formula) each day to help assure that calcium needs are met.
- Do not add salt, sugar, fat, or spices to a baby's food. Babies do not need them because their taste buds are more sensitive than an adult's. Added salt, sugar, or fat may also lead to poor eating habits later on.
- Certain foods should not be fed to infants and small children because they can cause choking. These include nuts, seeds, raw carrots, hot dogs, hard candies, whole grapes, popcorn, powdered sugar, and peanut butter.

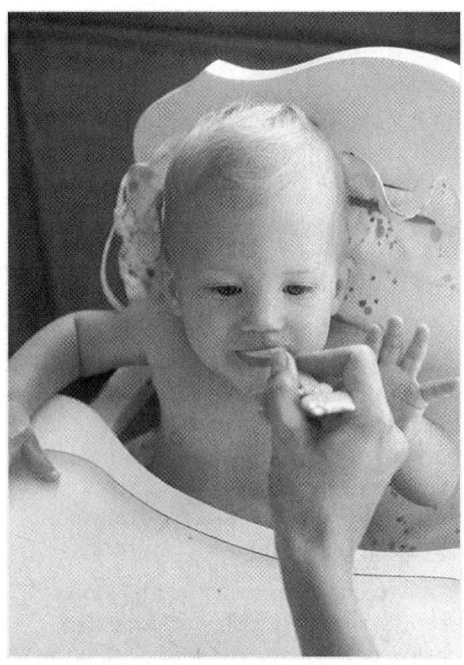

◆ **Introducing solid foods one at a time makes it easier to pinpoint any food allergies. Which solid food is usually introduced first?**

Extending Learning

Feeding Infants—Here are three infant feeding considerations:

- Besides being healthy for the baby, breast-feeding has other advantages. It costs less than formula and doesn't require sterile bottles, mixing, or heating.
- If the baby refuses certain foods, continue to offer them. In time, the baby may accept them.
- Homemade formula may not contain all the nutrients the baby needs. There is also a risk of bacterial contamination if it is not handled properly.

◆ Teaching children to prepare foods by themselves encourages good eating habits. Which areas of skills for food choices does this behavior reflect?

Childhood

Young children are active and growing. So it is essential that they receive a wide selection of nutritious foods from the five food groups in the Food Guide Pyramid.

At meals, food portions should be small. Many experts recommend beginning with 1 tablespoon (15 mL) of a food for each year of the child's life. That means the vegetable serving of a three-year-old should be about 3 tablespoons (45 mL). If the child is still hungry, he or she can be given more. The amount of food needed varies from child to child and from week to week.

During growth spurts—periods of very rapid growth—children may eat more than usual. At other times, they may want less food. Young children sometimes go through phases in which they insist on eating the same food at every meal or they hate a food at one moment and then love it the next. These food jags are usually temporary and don't create long-term nutritional concerns.

Young children need 2 cups (500 mL) of milk each day. It can be served in three or four small portions.

Children have very small stomachs that cannot hold very much food at one time. Therefore, they need between-meal snacks to help supply enough energy and nutrients. Healthful snacks include juice, yogurt, milk, pieces of fruit or vegetables, cooked meat, poultry, or fish, unsweetened cereal, and whole-grain crackers. Nutrient-dense foods should be encouraged.

Promoting Good Eating Habits

Do you have memories from early childhood of trying a food for the first time? Eventually, every child takes a chance with new foods. Introducing a young child to a previously untried food provides an excellent opportunity to add variety to the child's eating plan while simultaneously fostering good eating habits. Here are ways of making the most of that opportunity:

- Serve foods that vary in color and texture. If the food has eye appeal, children will be more likely to eat it—and to meet their nutritional needs.

- *Childhood (text pages 165-166)*

Childhood Memories Activity

Ask students to recall pleasant and unpleasant childhood memories that involved food. Based on the discussion, have students develop a list of guidelines for making mealtime pleasant for young children.

Student Demonstration

1. Have student groups plan fun food snacks for young children.
2. Suggest students include finger foods and foods that would have appeal for young children. One example: "Ants on a log"—celery filled with peanut butter and topped with raisins.
3. Have student groups arrange to prepare or bring their snack to class and share samples and preparation techniques with classmates.
4. Encourage students to share reasons for why and how snacking can be important for children and why their demonstrated snack is "kid-friendly." L1

Television Ad Activity

Have students observe commercials during one hour of Saturday morning children's television. Ask students to prepare a graph showing the types of foods that were advertised, the techniques advertisers used, and, in the student's opinion, how successful the ads may be.

Reinforcing Key Skills

Present the following problem to student groups. Allow time for them to discuss and compare their responses.

Leadership—A four-year-old boy you babysit is throwing a tantrum when you arrive. His mother just told him he couldn't have dessert unless he finished all his peas. How do you follow the parent's lead and, at the same time, reach the child?

- *Adolescence*
- *Adulthood*
  (text pages 166-167)

Categorizing Activity

Provide a list of 15–20 statements related to teens and food, such as "Eating chocolate causes acne." Have students form brainstorming groups in an effort to divide the list into categories: myths and facts. Suggest students research questionable statements.

Discussion Activity

Lead a class discussion on what happens when adults continue to eat as much food as when they were younger. Why is regular physical activity important for adults? What factors in modern lifestyles negatively impact healthy eating or regular exercise? Brainstorm ways to overcome these factors.

Field Trip

Conduct a field trip to a center for the aging adults. Ask the program director to identify the special challenges some elderly people face in meeting their nutritional needs. How do fixed incomes and health conditions contribute to the nutritional problems of the elderly? Have interested students find out how they can help out as volunteers in the feeding program or center.

Interview Activity

Have students interview an older relative or other individual in the community who lives alone, asking about eating patterns and habits. Ask students to write a "mock" newspaper article based on the interview.

- Eat meals with children, and make the meals enjoyable. Be a role model for good eating habits and behavior.
- Avoid using food as rewards or punishments. This practice gives young children the wrong impression about the purpose of food.
- Don't encourage children to become members of the "clean-your-plate club." Insisting that they finish all their food even after their hunger is satisfied can lead to overeating in later years.
- When possible, let children choose what foods they want to eat for some meals.
- Teach children how to prepare several simple, nutrient-rich foods by and for themselves.
- Invite children to help prepare part of a meal. Let them tear lettuce for a salad, make sandwiches, or aid with any other age-appropriate tasks.

Adolescence

Next to infancy, the second most rapid growth period of life is the one you are going through now—adolescence. Because of the dramatic physical and psychological changes associated with this period, you, as a teen, have an increased need for almost all nutrients.

Many teens don't get enough calcium, zinc, iron, vitamin A, or vitamin C in their eating plans. One easy way to avoid this problem is to be sure you get the minimum number of servings suggested for people your age in the Food Guide Pyramid. If you are highly active or still growing, aim for the maximum number.

As a teen, you are assuming more responsibility for your life, including your food choices. Developing food skills and fitness habits during this period will help set the stage for a healthy and productive future.

Adulthood

Mr. Carstairs, who is 45, has a "spare tire" around his midsection, while his next-door neighbor, who is the same age, does not. The difference relates in part to the fact that Mr. Carstairs eats the same way he did when he was younger, even though most adults require fewer calories.

Despite their decreased need for calories, adults still need their full share of nutrients. They can meet this demand by choosing a variety of low-fat, low-calorie foods from the Food Guide Pyramid. Continuing to get regular physical activity throughout adulthood is important as well.

Many adults don't realize they have slipped into poor eating and exercise habits until they develop a health problem. Developing healthful habits now, while you are in your teen years, may help reduce future health problems. It will also make it easier to continue these habits throughout life.

Older Adults

As people age, they continue to need the same nutrients, although in smaller amounts. If they remain physically active, they can continue to eat as much as younger adults.

With maturity, the body's thirst signal often declines and people don't drink as much water as their bodies require. Older people, like all other adults, need to drink eight cups (2 L) of water daily.

Reinforcing Key Skills

Present the following problems to student groups. Allow time for them to discuss and compare their responses.

Management—Financial management is very important for older adults on a fixed income. Have students develop a list of budget-stretching tips that might help an older adult maintain good eating habits during times when money is very tight.

Leadership—An aging relative rarely drinks water and seems to have a low overall fluid intake. How do you convey the importance of getting enough fluids?

◆ **With proper nutrition and other good health habits, many older adults remain very active.** Interview an older relative, neighbor, or other senior citizen who is active to learn about his or her eating habits.

Special Problems for Aging Adults

Some aging adults face special challenges in meeting their nutritional needs. Many live on fixed incomes that are too low to provide enough nutrient-rich food. Those who live alone may dislike preparing a meal just for one—or may be too frail to cook. Some older people have health problems that create nutritional risks.

In many communities, social service programs are available to help aging adults in situations like these. Senior and community centers often offer meals for older citizens at reduced rates. These programs provide nutrient-rich meals as well as an opportunity for socializing.

Living alone or on a limited income can make meal planning challenging for people of any age. In Chapter 11, you will learn helpful suggestions for coping with these challenges.

Section 6-1 Review & Activities

1. Why are good nutrition habits important for a woman even before she knows she is pregnant?
2. Identify three finger foods for infants and three healthy snack foods for young children.
3. How can adults get their full share of nutrients without getting too many calories?
4. **Synthesizing.** Hugh, a 21-year-old male, grew up learning always to eat everything served to him. What are some potential health problems that could result if he continues this behavior throughout adulthood?
5. **Analyzing.** Write a paragraph explaining how getting children involved in meal preparation can lead to good eating habits.
6. **Applying.** Think of a simple food that children can prepare for themselves. Write directions for preparing the food as you would explain it to a child. If possible, share the recipe with a young child in your home or community. Write about the experience in your Wellness Journal.

ASSESS

REVIEW

- Ask students to summarize the main ideas in this section.
- Have students complete the Section Review. (Answers appear below.)

EVALUATION

- Have students create simple, nutritious menus suitable for a small child, a teenager, an adult, and an older adult.
- Have students take the quiz for Section 6-1. (Use the quiz in the *Teacher Resource Guide,* or construct your own with the **Exam***View*® *Test Generator* on the *Effective Instruction CD-ROM.*)

RETEACHING

- Have students create a time line that represents a typical lifetime for a female. List special nutritional considerations at appropriate points. Discuss how the time line would be different for a male.
- Refer to the *Reteaching Activities* booklet for the Section 6-1 activity sheet.

CLOSE

Discuss nutritional and caloric requirements at different times in life. On the chalkboard, record a one-day meal plan for a five-year-old male or female. Then, have students suggest minor modifications for a nutritionally- and calorically-appropriate meal plan for an "average" 15-year-old, 45-year-old, and 75-year-old male or female; explain reasons for modifications.

Answers to Section 6-1 Review & Activities

1. A woman usually does not know she's pregnant for about a month or more.
2. Infants: see page 164; young children: see page 165.
3. By choosing a variety of nutrient-dense foods and practicing balance and moderation.
4. Will most likely result in overweight or obesity and the associated health risks.
5. Students should realize that the more children are involved with food, the more they will learn about it—and good eating habits.
6. Answers will vary. The directions, which may involve many steps, need to be written in very basic language.

SECTION
6-2
Managing Health Conditions

FOCUS

MOTIVATORS

- Ask students to describe dietary changes someone they know has been required to make as the result of a health condition. List the health conditions and the dietary changes on the chalkboard.
- Have students bring to class newspaper, magazine, or Internet articles that discuss special nutrition needs related to various health conditions. Have students categorize the articles by health condition and place them in Classroom Resource folders for reference as they study this and later sections.

VOCABULARY

Pronounce the terms listed under "Look for These Terms." Have students find the terms and their definitions in the section. Ask two students to identify what the acronyms *HIV* and *AIDS* represent. State that one other term has an acronym—MNT for *medical nutrition therapy*.

STUDY SKILLS

- **Listening.** Invite a group of volunteers each to prepare an oral reading on a page of text from the section, while others follow along silently.
- Have students read the section and complete the appropriate part of the Chapter 6 Study Guide in the *Student Workbook*.

SECTION
6-2

Managing Health Conditions

Have you ever lost sleep the night before a big exam or had butterflies in your stomach when you had to speak before a large audience? If so, you are not alone. Everyone at one time or another experiences these symptoms.

Objectives

After studying this section, you should be able to:

- Explain the relationship between stress and nutrition.
- Identify the role of nutrition in recovery from illness or injury.
- Identify positive and negative effects of using supplements.
- Give examples of how people with medical conditions or physical impairments can meet their nutritional needs.

Look for These Terms

stress
dietary supplements
megadose
herbal remedies
medical nutrition therapy
diabetes
HIV/AIDS
food allergy
food intolerance

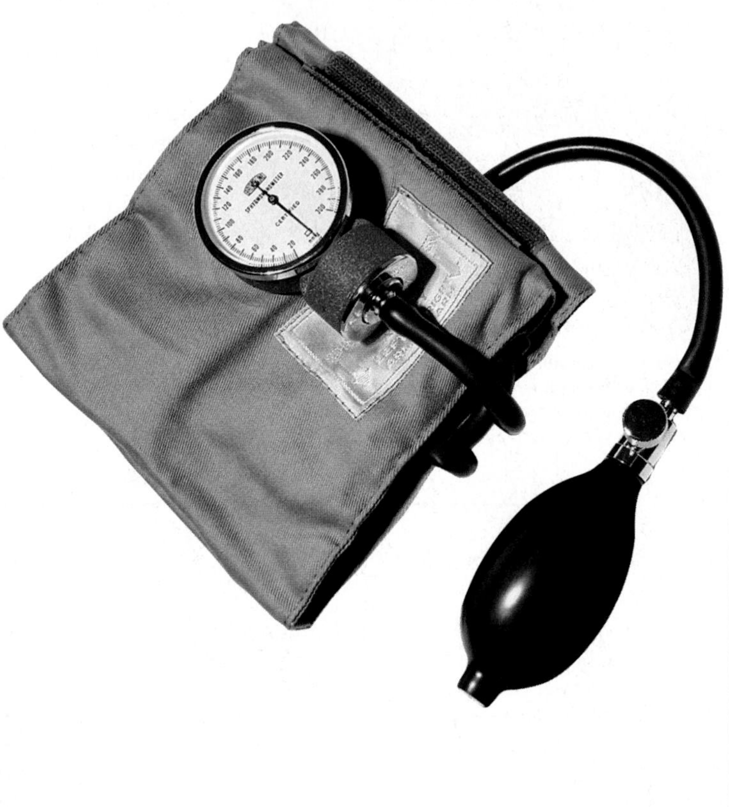

Stress

Physical reactions like the ones described above are symptoms of stress. **Stress** is physical or mental tension triggered by an event or situation in your life.

Not everyone finds the same situations stressful. Some people experience test anxiety, whereas others don't. At school, a teacher will experience types of job stress different from those experienced by a principal or a school counselor. Even going on a date, receiving an

Section 6-2 Resources

◆ **Student Workbook,** pp. 47, 51
◆ **Teacher Resource Guide**
Lesson Plan 6-2 Organizer
Section 6-2 Quiz
◆ **Effective Instruction CD-ROM**
Exam*View*® *Test Generator*

◆ **Student Motivation Kit**
Reteaching Activities, pp. 36–37
Enrichment Activities
Skills for Making Food Choices, pp. 17–18

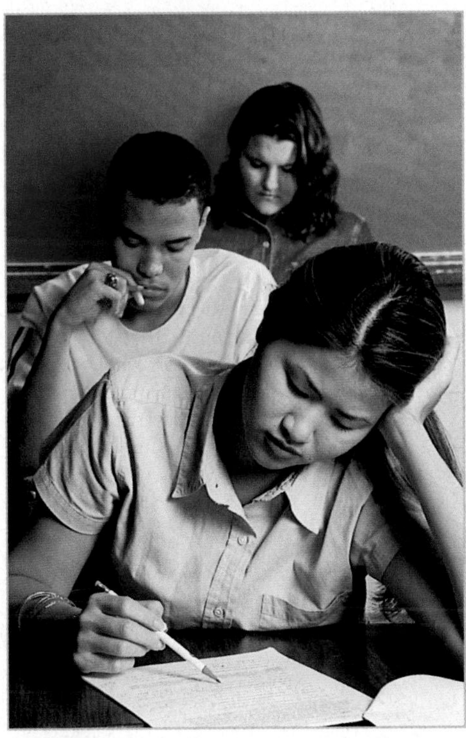

◆ No two people react in quite the same way to what can be a stressful situation. How does your level of stress when taking a test compare with that of a friend?

award, or experiencing some other positive event can be stressful.

Stressful situations are part of life. They can't be avoided. The key is to learn how to cope positively with these situations. When stress is not handled effectively, feelings of worry, fear, or anger can result, leading to depression and lack of energy. Stress may also cause headaches, backaches, or other physical symptoms. It even plays a role in high blood pressure and heart disease.

Nutrition and Stress

The effects of stress on the mind and body can have an impact on personal nutrition. Have you ever been too upset to eat? Negative emotions resulting from stress can cause heartburn, diarrhea, and other digestive problems. Some people overeat when they are feeling stress; others lose their appetite altogether.

Making poor food choices is not a positive way to deal with stress. It does nothing to help you cope with the actual cause of your stress. Poor eating habits can make you feel worse in the long run—often leading to an unhealthy weight and perhaps serious nutritional or health problems.

In contrast, good nutrition can help reduce stress. Eating right is one way to help prevent stress-related illnesses or manage their symptoms. By reacting to stressful situations in a positive way, you can take control of your life and reduce your risk of illness.

Illness and Recovery

Any type of illness puts a strain on the body. Whether you are fighting off a sore throat or have a broken ankle, a healthy, well-nourished body is better equipped to handle the problem. Even though a person who is ill may lose interest in eating, the body still has to have nutrients—often more of them than during healthy times.

If you are helping care for someone who is ill or recovering from an illness, follow these guidelines:

- ◆ Encourage fluids. The patient's physician or other health provider may specify how much is needed.
- ◆ Serve nutritious, eye-catching meals. Varying colors, shapes, textures, and temperatures can spice up any meal.

TEACH

- *Stress (text pages 168-169)*

Guest Speaker

Ask a local fitness instructor to explain how exercise can help alleviate stress. What types of exercises are effective in relieving stress? If possible, have the class practice the stress-relieving exercises.

One-Act Plays

Have groups of students write and stage original one-act plays that demonstrate positive and negative ways to cope with stress. After the presentation, arrange a roundtable discussion of the advantages of managing stress positively and the dangers of doing otherwise. L1

Discussion Activity

Discuss the various relationships between stress and nutrition. Why do some people over- or under-eat as ways of dealing with stress? On the chalkboard, record students' suggestions for ways to manage stress while making healthful food choices.

Critical Thinking Activity

Obtain a list of stress indicators or a self-test designed to measure the stress level in an adult's life. Ask students to redesign the test to make it applicable to the typical stresses in a teen's life. Ask for permission to conduct the test using another class. What do the results tell about the stress level among that group of teens? Have students write up the results.

Extending Learning

Stress and Vitamins—Stress hormones are released from the adrenal glands in response to stress. Vitamin C is needed to release these hormones. Because of this involvement of vitamin C, supplement manufacturers have used it as a basis for marketing some "stress formula" supplements. These supplements are usually a combination of B vitamins and vitamin C. The need for vitamin C during stress can be met just by aiming for the daily value. Including at least five servings of fruits and vegetables daily, especially vitamin C-rich choices, is a good start.

TEACH cont.

- *Illness and Recovery (text pages 169-170)*

USING CONNECTING FOOD AND HEALTH

After students have completed the "Think About It" activity, have students who believe they need improvement to repeat the activity again for another three days. Then compare pie graphs. Ask these students to share comparisons. Have all students share ideas for rearranging their days to include more time for themselves.

Display Activity

Have groups of students each create a display, using either props or poster board, to show stages of nutrition and immunity. Explain that the stages are as follows: (1) disease, (2) loss of appetite, (3) nutrition status declines, (4) immunity weakens, (5) disease worsens, and (6) further loss of appetite. Allow students to walk through and examine other groups' installations. Discuss how malnutrition and infection adversely affect each other. Ask the students how to break this chain with good nutrition.

Eating Plan Analysis Activity

Obtain from hospitals, physicians, or dietitians copies of recommended eating plans for people who are ill or are recovering. Distribute these to students. Discuss situations in which each eating plan might be prescribed. Ask students to provide possible explanations for specific components of eating plans, such as why increased fluids is recommended.

Connecting Food and Health

When the Pressure Is On

It's a vicious cycle that is all too common during the teen years: Pressures—from friends, from teachers, from family members—catch up with you. You begin to eat too much or too little, which takes a toll on your overall health and wellness.

How can you break the chain? Health experts offer a number of stress-busting solutions. Here are a few:

- Learn to manage your time. Keeping a daily planner can help. Be sure to set aside some time for you just to relax and enjoy yourself.
- If you're feeling angry or upset, listen to some calming music, read a funny book, or take your frustrations out by punching a pillow.
- Take positive action to solve a problem if you can. Share your feelings and problems with someone you trust.
- Stress can take the form of negative energy. Turn the negatives into positives. Try physical activity—run, walk, ride a bike, or clean a closet.
- Above all else, take time for eating well. Don't just grab whatever food is in sight. Include breakfast and exercise plans on your agenda for the day. Take care of your health.

Think About It

- In your Wellness Journal, make a list of your activities and responsibilities for a three-day period. As you carry out each task, note in the journal how much time it took. Also keep track of leisure time. At the end of the three days, make a pie graph showing how much time you devoted to each item. If the portion representing time for yourself is too small, think of ways of rearranging your day.

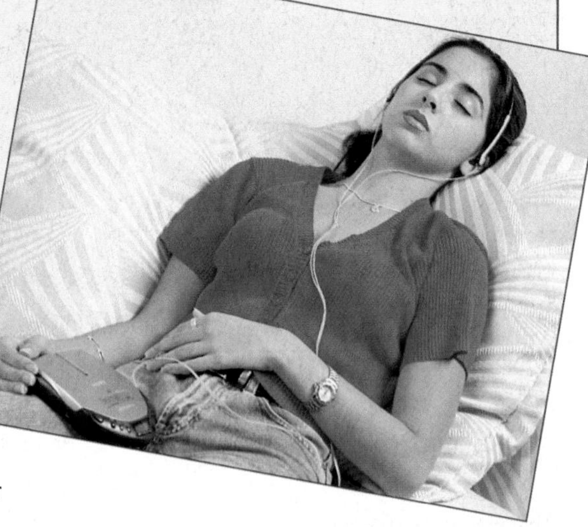

◆ **Taking time to relax can help you manage the stress in your life. In your Wellness Journal, list three activities you do or could try to help reduce stress in your life.**

◆ Be sure the patient gets enough rest for the healing process.

◆ Ask the physician or pharmacist whether the patient's medication affects the appetite or the way the body uses nutrients.

◆ Use disposable or plastic plates and cups if the patient has an illness that can spread to others.

Extending Learning

Illness and Sanitation—When caring for patients at home, follow these hints to keep illness from spreading to other family members:

- Wash your hands with soap and warm water for at least 20 seconds before and after every contact with the patient.
- Wash patient's dishes and utensils separately.
- To dispose of paper or plastic eating utensils and leftover food, put them in a paper bag in the sickroom. Then dispose of the bag immediately.

Nutrients and Disease Prevention

After Vince heard that eating oatmeal might reduce the risk of heart disease, he began having oatmeal each day for breakfast and lunch. Like Vince, many people jump on the bandwagon at the first report of a food or nutrient with supposed disease-fighting properties.

Two such classes of nutrients that have received much attention in the media are dietary supplements and herbal remedies. How can you as a consumer determine if these are for you? For an answer to his question, read on.

Dietary Supplements

Dietary supplements are nutrients people take in addition to the foods they eat. Usually, these supplements take the form of pills, capsules, liquids, or powders.

Dietary supplements may be useful for people taking certain types of medication, pregnant and nursing women, those recovering from illness, older people, and people with special nutritional needs. In such cases, these people may not be able to get enough nutrients from the foods they eat.

Food Science ◆ L A B ◆

Comparing Antacids

One common food-related health problem facing most people at one time or another is indigestion. In relieving the discomfort of indigestion or heartburn, is one over-the-counter product better than another? You are about to find out.

Procedure

1. Gather several antacid products. Dissolve a standard dose of one of the products in 8 ounces (250 mL) of water. Note the current time to the nearest second.
2. Begin adding vinegar to the cup, an eye dropper full at a time. After each addition, test the acidity of the solution with litmus paper. Keep track of how much vinegar you add.
3. Stop when the solution tests acidic, that is, when the litmus paper turns red.
4. Repeat the procedure for each product.

Conclusions

- ◆ Did one antacid neutralize the acid more quickly than the others? Did one neutralize more acid than the others?
- ◆ What ingredient or ingredients listed on the product's label do you think contributed to the antacid's effectiveness?
- ◆ What conclusions, if any, can you draw about the advertising of products as a whole?

- *Nutrients and Disease Prevention (text pages 171-172)*

USING THE Food Science ◆ L A B ◆

Explain to students that pharmaceutical companies often use more precise methods than those used in the classroom. State that stomach acid is not the same acidity as vinegar. Ask students to research the pH of stomach acid and suggest how it compares to vinegar. What conclusions can they draw from this finding?

Dietary Supplement Advisory

Have students form groups. Each group is to be on the alert over a two-day period for TV and magazine advertisements for dietary supplements. For each such ad, group members are to note the name of the supplement and the intended audience. Conclude with a discussion of how these manufacturers are helping to spread a false message. What action can be taken to prevent use and overuse of these products by an unsuspecting public? L2

Student Study

Ask students to develop a supplement use survey. The survey can be distributed to a random sampling of students and others in the community at large. Completed surveys can be placed anonymously in an enclosed box in a specified school location by a deadline date. Have your students compile survey findings in a chart or graph to be posted in the classroom. L3

Extending Learning

Dietary Supplements—There are many misconceptions about dietary supplements. One misconception is that they can provide energy. The three types of nutrients that directly provide energy are carbohydrates, proteins, and fats. Vitamin and mineral supplements do not supply energy. However, B vitamins do help indirectly provide energy from carbohydrates, proteins, and fats.

TEACH cont.

- ***Nutrients and Disease Prevention (text pages 171-172)***

News Research Activity

Have students research through the Internet or library resources cases of herbal remedy overdoses by people who assumed they were using a harmless product. An example is the innocent use of senna leaves—a powerful laxative—as tea, which landed two Vermont women in the hospital. Have students share their findings in a news program format.

Debate

Have students form two groups for a debate. One group is to argue the variety of benefits, or advantages, of herbal remedies, others the disadvantages. You may want to select a few specific herbs for students to debate. Allow time for students to research and plan for their debates. Have the teams stage each debate in front of an impartial jury of their peers. **L1**

Research

Encourage students to visit the National Council Against Health Fraud website and other sources to find out more about popular herbal remedies. Then, have students identify potential hazards related to herb use. Combine students' findings on a chart. **L3**

Most people, however, do not need supplements. They can get all the nutrients they need by following a balanced and varied eating plan. People who rely on supplements to make up for poor food choices are only short-changing themselves.

Safety Check

Children often confuse vitamin and mineral pills with candy. They can be harmed by large doses of supplements. In particular, iron supplements are the most common cause of poisoning deaths among children in the United States. If there are children in the home, be sure nutrient supplements are stored in child-resistant packages out of reach of children.

Nutrient Megadoses

Some people believe in taking megadoses (MEH-guh-dohs-es) of vitamins or mineral supplements. A **megadose** is an extra-large amount of a supplement thought to prevent or cure diseases. As noted in Chapter 2, excess amounts of some nutrients can accumulate in the body and cause harm. Excess amounts of those nutrients that are not stored by the body simply pass out of the body unused, making them a waste of money.

Your best choice is to try to get all your nutrients from food. If you decide to take supplements, avoid megadoses. Also, read the list of ingredients on the label of any supplement to be sure you know what you're getting. Avoid unrecognized nutrients.

Herbal Remedies

"Echinacea." "St. John's Wort." "Gingko." Strange and often hard-to-pronounce names like these have become commonplace in magazine and TV ads. You may see these items sold from booths at shopping malls.

They are but a few of hundreds of **herbal remedies**, nonstandardized products containing herbs known to have medicinal-like qualities. They may be advertised as the ultimate cure for illnesses or diseases. Many herbal remedies have been used in Europe and Asia for centuries. Most are just becoming popular in the United States. However, the safety, purity, and effectiveness of herbal products are questionable. Some of them can even cause serious illness or death.

Before experimenting with any herbal product, be sure to use critical thinking and the other food skills covered in Chapter 1. Remember: Scientific evidence has confirmed the benefits of physical activity and healthy eating.

Special Eating Plans

Some people, because of long-term medical conditions, must be especially aware of their food choices. Their physicians may prescribe special eating plans to help manage their medical conditions. A dietitian may need to provide **medical nutrition therapy**, an assessment of the nutritional status of a patient with a condition, an illness, or an injury that puts her or him at risk.

Extending Learning

St. John's Wort—One popular herbal product is St. John's wort. Promoters of this herb claim that it can improve sleep, decrease anxiety, and alleviate depression. In addition to the safety, purity, and effectiveness concerns of herbal products in general, here are facts about St. John's wort:

- It is sometimes, unfortunately, recommended as an alternative to drug therapy for people who suffer from severe depression.
- It may cause the skin to become more sun-sensitive.

• *Special Eating Plans (text pages 172-175)*

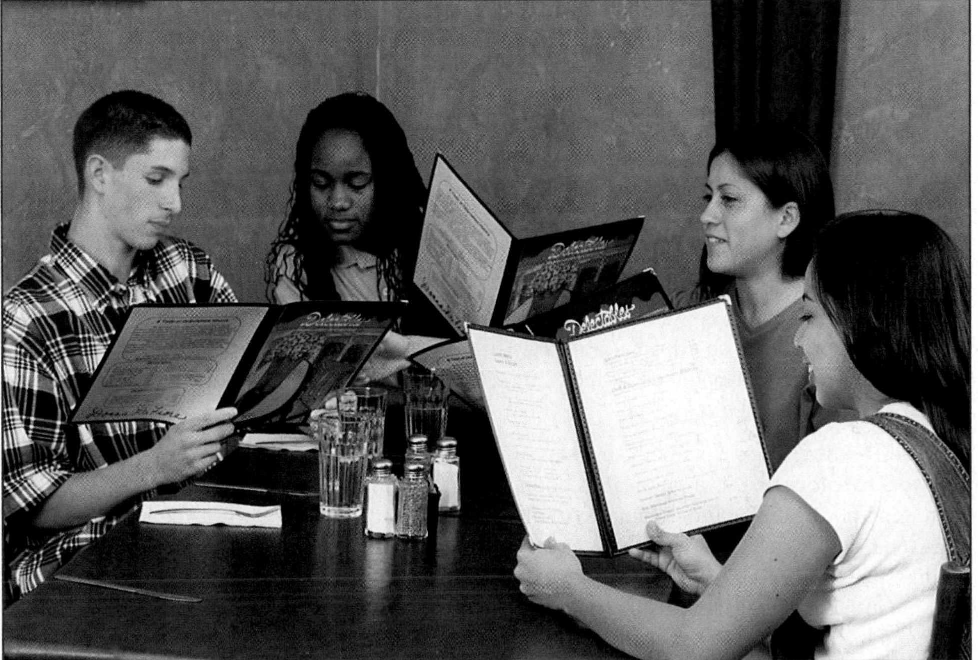

◆ **People with health conditions need to take special care when eating out. How can a person with diabetes use the skill of communication to ensure that he or she orders wisely from a restaurant menu?**

Here are a few conditions that require special eating plans:

◆ **High cholesterol.** People with high cholesterol may develop heart disease. Lowering total fat and saturated fat intake as well as increasing soluble fiber is commonly recommended. Starting the day with oatmeal, strawberries, and nonfat milk would fit well in this plan.

◆ **High blood pressure.** High blood pressure is also a risk factor for heart disease—and other medical conditions. A typical eating plan modification to help lower blood pressure may be to lower fat and sodium (including salt), while increasing potassium and calcium.

◆ **Diabetes. Diabetes** is a condition in which the body cannot control blood sugar levels. Diabetes may cause serious damage to the kidneys, eyes, and heart, as well as other parts of the body. Eating the right balance of food and counting grams of carbohydrate play a role in controlling the blood sugar level. Eating all foods in moderation also helps manage weight, which is very important for many diabetics.

◆ **HIV/AIDS.** For people living with **HIV/AIDS**—a disorder that interferes with the immune system's ability to combat disease-causing pathogens—proper nutrition needs to be a priority every day. Maintaining or improving appetite is vital. Plenty of fluids and regular snacks are important. Often, nutritional supplements are needed.

Interview

Have students interview someone on a specialized eating plan. Ask them to develop a list of questions prior to the interview. One example: "Is following the therapeutic eating plan difficult at a restaurant? If so, how?" Ask students to report their interview findings to class as a "television news anchor." **L1**

Ingredient Identification

Provide students with a packet of ten recipes. Assign students to develop a symbol-identification system for food ingredients that are common food allergens, then match appropriate symbols with recipes. Allow time for students to share chosen symbols and results. **L1**

Planning Specialized Eating Plans

Distribute a different medical condition topic to groups of students, such as "high cholesterol." Have each group plan a three-day meal plan for their assigned medical condition. Encourage students to research assigned conditions. Have each group present their eating plan to the class, discussing how it will improve the medical condition. **L2**

Reinforcing Key Skills

Present the following problems to student groups. Allow time for them to discuss and compare their responses.

Management—Have students plan three days of menus for a child who is allergic to milk. How can students see that the child gets enough calcium and other nutrients normally found in the Milk, Yogurt, and Cheese Group?

Communication—Imagine working in a restaurant, and a customer told you she could only eat sodium-free food due to high blood pressure.

TEACH cont.

- *Special Eating Plans*
- *Physical Challenges (text pages 172-175)*

Demonstration

Ask students to list ideas for foods that would be appropriate for someone who has dental problems and cannot eat hard rolls, raw vegetables, and some meats. Show students how to attractively present pureed foods using shaped molds and a variety of colors.

Discussion Activity

Discuss the effects physical impairments can have on the way people meet their nutritional needs. Have students research ideas and devices people have developed to make it easier to meet their nutritional needs. If possible, bring to class at least one such device.

Student Demonstration

1. Assign a physical challenge, such as blindness, to groups of students.
2. Allow time for each group to plan how to overcome the physical challenge during a meal.
3. Have students bring in food and, if needed, special equipment for a demonstration.
4. Have each group choose a representative to demonstrate to the class how to overcome the challenge, while other members of the group discuss the demonstration. L2

- **Food allergy.** For people afflicted with a **food allergy**, an abnormal, physical response to certain foods by the body's immune system, a single bite of an allergic food can cause symptoms. These range from itching, rash, and hives to abdominal pain, nausea, and even difficulty breathing. For adults, common allergy-causing foods are fish, shellfish, and nuts, especially peanuts. Common allergy-causing foods for children are cow's milk, eggs, peanuts, wheat, and soy. Special tests are used to determine which food or foods are responsible for an allergy.
- **Food intolerance.** Another sensitivity, **food intolerance**, is a physical reaction to food not involving the immune system. A food intolerance is most likely to cause digestive problems. One common example is an intolerance for lactose, the sugar found in cow's milk. Substituting lactose-reduced milk or soy milk for cow's milk is a typical solution.

INFOLINK
For more information on soluble fiber, including food sources, see Section 2-2.

Adjusting to a Special Eating Plan

It takes time for people who have been placed on a special eating plan to adjust to a new way of eating. Eating out and shopping for food pose special challenges. When in a restaurant, the person needs to learn to ask questions about how foods are prepared and to request special orders, when necessary. When at the supermarket, the individual needs to read food labels carefully, checking for ingredients to be limited or increased and looking for nutrient-modified products, such as calcium-fortified juice.

◆ **Adapting kitchens for easier use encourages independence and good nutrition among people with physical challenges. What are three differences you see between this specially built kitchen and others you have seen?**

Extending Learning

Oral Health—One eating challenge is related to dental problems. As people age, they may lose some or all of their teeth. This is often the result of gum disease, not cavities. Sometimes dentures replace teeth, usually allowing normal chewing to occur. However, sore teeth or gums, dry mouth, or swallowing problems sometimes exist. It is important for these oral health problems to be treated when they occur so they don't become barriers to eating healthfully.

People on special eating plans are often surprised at the variety of flavorful foods that can be prepared within the guidelines of their plans. Many are delighted to discover the various herbs and spices that can be pressed into use to make mouth-watering low-fat, low-sodium marinades and sauces. Many medical centers nowadays even offer specialized cooking classes.

If you know of anyone who must follow a special eating plan, offer your support and encouragement. Try to help the person view the special plan as an opportunity to try new foods.

Physical Challenges

Sometimes a physical challenge requires that a person make adaptations in order to meet his or her nutritional needs. Generally, the nutritional needs of such an individual are no different from those of anyone else of similar age, gender, and activity level. However, physical limitations may affect how those needs are met.

People with limited mobility, limited use of the hands, or vision problems may find it difficult to use standard kitchen equipment. In this case, the solution is to adapt the kitchen and its equipment. Design innovations, which are addressed in Chapters 7 and 14, have helped many such people lead independent and self-sufficient lives.

Section 6-2 Review & Activities

1. What is stress? Give three examples of how a negative reaction to stress can affect nutrition.
2. Give three suggestions for planning and preparing meals to fit a medically prescribed special eating plan.
3. In general, how do physical impairments relate to nutritional needs?
4. **Evaluating.** Discuss ways in which good nutrition might help you handle stress more effectively.
5. **Synthesizing.** When Franco complained to his cousin Paul about a lack of energy, Paul told him he needed an herbal remedy to "detoxify" his body. Do you think Franco should follow Paul's advice? Why or why not?
6. **Applying.** Imagine that you are caring for someone who is recovering from surgery. Identify at least six ways that you could make meals more enjoyable for this person.
7. **Analyzing.** Find information about a special diet, as for an allergy, diabetes, or high cholesterol. Use the Internet or other resources. Plan a day's menu for the diet and use nutrition analysis software to make sure the menu is healthful and appropriate for the condition. Present your menu to the class, explaining how it fits the Dietary Guidelines and why you recommend it.

ASSESS

REVIEW

- Ask students to summarize the main ideas in this section.
- Have students complete the Section Review. (Answers appear below.)

EVALUATION

- Provide students with two case studies: (1) female with a long-term medical condition and (2) male with a physical impairment. Have students write a short essay describing adaptations each person might require.
- Have students take the quiz for Section 6-2. (Use the quiz in the *Teacher Resource Guide,* or construct your own with the **ExamView®** *Test Generator* on the *Effective Instruction CD-ROM.*)

RETEACHING

- Have students work in pairs to list stressful situations for teens and ways teens can combat stress. Ask the pairs to role-play for the class how to combat one or more stressful situations.
- Refer to the *Reteaching Activities* booklet for the Section 6-2 activity sheet.

CLOSE

Give students a list of a dozen misconceptions related to stress, dietary supplements and special eating plans. Allow time for students to create statements dispelling the misconceptions. Invite several students to share their statements.

Answers to Section 6-2 Review & Activities

1. Physical or mental tension triggered by an event or situation in your life; examples will vary.
2. See bulleted list on pages 169-170.
3. They can make it more difficult to meet nutritional needs; special adaptations may be necessary.
4. Answers will vary. Generally, a well-nourished body is better able to cope with the physical impact of stress.
5. No; herbal remedy could be unsafe. Also, the use of the word *detoxify* is a red flag of junk science. A well-balanced, nutrient-dense meal plan needs to be emphasized.
6. Answers will vary but may focus on special touches.
7. Answers will vary.

SECTION
6-3
Eating Disorders

FOCUS

MOTIVATORS

- Show students pictures of individuals suffering from anorexia nervosa and bulimia nervosa. Ask if students can identify the problem these individuals are suffering from. Help students recognize that people with bulimia nervosa are hard to identify.
- On the chalkboard, write the headline "Ideal Weight Is Carried to Extreme." Ask students to imagine and discuss the story this headline might precede. Explain that in this section they will be reading "the story."

VOCABULARY

Pronounce the terms listed under "Look for These Terms." Have students find the terms and their definitions in the section.

STUDY SKILLS

- **Outlining.** Have students read the section and outline it by copying the headers on paper and leaving space after each one. Students are to write a sentence in their own words, summarizing the content under each header.
- Have students read the section and complete the appropriate part of the Chapter 6 Study Guide in the *Student Workbook.*

SECTION 6-3

Eating Disorders

Objectives

After studying this section, you should be able to:

- Identify the characteristics of anorexia nervosa and bulimia nervosa.
- Describe the effects of eating disorders on health.
- Explain what can be done to help someone with an eating disorder.

Look for These Terms

eating disorder
anorexia nervosa
binge eating disorder
bulimia nervosa

When Charlene began to lose excess weight, her friends supported her efforts. As the weeks passed, Charlene reached a healthy weight for her age and height. However, she continued to restrict her calorie intake.

Months later, Charlene had lost so much weight that she looked almost like a skeleton. She was light-headed and felt tired all the time. Concerned, her family scheduled a medical checkup. After a thorough evaluation, Dr. Cho diagnosed Charlene's problem as an eating disorder.

What Are Eating Disorders?

Eating disorders are conditions marked by extreme emotions, attitudes, and behaviors related to food, eating, and weight. Anorexia nervosa (a-nuh-REK-see-uh nur-VOH-suh), bulimia nervosa (boo-LEE-mee-uh), and binge eating are recognized disorders. These conditions can seriously impact health and even be life-threatening.

Eating disorders occur most among teens and young adults, especially females, but males, adults, and children as young as eight years old are also affected. Although the numbers are difficult to determine, estimates suggest that from 1 to 10 percent of all teens have an eating disorder. Both victims and their families struggle with the problems caused by eating disorders.

Anorexia Nervosa

People with **anorexia nervosa** have an irresistible urge to lose weight through self-starvation and other methods. They refuse to maintain a minimally normal body weight and have an obsessive fear of gaining weight. No matter how thin they become, they still feel fat and believe they are overweight.

Section 6-3 Resources

◆ **Student Workbook,** pp. 48, 52
◆ **Teacher Resource Guide**
Lesson Plan 6-3 Organizer
Section 6-3 Quiz
Chapter 6 Test
◆ **Effective Instruction CD-ROM**
Exam*View*® *Test Generator*
PowerPoint® Slide #18
◆ **Transparency Package,** CT-18
◆ **Student Motivation Kit**
Reteaching Activities, pp. 38–39
Enrichment Activities

◆ **During a binge eating episode, a person with an eating disorder might consume thousands of calories. What eating disorders involve binge eating? How do these disorders differ from each other?**

People with anorexia will do just about anything to "control" weight, even when their health is at risk. While becoming preoccupied with food and weight, they refuse to eat or they eat very little. They deny hunger and may avoid meals and other eating occasions. Sometimes food rituals become apparent as they rearrange food on a plate, cut it into tiny pieces, or chew for a long time.

Another method used by people with anorexia to control weight is frequent, strenuous exercise that lasts for long periods of time. Sensitivity to cold temperatures may occur. Spending less time with friends and former activities is also typical of people with this disorder.

Effects of Anorexia Nervosa

Anorexia can create serious health problems. A lowered heart rate and body temperature, constipation, and lowered blood pressure and breathing rate are possible. Heart problems, osteoporosis, and brain damage can also develop. Teens and children may experience stunted growth. Females past puberty may stop menstruating. Between 5 to 20 percent of all those with anorexia die from the disorder—a devastating statistic.

Binge Eating Disorder

People who have a binge eating disorder eat large quantities of food at one time, called bingeing. Since eating is out of control, no thought is given to whether feelings of hunger or fullness exist. An eating binge typically occurs when the person is alone and is followed by feelings of guilt.

Effects of Binge Eating Disorder

Because binge eating disorder causes weight gain, people with this condition develop the same health problems that overweight people have. These include high blood pressure, high cholesterol levels, heart disease, diabetes, and gallbladder disease.

TEACH

- *What Are Eating Disorders? (text pages 176-178)*

Chart Development Activity

Discuss the problems associated with eating disorders. What do researchers know about eating disorders? Ask students to develop a chart of the three eating disorders explained in the section and characteristics of each. Share select charts with the class during a discussion.

Building a Resource Folder

Challenge each class member to find and read one newspaper, magazine, journal, or Internet article about one of the three eating disorders covered in the section—anorexia nervosa, binge eating disorder, and bulimia nervosa. Students are to file their articles, along with a brief synopsis, in a Classroom Resource Folder. In their synopses, students are to share any new or startling details they learned from their articles. **L1**

Survey

Have the class develop a body image survey to be completed anonymously by students in the school and other individuals in the community. Students are to include questions about ideal body shape, size, and weight. One section of the survey is to deal specifically with weight loss methods, including extremely low-calorie diets, laxatives, diet aids, forced vomiting, and strenuous exercise for long periods. Tally the results and draw conclusions. **L2**

Reinforcing Key Skills

Present the following problems to student groups. Allow time for them to discuss and compare their responses.

Communication—A student in your school who you do not know well is losing weight and always seems just to pick at but not actually eat lunch. You fear that she may be suffering from an eating disorder but are not sure what action to take or to whom to speak.

TEACH cont.

- *What Are Eating Disorders? (text pages 176–178)*

Problem Solving Activity

Encourage students to use problem-solving skills to determine why people with eating disorders, who know the dangerous effects, continue to practice their self-destructive behaviors.

Research Activity

Have students investigate immediate and potential long-term effects of eating disorders on teens and young adults. Have students list the effects and then pool their information to create class lists.

Educational Tools

Ask each student to develop an educational brochure, flip-chart, or other tool for use in educating teens about the dangers of anorexia nervosa and bulimia nervosa. Encourage creativity and accuracy. Have students present their educational tools to another class in the school. Students are to self-assess the success of their presentation by the questions posed afterwards. L1

Bulimia Nervosa

With **bulimia nervosa,** people also have binge eating episodes, but these are followed with purging to rid the body of the food and calories and prevent weight gain. Purging methods include self-induced vomiting; abuse of laxatives, diet pills, and diuretics (water pills); and extreme exercise.

Like people with anorexia, those with bulimia have a preoccupation with food and a distorted sense of body shape and weight. Unlike people with anorexia, bulimics are usually within 10 to 15 pounds (5 to 8 kg) of a healthy weight.

Lack of control is typical during a binge episode. A total of 3,000 to 5,000 calories may be eaten at a time, usually within two hours and often while the person is alone. Unfortunately, the binge-purge cycle becomes a way of life, with two or more eating binges common in a week.

Because bulimia is so secretive, it can be hard to recognize in another person. Missing food may be a sign, as might the discovery of wrappers and containers for foods, laxatives, and diuretics. Time spent in the bathroom after meals can be another sign. Physical signs on the body are stained teeth, calluses on the hands from self-induced vomiting, and unusual swelling around the cheeks.

Effects of Bulimia Nervosa

With bulimia, vomiting damages the esophagus, teeth, and gums. The salivary glands, located on each side of the neck, enlarge. People with bulimia may rupture the esophagus. Many have constant sore throats.

Loss of fluid causes dehydration with this disorder. Potassium and sodium are also lost. These losses can cause fatigue and kidney problems. Even more serious, they can cause irregular heartbeats and possibly lead to heart failure.

Causes of Eating Disorders

All the results are not in on what causes eating disorders. Because the conditions are complex, the causes are too. Experts are looking at a number of possible connections.

How can I tell whether I have an eating disorder?

An eating disorder can begin in small ways. Weighing in regularly, counting calories, and exercising are all fine—until they become too extreme and start to cause problems. Does weight or body image worry you? Do you ever feel out of control when you eat or exercise? Do you feel obsessive about checking numbers on the scale or of fat grams and calories? Does eating bring feelings of shame or disgust? Do you ever eat in secret or hide other habits related to food? Has someone expressed concern about your eating and exercise habits or your weight? Even if any of your answers were yes, you might not have an eating disorder, but it could be the beginning. Talk to a trusted adult. Getting support early can help prevent a more serious situation from developing.

Extending Learning

Anorexia Nervosa and Brain Damage—Permanent brain damage can result from anorexia nervosa. This occurs because the brain needs a steady supply of glucose. When it doesn't get enough glucose from dietary or stored carbohydrate, protein is metabolized. However, people with anorexia nervosa may have little excess protein to break down into glucose. This lack of glucose can cause brain damage.

- **Psychological factors.** People with eating disorders may use food to cope with difficult emotions, such as feelings of low self-esteem and inadequacy. Loneliness, anxiety, anger, and depression are also possible contributors. The disorder itself further adds to these feelings.
- **Relationships.** Troubles with family and other relationships have been linked to eating disorders, especially when abuse or ridicule about weight takes place.
- **Body image.** Unrealistic images of body shape and weight in society put undo pressure on people to be something that isn't reasonable. Such images exist throughout the media. Dissatisfaction with appearance has been found in many eating disorder cases.
- **Chemistry.** Scientists are looking at the possibility of chemical imbalances in the brain as a possible link to eating disorders. Much is still to be learned in this area.

What Can Be Done?

The earlier an eating disorder is recognized and treated, the better the chance for recovery. Most people cannot stop the self-destructive behaviors on their own. They need professional help.

Resistance to treatment is common. The person may not recognize or acknowledge the problem. Embarrassment can also get in the way. Often someone else who sees what is happening has to step in and encourage the person to get help.

Getting Help

Facing up to an eating disorder takes strength, but it can be done. Acknowledging behaviors that don't seem quite right is the first step. The second step is finding a trusted adult to confide in. A family member or a school nurse or counselor is a good start. A professional counselor or nutritionist can provide the expert help needed. The Yellow Pages in the telephone directory often has references under "eating disorders."

Opening a door to communication is difficult for many. Choosing a private place and time to talk can help. Some people write down their concerns and specific history to make opening up a little easier. Realizing that health, now and in the future, is more important than moments of embarrassment gets many people started on the road to recovery.

◆ **Recovery from an eating disorder depends on getting help. Trained professionals are skilled and have experience in treatment. Why is it often difficult for a person to seek help? How can someone get over that hurdle?**

- *Causes of Eating Disorders*
- *What Can Be Done?*
- *Preventing Eating Disorders (text pages 179-180)*

Guest Speaker

Invite a health care professional or counselor to discuss symptoms of eating disorders, sources of help, and treatment procedures. If possible, have them bring a "spokesperson" (previous patient) who has been treated for an eating disorder.

Checklist

Ask groups of students to develop a checklist for identifying potential warning signs of eating disorders, using information in this section and independent research. Have the groups pool their ideas to develop a master checklist, in which all of the symptoms are listed. Invite students to create a poster from the checklist, and hang it in the classroom. L1

Oral Presentation Activity

Divide the class into five groups. Assign each group one of the five treatment options listed on page 180. Allow time for students to research the therapies. Have each class team "teach" their assigned therapy, using visual teaching tools.

HOME & COMMUNITY CONNECTION

Ask students to research and list all individuals, groups, associations, or treatment centers available in their community to help people with eating disorders. Have students compile their lists into one comprehensive list. Post the list on a school bulletin board or a school Web site.

ASSESS

REVIEW

- Ask students to summarize the main ideas in this section.
- Have students complete the Section Review. (Answers appear below.)

EVALUATION

- Have students write a short essay describing the topics they studied in this section.
- Have students take the quiz for Section 6-3. (Use the quiz in the *Teacher Resource Guide*, or construct your own with the **Exam***View*® *Test Generator* on the *Effective Instruction CD-ROM.*)

RETEACHING

- Have each student make flash cards on index cards, recording potential warning signs of the three discussed eating disorders on one side of the card and the name of the eating disorder on the other. Allow time for pairs of students to practice their flash cards with each other.
- Refer to the *Reteaching Activities* booklet for the Section 6-3 activity sheet.

CLOSE

State to the students: "You CAN make a difference." Then, have the class develop a list of ways they can potentially decrease the incidence of eating disorders at their school.

Treatment Options

Although the process is slow, people with eating disorders can recover. One or two years may be needed. Support from family and friends is vital along the way.

Treatment takes a team approach. The team may include health professionals to treat specific medical complications, dietitians, behavior therapists, psychotherapists, social workers, and nurses. Self-help groups offer sharing with others who have the disorder. Some treatment methods, which may be combined, are listed below.

- **Medical nutrition therapy.** Focuses on nutrition education.
- **Behavioral therapy.** Aims at changing eating habits.
- **Cognitive behavioral therapy.** Works on changing unrealistic thinking.
- **Family therapy.** Dvelops supportive family attitudes.
- **Drug therapy.** May involve antidepressant medication if a patient doesn't respond to other therapies.

Preventing Eating Disorders

The large number of people who have eating disorders is an alarm for society. While treatment is critical, prevention is equally important, but is that possible? Many say yes.

One focus of prevention is on identifying problem behaviors early—before they become full-blown eating disorders. Education and readily available opportunities to talk with professionals must be part of this effort.

A second focus is to prevent the behaviors from occurring at all. By addressing how society views physical appearance, changes in this area are possible. Most people know that a person's worth goes much deeper than looks alone, but unfortunately that message isn't clearly sent in society.

Section 6-4 Review & Activities

1. List four characteristics of anorexia nervosa.
2. Describe two key ways in which bulimia nervosa differs from anorexia nervosa.
3. What possible causes are there for eating disorders?
4. What treatments are available for people who suffer from eating disorders?
5. **Analyzing.** In recent years, a number of celebrities have admitted to having eating disorders. Do you think such publicity has a positive or negative effect? Explain.
6. **Applying.** Imagine that a good friend's eating habits have changed recently. You suspect bulimia nervosa. What is leading you to this conclusion? What actions will you take?
7. **Analyzing.** According to the National Eating Disorders Association, the average American model is 5′11″ tall and weighs 117 pounds. The average American female is 5′4″ tall and weighs 140 pounds. What connection can be made to eating disorders?

Answers to Section 6-3 Review & Activities

1. Any four: preoccupation with food; refusal to eat; food rituals; intense exercise; sensitivity to cold; less time with friends.
2. People with bulimia eat and purge; usually have close to healthy weight.
3. Coping with difficult feelings; troubled relationships; unrealistic body image; chemical imbalance.
4. See page 180.
5. Answers will vary. May encourage openness but also glamorize problem.
6. Answers will vary.
7. Media promotes unrealistic body image, which may contribute to eating disorders.

Career Wanted

Foods Writer

"Writing a good story is like making a good dinner."

Joyce Nitobe

Education and Training

- Degree in journalism, English, or communications
- Experience in food-related field, such as cooking or processing

Qualities

- Enjoy foods and food preparation
- Communication skills
- Ability to meet deadline

Q. Where do you get ideas for stories, Joyce?

A. Everywhere! When I hear about a restaurant opening or a new trend or nutrition issue, I see a story asking to be written. I think, "What else do I want to know about this?" and that directs my story.

Q. How do you develop a story?

A. Most stories involve some research. That might mean going to online resources or talking to experts. If it's a profile of someone in the business, I might shadow the person through a typical workday. Sometimes I test products or recipes. The magazine I write for has a test kitchen for that. They also help with getting photos.

Q. Do you have to be a good cook to be a good foods writer?

A. Many foods writers are good cooks because we enjoy cooking and do it often. Getting to try different foods and impressing your friends with your skills are fringe benefits of the job.

Related Career Opportunities

Entry Level

- Food service worker
- Newspaper intern
- Proofreader

Technical Level

- Food stylist
- Baker
- Newspaper stringer

Professional Level

- Consumer advocate
- Public relations specialist
- Chef

Making Career Connections

WRITING EXPERIENCE. Choose a topic in foods or nutrition from this chapter, or another that interests you. Write an article of at least 500 words, using the techniques mentioned in the interview. Illustrate with photographs or other graphics. Compile the class's contributions into a "Food and Nutrition Gazette."

Career Wanted

Foods Writer

Thinking About the Career

Have students think of other questions to ask Joyce Nitobe about being a foods writer. (Examples: What is the salary range for writing for a magazine? Is it similar for newspapers or the Internet? How long does it take you to create a full-length food and nutrition feature?)

Ask student volunteers to tell what they think would be the most exciting part of being a foods writer.

Career-Building Opportunities

Have students read the "About the Author" sections, when available, of food and nutrition books to determine authors' career backgrounds. Ask students to report interesting findings to class.

For More Information

For additional information about careers in food writing and journalism, encourage students to contact:

- National Council Against Health Fraud
  www.ncahf.org
- Association for Education in Journalism and Mass Communication
  234 Outlet Pointe Blvd.
  Columbia, SC 29210-5667
  www.aejmc.org
- Community Writers Association
  270 Westminster Street
  P.O. Box 12
  Providence, RI 02840-0312
  www.austensharp.com/cwa.htm
- Society for Technical Communication
  901 North Stuart St.
  Suite 904
  Arlington, VA 22203-1822
  www.stc.org
- The National Newspaper Association
  P.O. Box 7540
  Columbia, MO 65205-7540
  www.nna.org
- American Copy Editors Society
  3 Healy St.
  Huntington, NY 11743
  www.copydesk.org

REVIEW

- Have students complete the Chapter Review. (Answers appear below.)

EVALUATION

- Have each student develop a list of the 10 most important statements that they believe best represent the information in Chapter 6. Allow time for students to share their lists for a group study session.
- Have students take the test for Chapter 6. (Use the chapter test in the *Teacher Resource Guide,* or construct your own with the **ExamView®** *Test Generator* on the *Effective Instruction CD-ROM.*)

ANSWERS

Checking Your Knowledge

1. Because their bodies are still developing, growing, and changing.
2. Any three: pieces of skinless fruit, cooked vegetables, cheese, and crackers.
3. They eat the same amounts of the same foods, but their caloric requirements go down.
4. Any two: Extremely low budget; a reluctance to cook just for one; declining thirst signal; frailty; health problems.
5. Any two: Negative emotions resulting from stress can cause digestive problems, overeating, or loss of appetite.
6. Excess amounts of some nutrients can accumulate in the body and cause harm. Excess amounts of those nutrients that are not stored by the body simply pass out of the body unused, making them a waste of money.
7. A food allergy involves the immune system; a food intolerance does not.
8. Teens and young adults, especially females.

Chapter 6 Review & Activities

Summary

Section 6-1: Food and the Life Span

- At each stage of the life span, people experience changes in nutritional needs.
- Good nutrition during pregnancy is essential for the health of the baby.
- Infants and children need the right kinds of foods for health and growth.
- Children should be encouraged to develop good eating habits.
- Through adolescence and adulthood, changing energy needs are a consideration.
- Some older people face special challenges regarding nutrition needs.

Section 6-2: Managing Health Conditions

- Good nutrition is important in preventing and managing stress-related illnesses.
- Along with rest, nutritious food helps the body heal itself during illness and recovery.
- Most people can meet their nutritional needs without taking dietary supplements.
- The purity, safety, and effectiveness of herbal products are questionable.
- Some people have long-term medical conditions requiring medical nutrition therapy.
- Physical impairments sometimes require that a person make adaptations in order to meet nutritional needs.

Section 6-3: Eating Disorders

- Anorexia nervosa involves losing weight through self-starvation.
- Bulimia nervosa involves bingeing and purging.
- Binge eating disorder involves eating huge quantities of food at one time.
- All eating disorders can cause health complications—some of which are serious.
- Warning signs may indicate a problem.
- People with eating disorders need professional help.

Checking Your Knowledge

1. Why is nutrition of particular concern for pregnant teens?
2. Name three healthful finger foods a toddler might be given.
3. Why do people often tend to put on weight as they move from the teen years to adulthood?
4. Name two factors that may keep some older people from eating nutritious meals.
5. Name two ways in which stress and nutrition are related.
6. What dangers are associated with megadoses of dietary supplements?
7. What is the main difference between a food allergy and a food intolerance?
8. In which groups of people do eating disorders occur most often?
9. Describe the binge-purge cycle characteristic of bulimia nervosa.
10. Why is bulimia nervosa usually more difficult to recognize than anorexia nervosa?

Thinking Critically

1. **Identifying Cause and Effect.** The text states that using food to reward or punish children can lead to poor eating habits. Give some examples to show how this might happen.
2. **Determining Accuracy.** Some people believe that certain foods can help cure certain illnesses —for example, that chicken soup helps cure a cold. Do you think there is any truth to such beliefs? Why or why not? How might a scientist try to test such theories?

Working IN THE Lab

1. ***Foods Lab.*** List ideas for making nutritious foods that would appeal to young children. Consider using unusual colors, animal shapes, funny faces, and so on. Prepare samples of the foods. Serve them to classmates or to a group of young children, if possible.
2. ***Foods Lab.*** Find and prepare a simple recipe designed for a modified eating plan, such as a low-sodium or wheat-free plan. Rate the food for appearance, texture, and flavor.
3. ***Foods Lab.*** Prepare a simple meal, such as soup and a sandwich. Place it on a tray as if you were serving it to someone who was in bed recovering from an illness. Show how you would make the meal attractive as well as easy to eat.

Reinforcing Key Skills

1. **Leadership.** Many teens choose foods that don't provide enough calcium, zinc, iron, or vitamins A and C. What steps can be taken within a school cafeteria environment to heighten the awareness of these important nutrients?
2. **Directed Thinking.** What social influences exist that cause some teens to take supplements in place of food, to purge, and/or to eat very little?

Making Decisions and Solving Problems

Your 75-year-old neighbor has poor vision and no longer drives a car. He does his grocery shopping only when someone is available to drive him to the supermarket. You are worried that he isn't getting regular, nutritious meals.

Making Connections

1. **Science.** Using library or Internet sources, research the connection between herbs and health. Possible topics: What effect does echinacea have on colds? What effect does ginseng have on energy? Are there any herbs that help lower high blood pressure? Report your findings to the class. Reports need to include positive and negative uses of the herbs, in addition to your overall evaluation.
2. **Language Arts.** Work in groups to write, illustrate, and produce a pamphlet discussing the warning signs of eating disorders. Distribute the pamphlet in your school or community.

ANSWERS cont.

9. A person overeats (binges) and then purges by inducing vomiting, taking laxatives, or getting extreme amounts of exercise. Then the person feels guilty about it and resolves not to do it again. However, the cycle repeats itself.
10. People with bulimia realize that they have a problem and become skilled at hiding the symptoms. Also, they are usually within a normal weight range.

Thinking Critically

1. Answers will vary. An example: a parent constantly rewarded children with ice cream if they finished all their vegetables. This places special emphasis on ice cream—making it a desired food and possibly leading to a higher consumption of ice cream than of vegetables.
2. Answers will vary. A scientist might begin testing such a theory by finding several people with the same illness at the same stage, along with several healthy people. The scientist would feed chicken soup to half the ill people and half the well people. The other half of both groups would not get the soup. The scientist would then record the results and note any improvement that was due to consuming the chicken soup.

Reinforcing Key Skills

1. Answers will vary. Food choices high in certain nutrients can be highlighted on the menu, for instance, by using a different symbol for each nutrient. Nutrient tip sheets can be made available.
2. Answers will vary. The media has a very strong influence.

UNIT 2

Workspace, Tools, and Techniques

INTRODUCING UNIT 2

Assemble a panel of individuals (including students, if any fit the description) who have lived in other parts of the world. The panel is to discuss aspects of food preparation, cooking, and service in the country they lived in that are different from practices in the United States. (One example, prevalent in many countries, is storing eggs at room temperature rather than in the refrigerator.) Ask the guests to discuss food safety, kitchen safety, and storage. What concerns do people have for conserving natural resources during food preparation? How are foods prepared and cooked? What mealtime customs are observed?

UNIT 2

Workspace,

KEY TO ABILITY LEVELS Each section of the text contains skill-building activities. Each activity has been labeled for use with students of various learning styles and abilities.

L1 **Level 1** activities are basic activities and should be within the range of all students.

L2 **Level 2** activities are average activities and should be within the range of students working at average and above-average levels.

L3 **Level 3** activities are challenging activities designed for the ability range of above-average students.

Tools, and Techniques

UNIT 2 PROJECT

Divide the class into three groups representing the 19th, 20th, and 21st centuries. Ask each group to investigate the workspace, tools, and food preparation techniques of the assigned era. Explain that each group is to assemble images, facts, and data for its era to be presented as part of a multimedia, walk-through, in-class exhibit. (If there is not adequate classroom space for three such exhibits, ask groups to store relevant materials in a specific location in the classroom for presentation on a specified date close to the end of unit coverage.) For its multimedia display, each group is to make a checklist that contains the following questions: What are the major kitchen and food safety issues of the era? How is food stored? What concerns do people have about conserving natural resources during food preparation? What types of recipes are used? How are ingredients measured? What kitchen equipment is used? How are foods prepared and cooked?

PROJECT FOLLOWUP

At the end of unit coverage, have groups present their multimedia walk-throughs. Equip students with checklists as they walk through each installation, noting particular sounds, sights, and facts that apply equally well to the era they researched. Conclude by asking the entire class what generalizations they can make about the timelessness of certain food preparation customs.

FCCLA Projects

Applied Technology. Students develop a project on career technology. An aspiring dietitian might use specialized software to run nutrient analyses of classmates' lunches. A future pastry chef could customize prepared cakes or cookies by using the latest decorating tools and coloring agents.

Leaders at Work. Employed students implement a strategy to improve workplace safety or efficiency, recording results in photos. They identify the situation and ask permission to carry out the plan, using verifiable signs of success, such as fewer accidents, less time for tasks, or positive remarks from their coworkers.

CHAPTER 7

Kitchen Principles

Advance Planning Guide ☑

- Obtain a kitchen floor plan.
- Obtain pictures of basic kitchen work centers.
- Gather containers of hazardous chemicals.
- Invite a local firefighter to class to speak about kitchen fire safety.
- Prepare slides, drawings, or photos that show unsafe conditions in the kitchen.
- Bring to class a caulking "gun."
- Gather pictures of kitchens in 1900 and kitchens today.
- Arrange to bring to class opened, shelf-stable food packages.
- Gather freezer packaging materials for a display.
- Arrange to have a potential PSA presented over the school's public address, computer, or TV system.
- Gather articles describing the need for conserving natural resources.
- Arrange for a potential school-wide contest for voting on a trash-reduction advertising campaign.
- Arrange a field trip to a local recycling plant.

CHAPTER 7

Kitchen Principles

Working in the kitchen is more than just putting on a good show. It involves knowing rules of safety, including safe ways of storing food. After reading this chapter, you will know all about these topics.

MEETING DIVERSE NEEDS

Visual/Spatial Learner. If there are students in the class with an aptitude for drawing, building, or creating, invite a group of them to design an architecturally-detailed rendering of an ideal kitchen work center for the year 2025. Suggest they keep in mind safety, convenience, storage, conservation, and potential technological advances. Have them share their design with the rest of class, explaining how each part of the center positively correlates to safety, convenience, storage, conservation, and technology.

SECTION
7-1

Objectives

After studying this section, you should be able to:

- Define and give examples of major appliances, small appliances, and utensils.
- Explain what a work center is and identify the three basic kitchen work centers.

Look for These Terms

major appliance

small appliance

utensils

work center

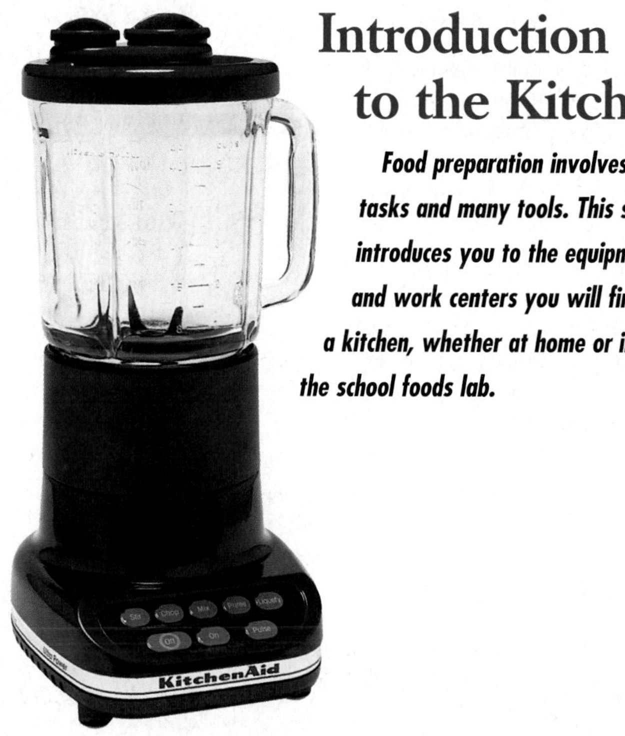

Introduction to the Kitchen

Food preparation involves many tasks and many tools. This section introduces you to the equipment and work centers you will find in a kitchen, whether at home or in the school foods lab.

Types of Kitchen Equipment

Kitchens contain three basic kinds of equipment: major appliances, small appliances, and utensils.

A **major appliance** is a large device that gets its energy from electricity or gas. Most kitchens have at least two major appliances: a refrigerator-freezer for cold storage and a range for cooking. Some kitchens have a separate cooktop and oven instead of a single range unit. Many kitchens also have a microwave oven and a dishwasher.

A **small appliance** is a small electrical household device used to perform simple tasks. The mixer, food processor, blender, and toaster are examples of small kitchen appliances.

Utensils are kitchen tools, such as measuring cups, knives, and peelers. Other kitchen utensils include pots, pans, and other cookware.

Safety Check

As any cook who has ever shorted out a microwave oven or burned a pot can tell you, appliances and utensils require careful use and regular care. Before using or cleaning any appliance, read the owner's manual.

SECTION
7-1

Introduction to the Kitchen

FOCUS

MOTIVATORS

- Have students prepare a bulletin board illustrating the various activities that take place in the kitchen.
- Ask students to work in groups to identify the major and small appliances and utensils they would need for a first apartment. Compare the lists developed by different groups.

VOCABULARY ACTIVITY

Pronounce the four terms listed under "Look for These Terms." Have students find the terms and their definitions in the section. Point out the noun *appliance*. Ask students to suggest if *appliance* always refers to kitchen devices. To what else can it refer? Repeat for *utensils* and *work center*.

STUDY SKILLS

- **Listening.** Invite a group of volunteers to prepare an oral reading of the section.
- Have students read the section and complete the appropriate part of the Chapter 7 Study Guide in the *Student Workbook.*

Section 7-1 Resources

◆ **Student Workbook,** pp. 53, 56
◆ **Teacher Resource Guide**
Lesson Plan 7-1 Organizer
Section 7-1 Quiz
◆ **Effective Instruction CD-ROM**
Exam*View*® *Test Generator*
PowerPoint® Slide #19
◆ **Transparency Package,** CT-19
◆ **Student Motivation Kit**
Reteaching Activities, p. 40
Enrichment Activities

TEACH

- *Types of Kitchen Equipment*
- *Kitchen Work Centers (text pages 187-188)*

Discussion Activity

Discuss the distinction between major and small appliances. Discuss why it is important to read the owner's manual before using or cleaning an appliance or utensil.

Stocking a Kitchen

Have students write a brief essay describing the appliances and utensils that would be included in their "perfect kitchen." Students may use drawings to illustrate points made in the essay but should concentrate on describing the kitchen vividly so the reader can envision it. L1

Planning

Suggest students think of situations when they tried to work or use something in the kitchen, but it wasn't possible or it wasn't easy due to the current kitchen plan. Then, ask students to describe the concept of work centers as it relates to the kitchen. Have students develop a written or drawn plan for a kitchen work center other than the centers listed on pages 188-189. Have students share their plans with the class and discuss how they fit the description of "well-designed" centers. L2

Kitchen Work Centers

You wouldn't store videotapes or CDs in a different location from the VCR or CD player. The same principle applies to kitchen organization. Organizing a kitchen efficiently can save time and energy by reducing the steps you need to take to carry out a task.

Most home kitchens and school foods labs are organized around work centers. A **work center** is an area designed for specific kitchen tasks. A well-designed work center has the equipment you need for a task, sufficient storage space, and a safe, convenient work space.

Technological advances are making kitchen designs more user-friendly. One example is an adjustable range cooktop that can be raised or lowered to a convenient height.

Basic Work Centers

The refrigerator-freezer, sink, and range—and the counters and cabinets around them—form the three basic kitchen centers.

- **Cold storage center.** The refrigerator-freezer is the focus of this center. Items stored nearby might include plastic storage bags, food wraps, and containers for leftover foods.
- **Sink center.** This center is the main source of water. It is used for a variety of tasks, including washing fresh fruits and vegetables, draining foods, and washing dishes. Dishpans and other cleanup supplies should be kept handy.

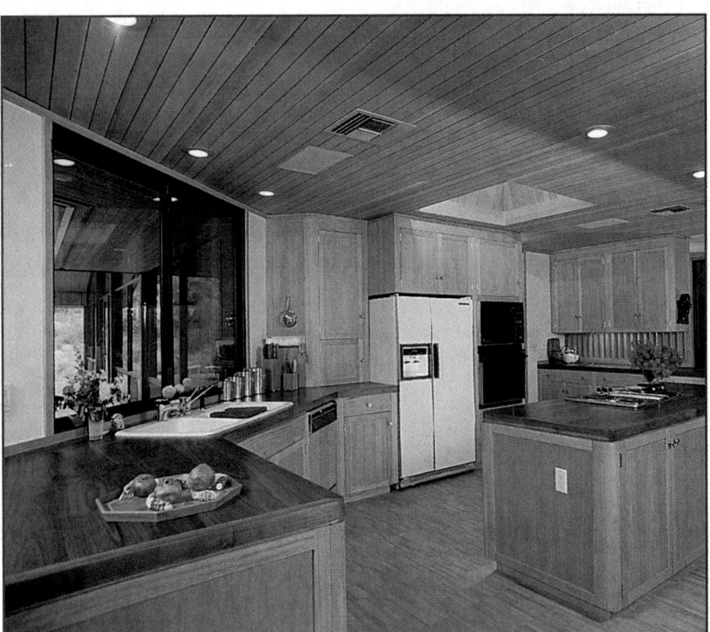

◆ **The overall design of a kitchen depends on lifestyle and budget. Which of the kitchen work centers can be seen in the kitchen shown here?**

Reinforcing Key Skills

Present the following problems to student groups. Allow time for them to discuss and compare their responses.

Communication—Lena wants utensils on a grid over the range. Pete thinks grease and cooking residues will get on them and wants to keep them in a drawer. Lena feels sharp implements could cause accidents. Resolve the problem.

Management—Dry spices used in your kitchen are stored right next to the range for easy access. Heat can decrease their shelf life. Where can these be conveniently placed out of harm's way?

- **Cooking center.** This center includes the range and related items, such as cooking tools, pots and pans, and potholders. Small cooking appliances might be kept near the range. Some canned and packaged foods might also be stored here.

Sometimes there is more than one logical place for equipment. For instance, a microwave oven may be part of the cooking center. However, it could also be placed near the refrigerator-freezer for quick heating of leftovers and frozen food. José's family keeps the microwave oven on a sturdy rolling cart so that it can be moved to wherever it's needed.

Other Work Centers

Some kitchens contain additional, separate work centers.

- **Mixing center.** This area is used for preparing and mixing foods. Measuring cups, bowls, mixing spoons, and an electric mixer are commonly stored here, along with foods such as flour and spices. In a small kitchen, this center might be combined with one of the others.
- **Planning center.** Some home kitchens include a planning center with space to store cookbooks, recipes, and coupons. A desk provides a convenient place for writing out meal plans and shopping lists. Other useful features are a calendar, a bulletin board, a telephone, and perhaps even a computer.

A well-organized and well-equipped kitchen is a place where good food can be prepared quickly, easily, and safely.

Section 7-1 Review & Activities

1. What is a major appliance? A small appliance? A utensil?
2. What is a kitchen work center?
3. Name three major work centers of the kitchen.
4. Why is it important to organize a kitchen around work centers?
5. **Analyzing.** Which of the three kinds of kitchen equipment do you think you could most easily get along without—major appliances, small appliances, or utensils? Explain your answer.
6. **Evaluating.** The Ameslers are designing a new kitchen. The family does a lot of baking. Identify which work centers they should plan their kitchen around. Explain your answers.
7. **Applying.** Draw a rough floor plan of your school foods lab kitchen. Show the location of the sink, major appliances, cabinets, and counters. Circle and label each work center. Identify the location of at least two small appliances and three kinds of utensils.

ASSESS

REVIEW

- Ask students to summarize the main ideas in this section.
- Have students complete the Section Review. (Answers appear below.)

EVALUATION

- Give students a floor plan of a kitchen. Have students identify the three basic work centers and list the items that might be included in each work center.
- Have students take the quiz for Section 7-1. (Use the quiz in the *Teacher Resource Guide,* or construct your own with the **Exam***View*® *Test Generator* on the *Effective Instruction CD-ROM.*)

RETEACHING

- Give students a picture of each basic work center and ask them to describe the appropriate work activity, appliances, and utensils for that work center.
- Refer to the *Reteaching Activities* booklet for the Section 7-1 activity sheet.

CLOSE

Remind students of the motivating activity in which they made lists of equipment for an apartment. Ask students to categorize the equipment according to work center.

Answers to Section 7-1 Review & Activities

1. A large device that gets its energy from electricity or gas; a small electrical household device used to perform simple tasks; a kitchen tool.
2. An area designed for specific kitchen tasks.
3. Cold storage center, sink center, cooking center.
4. To save time and energy by reducing steps you need to take to carry out a task.
5. Answers will vary. Possible answer: Small appliances, since most of their functions can also be performed by major appliances or utensils.
6. Answers will vary, but should include at least the centers in number 3 above.
7. Answers will vary according to your school foods lab layout.

SECTION
7-2
Preventing Kitchen Accidents

FOCUS

MOTIVATORS

- Ask students to describe major or minor accidents that have occurred in their home kitchens. Ask students to identify the causes of these accidents.
- Display containers of hazardous chemicals such as oven cleaners, drain cleaners, pesticides, and polishes. Ask students to identify those that are poisonous. When they are finished, announce that all are actually poisonous.

VOCABULARY ACTIVITY

Pronounce the three terms listed under "Look for These Terms." Explain that *CPR* stands for cardiopulmonary resuscitation—*cardio-* means heart; *pulmonary* refers to the lungs. Then have students find the terms and their definitions in the section.

STUDY SKILLS

- **Guided Reading.** Have students look at the headings within Section 7-2 to preview the concepts that will be discussed.
- Have students read the section and complete the appropriate part of the Chapter 7 Study Guide in the *Student Workbook*.

SECTION
7-2

Preventing Kitchen Accidents

Objectives

After studying this section, you should be able to:

- Identify ways to prevent common kitchen accidents.
- Discuss special safety needs.
- Describe what to do if a kitchen accident results in injury.

Look for These Terms

polarized plugs
Heimlich maneuver
CPR

As Kaneesha cracked eggs for an omelet, some egg white fell on the floor. "I'll clean that up later," she thought. Minutes later the telephone rang. As Kaneesha turned to answer it, she felt something slick underfoot. "The egg white!" she thought, as her foot slid out from under her.

An Accident-Free Kitchen

A kitchen should be a place to prepare enjoyable food. Yet, just a few seconds of carelessness can turn the kitchen into an accident waiting to happen. Falls, electrical shocks, cuts, burns, and poisoning are all kitchen hazards. The keys to preventing kitchen accidents are careful kitchen management and proper work habits.

General Safety Guidelines

Your work habits are vital to your safety in the kitchen. Here are some general guidelines:

- Don't let hair, jewelry, sleeves, or apron strings dangle. They could catch on fire or become tangled in appliances.
- Keep your mind on what you're doing.
- Prevent clutter. Put items back where they belong as you finish with them or after you've washed them.
- Close drawers and doors completely after you open them. You could be seriously hurt if you bump into an open door or drawer.
- Use the right tool for the job. Don't use a knife to pry off a jar cover, for example. Take the time to find the tool you need.
- Store heavy or bulky items, such as cookware, on low shelves so that you can reach them easily.

Section 7-2 Resources

◆ **Student Workbook,** pp. 53, 57
◆ **Teacher Resource Guide**
Lesson Plan 7-2 Organizer
Section 7-2 Quiz
◆ **Effective Instruction CD-ROM**
Exam*View*® *Test Generator*
◆ **Student Motivation Kit**
Reteaching Activities, pp. 41–42
Enrichment Activities
Food Science Resources, pp. 19–20

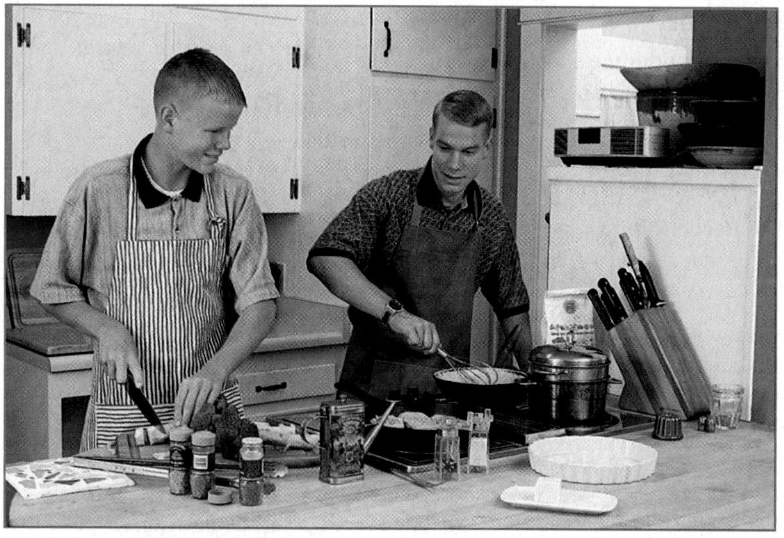

◆ Accident prevention in the kitchen begins with dressing appropriately. How might the saying "An ounce of prevention is worth a pound of cure" apply to work in the kitchen?

Preventing Falls

As Kaneesha learned, spills on the floor can cause accidents. To prevent falls, keep the floor clean and clear of clutter. Wipe up spills, spatters, and peelings so that no one will slip on them. Eliminate other hazards, such as slippery throw rugs, and replace damaged or worn flooring. Don't wear untied shoes, floppy slippers, or long clothing that could cause you to trip.

To reach higher shelves, use a firm stepstool. If you use a chair or a box, you could fall and be injured.

Preventing Cuts

Cuts are an everyday hazard for the cook. Here are some safety guidelines for handling knives, other sharp tools, and broken glass:

- ◆ Keep knives sharp and use them properly. You'll learn how in Section 8-4.
- ◆ Use a drawer divider, knife block, or knife rack for storing sharp cutting tools.
- ◆ Don't try to catch a falling knife—you might grab the blade instead of the handle. Step aside and let it fall.
- ◆ Don't soak knives or other sharp-edged utensils in a sink or dishpan with water in it. When you reach into the water, you could cut yourself.
- ◆ Sweep up broken glass from the floor immediately with a broom and dustpan. If you need to pick up pieces by hand, use a wet paper towel instead of bare fingers. Seal the broken glass in a paper or plastic bag; then place the bag in the wastebasket. Take out the trash as soon as possible.

◆ Storing knives in a block or special rack helps prevent cuts. Identify two other precautions to take when using knives.

TEACH

- *An Accident-Free Kitchen (text pages 190-195)*

Discussion Activity

Ask students to describe several types of injuries that can happen in the kitchen without careful kitchen management and safe work habits. Discuss the proper way to store and use knives and other sharp kitchen tools. Discuss precautions people should take to prevent serious shocks from electrical appliances.

Posters

Have students identify common types of kitchen accidents. Divide students into groups to create posters giving safety tips for preventing one type of kitchen accident. Have groups share their posters with the class, then post them in the foods laboratory. L1

Checklists

Have students develop a checklist for preventing falls and cuts in the kitchen. Have students use the checklist during meal preparation to check family's safety from these kitchen hazards. Any hazard should be shared with family members at home. L1

Extending Learning

Cuts—The Consumer Product Safety Commission estimates that over 137,000 people receive hospital treatment for injuries from kitchen knives each year. Most of these are for cuts on fingers, hands, and arms. To prevent injury, follow these tips:

- Always choose the right kind of knife for the job.
- When using scissors to snip food, hold the food so that your fingers are well away from the blades.

TEACH cont.

- *An Accident-Free Kitchen (text pages 190-195)*

Oral Presentation

Ask students to research the incidence of electrical shock, such as how often it occurs, what is the typical cause, and when is treatment necessary. Have students prepare a one-minute presentation on their findings. Encourage student creativity; suggest use of visuals and a television news format, for instance. L1

Home Survey

Have students find all the outlets and small, plugged-in appliances in their home kitchens. Using the information on page 192, review if they are being used properly. Report findings to the class. Suggest students report all findings to their families. L1

Press Release

Have students who are effective researchers team with writers to create a press release on using electricity safely. The release should list basic, informative steps learned from the text and from students' brainstorm sessions or research. If it can be arranged, students should send the press release for potential publication to a school publication or web site or a local newspaper. L2

Using Electricity Safely

Electrical appliances save both time and work in the kitchen. However, they can also be a source of shocks, burns, and other injuries.

To avoid accidents, carefully read the owner's manual that comes with each kitchen appliance. Follow the directions for using the appliance safely. In addition, remember these basic guidelines:

- **Water and electricity don't mix.** Never use an electric appliance when your hands are wet or when you are standing on a wet floor. Keep small electric appliances away from the water when you use them. Don't run cords around a sink. If an electric appliance falls into water or becomes wet, unplug it immediately without touching the appliance itself. Don't put small appliances in water for cleaning unless the owner's manual says it's safe to do so.
- **Avoid damage to electrical cords.** Even a single exposed wire could start a fire or produce a shock. To keep from damaging cords, don't run them over a hot surface or try to staple or nail them in place. Never disconnect an appliance by tugging on the cord. Instead, grasp the plug at the electrical outlet to remove it.
- **Use outlets properly.** Plugging too many cords into an electrical outlet can cause a fire. Some appliances are equipped with **polarized plugs**—plugs made with one blade wider than the other and designed to fit in the outlet in only one way. You may not be able to fit a polarized plug into an older outlet. If that's the case, don't try to force the plug in or change the shape of the plug. Instead, have the outlet replaced, or buy an adapter.
- **Use care with any plugged-in appliance.** Never put your fingers or a kitchen tool inside an appliance that is plugged in. You might touch parts that could shock you, or you might accidentally turn the appliance on and injure yourself. Don't let the cords dangle off the counter—an appliance could accidentally be pulled off while in use. Turn off small appliances as soon as you are through with them.
- **Watch for problems.** Don't try to use a damaged appliance or one that gives you a shock. Have it repaired before you use it again. If an appliance starts to burn, unplug it immediately.

◆ **Exercising electrical safety can help prevent a kitchen disaster.** In what way is the situation on the left an accident waiting to happen?

HOME & COMMUNITY CONNECTION

Ask students to bring to class one or more electrical appliance warning labels, instruction booklets, or package inserts, if possible, that provide safety information. Hold a class discussion on the safety guidelines from the students' collected information. What conclusions can be drawn?

Hazardous Chemicals

Hazardous chemicals are not limited to use in industries. Many can be found under most kitchen sinks. Hazardous household chemicals include oven cleaners, lighter fluid, drain cleaners, pesticides, and polishes. Some of these chemicals can cause burns, breathing difficulties, and poisoning.

Before you buy any household chemical, read the label carefully to be sure you understand the directions. You'll find important information about adequate ventilation, ways to protect yourself, and proper disposal of any unused product. You will also learn what to do if the product is accidentally swallowed or inhaled. Here are some additional tips:

- Never transfer a hazardous product to another container. You'll need the directions that appear on the original container each time you use the product.
- Never mix different chemical products. They could combine to give off poisonous fumes.
- With spray products, be sure you're pointing the spray nozzle where the product is supposed to go. Never point it at yourself or anyone else.

FOR YOUR HEALTH

Safe Cleaning Substitutes

Before reaching for a potentially hazardous cleaning product, consider using a safe substitute. The following cleaning solutions were used before household chemicals turned up on supermarket shelves.

Cleaning Product	Safe Substitute
Dishwashing liquid	Use a combination of soap flakes and vinegar.
Dishwasher detergent	Use equal parts borax and washing soda (hydrated sodium carbonate).
Oven cleaner	Use a paste of baking soda, salt, and hot water, or sprinkle baking soda on the soiled area and scrub it with a damp cloth after about five minutes. Be sure not to let the baking soda touch the heating elements.
Drain cleaner	Pour ¼ cup baking soda followed by ½ cup white vinegar in the drain. Cover the drain until the fizzing stops. Then flush by running hot water in the drain.
Window cleaner	Use alcohol to remove the residues. When the glass is dry, spray it with a mixture of equal parts white vinegar and water. You can recycle newspaper by drying the window with a crumpled page.

Following Up

1. Check the contents labels of three household cleaners you use regularly. Use a dictionary to check unfamiliar ingredients. How many of the ingredients are toxic?
2. Read the warnings on the labels for several cleaning products. How safe do you feel using these products? What effect could they have on the environment after being washed down household drains?

- *An Accident-Free Kitchen (text pages 190-195)*

Product Identification Activity

Ask students to develop a list of hazardous chemicals that can be found in their home kitchen. In class, discuss the problems the products can cause. Then ask students to list guidelines to use when buying and using products that contain hazardous chemicals.

Supermarket Survey

Assign students to visit a supermarket to find at least 10 different hazardous chemicals that might be found in kitchens. Ask them to create a table to show any warnings or special directions on the products they have identified. 

Computer Activity

Invite students to create pamphlets that summarize in a lively text format tips on storing and using hazardous chemicals. L2

FOR YOUR HEALTH

1. Divide the class into three groups.
2. Provide each group with ingredients to make one of the safe substitutes listed in For Your Health on page 193.
3. Have each group prepare their substitute.
4. Ask each group to demonstrate and discuss the proper use of their safe substitute to the rest of the class.
5. After each demonstration, moderate a discussion of the effectiveness of each safe substitute.

Reinforcing Key Skills

Present the following problems to student groups. Allow time for them to discuss and compare their responses.

Directed Thinking—Ask students why the instructions on lye drain cleaners tell them to flush the drain with cold water after use.

Communication—You have found hazardous chemicals stored within a child's easy reach at your relative's home. Your relative has two children under five years of age. Write the script of what you might say to ensure the health of the children.

TEACH cont.

- *An Accident-Free Kitchen (text pages 190-195)*

Poster Project Activity

Have students design and create posters to promote safety around ranges and microwaves. Have students share their posters in class while discussing guidelines for using ranges and microwaves. Display the posters in the foods laboratory or school cafeteria.

USING Safety Check

Ask students to bring to class the oldest potholder or oven mitt they can find from home. Set up a display, numbering the potholders and oven mitts. Have each student grade each as follows: STILL SAFE, UNSURE, and UNSAFE. Have one student tally the grades. Review the graded display with class. A potholder or oven mitt with mostly UNSAFE grades should be thrown away or recycled.

- ◆ Store hazardous chemical products away from food. Be sure children can't reach them. Flammable products, such as kerosene, lighter fluid, and aerosol sprays, must be stored away from any source of heat.
- ◆ Avoid using hazardous chemicals unnecessarily. Whenever you can, substitute simple, safe cleaners, such as lemon juice, vinegar, soap flakes, baking soda, washing soda, or borax.

Preventing Range and Microwave Accidents

The range is the most likely place for fires and burns to occur. The microwave oven also presents some hazards. Here are some rules for using these appliances safely:

- ◆ Use potholders or oven mitts when picking up or uncovering hot pots and pans.
- ◆ When uncovering a pot or pan, lift up the far edge of the cover first so that the steam will flow away from you. Otherwise, it could burn your face and hands.
- ◆ Use only pots and pans in good condition. A loose handle or warped bottom could cause an accident.
- ◆ Keep pan handles turned toward the back or middle of the range top. Otherwise, someone might bump into a handle, causing a spill, and possibly be burned by a hot liquid.
- ◆ Keep flammable items, such as paper towels, away from the range. A draft could blow them onto the range and start a fire. For the same reason, do not put curtains on a window that is close to the range.
- ◆ Do not use plastic items near the range except for those made of heatproof plastic, such as plastic turners and spoons for nonstick pans. Some plastics are highly flammable and give off poisonous fumes when they burn.
- ◆ Arrange oven racks properly before you start the oven. You risk being burned if you have to reposition them once the oven is hot.

◆ **Oven mitts provide more protection than potholders. Explain why both should be inspected from time to time.**

Extending Learning

Burns and Microwave Ovens— Microwave ovens are associated with an increase in burn injuries. The most common kinds result from heating whole eggs and baby bottles. The interiors develop high pressures when heated and can explode when handled.

Another common burn occurs when plastic wrap or a cover is removed from a container of hot food. People may be deceived if the container doesn't feel hot. The wrap or lid cover should always be tilted so the steam is directed away from the face.

- Stand to the side when you open the oven door. The heat rushing from the oven could burn your face.
- Don't reach into a hot oven. Pull out the rack first, using a potholder or an oven mitt.
- Clean up spills and crumbs after the oven has cooled. If allowed to build up in the oven, they could catch fire.
- Be sure cooktop and oven/broiler controls are turned off when not in use.
- Keep a fire extinguisher handy, and be sure everyone knows how to use it.

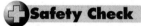

Safety Check

Be sure to inspect oven mitts and potholders for wear and tear from time to time. Worn or scorched spots will not protect you from getting burned by hot pots and pans.

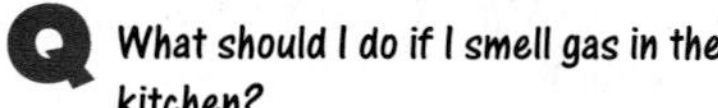

Q ***What should I do if I smell gas in the kitchen?***

A First check to see whether the pilot light on the range has gone out. If it has, light the match first; then turn on the burner and light it. Turning on the burner first will cause gas to accumulate, a condition that could lead to an explosion. If you still smell gas, turn off all controls and open the windows for ventilation. Alert others and leave the building immediately. Call your gas company from another location.

If a Fire Starts

You've followed all the proper safety procedures, but suddenly there's a fire in your kitchen. What should you do? What to do depends on where the fire occurs.

◆ **No kitchen should be without a fire extinguisher. Do you know how to use one correctly?**

- **Range top or electric skillet.** Turn off the heat. Put the cover on the pan, or pour salt or baking soda on the flames. Never use water—the grease will splatter and spread the fire, and it could burn you. Don't use baking powder—it could make the fire worse.
- **Oven, broiler, microwave, toaster oven.** Turn off or disconnect the appliance. Keep the oven door closed until the fire goes out.

Never attempt to carry a pan with burning contents. You could cause an injury or a bigger fire. If you can't immediately put out a fire, go outdoors and call the fire department.

- *An Accident-Free Kitchen (text pages 190-195)*

Discussion Activity

Ask students to describe two different places where fires may start in the kitchen. What should people do if a fire starts? Ask students to describe any kitchen fire situations where they were a witness. How was the situation handled?

VISUAL LEARNING ***Using the Photograph*** Ask students to state the location of the nearest fire extinguisher. Then demonstrate, step-by-step, how to use a fire extinguisher while students number each step on a blank piece of paper. Ask two student volunteers to repeat the demonstration to the class using their numbered steps.

Guest Speaker

Invite a local firefighter to come to class to speak about kitchen fire safety. If possible, this speaker might demonstrate techniques for putting out fires with baking soda or fire extinguishers.

HOME & COMMUNITY CONNECTION

Ask students to conduct a phone or live interview survey of three neighbors to determine if they own a fire extinguisher. Have students report results while one student tallies on the board the number of "yes" and "no" responses. Discuss the results. As a class, prepare a paragraph "position" statement of why having a fire extinguisher is recommended. Encourage students to provide copies of the statement to their neighbors without fire extinguishers.

TEACH cont.

- *Special Needs for Accident Prevention*
- *In Case of Accident (text pages 196-197)*

Educational Materials Activity

Have students identify ways to childproof a kitchen as you write them on the chalkboard. Ask students to compile suggestions in a booklet, mini-poster, or any other creative educational method.

Student Demonstrations

Have students work in pairs to demonstrate one poor example of child safety in the kitchen. Then, have the same pair demonstrate how to turn the poor example into an accident-preventing example. After the demonstration, encourage class discussion. L1

Developing First Aid Kit

Divide students into groups. Ask them to plan a first aid kit by (1) listing contents that go into it and (2) making the kit by bringing materials from home. For any materials students are not able to obtain, suggest they draw it or provide "mock" material. Have each group display their first aid kits. L1

Learning CPR Activity

Have students find one organization in your community that offers classes in CPR, how often the classes are offered, and what fees, if any, apply. Gather students' results in class. If there is more than one location, compile a list and distribute a copy to each student. Remind students that they can not perform CPR unless they are certified. Encourage students to become CPR certified.

Special Needs for Accident Prevention

As a rule, anything you could do to prevent accidents will benefit the entire family. The very young and old, however, may need special consideration.

Children

Small children like to be where adults are—especially the kitchen. They want to watch you and do what you're doing. If your household includes young children, follow these guidelines for accident prevention:

- Never leave young children alone in the kitchen, even for a few seconds.
- Protect toddlers by using safety latches on drawers and cabinet doors.
- If children want to help you work, set up a child-size table or a safe stepstool. Provide small utensils they can use easily for simple tasks such as mixing and mashing. Don't let young children use knives or work near the range. Supervise them at all times.
- Model safe work habits for children. Use the accident prevention skills you have learned. If you practice safe work habits in the kitchen, they will too.

Aging Adults and People with Disabilities

Kitchen safety is an important issue for those with physical challenges, such as poor eyesight or arthritis. Changes in the work space or equipment may be needed so that people with special needs can use the kitchen safely. Ask for their suggestions. What kitchen tasks are hard for them? How could the kitchen be reorganized to make jobs easier and safer? Here are some ideas for creating a barrier-free kitchen:

- Keep a magnifying glass in the kitchen to aid with reading small print.
- Relabel items in larger letters, if necessary, using stick-on labels and a marking pen.
- Add more or better lighting.
- Store frequently used equipment and foods in easy-to-reach places.
- Add a cart with wheels to the kitchen to make it easier to move food and equipment from place to place.
- Use nonbreakable dishes and glassware.
- Replace hard-to-open cabinet hardware with U-shaped or pull handles.
- Provide tongs or grippers to grab items that would otherwise be out of reach.
- Put mixing bowls on a damp dishcloth or a rubber disk jar opener to keep them from sliding on a slippery countertop during mixing.
- Use rubber disk jar openers for gripping appliance knobs.
- Provide a stool or tall chair so that the person can sit while working at the counter.

INFOLINK
For more information on designing barrier-free kitchens for people with special needs, see Section 14-3.

Reinforcing Key Skills

Present the following problems to student groups. Allow time for them to discuss and compare their responses.

Management—Someone is choking. You think you know what to do, but you aren't sure. Everyone else around you just stares and does nothing.

Directed Thinking—You have had first aid training. While you are in a restaurant, someone starts choking. They pass out. You are too scared to do anything because there are many adults who are trying to help. It is clear to you that none of them know the Heimlich maneuver.

In Case of Accident

In spite of all your precautions, an accident may happen when you are working in the kitchen. If you have practiced the management skills discussed in Chapter 1, you will be prepared for that possibility. You will have a list of emergency numbers next to the phone and a first aid kit in a handy location. If you don't know how to administer first aid, contact your local chapter of the American Red Cross to find out about training.

One first aid technique everyone should know is administering the **Heimlich maneuver**—a technique used to rescue victims of choking. The technique can even be performed on yourself. Another vital technique is **CPR**, or cardiopulmonary resuscitation (KARD-ee-oh-PULL-muh-nare-ee ree-SUSS-uh-TAY-shun), a technique used to revive a person whose breathing and heartbeat have stopped. Knowing these techniques can save a life.

If an accident does occur, stay calm. Panic will only keep you from thinking clearly. If necessary, take a few deep breaths to get yourself under control.

Never hesitate to call for help, whether for yourself or someone else. It is better to summon help, even though you may not need it, than to try to handle the accident yourself.

Section 7-2 Review & Activities

1. Name three ways to prevent falls.
2. Give three suggestions that might improve kitchen safety for an older person with special needs.
3. Name two things you should do in case an accident does occur in the kitchen.
4. **Analyzing.** What is the most serious kitchen accident you have ever had? Why did it happen? How could it have been prevented?
5. **Evaluating.** Some people are in the habit of unplugging toasters and other small kitchen appliances after every use. Besides being overly cautious, how might this practice actually lead to an accident situation?
6. **Applying.** Make a mini-poster for the school foods lab to remind class members of one of the accident prevention pointers discussed in this section. Compose a slogan that will help people remember the tip. Set aside one wall of the classroom to display posters.

ASSESS

REVIEW

- Ask students to summarize the main ideas in this section.
- Have students complete the Section Review. (Answers appear below.)

EVALUATION

- Have students write a short essay describing safety practices, precautions, and techniques for the kitchen.
- Have students take the quiz for Section 7-2. (Use the quiz in the *Teacher Resource Guide,* or construct your own with the **Exam***View*® *Test Generator* on the *Effective Instruction CD-ROM.*)

RETEACHING

- Prepare slides, drawings, or photos that show unsafe conditions in the kitchen. Ask students to identify what is wrong in each picture.
- Refer to the *Reteaching Activities* booklet for the Section 7-2 activity sheet.

CLOSE

In a contest style, give students exactly five minutes to list as many tips as possible for an accident-free kitchen, without allowing use of the text or notes. How many can they list?

Discuss home accidents mentioned at the beginning of this section. How could they have been prevented? What would students do if similar accidents did occur?

Answers to Section 7-2 Review & Activities

1. Any three: Wipe up spills immediately; remove area rugs that might slip; replace damaged or worn flooring; don't wear untied shoes, floppy slippers, or long clothing.
2. Refer to the bulleted list on page 196.
3. Stay calm, and never hesitate to call for help.
4. Answers will vary.
5. Answers will vary. Possible answers: It could cause an accident due to (1) dangling cords leading to appliance being pulled off the counter or (2) potential damage to cord from overuse/tugging.
6. Posters and slogans will vary.

SECTION
7-3
Keeping Food Safe to Eat

FOCUS

MOTIVATORS

- Tell the story of the old-time doctor who, upon making a house call, inevitably went first to the kitchen to thank the cook for providing him with a new patient. A grain of truth can be gleaned from this story: Anyone who selects, prepares, and serves food influences the health of those who eat it.
- Have students make a list of food safety guidelines that they already follow. Suggest that they keep their list handy and add items as they study ways to keep food safe.

VOCABULARY ACTIVITY

Pronounce the terms listed under "Look for These Terms." Have students find the terms and their definitions in the section. Point out that *cross-contamination* occurs when bacteria are transferred, or cross, from one source to another.

STUDY SKILLS

- **Outlining.** Have students read the section and outline it by copying the headers on paper and leaving space after each one. Students are to write a sentence in their own words, summarizing the content under each header.
- Have students read the section and complete the appropriate part of the Chapter 7 Study Guide in the *Student Workbook*.

SECTION 7-3

Keeping Food Safe to Eat

Objectives

After studying this section, you should be able to:

- Discuss the causes of foodborne illness.
- Explain how proper food handling practices can prevent foodborne illness.

Look for These Terms

food safety

microorganisms

toxins

cross-contamination

spores

Manuel checked the chicken sizzling on the grill. "It's done!" he called to his aunt. "I'll bring it in." He started to reach for the platter he had used to carry the raw chicken outside when his aunt stopped him. "Don't use that! It hasn't been washed. I'll get you a clean plate."

Food Safety

Manuel almost forgot an important rule of food safety. **Food safety** means following practices that help prevent foodborne illness and keep food safe to eat.

It's estimated that up to 80 million Americans suffer from foodborne illness, also known as food poisoning, every year. The illness may be mild, lasting just a day or two, or severe enough to require hospitalization. In some cases it can even result in death. Children, females who are pregnant, aging adults, and people with chronic illness are most at risk.

Most cases of foodborne illness can be traced to harmful **microorganisms**—tiny living creatures visible only through a microscope. In another sense, however, people are to blame. Improper food handling practices allow harmful microorganisms to grow and spread. It's up to you to handle food properly to prevent illness.

INFOLINK

For more on prevention of foodborne illness and other health risks associated with outdoor grilling, see Section 24-4.

Section 7-3 Resources

◆ **Student Workbook,** pp. 54, 59
◆ **Teacher Resource Guide**
Lesson Plan 7-3 Organizer
Section 7-3 Quiz
◆ **Effective Instruction CD-ROM**
Exam*View*® *Test Generator*
PowerPoint® Slide #20
◆ **Transparency Package,** CT-20
◆ **Student Motivation Kit**
Reteaching Activities, p. 43
Enrichment Activities

Harmful Microorganisms

Most harmful microorganisms associated with foodborne illness are bacteria—and they're everywhere. Bacteria are carried by people, animals, insects, and objects. Many bacteria are harmless, but others can cause illness. Sometimes the illness is not caused by the bacteria themselves but by the **toxins**, or poisons, they produce.

Most harmful bacteria can be tolerated by the human body in small amounts. When the amounts multiply to dangerous levels, however, they create a health hazard. Bacteria reproduce quickly in the presence of food, moisture, and warmth. In just a few hours, one bacterium can multiply into thousands. You can't tell whether food contains harmful bacteria. The food generally looks, smells, and tastes normal.

The chart below describes some bacteria that cause foodborne illness and where that bacteria are found.

Bacteria That Cause Foodborne Illness

Bacteria	*Where Bacteria Are Found*
E. coli	Contaminated water, raw or rare ground beef, unpasteurized milk or apple juice.
Listeria monocytogenes	Contaminated soil and water; meat and dairy products; ready-to-eat foods such as hot dogs, luncheon meats, cold cuts, dry sausages, and deli-style meats and poultry.
Salmonella	Raw or undercooked foods, such as poultry, eggs, and meat; unpasteurized milk.
Clostridium botulinum	Improperly processed canned foods, garlic in oils, vacuum-packed or tightly wrapped food—environments where there is little or no oxygen.
Campylobacter jejuni	Contaminated water, unpasteurized milk, or undercooked meat or poultry; on human skin, in nose, and in throat.
Staphylococcus aureus	On human skin, in nose, and in throat—spread by improper food handling.
Clostridium perfringens	Environments where there is little or no oxygen; spores can survive cooking; often called the "cafeteria germ" because it most often strikes food served in quantity and left for long periods on a steam table or at room temperature.

TEACH

- *Food Safety (text pages 198-199)*

Discussion Activity

Ask students to explain what is involved in sanitation. Why is sanitation important in the kitchen?

Listing

Ask students to list the people who are most at risk from foodborne illnesses. Ask students to list four ways in which microorganisms can cause foodborne illnesses. Encourage students to share their lists with other students and save their lists for a study tool. L1

Research

Have students research major outbreaks of foodborne illnesses in the United States, occurring from 1990 to present. Suggest students visit: www.foodsafety.gov. Ask students to identify the food that was contaminated and the food handling practices that caused bacteria development. Ask students to prepare a short research report. L2

Creating Cartoons

Have students draw cartoons featuring one type of foodborne illness. The cartoon should contain information on the type of food and the mode of transportation. State that important information can be presented in a fun way to enhance learning. L1

FOOD SCIENCE

Microorganisms Lab

Before class, prepare a sugar-sweetened gelatin mix, pour into small clear, plastic cups, and chill until set. Have students contaminate the gelatin with common items. Cover each plastic cup with plastic wrap and label with the name of the contaminant. Place on a tray and leave in a warm place for several days. (NOTE: Place warning signs that say "CONTAMINATED; DO NOT EAT" on each tray.) Check the cups each day for growth of microorganisms. Ask students to draw conclusions based on the results.

TEACH cont.

- *Cleanliness in the Kitchen (text pages 200-202)*

Demonstration

Ask for three student volunteers to demonstrate how they usually wash their hands before handling food. Ask students to note washing thoroughness while you time each demonstration. After all demonstrations are complete, have the class discuss the thoroughness of each washing technique. State the time of each. Have students repeat the hand washing demonstration using discussed improvements.

Interview

Have students interview a food service industry employee. Have students prepare a list of questions prior to the interview, including what hygiene rules he or she must follow. Ask students to present a 60-second report to class, in any reporting style, based on the interview. L1

Research Activity

Have students research other cultures to find customs dealing with personal hygiene and kitchen cleanliness. Emphasize that, although the methods may be different, most cultures have developed customs that ensure cleanliness in the kitchen and at meals. Discuss how and why such customs might be established.

Cleanliness in the Kitchen

Cleanliness is one of the keys to food safety. Whenever you work with food, be sure to keep yourself and the kitchen clean.

Personal Hygiene

When you're handling food, you don't have to scrub as surgeons do before operating. Remember, however, that keeping clean is important. Here are suggestions for minimizing the risk of introducing harmful microorganisms when you are working in the kitchen:

- Wear clean clothes and cover them with a clean apron. Spots and stains can harbor bacteria.
- Remove dangling jewelry, roll up long sleeves, and tie back long hair. That will help keep them out of food.
- Using soap and warm water, scrub your hands for 20 seconds before you begin to handle food. Use a brush to clean under and around your fingernails.
- Wear rubber or plastic gloves if you have an open wound on your hands. Because gloves can pick up bacteria, wash gloved hands as often as you wash bare hands.
- Scrub your hands immediately after using the toilet or blowing your nose.
- Do not sneeze or cough into food.
- Do not touch your face, your hair, or any other part of your body while working with food. If you do, stop working and scrub your hands.

Work Methods for Food Safety

In addition to keeping yourself clean, remember to follow these important guidelines:

- Be sure that work areas and equipment are clean before you start preparing food.
- Avoid **cross-contamination**—letting microorganisms from one food get into another. For example, the juices from raw meat, poultry, and fish and other seafood contain harmful microorganisms. A knife used to cut raw meat could contaminate raw vegetables. After you have handled raw meat, poultry, or seafood, wash everything that came in contact with those foods. This includes tools, work surfaces, and your hands.

◆ **Washing cutting boards and other equipment in between uses can prevent cross-contamination of foods. Explain why juices from raw meat, poultry, or seafood should not come in contact with other foods.**

Extending Learning

Foodborne Illness—If you suspect that you or someone else is suffering from foodborne illness, you can help health professionals diagnose the problem by:

- Wrapping a portion of the food you suspect caused the problem in a heavy plastic bag. Place it in a closed container clearly marked "DANGER" and chill it on ice.
- Writing the name of the food, when it was consumed, and the date of the illness on the outside of the container.
- Saving the original container in which the food was purchased.

◆ The kitchen items pictured here all have some potential risk as breeding grounds for microorganisms. Which of the items have the highest degree of risk?

- Do not use cutting boards made of porous materials, such as soft wood. Such materials provide a breeding ground for harmful bacteria.
- Wash the top of a can before opening it to keep dirt from getting into the food.
- If you use a spoon to taste food during preparation, wash it after each use to avoid transferring harmful bacteria from your mouth to the food you're preparing.
- Keep pets out of the kitchen.
- Keep two towels handy in the kitchen—one for wiping hands and a second one for drying dishes.
- Dishcloths and sponges can harbor harmful bacteria. Use a clean dishcloth each day. Wash sponges at the end of the day and allow them to air-dry before reuse.

Cleanup Time

After food has been prepared and eaten, it's time to clean up. A clean kitchen has no food particles and spills to encourage bacterial growth or to attract insects or rodents.

Using Cleanup Appliances

Many kitchens are equipped with a food waste disposal and a dishwasher to help speed cleanup. A food waste disposal system grinds food waste and flushes it down the drain. Always run plenty of cold water when grinding food. Don't overfill the disposal. Instead, grind small bunches at a time. To avoid clogging the disposal, don't put fibrous food, such as onion skins and corn husks, in it.

When using an automatic dishwasher, follow the instructions in the owner's manual. Be sure the dishwasher is full before running it. Small loads waste water and energy.

Washing Dishes by Hand

Washing dishes can go faster and more easily if you're well organized. The following suggestions can help you with this task.

Rinse soiled dishes and place them on one side of the sink. Group like items and arrange them in this order: glasses, flatware, plates, kitchen tools, and cookware. Keep sharp knives separate. If food is stuck to cookware, presoak it. Pour a little dish detergent in, add hot water, and let the pan stand for a while.

Fill a dishpan or sink with soapy water—hot enough to remove grease but not hot enough to burn your hands. Using a sponge or dishcloth, wash the dishes in the order you grouped them. Wash glasses first and greasy cookware last. When necessary, refill the sink or dishpan with clean, hot, soapy water.

- *Cleanliness in the Kitchen (text pages 200-202)*

Educational Material Development

Ask students to develop a numbered list of the steps in washing dishes properly by hand. Have students develop a mini-poster using their lists. Have the class choose the best poster to be posted in the school food lab. Encourage others to display their posters in their own kitchens. **L1**

Discussion Activity

Ask students to list all surfaces or appliances that need to be cleaned for kitchen cleanup. Discuss lists. Then ask students to explain the importance of placing garbage in a tightly closed plastic bag and putting it in the garbage can outside. What further precautions should you take regarding the outside can?

Environmental Activity

Caution students to use these or other proven methods of insect control, as opposed to relying on myths or traditions to rid the house of these pests. Ask students how they can determine whether a method is fact or fallacy. What are some advantages of using natural insecticides?

Reinforcing Key Skills

Present the following problems to student groups. Allow time for them to discuss and compare their responses.

Critical Thinking—Ask students to discuss the advantage of following the prescribed order when hand-washing dishes. Why should glassware be washed first and cookware last?

Leadership—You notice ants in the kitchen of your next door neighbor.

TEACH cont.

- *Cleanliness in the Kitchen (text pages 200-202)*

Demonstration

Bring a caulking gun to class to demonstrate how to properly caulk cracks and crevices. Ask a school repairperson to demonstrate caulking, if necessary. Then have students practice the technique. Discuss when and why this is helpful for controlling pests.

Skits

Divide the class into four groups. Have each group plan and present one of four skits on (1) use of the food waste disposal, (2) use of the automatic dishwasher, (3) procedures for washing dishes by hand, and (4) procedures for cleaning the work and eating areas of the foods lab. Encourage class discussion after each skit. L1

Field Research

Have students visit supermarkets to find cleaning solutions such as dishwashing liquid that make cleanup chores easier but are not harmful to the environment. Have them make a list of their findings. If possible, and if a parent approves the purchase, have students bring to class one bottle of a cleaning solution they discovered. L1

Rinse dishes thoroughly in hot water. Be sure the insides of containers are well rinsed. A safe and easy way to rinse the outsides is to put the dish rack in the sink and let hot water run over it. Let the dishes air-dry in the rack, or dry them with a clean, dry towel.

Safety Check

What if a glass or dish breaks in a sink full of water? Using a paper towel to protect your fingers, carefully reach into the sink and open up the drain. After the water has drained, use the wet paper towel to pick up the broken pieces. Remember to dispose of broken glass properly.

Cleaning the Work and Eating Areas

When you are through washing dishes, wipe the table. Clean all the work areas and appliances that were used. Don't forget to wash the can opener blade and the cutting board. Rinse the dishcloth often as you work, using hot, soapy water.

Wipe up any spills on the floor. Wash the sink to remove grease and food particles. If the kitchen is equipped with a disposal, run it a final time.

Finally, put any garbage in a plastic bag, close the bag tightly, and put it in the garbage can outside. Wash garbage cans regularly so that they don't attract insects and rodents.

Controlling Pests

Insects can bring disease into the kitchen. However, chemical insecticides can be hazardous to humans and the environment. Here are some ways to control household insects without using insecticides:

- Repair holes in walls and screens. Caulk cracks and crevices.
- Keep the kitchen and other areas clean.
- Sprinkle chili powder, paprika, or dried peppermint across ant trails.
- To control roaches, dust borax lightly around the refrigerator and range.

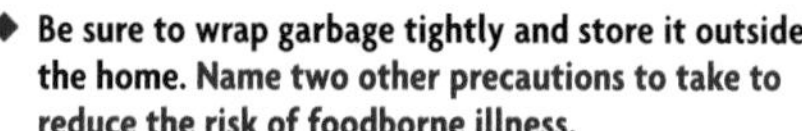

◆ **Be sure to wrap garbage tightly and store it outside the home. Name two other precautions to take to reduce the risk of foodborne illness.**

Extending Learning

Spores—The word spore is a derivative of the Greek word sporo, which means "seed." A spore is the reproductive body produced by molds, fungi, and ferns, as well as bacteria. This spore produces a parent body. Spores are very stable. They can be frozen and heated and still live. They will not form new bacteria until specific conditions, such as a specific temperature and moisture level, are reached.

Have students research (1) which bacteria produce spores, (2) the specific conditions necessary for spore production, and (3) how spores can be destroyed.

Proper Food Temperatures

Temperature is one of the most important factors in food safety. Keeping food at proper temperatures can be critical to preventing foodborne illness.

How Temperatures Affect Microorganisms

Bacteria multiply rapidly at temperatures between 60°F and 140°F (16°C to 60°C). Note that this range includes room temperatures. Most foodborne illnesses are caused by bacteria that thrive in these temperatures.

High food temperatures, from 160°F to 212°F (71°C to 100°C), kill most harmful bacteria. These temperatures are normally reached during cooking. However, some bacteria produce **spores**, cells that will develop into bacteria if conditions are right. Spores can survive cooking heat.

Cold refrigerator temperatures, below 40°F (4°C), slow down the growth of some bacteria but do not kill them.

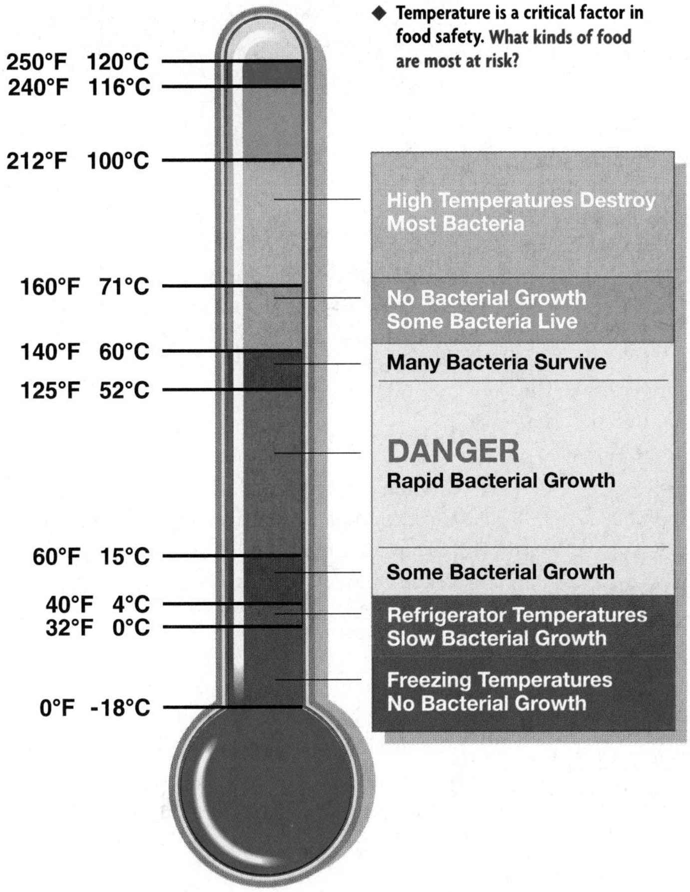

If food is frozen at 0°F (–18°C), bacteria stop growing. Bacteria or spores already present in food, however, will not be killed. When the food is thawed, bacteria will start to grow again.

The diagram on the left shows you the proper temperatures for storing and cooking food. Red is the danger zone—where bacteria grow rapidly. Bacteria also grow in the orange zone, but more slowly than in the red zone.

As you have learned, foodborne illness can also be caused by toxins. Some types of toxins are destroyed by heat. Others remain unchanged even after food is cooked.

◆ **Temperature is a critical factor in food safety. What kinds of food are most at risk?**

- *Proper Food Temperatures (text pages 203-205)*

VISUAL LEARNING ***Using the Artwork*** Ask students to re-create the temperature artwork in their own style using computer software. Have students show a print of their artwork to the class and share how they created it.

Rhymes

Have students create rhymes or raps to help them remember the proper temperatures for storing, cooking, and serving food. Have all interested students read their rhymes or perform their rap for the class. L2

Application

Have student groups apply principles of food sanitation to (1) holiday meals, (2) picnics, (3) brown bag lunches, and (4) parties. Ask groups to develop sanitation guidelines for each of these situations. Use the guidelines to prepare a series of articles on sanitation for potential publication in a community newspaper or web site. Have each group divide in half: one half will write and the other half will pitch the article series idea to local publication or web site editors. "Writers" and "pitchers" need to coordinate efforts. L1

HOME & COMMUNITY CONNECTION

Ask all students who have access to a refrigerator/freezer thermometer to record the temperature inside their own refrigerators at home. Have one student read the foods lab refrigerator temperature. Ask students to share temperature findings with the class. Were any refrigerator temperatures above 40°F (4°C)? What does this indicate?

TEACH cont.

- *Proper Food Temperatures (text pages 203-205)*

Discussion Activity

Ask students to describe three ways to thaw food safely. Why is it important not to thaw foods at room temperature?

Adapting Guidelines

Using the nine food handling guidelines on this page of the text, have students adapt the guidelines into basic language that elementary school-age children or some learning disabled individuals could understand. Encourage class discussion of the adapted guidelines. L3

Categorizing Activity

Provide students with a list of 20 food handling situations: 10 safe and 10 unsafe. Have students categorize each situation as safe or unsafe. Compare activity results in class.

Food Handling Guidelines

Many foods require special care to keep them out of the danger zone. Meat, poultry, fish and other seafood, eggs, and dairy products are some of these foods. When cooking food, follow these guidelines:

- Cook food to the proper internal temperature or until thoroughly cooked. Avoid partial cooking—cook the food completely at one time.
- Taste foods containing ingredients from animal sources only after they are fully cooked. Do not taste them when they are raw or during cooking.
- When microwaving, take steps to ensure even, thorough cooking.
- When reheating food that has been refrigerated, bring it to an internal temperature of 165°F (74°C) or higher to kill any bacteria. Keep in mind that if the food has not been properly stored, it can't be made safe just by reheating.

Thawing Food Safely

Never thaw food at room temperature. The outside of the item may contain millions of harmful bacteria by the time the inside is thawed. To thaw food safely, use one of these methods:

- Place food in the refrigerator where it will thaw slowly. Be sure packages of thawing food do not leak onto other foods.
- For faster thawing, put the package in a watertight plastic bag and submerge it in cold water. Change the water every 30 minutes. The cold slows down the growth of bacteria as the food thaws.

◆ **When thawing meat in the refrigerator, be sure to place it in a container to catch any drippings.**

- Use a microwave for quick, safe defrosting. Follow the manufacturer's directions. Foods thawed this way should be cooked immediately.

Serving Food

When serving food, cleanliness helps prevent the spread of microorganisms. Wipe the table before and after eating. Place a serving utensil in every serving dish. In addition, follow the personal hygiene guidelines on page 200.

Food safety principles also apply when serving food. To prevent contamination after food has been prepared, don't touch it with bare hands. Also hold cups and flatware by handles and glassware by the lower third. If

FOOD SCIENCE

Frozen Food Safety

Occasionally the power may go out and frozen foods may partially thaw. If a food still has ice crystal formation, it can be refrozen immediately, but should be used soon. Quality may be lost in this process. However, exercise caution if the frozen food had already been refrigerated for two days or more prior to freezing. In this case, it should not be refrozen. It can be used immediately.

If a frozen food has completely thawed, it should not be refrozen, and should be thrown out if it's been held at room temperature more than two hours.

you are preparing or carrying more than one plate, they should not overlap. Be sure to follow these food temperature guidelines as well when serving food:

- Do not leave food out more than two hours at room temperature or more than one hour if the temperature is above 90°F (32°C).
- Keep extra quantities of food either hot—on the range or in another cooking appliance—or cold—in the refrigerator.
- Do not add more food to a serving dish of food that has been out for a while. Instead, use a clean dish.
- Discard foods that have been held at room temperature for more than two hours.
- Refrigerate leftovers in shallow containers. Large, deep containers keep the food from cooling rapidly and evenly.

CLOSE-UP ON SCIENCE: BIOCHEMISTRY

Salmonella and Poultry

To reduce Salmonella contamination in poultry, scientists have developed a spray to use in the early stages of poultry production. The spray contains bacteria that are harmless to people and chickens, but hostile to Salmonella. After baby chickens are sprayed, they clean their feathers and ingest the spray. The bacteria live in the chicks' intestines, preventing Salmonella growth. Safe handling practices are still needed during poultry processing and preparation.

Section 7-3 Review & Activities

1. Identify three ways in which bacteria are spread.
2. Name five instances when you should wash your hands while working with food.
3. What temperature range is considered the "danger zone"? Why?
4. If you were serving a meal at home, what guidelines for food safety and cleanliness would you follow?
5. **Analyzing.** Why do you think so many Americans suffer from foodborne illness each year?
6. **Extending.** Learn what OSHA inspectors and local health inspectors look for as they monitor community health. What laws and policies guide them? Summarize your findings in a report.
7. **Evaluating.** With team members, prepare a dish assigned by your teacher. Afterwards, evaluate together how well the team followed food safety and cleanliness practices while handling the food and preparing the dish. List what your team did correctly as well as anything that should be done differently in future labs.

ASSESS

REVIEW

- Ask students to summarize the main ideas in this section.
- Have students complete the Section Review. (Answers appear below.)

EVALUATION

- Have students plan an indoor or outdoor picnic. Hot foods must be kept hot and cold foods must be kept cold. Preparation techniques must include safe use of equipment and good sanitation procedures before, during, and after the picnic.
- Have students take the quiz for Section 7-3. (Use the quiz in the *Teacher Resource Guide,* or construct your own with the **ExamView**® *Test Generator* on the *Effective Instruction CD-ROM.*)

RETEACHING

- Have students design a bulletin board display depicting bacteria and their modes of transportation to foods.
- Refer to the *Reteaching Activities* booklet for the Section 7-3 activity sheet.

CLOSE

Lead a discussion about the importance of sanitation to prevent foodborne illnesses. Then have the class brainstorm a one-line statement, or "mantra," that they can remember and repeat when necessary when working in the foods lab. Sample mantras: "Safety comes first" and "Practice safety for eating safely." Post the "mantra" on a classroom wall.

Answers to Section 7-3 Review & Activities

1. Any three: By people, animals, insects, and objects.
2. Before you begin to handle food; after using the bathroom or blowing your nose; after touching face, hair, or any other part of your body; after handling raw meat, poultry, or fish; after sneezing or coughing.
3. 60°F to 125°F (16°C to 52°C); most foodborne illnesses are caused by bacteria that thrive in these temperatures.
4. Answers will vary.
5. Answers will vary but may mention carelessness regarding food safety guidelines.
6. Answers will vary.
7. Answers will vary.

SECTION
7-4
Storing Food

FOCUS

MOTIVATORS

- Show students pictures of kitchens in 1900 and today. Point out differences in food storage and compare the advantages and disadvantages today and in the past. Discuss the time spent on food storage and preservation in 1900 and today. How would today's lifestyles be affected if everyone needed to preserve their own food?
- Show students a moldy piece of bread, tomato, or other vegetable or fruit. Ask students how they think it became moldy and if they would eat it.

VOCABULARY ACTIVITY

Pronounce the terms listed under "Look for These Terms." Have students find the terms and their definitions in the section. Then ask students to discuss why *shelf-stable* is a hyphenated term and why *shelf life* and *freezer burn* are not.

STUDY SKILLS

- **Note Taking.** Have students look at the headings within Section 7-4 to preview the concepts that will be discussed. Then, have students read the section while taking notes on the key concepts.
- Have students read the section and complete the appropriate part of the Chapter 7 Study Guide in the *Student Workbook*.

SECTION
7-4

Objectives

After studying this section, you should be able to:

- Identify causes and signs of food spoilage.
- Give examples of foods that are stored at room temperature and in cold storage.
- Give guidelines for each type of storage.

Look for These Terms

shelf life

shelf-stable

freezer burn

inventory

Storing Food

"The bread's moldy again!" Noelle exclaimed. "Why doesn't it keep longer?" One of the most common answers to Noelle's question is improper storage.

Spoilage and Nutrient Loss

When food is not properly stored, it begins to lose quality and nutrients. Eventually, it will spoil. Spoiled food often develops bad tastes and odors and must be thrown out. Some types of spoilage can cause foodborne illness.

What causes spoilage? Under the right conditions, harmful bacteria, yeasts, and molds can spoil food. Spoilage can also be caused by natural chemical changes within the cells of the food. Yet another cause is conditions in the environment, which can cause or speed up nutrient loss and spoilage.

- **Heat.** Heat speeds up chemical reactions that cause spoilage.
- **Air.** Exposure to oxygen can destroy some nutrients, such as vitamins C and E. It can also cause oils to become rancid and develop an unpleasant flavor.
- **Moisture.** Moisture is a double-edged sword. Too little moisture can cause fresh foods to dry out, wilt, and lose nutrients. Too much moisture can provide a breeding ground for bacteria and molds.
- **Light.** Light can destroy nutrients, especially vitamin C and riboflavin.
- **Dirt.** Dirt contains harmful microorganisms.

Section 7-4 Resources

◆ **Student Workbook,** pp. 54, 61
◆ **Teacher Resource Guide**
Lesson Plan 7-4 Organizer
Section 7-4 Quiz
◆ **Effective Instruction CD-ROM**
Exam*View*® *Test Generator*
◆ **Student Motivation Kit**
Reteaching Activities, p. 44
Enrichment Activities
Food Science Resources, pp. 116–120

- **Damage to food or packaging.** Both these conditions make spoilage by microorganisms more likely. Be alert for signs of spoilage in packaging, such as bulging cans, liquids that spurt when you open the container, or liquids that are cloudy when they should be clear.

INFOLINK

For more on bulging cans as an indicator of spoilage and other problems relating to nutrition, quality, and food safety when food shopping, see Section 12-3.

CLOSE-UP ON SCIENCE: CHEMISTRY

Enzymes in Food

The cells of living things contain *enzymes,* protein substances that cause chemical changes to occur. When a plant or animal is processed into a food, some of the enzymes remain active. Unless foods are heated to destroy the enzymes, chemical changes continue—destroying the cells and causing the food to spoil.

When Food Is Spoiled

How do you know when food is starting to spoil? Some fresh foods, such as apples and celery, may wilt, get wrinkled, or turn brown. Some foods become slimy, a sign that decay has started. Other signs of spoilage are spots of fuzzy mold; damage such as holes, tears, and bruises; bad flavors; and bad odors.

Spoiled foods should be discarded. Those that have turned moldy require special handling because mold gives off spores, which can easily spread. Very gently wrap the moldy food, or place it in a bag before discarding it. Examine other foods that may have been in contact with the moldy food. Clean the container that held the moldy food, and if necessary, wash out the refrigerator.

◆ **Blue cheese gets its flavor from a special type of mold. However, most foods with mold must be thrown out. Name two ways of retarding the formation of mold in the foods you store.**

FOOD SCIENCE

Microorganisms and Spoilage

Microorganisms such as bacteria, yeasts, and molds need food as a source of energy and nutrients. They produce waste products including acids and gases. These waste products create the bad tastes and odors typical of spoiled food. It's important for students to know that bad taste and odors are not always present. Using critical thinking is important to detect food spoilage when bad taste or odors do not exist.

TEACH

- ***Spoilage and Nutrient Loss (text pages 206-208)***

Charts

Ask students to develop a chart of the six factors that cause nutrient loss or spoilage (from the text on pages 206-207) and how they cause it. Encourage chart development utilizing a computer software program. Have students share charts with other students. Moderate a class discussion on conditions that you can control to eliminate or slow down nutrient loss and spoilage. **L1**

Discussion Activity

Ask students to describe symptoms that may indicate that food is spoiling. Ask students what types of moldy food should be discarded and what can be salvaged. How can these foods be salvaged? Ask students to describe the steps you should take to keep a mold from spreading.

USING THE Food Science LAB

Explain to students that food professionals often use methods other than those used in the classroom to achieve certain results.

Point out that the lab calls for leaving the Petri dish at room temperature for three days. Ask students why this is necessary. Leave the Petri dishes out one more day. Observe the results again. Compare results to those after three days.

- *Basic Storage Principles (text page 208)*

Chart Development Activity

Ask students what factors affect the shelf life of a product? Discuss guidelines people can follow to avoid loss of quality in food products. Then have each student develop a chart of room temperature storage tips that can be posted on a food cabinet door.

Student Demonstrations

Ask students to give examples of shelf-stable foods. Then provide groups of students with shelf-stable food packages that have been opened. Ask student groups to describe and demonstrate the ideal conditions for room temperature storage for each of the foods after they have been opened, including resealing foods or transferring contents into other containers. L1

Label Reading Activity

Provide students with a variety of food packages. Ask students to locate expiration dates on the packages. What types of foods have expiration dates? Compare length of expiration. During discussion, have students compile a list of product expiration dates. Have students develop graph based on dates.

Food Science ◆ LAB ◆

Growing Microorganisms

You can't see a single microorganism, but you can see colonies of microorganisms, called *cultures*. In this experiment, you'll discover just how widespread microorganisms really are.

Procedure

1. With a felt-tip pen, divide into quarters a Petri dish coated with nutrient agar. Number the quarters 1 to 4.
2. Touch the end of a 4-inch (10-cm) strip of cellophane tape to a doorknob, and press it into area 1 of the Petri dish. Touch another tape strip to a clean dish and a third strip to your hair, and press these into areas 2 and 3.
3. Touch a fourth piece of tape to the agar without letting it touch any other surface, including your fingers.
4. Leave the Petri dish at room temperature for three days. Observe it each day, and describe any growths that have appeared.

Conclusions

- Were any of the surfaces you tested free of microorganisms? Was the tape itself free of microorganisms?
- Which surfaces produced the most bacterial growth? Why?
- What changes in your food preparation practices might you consider making as a result of this experiment?
- How might restaurant managers use this information?

Basic Storage Principles

No food can be stored indefinitely. Each food has a **shelf life,** the length of time it can be stored and still retain its quality. Shelf life depends on the type of food, packaging, and storage temperature, as well as how the food is handled.

To avoid loss of quality in stored food, follow these guidelines:

- Buy only what you need.
- Follow the principle of "first in, first out." Store new food behind the same kind of older food. Use up the older food first.
- Look for "sell by" or "use by" dates on the containers. If there are none, you may want to write the purchase dates on the containers before storing them. Use canned food within a year.
- Clean storage areas regularly. Throw out food that has started to spoil or containers that have been damaged. Wash and dry surfaces thoroughly.

HOME & COMMUNITY CONNECTION

Have students look through packaged foods at home and find at least five with expiration dates. Ask students to note the many different forms these dates take. Have students design a system that would be clearer and more visible for using foods before they spoil. Encourage interested students to write to their local FDA office about their suggested expiration date system. If any students do so, have them share any FDA response with the class.

INFOLINK

For more information on "sell by" and "use by" dates, see Section 12-2.

Room Temperature Storage

Many canned, bottled, and packaged foods are **shelf-stable,** which means they are able to last for weeks or even months at room temperatures below 85°F (30°C). Examples are most unopened canned foods, dry beans and peas, oils and shortening, and many grain products (except whole grains). In general, foods that you find on grocery shelves can be stored at room temperature when you bring them home.

Kitchen cabinets are used for most room temperature storage. They should be clean and dry, with doors to keep out light and dirt. Temperatures should be no higher than 85°F (30°C) and no lower than freezing, 32°F (0°C). Do not store food on shelves near or above heat sources, such as a range, toaster, refrigerator, or radiator. Also avoid areas that may be wet, such as cabinets under the sink.

Once packages or containers have been opened, storage requirements differ. Some shelf-stable foods, including most canned goods, must be refrigerated after opening. Others, such as a bag of dry beans or a box of cereal, can remain at room temperature. Reseal the package if possible. Otherwise, transfer the contents to a storage container with a tight-fitting cover. Do the same with the foods you buy in bulk.

Safety Check

If you have to stack items to store them, put the lightest on top so that you'll be less likely to accidentally knock over heavy items that could cause injury. Boxes of dried soup mix, for example, can be stored on top of canned soups.

◆ **Shelf-stable foods may be stored at normal room temperature. Which of the two foods shown has telltale signs of possible bacterial contamination?**

- *Room Temperature Storage (text page 209)*

Display

Have students work in groups to create a display of one of the following: (1) Foods that may be stored in their original containers, (2) appropriate containers for room temperature storage, or (3) shelf-stable foods that need refrigeration after the package is opened. Allow time for students to view and discuss displays. L1

Research and Computer Writing Activity

Have students research new methods of food processing that may allow foods that have previously required refrigeration to be shelf-stable. Have students write a research report using a word-processing software program. Provide students font-size and word count instructions, such as font-size 12 and word count between 1000 and 1200. L2

USING Safety Check

Have students brainstorm safety tips that should be followed when storing foods, other than those discussed in the text on page 209. Write the tips on the chalk board or overhead transparency.

HOME & COMMUNITY CONNECTION

Ask students to perform a safety inspection of their home kitchen food storage cabinets. Ask them to create a list of any food that has expired; throw out the food. Record any other safety concerns. Ask students to share their findings in class. Specifically note common foods kept past expiration dates, if applicable.

TEACH cont.

- *Cold Storage (text pages 210-215)*

VISUAL LEARNING ***Using the Chart*** As shown on the chart on pages 210-211, some foods can be stored in the refrigerator or in the freezer. Ask students to discuss guidelines for choosing method of storing these foods. As students discuss guidelines, suggest they take notes.

Drawing Conclusions Activity

Have students compare the refrigerator storage guidelines in the chart on pages 210-211 to form conclusions about length of storage and types of food. Discuss similarities and differences. What foods can be stored the longest? Why? What foods can only be stored for a short period of time? Why?

Poster Project

Have students use the chart on pages 210-211 to make illustrated posters that could be mounted on a refrigerator door. Have them explain how they decided which foods to include. Encourage students to have their families use their poster. **L1**

Cold Storage

Perishable foods spoil quickly at room temperature. They require cold storage in the refrigerator or freezer, depending on the kind of food and how long you want to store it. The package may give instructions for storage. The chart below and on the next page gives you a general timetable for keeping foods in cold storage.

Refrigerator Storage

Foods normally refrigerated include:

- Foods that were refrigerated in the store, such as dairy products, eggs, delicatessen foods, and fresh meat, poultry, and fish and other seafood.
- Most fresh fruits and vegetables. Exceptions are onions, potatoes, and sweet potatoes, which should be stored in a cool, dry area.
- Whole-grain products, seeds, and nuts. They contain oils that can spoil and give foods an off-flavor.
- Leftover cooked foods.
- Baked goods with fruit or cream fillings.
- Any foods that according to label directions must be refrigerated after opening.

Cold Storage Chart

NOTE: —— means food should not be stored in that area.

Type of Food	*Refrigerator Storage 40°F (4°C)*	*Freezer Storage 0°F (–18°C)*
Meats, Poultry, Fish		
Beef, lamb, pork, or veal chops, steaks, roast	3-5 days	4-12 months
Chicken or turkey, whole	1-2 days	1 year
Chicken or turkey, pieces	1-2 days	9 months
Ground meats or poultry	1-2 days	3-4 months
Lean fish (cod)	1-2 days	6 months
Fatty fish (salmon)	1-2 days	2-3 months
Shellfish (shrimp)	1-2 days	3-6 months
Dairy Products		
Fresh milk, cream	7 days	3 months
Butter, margarine	1-3 months	6-9 months
Buttermilk	2 weeks	3 months
Sour cream	1-3 weeks	——
Yogurt, plain or flavored	1-2 weeks	1-2 months
Cottage cheese	1 week	——
Hard cheese (cheddar), opened	3-4 weeks	6 months
Hard cheese, unopened	6 months	6 months
Ice cream, sherbet	——	2-4 months

Extending Learning

Refrigerating Food

- Many accessories are available to help you organize the refrigerator storage area. They include turntables, racks, and stackable containers.
- The vegetable drawer helps fruits and vegetables retain moisture longer. Don't line the bottom with paper towels, which will get soggy. The extra moisture can encourage mold.
- Avoid using large containers to store small amounts of food. You waste space and cooling energy.

Cold Storage Chart (cont'd)

NOTE: —— means food should not be stored in that area.

Type of Food	Refrigerator Storage 40°F (4°C)	Freezer Storage 0°F (–18°C)
Miscellaneous Foods		
Bread	7-14 days	3 months
Cakes, pies (not cream-filled)	7 days	2-3 months
Cream pies	1-2 days	——
Fresh eggs, in shell	3 weeks	——
Raw yolks, whites	2-4 days	1 year
Hard-cooked eggs	1 week	——
Egg substitutes, opened	3 days	——
Egg substitutes, unopened	10 days	——
Mayonnaise, opened	2 months	——
Salad dressing, opened	3 months	——
Salsa, opened	3 months	——
Cookies	2 months	8-12 months
Cooked Foods, Leftovers		
Cooked meats, meat dishes	3-4 days	2-3 months
Fried chicken	3-4 days	4 months
Poultry covered in broth	3-4 days	6 months
Fish stews, soups (not creamed)	3-4 days	4-6 months
Cured Meats		
Hot dogs, opened	1 week	1-2 months
Lunch meats, opened	3-5 days	1-2 months
Hot dogs, lunch meats, unopened	2 weeks	1-2 months
Bacon	7 days	1 month
Smoked sausage (beef, pork, turkey)	7 days	1-2 months
Hard sausage (pepperoni)	2-3 weeks	1-2 months
Ham, canned (refrigerated, unopened)	6-9 months	——
Ham, fully cooked, whole	7 days	1-2 months
Ham, fully cooked, half or slices	3-5 days	1-2 months

- *Cold Storage (text pages 210-215)*

Creative Writing

Have students research how early home refrigerators compare with today's in size, appearance, cost, convenience, and other features. Have students write a creative story about a food stored in an early refrigerator compared to today's refrigerator, from the point-of-view of the chosen food. L2

Demonstration

Demonstrate how to properly use and read a refrigerator thermometer. Check temperatures in various parts of the refrigerator, including the top shelf, bottom shelf, door storage area, and crispers. Review the foods that should be stored in warmer and cooler parts of the refrigerator. Show how to control the interior temperature.

Student Demonstrations

Divide students into five groups. Have student groups prepare brief demonstrations on problems with (1) overloading the refrigerator, (2) selecting refrigerator storage containers, (3) storing meat, poultry, and fish, (4) storing fruits and vegetables, and (5) storing leftovers. L1

Extending Learning

Refrigerator/Freezer Thermometer—Point out to students that having a refrigerator/freezer thermometer is a good idea to help reduce potential spoilage if the refrigerator temperature rises about 40°F or the freezer temperature rises above 0°F. The thermometer should be placed near the front and top of the freezer. An accurate temperature can be read after the thermometer has been positioned there for more than six hours without the door opening. Temperature adjustments using refrigerator and freezer temperature regulators can be made based on the accurate thermometer reading.

TEACH cont.

• *Cold Storage (text pages 210-215)*

List Development Activity

Ask students to list foods that do not freeze well. Discuss what is meant by "freeze well." Why might these foods not be good candidates for freezing? Encourage discussion of specific foods and what specifically occurs upon freezing.

Demonstration

Display containers and packaging materials appropriate for use in the freezer. Demonstrate how to package foods frozen at home to avoid freezer burn. Allow students to practice packaging "foods" for the freezer. State that freezer burn alone affects texture and taste of food, but not safety.

Computerized Inventory

Demonstrate how to make a freezer inventory. Have students create a freezer inventory chart using a computer software program. Then have students create an inventory of the foods in their home freezers, using their computerized inventory chart. Suggest students use their inventory charts at home, updating their charts as needed. L1

◆ **Not all areas of the refrigerator have the same temperature. Which areas offer the coldest storage? Which foods should be stored in the door?**

Refrigeration Guidelines

Avoid overloading the refrigerator when storing foods. If the cold air can't circulate well, some areas may become too warm to store perishables safely. Be sure, also, that foods are tightly covered. This will keep them from drying out and will also prevent odors from being picked up by other foods. Opened canned foods may pick up an off-flavor from the can, so transfer them to another storage container.

Store meat, poultry, and seafood in the store wrap in a plastic bag to prevent leakage. Leaking foods can contaminate other stored foods.

When storing fruits and vegetables, wash them only if necessary to remove dirt. Wipe hard-skinned fruits and vegetables dry, and drain others well.

Leftovers require special care. To ensure thorough chilling, use shallow containers. Large, deep containers keep food from cooling rapidly and evenly. Cut large pieces of meat into smaller ones so that they cool quickly. Close the containers tightly, and label them with the current date. Be sure to use the food within a few days. (Remember that some foods can be frozen for longer storage.) You may want to keep all leftovers on the same shelf so that none get overlooked.

Every refrigerator has a temperature control or coldness setting. To promote freshness and retard spoilage of stored foods, follow the manufacturer's recommended settings. Do not let the temperature fall to a point where frost or ice forms. Foods with a high water content, such as lettuce, may freeze and be damaged.

FOOD SCIENCE

Freezing and Food Quality

Have students freeze small samples of foods that generally do not freeze well, such as potatoes (become watery and fall apart), lettuce (change in texture and flavor), mayonnaise (separates), and cooked egg whites (gets tough). They should package the food as for ordinary freezing. After several days, thaw the food and let students observe the results and draw conclusions. Suggest to students that the food is still safe to eat, even though the quality may be altered.

Freezer Storage

Freezing allows long-term storage of many foods. At temperatures of 0°F (–18°C) or below, foods keep from one month to a year, depending on the type of food and proper packaging.

Foods purchased frozen should be stored promptly in the home freezer. Many other foods can also be frozen to increase shelf life. These include fresh meats, poultry, and fish; baked goods such as breads and rolls; and many leftovers.

Some foods don't freeze well. Examples are fresh vegetables that are to be eaten raw, cooked or whole raw eggs, products made with mayonnaise, meat and poultry stuffing, cream- or egg-based sauces, custards, baked goods with cream filling, and many cheeses.

To freeze foods at home, you need a two-door refrigerator-freezer or a separate freezer unit. Separate freezer units generally maintain food quality longer than refrigerator-freezers.

Some refrigerators have only one outside door and a small freezer compartment inside. The freezer compartment maintains a temperature of 10°F to 15°F (–12°C to –10°C). It can be used for storing already frozen food for several weeks. However, it is not cold enough to freeze fresh or leftover food satisfactorily.

A freezer functions best when fairly full. Some freezers need regular defrosting.

Packaging and Freezing Foods

Foods that are purchased already frozen can be stored in their original packaging. However, foods frozen at home must be specially packaged to avoid freezer burn. **Freezer burn** is a condition that results when food is improperly packaged or stored in the freezer too long. The food dries out and loses flavor and texture.

◆ **These materials can help prevent freezer burn. What types of wraps and containers should not be used for freezing?**

- *Cold Storage (text pages 210-215)*

Product Comparison Activity

Ask students to list proper packaging materials for foods that will be frozen. Set up a display of the described packaging materials. Provide students a list of foods to be frozen. Have students suggest which packaging material they would choose for the food and why. Hold a class discussion of the material comparisons.

Public Service Announcement

Have students who are effective public speakers team with others who are effective researchers and writers to create a public service announcement (PSA) on keeping foods safe during a power outage. The announcement should list suggestions for keeping both frozen and refrigerated foods safe. If it can be arranged with the administration, students should present their PSA over the school's public address, computer, or television system. **L2**

FOOD SCIENCE

Freezer Burn

Have students freeze two samples of cooked food, one wrapped properly and one unwrapped. Several days later, have them examine and compare the samples before thawing, after thawing, and after re-heating. Discuss specific results, such as overall quality, appearance, texture, and taste.

TEACH cont.

- *Cold Storage (text pages 210-215)*

Discussion Activity

Discuss precautions people can take to prevent frozen food spoilage in case of a power outage. Discuss guidelines for deciding whether to keep and use food that was in the freezer and food that was in the refrigerator during a power outage.

Summarizing Activity

Ask students to write a summary describing the procedure you should use after a power outage to clean the refrigerator and freezer. In their summaries, have students suggest why it is important to clean the refrigerator freezer thoroughly after a power outage.

Safety Booklet

Have students work in groups to prepare safety booklets that explain how to determine whether to keep food after a power outage. Encourage use of computer software for development of the booklets. Have student groups provide copies of their booklet to the other students in class. L1

Packaging materials for freezing must be vapor- and moisture-resistant. Plastic containers with tight-fitting covers, heavy-duty plastic freezer bags, and wraps such as heavy-duty foil and freezer wrap are recommended. Don't use regular refrigerator storage bags or plastic tubs from such foods as margarine and yogurt. They do not provide enough protection. Fresh meat, poultry, and fish need additional wrap for freezing because the lightweight store wrapping does not provide sufficient protection.

When wrapping solid foods, such as meat, squeeze out as much air as possible to prevent freezer burn. Seal packages with freezer tape. When filling storage containers, leave enough space for food to expand as it freezes—about 1 inch (2.5 cm) in a quart (or liter) container. Then seal the container tightly. Label all packages and containers with the contents, amount (or number of servings), date frozen, and any special instructions.

For best quality, freeze food quickly. Spread packages out so they touch the coils or sides of the freezer. Leave enough space between packages for air to circulate. When the food is frozen (at least 24 hours later), you can stack it according to the kind of food.

Keep an **inventory**, or ongoing record, of the food in the freezer. Include the food, date frozen, and quantity. As you remove food, change the quantity on the inventory so that you know how much is left.

Power Outages

When the power goes off or the refrigerator-freezer breaks down, the food inside is in danger of spoiling. In general, avoid opening the door of the freezer or refrigerator. This will help maintain cold temperatures longer.

◆ **Meats should be wrapped carefully for freezing. Why should packages be dated?**

Keeping Frozen Foods Safe

A full freezer will keep food frozen for about two days after losing power. A half-full freezer will keep food frozen for about one day. If the freezer is not full, stack packages closely together so that they will stay cold. Separate frozen meat, poultry, and fish from other foods. That way, if they begin to thaw, their juices will not get into other foods.

If the power will be off longer than two days, you can put dry ice (frozen carbon dioxide) in the freezer. Be careful! Never touch dry ice with bare hands or breathe its vapors in an enclosed area. Carbon dioxide gas in high concentration is poisonous.

When the freezer is working again, follow these guidelines to decide what to do with the food:

- ◆ If ice crystals are still visible or the food feels as cold as if it were refrigerated, it's safe to refreeze. Some foods may lose quality, but they can still be eaten.
- ◆ Discard any food that thawed or was held above 40°F (4°C) for more than two hours. Discard any food that has a strange odor.

HOME & COMMUNITY CONNECTION

Mention to students that power-outages are sometimes associated with floods, hurricanes, fires, or other disasters. For specific advice about handling food in disasters, contacting the following experts is recommended:

- Local Red Cross chapter
- Cooperative Extension Service

Ask students to find the phone numbers for the community offices above or other emergency management organizations in the community.

Once the freezer is working again, wash up any food spills and wipe surfaces dry. If odors remain, wash again with a solution of 2 tablespoons (30 mL) baking soda dissolved in 1 quart (1 L) warm water. Leave an open box of baking soda inside the freezer to absorb odors.

Keeping Refrigerated Foods Safe

During a power outage, food will usually keep in the refrigerator for four to six hours, depending on the temperature of the room. If the power will be out for a long time, you can place a block of ice in the refrigerator.

When the refrigerator is working again, follow these guidelines to decide what to do with the food:

- Discard fresh meats, poultry, fish, lunch meats, hot dogs, eggs, milk, soft cheeses, and cooked foods if they have been held above 40°F (4°C) for more than two hours.
- Keep butter or margarine if it has not melted and does not have a rancid odor.
- Other foods, including fresh fruits and vegetables, are safe if they have no mold or sliminess and do not have a bad odor.

Once the refrigerator is working again, clean it as described for the freezer.

CLOSE-UP ON SCIENCE: MICROBIOLOGY

Food Storage Without Refrigeration

How did people keep food safe before refrigeration technology was developed? One of the oldest types of food preservation is dehydration, or drying. Dehydration denies germs the moisture they need to grow. Raisins and powdered drink mixes are two dehydrated products common today. Interestingly, "good" bacteria prevent the growth of "bad" bacteria in a process called fermentation. Fermentation extends the life of cucumbers (as pickles) and milk (as cheese). Canning, which uses high temperatures to kill bacteria and prevents their growth by sealing out air, is another food preservation method that was developed in 1809.

Section 7-4 Review & Activities

1. What is the difference between shelf-stable foods and perishable foods?
2. What is the ideal temperature range for room temperature storage? Refrigerator storage? Freezer storage?
3. Describe how you would wrap a package of fresh ground meat for freezing.
4. **Analyzing.** Most people have to throw away spoiled food now and then. What do you think is the major reason?
5. **Applying.** Use a refrigerator-freezer thermometer to check cold storage temperatures at home or in the school foods lab. Are the temperatures at safe levels?

ASSESS

REVIEW

- Ask students to summarize the main ideas in this section.
- Have students complete the Section Review. (Answers appear below.)

EVALUATION

- Give students a list of 10 food items. Ask them to write down how they would store each item, why they would use that method, and how long each item could be kept.
- Have students take the quiz for Section 7-4. (Use the quiz in the *Teacher Resource Guide,* or construct your own with the **ExamView®** *Test Generator* on the *Effective Instruction CD-ROM.*)

RETEACHING

- Stress that, in spite of refrigeration, most foods must be used quickly. Ask which refrigerated foods have the shortest and longest storage life. What should you do if food has been in the refrigerator a long time?
- Refer to the *Reteaching Activities* booklet for the Section 7-4 activity sheet.

CLOSE

Lead a discussion to tie in with the first section motivator. Discuss food storage in the past (circa 1900), today, and in the future (circa 2100). During the discussion, have three student volunteers write on the chalkboard the students' suggestions under each category heading.

Answers to Section 7-4 Review & Activities

1. Shelf-stable foods can be stored for much longer periods of time.
2. Room temperature: between 85°F and 32°F (30°C and 0°C); refrigerator: 40°F (4°C); freezer: 0°F (–18°C) or below.
3. Squeeze air out of heavy-duty plastic freezer bags and seal; wrap in freezer wrap and then heavy-duty foil, sealing with freezer packaging tape; leave enough space for food to expand in freezer containers and seal container tightly.
4. Answers will vary but may suggest that people keep food too long.
5. Answers will vary.

SECTION 7-5

Conserving Natural Resources

FOCUS

MOTIVATORS

- Bring to class articles describing the need for conserving natural resources. Ask students to relate the information in the articles to energy conservation in the kitchen.
- Begin a story describing family life in a time when natural resources have become very scarce. Ask each student to add something different to the story. What effects might scarcity have on the way people live?

VOCABULARY ACTIVITY

Pronounce the two terms listed under "Look for These Terms." Have students find the terms and their definitions in the section. Have one student volunteer to define the prefix *re-* in the term *recycle*.

STUDY SKILLS

- **Guided Reading.** Have students look at the headings within Section 7-5 to preview the concepts that will be discussed.
- Have students read the section and complete the appropriate part of the Chapter 7 Study Guide in the *Student Workbook*.

SECTION 7-5

Conserving Natural Resources

Objectives

After studying this section, you should be able to:

- Explain the importance of conservation.
- Identify ways to conserve resources when working in the kitchen.

Look for These Terms

conservation

recycling

Marcus was studying in the kitchen. He could hear the kitchen radio vaguely in the background—something about the environment. "Conserve natural resources. . . . Don't waste or pollute." Marcus went back to his homework. "I'm just one person," he said to himself. "There's not much I can do."

Conserve Energy

Ironically, the room in which Marcus was sitting—the kitchen—is a major producer of trash that threatens to choke the environment. It is also an energy-guzzler, filled with appliances that liberally use natural gas, electricity, and water. By failing to turn off the radio when he wasn't listening to it, Marcus missed a chance to help conserve energy. **Conservation** is concern about, and action taken to ensure, the preservation of the environment.

What can you as a consumer do to save energy? For starters, remember to turn off lights and appliances when they are not in use. Cook as many foods as possible when using the oven, and freeze the extra for future meals. Here are some other tips:

- Use small appliances or a microwave oven when cooking small amounts of food. They use less energy than the range.
- Match the pan size to the size of the burner or heating unit for top-of-range cooking so that less energy will be lost.
- Decide what you want to eat before opening the refrigerator door. The air in the refrigerator warms up if you leave the door open. Then more energy is needed to cool it down.
- Keep the refrigerator and freezer well organized so that you can find food easily.
- Don't run the dishwasher unless it's full.

Section 7-5 Resources

◆ **Student Workbook,** pp. 55, 62
◆ **Teacher Resource Guide**
Lesson Plan 7-5 Organizer
Section 7-5 Quiz
Chapter 7 Test
◆ **Effective Instruction CD-ROM**
Exam*View*® *Test Generator*
◆ **Student Motivation Kit**
Reteaching Activities, p. 45
Enrichment Activities

◆ **Pollution is a global problem. What decisions can you make to decrease its severity? What actions can you take to alert others to this problem?**

Safety Check

Never try to save energy by letting hot food cool to room temperature before refrigerating it. Remember, harmful bacteria grow quickly at room temperature.

Conserve Water

Clean, safe water is scarce in many areas. Water use may be restricted because of a shortage. Learn more about the water situation in your area. By conserving water in your home, you can help preserve this precious resource for all.

Look for ways to use less water during food preparation. For example, don't let tap water run unnecessarily as you pare vegetables.

Cleanup takes lots of water, but it is also possible to conserve in this task. When handwashing dishes, don't keep the water running. Wash all the dishes first; then rinse them at the same time, as quickly as possible.

Be sure to repair dripping faucets immediately. Water dripping from a kitchen or other faucet at the rate of a drop a second can waste about 700 gallons (2,800 L) a year.

FOOD SCIENCE

Heat Conduction Have students conduct an energy efficiency experiment to see how long it takes to boil water in glass, glass-ceramic, aluminum, and stainless steel utensils. Discuss the differences and how they relate to conservation.

TEACH

- *Conserve Energy*
- *Conserve Water*
  (text pages 216-217)

Discussion Activity

Discuss the need to conserve natural resources such as energy and water. Brainstorm with students a list of guidelines that people can follow to conserve energy in the kitchen. Then repeat for a list of guidelines that people can follow to conserve water in the kitchen.

Demonstration

Have students observe a two-pronged demonstration of (1) steaming vegetables and (2) boiling vegetables. During the demonstration, have students record observations related to conservation and nutrition. Discuss all conservation and nutritional advantages of steaming.

Efficient Meal Planning

Have students plan a meal with foods that can all be cooked together in the oven to save energy. Ask them to write out a menu for the lunch or dinner meal. Have student volunteers explain their choices to the class. Encourage class discussion on each of the presented meals. L2

TEACH cont.

- *Reduce Trash (text pages 218-220)*

Advertising Campaign

First, ask students to think of ways they could minimize the amount of trash they generate, by reducing, reusing, or recycling. Then, ask students to create a slogan and develop a logo to kick-off a trash-reduction campaign in their school. Have the class vote on the top three slogans and logos. Arrange to have a school-wide contest to vote for the best of the three. Have a team of students present all classrooms a copy of the winning slogan and logo. L2

Comparison Activity

Discuss how reusing certain kitchen items can help reduce trash. What types of items should people reuse? What types of items should people not reuse? Compare the differences.

Creative Solutions

Give students five minutes to think of as many uses as possible for plastic tubs, glass jars and bottles, or plastic or paper grocery bags. Have students with an interest in art design an appropriate award for the student who thinks of the most uses in each category. L1

◆ **Installing aerators on faucets cuts down on water waste. Identify three other regular habits that can help with this problem.**

Reduce Trash

Picture a four-lane highway running from Boston to Los Angeles, filled with trash about 6 feet (3 m) deep. That's about the amount of trash Americans create in one year. The trash usually ends up in landfills, which can pollute soil and water. Communities are running out of landfill space.

You can help minimize the trash problem. Start by remembering three key words: *reduce, reuse*, and *recycle*.

Reduce

One way to cut down on trash is to reduce food waste. Studies of residential garbage cans show that a significant percentage of all food an American family buys (not including bones and other inedible parts) gets thrown away. Reducing food waste will save you money. It will also help the environment. How can proper storage help reduce food waste?

Another way to cut down on trash is to reduce the use of disposable products. For example, use dishcloths instead of paper towels to wipe up spills. Use cloth napkins instead of paper ones. Buy or make cloth bags to carry groceries. Choose items in reusable or recyclable containers rather than disposable ones.

Reuse

Reusing gives second life to materials. Find creative ways to reuse items that might otherwise be thrown away. In the kitchen, you might:

- Wash plastic tubs from margarine, yogurt, and cottage cheese, and use them to refrigerate leftovers. Do not use them for freezing—they aren't heavy enough and food will dry out.

Extending Learning

Recycling—Suggest students shop for products in recyclable packaging, such as glass containers, steel cans, aluminum cans, and recycled plastic. State that the way to determine if a plastic container is recyclable is if it has a triangular recycling symbol with a number in it. The lower the number the easier it is to recycle. Ask students to bring to class one plastic container from home with a recycling symbol. Compare numbers to products. Ask if knowing this information affects their decision to purchase or use a product.

- Turn glass jars and bottles with tight-fitting covers into storage containers. Use them for foods such as rice, pasta, and dry beans. Wash the jars and covers carefully; then let them dry out for at least 24 hours to remove odors.
- Reuse plastic or paper grocery bags as trash bags.

Recycle

We could not live without water and many other resources the earth has provided for us. Recycling is a chance to give something back to the planet. **Recycling** is the treating of waste so that it can be reused, as well as an awareness of such practices.

The kinds of materials that are recycled can vary from community to community. Generally, newspapers, aluminum cans and foil, glass bottles, and some plastic containers are recycled. Learn about and cooperate with recycling efforts in your community.

Some communities have curbside pickup for recycled materials. In others, the items must be brought to the collection centers. Many supermarkets collect plastic shopping bags for recycling.

Precycling

You can do your part in the recycling effort before you even get your products home. Do you know how? The answer is *pre*cycling—

Connecting Food and Language Arts

Rachel Carson Speaks Out

Few writers or scientists have spoken out on the plight of the environment as eloquently as Rachel Carson, a pioneer of the modern ecology movement. Carson authored several best sellers, including *The Sea Around Us* and *Silent Spring,* and fought a lifelong crusade against the use of chemical pesticides.

In a speech, she voiced her concern about the use of pesticides, noting, "We are subjecting whole populations to exposure to chemicals which . . . have proved to be extremely poisonous and in many cases cumulative in their effect. These exposures now begin at or before birth and—unless we change our methods—will continue through the lifetime of those now living." Although her concerns have since echoed through the halls of government, prompting legislative action, during her life they met with frequent opposition—especially from the chemical industry, which she criticized in *Silent Spring* for feeding the public "little . . . pills of half-truths. We urgently need an end to these false assurances, to the sugar-coating of unpalatable facts."

Think About It

1. Imagine that you had written to Rachel Carson during her lifetime for her views on reducing household trash, including hazardous household wastes. In a level of language equivalent to that of the quotes in the above passage, write what you believe her reply would have been.
2. What do you think she was referring to in the phrase "sugar-coating of unpalatable facts"? Can you identify present-day food safety issues in which manufacturers in the private sector are attempting to sugar-coat unpalatable facts?

- *Reduce Trash*
- *Show Your Concern*
(text pages 218-220)

Poster Project

Have students prepare posters to illustrate the advantages of recycling. Display the posters around school, especially near the garbage cans in classrooms and the cafeteria. L1

Field Trip

Arrange a field trip to a local recycling plant. Prior to the trip, ask students to develop one question each to potentially ask the plant guide. After the trip, have students write a summary of the trip.

HOME & COMMUNITY CONNECTION

Have students identify recycling centers in the community. Also have students identify any recycling campaigns that are promoted in the community. Discuss with students how they can help play a role in encouraging others in the community to recycle newspapers, glass, aluminum cans, and more. Ask students to describe specific ways they can influence business, industry, and government to conserve natural resources.

ASSESS

REVIEW

- Ask students to summarize the main ideas in this section.
- Have students complete the Section Review. (Answers appear below.)

EVALUATION

- Ask students to create a list of ten specific ways to conserve natural resources and a list of ten reasons why it's important to conserve natural resources.
- Have students take the quiz for Section 7-5. (Use the quiz in the *Teacher Resource Guide,* or construct your own with the **Exam***View*® *Test Generator* on the *Effective Instruction CD-ROM.*)

RETEACHING

- Bring to class magazine or newspaper pictures of natural resources being wasted. Ask students to describe what's wrong and suggest ways to correct it.
- Refer to the *Reteaching Activities* booklet for the Section 7-5 activity sheet.

CLOSE

Repeat the section motivator in which you began a story and students contributed; this time, encourage students to relate ways the family can reduce, reuse, and recycle.

choosing packaging and products that can ultimately be reused. Here are some tips:

- Avoid products packaged in plastic—a material that cannot be recycled—or polystyrene, which releases harmful chemicals into the atmosphere.
- Avoid items that you use once and throw away, such as disposable razors and paper cups and plates.
- Buy in bulk. Bulk quantities use less packaging than small or single-serving sizes.

◆ **Many materials can be recycled and used again. Find out what steps your community has taken to recycle waste.**

Show Your Concern

Some people, like Marcus, believe they can't do much to help solve environmental problems. Yet conservation begins with the individual. If each person does his or her share, waste and pollution can be reduced.

Some people blame business, industry, and government for environmental problems. Even in those areas, individual consumers have a voice. Every time you buy a product or use a service, you "vote" for it and for the company that sells it. Every time you buy items or services that conserve energy, the producers will expand such choices. Consumer power is an effective way to conserve natural resources.

By making the right choices and cooperating with community programs, you can do your share to help conserve natural resources.

Section 7-5 Review & Activities

1. Why is it important for individuals to conserve resources?
2. Name five ways to conserve energy in the home.
3. Name three keys to reducing trash, and give an example of each.
4. **Extending.** Describe some ways you can influence business, industry, and government to conserve natural resources.
5. **Synthesizing.** How might you convince someone who doesn't recycle to start recycling?
6. **Applying.** Develop a plan to reduce, reuse, and recycle at home. Where can you start? How can you proceed? How might you persuade family members to take part in your plan?

Answers to Section 7-5 Review & Activities

1. Environmental problems are becoming steadily worse; everyone needs to help solve them.
2. Any five: See list on page 216.
3. Reduce, reuse, and recycle; examples will vary.
4. By choosing products that are environmentally friendly and that can be recycled; by not using products that have unnecessary packaging.
5. Answers will vary.
6. Answers will vary.

Career Wanted

Local Health Inspector

"Food safety is more than meets the eye."

Sasha Rafidi

Education and Training
- Degree in food science
- Completion of supervised internship

Qualities
- Analytical skills
- Communication skills
- Attention to detail

Q. Basically, Sasha, what is a local health inspector's job?

A. My main duty is making sure that food sellers comply with the safety and sanitation code. I inspect restaurants, food booths at fairs, caterers—any place food is sold to the public. Basically I look at three things: cleanliness, freshness, and safe temperatures.

Q. Are inspections mostly visual?

A. Many violations are obvious if you're trained where to look and what to look for, like mice nests in the boiler room. I also use a special thermometer to measure food temperature, heat-sensitive tape for water temperature, and pH paper to test food acidity.

Q. What's the biggest challenge in your job?

A. I think it's persuading people that little things count. Handing a customer a sandwich without wearing gloves may seem minor, but infections can spread to dozens of people. Fortunately, most managers are good about correcting problems. They may even earn a perfect score the next time.

Related Career Opportunities

Entry Level
- Food service worker
- Restaurant food grader

Technical Level
- Chemical technician
- Produce department manager
- Occupational health and safety technologist

Professional Level
- Consumer safety officer
- Agricultural inspector
- Microbiologist

Making Career Connections

INSPECTION EXPERIENCE. Arrange to inspect the foods lab for safety and sanitation, accompanied by your school cafeteria manager or other food service professional. Record your evaluation separately; then compare. Did the professional notice problems that you didn't? Share results in class. Carry out any suggested improvements.

Career Wanted

Local Health Inspector

Thinking About the Career

Have students think of other questions they would like to ask Sasha Rafidi. (Examples: How do you check for violations? Do you have a laboratory to which you can send samples of foods to inspect? What's the salary range for health inspectors?)

Ask student volunteers to tell what they think would be the most exciting part of being a health inspector.

Have students discuss the responsibilities inherent in the health inspection business.

Career-Building Opportunities

Ask students to write a job description of an epidemiologist, based on their research. Research can be conducted through phone calls, classified ads, and library or Internet research. Have a few student volunteers read their descriptions. Discuss the job description similarities and differences.

For More Information

For additional information about careers in health inspection, encourage students to contact:

- Higher Education Programs
  USDA/CSREES/SERD
  1400 Independence Ave., SW
  Stop 2251
  Washington, DC 20250-2251
  www.reeusda.gov
- Food Safety and Inspection Service
  U.S. Department of Agriculture
  1400 Independence Ave., SW
  Room 2932-S
  Washington, DC 20250-3700
  www.fsis.usda.gov
- U.S. Food and Drug Administration
  5600 Fishers Lane
  Rockville, MD 20857-0001
  www.fda.gov

REVIEW

- Have students complete the Chapter Review. (Answers appear below.)

EVALUATION

- Divide the class into two teams. Each team should brainstorm questions about Chapter 7. Then allow the teams to take turns asking each other the questions they listed. At the end of the questioning period, the team with the most correct answers wins.
- Have students take the test for Chapter 7. (Use the chapter test in the *Teacher Resource Guide,* or construct your own with the **Exam***View*® *Test Generator* on the *Effective Instruction CD-ROM.*)

ANSWERS

Checking Your Knowledge

1. Possible answers: Cold storage center—storage bags, food wraps, containers for leftover foods; sink center—dishpans, cleanup supplies, dish towels and cloths; cooking center—cooking utensils, pots and pans, pot holders, small appliances.
2. Any two: Keep knives sharp and use them properly; don't try to catch a falling knife; don't soak knives in sink or dishpan of water.
3. Never mix chemical products; store hazardous chemicals away from food; store flammable products away from a heat source.
4. Answers will vary. Possible answer: Model safe work habits; allow children to watch you; assign them simple tasks.
5. Any two: Wear clean clothes covered with a clean apron; remove dangling jewelry, roll up long sleeves, and tie back long hair; scrub hands for 20 seconds before handling food; use gloves if you have open wounds on hands; scrub hands immediately after

Chapter 7 Review & Activities

Summary

Section 7-1: Introduction to the Kitchen

- Kitchens are equipped with major appliances, small appliances, and utensils.
- Kitchens are organized around work centers; the three basic ones are the cold storage, sink, and cooking centers.

Section 7-2: Preventing Kitchen Accidents

- Good management and safe work habits are the keys to kitchen safety.
- Common kitchen hazards include falls, cuts, shock, and burns.
- People with special needs require special safety measures.
- Learn first aid, including the Heimlich maneuver and CPR.

Section 7-3: Keeping Food Safe to Eat

- If food is handled improperly, microorganisms can multiply and cause foodborne illness.
- Prevent illness by practicing good personal hygiene, using sanitary work methods, keeping the kitchen clean, and keeping food at proper temperatures.

Section 7-4: Storing Food

- Proper food storage prevents spoilage and nutrient loss.
- Shelf-stable foods may be stored at room temperature.
- Store perishable foods in the freezer or in the refrigerator.
- Frozen and refrigerated foods require special handling after a power outage.

Section 7-5: Conserving Natural Resources

- Conservation begins with the individual.
- Consider measures for saving energy and conserving water.
- To reduce trash, identify ways to reduce, reuse, and recycle.

Checking Your Knowledge

1. Name three items that might be found at each of the three basic kitchen work centers.
2. List two knife safety rules.
3. Give three guidelines for storing hazardous household chemicals.
4. How can you help children learn safe kitchen work habits?
5. List two personal hygiene habits that can help prevent foodborne illness.
6. What is cross-contamination? How can you prevent it?
7. Describe two procedures for thawing food safely.
8. What is shelf life?
9. Name two ways to keep frozen foods safe when the power goes off.
10. Give three alternatives to using disposable items.

Working IN THE Lab

1. ***Food Preparation.*** Prepare a food using a recipe that requires the use of the three basic kitchen work centers. Analyze how organizing a kitchen by work centers helped ease and speed this food preparation task.
2. ***Food Science.*** Observe spoilage in fresh fruits with this experiment. Label small samples of fresh fruits with the type of fruit and the date. Leave the samples out at room temperature (along with a sign warning "Do Not Eat"). Each day, record changes in appearance and smell.

Thinking Critically

1. **Recognizing Assumptions.** Elaine's mother uses a toaster with a damaged wire. She says that the toaster still works and refuses to have it fixed or buy a new one. What assumption is she making? Is it a correct one? Explain your answer.
2. **Distinguishing Between Fact and Opinion.** Analyze this statement: "I use up leftovers, even if they smell a little spoiled. After all, if I boil food long enough, it can't make people sick." Which of these sentences is a fact? Which is an opinion? Defend your answer and suggest possible consequences of this attitude.
3. **Analyzing Behavior.** Think about or observe your family's everyday habits over the space of several days. Make a checklist of habits you observe (for example, water usage), and consider the impact of each on the environment (for example, older brother leaves water running while he shaves). Using the information from the chapter, make a list of recommendations for alternatives that can help reduce, reuse, and recycle the products your family uses. Share your recommendations with family members.

Reinforcing Key Skills

1. **Leadership.** It seems that whenever Tanya needs a utensil to prepare a dish, she can't find it. Things are thrown into drawers in a haphazard fashion by whoever empties the dishwasher. Covers might be at the opposite end of the kitchen from pots. How can Tanya work with her family to solve this problem?
2. **Communication.** Rick has noticed that the school cafeteria does not practice recycling. All trash, including recyclable cans and glass jars, goes into the same dumpster. What steps would you suggest to Rick to bring this problem and possible solutions to the attention of the school community?

Making Decisions and Solving Problems

Kim's family has a hard time functioning in the kitchen on weekday mornings. Some family members are making bag lunches while others are preparing a quick breakfast. As family members get in each other's way, accidents and spills sometimes occur. What could Kim's family do?

Making Connections

1. **Health.** Working with a partner, use library or online resources to investigate treatment for the foodborne illnesses caused by the bacteria in the chart on page 199. Gather statistics on how many people have become victims of each illness and what steps safety officials are taking to curb each problem. Share your findings in a report.
2. **Social Studies.** Create a timeline showing how contaminated water represented a life-threatening problem in earlier periods of civilization, how efforts in the early twentieth century helped clean up the water supply, and how carelessness in the second half of the twentieth century reintroduced the problem. Project the timeline into the future with your own ideas and innovations for how water pollution can be stopped permanently.

ANSWERS cont.

using bathroom or blowing nose; don't touch face or hair while working with food.

6. Letting microorganisms from one food get into another. Use clean dishcloths and sponges; wash top of can before opening; use clean spoon each time you taste food; keep pets out of the kitchen; use separate towels for wiping hands and drying dishes.
7. Any two: Place food in refrigerator; put package in watertight plastic bag and submerge in cold water (change water every 30 minutes); use microwave oven.
8. The length of time a food can be stored and still retain its quality.
9. Any two: Stack packages closely together so that they will stay cold; separate frozen meat, poultry, and fish from other foods; put dry ice in freezer.
10. Any three: Use dishcloths instead of paper towels; use cloth napkins instead of paper ones; buy or make cloth bags to carry groceries; choose items in reusable or recyclable containers rather than disposable ones.

Thinking Critically

1. The assumption is that since the toaster still works without a problem, there's not need to replace it. This assumption is not correct. Even though the toaster still works, the damaged wire is a potential fire hazard; the toaster needs to be replaced.
2. Fact: "I use up leftovers, even if they smell a little spoiled." Opinion: "After all, if I boil food long enough, it can't make people sick." This person's opinion is based on an inaccurate belief that if food is boiled long enough it can't make people sick. It can make people sick.
3. Observations, checklists, impact, and recommendations will vary. Suggest students make sure their recommendations directly correlate with their family observations.

Reinforcing Key Skills

1. Answers will vary but should include reorganizing the kitchen so that equipment and utensils are stored near the work center where they are used most often.
2. Answers will vary. A logical plan might include Rick involving some other students with an interest in recycling; approaching a teacher to help them get organized and formulate a plan; taking the plan to the administration for possible implementation.

CHAPTER

8

Recipe Skills

Advance Planning Guide ☑

- Obtain a recipe dating from the 1800s or earlier.
- Bring a variety of cookbooks to class.
- Prepare a poorly formatted recipe for students to revise.
- Prepare a display of tools used for measuring.
- Prepare a list of ingredients in amounts that require the use of combinations of measures.
- Bring to class a recipe for vanilla pudding.
- Bring to class a loaf cake recipe with a yield of 12.
- Find a recipe you know will fail.
- Bring to class simple recipes for foods that are high in fat and/or sodium.
- Make arrangements for a chef, dietitian, or other food professional to come to class.
- Bring to class a map of the United States.
- Arrange an assortment of knives by size, shape, and use.
- Obtain or create a work flow chart, employee work schedule, duty roster, and memo of instructions.
- Create or find a menu for a multi-course evening meal.
- Arrange a field trip to the school cafeteria or a local restaurant.

CHAPTER

8

Debra tried a cake recipe she saw on a TV cooking show. Her cake was heavy and coarse and didn't look like the one on TV.

Why did Debra get different results using the same recipe? This chapter will explain the possible answers.

Recipe Skills

MEETING DIVERSE NEEDS

Visually Impaired Students. If there are students within the class who are visually impaired, provide them with a variety of large-type cookbooks (such as *The New York Times Large Type Cookbook* by Jean Hewitt). Partner visually impaired students with students who have no visual impairments. The latter can transcribe recipes or read them aloud as needed.

SECTION
8-1

Objectives

After studying this section, you should be able to:

- List the kinds of information a good recipe provides.
- Give guidelines for evaluating and collecting recipes.

Look for These Terms

recipe

yield

assembly directions

Recipe Basics

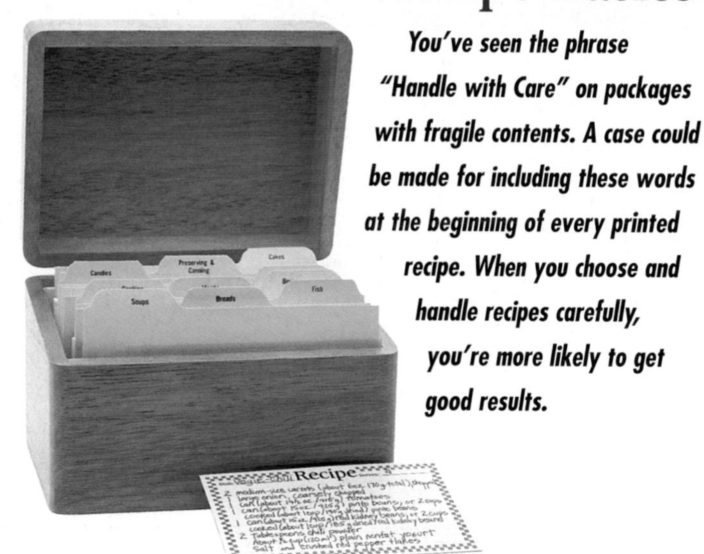

You've seen the phrase "Handle with Care" on packages with fragile contents. A case could be made for including these words at the beginning of every printed recipe. When you choose and handle recipes carefully, you're more likely to get good results.

Recipe Information

A **recipe** is a set of directions for making a food or beverage. Success with a recipe depends not only on the cook's skill but also on the recipe itself. Here are the components of a well-written and complete recipe:

- **Ingredients.** The ingredients should be listed in the order in which they are used. This makes it easier to follow the recipe and not omit an ingredient. Amounts of ingredients are also given.
- **Yield.** The **yield** is the number of servings or amount the recipe makes. The yield of a recipe can be increased or decreased, as necessary. You will learn more about this in Section 8-3.
- **Information about temperature, time, and equipment.** This may include pan size and type, oven temperature or power, and cooking time. A well-written recipe will also tell you if a conventional oven needs to be preheated.
- **Step-by-step directions.** The directions should be clear and easy to follow. Steps may be numbered so that you won't skip any or lose your place. Some recipes include more than one set of directions, such as a conventional method and a microwave method.

SECTION
8-1
Recipe Basics

FOCUS

MOTIVATORS

- Obtain a recipe dating from the 1800s or earlier. (Check your public library for reprints of old cookbooks or conduct an online search.) Distribute recipe copies and/or show the recipe on the overhead projector. Ask students how the recipe differs from those used today. What might account for the differences? What information should a recipe provide?
- Distribute a variety of cookbooks to the class. Ask students to choose a cookbook they would likely use and explain why they chose it.

VOCABULARY ACTIVITY

Pronounce the terms listed under "Look for These Terms." Then, as a class, brainstorm definitions for *recipe*. Decide on one best class definition; then compare it to the definition in the section. Repeat for *yield*.

STUDY SKILLS

- **Guided Reading.** Have students look at the headings within Section 8-1 to preview the concepts that will be discussed.
- Have students read the section and complete the appropriate part of the Chapter 8 Study Guide in the *Student Workbook*.

Section 8-1 Resources

◆ **Student Workbook,** pp. 63, 66
◆ **Teacher Resource Guide**
Lesson Plan 8-1 Organizer
Section 8-1 Quiz
◆ **Effective Instruction CD-ROM**
Exam*View*® *Test Generator*
PowerPoint® Slide #21
◆ **Transparency Package,** CT-21
◆ **Student Motivation Kit**
Reteaching Activities, p. 46
Enrichment Activities
Foods Lab Resources, pp. 35–36

TEACH

- *Recipe Information*
- *Collecting Recipes (text pages 225-227)*

Discussion Activity

Ask students to list and describe the elements of a well-written, complete recipe. Discuss the advantage of compiling your own collection of recipes.

Checklist Activity

Ask students to explain why it's important to analyze a new recipe before you use it. What questions should you ask? As a class, develop a checklist of questions to ask when selecting recipes.

Categorizing

Divide students into three working groups. Provide each group with the same ten recipes. Assign students to categorize the recipes, organizing them in the most user-friendly way. This may involve cutting and pasting or computer filing. **L1**

History

At home, have students trace the recipe history of a favorite family food. Encourage them to determine how it has remained the same over time? How the recipe information or format has changed over time? Invite students to share their family recipe history to the class. **L1**

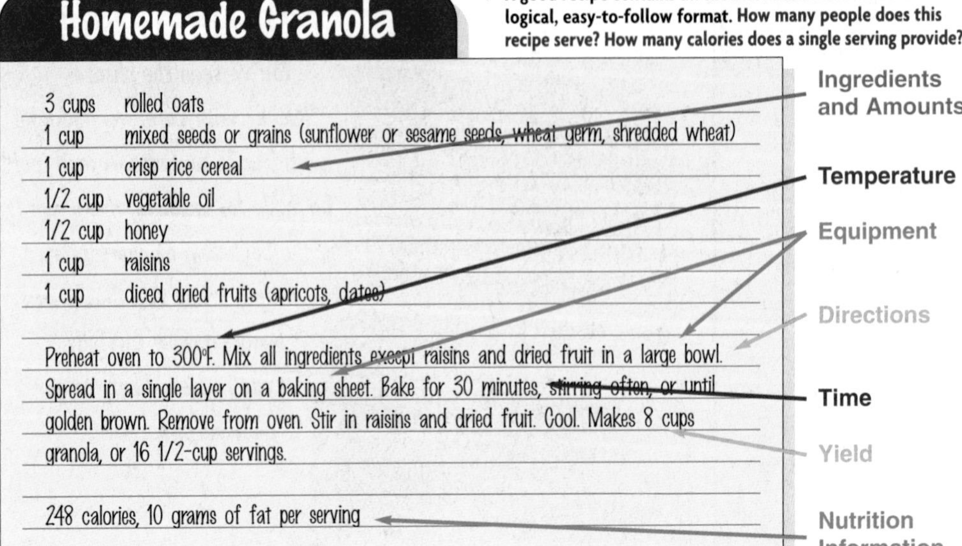

Homemade Granola
3 cups rolled oats
1 cup mixed seeds or grains (sunflower or sesame seeds, wheat germ, shredded wheat)
1 cup crisp rice cereal
1/2 cup vegetable oil
1/2 cup honey
1 cup raisins
1 cup diced dried fruits (apricots, dates)
Preheat oven to 300°F. Mix all ingredients except raisins and dried fruit in a large bowl. Spread in a single layer on a baking sheet. Bake for 30 minutes, stirring often, or until golden brown. Remove from oven. Stir in raisins and dried fruit. Cool. Makes 8 cups granola, or 16 1/2-cup servings.
248 calories, 10 grams of fat per serving
Ingredients and Amounts
Temperature
Equipment
Directions
Time
Yield
Nutrition Information

◆ **A good recipe contains all the information shown here in a logical, easy-to-follow format. How many people does this recipe serve? How many calories does a single serving provide?**

◆ **Nutrition information.** This information is not essential, but it can be useful in helping you choose recipes that provide vital nutrients and that fit in with your eating plan. Typical nutrition information tells you the number of calories and the amount of fat and sodium for each serving of food. Some recipes also include information about carbohydrates, fiber, protein, cholesterol, both saturated and unsaturated fats, vitamins, and minerals.

Recipe Formats

The standard, or most common, format for a recipe lists the ingredients first, followed by the **assembly directions**, the step-by-step procedure that explains how to combine the ingredients in a recipe. Recipes in this book are in the standard format.

A less common recipe format combines the ingredients and assembly directions. You may see a recipe written this way on a food package, for example. This format takes less space than the standard format.

Collecting Recipes

A reliable recipe source is a basic cookbook that gives standard recipes for common foods. You probably have several in your classroom or school library. If you don't find one you like, ask your teacher for recommendations. Other reliable recipe sources are magazines, newspapers, package labels, and Web sites.

How can you tell if a recipe is accurate and complete? When you first read a recipe, analyze it. Are basic ingredients missing? Are descriptions of ingredients clear? Is a direction included for each ingredient? Do you have all the information needed to prepare the recipe? If the answer to any of these questions is no, look for another recipe.

DID *You* Know?

- Culinary historians estimate that the first known cookbook existed 2300 years ago!

Technology TIE-IN

The format of the first known cookbook is vastly different from today's technologically-advanced cookbooks.

Today's computerized cookbooks are quite a bit easier to use than cookbooks of the past. Using computerized recipes enables you to plan menus and shopping lists, count fat grams, and more with the ease of a few clicks of a mouse. In class, discuss the evolution of the cookbook and the advantages of technology related to recipe use.

Once you have a reliable recipe source, you can expand a recipe collection in whatever direction you choose, depending on the kinds of food you enjoy. Why not start a collection of recipes that are tasty, healthful, and easy to prepare? After trying a particular recipe, decide whether to add it to your list of favorites. If you plan to use a new recipe on a special occasion, try it ahead of time first and evaluate the results.

Organizing Recipes

Organizing recipes in your collection can help you find them when you need them. You can paste your recipes on index cards and use a card file box for storage. If you have access to a computer, you can use a word processor file or cookbook software to save recipes. You can then print a particular recipe any time you need it. Use whatever system of organization works best for you.

Connecting Food and Language Arts

Recipe Language

Before cookbooks became popular, recipes were typically handed down within families or traded among friends. As a result, amounts and instructions were sometimes less exact than those given today. Thus, cooks of generations past relied more on "insider" information when preparing foods. They could follow a cake recipe that called for "a lump" of butter, "a coffee cup" of sugar, and "a handful" of raisins, with the batter to be cooked in "a slow oven." They knew from experience what the recipe writer meant.

Think About It

- Ask an older adult in your family about long-standing family recipes that might be inexact. Do you have any familiar favorites? Work with the family member to write an up-to-date recipe that you would be able to follow. Try the recipe, adjust quantities as needed, and add it to your family-heirloom recipe collection.

Section 8-1 Review & Activities

1. What basic information should be found in a well-written recipe?
2. What information does the yield of a recipe give?
3. Identify three things to look for when evaluating a new recipe.
4. **Evaluating.** What characteristics make a recipe difficult or easy to follow?
5. **Extending.** Antonia wants to make a low-fat recipe that she has found in a newspaper. The recipe is complete except for the nutrition information. What would you advise Antonia to do?
6. **Applying.** Find a recipe on a food package or in a magazine or newspaper. Use the guidelines given in this section to determine whether you would want to try it. Write down any questions you have about the recipe. What are some ways this recipe could be improved?

ASSESS

REVIEW

- Ask students to summarize the main ideas in this section.
- Have students complete the Section Review. (Answers appear below.)

EVALUATION

- Give students a recipe. Ask them to identify its parts and explain the function of each in meal planning and food preparation.
- Have students take the quiz for Section 8-1. (Use the quiz in the *Teacher Resource Guide,* or construct your own with the **Exam***View*® *Test Generator* on the *Effective Instruction CD-ROM.*)

RETEACHING

- Provide students with a recipe in which some information has been omitted. Ask students to (1) identify the missing parts and (2) discuss ways to make the recipe complete.
- Refer to the *Reteaching Activities* booklet for the Section 8-1 activity sheet.

CLOSE

As a class, develop a "top ten list" of the most important points learned in this section regarding clarity and specific instructions in recipes.

Answers to Section 8-1 Review & Activities

1. See bulleted list on pages 225-226.
2. Number of servings or amount the recipe makes.
3. Any three: Missing ingredients, clear descriptions of ingredients, directions for use of each ingredient, all other necessary information.
4. Answers will vary. Possible answer: Should be well-written and, preferably, in the standard format.
5. Answers will vary. Possible answers: Find a similar recipe that has this information. Look up the nutritive values of the ingredients in a reputable source.
6. Questions will vary. Typically, recipes can be improved by including more specific information and by simplifying the format.

SECTION
8-2

Measuring Ingredients

FOCUS

MOTIVATORS

- Demonstrate how pioneer women used their hands, bowls, teacups, and other containers to measure ingredients. Did these techniques work? Why? Why was it difficult for these cooks to share their recipes with others?
- Demonstrate that a cup is not always a cup. Pack flour into a cup and level. Then sift the flour onto waxed paper, spoon lightly into the cup, and level with a straightedge spatula. Measure the difference. Repeat using brown sugar, packed and not packed. Measure the difference.

VOCABULARY ACTIVITY

Pronounce the two terms listed under "Look for These Terms." Ask students to define the prefix *equi-* (equal). Then have students find the terms and their definitions in the section.

STUDY SKILLS

- **Outlining.** Have students read the section and outline it by copying the headers on paper and leaving space after each one. Students are to write a sentence in their own words, summarizing the content under each header.
- Have students read the section and complete the appropriate part of the Chapter 8 Study Guide in the *Student Workbook*.

SECTION
8-2

Objectives

After studying this section, you should be able to:

- Identify customary and metric units of measure.
- Identify measuring tools.
- Describe the proper procedures for measuring various types of ingredients.

Look for These Terms

volume

equivalents

Measuring Ingredients

Logan bought a glass of lemonade at his brother Carl's lemonade stand.

"How much sugar did you put in this?" Dom asked, after one sip of the very sweet drink.

"The directions said 1 cup," Carl replied, "and that's what I used." He held up an oversized coffee mug. As Carl found out, measuring properly is very important.

Units of Measurement

In a recipe, amounts of ingredients can be given in several ways. Most ingredients are measured by **volume**, the amount of space an ingredient takes up. For instance, a pasta salad recipe might list "1 cup cooked pasta." Some ingredients are measured by weight: 1 pound of shrimp and 8 ounces of baking chocolate are examples. A few ingredients may be measured by the number of items, such as one medium banana or two eggs.

Customary Units

Units of measure may be expressed in one of two ways—customary or metric. The customary system is the system of weights and measures used in the United States. Following are the most common customary units found in recipes, with their abbreviations in parentheses.

- ◆ **Volume:** teaspoon (tsp.), tablespoon (Tbsp.), cup (c.), fluid ounce (fl. oz.), pint (pt.), quart (qt.), gallon (gal.).
- ◆ **Weight:** ounce (oz.), pound (lb.).
- ◆ **Temperature:** degrees Fahrenheit (°F).
- ◆ **Length:** inches (in.).

Notice that *ounce* is used to express both volume (in fluid ounces) and weight. The two are not the same. To understand the difference, imagine a cup of popcorn and a cup of water. Both take up the same amount of space, but the popcorn is mostly air and, therefore, is much lighter. To find out how much each *weighs*, you would use a scale, not a measuring cup.

Section 8-2 Resources

◆ **Student Workbook,** pp. 63, 67
◆ **Teacher Resource Guide**
Lesson Plan 8-2 Organizer
Section 8-2 Quiz
◆ **Effective Instruction CD-ROM**
Exam*View*® *Test Generator*

◆ **Student Motivation Kit**
Reteaching Activities, p. 47
Enrichment Activities
Foods Lab Resources, pp. 37–38

Metric Units

The metric system is based on multiples of ten. For instance, just as there are 100 pennies in one dollar, there are 100 centimeters in one meter. Once you become familiar with it, the metric system is easier to use than the customary system.

Here are the metric units and symbols most often found in recipes.

- **Volume:** milliliter (mL), liter (L).
- **Weight:** milligram (mg), gram (g), kilogram (kg).
- **Temperature:** degrees Celsius (°C).
- **Length:** centimeter (cm).

Equivalents

You can express the same amount in different ways by using **equivalents**, different units of equal measure. For instance, 4 tablespoons of flour is the same amount as ¼ cup of flour, or about 50 milliliters. The chart on page 230 shows equivalents for food preparation.

Connecting Food and Math

Converting Temperatures

Most customary-to-metric conversions are fairly straightforward. One that is not is temperature. The table of equivalents on page 230 gives you some general temperature conversion guidelines, but you may need to use an oven temperature that is not listed. What would you do if a recipe specified setting your oven to 145°C? A simple solution is to use the following formula:

$$1.8 \times {}^\circ C + 32 = {}^\circ F$$

Doing the computation for the above example reveals that the correct Fahrenheit setting is 300°F ($1.8 \times 145 = 261$; $261 + 32 = 293$, which can be rounded to 300).

To convert from Fahrenheit to Celsius is just as easy. The formula is:

$$({}^\circ F - 32) \times 0.56 = {}^\circ C$$

Think About It

- Paula is sending a recipe to her cousin Esteban, who lives in Spain. The recipe contains this instruction: "Bake at 375°F for 15 minutes." At what temperature should Paula instruct her cousin to set his oven?

◆ **Accurate measurements are the key to successful food preparation. Why is accuracy important when cooking?**

TEACH

- ***Units of Measurement (text pages 228-230)***

Chart Making Activity

On the chalkboard, invite students to list in a chart format (similar to the chart on page 230) the most common units for volume, weight, and temperature in the customary and metric systems. Discuss the difference between an ounce and a fluid ounce. In what way does the metric system make this distinction clearer?

Measurement Review Activity

Review the two different systems of measurement, customary and metric. In the United States, which system is predominantly used in recipes? Why is the United States moving toward adopting the metric system? Discuss metric systems advantages.

Equivalent Measures Cards

Have students work in groups to make cards listing equivalent measurements. Have students use the cards to play a card-matching game, like rummy. Give points for correctly matching equivalent measurements. L1

Adapting Recipes

Provide a recipe to students that uses customary measures. Using the chart on page 230, have students list the approximate metric equivalent for each recipe ingredient. L1

Extending Learning

Equivalents—Here are equivalents of some basic foods, before and after preparation:

1 cup dry beans or pasta = about 2 cups cooked

1 slice bread = ¾ cup soft or ¼ cup fine dry crumbs

¼ pound cheddar cheese = 1 cup grated

1 medium apple = 1 cup sliced

1 medium orange = ⅓ cup juice

1 medium onion = ½ cup chopped

1 pound raw chicken breast = 2 cups cooked, chopped

TEACH cont.

- *Equipment for Measuring (text pages 230-231)*

Discussion Activity

Ask students to describe measuring tools commonly found in a well-equipped kitchen. Discuss the importance of using standard measuring cups and spoons for recipes. What can happen from using non-standard measures?

USING CONNECTING FOOD AND MATH

The feature is found on page 229. Explain to students that in mathematical sequences containing multiple operations, multiplication and division come before addition and subtraction, unless otherwise grouped.

To help students familiarize themselves with the Celsius temperatures, use the formula to develop with students a pocket-guide of 10 common Fahrenheit temperatures with their Celsius equivalents.

Student Demonstrations

Allow students to experiment with liquid and dry measuring cups to demonstrate for themselves the importance of using correct measures. Ask students to write a brief report describing their experiments and results. L1

Demonstration

Demonstrate how non-standard measuring cups can not accurately be used for standardized recipes. Show the actual amount of liquid in a coffee mug and beverage glasses versus one liquid measuring cup and a soup spoon versus one measuring tablespoon.

Equivalents

Customary Measure	Customary Equivalent	Approximate Metric Equivalent
Volume		
1 tsp.		5 mL
1 Tbsp.	3 tsp.	15 mL
1 fl. oz.	2 Tbsp.	30 mL
1/4 cup		50 mL
1/3 cup		75 mL
1/2 cup		125 mL
2/3 cup		150 mL
3/4 cup		175 mL
1 cup	8 fl. oz. or 16 Tbsp.	250 mL
1 pt.	2 cup or 16 fl. oz.	500 mL
1 qt.	2 pt. or 4 cup or 32 fl. oz.	1000 mL or 1 L
1 gal.	4 qt.	4 L
Weight		
1 oz.		28 g
1 lb.	16 oz.	500 g
2 lb.	32 oz.	1,000 g or 1 kg
Temperatures		
0°F		–18°C
32°F		0°C
350°F		180°C
400°F		200°C

Equipment for Measuring

Now that you understand the different units for measuring ingredients, you'll want to be sure you have the right tools for measuring. A well-equipped kitchen includes the following measuring tools. Each has specific uses, as you will learn.

- **Dry measuring cups** usually come in a set of several sizes. A typical customary set includes 1/4-cup, 1/3-cup, 1/2-cup, and 1-cup measures. A metric set includes 50-mL, 125-mL, and 250-mL measures.

Dry measuring cups are used for accurate measuring of dry ingredients. Give the metric equivalent of each volume shown.

Reinforcing Key Skills

Present the following problems to student groups. Allow time for them to discuss and compare their responses.

Management—If your kitchen was supplied with measuring spoons but without measuring cups, how could you accurately measure 1/4 cup of sugar?

Communication—Your best friend was baking a cake for a graduation party. To measure the flour she packed it down into a liquid measuring cup. How would you inform her of her error?

- **Liquid measuring cups** are transparent and have measurement markings on the side. They are typically marked in fractions of a cup, fluid ounces, and milliliters. A head space of about ¼ inch above the top marking makes it easier to move a filled cup without spilling. A spout makes pouring easier. Common sizes are 1-cup (25-mL) and 2-cup (500-mL).
- **Measuring spoons** generally come in sets of four or five. Most customary sets, as you'll notice in the photo on the right, include these four sizes: ¼-teaspoon, ½-teaspoon, 1-teaspoon, and 1-tablespoon. Metric sets include these five: 1-mL, 2-mL, 5-mL, 15-mL, and 25-mL measures.

Always use standard measuring cups and spoons. A standard 1-cup measuring cup, no matter how it is shaped or designed, always holds the same amount. Coffee mugs, beverage glasses, soup spoons, and other nonstandard items used for serving or eating food vary in size.

Other helpful measuring tools are a straightedge spatula for leveling off dry ingredients, a rubber scraper for removing ingredients from measuring cups, and a food scale for measuring ingredients by weight.

Using Combinations of Measures

What happens if you need a dry measurement but lack a measuring cup or spoon for that exact amount? The answer is to use a combination approach. For instance, if you need ¾ cup flour, use the ½-cup and ¼-cup measures. For ⅔ cup, measure ⅓ cup twice.

Sometimes you may need to measure unusual amounts of an ingredient, such as ⅝ cup. How would you measure such an amount? First, measure out the closest amount you can with a standard-size measure. For example, the closest measure to ⅝ cup is ½ cup (since ½ = 4/8). This leaves you with ⅛ cup left to measure. Since ⅛ cup is a small amount, you will need to use measuring spoons. Here is where equivalents come in handy. Using the equivalents chart on page 230, you'll note there are 16 tablespoons in one cup. Therefore, ⅛ cup equals 2 tablespoons (⅛ × 16 = 16/8 = 2). You would add 2 tablespoons to ½ cup to get ⅝ cup.

◆ **Standard measuring spoons come in sets of four as shown here. Metric spoons come in sets of five. How many ½ tsp. measures would you need to make up the volume of 1 Tbsp.?**

You can also remove small amounts from a measuring cup to get the exact amount called for in a recipe. To get ⅞ cup milk, you would first measure one cup and then remove 2 tablespoons (⅛ cup). How would you measure ⅜ cup?

Techniques for Measuring

In addition to the correct tools, the proper procedures are essential to accurate measuring and a successful recipe. The guidelines that follow will help you.

- *Equipment for Measuring (text pages 230-231)*

Display Activity

Prepare a display of tools used for measuring. Differentiate between dry and liquid measuring cups. Point out that measuring spoons can be used for measuring small amounts of both liquid and dry ingredients. Stress the importance of using standard measuring cups and spoons.

Demonstration

Demonstrate how to properly use a rubber scraper for removing ingredients from measuring cups. Then demonstrate the difference in measurement when not using a rubber scraper.

Measuring Math Activity

Provide students with a list of ingredients in amounts that require the use of combinations of measures. Ask students to identify the proper types and sizes of measuring cups or spoons needed. Then have students practice measuring specific combination amounts.

HOME & COMMUNITY CONNECTION

Ask students to do a survey of their kitchens at home. Make a list of all the equipment used for measuring. Have students determine what additional measuring equipment may be useful. Did they find any uncommon measuring equipment, such as a ⅔ cup dry measuring cup?

RECIPE FILE

Banana Citrus Smoothie

This recipe uses a variety of measuring equipment.

USING THE RECIPE

- Have students read the recipe and discuss each step.
- Review food and kitchen safety procedures that apply to this recipe.
- Remind students to be careful with the sharp blade on the blender, and caution them never to run the blender without first placing the cover on it.
- Have each lab team fill out a work plan. (See the *Foods Lab Resources* booklet.)
- Have students check off the ingredients and equipment listed on the recipe worksheet and prepare the recipe.
- Have students complete the evaluation and questions on the recipe worksheet.

SEE ALSO...
The *Foods Lab Resources* booklet for the "Banana Citrus Smoothie" recipe worksheet and other recipe alternatives.

RECIPE FILE

Banana Citrus Smoothie

When a big thirst strikes, a refreshing smoothie can be the perfect answer. As you prepare this recipe, note the various measuring tools and methods called for.

Customary	***Ingredients***	***Metric***
1 cup	orange juice	250 mL
⅓ cup	plain nonfat yogurt	75 mL
½ cup	crushed ice	125 mL
½ cup	nonfat dry milk	125 mL
½ medium	banana	½ medium
¼ cup	powdered sugar	50 mL

Yield: Three servings, each 8 fl. oz. (250 mL)

Directions

1. Place all ingredients in blender container.
2. Cover and blend until smooth.
3. Pour into glasses and serve immediately.

Nutrition Information

Per serving (approximate): 139 calories, 6 g protein, 29 g carbohydrate, trace fat, 2 mg cholesterol, 83 mg sodium
Good source of: potassium, vitamin C, B vitamins, calcium, phosphorus

Food for Thought

- For which ingredient(s) would you use a liquid measuring cup? A dry measuring cup? Measuring spoons?
- What should be done to the powdered sugar before measuring it?

Measuring Liquids

Liquid measuring cups are used to measure all liquids, including oils and syrups. To measure liquids, follow these steps:

1. Set the cup on a level surface. If you try to hold it in your hand, you may tip it and get an inaccurate reading.
2. Carefully pour the liquid into the measuring cup.
3. Bend down to check the measurement at eye level for an accurate reading.
4. Add more liquid or pour off excess, if needed, until the top of the liquid is at the desired measurement mark.

Answers to **Food for Thought**

1. Liquid measuring cup: orange juice, yogurt (optional); dry measuring cup: yogurt (optional), crushed ice, nonfat dry milk, powdered sugar; measuring spoons: none.
2. Sift powdered sugar before measuring to add air and remove any lumps for accurate measurement.

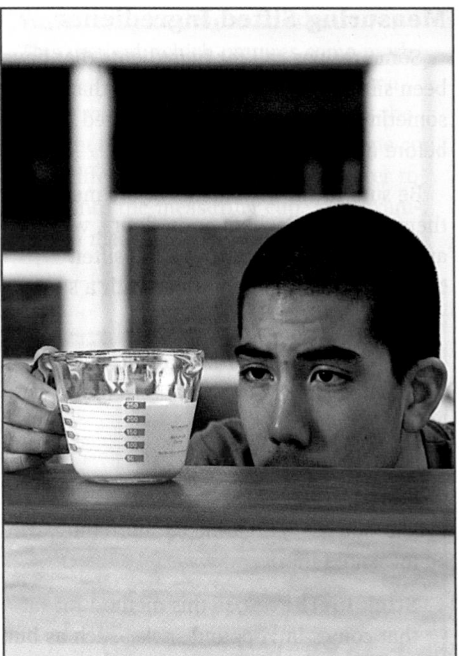

◆ **Check the measurement of liquids at eye level. Explain why this is important.**

Measuring Dry Ingredients

Dry measuring cups are used to measure flour, sugar, dry beans, and other dry ingredients. They can also be used for foods such as diced meat, chopped vegetables, and yogurt. Here are the steps to take when measuring dry ingredients:

1. Put a piece of waxed paper under the measuring cup to catch any extra ingredient. Don't measure an ingredient while holding the cup over the bowl in which you are mixing.
2. Fill the cup with the ingredient. Some ingredients must be spooned into the cup lightly. Others can be packed down if specified in the recipe.
3. Level off the top of the cup using the straight edge of a spatula. Let the excess fall on the waxed paper. Put the excess back into the original container.
4. Pour the ingredient into the mixture. With semisolid foods, such as yogurt, use a rubber scraper to be sure the entire ingredient has been emptied out of the cup.
5. Pour the ingredient into the mixing container. If needed, use a rubber scraper to empty the cup completely.

For small amounts of liquids, use measuring spoons. To measure ⅛ teaspoon of a liquid ingredient, dribble it into the ¼-teaspoon measure until it looks half full.

◆ **Carefully level off the measure of dry ingredients with a straight-edged instrument, such as a spatula. Why has this teen set waxed paper on his work space?**

- *Techniques for Measuring (text pages 231-235)*

Discussion Activity

Ask students to list the steps for measuring liquids. How should you measure ⅛ tsp. of a liquid if you do not have a ⅛ tsp. measuring spoon?

Measuring Liquids

Have students work in groups of three. One person in each group should fill a glass measuring cup with ⅜ cup, ¼ cup, ½ cup, ⅝ cup, or ⅞ cup water, making sure the measurement is accurate. He or she should not tell the other students the amount in the cup. Have another student read the measurement from eye level. Have the third student read the measurement by looking down into the cup. Ask students to write a summary explaining their results. L1

Student Demonstrations

Have students work in small groups to demonstrate procedures for measuring dry ingredients. Discuss how proper procedures were necessary for accurate measurement. L1

Creative Writing

Assign your students to write a one-page, how-to story about measuring one cup of brown sugar from the point of view of brown sugar. L2

FOOD SCIENCE

Meniscus

Have students pour water into a clear measuring cup. Tell them to look carefully at the surface of the water and note the *meniscus*, the curve formed by the surface of the liquid. Explain that when you measure clear liquids, you should make sure that the bottom of the meniscus is at the marking for the amount you want. Have students practice measuring water and other clear liquids. Walk around and make sure they are measuring properly.

SECTION
8-3
Changing a Recipe

FOCUS

MOTIVATORS

- Provide students with a vanilla pudding recipe. Ask students what changes would be needed to increase or decrease the number of servings (yield). What changes would be needed to vary the flavor of the pudding? What changes could be made in the recipe to decrease the amount of fat?
- Ask students how they think new recipes are created. What would a chef need to know to create a new recipe? Why might a chef want to change a recipe? What would a chef need to know to change it?

VOCABULARY ACTIVITY

Pronounce the term listed under "Look for This Term." Have students find the term and its definition in the section.

STUDY SKILLS

- **Guided Reading.** Have students look at the headings within Section 8-3 to preview the concepts that will be discussed.
- Have students read the section and complete the appropriate part of the Chapter 8 Study Guide in the *Student Workbook*.

SECTION
8-3

Objectives

After studying this section, you should be able to:

- Explain how to increase or decrease recipe yield.
- Give basic strategies for changing a recipe to decrease fat and sodium.
- Describe how high altitudes affect the cooking process.

Look for This Term

desired yield

Changing a Recipe

Heather was getting ready to make drop biscuits for dinner when she realized that she did not have any buttermilk. That didn't stop her. She knew she could substitute a mixture of fat-free milk and vinegar and the recipe would come out fine.

Why Change a Recipe?

From time to time, you may find that, like Heather, you have to change a recipe. Perhaps you don't have one of the ingredients and can't take the time to go out to buy it. You might want to substitute a more healthful or less expensive ingredient for one in the recipe. You might want to increase or decrease the recipe yield.

Changes are more likely to be successful in some recipes than in others. Mixtures such as salads, stir-fried foods, soups, and stews can usually be changed easily. On the other hand, recipes for baked products such as muffins and custards are like chemical formulas. Because each ingredient does a job in the recipe, the ingredients must be used in specific amounts in relation to each other. If one amount is changed or one ingredient is omitted, you risk having the recipe not turn out right.

When you change the ingredients in mixtures, you may notice a difference in flavor and texture. For instance, Paige sometimes substitutes cooked turkey for beef when making tacos. How might this change affect the flavor and texture of the dish?

236 **Chapter 8 ◆ Recipe Skills**

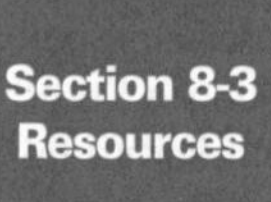

◆ Student Workbook, pp. 64, 68
◆ Teacher Resource Guide
Lesson Plan 8-3 Organizer
Section 8-3 Quiz
◆ Effective Instruction CD-ROM
Exam*View*® *Test Generator*

◆ Student Motivation Kit
Reteaching Activities, p. 48
Enrichment Activities
Food Science Resources, pp. 50–52, 90–92, 108–109

◆ The success of a recipe depends on choosing appropriate substitutes and measuring them carefully. What might be used in place of the apples in this loaf cake?

Changing the Yield

Recipes may need to be changed if the yield is not what you need. Most recipes, even those for baked goods, can be successfully doubled. Remember that larger equipment may be needed for mixing and cooking, and cooking times often need adjustment. For baked goods, it is best to use two baking pans of the original size rather than one larger one.

Many recipes for mixtures such as casseroles and soups can be not only doubled, but halved, tripled, and so on. The same process is used for both increasing and decreasing.

1. ***Determine the desired yield.*** The **desired yield** represents the number of servings you need.
2. ***Use the formula.*** To adjust the yield of a recipe, multiply the amount of each ingredient in the same number. That number is determined by using a simple formula:

   desired yield ÷ regular yield = number to multiply by

   Example: Your chili recipe serves eight and you need to serve only four: 4 ÷ 8 = 0.5.
3. ***Multiply each ingredient amount by that number.*** This keeps all the ingredients in the same proportion as in the original recipe.

TEACH

- *Why Change a Recipe?*
- *Changing the Yield (text pages 236-238)*

Discussion Activity

Ask students why a person might want or need to change a recipe. Ask students to explain why it might be easier in some cases to double a recipe than to reduce it by half. Discuss the importance of considering changes needed to equipment, temperature, and cooking time when you change the yield.

Calculations

Using recipes, have students practice halving, doubling, and tripling the yields. Ask what problems they encountered. What changes, other than in measurement, were needed? L1

Prediction Activity

Provide students with a loaf cake recipe with a yield of 12. Ask students to predict the effects of increasing or decreasing the yield of the recipe. How might doing so affect the results? Then, have students double the yield and determine all adjustments needed in ingredients, equipment, temperature, or time?

Solving Problems

Provide student "detectives" with a recipe that you know will fail. Ask students to solve the recipe failure mystery by analyzing ingredients, yield, directions, and other important information. Discuss their solution to have a successful recipe. L1

Reinforcing Key Skills

Present the following problems to student groups. Allow time for them to discuss and compare their responses.

Directed Thinking—You need to decrease by half a recipe that calls for one egg. How would you do so? How could you use the leftover egg?

Management—You want to double the yield of your lasagne recipe, but you don't have double the time.

- *Making Ingredient Substitutions*
- *High-Altitude Cooking (text pages 238-241)*

USING THE Food Science LAB

Explain to students that when food professionals develop nutrient-modified food, they often use methods other than those used by the general public or in the classroom to achieve more desirable results. Amplify on this by providing students with low-fat sour cream.

Have them repeat steps 3 and 4, this time using low-fat sour cream in addition to the regular sour cream and lab-developed sour cream.

Ask what difference, if any, they can discern in the flavor of the three products? In the appearance? Texture?

Point out that the lab calls for the addition of lemon juice to the low-fat cottage cheese. Ask: What is the purpose of the lemon juice?

Compare ingredient differences on the product labels.

Display Activity

Place a map of the United States on a bulletin board. Identify, with flagged pins, several areas that are above 1000 m (approximately 3000 ft.). Describe the effects of high altitude. What adjustments are needed when cooking at high altitudes? Brainstorm a list of food products that people living in these high-altitude areas may need to prepare differently.

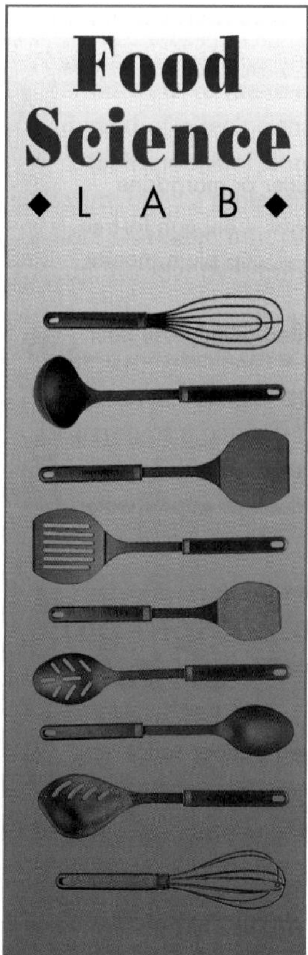

Taste-Testing a Reduced-Fat Product

According to an old saying, the proof is in the eating. You are about to test the truth of this saying by conducting a taste test of a full-fat dairy product and a lower-fat version made in the food lab.

Procedure

1. Place 8 ounces (250 mL) of low-fat small-curd cottage cheese in a blender. Blend until smooth. Add 1 tablespoon (5 mL) of lemon juice and blend again.
2. Force the cottage cheese through a strainer. Remove as much of the solid contents as possible.
3. Have classmates taste small samples of both this cottage cheese blend and full-fat sour cream. Record their reactions in a chart.
4. Add commercial onion soup mix to both foods to make dips. Repeat step 3.

Conclusions

- ◆ How did the subjects rate the cottage cheese blend in comparison with the sour cream? Did all the subjects have the same reaction to the two samples? If not, explain.
- ◆ Did the results of the experiment differ when you added the onion soup mix? If so, how? What can you infer?
- ◆ How can the results of this food science lab help you use recipes in the future?

High-Altitude Cooking

Unless otherwise indicated, recipes are intended to be used at altitudes of 3,000 feet (about 1,000 m) or below. If used at higher altitudes, they may not turn out right. Why? As the altitude gets higher, the air pressure gets lower. This affects food preparation in two main ways.

First, water boils at a lower temperature. This means that foods that are boiled, such as pasta, take longer to cook. Second, when the air pressure is low, bubbles of gas that form in liquids escape into the atmosphere more readily. As a result, baked goods are likely to rise less and be heavy. Sometimes reducing the amount of baking powder or soda and sugar and increasing the liquid can help.

People who live in high-altitude areas often can get helpful information about adapting recipes from their local utility company, newspapers, or nearest cooperative extension office. Many packaged foods include special directions for preparation at high altitudes.

HOME & COMMUNITY CONNECTION

Ask students to develop a list of five cities that they have visited or would like someday to visit. Ask them to identify the country (and state, province, etc.) in which the city is located and research the altitude of the city. In class, have students point to their selected cities on a globe and state the altitude and whether the specific populations need to follow high-altitude cooking instructions. Discuss conclusions related to high-altitude cooking and different regions of the world.

FOR YOUR HEALTH

Adding by Subtracting

According to a mathematical principle, subtracting one amount from another yields a lower number. Nutritionists, however, are discovering that it is possible to *add* to the flavor of a recipe *and increase* its nutritional value, *while cutting down* on certain ingredients. Here are some examples of this new food math:

- Toast nuts before using them in dishes. That way, you can use fewer nuts to get the same nutty flavor.
- Add a pinch of cinnamon, nutmeg, or other sweet spice to a recipe and use less sugar.
- Add dried fruits or pureed dried fruits to a sweet recipe. They will pack in more nutrition while allowing you to cut down on the amount of sugar called for.
- Subtract heavy, fatty sauces on meats, vegetables, and other foods. In their place, add light, tangy salsas instead. You will be surprised at the boost in flavor.

Following Up

- Think of at least two ways to add flavor to foods while subtracting ingredients high in sodium, such as salt and ketchup. Be creative.

Section 8-3 Review & Activities

1. Name three reasons to change a recipe.
2. List the basic steps in changing recipe yield.
3. Name three changes that can be made to a recipe for health reasons.
4. **Synthesizing.** What are some other ways Tony might modify the spaghetti sauce to make it healthful while maintaining its good flavor?
5. **Comparing and Contrasting.** What are the pros and cons of modifying favorite recipes to lower their fat content as compared with buying a cookbook with low-fat recipes?
6. **Applying.** Find a simple recipe that makes 4 servings. Show how you would change the ingredient amounts to make 12 servings or 2 servings.

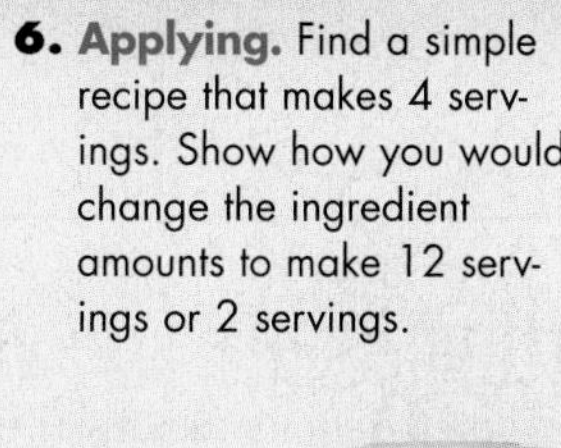

ASSESS

REVIEW

- Ask students to summarize the main ideas in this section.
- Have students complete the Section Review. (Answers appear below.)

EVALUATION

- Ask students to double the yield of a popular food recipe and to reduce the amount of fat and sodium it contains.
- Have students take the quiz for Section 8-3. (Use the quiz in the *Teacher Resource Guide,* or construct your own with the **Exam***View*® *Test Generator* on the *Effective Instruction CD-ROM.*)

RETEACHING

- Give students a standard biscuit recipe and help them make the adjustments needed to bake the biscuits at high altitudes.
- Refer to the *Reteaching Activities* booklet for the Section 8-3 activity sheet.

CLOSE

Ask students again how they think new recipes are created. Note that many new recipes are made by altering existing recipes. Emphasize that different locations, food preferences, altitudes, and diet needs could all be reasons. As a class, review a fettucine Alfredo recipe, for example. Brainstorm a list of all the possible changes that could be made based on food preferences, altitude, health, and missing ingredients.

Answers to Section 8-3 Review & Activities

1. When you're missing an ingredient, for health reasons, or to change the yield.
2. See numbered list on pages 237-238.
3. Ingredient changes, modifications to the cooking method, reduction of portion sizes.
4. Answers will vary. Have students give suggestions for additions rather than reductions to the recipe.
5. Answers will vary. Possible pro: can adjust to exact fat content and flavor desired. Possible con: may need to try several modifications until reaching desired result.
6. Answers will vary but should describe a procedure that follows the steps on pages 237-238.

SECTION 8-4

Preparation Tasks

FOCUS

MOTIVATORS

- Show students an assortment of knives. From the shape and size of each knife, can they guess the purpose of the knife?
- Without instructions, have small groups of students cut up half an apple as if for muffins. Then have each group explain how theirs was chopped. Which method produced the most finely chopped apple? What were the differences in the results? What else did the groups need to know?

VOCABULARY ACTIVITY

Direct students' attention to "Look for These Terms." Using a classroom dictionary reference, have three student volunteers find the multiple definitions for *score, whisk,* and *fold(ing)*. Discuss which definitions of each term are related to this section.

STUDY SKILLS

- **Outlining.** Have students read the section and outline it by copying the headers on paper and leaving space after each one. Students are to write a sentence in their own words, summarizing the content under each header.
- Have students read the section and complete the appropriate part of the Chapter 8 Study Guide in the *Student Workbook*.

SECTION 8-4

Preparation Tasks

Objectives

After studying this section, you should be able to:

- Describe the techniques that correspond with common recipe terms.
- Identify the kitchen equipment used for each technique.

Look for These Terms

sharpening steel

pare

serrated

score

whisk

folding

purée

If you were lost in a foreign country, you would need to know the language in order to ask directions. In the same way, success with a recipe depends on the ability to navigate through the directions, which may include terms that are "foreign" to a new cook. In this section, you will learn about these terms.

Cutting Foods

Food preparation often involves a variety of cutting tasks. You may need to trim unwanted parts from food or cut food to the desired size. With practice, you can become a cutting expert. Knowing how to use cutting tools properly is the first step to succeeding in the kitchen as well as to preventing accidents.

Equipment for Cutting

Two key cutting tools for a well-equipped kitchen do no actual cutting. One of these is a cutting board, a specially-designed surface to help protect kitchen counters. To reduce the risk of foodborne illness, choose a cutting board made of a nonporous material.

The second cutting tool, a **sharpening steel**, is a long, steel rod on a handle used to help keep knives sharp. Regular and correct use of a sharpening steel is an essential skill to learn. Here is what to do (reverse the directions if you are left-handed):

1. Hold the handle of the steel in your left hand. Place the point straight down, very firmly, on a cutting board. In your right hand, hold the knife by the handle, blade down.

Section 8-4 Resources

◆ **Student Workbook,** pp. 64, 69
◆ **Teacher Resource Guide**
Lesson Plan 8-4 Organizer
Section 8-4 Quiz
◆ **Effective Instruction CD-ROM**
Exam*View*® *Test Generator*

◆ **Student Motivation Kit**
Reteaching Activities, p. 49
Enrichment Activities
Foods Lab Resources, pp. 39–40
Food Science Resources, pp. 90–92

2. Place the knife blade against the right side of the steel. The knife blade and steel should touch near the handles. Tip the knife away from the steel at a 20-degree angle.

3. Draw the blade down the steel and toward you, keeping it at a 20-degree angle to the steel. Use gentle pressure.

4. When the tip of the knife reaches the tip of the steel, repeat the process, holding the knife against the steel on the left. Draw the blade down along the steel four or five times, alternating right and left sides.

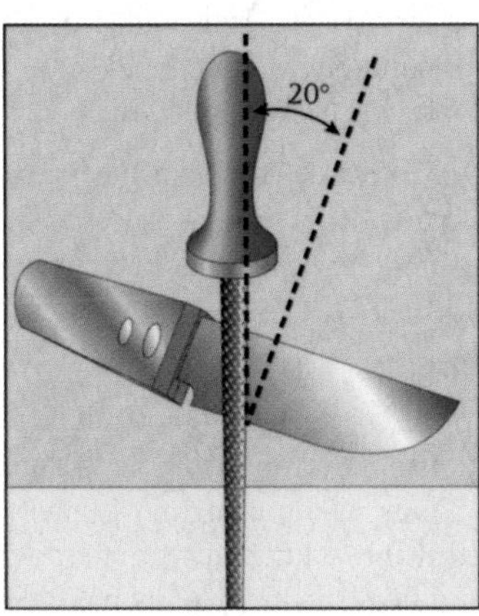

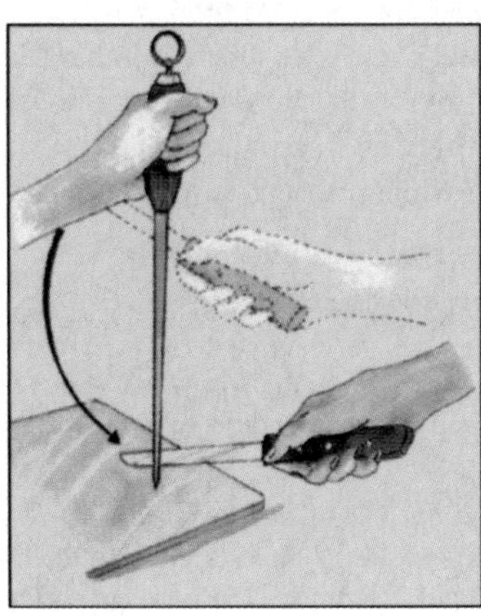

INFOLINK

For more information on ways to reduce the likelihood of foodborne illness, see Section 7-3.

Knives

Many cutting tasks require the use of a knife. The basic types of knives include:

- **Chef's knife.** Also called a French knife. Has a large, triangular blade. Ideal for slicing, chopping, and dicing.
- **Slicing knife.** Used for cutting large foods, such as meat and poultry.
- **Utility knife.** Similar in shape to a slicing knife but smaller. Used for cutting smaller food items, such as tomatoes and apples.
- **Paring knife.** Used to **pare**—cut a very thin layer of peel or outer coating from—fruits and vegetables.

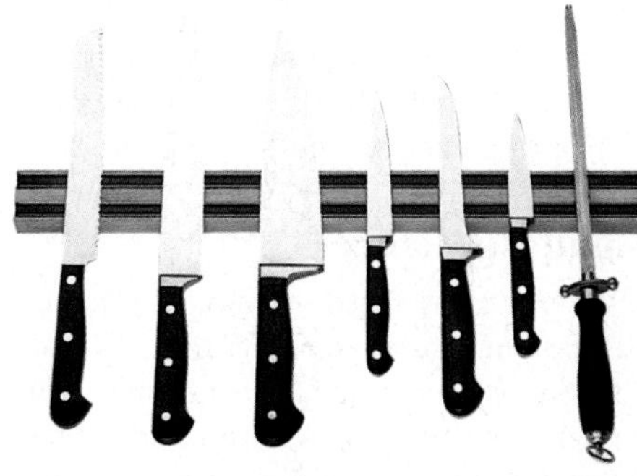

◆ From left to right: bread knife, slicing knife, chef's knife, utility knife, boning knife, paring knife, sharpening steel. Identify the task you would perform with a utility knife.

TEACH

- *Cutting Foods (text pages 242-246)*

Display Activity

Prepare a display of the six basic knives discussed in this section. Ask students to identify the knives and describe the function of each.

Demonstration

Demonstrate how to use a sharpening steel to sharpen knives. Point out that sharp knives are safer than dull ones. Emphasize this point by cutting a tomato with a sharp knife, then a dull one. Discuss other knife-safety suggestions.

Skill-Matching Activity

Bring foods to class to be cut in specific manners. For instance, bread/sliced for sandwiches with a bread knife; apple/peeled with paring knife for use in a baked recipe. Assign each food to a student volunteer. The volunteers will then pick the appropriate knife for the specified task, state why they chose it, and demonstrate to the class how they recommend cutting the food. Closely monitor the students while cutting and provide guidance when needed.

Extending Learning

Chopping Garlic—One way to prepare garlic: Place garlic clove on cutting board, hold chef's knife blade flat on top of the garlic, firmly strike the top flat-side of the knife with the palm of your free hand, easily peel, and mince it with the knife tip or mash it with the back of the knife blade for "paste."

Another way to prepare garlic is with a garlic press. Point out to students that the garlic press is a device that minces or chops garlic into fine pieces by pressing the cloves of garlic through small holes. Electric models are also available.

TEACH cont.

- *Cutting Foods (text pages 242-246)*

Checklist

Remind students that *all* cutting tools, not just knives, are sharp. Ask students to brainstorm safety guidelines for using tools such as peelers, graters, and kitchen shears safely. Format guidelines in a checklist format. L1

VISUAL LEARNING ***Using the Illustration*** Have students study the illustration of the chef's knife on page 244. Have students practice holding the knife properly. Then practice slicing a stalk of celery while holding the knife properly.

Food Art

Divide the class into three groups. Provide each group with the same variety of fruits and vegetables. Using appropriate and available knives and alternative cutting tools, challenge each group to create imaginative food art, like animal shapes. Award gold, silver, and bronze awards for cutting techniques and creativity. L1

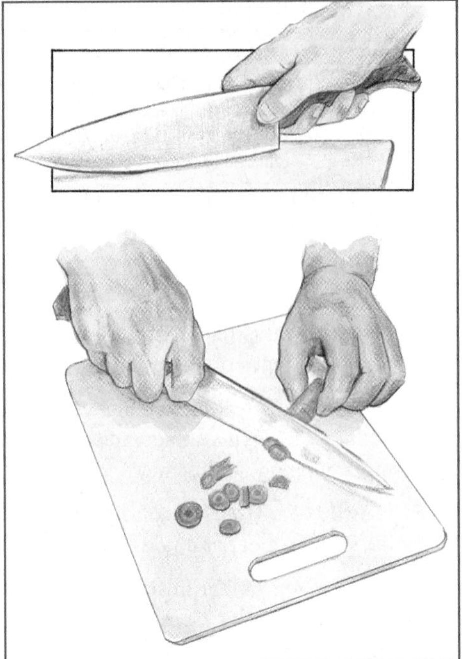

◆ **Note the correct hand position for holding a chef's knife. Identify two techniques for safe use when cutting.**

◆ **Boning knife.** Has a thin, angled blade, well suited to removing the bones from meat, poultry, and fish. May also be used to trim fat from meat.

◆ **Bread knife.** Has a **serrated**, or saw-tooth-patterned, blade for slicing through coarse-grained breads.

Small Appliances

With its many speed settings, an electric blender can be used to cut, grind, and mix. A food processor is similar to a blender, but is often more powerful and versatile. This heavy-duty cutting machine comes with an assortment of blade attachments for various jobs such as slicing and grinding meats. Some food processors may have a blade for kneading bread dough.

Alternative Cutting Tools

Other simpler cutting tools and their uses include:

◆ **Vegetable peeler.** Has blade that swivels. Perfect for paring fruits and vegetables.

◆ **Poultry shears.** Scissors-like tool, capable of cutting through bone. May also be used for snipping, trimming, or cutting dried fruit, pastry, or fresh herbs.

◆ **Food chopper.** Ranges in size from small hand-held nut chopper to large chopper with several blades.

◆ **Food grinder.** Grinds meat, poultry, nuts, and many other foods. Also good for grating, shredding, and other fine cutting needs.

Techniques for Cutting

Although some cutting tools require you only to push a button, using knives requires specific skills. When using most knives, hold the food firmly on the cutting board with one hand and hold the knife by its handle with the other. For rounded foods, such as some fruits and vegetables, first cut a thin slice from the bottom so the item will sit flat. Grip the knife firmly and use a back-and-forth, sawing motion while pressing down gently.

Safety Check

Keep knives sharp. A dull knife is much more likely to slip and cut you because you will have to exert more pressure.

When using a knife, keep your fingers away from the sharp edge of the blade. Be sure the fingertips of the hand holding the food are curled under. Never hold the food in your hand while cutting, and never cut with the blade facing your body.

Extending Learning

Retaining Nutrients—Many fruits and vegetables have a store of nutrients just beneath their skins. When paring these foods, as little of the skin as possible should be removed so that nutrients can be retained. Discuss with students the best way to accomplish this. Have students practice with and compare the use of a paring knife and a peeler. Ask students to write a report of their findings.

Common Cutting Tasks

Recipes often use terms such as *cube, grate,* or *score* to indicate how foods are to be cut. To prepare food successfully and prevent accidents, you need to know what each term means and how to perform the technique correctly. Here is a guide to some common cutting tasks.

Look and Learn:

What are the safety precautions being taken in each of these diagrams?

Slice. To cut a food in large, thin pieces.

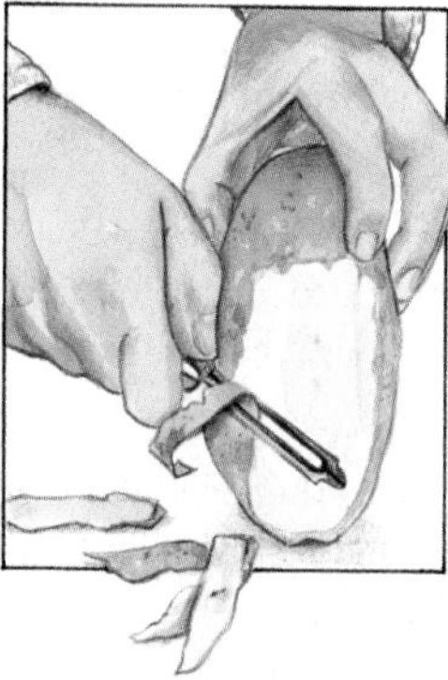

Pare. To cut off a very thin layer of peel. A peeler or paring knife works best.

Cube and dice. Both these terms refer to cutting food into small, squared pieces. Make the pieces about ½ inch (1.3 cm) on each side when cubing and ⅛ to ¼ inch (3 to 6 mm) when dicing.

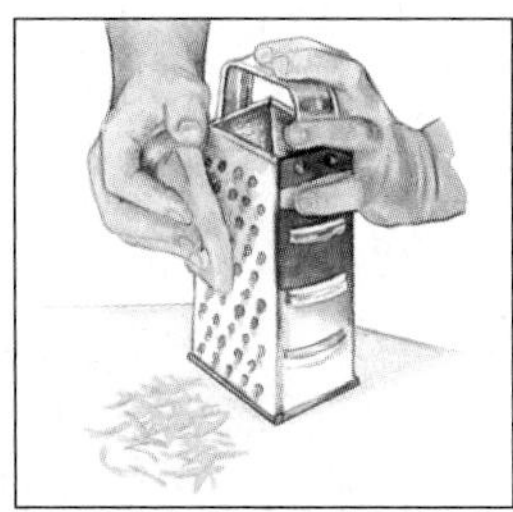

Grate. Cut food into smaller pieces or shreds by pressing and rubbing the food against the rough surface of a grater.

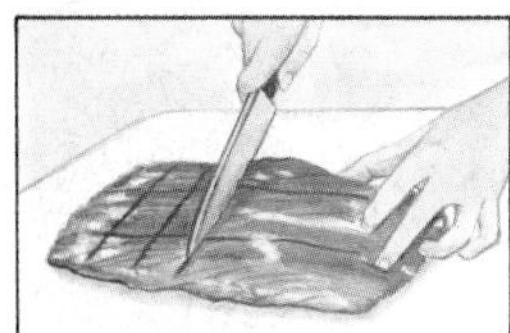

Score. To **score** means to make shallow, straight cuts in the surface of a food, such as a flank steak. Scoring helps tenderize meat. A slicing knife is most often used to score meats.

Chop and mince. Both these terms refer to cutting food into small irregular pieces. Minced pieces are smaller than chopped pieces. To use a chef's knife to chop or mince, hold the knife handle with one hand, pressing the tip against the cutting board. The other hand should rest lightly on the back of the blade, near the tip, as in the picture. Rock or pump the knife handle up and down, keeping the tip of the blade on the board so that the blade chops through the food.

- *Cutting Foods (text pages 242-246)*

Demonstration

Emphasize that you should never hold food in your hand while cutting, and never cut with the blade facing your body. Demonstrate how to properly cut rounded foods.

Recipe Reading

Have students work in groups to find recipes that call for various cutting techniques. Ask groups to share the terms they found and the foods involved. L1

VISUAL LEARNING ***Using the "Common Cutting Tasks" Feature***

Divide the class into six groups. Assign each group one of the six common cutting tasks depicted on this page. Each group will need to develop a presentation with a demonstration for their cutting task. The presentation is to be geared toward people who have never tried the cutting task. Have each group instruct the class, allowing time for a question and answer period.

Technology TIE-IN Point out that some cutting tools and techniques used today have improved the speed of cooking and accuracy of cutting. Have students work in small teams to research and create recipe comparison posters. For instance, have students compare a cole slaw recipe from 1900 with a current recipe. On their poster displays, have them highlight the difference between cutting equipment, cutting tasks, preparation time, and appearance. Display the posters in the classroom.

- *Mixing Foods (text pages 246-248)*

Discussion Activity

Ask students to list and describe tools used for mixing. *(See photo on page 248.)* The electric mixer does many of the same tasks done by the wire whisk, the wooden spoon, and the rotary beater. Ask students to explain tasks for which a chef might prefer one of these tools over another. Discuss mixing terms often found in recipes. Have students describe each technique. *(See page 247.)*

Research

Have students research and report on food preparation tools used by colonial or pioneer families. Their reports should conclude with comparisons to mixing equipment used today. L1

◆ **Small appliances and other cutting tools include: (from left to right) food chopper, blender, grater, food processor, food grinder (in front) poultry shears, peeler. Name two advantages to owning a food processor rather than just a blender.**

Mixing Foods

Another common recipe task is combining ingredients through mixing. You can use different mixing tools and techniques, depending on the food and the desired results.

Equipment for Mixing

Many kinds of mixing tools, from small hand-held utensils to electrical appliances, are used for mixing tasks. Two mixing appliances, the blender and food processor, were mentioned earlier in connection with cutting.

Other tools commonly used when mixing include:

- ◆ **Electric mixer.** Used to blend, beat, and whip ingredients. Lightweight, hand-held models are convenient. Heavy-duty models are attached permanently to a stand.
- ◆ **Rotary beater.** Used to mix and whip foods more quickly and easily than can be done with a spoon or whisk. Often used to beat egg whites.
- ◆ **Mixing bowls.** Come in many different sizes. May be of stainless steel, glass, pottery, or plastic.
- ◆ **Mixing spoon.** Used for many mixing tasks. Different sizes and shapes are available.
- ◆ **Sifter.** A container with a fine wire screen at the bottom and a blade that forces dry ingredients through the screen.
- ◆ **Wire whisk.** A **whisk** is a balloon-shaped device made of wire loops held together by a handle. Used for mixing, stirring, beating, and whipping.
- ◆ **Rubber scraper.** Used to scrape food from bowls, pans, and other containers. Helpful in moving thick ingredients from the sides of the bowl to the middle while mixing. Also used for folding, which is described on page 247.

Extending Learning

Equipment Comparison—Have students beat an egg using a wire whisk and another egg using a rotary beater, beating both eggs the same length of time. Ask students what the differences are in the two eggs after beating. In what types of recipes would each method be used? Discuss other equipment that may be used interchangeably, pointing out preferred uses.

Techniques for Mixing

As with cutting, the techniques of mixing have a vocabulary all their own. Some of these terms found in recipes will be readily familiar to you. Others will not.

Look and Learn:

Name one recipe in which you would use each of the following mixing techniques.

Mix, combine, blend. To thoroughly incorporate one ingredient into another, using a spoon, wire whisk, rotary beater, electric mixer, or electric blender.

Stir. To mix by hand, using a spoon or wire whisk in a circular motion. Can also be done while cooking to keep food from sticking to the pan and to distribute heat throughout foods.

Beat. To thoroughly mix foods using a vigorous over-and-over motion. Egg whites may be beaten to add air to them.

Cream. To beat together ingredients, such as shortening and sugar, until soft and creamy.

Whip. To incorporate air into a mixture to make it light and fluffy.

Fold. **Folding** is a technique used to gently mix delicate ingredients, usually with a rubber scraper or spoon. The technique involves cutting down through the mixture, moving the utensil across the bottom of the bowl, and bringing it back up to the surface along with some of the mixture from the bottom. The utensil is never lifted out of the mixture.

Sift. To force one or more dry ingredients—for example, flour—through a sifter or strainer to add air, remove small lumps, or mix two ingredients.

- *Mixing Foods (text pages 246-247)*

Discussion Activity

Discuss the importance of understanding the terms used to describe food preparation techniques. Discuss possible results of misunderstanding a food preparation term.

Demonstration

Demonstrate how to mix, combine, blend, stir, beat, cream, whip, fold, and sift ingredients. Have students work in groups to find recipes that call for each mixing technique described in "Techniques for Mixing" on this page. Ask groups to share the terms they found and the foods involved.

- *Other Tasks (text pages 248-249)*

Categorizing Activity

Ask students to list specific occasions when each of the "other tasks" described on this page may be used. As a class, develop a list of all the possibilities for each task category. Discuss the importance of understanding the terms used to describe food preparation techniques. Discuss possible results of misunderstanding a food preparation term.

Word Games

Have students develop word games, such as word searches and crossword puzzles, or flash cards, using food preparation terms discussed in this section. L1

Research

Have students research and report on traditional food preparation techniques used in other cultures of the world. Include in the research how they are different from and similar to our own. Reports on developing nations or cultures without the use of electricity should be encouraged. L1

◆ These are common mixing tools. In back (left to right): electric mixer (with extra attachments), sifter, hand-held electric mixer, mixing bowls; in front: rotary beater, wooden spoons, wire whisk, rubber scrapers. Why are rubber scrapers such an important tool to have when cooking or baking?

Other Tasks

A variety of other tools and techniques are used in food preparation. Here are some additional terms you may find in recipes:

- **Strain.** To separate solid particles from a liquid, such as broth or juice. The liquid is poured through a bowl-shaped fine screen called a strainer or sieve (SIV).
- **Drain.** To drain from a solid food, such as fruits, vegetables, or cooked pasta. This is done by putting the food in a colander—a bowl with small holes in the bottom—or a large strainer.
- **Purée (pyoo-RAY). Purée** means to make food smooth and thick by putting it through a strainer, blender, or food processor.
- **Baste.** To brush or pour a liquid over a food as it cooks.
- **Dredge.** To coat a food with a dry ingredient, such as flour or crumbs.

Many heating and cooking tasks are also involved in food preparation. These techniques and the equipment needed are explored in the next chapter.

Reinforcing Key Skills

Present the following problems to student groups. Allow time for them to discuss and compare their responses.

Management—People in other cultures often use equipment and techniques for preparing food that differ from those we use. Ask students to discuss the problems someone from the United States might encounter while trying to cook in India, and vice versa.

Communication—At the home of relatives you are served a new recipe for baked chicken. The exterior is tough and dry. Your relatives ask if you liked the recipe. What kind but truthful reply can you give?

Sanitary Use and Care

Proper sanitation techniques help prevent illness when using tools and equipment. Tools used for tasting should be washed before returning them to the food. Otherwise, bacteria from your mouth can enter the food. Also remember the cross-contamination principle: wash any tools used with raw meat, poultry, and seafood before using them with other foods.

Be sure to clean tools and equipment after every use. Any old food that remains could become contaminated, causing foodborne illnesses. To clean appliances that can't be placed in dishwater, wipe them thoroughly. The owner's manual provides specifics about cleaning.

Safety Check

When using such tools and equipment as graters, peelers, chopping tools, and mixers, remember that carelessness can cause injuries. Keep fingers away from any rough or slicing edges. Cut away from yourself when using a peeler. When using a mixer, keep fingers away from the beaters. Spoons and other tools should not be used while the mixer is running.

When caring for tools and equipment, also follow safety practices. Unplug mixers before removing the beaters for washing. Find out which parts of an appliance can be submersed in water and always unplug the appliance before cleaning. To prevent cuts, don't leave sharp tools in dishwater, where suds and other dishes may hide them. Wipe knife blades slowly and carefully, with the blade pointed away from you. Store all items properly to prevent accidents.

Section 8-4 Review & Activities

1. Describe the differences between a paring knife, a boning knife, and a chef's knife.
2. What does *beating* mean when used to describe a mixing technique? Name three tools that could be used to beat a mixture.
3. Name two small electrical appliances that are useful for both cutting and mixing tasks.
4. When you're working in the kitchen, what practices demonstrate the sanitary use and care of tools and equipment?
5. **Evaluating.** What might happen if you tried to follow a recipe without understanding the meaning of food preparation terms?
6. **Applying.** Develop a checklist for use in your school foods lab on which cutting equipment to use with which foods. Post your checklist on a wall in the classroom.
7. **Applying.** Demonstrate the safe use of the following tools and equipment: chef's knife; paring knife; grater; peeler; mixer; and hand beater.
8. **Applying.** Demonstrate safe practices when cleaning the following tools and equipment: a hand-held mixer; a stand mixer; a sharp knife or other sharp tool.

ASSESS

REVIEW

- Ask students to summarize the main ideas in this section.
- Have students complete the Section Review. (Answers appear below.)

EVALUATION

- Have students write a short essay describing the food preparation tasks discussed in this section.
- Have students take the quiz for Section 8-4. (Use the quiz in the *Teacher Resource Guide,* or construct your own with the **Exam***View*® *Test Generator* on the *Effective Instruction CD-ROM.*)

RETEACHING

- Create flashcards that show different cutting and mixing tools. Have students use the cards to practice identifying each tool and describing its purpose.
- Refer to the *Reteaching Activities* booklet for the Section 8-4 activity sheet.

CLOSE

Refer students to the motivator for this section in which they cut the apple. Which tool would they choose now? Ask students to give reasons for their choices.

Answers to Section 8-4 Review & Activities

1. See bulleted list on pages 243-244.
2. Thoroughly mixing foods using a vigorous over-and-over motion. Any three: Rotary beater, electric mixer, mixing spoon, wire whisk.
3. Blender and food processor.
4. See "Sanitary Use and Care," on page 249.
5. Answers will vary but should suggest that the recipe may not turn out as expected.
6. Checklists will vary.
7. Demonstrations should present safe use of tools and equipment.
8. Demonstrations should present safe cleaning techniques.

Recipe File

Easy English Trifle

This recipe requires accurate cutting skills for the cake and folding technique for the whipped topping. Prior to assigning the lab, you may wish to have students review "Common Cutting Tasks" on page 245 and "Techniques for Mixing" on page 247.

Using the Recipe

- Have students read the recipe and discuss each step.
- Review safety and sanitation procedures that apply to this recipe.
- Remind students never to run the blender without first placing the cover on it.
- Have each lab team fill out a work plan. (See the *Foods Lab Resources* booklet.)
- Have students check off the ingredients and equipment listed on the recipe worksheet and prepare the recipe.
- Have students complete the evaluation and questions on the recipe worksheet.

SEE ALSO. . .
The *Foods Lab Resources* booklet for the "Easy English Trifle" recipe worksheet and other recipe alternatives.

Recipe File

Easy English Trifle

This recipe can be a light, refreshing dessert. Try using a variety of canned, frozen, or fresh fruits to create your own combinations.

Customary	***Ingredients***	***Metric***
1	Angel food cake*	1
20-oz. can	Fruit cocktail packed in juice	567-gram can
3-oz. package	Instant vanilla pudding and pie filling mix	95-gram package
2 cup	Fat-free milk	500 mL
4-oz. carton	Light, nondairy whipped topping, thawed	112-gram carton

Yield: 8-10 servings

* May be either made from a packaged mix or bought already baked.

Directions

1. Cut the cake into slabs about 1 inch (2.5 cm) thick. Use the slabs to line the inside of a large serving bowl.
2. Spoon half the fruit cocktail and all the juice over the cake.
3. Prepare the pudding mix according to the package directions, using the 2 cups (500 mL) of milk.
4. Fold in half the thawed whipped topping. Spoon the mixture over the cake and fruit. Add the remaining fruit.
5. Spread the remaining whipped topping over all. Refrigerate for at least 2 hours before serving.

Nutrition Information

Per serving (approximate): 160 calories, 7 g protein, 31 g carbohydrate, 1 g fat, 0 mg cholesterol, 85 mg sodium
Good source of: vitamin E, B vitamins, calcium, phosphorus

Food for Thought

- How many different mixing tools mentioned in the text could you use to prepare the pudding mix?
- Why does the recipe instruct you to "fold in," rather than merely blend in, the whipped topping?

Answers to **Food for Thought**

1. A rotary beater, a wooden spoon, or a wire whisk.
2. Folding is directed so that the airy, fluffy texture of the whipped topping does not deflate.

SECTION
8-5

Objectives

After studying this section, you should be able to:

- Describe a work plan and a schedule, and explain the usefulness of each.
- Give examples of efficient work techniques.
- Give guidelines for working cooperatively in the school foods lab or at home.

Look for These Terms

work plan

pre-preparation

dovetail

Time Management and Teamwork

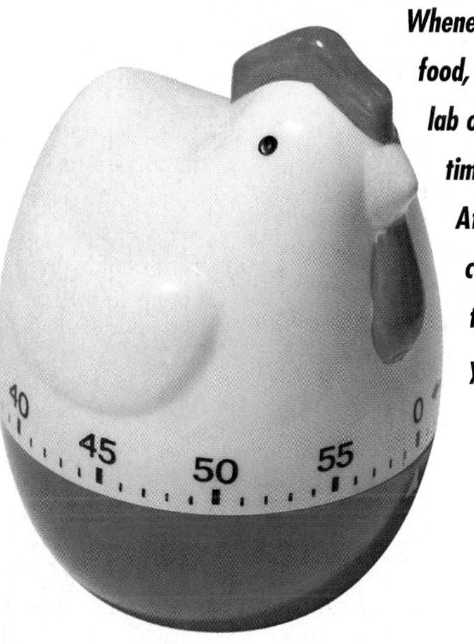

Whenever you are preparing food, either in the school foods lab or for your family's dinner, time is likely to be a concern. At such times, management, communication, and critical thinking can help you meet your deadlines.

Time Management in the Kitchen

Winning a race takes strategy, speed, and skill. These same properties are the keys to time management in the kitchen.

Strategy: A Work Plan

Food preparation involves more than choosing a recipe and starting to work. Rather, it involves mapping out all the procedures and tasks that play a part in your recipe or meal. Do you have the ingredients and equipment you need? Are you familiar with the cooking techniques called for in the recipes? Can you complete the food preparation and cleanup in the time available?

A smart strategy is to always start with a **work plan**. Basically, this is a list of all the tasks required to complete the recipe and an estimate of how long each task will take.

Developing a Work Plan

Recipes and package directions often provide help in estimating time. The directions on a spaghetti package, for example, may tell you that the product requires 9 minutes to cook. As an effective manager, however, you will need to draw on your ability to think critically to help you identify other tasks and

Section 8-5 Resources

◆ **Student Workbook,** pp. 65, 70
◆ **Teacher Resource Guide**
Lesson Plan 8-5 Organizer
Section 8-5 Quiz
Chapter 8 Test
◆ **Effective Instruction CD-ROM**
Exam*View*® *Test Generator*
◆ **Student Motivation Kit**
Reteaching Activities, p. 50
Enrichment Activities
Foods Lab Resources, pp. 41–42
Skills for Making Food Choices, pp. 21–22

SECTION 8-5 Time Management and Teamwork

FOCUS

MOTIVATORS

- Display a work flow chart, employee work schedule, duty roster, memo of instructions. Ask how these relate to food preparation. Explain they help ensure efficiency.
- Describe a typical family in the 1950s and tell a story of a "housewife" who prepared a well-rounded dinner every evening. Ask students to identify the differences between that story and a "typical" family dinner today. What factors created these changes? Explain the increased importance today for time management and teamwork.

VOCABULARY ACTIVITY

Direct students' attention to "Look for These Terms." Pronounce aloud the word *dovetail.* Ask a volunteer to investigate the meaning of this combined form. Have students find the other definitions within the text. How does dovetailing relate to them?

STUDY SKILLS

- **Listening.** Invite a group of volunteers to each prepare an oral reading of a page of text from the section, while others follow along silently. At the end of the reading, the class is to list as many key concepts as they can recall.
- Have students read the section and complete the appropriate part of the Chapter 8 Study Guide in the *Student Workbook.*

TEACH

- *Time Management in the Kitchen (text pages 251-254)*

Discussion Activity

Ask students to name the three keys to time management in the kitchen. Discuss the purpose of a work plan. What does a work plan include? Ask students to explain the difference between a work plan and schedule. Discuss the concept of "pre-preparation tasks." Ask students to individually think of three tasks that are frequently included in pre-preparation tasks. Share and discuss tasks.

Developing a Computerized Work Plan

Provide students with a recipe. Assign them to read it and develop a computerized work plan for preparing that recipe. L1

Developing Skits

Have students work in small groups to develop a short skit based on one of the keys to efficiency described in the text. Have groups present their skits to the class. Discuss how these techniques save time and energy. L1

Goal Setting

Assign students a goal-setting project. Students can set one 1-week goal for teamwork at home. Have them record their goal and turn it in to you. One week later, return it to students to determine if goals were met. Allow time for discussion. L1

find or estimate the time each requires—for example, boiling water for the pasta, chopping vegetables for the sauce, and cleaning salad greens. A good rule of thumb for beginning cooks is to allow more time than you think you will need. As your skills improve, you will be able to work faster and make more accurate time estimates.

Look at the recipe for "Pizza Snacks" below and the work plan Naomi made for it on the next page. Note that some of the first steps on the work plan come from the list of ingredients, not the assembly directions. Naomi saw from this list that the tasks would include halving the English muffins, shredding the cheese, and chopping and slicing the toppings.

Even before these steps comes the **pre-preparation**, tasks done before actual recipe preparation. In Naomi's case, these tasks included washing the green pepper and onion and measuring out the other ingredients.

A successful work plan might even include important tasks like washing your hands and setting the oven temperature. Including such steps ensures that a new cook won't forget to do them.

Pizza Snacks

2 English muffins, split in halves
1/2 cup prepared pizza sauce
1 Tbsp. chopped green pepper
1 Tbsp. sliced mushrooms
1 Tbsp. chopped onions
1/2 cup shredded low-fat mozzarella cheese

1. Place English muffin halves, crust-side down, on broiler pan.
2. Spread each muffin half with 2 Tbsp. pizza sauce.
3. Top with green pepper, mushrooms, and onion.
4. Sprinkle each muffin half with 2 Tbsp. cheese.
5. Position broiler pan so the tops of the muffins are about 4 inches from the heat. Turn on broiler.
6. Broil until cheese is bubbly, about 2 to 4 minutes. Remove immediately and serve hot.

NOTE: Broiling time may vary.

Yield: 4 small pizzas

Extending Learning

Work Plans and Schedules—Some chefs make a combination work plan and schedule. To do this, you must be certain your work plan lists tasks in the exact order they should be started. Then add a column giving the starting time for each task. In class, develop a combination work plan and schedule for preparing buttered toast, grapefruit half, and cereal with milk for breakfast.

Work Plan-Pizza Snacks

Task	Approx. Time
Gather ingredients and equipment. Scrub hands.	8 min.
Split English muffins in half.	2 min.
Chop green pepper and onion. Slice mushrooms.	7 min.
Shred cheese.	3 min.
Put muffins on broiler pan and put on toppings.	3 min.
Broil until cheese is bubbly.	6 min.
Prepare to serve.	1 min.
	Total: 30 min.

Speed: A Schedule

Once you have a work plan, you can use it to make a schedule that shows when each task must be started. If you have developed a sound work plan, making a schedule should be a snap. Simply do the following:

1. Consult your work plan for the estimated time each task will take to complete.
2. Add these times to find the total preparation time.
3. Subtract the total preparation time from the time you want the food to be ready. This step tells you what time to start.

Naomi's estimated total preparation time is 30 minutes. She plans to serve the pizzas at 6:30, so she needs to start at 6:00. To keep to her schedule, Naomi decides to chop and slice the vegetables first, shred the cheese next, and then split the English muffins. For this recipe, the remaining tasks match the order of the recipe directions.

When you are learning to prepare food, it's a good idea to make a work plan and schedule every time. Eventually, you may need to do so only when you prepare a new dish or plan a special meal.

Schedule-Pizza Snacks

6:00	Get ready.
6:08	Split English muffins.
6:10	Chop and slice vegetables.
6:17	Shred cheese.
6:20	Assemble pizzas.
6:23	Broil pizzas.
6:29	Prepare to serve.
6:30	Serve pizzas.

- *Time Management in the Kitchen (text pages 251-254)*

Mnemonic Activity

Ask students the keys to working efficiently in the kitchen. Develop a *mnemonic*, or memory device, with students for remembering the six keys to working efficiently. This might take the form of a short tune or rhyme.

Scheduling Activity

Give students a recipe for a main dish and tell them that dinner is to be served at 6:00 P.M. Have students develop a schedule (preferably computerized) that will allow them to serve the meal on time. Remind students that they should first complete a work plan. To be sure students understand the difference between efficiency and carelessness, propose several examples of short-cuts in the kitchen (some that increase efficiency and some that are just carelessness). Have students decide which are true efficiency measures and which are carelessness.

Dovetailing

Give students a menu for an evening meal to be served at 7:00 P.M. Include recipes for all the foods on the menu. Have students prepare a work plan and schedule, dovetailing the tasks associated with each recipe. L2

HOME & COMMUNITY CONNECTION

To demonstrate the ever-present importance of time management skills in the home or community, have students act as reviewers. Their review can take place at home or a restaurant. Have them observe the time management skills that are used effectively, and those that are not. Have them establish their own scoring system and then write a summary of time management findings. Was it a passing or failing review? Suggest areas for improved efficiency.

TEACH cont.

- *Teamwork in the School Kitchen*
- *Teamwork at Home (text pages 254-256)*

Writing Activity

Ask students to write a poem, non-fictional story, or TV sit-com feature on why it is important to be organized and to cooperate with other team members in the foods lab. When writing, consider these statements or questions: How can this concept be applied in students' homes? Discuss the process of evaluating the results of a foods lab experiment or meal preparation process. What questions should be asked?

Developing Skits

Have small groups develop a short, two-part skit. The first part should show how "teamwork" can create a problem if everyone doesn't help; the second part should show how teamwork can be a big advantage if everyone works together properly. L1

Skill: Working Efficiently

As you gain food preparation experience, you will notice an obvious improvement in your skills. You'll be able to complete some tasks in half the time they once took. Yet there is more to efficiency than just experience. Even a beginner can be efficient by knowing how to save time and energy. Here are some keys to efficiency:

- **Organize the kitchen.** Always store items in the same place so that you won't waste time looking for them.
- **Learn to use equipment properly.** Take the time to read the owner's manuals for the small and large appliances in the kitchen. Besides learning to use them safely, you may find they can be helpful in ways you didn't realize. Practice using tools until you are comfortable with them.
- **Look for ways to simplify.** Could a different piece of equipment complete a task more quickly? Would a different cooking method be more efficient? Thinking through your options can help you save time and energy.
- **Gather equipment and ingredients.** Assembling what you need before you start has advantages. First, you won't discover halfway through a recipe that you are out of an ingredient. Second, it will be easier to check whether you used every ingredient. Third, and perhaps most important, you will have everything you need right at your fingertips.
- **Dovetail tasks.** To **dovetail** means to fit different tasks together smoothly. Not every preparation step needs your undivided attention. You could, for example, make a tossed salad while chicken pieces are roasting. Dovetailing is especially important when you are preparing a whole meal. If you plan to dovetail tasks, be sure to adjust your time schedule.
- **Clean up as you work.** Before you start work, fill the sink or a dishpan with hot, sudsy water. Whenever you have a few free moments, wash the equipment you have finished using. Also keep a clean, wet dishcloth handy to wipe up spills as they happen. Put away ingredients as you finish with them. Your final cleanup will take much less time.

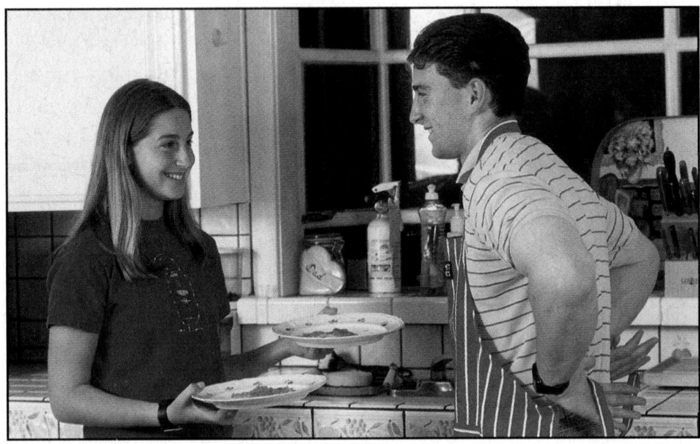

◆ Cleaning up is part of the job when working in the kitchen. By cleaning up as you prepare foods, the job is easier after you eat. Working together also makes the effort more fun and gets it done faster.

Teamwork in the School Kitchen

In the foods lab at school, you work as part of a team. You also work against the clock. Every lab activity needs to be completed—including cleanup and evaluation—within a limited period of time. Success depends on organization and cooperation.

- **Organizing the job.** As a team, you and your classmates need to start with a basic work plan. When you plan your schedule, decide not only when each task should start, but also who will do it. With every team member working, several tasks can be accomplished at the same time. You may want to use a schedule that has five-minute blocks of time down the left and columns with each person's name across the top. That way, the schedule shows what each person should be doing throughout the lab period. Be sure to consider work space and equipment as you plan your schedule.
- **Cooperating.** As in many school and work situations, success in the foods lab depends on everyone working together. Work quickly and efficiently. Since accuracy is essential, ask another team member for help if you have a question or problem. Be willing to help if someone else falls behind or makes a mistake. Keeping a sense of humor helps the work go smoothly.
- **Taking responsibility.** When you work with others, what do you want from them if the group is to succeed? You probably hope they will do their share of the work. It is only fair for them to expect the same from you. Taking responsibility means doing your part without being pressured. Shared responsibility helps the whole group do well, which allows each person to also share the group's success.
- **Cleaning up.** Cleaning as you go will make end-of-class cleanup easier and faster. Be sure all equipment is clean and dry. Most important, return everything to its proper place. Otherwise, you will slow down the next team using the kitchen. Be sure all work surfaces and appliances are clean and that you have disposed of waste properly.

Q ***I work best with my friends. Shouldn't I try to get with them when we team up in the foods lab?***

Although working with friends makes a foods lab enjoyable, think of the advantages in working with others. Learning to team successfully with all kinds of people is good practice since that's what you'll do in the work world. In the lab and on the job, you'll have to adjust to different personalities, some easy and some difficult. As you search for new ways to get along, your cooperation skills grow. Try looking at teamwork as an opportunity. Be open to new contacts and challenges. You already know how to work with your friends, but you can learn something by teaming up with people who have different perspectives, skills, and knowledge. Every person has something positive to share. Getting to know someone better can be good for both of you.

- ***Teamwork in the School Kitchen***
- ***Teamwork at Home (text pages 254-256)***

Discussion Activity

Discuss ways food preparation in the foods lab is similar to and different from food preparation at home. Discuss the importance of organization and cooperation. Why is it important to clean up as you go? What can you learn by evaluating the results of each lab?

Field Trip

Take the class to the school cafeteria or a local restaurant. In small groups, have students observe the workers in the kitchen and their use of teamwork; record observations. In class, discuss the observations, positive and negative.

Extending Learning

Teamwork—There are advantages to working with others in the foods lab at school or your kitchen at home. You can share both the work and the fun of food preparation.

There are also potential pitfalls. When two or more people share a small space, they can get in each other's way, creating less efficiency.

When working with others in the kitchen, success depends on working well as a team. Teamwork requires good organization and communication. Each person's responsibilities must be clear.

ASSESS

REVIEW

- Ask students to summarize the main ideas in this section.
- Have students complete the Section Review. (Answers appear below.)

EVALUATION

- Give students a recipe and have them develop a work plan and time schedule for preparing the recipe.
- Have students take the quiz for Section 8-5. (Use the quiz in the *Teacher Resource Guide,* or construct your own with the **Exam***View*® *Test Generator* on the *Effective Instruction CD-ROM.*)

RETEACHING

- Have students observe family members at home to identify pre-preparation tasks and work simplification practices.
- Refer to the *Reteaching Activities* booklet for the Section 8-5 activity sheet.

CLOSE

Refer students to the first section motivator. Ask students to review how having a work plan can help structure and organize meal preparation tasks. Have students each name one new time management or teamwork skill they plan to practice.

- **Evaluating the results.** Labs usually involve evaluation of the finished product and the preparation process. Thoughtfulness and honesty are important. This is especially true if the food did not turn out as expected, if you had preparation problems, or if your team did not work together well. Think about what you learned from the experience and what you might do differently the next time.

Teamwork at Home

In many ways, teamwork in your kitchen at home is as important as it is in the foods lab. Organization, cooperation, and cleanup are again the watchwords of a successful effort when working with family members.

Whether you are responsible for helping prepare family meals on a regular basis or just occasionally, you need to remember that these can be enjoyable times. You might help a younger brother or sister learn a new cooking skill or just take time to talk with a family member. When you have more time, try out a new recipe together. Daily food preparation can be a chore or an opportunity to build togetherness. It all depends on your attitude.

Section 8-5 Review & Activities

1. What is a work plan? How can it help you manage time when preparing food?
2. Give three examples of ways to work efficiently in your kitchen or the school foods lab.
3. What should you think about when evaluating a completed foods lab?
4. **Synthesize.** What are some specific problems that can occur in the kitchen or foods lab if you don't work efficiently?
5. **Analyze.** Imagine that you are preparing a dinner of salad (chopped tomato, shredded lettuce, French dressing) and sandwiches (turkey, cheese, sliced tomatoes, whole wheat bread, deli mustard). Explain how you could dovetail tasks in the preparation of these foods.
6. **Applying.** Working in groups, design a work plan and schedule form to use when planning school foods labs. Use the forms in the next foods lab and evaluate how much more or less efficiently your group worked in the lab. If necessary, redesign the forms.
7. **Applying.** Test your skills at problem solving in the foods lab by describing what you would do in these situations: (a) your team is preparing a salad, but one person is spending the time talking to someone on another team; (b) your team is going to bake a cake but members cannot agree on the specific tasks that each should do.
8. **Applying.** List specific actions that demonstrate cooperation among three team members who are making a vegetable salad in the lab.
9. **Evaluating.** Work with a team in the lab, preparing a dish assigned by your teacher. Plan the responsibilities of each team member. Afterwards, evaluate how well you each demonstrated responsibility.

Answers to Section 8-5 Review & Activities

1. A list of all tasks needed to complete a recipe and how long each one takes; by organizing the tasks so that you can create a schedule.
2. See bulleted list on page 254.
3. The finished product and the preparation process, what you learned from this experience, and what you might do differently next time.
4. Answers will vary. You may not finish in time or may work unsafely.
5. Answers will vary.
6. Plans and forms will vary.
7. Possible answers: (a) remind talkers that grade includes lab; (b) write tasks on papers and have each person draw one.
8. Answers will vary.
9. Answers will vary.

Career Wanted

Research Lab Technician

"A lot of people are counting on my numbers."

Freda Cisco

Education and Training
- Associate's degree in food science or related field
- Experience in laboratory procedures

Qualities
- Organization skills
- Attention to detail
- Communication skills
- Ability to work alone

Q. What are a lab technician's typical duties, Freda?

A. We assist the scientists who lead the research. They design the experiments. We run them and record the data. For instance, one project compared edible and non-edible parts in crop samples. I weighed each sample, ground and freeze-dried it, and weighed it again when the sugars and fiber had been separated.

Q. So you're involved in research at a fundamental level.

A. Yes. I have to understand and follow directions exactly, or we'll waste time on faulty experimentation. I also need enough understanding of chemistry to know when results are unusual and may need double-checking.

Q. How did you pick this line of work?

A. I've always enjoyed the investigation of science. While working in a food maker's lab, I feel like I'm doing my part to put food on the world's table, maybe even feeding people who wouldn't have enough to eat otherwise.

Related Career Opportunities

Entry Level
- Lab assistant
- Food preparation kitchen worker

Technical Level
- Chemical engineering technician
- Preservationist

Professional Level
- Research lab director
- Federal food inspector
- Food packaging engineer

Making Career Connections

EQUIPMENT COMPARISON. Learn about the measuring equipment used in a scientific research lab. What tools have the same purpose as the kitchen utensils discussed in this chapter? How are they similar and different in use and design? Display side-by-side comparisons of lab and cooking tools in a chart or poster.

Career Wanted

Research Lab Technician

Thinking About the Career

Many careers are directly impacted by advancements in technology. The job of a research lab technician is high on the list. Ask students to brainstorm a typical food research lab technician's job today along with what it may have been in 1975. Compare and contrast the differences. After thoroughly analyzing the differences, ask students to brainstorm the possible job description in 2025.

Career-Building Opportunities

Using online resources, encourage students to learn about the careers of senior food chemists. Students should answer these questions: Which skills beyond educational requirements are useful? Which skills could be developed or refined prior to college?

For More Information

For additional information about careers in laboratory research, encourage students to contact:

- Institute of Food Science and Engineering
  Texas A&M University
  ifse.tamu.edu
- AOAC International
  481 North Frederick Avenue
  Suite 500
  Gaithersburg, MD 20877-2417
  www.aoac.org

REVIEW

- Have students complete the Chapter Review. (Answers appear below.)

EVALUATION

- Provide a list of five scenarios to small groups of students. Each scenario is a negative situation representing each section of Chapter 8. Each group is to turn the negative situations into positive ones. Allow each group time to present one scenario each.
- Have students take the test for Chapter 8. (Use the chapter test in the *Teacher Resource Guide,* or construct your own with the **Exam***View*® *Test Generator* on the *Effective Instruction CD-ROM.*)

ANSWERS

Checking Your Knowledge

1. Directions should be clear and easy to follow; steps should be numbered; more than one set of directions may be included.
2. The same amount expressed using a different measure. Examples will vary.
3. Set liquid measuring cup on level surface; carefully pour liquid into cup; bend down to check the measurement at eye level; add more or pour off excess, if needed.
4. Recipes for baked products; if one amount is changed or an ingredient is omitted, the recipe may suffer poor results due to the "chemical formula" nature of baking. Poor results may include altered taste, texture, color, moistness, and more.
5. Desired yield ÷ regular yield = number to multiply by.

Chapter 8 Review & Activities

Summary

Section 8-1: Recipe Basics

- Before using a recipe, check to be sure it includes certain basic information and is clearly written.
- Recipes are available from many sources.
- A well-organized recipe collection is easy to use.

Section 8-4: Preparation Tasks

- To follow a recipe, you need to understand the meaning of the terms used.
- You need to know which utensil or appliance to use and the correct technique.

Section 8-2: Measuring Ingredients

- Recipes include weight and volume measurements in customary or metric units.
- For accurate measurements, select the right tools and follow the correct procedures.

Section 8-5: Time Management and Teamwork

- A work plan helps you identify the tasks that must be done.
- A schedule tells you when to do the tasks.
- Look for ways to make the job easier and more efficient.
- Teamwork is essential when working in the kitchen.

Section 8-3: Changing a Recipe

- You can alter the yield of a recipe by changing the amounts of ingredients.
- To make a recipe healthier, you can change ingredients, modify the way food is prepared, or reduce portion sizes.
- High-altitude cooking may require changes in cooking time or ingredients.

Checking Your Knowledge

1. What are important features of step-by-step directions?
2. In measuring, what is an equivalent? Give an example.
3. Describe how to measure liquids accurately.
4. What type of recipe is difficult to alter? Why?
5. When changing the yield of a recipe, by what number do you multiply or divide each ingredient?
6. Define *score* and *pare.* What do *mince* and *grate* mean?
7. What is the difference between straining and draining? What equipment is used for each purpose?
8. Describe the technique for folding one ingredient into another.
9. Why should you clean up as you work in the foods lab?
10. Describe how a work plan for a team differs from a work plan for an individual.

Working IN THE Lab

1. ***Food Preparation.*** Choose a recipe from a cookbook or use one provided by your teacher. Make at least one ingredient substitution to lower the fat or improve the nutrient content. Evaluate the results.
2. ***Food Preparation.*** Pare a raw potato. Cut it into slices ½ inch (1.3 cm) thick. Set two slices aside; then cube the rest. Set some of the cubed pieces aside; then dice the rest. Have your teacher check your work.

Thinking Critically

1. **Analyzing Decisions.** Peggy looked through several cookbooks trying to find a recipe for a special meal for her friends in the chess club, who had just won a state championship. Some of the recipes she examined were complex, involving many steps and techniques, while others were less so. In the end, Peggy decided to make a dish she had prepared many times before. Do you think Peggy's decision was a wise one? Explain your answer.
2. **Recognizing Assumptions.** Part way through preparing a batch of banana pudding, Dana discovered that she had only four bananas, instead of the six called for in the recipe. She decided to subtract two from every ingredient listed. Do you think the recipe will turn out well? Why or why not?
3. **Identifying Evidence.** Some people may believe that it's not worth spending the time to make a work plan and schedule. Why might they feel this way? What could you say to change their opinion?

Reinforcing Key Skills

1. **Directed Thinking.** It is Portia's turn to cook the family's dinner. She would like to do something different. While looking through the kitchen cookbook collection, she finds a recipe for fish in a hand-stapled batch of recipes. Before gathering ingredients for the dish, what questions about this recipe source does Portia need to ask?
2. **Communication.** Manto is planning a dinner party to help celebrate his aunt and uncle's wedding anniversary. While preparing his work plan, he finds that one of the foods he is using—an imported grain product—does not list a cooking time on the package. What would you advise Manto to do?

Making Decisions and Solving Problems

You've found a recipe for a casserole that you want to try. The ingredients list includes shredded cheese, but the directions do not tell you what to do with it. What would you do?

Making Connections

1. **Math.** Find a recipe that makes twelve or more servings. Change the recipe so that it yields four servings.
2. **Social Studies.** Using the library or other resources, find information about food preparation in colonial America or another historical period. Describe at least three tools that were commonly used for food preparation tasks. How did the tools differ from what is used today?

ANSWERS cont.

6. *Score:* make shallow, straight cuts in the surface of a food; *pare:* cut off a very thin layer of peel; *mince:* cut food in small, irregular pieces (pieces are smaller than chopped foods); *grate:* rub food against the rough surface of a grater.
7. Straining is separating solid particles from a liquid using a bowl-shaped fine screen called a strainer or sieve. Draining is allowing liquids to drain from a solid food by putting the food in a colander or a large strainer.
8. Use a rubber scraper or wooden spoon to cut down through the mixture, move the utensil across the bottom of the bowl, and bring it back up to the surface. Never lift the utensil out of the mixture.
9. It will make end-of-class cleanup easier and faster. It won't slow down the next team in the kitchen.
10. For a team, the schedule should specify not only when each task should start, but who should do it.

Thinking Critically

1. Answers will vary. Possible answer: Peggy may have decided not to try something for the first time on a special occasion. She may have felt more comfortable with a recipe she knew would work.
2. It will most likely not turn out right since Dana did not reduce all the ingredients proportionately.
3. Answers will vary. Possible answer: Some people may believe that recipes have all the necessary information in the recipe directions. Directions don't include all information needed, especially any required pre-preparation work. Having a plan can help you finish earlier.

Reinforcing Key Skills

1. Answers will vary. May note that Portia needs to know the source of these recipes before assuming they are worthy of use. Recipe reliability is correlated with the recipe source.
2. Answers will vary. Possible answer: Look for an 800 number for the manufacturer (on the package or in the telephone directory) and place a call to a customer help line. If time permits, look online for helpful information about this product.

CHAPTER

9

Cooking Methods

Advance Planning Guide ☑

- Arrange a field trip to a local appliance store.
- Gather appliance advertisements.
- Gather drawings or photos of cookware.
- Develop a list of prepared food items and a list of cookware.
- Arrange to have available four same-sized saucepans, including one anodized aluminum and one stainless-steel saucepan.
- Invite a registered dietitian to demonstrate cooking methods that preserve nutrients.
- Obtain a meat thermometer and a candy thermometer.
- Create flash cards that show different cookware and bakeware items.
- Obtain directions for using a pressure cooker.
- Arrange the purchase of broccoli, eggs, chicken breasts, raw baby carrots, condensed, creamy carrot or potato soup, quick bread mixes, and baking potatoes.
- Obtain microwave oven ads (or descriptions).
- Gather cookbooks with both conventional and microwave recipes.
- Obtain microwave-safe and non-microwave-safe coverings and containers.

CHAPTER

9

Cooking Methods

Lisa stared at the package of pork chops thawing in the refrigerator. She had never cooked pork chops and wondered how to cook them for her family's dinner.

What should Lisa do? This chapter describes different types of cooking equipment and techniques.

MEETING DIVERSE NEEDS

Celebrating Cultural Diversity. If there are students in the class who are first- or second-generation residents of the United States, ask them to demonstrate a cooking method that was originally discovered or is more utilized in their culture. Suggest that these students bring to class any unique cooking equipment needed for the demonstration. If possible, have these students bring a traditional basic recipe they will demonstrate to the class.

SECTION

9-1

Equipment for Cooking

Look around any kitchen, and you'll find many kinds of equipment designed for cooking. These include major appliances, small appliances, and a variety of utensils.

Objectives

After studying this section, you should be able to:

- Describe how cooktops and conventional, convection, and microwave ovens work.
- Identify small cooking appliances and describe their uses.
- Identify cookware, bakeware, and cooking tools.

Look for These Terms

heating units

cookware

bakeware

Major Cooking Appliances

The major appliances used for cooking are the conventional range, the convection oven, and the microwave oven. At least one of the first two appliances is found in almost every kitchen. Some kitchens have all three.

The Range

A range usually consists of a cooktop, an oven, and a broiler. The cooktop has either dials or push buttons to control the heat. The heat is generated by **heating units**—energy sources in ranges used to heat foods. Ovens have thermostatic controls so that you can set precise temperatures. Oven temperature settings vary from "warm"—below 200°F (93°C)—to "broil," which is generally about 500°F (260°C). The broiler cooks food by direct heat from a heating unit located in the top of the compartment.

Instead of a freestanding range, some kitchens have separate cooktop and oven units built into cabinets. Other kitchens have a portable oven that can be placed on a countertop or cart.

Ranges use either gas or electricity for heat. The two types of ranges have slightly different features.

Section 9-1 Resources

◆ **Student Workbook,** pp. 71, 74
◆ **Teacher Resource Guide**
Lesson Plan 9-1 Organizer
Section 9-1 Quiz
◆ **Effective Instruction CD-ROM**
Exam*View*® *Test Generator*
PowerPoint® Slide #22
◆ **Transparency Package,** CT-22
◆ **Student Motivation Kit**
Reteaching Activities, p. 51
Enrichment Activities
Skills for Making Food Choices, pp. 23–24

SECTION

9-1

Equipment for Cooking

FOCUS

MOTIVATORS

- Have students compare equipment used by backpackers and campers with that used in a home kitchen.
- Have students make predictions regarding cooking equipment in the latter part of the twenty-first century. What changes do they predict? Will families continue to prepare food at home as they do today? If not, how might food preparation be done?

VOCABULARY ACTIVITY

Pronounce the three terms listed under "Look for These Terms." Have students find the terms and their definitions in the section. Direct students' attention to *cookware* and *bakeware*. Ask students if *ware* is a complete word. Is it a noun, verb, or adjective? What is its definition?

STUDY SKILLS

- **Guided Reading.** Have students look at the headings within Section 9-1 to preview the concepts that will be discussed.
- Have students read the section and complete the appropriate part of the Chapter 9 Study Guide in the *Student Workbook*.

TEACH

- *Major Cooking Appliances (text pages 261-263)*

Debate

Have students form two groups for a debate. One group is to argue that food preparation using a gas range is preferable to using an electric range, others the reverse. Encourage each team to review text page 262. Suggest additional research. Have teams stage a debate for an impartial jury of their peers. L1

Listing Activity

Ask students to list and describe the types of cooktops available for electric ranges. Ask students if they suggest any characteristics be added to the list on page 262.

Computerized Chart Making

Have students make a chart using a computer software program comparing the features of gas and electric ranges. Suggest students share and compare charts as well as discuss their chart-making techniques. L2

Field Trip

Take a field trip to a local appliance store. Ask the salesperson to point out features of gas and electric ranges and ovens and to explain the characteristics of coil elements and induction cooktops available on electric ranges.

Gas Range

In a gas range, the oven and broiler are often in separate compartments. The broiler is generally located below the oven. When you're broiling in a gas range, keep the compartment door closed.

The heating units in a gas range are called *burners.* The burners in gas cooktops heat with a flame that is easily regulated. The change in heat level is almost immediate. Some gas ranges have sealed burners that show no visible flame.

In most newer ranges, when a burner is turned on, gas flows through and is ignited by an electronic spark. Older ranges contain pilot lights—small gas flames that burn continuously. When the burner is turned on, the pilot light ignites the gas. Sometimes, however, the pilot light goes out and must be relighted. This should be done by lighting a match and *then* turning on the burner. If the burner is turned on first, gas will accumulate and could cause an explosion when you strike the match.

Air flow is needed for burning gas, so take care not to block the vents in a gas range (by, for example, lining the burner bowls with foil). If air flow is blocked, the gas will not burn properly, resulting in the release of carbon monoxide, a deadly gas.

Electric Range

The heating units in electric ranges are called *elements.* Electricity passes through the element, causing it to heat up.

The oven and broiler in an electric range are in the same compartment. The compartment has two heating elements, one at the top and one at the bottom. The bottom element heats the compartment for all cooking purposes except broiling. For broiling, only the top element comes on. When you're broiling food in an electric range, leave the door slightly open.

There are two main cooktops available in electric ranges, each with unique characteristics:

- **Coil elements.** Elements heat up and cool down relatively quickly, although more slowly than gas burners. Coils may vary in size to fit smaller and larger cooking containers.
- **Induction cooktops.** A glass-ceramic top covers the heating elements, making this cooktop very easy to keep clean. With induction cooktops, heat is produced when a ferrous metal pan—such as stainless steel or cast iron—is placed on the element. The magnetic attraction between the pan and the heating element produces heat. This cooktop stays cool, except for any heat transferred from the pan.

◆ **The two most common types of cooktops for electric ranges are coil elements (below) and induction. Name two things that might make an induction cooktop preferable to one with coil elements.**

Extending Learning

Down-draft Ranges—Down-draft ranges have a built-in ventilating system that eliminates the need for a ventilating hood or fan. A duct connects the range ventilating system to the outside of the home. During cooking, blowers inside the range pull smoke, heat, and odors out through the appliance and exhaust them outdoors through the ductwork.

CLOSE-UP ON SCIENCE: PHYSICS

Electrical Resistance and Heat

As electricity passes through a material, its flow is interrupted by a characteristic of the material called *resistance*. The result is that the material heats up. The greater the current flow and the higher the resistance of the material, the greater the heat produced. Cooktop elements have high resistance to produce the heat needed for cooking.

The Convection Oven

A convection oven is similar to a conventional oven except that a fan circulates the heated air. This speeds up cooking time and keeps temperatures even throughout the oven. As a result, foods brown more evenly than in a conventional oven. A convection oven cooks more quickly than a conventional oven, but not as quickly as a microwave oven.

A convection oven can be combined with either a conventional or a microwave oven. The combination oven has more advantages than any single type.

The Microwave Oven

Microwaves are a form of energy that travels like radio waves. In a microwave oven, a magnetron (MAG-nuh-trahn) tube turns electricity into microwaves. The microwaves are distributed throughout the oven by a stirrer blade, a fanlike device. The microwaves bounce off the oven's walls and floor until they are absorbed by the food. Microwave energy is reflected from metal but passes through glass, paper, and plastic to get to food.

Microwaves make food molecules vibrate against each other, producing friction. This friction produces heat that cooks the food. Microwave ovens cook many foods in one-fourth the time that it takes to cook them conventionally, making this an energy-efficient way to cook.

◆ **Convection ovens use a built-in fan to circulate hot air in the oven compartment. Explain the advantages of this method of cooking.**

- ***Major Cooking Appliances (text pages 261-263)***

Appliance Ad Activity

Provide students with appliance ads. Have students study appliance ads to identify features available on ranges, conventional ovens, convection ovens, and microwave ovens. Which features are basic? Which are extras? How do the extra features affect the price of the appliance?

Research

Ask students to research what specific changes need to be made in a recipe for baking in a convection oven, since the recipe is based on baking in a conventional oven. Have students adapt a baking recipe based on their research results. **L1**

Comparison Activity

Have students compare the features of conventional ovens, convection ovens, and microwave ovens and write a critical analysis reporting the advantages and disadvantages of each type of oven in terms of cooking time, energy use, and food quality.

Extending Learning

Commercial Ranges—Commercial ranges, commonly used in restaurants, are also available for home use. They usually have cast iron cooking surfaces, and a minimum of six burners. They are slightly deeper than standard home ranges, with well-insulated ovens. Because of their durable construction, they can last a life-time. They do, however, lack popular features such as self-cleaning ovens, clocks, timers, and glass doors. The outside is usually finished in stainless steel, copper, black, or gray.

- *Small Cooking Appliances (text page 264)*

Science Connection Activity

Point out that many small electric appliances also use high-resistance and current flow to produce heat. Ask students why these appliances need to be watched more carefully than appliances that don't produce heat by this method.

Listing Activity

Ask students to name several small cooking appliances that make certain cooking tasks faster and easier. List them on the chalkboard while students write in their notes any small appliances not already listed on this page. Have volunteer students give a one-sentence description for these appliances.

Poster Project Activity

Have students prepare "then and now" posters comparing small appliances of the past with current versions. How have small cooking appliances changed? Which changes are functional improvements? Which are aesthetic changes?

Research Activity

Ask students to research how the energy use of small appliances compares with the energy use of major appliances for the same purpose. Discuss students' results.

Small Cooking Appliances

Many small appliances are available to help you perform certain cooking tasks quickly and easily. Here are some basic ones:

- **Toaster.** Browns bread products on both sides at the same time. You set the controls for the degree of browning. Two- and four-slice models are available.
- **Toaster oven.** Toasts bread, heats up foods, and bakes small amounts of many foods. Some toaster ovens can broil food.
- **Electric skillet.** A thermostat controls the temperature of the skillet. This appliance is useful for frying, roasting, steaming, and baking.
- **Portable electric burner.** A small appliance that works like the cooktop on a range.
- **Slow cooker.** A deep pot with a heating element in the base that allows food to cook slowly over many hours. It's a convenient way to cook one-dish meals such as stews.
- **Broiler/grill.** A small, portable electric grill used to broil or grill food indoors.
- **Rice cooker/steamer.** Used to cook large quantities of rice or to steam vegetables. The controlled heat cooks all types of rice perfectly.

Cookware and Bakeware

Cookware is equipment for cooking food on top of the range. **Bakeware** is equipment for cooking food in an oven. Both cookware and bakeware are available in a variety of materials. Microwave ovens have special requirements for cooking containers.

As a general rule, all types of cookware and bakeware should be washed in hot water with dish detergent. To remove baked-on food, soak pans in hot water with a little detergent prior to washing them.

Extending Learning

Small Appliances

- *Cordless appliances.* These operate on rechargeable batteries built into a special storage-charger base. The appliance recharges during storage.
- *Compact or mini-appliances.* Their popularity is linked to the increase in one- and two-person households. Even in larger households, family members often prepare their own meals and eat on staggered schedules. Smaller appliances are easier to store.

Cookware

If you were packing for an overnight trip, you'd use a lightweight travel bag, not a huge trunk. In much the same way, you can choose cookware, which comes in many shapes and sizes, depending on how you plan to use it. Here is a guide to some common items:

- **Saucepans.** Saucepans have one long handle and often come with a cover. Some types have a small handle on the opposite side as well. Sizes range from ½ quart to 4 quarts (500 mL to 4 L). Saucepans are usually made of metal or heatproof glass.
- **Pots.** Larger and heavier than saucepans, pots range in size from 3 to 20 quarts (3 to 20 L). Pots have two small handles, one on either side, which make it easier to lift a heavy pot. Most pots come with covers.
- **Skillets.** Sometimes called "frypans" or "frying pans," skillets are used for browning and frying foods. They vary in size and often have matching covers.
- **Double boiler.** A double boiler consists of two saucepans—a smaller one fitting into a larger one—and a cover. Boiling water in the bottom pan gently heats the food in the upper pan. This type of cookware is used for heating foods that scorch easily, such as milk, chocolate, sauces, and cereal.
- **Dutch oven.** This is a heavy-gauge pot with a close-fitting cover. This type of pot may be used on top of the range or in the oven. Some Dutch ovens come with a rack to keep meat and poultry from sticking to the bottom.
- **Steamer.** This basketlike container is placed inside a saucepan containing a small amount of boiling water. Holes in the steamer allow steam to pass through and cook the food.
- **Pressure cooker.** This heavy pot has a locked-on cover and steam gauge. Steam builds up inside the pot, causing very high cooking temperatures that cook food more quickly than in an ordinary pot.

- *Cookware and Bakeware (text pages 264-268)*

Bulletin Board Activity

Number and arrange mounted photos or drawings of cookware on the bulletin board, including more than those in the photograph on this page. Ask students to write each item number and name under one of the three columns: "Necessities," "Clutter," and "Luxuries." Discuss the differences between needs and wants and talk about how to distinguish between the two. Why might people differ on their evaluation of certain items?

Matching Activity

Provide students a list of prepared food items and a list of cookware. Have students match the food item with its appropriate cookware. Discuss results with the class.

Home Survey

Ask students to write a list of all the cookware that is used in their homes and at least one example of how it's used, such as a double boiler for melting chocolate and reheating cabbage rolls. Have students bring their lists to class. Have one student compile a master list of the students' surveys. Provide master list copies to each student. L1

Reinforcing Key Skills

Present the following problems to student groups. Allow time for them to discuss and compare their responses.

Management—Ask students to figure potential costs in time and materials to clean an oven by hand. How much energy is expended when a self-cleaning oven burns off baked-on food? What is the cost of this energy? What does the self-cleaning feature add to the cost of an oven?

Communication—You see a classmate boiling water in a stockpot in the foods lab for boiling just a 1-cup portion of pasta. What might you say?

- *Cookware and Bakeware (text pages 264-268)*

VISUAL LEARNING ***Using the Chart*** Using the chart on pages 266-267, have student groups write each material's name, advantages, disadvantages, and use and care suggestions on note cards. Have students use the note cards to play a "match game."

Product Comparison

Discuss the advantages and disadvantages of using anodized aluminum versus stainless steel. Arrange to have available the same-sized anodized aluminum and stainless steel saucepans. Have two student volunteers prepare the same rice mix, using the two types of cookware. When finished with rice preparation, have all students compare and contrast the two finished rice products and the pans for stuck-on rice. Encourage students to draw conclusions. L2

Safety Activity

Tell students that copper is not the only metal that releases metal ions into food. When acidic foods such as tomato sauce are cooked in iron cookware, the iron content of the food increases. Why is this not considered to be dangerous?

Materials Used for Cookware

Material	*Advantages*	*Disadvantages*	*Use and Care*
Aluminum	• Conducts heat quickly, evenly. • Lightweight. • Durable. • Comes in a variety of finishes.	• Warps, dents, and scratches easily. • Darkens and stains, especially in dishwasher. • Pits if used to store salty or acid foods.	• Cool before washing to prevent warping. • Avoid sharp tools like knives and beaters. • Do not use to store salty or acid foods.
Anodized Aluminum	• Maintains an even, consistent cooking temperature. • Durable. • Will never peel, chip, or crack. • Resists sticking and scratching.	• Heavy. • Can be expensive.	• Use nonabrasive cleaners and nylon scrubbers.
Stainless Steel	• Durable, tough, hard. • Will not dent easily. • Attractive.	• Conducts heat unevenly. • Stains when overheated or from starchy foods. • Can develop hot spots. • Pits if used to store salty or acid foods.	• Use nonabrasive cleaners and nylon scrubbers. • Use stainless steel cleaner to remove stains. • Do not use to store salty or acid foods.
Copper	• Excellent heat conductor. • Attractive.	• Discolors easily. • Discolors food and may create toxic compounds. Inside must be lined with tin or stainless steel.	• Dry after washing. • Do not scour inside—the thin lining may be worn away. • Polish with copper cleaner or mixture of flour and vinegar.
Cast Iron	• Distributes heat evenly. • Retains heat well.	• Heavy. • Rusts if not wiped dry after washing.	• Store in dry place. • Store cover separately—pan may rust if stored covered.

FOOD SCIENCE **Materials Experiment** Bring to class samples of four or more types of saucepans of equal size. Ask students to hypothesize which pan will cook fastest based on the chart information. They can test their hypotheses by heating 2 cups (500 mL) of refrigerated water in each pan using the same burner preheated to the same temperature. With a candy thermometer and a stop watch, students can test how fast the water reaches a given temperature. Which pan cools most quickly? What conclusions can be drawn?

Materials Used for Cookware (cont'd)

Material	*Advantages*	*Disadvantages*	*Use and Care*
Glass	• Attractive; can be used for cooking and serving. • Easy to clean.	• Breaks easily, especially if exposed to extreme temperature changes. • Some can be used only on the cooktop; others only in the oven. • Holds heat, but does not conduct heat well.	• May need a wire grid if used on an electric cooktop. • Use nonabrasive cleaners and nylon scrubbers. • Do not plunge hot pan into cold water or put into the refrigerator.
Glass-Ceramic	• Goes from freezer to oven or cooktop. • Durable, heat-resistant, attractive. • Used for roasting, broiling, and baking in conventional or microwave ovens.	• May break if dropped. • Holds heat well—reduce oven temperatures by 25°F (14°C) for baked goods.	• Use nonabrasive cleaners and nylon scrubbers. • Dishwasher-safe. • Use manufacturer's care instructions.
Stoneware	• Attractive; can be used for cooking and serving. • Retains heat.	• Breaks easily.	• Dishwasher-safe. • Use nonabrasive cleaners and nylon scrubbers.
Enamel (glass baked on metal)	• Attractive; can be used to cook and serve.	• Chips easily.	• Dishwasher-safe. • Use nonabrasive cleaners and nylon scrubbers.
Microwave-safe Plastic	• Durable. • Stain-resistant. • Easy to clean.	• Some cannot be used in conventional ovens. • Can be scratched by sharp kitchen tools.	• Dishwasher-safe. • Use nonabrasive cleaners and nylon scrubbers.
Nonstick Finishes	• Keeps food from sticking to pans—fat may not be necessary for browning, sautéing, or frying.	• Easily scratched by metal kitchen tools or abrasive cleaners. • High heat may stain finish or warp pan.	• Follow manufacturer's directions for use and care. Some cannot be washed in dishwasher. • Use nonmetal tools to prevent scratching.

• *Cookware and Bakeware (text pages 264-268)*

Evaluating Cookware

Have students work in groups to evaluate the quality of several types of cookware. Ask students to compare the quality of construction, balance, handles, covers, weight, potential uses, and potential benefits for healthier cooking. Ask groups to report their findings to the class. Add additional points as needed after each presentation. **L2**

Flash Cards

Ask students to make flash cards of appliances, cookware, and cooking tools. Have students practice their flash cards with each other, identifying each item and its uses. **L1**

Research Activity

Have students research nonstick cooking materials. How and when was the coating material first discovered? What other uses does it have? Do they believe the utilization of nonstick cookware will grow during the 21st century? Why? Ask students to write a report of their research findings using a computer word-processing program.

Extending Learning

Minimizing Nutrient Loss—Emphasize that students should check cookware thoroughly before making a purchase. Point out that one purpose of a tight-fitting cover is to prevent nutrient loss. Ask students how the nutrients would be lost if the cover was loose-fitting or not used.

TEACH cont.

- *Cookware and Bakeware (text pages 264-268)*

Materials Analysis Activity

Ask students to list and describe basic types of bakeware, including the materials used to make the bakeware. Discuss the advantages and disadvantages of the materials used for the listed bakeware. Ask students why it is necessary to reduce the heat if you bake in glass.

VISUAL LEARNING ***Using the Photograph*** Have students identify the bakeware items shown in the photo on this page and discuss uses for each item. Which would they consider most versatile, or have the most uses? Why might it be best to consider buying bakeware that has multiple uses?

Lab Experience Activity

Test the effects of different bakeware materials on the finished product. Pour banana bread or other quick bread batter into loaf pans or muffin pans made from various materials or with different finishes. Place the pans in the same preheated oven and bake for the same amount of time. Have students compare the results and draw conclusions.

Safety Check

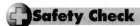

Don't use copper cookware if it's unlined or if the lining wears out. Acidic foods can cause copper to be released into food. Too much copper in the body can cause nausea, vomiting, and diarrhea.

Bakeware

Most bakeware consists of pans of different sizes and shapes. Light-colored pans transfer oven heat to food quickly and give baked products a light, delicate crust. Dark pans absorb more heat from the oven and can produce thick brown crusts in baked products, though not in other foods.

Glass pans absorb more heat than metal bakeware does. If you use a glass pan for baking, reduce the oven temperature by 25°F (14°C).

Here are some basic types of bakeware:

- **Loaf pan.** A deep, narrow, rectangular pan used for baking breads and meat loaf.
- **Cookie sheet.** A flat, rectangular pan designed for baking cookies and biscuits. A cookie sheet has two or three open sides.
- **Baking sheet.** Similar to a cookie sheet, except with four shallow sides about 1 inch (2.5 cm) deep. Baking sheets are used for baking sheet cakes, pizza, chicken pieces, and fish.
- **Cake pans.** Available in assorted sizes and shapes.
- **Tube pan.** A variation on the standard cake pan with a central tube to help trap added air in angel food and sponge cakes.
- **Pie pans.** Shallow, round pans with slanted sides. Pie pans are used for pies, tarts, and quiches.
- **Muffin pans.** Used for baking muffins, rolls, and cupcakes. These pans are available in 6- and 12-cup capacities.
- **Roasting pans.** Large, heavy pans, oval or rectangular in shape, and used for roasting meats and poultry. Roasting pans may be covered or uncovered.
- **Casserole.** A covered or uncovered pan used for baking and serving main dishes and desserts. Various sizes are available.
- **Aluminum foil pans.** Disposable pans made of foil. These pans are useful for special, one-of-a-kind occasions and can be recycled.

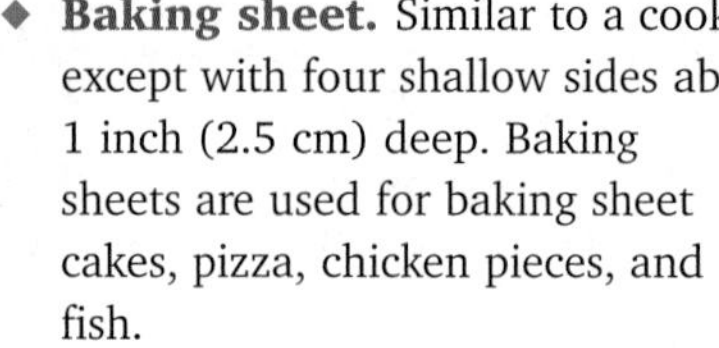

◆ **A variety of bakeware is available. Compare and contrast the results achieved by cooking with shiny vs. darker metal pans.**

Reinforcing Key Skills

Present the following problems to student groups. Allow time for them to discuss and compare their responses.

Directed Thinking—When making a purchase, do you ever have trouble deciding which brand, color, model, or size you should buy? Is it easier to make a selection when you know more or less about the item you are buying?

Communication—You see an indecisive buyer in the bakeware section of a kitchen supply store. Think of how you might help the person decide.

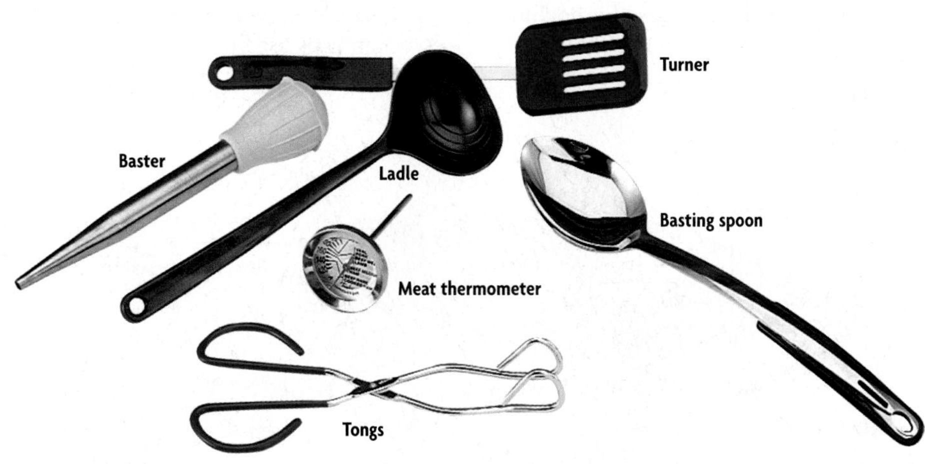

Cooking Tools

A variety of tools are available for the many different cooking tasks. Here are some you might find helpful:

- **Turner.** Used to lift and turn flat foods such as hamburgers and pancakes.
- **Tongs.** Used to grip and lift hot, bulky foods, such as broccoli spears.
- **Basting spoon.** Used to stir and baste foods during cooking.
- **Baster.** A long tube with a bulb on the end used for suctioning up juices for basting.
- **Ladle.** Has a small bowl and a long handle for dipping hot liquids from a pan.
- **Pastry brush.** Used to brush hot foods with sauce or pastry with a glaze.
- **Skewers.** Long rods made of metal or bamboo, with one pointed end. Pieces of food are threaded onto skewers for cooking or serving.
- **Oven meat thermometer.** Used to measure the internal temperature of meat and poultry as it roasts in the oven. This type of thermometer cannot be used with thin food or in a microwave oven.
- **Instant-read thermometer.** Used to measure the internal temperature of food at the end of cooking time, including foods prepared in a microwave or conventional oven. This type of thermometer cannot be used while food is cooking in the oven. To gauge the internal temperature of thin foods, insert the thermometer sideways. Both digital and analog models of instant-read thermometers are sold, with the digital version being easier to read.

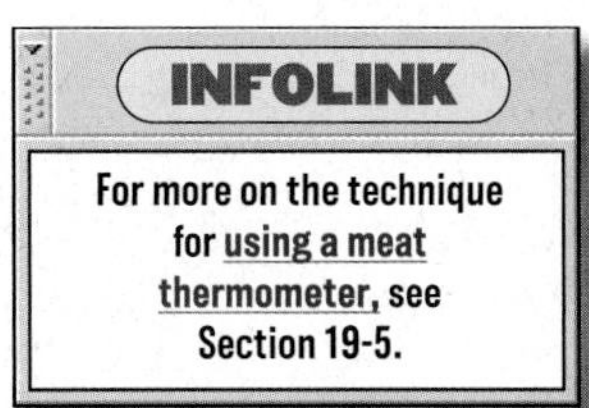

For more on the technique for using a meat thermometer, see Section 19-5.

- *Cooking Tools (text pages 269-270)*

Discussion Activity

Ask students to describe cooking tools that a chef might need. Discuss the reasons a person might need two different kinds of thermometers: one for meat and one for candy. Show students the two types of thermometers. Note the temperature ranges for each thermometer.

Demonstration

Hand students a cooking tool as they come into class. Provide students a few minutes to determine the name of the tool and all potential uses of the tool. As you call on each student, ask him or her to identify the tool, suggest at least three potential uses of the tool, and show how to use the tool.

Foods Lab Survey Activity

Have students locate the cooking tools in the foods lab. Point out that these items are stored near the range. Have students make a list of the name of the tools they find. Discuss potential uses for each tool.

Reinforcing Key Skills

Present the following problems to student groups. Allow time for them to discuss and compare their responses.

Directed Thinking—Have students visit a discount store and a department store to record the prices of several different types of cooking tools. Were the same types and brands available in both places? At which were items in general more expensive? Were there any exceptions? Ask students to draw conclusions.

Management—You just finished baking a cake, but you can't find a cooling rack.

ASSESS

REVIEW

- Ask students to summarize the main ideas in this section.
- Have students complete the Section Review. (Answers appear below.)

EVALUATION

- Ask students to write a short essay describing the appliances, cookware, bakeware, and cooking tools that should be found in a well-equipped kitchen.
- Have students take the quiz for Section 9-1. (Use the quiz in the *Teacher Resource Guide,* or construct your own with the **Exam***View*® *Test Generator* on the *Effective Instruction CD-ROM.*)

RETEACHING

- Create flash cards that show different cookware and bakeware items. Have students use the cards to practice identifying each item and describing its purpose.
- Refer to the *Reteaching Activities* booklet for the Section 9-1 activity sheet.

CLOSE

Lead a class discussion on the importance of having the proper tools and equipment in the kitchen. Ask students to brainstorm food items they couldn't prepare or couldn't prepare well if the only kitchen equipment available was a basting spoon, an aluminum saucepan, and a cookie sheet. Encourage students to visualize a preparation situation.

- **Wire cooling racks.** Used for holding baked goods during cooling or hot pans when they are removed from the heat.
- **Potholders and oven mitts.** Thick cloth pads used to protect hands while handling hot containers.

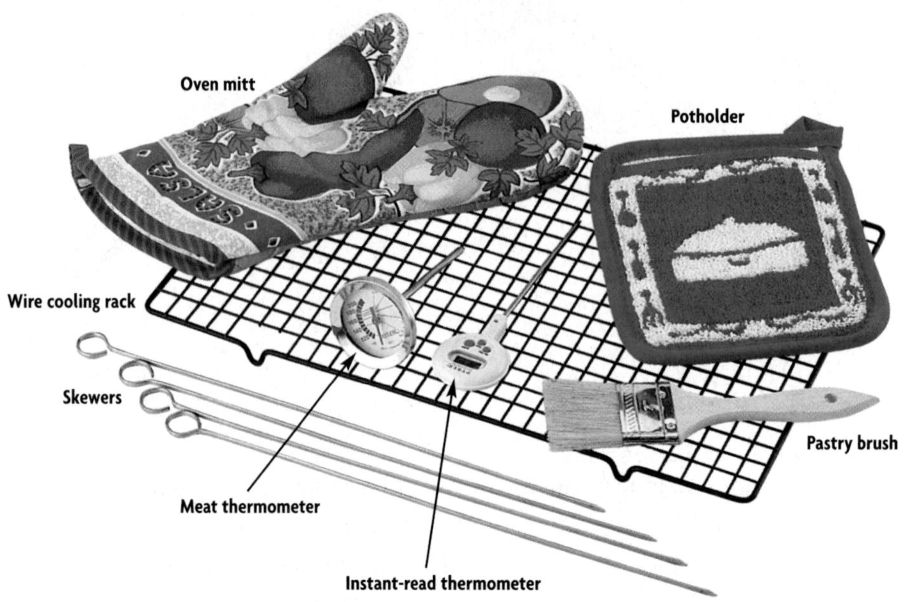

Section 9-1 Review & Activities

1. Name four small appliances for cooking foods.
2. What are the key differences between a saucepan and a pot? Between a cookie sheet and a baking sheet?
3. What is the difference between cookware and bakeware?
4. What are the main differences between conventional, convection, and microwave ovens?
5. **Applying.** Choose three kitchen equipment items that require different types of sanitary care. Demonstrate for the class the correct sanitary practices to use in caring for each item.
6. **Synthesizing.** Bret's family is on a limited budget. What small cooking appliances might you advise them to buy or not to buy? Explain your answer.
7. **Applying.** Working in groups, identify the cooking equipment found in the foods lab kitchen and note where it is located. Be prepared to report orally to your teacher.

Answers to Section 9-1 Review & Activities

1. See bulleted list on page 264.
2. See bulleted list on page 265; see bulleted list on page 268.
3. Cookware is used for cooking food on top of the range; bakeware is used for cooking food in an oven.
4. Conventional ovens often have a heating element for broiling. Convection ovens have a fan that circulates the heated air. Microwave ovens use microwaves to heat the food, and they cook food faster than the other two; conventional ovens are the slowest.
5. Demonstrations will vary.
6. Answers will vary.
7. Answers will vary.

SECTION
9-2

Objectives

After studying this section, you should be able to:

- Explain how heat is transferred by conduction, convection, and radiation.
- Describe some changes in food brought about by cooking.

Look for These Terms

conduction

convection

convection current

radiation

Heat and Cooking

Wonderful things happen in the kitchen. A mixture of vegetables, meat, and water becomes a savory stew. A turkey browning in the oven or soup simmering on top of the range creates delicious aromas. These are just a few of the delightful changes that result from applying heat to food.

Methods of Heat Transfer

When any material—metal, glass, or a food—is heated, its molecules vibrate. The greater the heat, the higher the vibration. Depending on the heat source, these vibrations can come from different forms of energy. The three types of energy transfer central to all cooking are *conduction, convection,* and *radiation.*

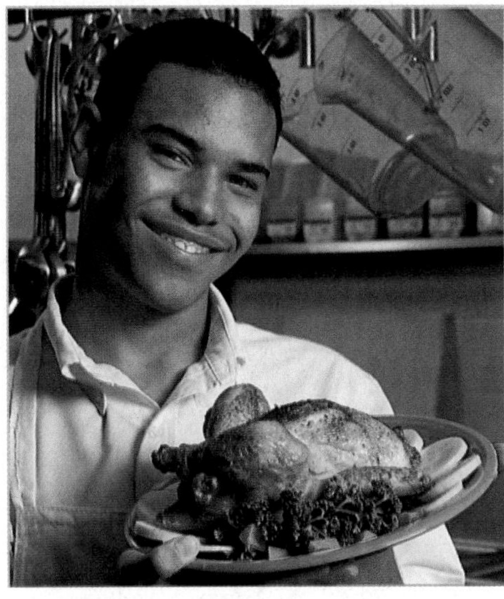

◆ **Heat affects the flavor of foods. Name two other senses besides taste to which browned foods might appeal.**

SECTION
9-2
Heat and Cooking

FOCUS

MOTIVATORS

- Discuss how the discovery of fire led to cooking as we know it today.
- Have students make a list of foods they eat raw or cooked, such as broccoli and cheese. Have students share their lists while describing the difference between the cooked and raw forms, including color, flavor, and texture differences.

VOCABULARY ACTIVITY

Pronounce the four terms listed under "Look for These Terms." Have students find the terms and their definitions in the section. Direct students' attention to the suffix *-tion*. Are the terms in this section nouns, verbs, or adjectives? What words are created when *conduction, convection,* and *radiation* are without this suffix? Are they nouns, verbs, or adjectives?

STUDY SKILLS

- **Listening.** Invite a group of volunteers to each prepare an oral reading of a page of text from the section, while others follow along silently. At the end of the reading, the class is to list as many key concepts as they can recall. Share and compare summaries.
- Have students read the section and complete the appropriate part of the Chapter 9 Study Guide in the *Student Workbook*.

Section 9-2 Resources

◆ **Student Workbook,** pp. 71, 75
◆ **Teacher Resource Guide**
Lesson Plan 9-2 Organizer
Section 9-2 Quiz
◆ **Effective Instruction CD-ROM**
Exam*View*® *Test Generator*

◆ **Student Motivation Kit**
Reteaching Activities, p. 52
Enrichment Activities
Food Science Resources, pp. 50–52, 101–103

TEACH

- *Methods of Heat Transfer (text pages 271-273)*

Discussion Activity

Ask students to list three ways in which heat travels to or through foods. Ask students to explain what a convection current is. How is this related to cooking food?

Menu Planning

Have each student plan a menu that includes all three methods of heat transfer. Suggest that a few students record their menus on the chalkboard, identifying which method is used for which food. Example: Broiled sirloin steak (radiation and conduction), boiled new potatoes (convection), and sautéed red peppers in a non-stick skillet (conduction), fat free milk, and mixed fruit. L1

Recipe Search

Have students bring to class recipes that specify various ways of heating or cooking foods. Have students make a chart classifying the recipes according to the three types of energy transfer. Ask several student volunteers to share their charts with the class. Discuss how common it is to find more than one method of heat transfer in one recipe. L2

Conduction

Think of a pancake cooking in a skillet. Heat from the cooktop heating unit is conducted into the skillet, which in turn passes the heat along to the bottom of the pancake and finally to the inside of the food. This heat transfer by direct contact is known as **conduction**.

As molecules are heated, they pass the heat on to neighboring molecules. In this way, heat can travel within an object and to other objects that are in direct contact. To cook the top of the pancake, you flip it over. Can you see why?

Convection

Transfer of heat by the movement of air or liquid is called **convection**. As air or liquid is heated, the hotter portions rise above the colder ones. This creates a **convection current**—a circular flow of air or liquid resulting from uneven heating. Imagine a saucepan of water heating on the cooktop. The water nearest the bottom of the saucepan gets warm and rises through the colder water to the surface. The colder water on the surface is forced down to the saucepan bottom. As the cold water on the bottom of the saucepan warms up, it rises to the surface. This process continually repeats, creating a convection current. This same process also occurs with heated air in an oven.

◆ **Conduction and convection are alternative methods of transferring heat to food. Write a brief paragraph that explains how each method works.**

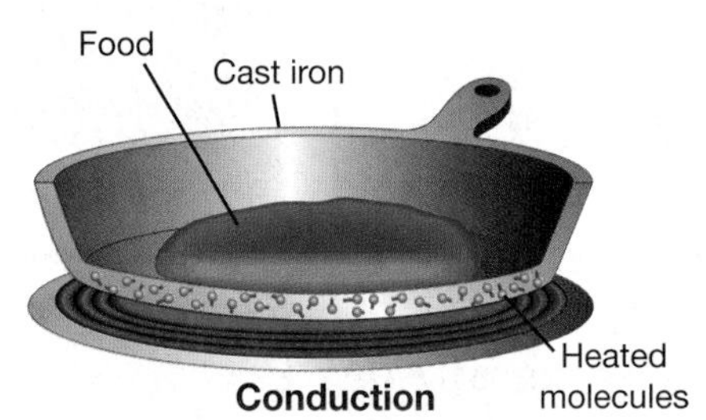

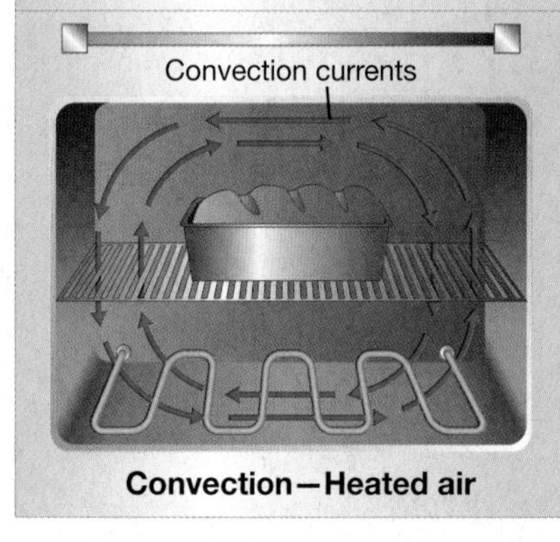

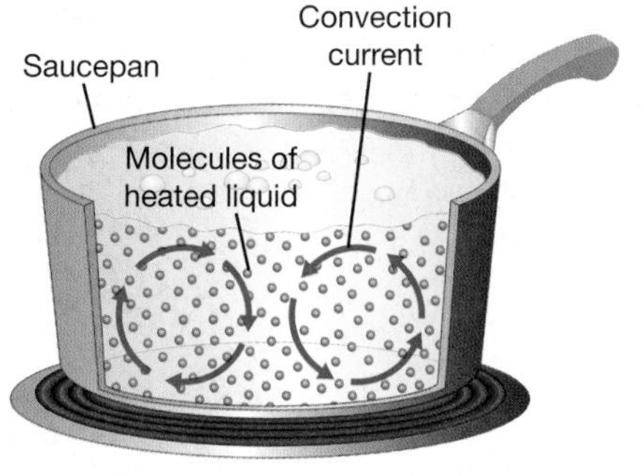

FOOD SCIENCE: Convection Currents

Convection currents create a continuous movement of air or liquid. In a convection oven, for example, as air near the heating element becomes warmer, it begins to rise, displacing the relatively cool air toward the top of the oven. Because the warmer air is now away from the heating element, it begins to cool slightly. In the meantime, the cooler air cannot escape the oven, so it is forced down toward the burner. As it gets near the burner, it begins to warm and rise back to the top of the oven, again displacing the cooler air.

Radiation

The sun radiates heat to warm the earth. In a similar way, radiant heat from a broiler strikes and warms the food below. This type of heat transfer method that uses infrared rays to strike and warm an object is called **radiation**.

Most cooking techniques use a combination of some or all the heat transfer processes described here. For example, a broiler heats the surface of a food by radiation. The heat then travels through the food by conduction.

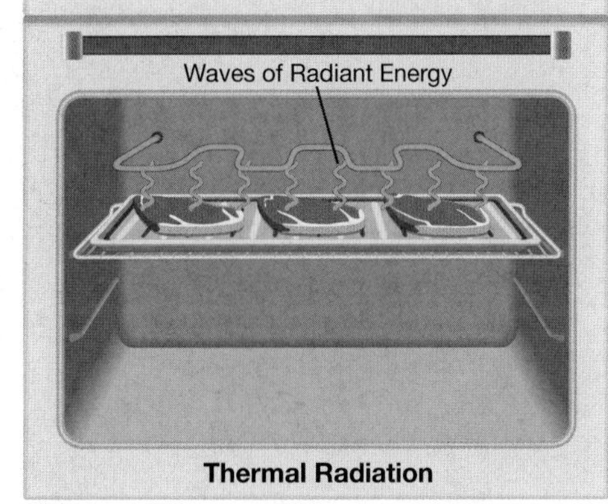

◆ **Heat can also be transferred through infrared rays. Name two cooking methods that use these rays.**

How Does Heat Affect Aroma?

Some experts claim that as much as 85 percent of what we call "taste" is actually smell. How much of a role does heat play in the aroma of foods and whether those aromas are pleasant?

Procedure

1. Ask several classmates to serve as aroma testers. Have them stand 6 feet or more from your work area.
2. Slice half a large onion. Have the aroma testers begin walking toward you. They should stop when they can detect an aroma. Have the testers rate the aroma in terms of how pleasant they found it. Note their responses. Remove the onion and have the testers return to their original positions.
3. Slice the other half of the onion. Place it in the microwave oven and cook it for 3 minutes at 100 percent power. Again, have the testers walk toward you and stop when they detect an aroma. Record their ratings as before.
4. Repeat steps 2 and 3, using celery ribs and bacon strips.

Conclusions

- ◆ How did the before and after ratings compare? How do you account for any differences?
- ◆ What generalization can you make about the effects of heat on foods that require cooking as opposed to those that can be eaten cooked or raw? How can you test this generalization?

Extending Learning

Irradiation—The cooking method of radiation should not be confused with the shelf-life prolonging process of radiation, known as irradiation. Irradiation is an FDA-approved process to extend shelf-life and slow decay or maturation of food through destruction of insects and microorganisms. All irradiated foods display a symbol of a plant inside a broken circle, except for herbs, spices, and other foods that are used as ingredients in other food products. Irradiation can help reduce the amount of chemicals and preservatives in processed foods.

- *Methods of Heat Transfer (text pages 271-273)*

Ask students to use critical thinking to answer the following questions based on the lab:

How can heat (and aroma) affect someone trying to eat less to lose weight? Eat more to gain weight?

How may heat (and aroma) affect someone with nausea? Someone with a cold?

Research Activity

Have students use library references to find magazine or journal articles that refer to the different methods of heat transfer. Ask students to write a brief written summary of the articles.

Taste Test

1. Divide the class into groups; provide each group 2 cups (500 mL) of raw baby carrots.
2. Have students develop a chart with rows labeled "raw" and "cooked," and columns headed "taste," "aroma," "texture," and "color."
3. Ask students to taste one cup (250 mL) of carrots raw and record their findings in the "raw" row.
4. Have students boil 1 cup (250 mL) of carrots and record their findings in the "cooked" row.
5. Encourage class discussion of the findings.

TEACH cont.

- *How Heat Affects Nutrients (text pages 274-275)*

Public Service Announcement

Have students who are effective public speakers team with others who are effective researchers and writers to create a public service announcement (PSA) on why and how to prepare foods to retain nutrients. If it can be arranged with the administration, students should present their PSA on school's public address, computer, or TV system. L2

Guest Speaker

Ask a registered dietitian to speak to the class regarding cooking methods that preserve nutrients in foods. Suggest the speaker demonstrate one or more of the methods while discussing which nutrients can be lost and why. Discuss why we want to preserve these nutrients.

Recipe R & D

Divide students into pairs or small groups. Each group is to locate and modify an existing recipe so as to retain as many nutrients as possible. Groups are to write their recipes in standard format. They are to write a brief introduction that explains their nutrient-loss prevention suggestions. L3

◆ Bread that is browned actually tastes better than bread with a light color. That's because the chemical reactions that cause the browning also affect the internal flavor. A crust that is brown and glossy can be obtained by coating the surface with egg, placing a pan of hot water in the oven, or spraying the loaf's surface with water.

How Heat Affects Food

As Matt removed a loaf of freshly baked bread from the oven, he breathed in its delicious aroma. Heat waves rose from the crisp brown crust. He could hardly wait to cut himself a slice.

CLOSE-UP ON SCIENCE: CHEMISTRY

Taste and Temperature

The temperature at which a food will be served is important for food scientists to consider as they create new food product recipes and modify older ones. Heat releases food odors (as you know if you have ever cooked cabbage), and stronger odors intensify a food's taste. Recipes for hot foods must be balanced so that more aromatic ingredients do not overwhelm the others. Similarly, cold dulls the taste buds. Flavors in cold foods must be more intense to be fully enjoyed.

The oven's heat brought out the aroma of the bread and baked its crust to a golden brown. These are two ways in which heat affects food. Heat releases flavor and aroma from foods. Cooking different foods together allows flavors to mingle, creating a pleasing combination. Heat also changes the color of foods. Some foods become darker when cooked and some become lighter. Heat brightens the color of some foods.

Heat also changes the texture of foods. Some foods become harder, some softer, some crispy, and some tender. In addition, heat has an effect on nutrients.

How Cooking Affects Nutrients

One of the goals of food preparation is to retain nutrients, such as vitamins and minerals. You've already learned that proper storage helps retain nutrients. Another key is to choose cooking methods that minimize nutrient loss and to use those methods properly.

Some nutrients can be destroyed by cooking heat. These include vitamin C, thiamin, and folate.

FOOD SCIENCE **The Effects of Cooking on Vitamin C**

Have one or more students research all the factors, including cooking heat, that can destroy vitamin C, such as light and oxygen. Encourage students to include any specific percentage-of-loss information they can find. How much vitamin C is lost by boiling broccoli for one minute versus steaming broccoli for one minute? How much vitamin C is lost in one cup (250 mL) of orange juice stored in an opaque container versus the same amount stored in a glass container? Have students report on their findings.

When foods are cooked in liquid, water-soluble vitamins and some minerals dissolve into the liquid. Unless the cooking liquid is consumed, these nutrients are lost. Some minerals and fat-soluble vitamins may be lost as fats and juices drip from meat, poultry, and fish.

Although very little protein is lost during cooking, animal proteins are sensitive to high temperatures. Overcooking in dry heat toughens them, making them unpleasant to eat.

The exact effect of heat on food depends on both the food and the cooking method. In the next section you will learn more about various cooking methods, as well as ways to retain vitamins and minerals and to reduce fat.

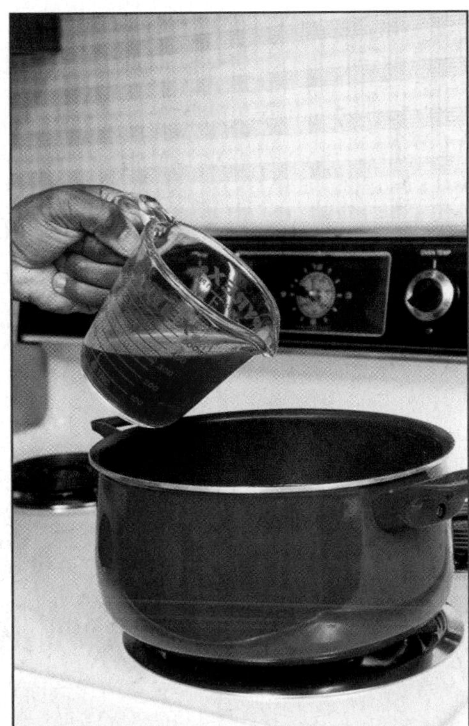

◆ **Making soup by using the liquid that the vegetables were cooked in is one way of conserving nutrients. What are some others?**

Section 9-2 Review & Activities

1. Briefly describe the three ways heat can be transferred to food during cooking.

2. Name three general ways heat can affect food.

3. Name ways in which nutrients, such as vitamins and minerals, can be lost during cooking.

4. **Synthesizing.** How might understanding heat transfer processes help you in using appliances to cook food?

5. **Extending.** Explain the effect of heating on vitamin C, thiamin, and folate. Suggest ways to prevent loss of these vitamins during cooking.

6. **Applying.** Prepare a lesson plan for teaching young children about safety in and around kitchen ranges. Include a definition of the term *heating unit,* as well as original pictures of heating units that transfer energy visibly, such as gas, and those where the heat is invisible—radiation, for example. If possible, teach your lesson to an elementary school class in your community.

ASSESS

REVIEW

- Ask students to summarize the main ideas in this section.
- Have students complete the Section Review. (Answers appear below.)

EVALUATION

- Ask students to prepare an outline of the topics covered in this chapter, using "Methods of Heat Transfer" and "How Heat Affects Food" as main topics.
- Have students take the quiz for Section 9-2. (Use the quiz in the *Teacher Resource Guide,* or construct your own with the **ExamView®** *Test Generator* on the *Effective Instruction CD-ROM.*)

RETEACHING

- Ask students to draw simple diagrams to illustrate the differences between conduction, convection, and radiation in cooking.
- Refer to the *Reteaching Activities* booklet for the Section 9-2 activity sheet.

CLOSE

Based on information learned in this section, brainstorm a list with students of several suggestions for nutritious cooking.

Answers to Section 9-2 Review & Activities

1. See pages 272-273.
2. It changes the color, flavor, and texture of foods.
3. See text copy on this page.
4. Answers will vary. Possible answer: You can make adjustments when necessary for the amount of food, type of food, or cooking time.
5. They are destroyed by heat or lost in cooking water or steam. Cook vegetables quickly; steam them or use small amounts of cooking water; use leftover liquid in soup, stew, or a sauce; cover food during cooking.
6. Answers will vary.

SECTION
9-3
Conventional Cooking Techniques

FOCUS

MOTIVATORS

- Have students make a list of conventional cooking techniques. Compare the list made by students with the cooking techniques listed in the text. With which techniques are students most familiar?
- Name and briefly describe a cooking technique. Ask students to name foods that may be prepared using the technique. Point out other familiar foods that may be prepared by each technique.

VOCABULARY ACTIVITY

Pronounce the terms listed under "Look for These Terms." Have students find the terms and their definitions in the section. Direct students' attention to the suffix *-ing* in *cooking, stewing, poaching, preheating,* and *frying*. In what way does it change the root of these terms?

STUDY SKILLS

- **Outlining.** Have students read the section and outline it by copying the headers on paper and leaving space after each one. Students are to write a sentence in their own words, summarizing the content under each header.
- Have students read the section and complete the appropriate part of the Chapter 9 Study Guide in the *Student Workbook*.

SECTION
9-3

Conventional Cooking Techniques

Objectives

After studying this section, you should be able to:

- Explain basic differences between moist-heat cooking, dry-heat cooking, and frying.
- Identify specific types of moist-heat cooking, dry-heat cooking, and frying, as well as combination methods.
- Give guidelines for conventional cooking.

Look for These Terms

moist-heat cooking
stewing
poaching
dry-heat cooking
preheating
hot spot
frying
sauté
smoking point
wok

Kristie wanted to try something new, so she bought and cooked a chuck roast for her family. She cooked it the way her mother always cooked roasts—in an open pan in the oven. The roast turned out so tough and dry that it was barely edible.

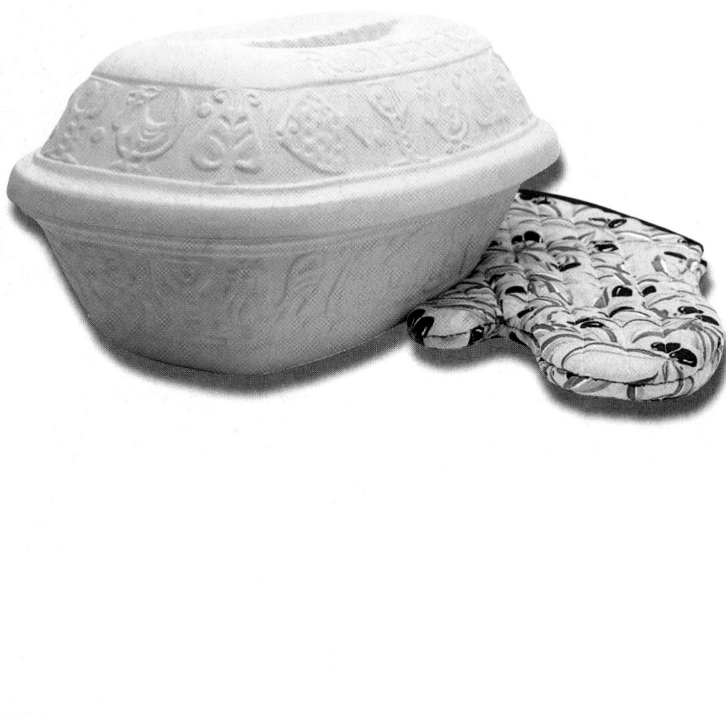

Moist-heat Methods

Cooking methods vary depending on the kind of food being cooked and the results desired. **Moist-heat cooking** includes methods in which food is cooked in hot liquid, steam, or a combination of the two. Moist heat may be used for a number of reasons. Long, slow moist-heat cooking can help tenderize meat. Some foods, such as rice or dry beans, must absorb liquid as they cook.

Section 9-3 Resources

- ◆ **Student Workbook,** pp. 72, 76
- ◆ **Teacher Resource Guide**
  - Lesson Plan 9-3 Organizer
  - Section 9-3 Quiz
- ◆ **Effective Instruction CD-ROM**
  - Exam*View*® *Test Generator*
- ◆ **Student Motivation Kit**
  - Reteaching Activities, pp. 53–54
  - Enrichment Activities
  - Food Science Resources, pp. 66–68

◆ **Moist-heat cooking can produce tender, flavorful one-dish meals. What other types of foods are best cooked with moist heat?**

Sometimes cooking foods together in broth or a sauce helps blend their flavors.

Many cooking appliances, including the microwave and slow cooker, use moist heat. When using a conventional range, you can choose any of these moist-heat methods: boiling, simmering, steaming, and pressure cooking.

Boiling

When a liquid reaches boiling temperature, it forms large bubbles that rise to the surface and break. Water boils at 212°F (100°C). Boiling is suitable for only a few foods, such as corn on the cob and pasta. Many other foods tend to overcook easily or break apart when boiled. Nutrient loss is higher with boiling than with other methods. Boiling also toughens foods high in protein, such as eggs.

When boiling foods, be sure to use a saucepan or pot large enough to hold the food and the boiling liquid. Bring the liquid to the boiling point; then add the food. Be sure the liquid continues boiling as the food cooks.

Boiling is also useful when you want liquid to evaporate quickly. For instance, you might boil a sauce to thicken it or boil a soup to concentrate the flavor.

Simmering

Simmering differs from boiling in that bubbles in the liquid rise gently and just begin to break the surface. Water simmers at about 186°F to 210°F (86°C to 99°C). Simmering is used to cook many types of food, including fruits, vegetables, and less tender cuts of meat and poultry. Some foods that would break apart or toughen if boiled can be successfully simmered. As with boiling, some nutrients, especially water-soluble vitamins, are lost during simmering. For this reason, it is wise to use the cooking liquid from simmered foods, such as vegetables and dry beans, whenever possible.

To simmer food, bring the liquid to a boil and then add the food. After the liquid returns to a boil, reduce the heat so that the food simmers. A slow cooker can also be used to simmer some foods, such as meats and dry beans.

Safety Check

When adding food to boiling liquid, use tongs or a long-handled spoon to hold the food just above the surface of the liquid. Then ease the food in. Dropping the food from high above the liquid can cause the liquid to splash up, resulting in burns.

TEACH

- *Moist-heat Methods (text pages 276-278)*

Discussion Activity

Ask students to explain why boiling is suitable for only a few foods. Ask students to name two foods that can be boiled. Ask students to explain the difference between simmering and boiling.

Using Safety Check

Ask two student volunteers to demonstrate the proper way to use tongs and a long-handled spoon to add raw vegetables to boiling water. Have students discuss the techniques.

Demonstration

Prepare a creamy potato or carrot soup, made with too much liquid. Show students the runny quality of the soup. If possible, have them taste it. Ask them how they would improve the soup quality for a creamy consistency and concentrated flavor. Boil the soup for several minutes until the desired consistency is reached. Show students the creamy quality. If possible, have them taste the flavor-concentrated, creamy soup. Compare the differences with students.

FOOD SCIENCE

Boiling Point and Altitude

Water boils at 212°F at sea level. It boils at a lower temperature at a higher altitude, however. For instance, at an altitude of 7,500 feet, water boils at approximately 198°F. This happens because there is less air pressure to counteract the action of boiling. Since foods boil at a lower temperature at higher altitudes, it will take longer for foods to cook in the boiling water.

TEACH cont.

- *Moist-heat Methods (text pages 276-278)*

Brainstorming Activity

What are the basic differences among the four moist-heat methods of cooking? How would you decide which method to use? Have students brainstorm a list of foods associated with each moist-heat cooking method.

Reading Instructions

Provide students with directions for using a pressure cooker. Have students read the directions. Ask them to make a list of safety precautions for working with pressure cookers. L1

Lab Experience Activity

Divide students into four groups. Provide each group with the same amount of broccoli and general cooking instructions. Have student groups use the moist-heat methods to prepare broccoli to the al dente stage by (1) boiling, (2) simmering, (3) steaming, and (4) pressure cooking. Have all students analyze each group's cooked broccoli for color, texture, and flavor based on the cooking method. Have students compare the results. Which received the highest ratings? Lowest ratings?

FOR YOUR HEALTH

Full Steam Ahead

Steaming not only locks in flavor and nutrients but also is a simple way of cooking certain foods, such as rice, which can become sticky when simmered. Here are some healthful steaming suggestions:

- Steam chunks of boneless chicken breast with broccoli florets, carrot strips, and slices of onion for a nutrient-rich alternative to stir-frying.
- When steaming vegetables or rice, steam them over seasoned, canned chicken or vegetable broth instead of water. This method adds flavor without adding fat.

Following Up

- Experiment with steaming foods that you ordinarily enjoy cooked by other methods. Try different vegetables and vegetable combinations. Introduce any pleasant discoveries to members of your household and ask for their reactions. Write about the experience in your Wellness Journal.

◆ **Steaming foods locks in flavor and nutrients. Can you explain why?**

Two special cooking techniques that make use of simmering are stewing and poaching. **Stewing** involves covering small pieces of food with liquid and then simmering until done. **Poaching** refers to simmering whole foods in a small amount of liquid until done. Eggs, fish, and whole fruits can be poached.

Steaming

Steaming is a method of cooking food over, but not in, boiling water. The food is usually placed in a steamer basket that fits inside a saucepan. Steam is created by a small amount of boiling water in the bottom of the pan. The boiling water does not come in contact with the food. The pan is covered during cooking to trap the steam. You can also use an electric steamer to cook food.

Many foods can be cooked in steam, including vegetables and fish. Foods retain their color, shape, and flavor well when steamed. Few nutrients are lost. Cooking time is longer with steaming than with boiling or simmering.

Pressure Cooking

A pressure cooker cooks food in steam under pressure. Because pressure makes temperatures above 212°F (100°C) possible, the food cooks 3 to 10 times faster than with other methods.

A pressure cooker is best used with foods that take a long time to cook. Examples are less tender cuts of meat and poultry, dry beans, soups, one-dish meals, and vegetables. This method has all the advantages of steaming plus faster cooking times. Follow the manufacturer's directions and accident prevention guidelines carefully. The food in a pressure cooker is superheated and under high pressure.

Extending Learning

Pressure Cookers—Since atmospheric pressure affects the boiling point of water, the higher the pressure, the hotter water will get before it starts to boil. The lid of a pressure cooker is tightly sealed to trap steam, creating high pressure. The rise in pressure causes the boiling point of water to rise. The temperature of the water goes up, and food cooks faster.

Dry-heat Methods

Dry-heat cooking means cooking food uncovered without added liquid or fat. Dry-heat methods include roasting and baking, broiling, and pan-broiling.

Roasting and Baking

Roasting and baking both involve cooking food uncovered in a conventional or convection oven. *Roasting* generally refers to cooking large, tender cuts of meat or poultry. *Baking* is the term used with foods such as breads, cookies, vegetables, and casseroles, though some meat, poultry, and fish preparations are also baked. Baked ham and baked chicken are examples.

Roasting gives tender meat and poultry a flavorful, crispy, brown crust. Use a shallow, uncovered roasting pan with a rack. The roasting rack allows fat to drain away from the food—a real benefit for those trying to reduce their fat intake.

For baked goods such as breads, cookies, and cakes, preheating is important. **Preheating** means turning the oven on about 10 minutes before using it so that it will be at the desired temperature when the food is placed inside.

CLOSE-UP ON SCIENCE: CHEMISTRY

The Maillard Reaction

Food cooked in dry heat or in fat goes through a browning process. As food browns, the color, flavor, and texture are altered as the result of complex chemical changes. One of these changes is the Maillard reaction. It occurs when carbohydrates (either sugar or starch) and amino acids combine on the surface of a food such as roasting meat. The reaction occurs only at temperatures over 300°F (150°C). The surface of the food cooked in dry heat or in fat reaches that temperature. With moist heat, the cooking temperature is limited to the boiling point of water, 212°F (100°C). That is why foods cooked in moist heat don't brown.

◆ **Roasting and baking are dry-heat cooking methods. Name two more foods that would be cooked using these methods.**

- *Dry-heat Methods (text pages 279-282)*

Discussion Activity

Ask students to describe the proper method for roasting meat and poultry. Ask students to define "preheating" and to explain why preheating is important when baking breads and cakes.

Lab Experience

Provide students with raw chicken breasts. Ask each group of students to prepare the chicken breasts—half roasted in an oven and the other half grilled or pan-broiled. Have students compare their end results, including the effect of the Maillard reaction on color, flavor, and texture. Was one method preferred over the other? Why? L3

USING THE CLOSE-UP ON SCIENCE: CHEMISTRY

Provide students with meat, poultry, and fish recipes. Ask students to determine in which recipes the Maillard reaction will occur. Have students discuss their results in class. If there is time, prepare one of the recipes, that is roasted or baked, for a demonstration in which the Maillard reaction occurs.

Extending Learning

Cooking in a Plastic Bag—Plastic cooking bags are made specifically for cooking. It is not necessary to brown meat or poultry before placing it in a cooking bag.

Place the food in a plastic cooking bag, along with a small amount of liquid. Vegetables may be added, depending on the recipe. Close the bag and place it in a baking pan large enough to hold it. Cut slits in the bag to allow steam to escape. Follow manufacturer's directions carefully when using a plastic cooking bag.

TEACH cont.

- ***Dry-heat Methods (text pages 279-282)***

Demonstration

Demonstrate how to set the oven correctly. Discuss the importance of preheating the oven for baked goods. Show correct placement of pans in the oven, based on the diagram on page 280. Emphasize the importance of air circulation for proper baking.

Discussion Activity

Talk about how broiling and pan broiling differ from roasting and baking. Encourage discussion of nutritional advantages of all these dry-heat cooking methods. Also encourage discussion of safety precautions when broiling and pan broiling to prevent grease fires.

Developing Instructions

Have students develop an instruction sheet for pan placement in the oven. Encourage students to design a format (such as boxed and numbered) for their instruction sheet using the computer. Suggest students take the instruction sheet home to be followed when using the oven at home. L1

Pan Placement in the Oven

When baking, placement and spacing of pans are important. The pans must be placed so the hot air in the oven can circulate freely. If pans touch each other or the oven walls, they create a hot spot—an area of concentrated heat. The food overcooks in these areas. When baking several pans of food at one time, place them diagonally opposite one another, as shown here.

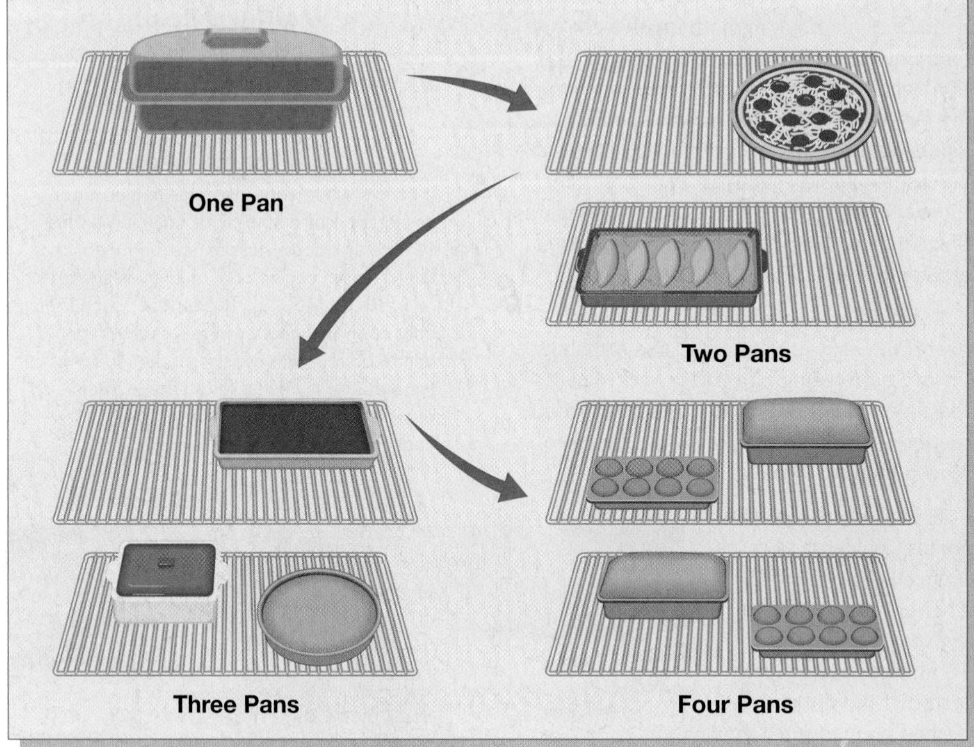

It is also important to place pans in such a way that the hot air in the oven can circulate freely. If pans touch each other or the oven walls, they create a **hot spot**—an area of concentrated heat—that can cause the food to overcook. When baking several pans of food at one time, place them diagonally opposite one another.

HOME & COMMUNITY CONNECTION

Using the "Pan Placement in the Oven" boxed information on page 280, have students quiz their family members, relatives, or neighbors on pan placement for one, two, three, and four pans. Ask students to discuss results in class. Who quizzed somebody that missed at least one placement? Which placement was most commonly done incorrectly? Encourage students to make sure those whom they quizzed understand all four appropriate placements.

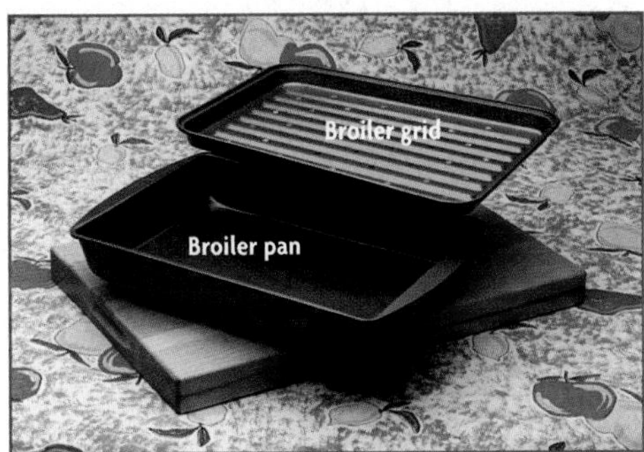

◆ **A broiler pan consists of two parts that fit together. What makes broiling a low-fat cooking method?**

Broiling

Broiling refers to cooking food under direct heat. The broiler pan is placed below a burner or heating element. The heat radiates down onto the food, cooking it quickly.

Broiling works well with tender cuts of meat and poultry as well as fish, fruits, and some vegetables. Foods that are already cooked may be broiled for a short time to brown them. Broiling may also be used to melt cheese toppings.

A broiler pan has two parts. A slotted grid holds the food. The grid fits on top of a shallow pan that catches drippings. This allows fat to drain away during cooking.

For broiling in most ranges, set the oven control on "broil." You can't control the broiling temperature. To control the cooking, you can vary the distance of the pan from the heat source and the cooking time. For thicker foods, position the pan farther from the heat and increase the cooking time. This allows the food to cook all the way through without burning on the outside. Check a cookbook for guidelines about positioning specific foods for broiling.

Outdoor cooking on a grill or spit is similar to broiling except that the heat source is below the food. The food is placed on a wire grid.

INFOLINK

For more on outdoor cooking methods and how to perform them safely, see Section 24-4.

Q&A

What are some tips to help me broil successfully?

Pat meat and poultry dry. Moisture can keep food from becoming brown and crisp. Don't salt foods before broiling. Salt draws moisture from foods, causing them to dry out. Brush fish, fruit, and vegetables lightly with oil or melted butter or margarine to keep them from charring. To prevent foods from sticking, always start with a cold broiler pan. Use tongs, not a fork. The fork pierces the food, making holes that allow juices to escape.

Safety Check

Never cover the broiler grid with foil. Foil keeps drippings from falling through, which could cause a grease fire.

Never put your hands into the broiler compartment to turn or remove food. The intense heat can cause severe burns. Instead, take the broiler pan from the compartment first. Remember to use potholders or oven mitts. Put the pan on a heatproof surface or wire rack; then turn or remove the food.

- *Dry-heat Methods (text pages 279-282)*

USING Safety Check

Ask students to suggest other safety tips for broiling foods. Remind students that foods that contain a large amount of fat may spatter grease as you are removing the food from the oven and even after you place it on the wire rack or heatproof surface.

Poster Project

Using the Q & A on page 281, have students create a poster depicting tips, in an illustrated format, for successful broiling. If desired, hang the posters around the classroom until this chapter is completed. Afterwards, encourage students to use their illustrated posters at home when broiling. **L1**

Recipe Comparisons

Have students locate recipes for preparing food by one of the dry-heat methods. Collect several select recipes into a multi-page document. Give each student a copy, then ask all students to review the recipes for class discussion. Discussion can include:

Which recipes use the cooking method of broiling? Pan-broiling? Baking? Roasting?

Which recipes will undergo the Maillard reaction? **L2**

Extending Learning

Cooking in Fats—Low-fat recipes sometimes recommend the use of a liquid for sautéing food rather than a small amount of fat. One purpose of sautéing is to brown the food to develop the flavor. The liquid substituted for the fat will not allow the food to reach a high enough temperature for proper browning to take place. Instead, the food will steam. Once the liquid evaporates, the food may begin to burn. A better low-fat alternative is using nonstick cooking spray and a skillet with a nonstick finish.

TEACH cont.

- *Frying*
- *Combination Methods (text pages 282-283)*

Discussion Activity

Ask students to list and describe the three basic methods of frying. Can fried foods fit into a healthy eating plan? How? Ask students to explain the combination methods of braising and stir-frying. Why might someone choose to braise a cut of meat? Stir-fry a cut of meat?

Categorizing Activity

Have students form a brainstorming group in an effort to list as many foods as possible that typically use the dry-heat methods of sautéing, pan-frying, deep-fat frying, braising, and stir-frying. Ask students why each one of these methods are chosen for the mentioned foods.

Student Reports

Have students investigate and write a short report on the smoke point, flash point, and fire point of different oils. What happens to the smoke point after the oil is used? **L1**

Finding Recipes

Have students look for recipes that utilize combination methods. Have students study the recipes to determine which combination methods are used for each? Have students draw conclusions. **L2**

Pan-Broiling

Pan-broiling is a range-top method of dry-heat cooking. Foods such as hamburgers, tender cuts of steak, and some cuts of pork may be pan-broiled. The food cooks quickly and retains a minimum amount of fat.

To pan-broil, cook the food in a heavy skillet over medium heat. Don't add fat. As fat accumulates in the pan during cooking, pour it off or remove it with a baster.

Frying

Frying involves cooking food in oil or melted fat. Here are several different methods:

- **Sautéing.** To **sauté** (saw-TAY) means to brown or cook foods in a skillet with a small amount of fat. Low to medium heat is used. This method is often used for chopped vegetables, such as onions and peppers, and small pieces of meat and fish.
- **Pan-frying.** Pan-frying is similar to sautéing but usually involves larger pieces of meat, poultry, or fish. The food may need to be turned several times during the cooking process for complete, even cooking. Pan-frying is often used to brown meat before cooking it in moist heat.
- **Deep-fat frying.** This method is also called "french frying." Food is immersed in hot fat and cooked until done. This method is used for tender foods, such as vegetables, and some breads, such as doughnuts. For best deep-fat frying results, use a deep-fat thermometer to keep the fat at the correct temperature.

Note that every fat has a **smoking point**—a temperature at which fats begin to give off irritating smoke and break down chemically. Oil that has reached its smoking point is no longer good for cooking. Animal fats, such as butter and lard, have low smoking points. Safflower, soybean, corn, and peanut oils have relatively high smoking points. They make the best choices for frying.

Combination Methods

Sometimes the best way to cook a food is by a combination of methods. Braising and stir-frying are two popular cooking methods that combine dry-heat and moist-heat cooking.

Braising

Braising combines browning food (frying) with a long period of simmering to tenderize the food and enhance the flavor. It is often used for large, less tender cuts of meat and poultry.

Use a Dutch oven or other heavy pot with a tight-fitting cover. Brown the food first on all sides. Then add seasonings and a small amount of liquid to the food and cover the pot. The cooking may be completed in the oven (usually at 350°F or 180°C) or on top of the range. Vegetables are sometimes added to braised meat or poultry near the end of the cooking time.

Safety Check

When frying, don't overheat the fat or oil. It could catch fire.

Be sure the food to be fried is dry. Moisture could cause the fat or oil to spatter and burn you. Be prepared to act quickly in case of a grease fire. Have a fire extinguisher handy.

FOOD SCIENCE

Frying Temperatures Have students research and/or test the effect of cooking temperature on deep-fat fried foods. What happens when you fry foods at the proper temperature? What if the oil temperature is too low? What if the oil temperature is too high?

◆ **Braising combines frying and moist-heat cooking. What is another combination method of cooking?**

Stir-Frying

Stir-frying also combines frying and moist-heat cooking. In this method, small pieces of food are fried quickly in a small amount of oil at high heat. Stir the food constantly to keep it from sticking to the pan. During the last few minutes of cooking, add a small amount of liquid to the food and cover the pan, allowing the food to steam briefly.

Stir-frying, which began in Asia, is most often used for cooking mixtures of vegetables and other foods. A special bowl-shaped pan called a **wok** is traditionally used, but a skillet also works well.

Section 9-3 Review & Activities

1. What are three basic categories of cooking methods? Which could you use to make meat more tender? Which could you use to brown meat?
2. List the methods of dry-heat cooking.
3. Name and describe three methods of frying.
4. Rank these cooking methods according to how well they retain nutrients in food: frying, simmering, pressure cooking, roasting, boiling, steaming.
5. **Evaluating.** Woks, commonly used in Eastern cultures, have become very popular with cooks in the West in recent decades. Explain this from both a cultural and nutritional standpoint.
6. **Synthesizing.** Raina would like to cut down on the amount of fat in the foods her family eats but hesitates to give up on cooking the fried foods the family enjoys. What recommendations can you make for a healthy compromise?
7. **Applying.** Find several recipes for the following: eggs for breakfast, a vegetable side dish, a ground beef dish, soup, and chicken. What basic cooking method does each recipe use?
8. **Applying.** Demonstrate for the class how you would use a pressure cooker to prepare dry beans for a dish. Explain the steps involved, providing details and including safety information.

ASSESS

REVIEW

- Ask students to summarize the main ideas in this section.
- Have students complete the Section Review. (Answers appear below.)

EVALUATION

- Ask students to make a chart describing different methods of cooking using moist heat, dry heat, and frying.
- Have students take the quiz for Section 9-3. (Use the quiz in the *Teacher Resource Guide,* or construct your own with the **Exam***View*® *Test Generator* on the *Effective Instruction CD-ROM.*)

RETEACHING

- Show students several pictures of foods that were obviously cooked using one of the methods mentioned in this chapter. Have students identify the method used to prepare each food.
- Refer to the *Reteaching Activities* booklet for the Section 9-3 activity sheet.

CLOSE

Lead a discussion about the various methods of conventional cooking. Ask students to do a 24-hour eating plan recall. Have student volunteers determine which (if any) of the conventional cooking methods were used to prepare their food choices.

Answers to Section 9-3 Review & Activities

1. Moist heat, dry heat, and frying; moist heat; frying.
2. Roasting, baking, broiling, and pan broiling.
3. See bulleted list on page 282.
4. Possible ranking: steaming, pressure cooking, roasting, simmering, frying, boiling.
5. Answers will vary. Possible answer: Culturally, nations are less isolated and more diverse; nutritionally, stir-frying uses very little fat and preserves more nutrients in the food.
6. Answers will vary.
7. Answers will vary.
8. Demonstrations should reflect safe procedures.

SECTION 9-4

Microwave Cooking Techniques

FOCUS

MOTIVATORS

- Ask students how many have used microwave ovens. Where have they used them? What foods have students cooked in them? What do students perceive as their advantages and disadvantages?
- Show two examples of banana bread or another quick bread—one baked in a conventional oven and the other baked in a microwave oven. Ask students to identify which bread was baked in which oven? Have them explain their answers. Have students taste the two samples and compare. Which sample do they prefer?

VOCABULARY ACTIVITY

Pronounce the terms listed under "Look for These Terms." Have students find the terms and their definitions in the section.

STUDY SKILLS

- **Outlining.** Have students read the section and outline it by copying the headers on paper and leaving space after each one. Students are to write a sentence in their own words, summarizing the content under each header.
- Have students read the section and complete the appropriate part of the Chapter 9 Study Guide in the *Student Workbook.*

SECTION 9-4

Microwave Cooking Techniques

Objectives

After studying this section, you should be able to:

- Explain why the choice of power setting, foods for cooking, and cookware are important in microwave cooking.
- Describe the techniques necessary for successful microwaving.
- Identify safety precautions for microwave oven use.

Look for These Terms

watts

arcing

standing time

Tori put a dish of leftovers in the microwave and punched in the time and power setting. In two minutes she had a hot, nutritious meal. "What did people do before the microwave was invented?" she said to herself as she sat down to eat.

Microwave Oven Basics

Microwaving is a fast, healthful way to cook. Food cooks quickly with less fat and liquid than in most conventional methods. That means more of the water-soluble vitamins are retained, and fewer vitamins are destroyed by heat.

Microwave cooking isn't complicated, but it is different from conventional cooking methods. Start by reading the owner's manual. It will give specific directions for using your microwave oven. It will also help you understand how the microwave power settings work, the kinds of foods that can be microwaved, and the proper equipment to use.

Power Settings

When you cook foods in a microwave oven, you have to choose the power setting. The equation between power setting and the speed with which you get your food to the table is a simple one: The higher the power setting, the faster the cooking.

On some microwave ovens the power setting is identified as a percentage, such as 50 or 100 percent power. On others it is a

Section 9-4 Resources

◆ **Student Workbook,** pp. 72, 78
◆ **Teacher Resource Guide**
Lesson Plan 9-4 Organizer
Section 9-4 Quiz
Chapter 9 Test
◆ **Effective Instruction CD-ROM**
Exam*View*® *Test Generator*

◆ **Student Motivation Kit**
Reteaching Activities, pp. 55–56
Enrichment Activities
Foods Lab Resources, pp. 43–44

description—for example, "low" or "medium." The chart below gives typical equivalents for these two kinds of power settings. Because microwave ovens do differ, be sure to check your owner's manual for information on power settings.

Microwave Power Levels

Description	Percentage of Power
High	100
Medium-High	70
Medium	50
Medium-Low	30
Low	10

Safety Check

Standards for microwave ovens require at least two independent interlock systems. Each of these systems stops the production of microwaves the moment the latch is released or the door is opened. If an interlock system fails, a monitoring system stops the oven. Don't operate the oven if the door is bent, the latches are broken or loosened, or the door seals are damaged.

Microwave ovens vary in the amount of microwaves they produce at each setting because they have different power ratings. These ratings are based on units of electrical power called **watts**. The higher the oven wattage, the more microwaves it produces at various settings. Compact models produce about 600 to 700 watts. Midsize and large models produce between 800 and 1,000 watts. You'll usually find the wattage rating on the back of the oven, along with the serial and model numbers.

◆ **Microwaves produced by the magnetron hit the walls and bounce back to the food. Which foods microwave successfully? Which do not?**

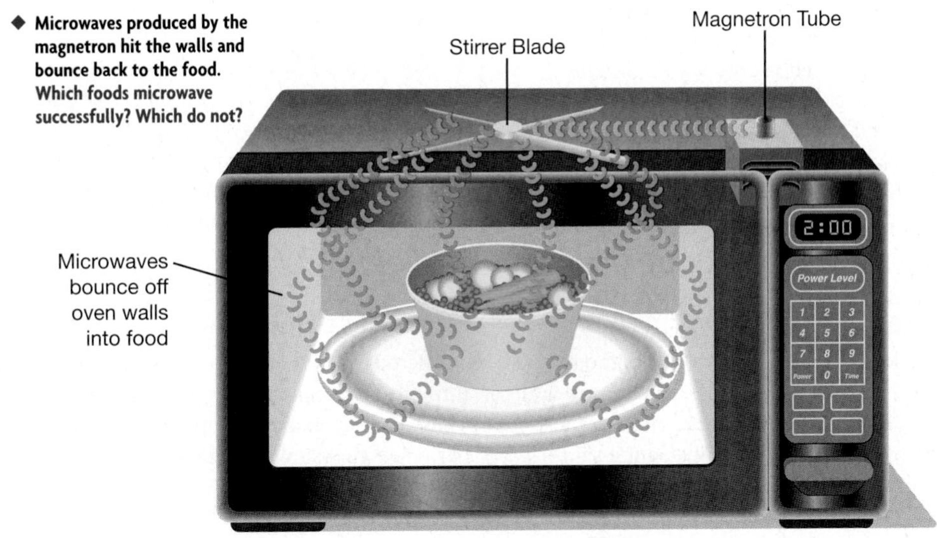

Microwave Oven

TEACH

- *Microwave Oven Basics (text pages 284-287)*

Discussion Activity

Ask students to explain how the power setting affects cooking in a microwave oven. Ask students to explain why some microwaves produce more microwaves than others at the same power setting.

Ad-Reading Activity

Provide students with microwave oven ads (or descriptions). Have students read the ads to determine the range of wattage available. Discuss how the wattage of the microwave oven affects cooking times.

Finding Recipes

Provide students with cookbooks. Make sure that the cookbooks contain recipes with both microwave and conventional recipes. Have students find a recipe that gives directions for conventional cooking and microwave cooking. Have students write a brief report on the differences between the two methods and potential differences between the prepared recipe results. Ask a few student volunteers to share their recipe findings in class. L1

FOOD SCIENCE

Nutrient Retention and Microwaving

In general, there is less nutrient loss in foods cooked in a microwave oven than in those cooked conventionally. Fewer heat-sensitive nutrients are destroyed due to shorter microwave cooking times. Because less liquid is needed in many microwave recipes, there is less chance for water-soluble nutrients to dissolve in liquid. Have interested students research scientific studies of nutrient loss percentage for food prepared in the microwave compared to food prepared by other methods, including the conventional oven.

TEACH cont.

- *Microwave Oven Basics (text pages 284-287)*

Comparisons Activity

Discuss the advantages and disadvantages of cooking various foods in the microwave oven. Which foods cook faster? Which require as much time as by conventional methods? Which foods produce high quality results? Which are less satisfactory when cooked in the microwave?

Chart Making

Have students make a chart showing the effects of food's composition, including the "Other Factors" listed on page 286, on the way it cooks in the microwave. Encourage students to prepare their charts using a computer software program. Allow time for students to share and compare charts. **L1**

Lab Experience

1. Provide student groups with four large baking potatoes each.
2. Have students cut potatoes, using proper cutting techniques, into various sizes and shapes.
3. Have them microwave the pieces of potato on High, rotating frequently and checking frequently to see whether the pieces are done.
4. Ask students to draw conclusions. Which piece was done first? Last? Why? **L1**

How Microwaves Cook

Microwaves cook by making food molecules vibrate. The microwaves penetrate food to a depth of about 1½ inches (3.8 cm). There, they agitate food molecules and produce heat. If the food is thicker, conduction moves the heat deeper into the food and eventually cooks it throughout.

Microwave cooking is a better choice for some foods than others. Generally, the best choices are foods that are moist to begin with or that can be cooked in moist heat.

Food Composition

A food's composition—what it is made of—affects the way it cooks in the microwave. Foods high in water, such as vegetables, will cook faster than foods with a lower water content, such as meat.

Fat, sugar, and salt also attract microwaves; however, you must be careful when heating these items. Concentrations of fat or sugar can create hot spots when exposed to microwaves. If you microwave a jelly doughnut, for example, the jelly will be superheated while the doughnut itself is only warm. Serious burns on the skin or mouth could result. Food under salted areas will cook faster than that under unsalted areas. Therefore, don't sprinkle salt on food before microwaving—wait until after cooking.

Some foods—pasta and rice, for example—need time to absorb liquids as they cook. As a result, no real time is saved when cooking such foods in the microwave. Other foods, such as potatoes and winter squash, have a tough skin that keeps moisture from evaporating. Steam can build up inside the skin and cause the food to burst. Pierce foods like these with a fork to allow steam to escape. For the same reason, do not cook eggs in the shell in the microwave oven—they will burst.

Other Factors

Here are some additional principles to guide you in microwave cooking:

- **Food density.** The heavier a food feels for its size, the more dense it is. For example, a slice of bread is less dense than a slice of meat the same size. The denser a food, the longer the cooking time.
- **Shape and size of food.** Foods of a uniform thickness cook most evenly. If foods are unevenly shaped, the thinner parts will cook through before the thicker parts. Small pieces cook faster than large ones.
- **Starting temperature of food.** The colder the food is to start with, the longer it will take to cook. Thaw most frozen foods, except vegetables, before microwaving. For commercially frozen foods, follow package directions.
- **Amount of food.** The more food you're cooking, the longer it will take. The same number of microwaves are produced no matter how much food you put in the oven. One potato cooks quickly, but cooking four potatoes takes longer because they must share the microwaves.

Microwave Cookware

Microwaves are reflected by metal but pass through glass, plastic, and paper materials. These characteristics are important to remember when choosing and using containers for microwave cooking.

Extending Learning

Microwaves—Dr. Percy L. Spencer, of Massachusetts, experimented with radar in 1945. Noticing that a chocolate bar in his pocket melted, he wondered if microwave energy could be used for cooking. He popped corn with microwaves and filed a patent for a microwave oven in 1945. At first, microwave ovens were large and expensive. By 1967, they were modified, becoming practical for consumers. Microwave ovens are now a major appliance. Have a few students research this topic and develop a timeline.

Metal and foil are not generally used in microwave ovens. They can cause **arcing**, electrical sparks that can damage the oven or start a fire. Use metal and foil only if your owner's manual specifies. Never leave metal tools, such as a spoon, in any food being microwaved.

Some general guidelines for choosing containers for microwave cooking follow. Some containers that cannot withstand high cooking temperatures are safe for heating foods at lower temperatures.

- **Glass and glass-ceramic.** Use oven-proof glass and glass-ceramic for cooking. Regular glass may be suitable for heating.
- **Stoneware, china, and pottery.** Most items are suitable for cooking unless they have metal trim. Avoid pottery with metallic glazes.
- **Plastic.** For cooking, use only plastic items that are marked "microwave-safe." Some special plastics can be used both in the microwave and at low to moderate temperatures in conventional ovens.
- **Paper.** Use paper plates only if they are firm enough to hold food. Choose paper towels labeled "microwave-safe." Avoid products containing recycled paper. They may contain metal fragments or chemicals that could catch fire.

The size and shape of microwave cookware also affects the way food cooks and the cooking time. Pans should be shallow with straight sides. Round pans allow for even cooking. Square and rectangular pans should have rounded corners.

◆ **Be sure to choose cookware that can safely be used in a microwave oven. What are some types that would not be suitable?**

Q *If a glass or pottery container isn't marked "microwave-safe," how can I tell whether or not I can use it for microwave cooking?*

A Here's a simple test: Fill a glass measuring cup with water and place it in the oven next to the empty container you're testing. Heat for 2 minutes at 100 percent power. If the empty container is too hot to touch, don't use it in the microwave oven.

- *Microwave Oven Basics (text pages 284-287)*

Display Activity

Prepare a display of cooking containers. Ask students to sort the containers into two groups: those that can be used safely in the microwave oven and those that cannot. Summarize characteristics of microwave safe containers. Explain why metal causes arcing in a microwave oven.

Analysis Activity

Discuss how type of food and cooking time may affect the choice of container for microwaving. Refer students back to the "Materials Used for Cookware" chart on pages 266-267.

Using 

Provide a couple of student volunteers two containers without "microwave-safe" marking. One should be microwave safe and the other not. Have the two students follow the instructions given on page 287 to test the containers to determine whether they can be used safely in a microwave oven. Ask them to show and explain results to the class. Discuss what conclusions can be drawn from their findings.

Extending Learning

Containers—The shape of the container is important in microwaving cooking:

- A ring shape is most efficient because microwaves enter the food from any angle. The result is faster, with more even cooking. This shape is recommended for foods that cannot be stirred during cooking. A round or oval shape ranks next.
- Containers should have vertical rather than slanted sides. If the sides slope, some of the food is more shallow than the rest. Therefore, it receives more microwaves and may overcook.

- *Microwaving Successfully (text pages 288-289)*

Student Demonstrations

Provide a group of student volunteers with several foods to be microwaved at one time. Ask students to demonstrate proper food placement and proper food covering in the microwave oven. Encourage class discussion. L1

Display Activity

Set up a display of coverings, some microwavable and some not. Ask students to suggest which coverings are appropriate in a microwave oven and why.

Demonstration

Microwave two portions of a food, covering one with microwavable plastic wrap and the other with plastic wrap not suitable for use in the microwave. What happens to each type of plastic wrap? Have students write a paragraph explaining their conclusions.

COMPUTER ACTIVITY
Creating a Brochure

Invite students to prepare a brochure explaining and illustrating techniques for successful microwave cooking. The brochures may be run-off on the classroom or a home computer, using either word-processing or desktop publishing software. Students may illustrate their brochures with original or computer art.

Microwaving Successfully

A few special techniques are needed in microwave cooking. They involve placing food in the oven and in the pan, covering, stirring, rotating, turning, and timing.

Food Placement

When he's in a hurry for a meal, Beau usually tosses a few leftovers into the microwave. He's often annoyed to find that one or more of the foods hasn't heated through. How you place food in a microwave is a factor in successful heating and cooking.

The best arrangement of food for microwaving is a ring shape. This allows microwaves to enter food from as many sides as possible.

◆ **For even cooking, arrange foods for microwaving with the thickest or toughest parts toward the outside. Explain the reasons for this instruction.**

A meatloaf can be shaped into a ring in a pan or cooked in a ring mold.

When possible, leave space between pieces of food to allow better microwave penetration.

When cooking foods of uneven thickness, use the characteristics of microwave patterns to your advantage. Food in the center of the oven cooks more slowly. Arrange food like the spokes of a wheel, with the thickest or toughest parts toward the outside and the thinnest or most tender parts toward the center. With broccoli spears, for example, place the tops toward the center and the stalks toward the outside.

Covering Food

A cover holds in steam, keeps foods moist, and shortens cooking time. It also keeps food from spattering in the oven.

Foods you would cover for conventional cooking are usually covered for microwave cooking. If you want foods to steam, cover them tightly. For drier foods, cover loosely.

Foods may be covered with microwave-safe glass or plastic covers. An inverted plate is another option. Here are still other options:

- **Waxed paper and cooking parchment.** Waxed paper and cooking parchment prevent spatters and allow some steam and moisture to escape. Use them on foods such as casseroles.
- **Paper towels.** Paper towels absorb excess moisture and prevent spatters. Wrap rolls, breads, and sandwiches in paper towels before microwaving to keep them from becoming soggy.

When you remove covers or inverted plates, use a potholder or an oven mitt. Tilt the cover away from you to prevent the escaping steam from causing burns.

Reinforcing Key Skills

Present the following problems to student groups. Allow time for them to discuss and compare their responses.

Management—Why it is sometimes necessary to make adjustments to the cooking time recommended in a microwave cookbook?

Communication—You see a family member covering food to be microwaved with plastic wrap that's not microwave safe. What do you say?

◆ In microwaves not equipped with turntables, it is important to rotate foods a half turn so they cook more evenly. What other measures can you take to ensure that microwave foods cook evenly?

Stirring, Rotating, and Turning

Microwaves may not be distributed evenly throughout the oven, especially in older models. To be sure that food cooks as evenly as possible, stir, rotate, or turn it during cooking. Unless directed otherwise, stir or turn foods after half the cooking time.

Stirring helps foods cook evenly. If the food can't be stirred, rotate the pan. To rotate, use a potholder to grasp the pan and give it a half turn. Dense foods such as meat and poultry should also be turned over. Use tongs to turn foods over.

Most newer ovens have turntables that rotate the food as it cooks. Follow directions in the owner's manual.

Determining Cooking Time

Microwave cooking has two parts. The first part occurs when the oven is on and microwaves are being produced. After the oven turns off, the heat trapped inside the food continues cooking it. This period during which heat buildup in a microwaved food completes its cooking is called **standing time**. Microwave recipes give directions for both cooking and standing time. If you cooked the food uncovered, cover it during standing time to retain heat.

Check a food's progress as it cooks. Test food for doneness after the standing time, not before. Avoid overcooking. Foods overcooked in the microwave oven become hard and tough.

Food will cook slightly faster in higher-wattage ovens. Some ovens have sensors that will turn the oven off when the food is done.

Even with turntables, microwave ovens may not cook evenly. To be sure microwaved foods such as meat, poultry, fish, and casseroles are thoroughly cooked, use an instant-read thermometer at the end of cooking and standing times. Insert the thermometer in several different areas to be sure the food is evenly done.

- *Microwaving Successfully (text pages 288-289)*

Demonstration

Microwave two small glass bowls of green vegetables for the time suggested in the instruction book. At the end of microwave time, have students observe one bowl and evaluate for color, degree of doneness, and texture. At the end of standing time, have students observe and evaluate the other bowl. What effect did standing time have upon the vegetables?

Student Lab Demonstration

Provide three student groups with directions and ingredients for microwaving scrambled eggs. Have one group follow the recipe, but not stir or rotate the eggs during microwaving. Have the second group follow the exact directions. Have the third group overcook the eggs by 60 seconds. Have students display all finished products in the front of the classroom. Ask a representative from each group to show and describe results to the class. Encourage students to draw conclusions. L2

Reinforcing Key Skills

Present the following problems to student groups. Allow time for them to discuss and compare their responses.

Management—Have students explain why seasoning should be reduced in adapting a recipe to microwave cooking.

Directed Thinking—You accidentally throw away the owner's manual to your new microwave before you have a chance to read it. What action do you take?

TEACH cont.

- *Microwave Recipes*
- *Microwave Care and Accident Prevention (text pages 290-291)*

Checklists

Have students develop a checklist of safety rules for microwave cooking. Have students use the checklist to examine accident prevention during microwave use at home and in foods lab. Any improper use should be shared with family members at home. L1

Safety Campaign

After reading the section "Microwave Care and Accident Prevention," have students consider how they might go about raising awareness of microwave oven accident prevention. In small groups, have students identify a target audience and/or safety concern, then develop a plan to increase awareness. L3

Supermarket Survey

Have students visit one supermarket and record the name and type of at least five food products that provide both conventional and microwave preparation instructions. How do the ingredients and cooking times vary? Permit time for them to discuss and compare their findings. L1

Sometimes people in my family use margarine tubs to heat foods in the microwave. Is that okay?

This is not a good idea. Cold storage containers like these can melt from the hot food. That can cause chemicals from the container to transfer to the food. The person who eats the food could be consuming harmful substances. For this reason, it is best to store cold foods in margarine containers but not use them for reheating. Stick to "microwave-safe."

Microwave Recipes

Amanda has a favorite recipe for chicken with orange sauce, but it takes so long to prepare that she seldom uses it. She'd love to be able to use the microwave instead of a conventional oven.

Adapting a standard recipe for cooking in the microwave oven works best if you can find a similar microwave recipe. A basic microwave cookbook can help you ease into microwave cooking successfully. With experience, you can begin experimenting.

A well-written microwave recipe has the same features as a conventional recipe. In addition, it specifies:

- The size and shape of the cooking container.
- How to arrange food for even cooking.
- Whether or not to cover the dish.
- A range of cooking and standing times.

Microwave Care and Accident Prevention

Accident prevention rules for conventional cooking also apply to microwave cooking. Here are some additional microwave accident prevention rules:

- Never turn on the oven unless there's food in it. You could damage the oven.
- Follow the manufacturer's directions for preparing commercially frozen foods in the microwave oven. Don't eat the food if the package turns brown. Don't reuse containers.
- Loosen tight-fitting covers or caps before microwaving. Otherwise, a buildup of steam pressure could cause the container to explode.
- Never attach kitchen magnets to the microwave oven. They can affect the electronic controls.
- Have your microwave oven tested by an authorized repairperson if you're concerned about microwaves leaking from the oven. Microwave leakage meters available for home use are often not reliable.

Safety Check

Foods that are cooked or heated in a microwave oven can have "cold spots" as well as "hot spots." When microwaves enter the food irregularly, the food may not cook or heat evenly. Where the food stays cooler, bacteria could survive and cause foodborne illness when the food is eaten. This is the safety reason for stirring or rotating foods as they cook or heat.

FOOD SCIENCE

Vegetable Cooking Experiment

See the *Food Science Resources* booklet for the "Cooking Vegetables by Conventional and Microwave Methods" teaching guide and student experiment worksheet. The experiment compares the effect of conventional and microwave cooking on fresh broccoli.

Cleaning the Microwave Oven

Clean spots and spills after every use. If allowed to build up, they will absorb microwaves and cut down on the cooking power. Keep the door seal clean. Spilled food also allows bacteria to grow.

To clean the interior of the oven, wipe it with a clean, wet dishcloth. Dry it thoroughly. Don't use abrasive cleaners.

INFOLINK

For more on preventing kitchen accidents, see Section 7-2.

Section 9-4 Review & Activities

1. Describe the factors involved in the choice of power setting, foods for cooking, and cookware.
2. What is the purpose of stirring, rotating, and turning food during cooking?
3. Give three guidelines for accident prevention when using a microwave oven.
4. **Synthesizing.** Many families limit their use of microwave ovens to thawing frozen foods and heating leftovers. Why do you think more people don't use the microwave oven for other types of cooking?
5. **Analyzing.** You have been asked to create an advertising campaign for a line of microwave ovens. Write three persuasive facts about microwave cooking that might lead a consumer to consider buying a microwave oven.
6. **Applying.** Check plastic containers, tools, and cookware in the foods lab. Which items are marked "microwave-safe"?

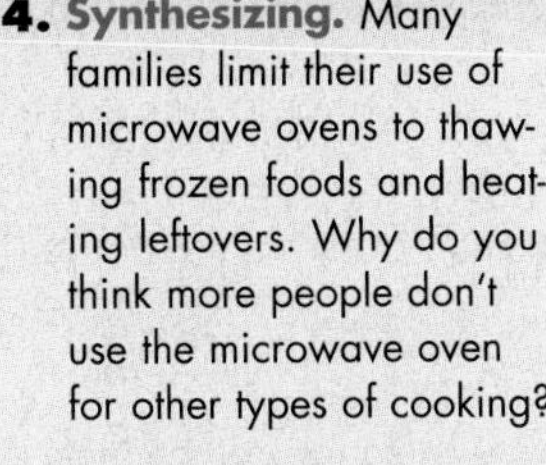

ASSESS

REVIEW

- Ask students to summarize the main ideas in this section.
- Have students complete the Section Review. (Answers appear below.)

EVALUATION

- Ask students to prepare a written summary of rules to follow when cooking in a microwave oven.
- Have students take the quiz for Section 9-4. (Use the quiz in the *Teacher Resource Guide,* or construct your own with the **Exam***View*® *Test Generator* on the *Effective Instruction CD-ROM.*)

RETEACHING

- Divide students into groups and assign one or more specific foods to each group. Have the groups review a microwave cookbook and report to the class how much microwave time and standing time is needed to cook each assigned food.
- Refer to the *Reteaching Activities* booklet for the Section 9-4 activity sheet.

CLOSE

Lead the class in the development of a step-by-step instruction sheet on properly using a microwave.

Answers to Section 9-4 Review & Activities

1. Power setting determines the speed of cooking time; some foods don't cook well in a microwave; not all cookware is appropriate for microwave use.
2. To be sure the food cooks evenly.
3. See second bulleted list on page 290.
4. Answers will vary. Possible answer: They prefer food that's browner and crisper than a microwave can produce.
5. Answers will vary. Three examples: Microwave ovens can help you cook faster; can help retain food nutrients for healthier eating; use less energy for food preparation.
6. Answers will vary according to the items in the foods lab.

Recipe File

Chicken Quesadillas

This recipe uses the cooking method of microwaving. Prior to assigning the lab, you may wish to have students review the portion of the text under the heading "Microwaving Successfully" on pages 288-289.

USING THE RECIPE

- Have students read the recipe and discuss each step.
- Review safety and sanitation procedures that apply to this recipe.
- Remind students that it is very important to use a microwave-safe tray or plate.
- Have each lab team fill out a work plan. (See the *Foods Lab Resources* booklet.)
- Have students check off the ingredients and equipment listed on the recipe worksheet and prepare the recipe.
- Have students complete the evaluation and questions on the recipe worksheet.

SEE ALSO...

The *Foods Lab Resources* booklet for the Chicken Quesadillas recipe worksheet and other recipe alternatives.

Recipe File

Chicken Quesadillas

This zesty recipe is great for lunch, along with a tossed salad and fresh fruit.

Customary	*Ingredients*	*Metric*
1	Boneless, skinless chicken breast, cooked and shredded	1
2	12-in. flour tortillas	2
1	Tomato, diced	1
Dash	Ground cumin	Dash
1 tsp.	Chili powder	5 mL
½ cup	Shredded low-fat Monterey jack or cheddar cheese	125 mL

Yield: Two servings

Equipment: Microwave-safe tray or large plate
Power level: 100%

Directions

1. Place the tortillas on a microwave-safe tray or large plate. Distribute half the shredded chicken on each tortilla.
2. In a small bowl, combine the diced tomato, cumin, and chili powder. Gently toss to mix.
3. Spread half the seasoned tomato on each tortilla. Top each with half the cheese.
4. Microwave at 100% power for 30 seconds to 1 minute. Let stand 1 minute.
5. Fold each quesadilla in half. Serve hot.

Nutrition Information

Per serving (approximate), based on use of boneless, skinless, roasted chicken breast: 337 calories, 39 g protein, 22 g carbohydrate, 10 g fat, 87 mg cholesterol, 150 mg sodium
Good source of: potassium, magnesium, iron, vitamin C, phosphorus, B vitamins

Food for Thought

- What kitchen tool would you use to dice the tomato? To shred the cheese if it came in a block?
- What substitutions could you make for the chicken? What adjustments, if any, would you need to make to the power setting or cooking time?

Answers to **Food for Thought**

1. Chef's knife. Shredder.
2. Turkey breast, lean beef, lean pork. No adjustments as long as they were all pre-cooked, shredded, and at the same temperature prior to microwaving.

Career Wanted

Caterer

"My food has to look as good as it tastes."

Storey Peak, Jr.

Education and Training

- Degree or certificate from cooking school
- Additional courses in food science and business management

Qualities

- Organization skills
- Self-discipline
- Communication skills
- Creativity

Q. Besides preparing food, Storey, what does a caterer do?

A. Catering an event starts with meeting with the client to choose a menu, based on the type and size of the event, where it's held, and the budget we're working with. We set up, serve, and clean up afterward.

Q. What skills are most important in your job?

A. Cooking skill, of course, but management is essential, too. Even a small event is a real production, between packing all the equipment, arranging food attractively, and keeping trays filled or clearing dishes. Fortunately I have a great crew. We've worked out a routine.

Q. What's your favorite part of the job?

A. Again, it's the cooking. Especially when I hear guests say how much they like the food and ask if we can do their next party. As a chef and business owner, that's very flattering.

Related Career Opportunities

Entry Level
- Personal shopper
- Fruit and vegetable grader
- Salad preparer

Technical Level
- Food stylist
- Baker

Professional Level
- Executive chef
- Hotel banquet manager
- Hospital food service manager

Making Career Connections

CAREER INTERVIEW. Interview a caterer. Find out what cooking methods are most successful for catering. How does catering equipment compare to that used in the home? What special concerns arise when multiple people work together to serve a meal? Transcribe your interview and summarize it for the class.

Career Wanted

Caterer

Thinking About the Career

Have students think of other questions they would like to ask Storey Peak, Jr., about the catering occupation. (Examples: "How many hours a week do you usually work? What resources did you need to get started in this business? What size are the events you cater?")

Ask student volunteers to tell what they think would be the most exciting part of the catering business.

Have students brainstorm decisions that might have to be made in the catering business and use the decision-making steps to develop logical answers.

Career-Building Opportunities

In a catering career, you can gain experience as a caterer's assistant, earn your reputation as a caterer, and then either join a large catering firm or start your own catering business. As a caterer, you have the opportunity to take part in a business as big or as small as you want it to be. Have students interview a caterer in their community, asking probing questions about education and work experience.

For More Information

For additional information about careers in the field of catering, encourage students to contact:

- American Culinary Federation
  10 San Bartola Dr.
  St. Augustine, FL 32086
  www.acfchefs.org
- International Association of Culinary Professionals
  304 W. Liberty St., Suite 201
  Louisville, KY 40202
  www.iacp.org
- Small Business Administration (SBA)
  409 3rd Street SW
  Washington, D.C. 20416
  www.sba.gov
- Small Business Directors' Association
  www.cba.uc.edu

REVIEW

- Have students complete the Chapter Review. (Answers appear below.)

EVALUATION

- Give students a simple recipe and ask them to describe how they would prepare it, naming the equipment they would use and specific method of cooking.
- Have students take the test for Chapter 9. (Use the chapter test in the *Teacher Resource Guide,* or construct your own with the **Exam***View*® *Test Generator* on the *Effective Instruction CD-ROM.*)

ANSWERS

Checking Your Knowledge

1. Below the oven; at the top of the oven compartment.
2. Heating foods that scorch easily, such as milk, chocolate, sauces, and hot cereal.
3. Any four: *Turner:* lift and turn flat foods; *tongs:* grip and lift bulky foods; *basting spoon:* stir and baste foods; *baster:* suction up juices for basting; *ladle:* dip hot liquids; *pastry brush:* brush foods with sauce or glaze; *skewers:* thread food for cooking or serving; *meat thermometer:* measure internal temperature; *wire cooling racks:* hold foods and hot pans during cooling; *potholders, oven mitts:* protect hands.
4. A method by which heat is transferred by the movement of air or liquid. It differs from conduction in that conduction requires direct contact between the heat source and the item being heated.
5. To help tenderize meat; to allow foods to absorb liquid; to blend flavors.

Chapter 9 Review & Activities

Summary

Section 9-1: Equipment for Cooking

- Major cooking appliances include gas and electric ranges and convection and microwave ovens. Each is different.
- Small cooking appliances are useful for specialized tasks.
- Cookware and bakeware items have specific uses and come in a range of materials.
- A variety of small tools are used in cooking.

Section 9-2: Heat and Cooking

- Heat travels by conduction, convection, or radiation.
- When food is heated, the color, flavor, aroma, and texture are all affected.
- Take steps to minimize nutrient losses during cooking.

Section 9-3: Conventional Cooking Techniques

- The three basic types of cooking methods—moist-heat, dry-heat, and frying—affect food differently.
- Braising and stir-frying are cooking techniques that combine two basic methods.

Section 9-4: Microwave Cooking Techniques

- Microwave cooking requires an understanding of the power settings and how microwaves affect different foods and materials.
- Follow instructions for arranging, covering, stirring, rotating, turning, and timing foods.
- Use guidelines for preventing accidents when using the oven, and care for it properly.

Working IN THE Lab

1. ***Presentation.*** Collect several cookware and bakeware items. Give a presentation explaining how the differences in size, shape, materials, and handle placement make each item helpful for particular kinds of cooking tasks.
2. ***Food Science.*** Cook potato slices by baking, simmering, boiling, and frying. Compare the flavors and textures.

Checking Your Knowledge

1. Where is the broiler in a gas range? In an electric range?
2. What is a double boiler used for?
3. List four cooking tools and tell what they are used for.
4. What is convection? How is it different from conduction?
5. Name three possible reasons for using moist heat in certain situations.
6. What is the difference between stewing and poaching?
7. What kinds of foods can you roast successfully?
8. How is pan-broiling different from broiling?
9. What happens when you change the power setting of a microwave oven from high to medium? How does this affect the cooking time?
10. Name four specific materials suitable for microwave cooking.

Review & Activities Chapter 9

Thinking Critically

1. **Recognizing Values.** Imagine that you saw an advertisement for a microwave oven that specified the product as "ideal for the modern American family." Identify the value that you believe this ad is addressing. In what way is the value you have identified responsible for the popularity of microwave ovens and similar appliances?
2. **Identifying Cause and Effect.** Soo-Kim used a recipe that she cut out of a magazine to braise a mixture of meat and vegetables. When the cooking time ended, she was upset when she found the food dried out and charred on the bottom. What might have caused this? What advice can you give Soo-Kim for the future?

Reinforcing Key Skills

1. **Communication.** Julio knows that he needs to reduce fat and calories in his eating plan. He loves to cook, and pan-fried steak and french fries are two of his specialties. What changes in cooking methods can you suggest to Julio that would help him prepare his favorite foods in a more healthful way?
2. **Management.** You are a member of a group of students who have taken on the task of preparing a guidebook to accident prevention in the foods lab kitchen. List the procedure you would suggest the group follow in accomplishing this task.

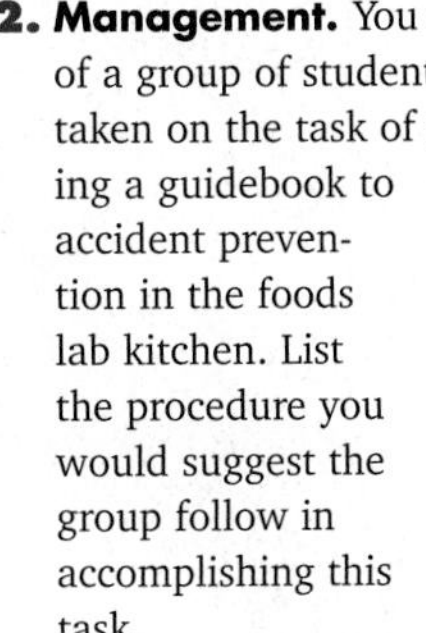

Making Decisions and Solving Problems

Your family is packing for a week's vacation at a lakeside cabin that has a small gas range. Your parents have asked you to choose the cookware, bakeware, and kitchen tools to pack. You can take only as much as you can fit in a small cardboard box. How would you use management skills to help you solve this problem?

Making Connections

1. **Science.** Place a long, all-metal kitchen tool, such as a ladle, in a saucepan of boiling water. Using a watch with a second hand, time how long it takes for the handle to become hot to the touch at the midpoint and at the end. What kind of heat transfer is involved in the movement of heat through the metal handle?
2. **Art.** Develop a diagram that shows how to arrange fresh broccoli in a casserole for microwaving. Indicate how the microwaves will be absorbed by the food.

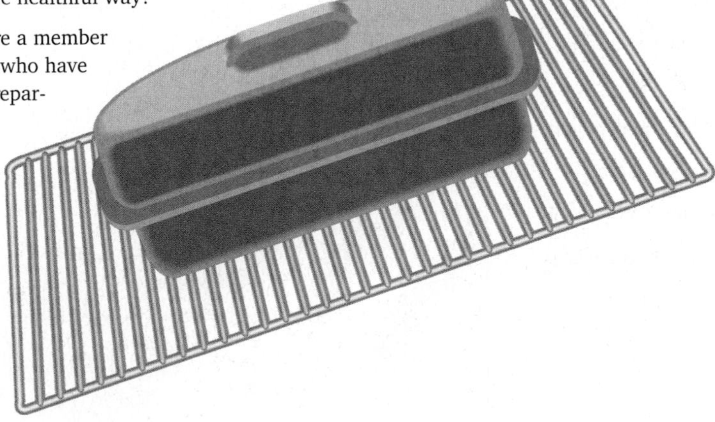

ANSWERS cont.

6. *Stewing:* covering small pieces of food with liquid, then simmering until done. *Poaching:* simmering whole foods in a small amount of liquid until done.
7. Large, tender cuts of meat or poultry.
8. Pan-broiling is done on top of the range.
9. The percentage of cooking power is reduced by 50%; cooking time increases.
10. Any four: Glass, glass-ceramic, stoneware, china, pottery, plastic, paper.

Thinking Critically

1. Answers will vary. Quick-cooking convenience—it's valued by fast-paced, modern American families with typical complaints of too little time for cooking. Microwave ovens and similar appliances help speed the time of cooking.
2. Answers will vary. Possible answer: Insufficient liquid may have been added. In the future, add more liquid during the simmering stage when necessary.

Reinforcing Key Skills

1. Answers will vary. Possible answer: Cook steak and fries with a dry-heat method, such as pan-broiling the steak and baking the French fries.
2. Answers will vary. Suggest that the students first develop an outline of topics to cover. Then assign each student in the group a specific section of the outline.

CHAPTER

10 Mealtime Customs

Advance Planning Guide ☑

- Prepare a sloppily set table for a motivation activity.
- Set up individual table settings for a table-setting lab.
- Arrange a display of tableware with individual items numbered 1-8.
- Arrange a field trip to a local full-service restaurant.
- Obtain menus (perhaps take-out menus) from different types of restaurants in the community.
- Obtain restaurant bills from different types of restaurants.
- Arrange with an etiquette consultant to speak to the class about mealtime etiquette, especially restaurant etiquette.

CHAPTER 10

Section 10-1
Serving Family Meals

Section 10-2
Mealtime Etiquette

Mealtime customs may vary, but the purposes of sharing meals with others are generally the same—to enjoy food, to socialize, or to conduct business. Meals give families a chance to spend time together and strengthen the family as a unit. In this chapter, you'll learn strategies for making family meals and other mealtimes a success.

MEETING DIVERSE NEEDS

Celebrating Cultural Diversity. If there are students within the class who are first- or second-generation residents of the United States, ask them to demonstrate mealtime table etiquette customs that traditionally differ from those of Americans. Some examples: eating with the fork exclusively in the left hand and the knife in the right, eating with hands, scooping foods with breads, or eating with chopsticks. Ask students why it's important to be aware of cultural etiquette practices.

SECTION

10-1

Serving Family Meals

"I won't be home for dinner, Mom—my debate team meets tonight."

"I'll be working late. I'll pick something up on the way home."

Does this sound familiar? In this section, you will learn about the importance of having meals together as a family.

Objectives

After studying this section, you should be able to:

- Explain why meals together can be important to the family.
- Demonstrate how to arrange tableware for a simple family meal.
- Describe family service and plate service.

Look for These Terms

tableware

place setting

serving pieces

cover

Family Meals

In today's fast-paced society, finding time to sit down and enjoy a meal as a family can be a challenge. The good news is that more and more families are meeting this challenge. Whether it is only once a week for dinner or each day at breakfast, eating together is important to a family's social health. Family meals are a time when everyone can relax, enjoy food, talk with one another, catch up on family news, and just have fun.

To make the most of family meals, you need to follow a few simple guidelines. These include keeping a positive mealtime atmosphere and paying attention to the table's appearance.

Mealtime Atmosphere

Sierra's family keeps the TV on during dinner. Dinner at Mark's house often erupts into complaints and accusations involving Mark, his sister, and their parents. What is wrong with these scenarios? Both families do not realize the importance of a positive mealtime atmosphere. An upbeat atmosphere can be as essential to your family's health as nutritious food. Mealtime isn't the time to complain, criticize, or air the day's problems. Keep family meals fun. Focus on the pleasure of eating and of each other's company. What interesting topics can you think of to discuss with your family?

Section 10-1 Resources

◆ **Student Workbook,** pp. 79, 81
◆ **Teacher Resource Guide**
Lesson Plan 10-1 Organizer
Section 10-1 Quiz
◆ **Effective Instruction CD-ROM**
Exam*View*® *Test Generator*
PowerPoint® Slide #23
◆ **Transparency Package,** CT-23
◆ **Student Motivation Kit**
Reteaching Activities, p. 57
Enrichment Activities
Skills for Making Food Choices, pp. 25–26

SECTION 10-1 Serving Family Meals

FOCUS

MOTIVATORS

- Before class, set a table haphazardly, perhaps using mismatched plates, no tablecloth or centerpiece, silverware tossed on plates, etc. Ask students: What is wrong with this table setting? Why? Discuss how proper table presentation contributes to a pleasant mealtime environment.
- Have students collect and display pictures of attractive table settings using tablecloths, placemats, runners, napkins, and centerpieces. Display pictures on a bulletin board titled "Serving Food with Flair."

VOCABULARY ACTIVITY

Pronounce the terms listed under "Look for These Terms." Have students find the terms and their definitions in the section. Point out that *ware,* as in *tableware,* means "manufactured items," and is often used in combination with another word. Ask students to give examples of other terms that use this stem. *(dinnerware, flatware, glassware, earthenware, warehouse)*

STUDY SKILLS

- **Listening.** Invite a group of volunteers each to prepare an oral reading of a page of text from the section, while others follow along silently.
- Have students read the section and complete the appropriate part of the Chapter 10 Study Guide in the *Student Workbook.*

TEACH

- *Family Meals (text pages 297-299)*

Writing Activity

Ask students to write a vivid description of a pleasant, mealtime atmosphere, using adjectives to help the reader visualize the situation. Select several of the descriptions to read anonymously to the class. Ask students how each of the situations makes them feel.

Table Setting Lab

Divide students into groups. Provide groups with one place setting: dinner plate, dinner fork, salad fork, knife, teaspoon, beverage glass, napkin, and cup and saucer. While one student creates the cover, have others evaluate it based on guidelines and measurements on pages 298-299. Repeat until each group member has practiced table setting. L1

Identification Activity

Set up a display labeled 1–8, with eight different pieces of flatware. Ask students to write numbers 1–8 on a blank sheet of paper and then identify the name of each type of flatware and one example of when each might be used. Ask students to share their answers.

Using Recipes

Provide students with a variety of recipes. Then, ask students to list the piece of place setting on or in which to serve the prepared recipe and which piece of flatware they would use for eating the prepared recipe. Allow time for students to share responses with each other. L1

Even when you are eating alone, it is important to sit down and take time to enjoy yourself and your food. People who read or watch television as they eat pay little attention to what and how much they eat. They often eat more than they would if they relaxed, concentrated on the food, and enjoyed the meal.

Setting the Table

How the table looks at mealtime can be as significant as how the people around it behave. Start by making the eating area easy on the eye. Be sure the table is free of papers and other clutter. Place a simple decoration on or near the table—for example, a vase with a single garden flower or a few interesting seashells.

Table settings include the following components:

- **Tableware. Tableware** includes any items used for serving and eating food. Types of tableware are dinnerware (plates, bowls, and cups), flatware (knives, forks, and spoons), glassware, and "linens" (anything from a cloth tablecloth and napkins to wipe-clean placemats).
- **Place setting.** The pieces of tableware used by one person to eat a meal are called a **place setting**.
- **Serving pieces.** Platters, large bowls, and other tableware used for serving food are known as **serving pieces**.
- **Cover.** The arrangement of a place setting for one person is called a **cover**. The rules for this arrangement are based on both tradition and practicality.

Table-Setting Basics

Knowing how to set a table will help you serve family meals, entertain guests, and feel comfortable when you eat out.

The cover is usually on the table before people sit down to eat. The plate goes in the center of the cover, about 1 inch (2.5 cm) from the edge of the table.

◆ Place settings can be formal or simple, depending on the meal to be served. Devise a menu for a formal meal. Tell what would go on each serving piece shown in the illustration on the left.

Reinforcing Key Skills

Present the following problems to student groups. Allow time for them to discuss and compare their responses.

Management—Ask students to describe a situation in which they might include in their preparatory task list making sure that cloth table linens are clean.

Communication—You have been asked to help serve a formal dinner for a group of adults at your neighbor's home. You noticed that there is a salad to serve, but no salad forks or salad plates are available.

Arrange flatware in the order in which it is used, starting at the outside and working in toward the center. Forks go to the left of the plate, knives to the right. Place spoons to the right of the knives. If you have both a soup spoon and a teaspoon, you'd probably use the soup spoon first. Place it to the right of the teaspoon.

Place a beverage glass just above the tip of the dinner knife. The cup and saucer or mug go to the right of the spoon, about 1 inch (2.5 cm) from the edge of the table. The napkin is usually placed to the left of the fork.

Settings for Family Meals

Most families choose simple table settings for everyday meals. For most meals, you need at least a dinner plate, fork, knife, teaspoon, and beverage glass. Add a cup and saucer or a mug if a hot beverage is being served. If salad is on the menu, add a salad plate or bowl. For soup, you'll need a bowl and a soup spoon.

At home, the same fork can be used to eat both a salad and the main dish. For a formal meal, separate forks would be used.

Serving Family Meals

In Ray's family, serving bowls are passed around the table, and everyone takes whatever she or he wants. Julie's dad prefers to dish food onto plates at the range. These two most common styles of serving food are known as *family service* and *plate service*.

Family Service

In family service, the cover is set with the necessary tableware. The food is placed in serving dishes and passed around the table, with people helping themselves. It's less confusing if all the foods are passed in the same direction, generally to the right.

Sometimes, if a serving plate is too hot or a roast or ham is sliced at the table, a family member serves the food at the table. In that case, the dinner plates are stacked in front of the server. The food is placed on a plate and passed along to the diners, who then help themselves to other foods in the meal.

The main advantage of family service is that people can serve themselves the amount they want. This is especially helpful for those who are limited in the kinds or amounts of food they can eat. There are, however, several disadvantages. The hot food left on the table in serving dishes may cool to room temperature quickly. This allows harmful bacteria to multiply. Family service also makes it difficult to practice portion control, which can lead to overeating. A third disadvantage is that excess food left on a plate must be thrown away, which wastes food and money.

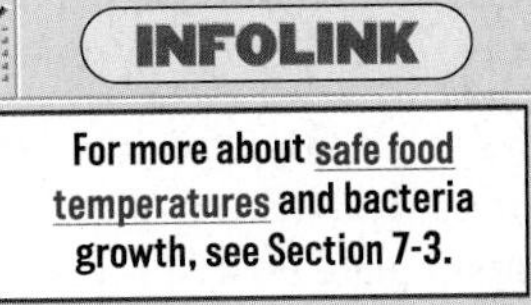

INFOLINK
For more about safe food temperatures and bacteria growth, see Section 7-3.

- *Serving Family Meals (text pages 299-300)*

Discussion Activity

Ask students to describe family service. What are its advantages and disadvantages? Discuss plate service. How is it different from family service? What advantage does it have over family service? Ask students to describe how bread or rolls, salads, and desserts are handled for each style.

Class Survey Activity

Ask students to read the descriptions of family service and plate service. Survey the class to determine which style is most popular in their families. What other styles of service are used?

Lab Experience

1. Divide the class into two groups.
2. Ask students to prepare a simple meal in the foods lab. Have one group serve it using family service and the other using plate service.
3. Have students observe the general guidelines while eating, such as serving breads and rolls, salads, and desserts.
4. After finished with the meal, ask students to compare and contrast the different types of service, including general guidelines and specifics—the atmosphere, length of mealtime, safety concerns, and cleanup time.  L1

Extending Learning

Kids and Family Meals—With young preschool-aged children in the household, peaceful family meals are generally the exception, not the rule. To create more pleasant family mealtimes, young siblings can be encouraged to help plan meals. Parents and older brothers and sisters can use the following guidelines:

- Parents provide: What foods are served; where they're served; when they're served.
- Children need to decide: Which of the served foods to eat; How much to eat.

TEACH cont.

- *Serving Family Meals (text pages 299-300)*

Guideline Development Activity

Ask students to form brainstorming groups in an effort to develop mealtime safety guidelines for use in family service. Then have each group share its guidelines. As a class, choose the ten best guidelines. Suggest that each student post the guidelines in his or her home kitchen.

Checklists

Have students each develop a checklist for teaching children how to serve family meals. Suggest students write in basic, descriptive language. Ask a few volunteer students to share their checklists with the class. If possible, have students provide checklists to a classroom of younger students. L1

USING CONNECTING FOOD AND LANGUAGE ARTS

Have interested students read their stories to the class. While they're reading their stories, have the rest of the students close their eyes to help visualize the meal experience. After each story, ask the class to discuss several reasons why they believe each meal was memorable. Which words helped create a visual image or feeling associated with the meal?

◆ Some families use plate service at home. How is plate service different from other ways of serving family meals?

Plate Service

Plate service is generally used for family meals and in restaurants. The table is set without dinner plates, though space is left on each cover for the plate (and salad bowl if a salad is to be served). Food is placed on the plates directly from the containers in which it was cooked, and the plates are then brought to the table. The food remaining in pans can be kept hot on the range or in the oven. The only exception is salad. This may be passed around the table in a serving bowl so that people can help themselves.

Besides cutting down on waste and bacteria buildup, and discouraging the tendency to overeat, plate service saves cleanup time. Because no serving dishes are used, there are none to wash.

General Guidelines

Place breads and rolls on a plate or in a basket, and pass it around the table. If a basket is used, line it with a napkin. Diners can place bread or rolls on the edge of their dinner plates. At more formal meals, provide a small bread-and-butter plate above the forks.

Serve salads either in individual bowls at each place setting or in a serving bowl to be passed around the table. If possible, serve salad dressing separately so that people can use the amount they want.

Serve dessert after the dinner plates, salad bowls, and serving dishes have been cleared from the table. If forks or spoons are needed, bring them to the table with the dessert.

Extending Learning

Buffet-type Service—Another popular style of serving food is buffet-type service. A buffet is a meal where diners serve themselves from a variety of prepared dishes that are all set out together on a sideboard or table. Buffet-type service allows the diner flexibility over the type and amount of foods chosen. Buffets need to be closely managed to keep hot foods hot and cold foods cold. Someone trying to lose weight needs to be aware that this type of service can be associated with overeating.

Connecting Food and Language Arts

Remembrances of Meals Past

Do you recall the best meal you ever had? As the following passage from Charles Dickens's *A Christmas Carol* reveals, size is not the only measure of a meal's success.

"At last the dishes were set on, and . . . [followed] by a breathless pause as Mrs. Cratchit, looking slowly all along the carving-knife, prepared to plunge it in the breast [of the goose]; but when she did, and when the long-expected gush of stuffing issued forth, one murmur of delight arose all [a]round. . . .

"There never was such a goose. . . . Its tenderness and flavour, size and cheapness, were the themes of universal admiration. Eked out by apple-sauce and mashed potatoes, it was a sufficient dinner for the whole family; indeed, as Mrs. Cratchit said with great delight (surveying one small atom of a bone upon the dish), they hadn't ate it all at last! Yet every one had had enough, and the youngest Cratchits in particular, were steeped in sage and onion to the eyebrows!"

Think About It

1. What does the server do to make the meal one that the whole family will remember for years to come? What word or phrase in the passage clues you in to the fact that this practice is probably a family tradition?
2. Write your own story describing a meal (real or imagined) you found memorable and really enjoyed. Include specific details that show how the presentation of the meal made it special.

Section 10-1 Review & Activities

1. Identify two benefits of a pleasant mealtime atmosphere.
2. Name the items included in a simple, everyday table setting.
3. Traditionally, how is flatware arranged with respect to the dinner plate?
4. Compare and contrast family service and plate service.
5. **Analyzing.** With several classmates, brainstorm obstacles a family can face in planning meals together. Devise strategies for overcoming each problem. Share your findings with the class.
6. **Extending.** Plate service can cut down on the tendency to overeat. Identify other factors of meal service that can help cut down on this tendency.
7. **Applying.** Set a cover incorrectly. Challenge a classmate to identify and correct the errors in the setting.

ASSESS

REVIEW

- Ask students to summarize the main ideas in this section.
- Have students complete the Section Review. (Answers appear below.)

EVALUATION

- Have students plan and describe a pleasant eating area, complete with table settings, and explain the purpose of each item.
- Have students take the quiz for Section 10-1. (Use the quiz in the *Teacher Resource Guide,* or construct your own with the **ExamView®** *Test Generator* on the *Effective Instruction CD-ROM.*)

RETEACHING

- Have students work in pairs to arrange a cover for a specific meal.
- Refer to the *Reteaching Activities* booklet for the Section 10-1 activity sheet.

CLOSE

Refer to the bulletin board "Serving Food with Flair" that students helped to create in the chapter motivator. Have students identify the type of service and guess what foods will be served for each display.

Answers to Section 10-1 Review & Activities

1. It helps you enjoy your meal and digest your food.
2. Dinner plate, fork, knife, teaspoon, beverage glass; other items may be added if needed.
3. Forks—to the left of the plate; knives—to the right of the plate; spoons—to the right of the knives.
4. See pages 299-300.
5. Answers will vary. Schedule conflicts may be the most common obstacle.
6. Answers will vary. Possible answers: Soothing atmosphere, smaller plates.
7. Answers will vary.

SECTION
10-2
Mealtime Etiquette

FOCUS

MOTIVATORS

- Ask students to describe or demonstrate poor mealtime etiquette. Discuss the impression poor mealtime etiquette makes on others.
- Ask students to make a list of mealtime etiquette guidelines they observe. Have students keep the list in a handy place so they can add additional guidelines as they study mealtime etiquette.

VOCABULARY ACTIVITY

Pronounce the terms listed under "Look for These Terms." Have students find the terms and their definitions in the section. Point out that the word *reservation* comes from the verb *reserve*, meaning "to keep for future use or set apart." Ask students to find several meanings of reservation in a dictionary.

STUDY SKILLS

- **Guided Reading.** Have students look at the headings within Section 10-2 to preview the concepts that will be discussed.
- Have students read the section and complete the appropriate part of the Chapter 10 Study Guide in the *Student Workbook*.

SECTION
10-2

Objectives

After studying this section, you should be able to:

- Explain the importance of knowing simple table etiquette.
- Describe basic etiquette guidelines.

Look for These Terms

table etiquette

reservation

gratuity

Mealtime Etiquette

"You should have seen the game!" Aaron shouted with his mouth full. "We really creamed Central." He reached across the table for the salsa. His twin sister Kayla swallowed, then quietly asked, "Would someone please pass the tortillas?"

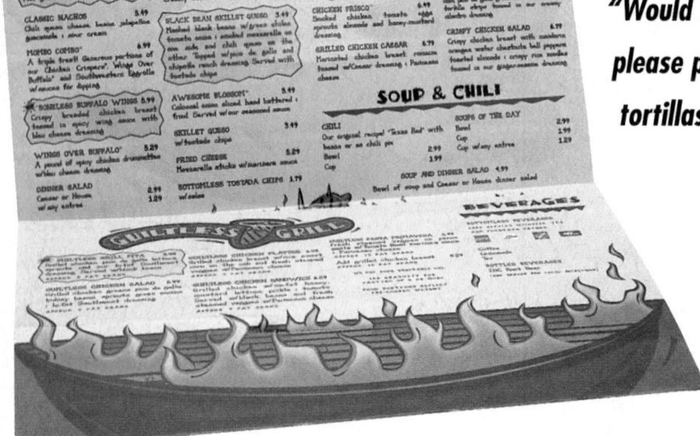

Table Etiquette

Aaron and Kayla are twins, but there is one important difference between them: table etiquette. **Table etiquette** is the courtesy shown by using good manners at meals.

Good table manners help put you at ease in social situations. They can also be an asset in the working world. Many business transactions take place over meals. Often, when companies consider an applicant for a job, the interview may include a meal. This gives the interviewer a chance to observe how the applicant would act during similar business situations.

Basic Etiquette

Here are some general etiquette guidelines:

Before Eating

- Place the napkin on your lap before you start eating. Don't tuck it into a belt or under your chin.
- If there are six or fewer people at the table, wait until everyone is served before you begin to eat. If there are more, wait until two or three have been served.
- You may reach for serving dishes as long as you don't have to lean across your neighbor. If you can't reach the food easily, politely ask the person nearest the food to pass it to you.

Section 10-2 Resources

◆ **Student Workbook,** pp. 80, 82
◆ **Teacher Resource Guide**
Lesson Plan 10-2 Organizer
Section 10-2 Quiz
Chapter 10 Test
◆ **Effective Instruction CD-ROM**
Exam *View*® *Test Generator*
PowerPoint® Slide #24
◆ **Transparency Package,** CT-24
◆ **Student Motivation Kit**
Reteaching Activities, p. 58
Enrichment Activities

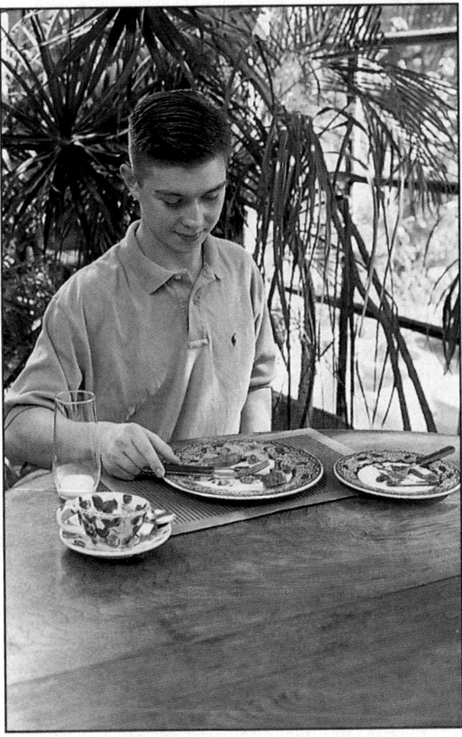

◆ **At the end of the meal, place your knife and fork on your plate as shown. Give two other do's and don'ts of table etiquette.**

While Eating

- ◆ Don't talk with your mouth full. Finish chewing, swallow the food, and then talk.
- ◆ If you're having problems getting foods (such as peas) onto your fork, push them on with a piece of bread. If you have no bread, use the tip of your dinner knife to push the food onto the fork.
- ◆ Break bread into smaller pieces before buttering or eating it.
- ◆ If you're dining at someone's home and aren't sure what to do, use your host's actions as a guide.
- ◆ Cut food into small pieces for eating. If you try to eat large pieces, you may have difficulty chewing and may choke.
- ◆ Sit up straight when you eat, and don't lean on your elbows.
- ◆ If you must cough or sneeze, cover your mouth and nose with a handkerchief or a napkin. If your coughing continues, excuse yourself and leave the table.

After Eating

- ◆ Never comb your hair or apply makeup while at the table.
- ◆ Don't leave a spoon in your cup. You might knock the cup over if your hand accidentally hits the spoon.
- ◆ When you have finished eating, place your fork and knife on your plate, pointing toward the center.

Finally, remember that people from other countries and cultures have table manners that may be different from yours. Respect and accept people with other customs.

Q ***Is it all right to eat fried chicken with my fingers?***

A That depends. When you're at home or in a fast-food restaurant, feel free to eat fried chicken with your fingers. When in someone else's home, follow the lead of your host. In fine restaurants, eat all meat except crisp bacon with a knife and fork. Note that some foods—namely breads, celery, olives, carrot sticks, pickles, and most sandwiches—are normally eaten with the fingers regardless of where you are eating.

TEACH

- ***Table Etiquette***
- ***Basic Etiquette (text pages 302-303)***

Discussion Activity

Ask students to each brainstorm a list of ten reasons for using table etiquette. Then, on the chalkboard, have each student record one reason. Discuss the list.

Oral Presentation

Have students study etiquette customs of the past or of another culture using library references and the Internet. To enhance students' research, encourage them to conduct a personal interview with a grandparent or a person of different culture, if possible. Have students each prepare and give a two-minute oral presentation to the class. L2

Field Trip

Take students on a field trip to a local full-service restaurant. Have students order meals and demonstrate appropriate restaurant etiquette. During the meal, make a point to commend students who demonstrate exemplary etiquette.

Reinforcing Key Skills

Present the following problems to student groups. Allow time for them to discuss and compare their responses.

Communication—Present this scenario to students: You have applied for a job with a large company. A representative contacts you and invites you to dinner at a nice restaurant. He orders baked chicken and proceeds to eat it with his fingers, although other people in the restaurant are eating it with a knife and fork. He displays poor table manners. What should you do?

- *Restaurant Etiquette (text pages 304-306)*

Critical Thinking Activity

Share with students the following two situations: (1) You have a 7:00 P.M. reservation at an exclusive restaurant but you are going to be 30 minutes late; (2) You have a 7:00 P.M. reservation at an exclusive restaurant, but you decide not to go. Ask students to identify possible problems that may arise, in each instance, by not calling. Have two students role-play the proper way to notify the restaurants.

Menu Reading Activity

Provide students with menus from different types of restaurants. Ask students to look at the menus to determine how foods are priced. Are foods priced by the meal or individually? Ask students to make a list of unfamiliar terms on the menus. Discuss these terms.

Skits

Provide small groups of students with a variety of menus. Divide students into small groups to create and present skits demonstrating proper procedures for ordering meals at different types of restaurants, using the provided menus. Discuss variations in procedures. L1

Restaurant Etiquette

Restaurant etiquette involves the same good manners that you use anywhere else. Still, there are a few basic guidelines that deal with situations found only in restaurants.

When You Arrive

When you enter a restaurant, you may be asked whether you have a reservation. A **reservation** is an arrangement made ahead of time for a table at a restaurant. When calling, give your name, the number of people in your group, and the time you plan to arrive. If you will be late or decide not to go, call and ask to change or cancel the reservation.

Near the entrance, you may see a checkroom. If you do, leave coats, umbrellas, packages, books, and briefcases. You are expected to tip the attendant.

Unless a sign states otherwise, never seat yourself. A restaurant employee will direct you and your group to a table.

◆ **When eating at a restaurant, be sure and look at the menu carefully and ask any questions before placing an order. What types of questions might be good to ask?**

FOR YOUR HEALTH

Safe Practices = Safe Food

Personal hygiene and sanitation practices are just as important when you are serving and eating food as when you are preparing it. For example, if hand-washing practices are not followed, bacteria on your skin can be transferred to the food. Regardless of these precautions, many bacteria remain. Whether you are eating in a restaurant or at home, or are a guest in someone else's home, follow these safety guidelines when you serve yourself:

- Never touch food that someone else will be eating.
- If a dip is served, dip a piece of food in the dip mixture just once. Try to take enough dip for the whole piece. If you need more dip for the piece you've already bitten, use a serving spoon and put some on a small, individual plate.
- Don't use your fingers to pick up and taste food as you make your selections.

Following Up

- What might you provide along with finger foods that people could use to safely transfer food to their own plates? What precautions should you take when you are preparing food and need to taste it for seasonings from time to time?

The Meal

Jorge was puzzled by the term *á la carte* on his restaurant menu. Instead of ordering and possibly making a mistake and not getting what he wanted, he asked his server to explain it.

Reinforcing Key Skills

Present the following problems to student groups. Allow time for them to discuss and compare their responses.

Leadership—Many people feel awkward asking to have leftover food wrapped. Discuss why asking for a "doggie bag" is appropriate etiquette.

Communication—You ordered your meal at a nearby steakhouse over 40 minutes ago and you haven't been served. How do you approach the waitperson and/or manager?

◆ **If the server takes care of the payment of the check, the money or credit card should be given to the server. How can the tip can be handled in this situation?**

When dining out, don't be afraid to ask a few questions. This can be especially important when it comes to the restaurant's pricing policy. Sometimes the price of the entrée, or main dish, includes side dishes such as vegetables and salad. Other restaurants price each item individually. Knowing the policy can help you avoid an embarrassing and uncomfortable situation.

On occasion, each person in a group will want to pay for his or her own meal. If the group is small, ask the server for separate checks before you order. Alternatively—or if the restaurant's policy is to make out only one check for each table—you might ask the server to figure out the cost for each person. In some restaurants, meals are itemized on the check individually and collectively.

Restaurants may serve more food than some people can eat. If you have leftover food, such as part of a steak or chicken, ask to have it wrapped so you can take it home. Most restaurants have special containers and supply them for diners. This does not apply to all-you-can-eat buffets and salad bars.

In fast-food restaurants, self-serve restaurants, and some delicatessens, customers are expected to clear their own table after eating. Trays and disposables are deposited in specified containers.

Communicating with Servers

Be polite to servers, whether in a fast-food or an elegant restaurant. Remember, they're working hard to serve you and a number of other people at the same time. Be considerate and patient, especially during busy periods.

To call your server, catch his or her attention by calmly raising your hand. If necessary, ask one of the other servers to get your server. Never call out or disturb other diners.

Paying the Check

At the meal's end, the server will bring you the check. In some restaurants you pay your server. In others you take the check to the cashier for payment. If you're not sure what to do, ask the server.

Look over the check carefully and add up the items. If there is a mistake, quietly point it out to the server. The server should correct any mistake or explain why the amount shown is right.

In most restaurants you are expected to leave a **gratuity** (gruh-TOO-uh-tee). Also known as a "tip," this is extra money given to the server in appreciation for good service. Servers rely on tips as an important part of their pay. Sometimes the tip has been added to the check. A standard amount to tip is 15 percent of the pretax food bill. The chart on the next page shows how much to leave depending on the type of restaurant and other circumstances.

• *Restaurant Etiquette (text pages 304-306)*

VISUAL LEARNING ***Using the "How Much to Tip" Chart***

Provide students with sample restaurant bills from four types of restaurants noted in the chart in the textbook on page 306. Have students practice using the restaurant bills by adding the appropriate tip for each situation. Discuss calculated tips for each situation.

Guest Speaker

Invite an etiquette consultant to speak to the class about mealtime etiquette, especially restaurant etiquette. Prior to the presentation, have each student write a "Dear Ms. or Mr. Manners" question that they would like a response for by the consultant.

Role Play Activity

Have students form pairs. Provide each pair with a complaint or a compliment. Have each pair of students decide who is going to be the "customer" and who is going to be the "server," and possibly the "manager," too. Allow students time to plan their role-play scenarios. Ask each pair of students to role-play for the class. Discuss how well each situation was handled.

Technology TIE-IN One goal of restaurants is to provide efficient service to improve customer satisfaction. Advances in technology have created more efficiency in the dining areas (i.e. computerized registers) and kitchen operations (i.e. microwaves). Have interested students research restaurant operations from the early 1970s to today, focusing on how technology has improved aspects of the restaurant, including efficiency. Ask them to share findings with the class.

ASSESS

REVIEW

- Ask students to summarize the main ideas in this section.
- Have students complete the Section Review. (Answers appear below.)

EVALUATION

- Have individual students demonstrate appropriate table manners for specific situations.
- Have students take the quiz for Section 10-2. (Use the quiz in the *Teacher Resource Guide,* or construct your own with the **Exam***View*® *Test Generator* on the *Effective Instruction CD-ROM.*)

RETEACHING

- Have students work in pairs to practice demonstrating good table manners in a variety of situations.
- Refer to the *Reteaching Activities* booklet for the Section 10-2 activity sheet.

CLOSE

Create two class lists of etiquette guidelines: One for use at home and the second for use in a restaurant. Have students record the guidelines on index cards and then post one on a refrigerator and carry the other in a wallet.

How Much to Tip

Average	15 percent—more if service was exceptionally good.
Fancy restaurants	20 percent
Coffee shops	• No less than 25 cents if just a beverage was ordered. • If food is ordered, 15 percent of the bill or at least 50 cents, whichever amount is greater.
Buffet-type restaurant	10 percent if a server filled water glasses, brought beverages, and cleared the table.
Fast-food restaurants	No tip required.

Methods of Payment

When paying for a meal in cash, leave the money, including the tip, on the table or in the tray on which the check was presented. If you use a credit card, the server or cashier will process the card and hand you the credit card slip. Again, go over the math to be sure the totals are correct. The slip has a space for a tip. Fill in the amount, add the final total, sign the slip, and hand it back to the server or cashier. Be sure to get your copy of the credit card slip for your records—and don't forget the credit card.

Complaints and Compliments

If you have any complaints about the food, tell the server. If nothing is done, complain to the manager. You can also complain to the manager if the service was poor.

While people rarely hesitate to voice their complaints, few remember to express their appreciation for exceptional food and service. Compliments are just as important to the management as are complaints.

Section 10-2 Review & Activities

1. What is the importance of using good table manners?
2. Explain two ways of solving the problem of getting food onto your fork.
3. Describe two polite ways of calling your server to the table.
4. **Analyzing.** Why do you think a meal is part of many job interviews? What might an employer learn about a job applicant by his or her dining etiquette?
5. **Evaluating.** Which points covered in the lesson could help a person avoid an awkward or embarrassing situation? Explain.
6. **Applying.** With one or two classmates, write and perform a skit demonstrating at least three dining etiquette errors. Have the rest of the class identify the errors and offer suggestions to correct them.

Answers to Section 10-2 Review & Activities

1. They help you feel more comfortable in social and work situations.
2. Use a piece of bread if you have any; if not, use the tip of your knife.
3. Raise your hand or ask another server to get him or her.
4. Answers will vary. Possible answer: Dining etiquette usually tells a lot about people. The potential employer may want to see how you act in company and how you might look to your clients during a meal.
5. Answers will vary.
6. Answers will vary.

Career Wanted

Etiquette Consultant

Education and Training
- Certificate from school of etiquette and protocol
- Background in human resources

Qualities
- Communication skills
- Self-confidence
- Outgoing personality

"Showing good manners gives you an edge in life."

Terrie Tilghman

Q. Terrie, how did you come to be an etiquette consultant?

A. As a personnel director, I saw problems caused by people who didn't know how to interact. Morale, productivity, and profits suffered. With a business of my own, solving these problems became my focus.

Q. Who hires you, and why?

A. Most of my clients are businesses that need a confidence-inspiring image, like banks and professional fundraisers. Universities also hire me to give business etiquette seminars to students.

Q. What about international business travelers?

A. To learn foreign etiquette, you need an expert in that culture. Different societies have different rules.

Q. What's the biggest misconception people have about etiquette?

A. They think etiquette applies only to fancy restaurants and diplomats. Etiquette is for everyone. Saying "please" and "thank you" is just one small example of the everyday etiquette that affects all aspects of life.

Related Career Opportunities

Entry Level
- Restaurant hostess or host
- Preschool teacher's aide

Technical Level
- Sales representative
- Employment agency interviewer

Professional Level
- Image consultant
- Newspaper columnist
- Labor relations specialist

Making Career Connections

TEACHING EXPERIENCE. Become an "expert" in a certain situation, such as interviewing for a job, hosting a party, attending a formal dinner, or using e-mail. Prepare and give a short etiquette lesson to the class.

Career Wanted

Etiquette Consultant

Thinking About the Career

Have students think of other questions they would like to ask Terrie Tilghman about being an etiquette consultant. (Examples: Do you maintain an office, or do you travel to each client location, or both? What are the business implications of being self-employed?)

Ask students why courses in communications are valuable to an etiquette consultant.

Career-Building Opportunities

Have interested students set up an appointment with a Small Business Administration representative to discuss possible ways individuals go about becoming self-employed.

For More Information

For additional information about self-employment, encourage students to contact:

- Association of Professional Consultants
  P.O. Box 51193
  Irvine, CA 92619-1193
  www.consultapc.org
- Small Business Administration
  409 Third St., SW
  Washington, D.C. 20416
  www.sba.gov
- Professional and Technical Consultants Association
  1060 N. Fourth St.
  San Jose, CA 95112
  www.patca.org

REVIEW

- Have students complete the Chapter Review. (Answers appear below.)

EVALUATION

- Give students several scenarios that require the proper use of etiquette. Have students take turns demonstrating how they would act.
- Have students take the test for Chapter 10. (Use the chapter test in the *Teacher Resource Guide,* or construct your own with the **Exam***View*® *Test Generator* on the *Effective Instruction CD-ROM.*)

ANSWERS

Checking Your Knowledge

1. Make the eating area attractive; keep meals fun; take the time to sit down and eat, relax, and enjoy yourself.
2. For a formal meal, separate dinner, salad, and dessert forks are used; for an informal meal, generally only one fork is used. A formal meal may include more dinnerware and glassware.
3. Place the plate in the center. Arrange flatware in the order in which it is used, starting at the outside and working in toward the center: all forks to the left of the plate; all knives to the right; spoons to the right of the knives. Place the beverage glass above the dinner knife and the cup and saucer to the right of the spoon.
4. Food remaining in cookware can be kept hot; serving dishes aren't used, which saves cleanup time; overeating and bacterial growth are discouraged.
5. Answers will vary. Possible answer: Advantage—people can serve themselves the amount they want; disadvantage—hot food cools quickly on the table.

Chapter 10 Review & Activities

Summary

Section 10-1: Serving Family Meals

- Family meals are important for strengthening family bonds.
- Creating a pleasant mealtime atmosphere, including the table setting, helps make meals more enjoyable.
- A basic cover includes a dinner plate, fork, knife, teaspoon, and beverage glass. The items are arranged in a specific way based on tradition and convenience.
- Meals may be served using either family service or plate service.

Section 10-2: Mealtime Etiquette

- The purpose of table manners is to make eating a pleasant experience for everyone at the table.
- Rules of etiquette involve common sense and consideration for others.
- When dining in a restaurant, follow the accepted etiquette for making reservations, ordering and paying for the meal, and leaving a tip.
- Be courteous to food servers, and offer your compliments for good food service.

Checking Your Knowledge

1. Give three general guidelines for creating a pleasant mealtime atmosphere.
2. In what way are the components of a place setting for a formal meal different from those for an informal family meal?
3. Describe how to arrange a cover.
4. What are the advantages of plate service?
5. Name one advantage and one disadvantage of family service.
6. When dining with others, when may you begin to eat?
7. Give five examples of acceptable finger foods.
8. Explain the procedure for paying the bill and leaving a tip when paying with cash and by credit card.
9. How much should you tip food servers in an elegant restaurant? A buffet-style restaurant? A coffee shop?
10. If your food or service was poor, how should you register your complaint?

Working IN THE Lab

1. ***Presentation.*** Design and carry out a table setting, using items available in the foods lab or brought from home. Choose a specific meal and theme. Include table linens and decoration as well as all necessary tableware items in their proper places.
2. ***Simulation.*** Simulate a family meal using either family service or plate service. Include the proper arrangement of tableware, the rules of mealtime etiquette, and conversation that would contribute to a pleasant dining atmosphere.
3. ***Demonstration.*** Demonstrate rules of restaurant etiquette for one of the following situations: arriving at the restaurant and being seated; ordering and eating the meal; paying the bill and leaving the tip; registering a complaint or compliment with the manager.

Thinking Critically

1. Identifying Cause and Effect. How might eating family meals together affect family members' attitudes toward food and nutrition?

2. Analyzing Behavior. Suppose you and a friend are at a restaurant and see someone eating food in a manner that seems strange to you. Your friend thinks that person is either uneducated or deliberately rude. Is this a fair judgment? What are some possible explanations for the person's behavior?

Reinforcing Key Skills

1. Communication. Although your family often eats meals together, there is little conversation at the table. You would like to encourage family members to be more open and sharing at mealtime. How can you use your own communication skills to improve communication among family members?

2. Leadership. A friend is eating dinner with your family. She has made some etiquette mistakes that are embarrassing to her and your family. What steps can you take to put everyone at ease?

Making Decisions and Solving Problems

You are being considered for a job that you want very much. Your potential employer has asked you to lunch at a fancy restaurant. You are worried about making a good impression.

Making Connections

1. Social Studies. Use library resources to find information about table settings and mealtime etiquette in another culture. How are meals served? What is the proper way to eat the meal? Prepare a brief presentation for the class in which you act out a typical meal in that culture.

2. Math. Conduct a survey of tipping practices in local food establishments. By questioning servers, cashiers, or other personnel, determine the average percentage of tip that is left in each type of establishment. Create a bar graph comparing these percentages with the percentages suggested in this chapter.

Guest Check
TABLE NO. NO. PERSONS CHECK NO. SERVER NO
800529
TAX
THANK YOU!

ANSWERS cont.

6. If there are six or fewer people at the table, wait until everyone is served; if there are more than six, wait until two or three others have been served.
7. Any five: Breads, celery, olives, carrot sticks, pickles, crisp bacon, most sandwiches.
8. *Cash:* look check over carefully, pay server or go to cashier to pay, leave a tip on the table or on the check tray (15 percent is average). *Credit card:* look check over carefully, submit credit card to server or cashier, check amount on credit card slip, add tip, and sign. Remember to get your copy of the credit slip.
9. *Elegant restaurant:* 15 percent. *Buffet-style restaurant:* 10 percent. *Coffee shop:* no less than 25 cents for beverage only or 50 cents for food; should average 15 percent.
10. Tell the server or the manager if necessary.

Thinking Critically

1. Answers will vary. Pleasant meals can create positive association with foods, eating, and nutrition. They can be a chance for parents to teach positive eating habits.
2. Answers will vary. No, this isn't a fair judgment. Students should realize that mealtime etiquette differs in other cultures. Perhaps the person is using the etiquette accepted in his or her own country or culture.

Reinforcing Key Skills

1. Communication techniques will vary. First, make sure a pleasant atmosphere is provided. Calmly ask open-ended questions.
2. Steps will vary.

UNIT 3

Consumer Decisions

INTRODUCING UNIT 3

Ask whether students think of themselves as smart consumers. Follow up with questions that show the amount of brainwork that goes into smart shopping. (For example: What are the benefits to planning a week's worth of meals at a time? What is the benefit of keeping a food budget? How can you reduce food spending through wise meal planning? How can a shopping list save you money? How can you get the most for your money when food shopping?)

UNIT 3

Consumer

KEY TO ABILITY LEVELS Each section of the text contains skill-building activities. Each activity has been labeled for use with students of various learning styles and abilities.

L1 **Level 1** activities are basic activities and should be within the range of all students.

L2 **Level 2** activities are average activities and should be within the range of students working at average and above-average levels.

L3 **Level 3** activities are challenging activities designed for the ability range of above-average students.

Decisions

FCCLA Projects **Financial Fitness.** Students research the costs of a kitchen "starter kit" for young adults. They compare the prices and quality of food staples and basic cookware, assembling results in a "Best Buys" booklet that is offered to graduating seniors or others.

Community Service. Students volunteer at a food bank, soup kitchen, or meal delivery program and record their experiences and impressions in a journal. They learn who is served, why foods are chosen, how food is obtained, what causes hunger, and how communities respond.

UNIT 3 PROJECT

Have students maintain a running log of all the purchases—food and otherwise—that they make during work on this unit. Instruct students to note each item bought, the amount of the purchase, and any factors that prompted the purchase (for example, sheer need, advertising, word of mouth). Instruct students to keep a running tally of how much money went in and out each week.

PROJECT FOLLOWUP

Have students review their spending logs, calculating what they spent the most money on and who or what had the greatest influence on them. Allow students to share and compare their findings as a bridge to a discussion of how sensible students felt their purchases were as a whole. Ask: What could you have done to enable yourself to spend more wisely?

CHAPTER

11

Planning Meals

Advance Planning Guide ☑

- Gather cookbooks with a variety of ethnic recipes and cookbooks representing specific cultures.
- Find three culturally-diverse recipes.
- Gather recipes for a simple family meal.
- Prepare a list of the "mock" contents of a freezer, refrigerator, and kitchen cabinets.
- Arrange for the school food service director to speak to the students.
- Prepare a written, unappetizing dinner meal.
- Obtain a world map and place it on a bulletin board.
- Obtain push pins, with flags to stick on the pins.
- Develop one meal challenging situation per student in class.
- Prepare menus for several meals.
- Purchase three name-brand products and their cheaper counterparts (such as crackers, cereals, and pretzels).
- Arrange a field trip to a local soup kitchen or food bank.
- Develop a spending record for a hypothetical family.
- Prepare index cards showing nutritious foods and their prices.

CHAPTER

11

Section 11-1
Basic Meal Planning

Section 11-2
Challenges in Meal Planning

Section 11-3
Food Costs and Budgeting

It was Li's turn to make dinner. With notepad in hand, she mapped out an ingredients list, a work plan, and a schedule. Within minutes, Li had built the foundation for a nutritious and delicious meal.

After reading this chapter, you—like Li—will know how to plan and produce healthful and delicious meals within a budget.

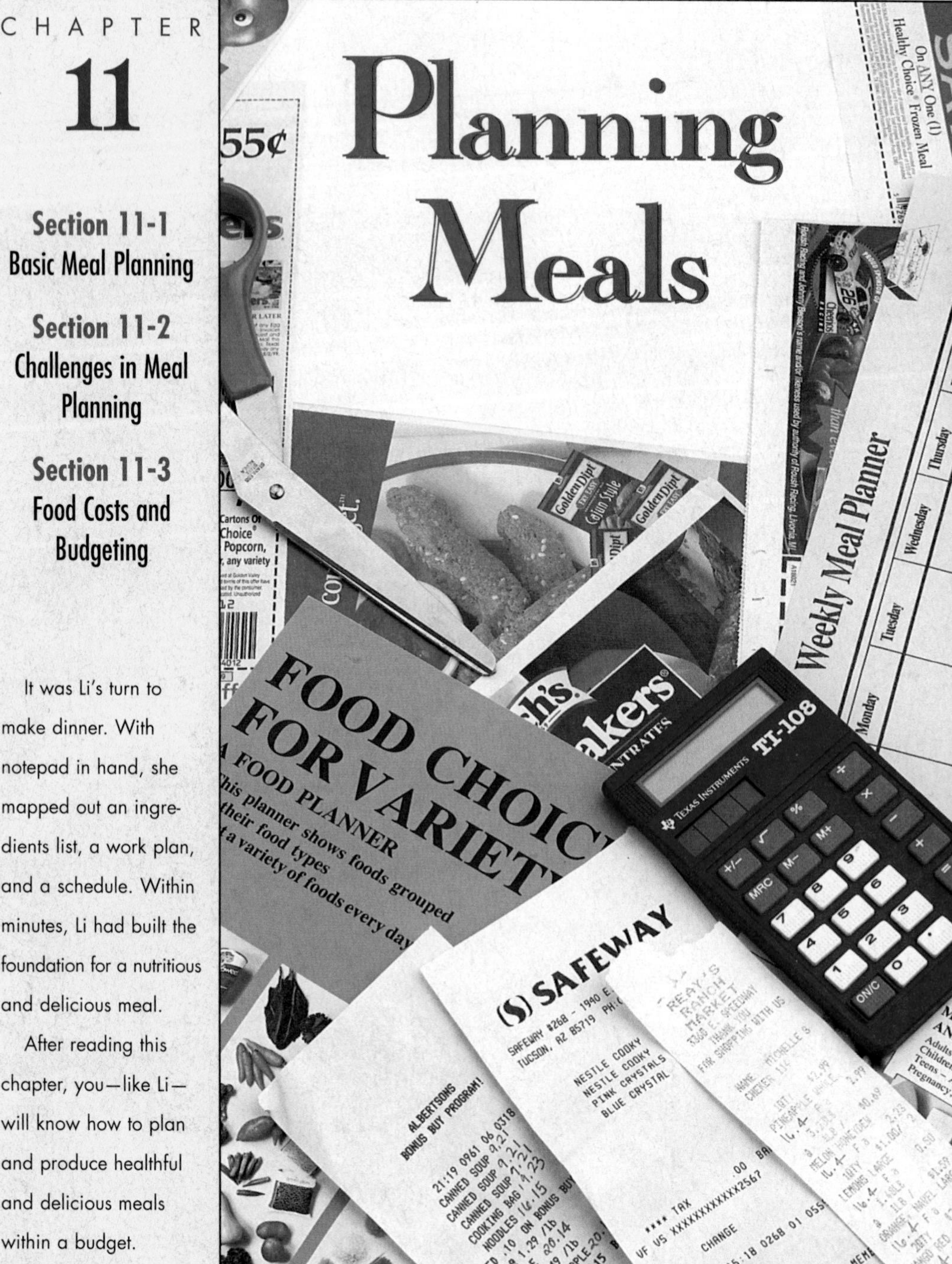

MEETING DIVERSE NEEDS

Logical/Mathematical Learner. If there are students in the class who have an aptitude for numbers, invite them to plan a week's worth of menus for a family of four with a weekly food budget of $70. Students will need to visit a supermarket or use supermarket ads to find prices for all food items within their menus. Have students provide copies of their menus for class inspection, along with the total cost of meals per day.

SECTION
11-1

Objectives

After studying this section, you should be able to:

- Identify factors that affect meal planning.
- Describe characteristics that make meals appealing.
- Explain how to coordinate a work plan and schedule for preparing a meal.
- Discuss the benefits of weekly meal planning.

Look for These Terms

meal appeal

texture

Basic Meal Planning

Before you can play ice hockey, you must know how to skate. Similarly, before you can plan an entire meal, you need to know how to plan a recipe. Many of the skills involved in meal planning and recipe planning are the same.

Factors to Consider

Planning a meal involves making decisions about what foods to include and how to prepare them. As you begin to plan, keep in mind a number of factors. One is nutrition. Use what you have learned about the Dietary Guidelines and the Food Guide Pyramid to create healthful menus.

Another factor is how the meal fits in with the day's eating pattern. You might choose different foods for the main meal of the day than you would for a light lunch or supper. A third factor to think about is the people who will be eating the meal. What are their individual nutrition needs? What foods do they like and dislike? Are there certain foods that must be avoided for medical or other reasons? Finally, consider your resources. Good meal planning makes use of resource management.

INFOLINK

For specific nutrition recommendations found in the Dietary Guidelines and Food Guide Pyramid, see Sections 3-1 and 3-2.

SECTION
11-1
Basic Meal Planning

FOCUS

MOTIVATORS

- Ask students to work in pairs to identify factors to consider when planning a meal. Ask several pairs to share their responses with the class.
- Ask students to describe their favorite meals. Discuss the appealing characteristics of the meals in terms of flavors, textures, colors, shapes, and sizes.

VOCABULARY ACTIVITY

Pronounce the two terms listed under "Look for These Terms." Have students find the terms and their definitions in the section.

STUDY SKILLS

- **Guided Reading.** Have students look at the headings within Section 11-1 to preview the concepts that will be discussed.
- Have students read the section and complete the appropriate part of the Chapter 11 Study Guide in the *Student Workbook*.

Section 11-1 Resources

◆ **Student Workbook,** pp. 83, 85
◆ **Teacher Resource Guide**
Lesson Plan 11-1 Organizer
Section 11-1 Quiz
◆ **Effective Instruction CD-ROM**
Exam*View*® *Test Generator*
PowerPoint® Slide #25
◆ **Transparency Package,** CT-25
◆ **Student Motivation Kit**
Reteaching Activities, p. 59
Enrichment Activities
Skills for Making Food Choices, pp. 27–28

TEACH

- *Resources for Meals*
- *Meal Appeal (text pages 314-315)*

Listing Activity

Ask students to list and describe the resources used for meal planning and preparation in their notes. Then have several student volunteers share a description of one of the resources they listed. Ask students to explain how an individual's meal preparation skills can be considered a resource.

Using Recipes

Provide students with cookbooks; ask them to choose three recipes. Have students analyze the recipes to determine the resources needed to prepare them. Ask several students to share their recipes, while discussing the resources needed. L1

Comparing Alternatives Activity

Define *trade-off* and read the examples on text page 314. Ask students to think of another example of a situation in which a trade-off must be made when planning and preparing meals.

Demonstration

Demonstrate how to take a bland, "white" food meal and make it more appealing by making a few minor changes, such as adding salsa to baked chicken, peas or diced green onions to rice, and a sprinkle of cinnamon on applesauce. Discuss other suggestions.

Resources for Meals

What resources are involved in meal planning and preparation?

- **Time and energy.** If time or energy for meal preparation is limited, plan a meal that's simple to fix. You might look for a quick and easy recipe or think about using convenience foods along with fresh ones.
- **Food choices and availability.** Supermarkets offer an amazing variety of food. Still, your choices may be limited. Some foods are seasonal, especially fresh fruits. Your food store may not carry the items needed to prepare a special recipe. You might have to substitute an ingredient or choose another recipe.
- **Money.** Most people have a limited food budget. With careful planning, however, you can stretch your food dollars. You'll find helpful suggestions in Sections 11-3 and 12-3.
- **Preparation skills.** If you are just learning to cook, choose simple recipes that you can prepare with confidence. As you develop your skills, you can choose more complex recipes.
- **Equipment.** When you find a new recipe you think you might like, consider whether you have the necessary tools and equipment. If you don't, think about other items you might substitute. For example, a chicken stir-fry dish could be cooked in a skillet instead of a wok.

Using resources wisely often means making trade-offs. For instance, a microwave oven lets you use one resource (equipment) to save another (time). Cooking with convenience foods also saves time but may cost more than cooking meals from scratch. You must decide which is most important to you, time or money.

◆ **With practice, you can plan meals that are simple and delicious. Identify two factors to think about when planning a meal.**

Meal Appeal

Usually, meal planning begins with choosing a main course. Then you add side dishes that will complement it.

When selecting a main course, think about **meal appeal**—the characteristics that make a meal appetizing and enjoyable. In particular, consider:

- **Color.** Think of your dinner plate as an artist's palette. Plan meals that include an array of colors. Colorful fruits and vegetables, for example, can help brighten any meal.
- **Shape and size.** Food is most appealing when the shapes and sizes vary. For example, cut carrots into strips and tomatoes into quarters. To vary the shape, chop, dice, cube, serve whole, or cut food with decorative cutters.

HOME & COMMUNITY CONNECTION

Provide students with three recipes calling for exotic ingredients and/or equipment. Ask them to list all resources needed for recipe preparation and to compare this list with resources in their home kitchen or the class foods lab. If students lack ingredients, skills, or other resources, have them identify trade-offs they could make to eliminate the roadblocks to preparation. Ask students to share trade-off suggestions.

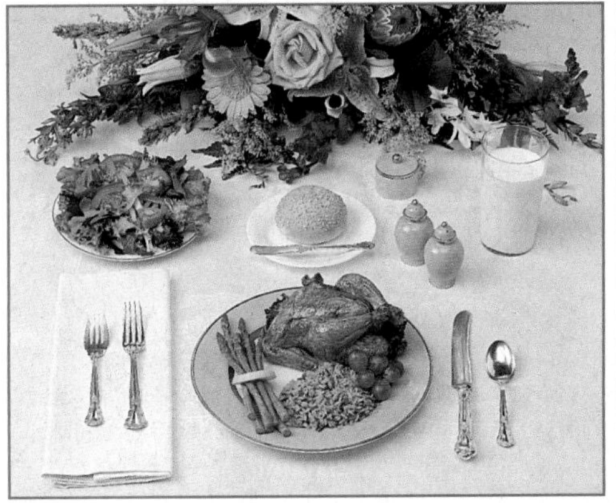

◆ Planning for eye appeal is critical. Which of these two meals would you rather eat?

- **Flavor and aroma.** Try to avoid using foods with similar flavors or aromas in one meal. If all the foods are strongly flavored—for example, spicy chili with garlic bread—the combination can clash. What type of bread would be better suited to this dish? Why?
- **Texture. Texture** is the way food feels when you chew it—for example, soft or hard, crisp or chewy. A meal should include a variety of textures. For example, with a soft main dish, such as pasta, you might serve a crisp tossed salad.
- **Temperature.** If you were planning lunch for a cold winter day, steaming hot soup would be more welcome than a chilled salad. Keep meal appeal in mind when you serve the food, too. Hot foods should be piping hot and cold foods crisply chilled. To be sure they stay that way, serve hot and cold foods on separate plates.

INFOLINK

For the basics of putting together a work plan and schedule for a recipe, see Section 8-5.

Planning a Meal

Drew's plan—to make a surprise Sunday brunch to celebrate his parents' wedding anniversary—started off well. In a magazine, he found a delicious-sounding recipe for French toast with a cherry topping. When his parents entered the kitchen, however, they found Drew fuming over burned food, an empty coffee pot, and still-frozen orange juice.

What went wrong? Drew didn't prepare a work plan and schedule. After deciding on his menu, Drew should have listed the basic steps in preparing each item. He should then have estimated the preparation and cooking time needed for each step, including the time needed for general tasks such as getting ready to cook and setting the table. Finally, Drew should have considered the best way to combine the separate tasks for each food into one plan for the meal by noting which tasks would take the most time.

- *Meal Appeal*
- *Planning a Meal (text pages 314-317)*

Poster Project

Have students collect and display pictures that illustrate various ways to make meals appealing, as in the left photo on page 315. Ask several students to identify ways variety is provided in color, shape and size, texture, flavor, and temperature in their posters. L1

Brainstorming Activity

Ask students to brainstorm ways they could conserve natural resources in the kitchen by planning ahead. Record suggestions on the chalkboard. What resources are most likely to be wasted in the kitchen?

Student Demonstrations

Have students work in groups to plan a demonstration of a lunch with meal appeal. Suggest that students have each person in their group bring one food item for the planned demonstration. Allot each group ten minutes to show the class its lunch menu and discuss why their meal has appeal. Encourage other students to comment on each demonstration. If possible, have students provide sample taste tests. L1

Reinforcing Key Skills

Present the following problems to student groups. Allow time for them to discuss and compare their responses.

Management—Give students a menu that is nutritious but not appealing. Challenge students to identify ways to make the meal more appealing.

Communication—You are in charge of preparing a dinner for a party next week. The requested dinner is roast turkey breast, mashed potatoes, and steamed cauliflower. What might you say to the person who is requesting this meal?

TEACH cont.

- *Planning a Meal (text pages 315-317)*

VISUAL LEARNING ***Using the Photograph*** Direct students to the caption of the photo on this page. Extend the questions by asking: What kinds of foods would you not make in advance? Why?

USING THE Food Science LAB

Assign the Food Science Lab, "The Role of the Senses in Meal Appeal." Prior to attempting the lab, students should read through the procedure and attempt to form hypotheses. Explain that this is a vital first step in carrying out any experiment.

After students have completed the activity, discuss the role of the sense of sight alone as a visual stimulus to food appreciation. Ask: In what way is the sense of sight important to enjoying a meal?

Discussion Activity

Ask students to describe the steps required to make a work plan for an entire meal. Discuss ways to cut down on last-minute tasks in meal preparation.

Meal Planning Activity

Define *dovetailing*. Remind students that dovetailing the preparation of two or more dishes should be considered at the meal planning stage. Experienced cooks do so almost automatically. Provide students with a menu for a family meal. Ask students to identify all the tasks necessary for preparing the meal.

Safety Check

As you make your work plan, remember to allow time for:

- Washing utensils and work surfaces to prevent cross-contamination.
- Returning perishable foods to the refrigerator or freezer.
- Cooking or chilling foods thoroughly.

◆ **A tossed salad can be made ahead and refrigerated until mealtime. What other foods might be prepared in advance?**

Food Science ◆ LAB ◆

The Role of the Senses in Meal Appeal

What role do your senses play in your enjoyment of a meal? As you will see, the solution involves using not just your eyes, nose, and mouth but also your mind.

Procedure

1. Arrange nine different foods on a table. Ask each of three groups of volunteers to select three foods. Foods used in the experiment should range from fairly bland and colorless (for example, cottage cheese) to fairly spicy and bold (such as salsa).
2. Invite each group to arrange its three foods on a plate as attractively as possible. Then ask each group to smell the combined foods and, finally, to taste them.
3. Ask each group to rate the combinations from 1 to 5 in terms of sight, taste, and smell. Record the reactions.

Conclusions

- ◆ Which sense—sight, smell, or taste—appeared to play the greatest role in a group's reaction?
- ◆ Was variety a factor in the results? Explain.
- ◆ Repeat the experiment. This time carefully choose combinations for each group that have meal appeal. How, if at all, did the ratings differ?

A Meal Work Plan

A basic principle in any meal work plan is to start with the food that takes the longest time to prepare. Suppose you plan to bake chicken pieces in the oven for an hour. If the other foods will take less time, plan to get the chicken ready to bake first. Then you can work on other parts of the meal while the chicken is in the oven.

Extending Learning

Dovetailing—The term *dovetail* is used in the furniture construction industry to describe the process of fitting two pieces of wood tightly together in an interlocking joint that resembles a dove's tail. In meal preparation, dovetailing means organizing various tasks so that they fit together for efficient use of time.

To cut down on last-minute tasks, consider whether foods can safely be prepared early. For instance, you could assemble a tossed salad (except for the dressing) and then put it in the refrigerator. Setting the table can also be done ahead of time, or you might plan on asking a helper to do it for you.

After you've decided on the sequence of steps in your work plan, figure out the total time needed. If the meal will take too long to prepare, think about changes that would help. For example, would chicken pieces cook faster than a whole chicken? Would changing to a different cooking method cut down on time?

A Meal Schedule

When you're satisfied with the work plan, you can use it to make a schedule for meal preparation. Decide what time you want to serve the meal. Count backward from that time to determine when you need to start preparation.

The work plan and schedule on page 318 show how the planning process could have prevented Drew's surprise brunch from turning into a catastrophe.

Weekly Meal Planning

Most people find it helpful to plan meals for a week or more at a time. Long-range planning has several advantages. It cuts down on anxiety and time spent on deciding what to serve every day. It promotes a greater variety of meals and helps you get the most for your food dollar. It decreases unneeded trips to the supermarket for forgotten items. It also makes food preparation more organized and efficient.

When planning a week's worth of meals, use what you have already learned about planning menus. Here are some additional tips:

- ◆ Aim for balanced nutrition and variety in meals and snacks over the course of the week. Check to see that the menus for each day provide enough servings from the Food Guide Pyramid.
- ◆ Set aside a regular time and place for meal planning.
- ◆ Ask family members about their plans for the week. Knowing when family members need to eat early, late, or away from home can affect the menus and recipes you choose.
- ◆ Check the refrigerator, freezer, and kitchen cabinets to see what foods you have on hand. Think of ways to use these foods (especially perishables, such as leftovers and fresh fruits and vegetables).
- ◆ Check newspaper ads to see what foods are on sale.
- ◆ Plan nutritious snacks as well as meals.

Work Plan and Schedule
7:00 Get ready to cook
7:10 Set table
Mix juice and refrigerate
7:20 Turn on oven to preheat
7:25 Grease baking dish
Mix batter; dip bread slices;
7:30 put in baking dish
Put French toast in oven; set timer
7:40 for 8 min. Start coffee
Start preparing cherry mixture
7:45 Turn French toast, set timer for 8 min.
7:48 continue preparing cherry mixture
Remove French toast from oven, put on
7:56 platter; put cherry topping in serving dish
Pour juice and milk
7:58 Serve coffee; breakfast is ready!
8:00

- *Weekly Meal Planning (text pages 317-320)*

Brainstorming Activity

Divide the class into brainstorming teams. Instruct each team to make a list of all the foods served in their favorite family meals. Then, working on one meal at a time, groups are to make a second list of those foods that can be prepared in advance. Have groups share lists. Ask: What does this experience reveal about the importance of planning?

Lab Experience

1. Provide students with recipes for a simple family meal.
2. Have students work in lab groups to study the recipes and plan the time and sequence for preparing a simple family meal.
3. Assign one member of each group the role of observer.
4. Have students prepare and serve the meal.
5. The observer should evaluate how well the group did each of the following: assemble equipment and ingredients, do pre-preparation, follow a logical work plan/schedule, simplify work techniques, and clean up.
6. After the lab, discuss the strengths and opportunities for improvement observed in each group. How did any problem areas or areas of strength effect the meal results? L1

HOME & COMMUNITY CONNECTION

Have students plan and prepare a family meal. Before preparing the meal, they should read the recipe and prepare a work plan and schedule. When preparing the meal, the students should assemble equipment and ingredients first, do pre-preparation tasks, simplify work techniques, and clean up as they go. After the meal, family members should evaluate the results. Have a few students share their experience with the class.

- *Weekly Meal Planning (text pages 317-320)*

Listing Activity

While you record responses on the chalkboard or overhead projector, ask students to brainstorm a list of all the advantages of planning meals a week or more in advance. Then ask students to brainstorm all the problems that could result when not planning meals. Compare the lists.

Checklists

Have students develop a checklist of tips for planning meals in advance. Have students use the checklist to help plan a meal for their families. Encourage students to create a computerized checklist and provide a disk of it to their family to help them plan all family meals. L1

Menu Development Activity

Provide students a list of the "mock" contents of a freezer, refrigerator, and kitchen cabinets. Challenge students to plan a breakfast, lunch, and dinner based on the choices available. Encourage nutritious meal planning with meal appeal. Have several student volunteers share their one-day menus with the class. Note the numerous menu possibilities based on the same foods.

Work Plan and Schedule

Task	Preparation Time	Cooking Time
General Tasks:		
Get ready to cook.	10 min.	
Set table.	10 min.	
Oven French Toast:		
Preheat oven.		15 min.
Grease baking dish.	5 min.	
Mix egg batter; dip bread slices in batter; put in baking dish.	10 min.	
Bake on first side.		8 min.
Turn and bake on other side.		8 min.
Glazed Cherry Topping:		
Open canned cherries; put in saucepan; mix cornstarch and water and add to cherries.	5 min.	
Cook cherry mixture as directed in recipe.		4-6 min.
Orange Juice:		
Mix frozen concentrate in pitcher; refrigerate.	5 min.	
Coffee:		
Prepare in coffeemaker.	5 min.	15 min.
Serving Tasks:		
Put food in serving dishes.	2 min.	
Pour beverages.	2 min.	

Time	Task
9:00	Get ready to cook.
9:10	Set table.
9:20	Mix juice and refrigerate.
9:25	Turn on oven to preheat. Grease baking dish.
9:30	Mix batter; dip bread slices; put in baking dish.
9:40	Put French toast in oven; set timer for 8 min. Start coffee.
9:45	Start preparing cherry mixture.
9:48	Turn French toast; set timer for 8 min. Continue preparing cherry mixture.
9:56	Remove French toast from oven; put on platter; put cherry topping in serving dish.
9:58	Pour juice and milk.
10:00	Serve coffee; brunch is ready!

Extending Learning

Meal Management—When it comes to the final steps of planning meals, there are many management styles you can use, such as:

- One person is primarily responsible for planning and preparing meals.
- Two or more people in the household share responsibility for the meals.
- The whole family is involved in meal planning and shopping. When involved, members are more likely to try to be home for mealtime.

Once you have the menus for the week, you can use them to make your shopping list. As you will learn in Chapter 12, a shopping list can help you manage money as well as time.

When you first try it, planning a week's worth of meals may seem time-consuming. However, it becomes easier with practice. Once you have planned meals for several months, you can use them over and over again. In the long run, weekly planning is well worth the initial investment of time.

Sample Weekly Menu Plan

	Breakfast	Lunch	Dinner	Snacks	Memos
MONDAY	Bran Cereal Sliced Bananas Rye Toast Milk/Coffee	(Packed) Turkey Sandwich Carrot/Celery Sticks Pretzels Apple Milk (buy)	Spaghetti and Meatballs Tossed Salad Garlic Bread Milk/Coffee Italian Ice	Fresh Fruits or Vegetables Trail Mix Cranberry Juice	Krystal—not home for dinner, swim team banquet.
TUESDAY	French Toast Kiwi Halves Milk/Coffee	(Packed) Peanut Butter–Whole Wheat Sandwich Broccoli/Carrots Pear Milk (buy)	Beans and Rice Corn Tortillas Spinach Salad Milk/Coffee Sliced Fruit	Fresh Fruits or Vegetables Popcorn Vegetable Juice	Everyone home for dinner.
WEDNESDAY	Bagels with Nonfat Cream Cheese Orange Slices Milk/Coffee	Mom and Dad—lunch out Jason and Krystal—school lunch	Baked Chicken Brown Rice Broccoli Spears Whole Wheat Rolls Coleslaw Milk/Coffee	Fresh Fruits or Vegetables Pretzels	Dad—late for dinner, grocery shopping after work.
THURSDAY	Oatmeal with Raisins Whole Wheat Toast Milk/Coffee	(Packed) Leftover Chicken Sandwiches Carrot/Celery Sticks Banana Milk (buy)	Spicy Chili with Beans Cornbread Tossed Salad Milk	Popcorn Strawberry Frozen Yogurt	Jason's basketball game—eat early.

• ***Sample Weekly Menu Plan (text pages 319-320)***

Review Activity

Review the steps for preparing a recipe. Refer students to the list of tasks and the work schedule in the text on page 318. Discuss the steps in making the work plan and schedule.

Guest Speaker

Invite the school food service director to describe how school menus are planned. Have students prepare at least one question each to potentially ask the food service director about school menus. Do the menus need to meet national standards? What are cycle menus? Why are they used? How do they save time? Are they always reused exactly? If not, what changes are likely to be made and why?

Menu Planning

Have students plan a week's menus for their own families using the suggestions and model on pages 319 and 320. Suggest they interview their family members for menu suggestions and to make sure they have or can obtain all resources needed for the menu. Encourage students to plan the menu on the computer. Invite students to share their family menus with the class. L1

Reinforcing Key Skills

Present the following problems to student groups. Allow time for them to discuss and compare their responses.

Management—Tamara suggests that her family plan menus a week in advance, but her mother complains that her job is taking all of her time and that meal planning is too time-consuming. What action might Tamara take both to help out at home and to demonstrate the usefulness of such a plan?

ASSESS

REVIEW

- Ask students to summarize the main ideas in this section.
- Have students complete the Section Review. (Answers appear below.)

EVALUATION

- Provide students with a copy of a menu for an unappetizing dinner meal. Have students give it a meal "makeover" to make it more appealing yet nutritious.
- Have students take the quiz for Section 11-1. (Use the quiz in the *Teacher Resource Guide,* or construct your own with the **Exam***View*® *Test Generator* on the *Effective Instruction CD-ROM.*)

RETEACHING

- Have students work in pairs. One partner is to read aloud a general heading from the section. The other is to write two useful facts contained in that section. The partners are to take turns.
- Refer to the *Reteaching Activities* booklet for the Section 11-1 activity sheet.

CLOSE

Have three groups work together to create a one-day menu that takes into account all characteristics of meal appeal. Discuss all the positive characteristics of each meal on the menu.

Sample Weekly Menu Plan (cont'd)

	Breakfast	*Lunch*	*Dinner*	*Snacks*	*Memos*
FRIDAY	Assorted Cereals Bananas Whole Wheat Toast with Fruit Spread Milk/Coffee	(Packed) Leftover Chili Red and Green Pepper Sticks Corn Chips Mixed Fruit Cup Milk (buy)	Take-out Pizza Tossed Salad Mixed Fruit Juice	Fresh Fruits with Plain Yogurt Brownie	Jason—eating out with friends.
SATURDAY	Scrambled Eggs Bacon Whole Wheat Toast Orange Juice Milk/Coffee	Hearty Vegetable Soup Corn Muffin Fruit Milk	Grilled Burgers with Buns Potato Salad Sliced Tomatoes Milk/Coffee	Popcorn Flavored Yogurt Mixed Fruit Juice	Rob and Kara coming over for dinner.
SUNDAY	Bran Muffins Grapefruit Milk/Coffee	Baked Ham Sweet Potatoes Broccoli Fruit Salad Milk Angel Food Cake	Sandwiches or Leftover Pizza Coleslaw	Fresh Fruits or Vegetables Rice Cakes	Plan next week's menus.

Section 11-1 Review & Activities

1. Identify four factors that affect your decisions when planning meals.
2. What is meal appeal?
3. What is the first step in making a work plan for a meal?
4. **Evaluating.** Do you think it is necessary to make a work plan and schedule for every meal? Why or why not? What are the pros and cons of doing so?
5. **Comparing and Contrasting.** Make a Venn diagram showing how energy, time, and money management are related in meal planning.
6. **Applying.** Plan a basic meal for you and your family. Develop a work plan and schedule for preparing this meal. If possible, proceed with the preparation; then write about the experience in your Wellness Journal.

Answers to Section 11-1 Review & Activities

1. See page 313.
2. The characteristics that make a meal appetizing and enjoyable.
3. List the basic steps in preparing each dish.
4. Answers will vary. It's helpful, especially at first. It's the best way to ensure successful meal preparation and may help save time. Possible con: Difficulty sticking to the plan due to unpredictable situations that arise.
5. Answers will vary.
6. Answers will vary.

SECTION
11-2

Challenges in Meal Planning

Serena's mother has a full-time job and her brother plays several school sports. With Serena's own busy schedule, it is anyone's guess which family members will be home for dinner!

Situations like this one are a real challenge to meal planning. A busy lifestyle, however, does not have to interfere with enjoying nutritious, tasty foods. In this section, you will learn about ways of dealing with the challenges of meal planning.

Objectives

After studying this section, you should be able to:

- Identify meal planning strategies for families with busy schedules.
- Give suggestions for planning meals for one person.
- Discuss ways to handle unexpected changes in mealtime plans.

Look for This Term

versatility

Multiple Roles

The family is really hungry, but who has time to cook? This is a common dilemma today as busy people manage multiple roles. Each role a person has—in the family, in the community, and at work or school—has responsibilities that demand time. As a result, such responsibilities as cooking wholesome meals get squeezed into shorter time frames.

Management skills help people who are pressed for time. Those who plan and set priorities know what needs to be done first. By identifying resources, they know where to turn for support. After listing tasks, they develop schedules and assign responsibilities. During a family meeting, for example, they might decide who will plan meals, shop, cook, and clean up. Tasks can be rotated periodically. With a little creative thought, busy schedules don't have to put mealtimes and other responsibilities at risk.

Tips for Busy Schedules

When schedules are full, preparing meals can be a challenge. The following tips are useful:

- ◆ Plan weekly menus at one time instead of deciding what to eat at the last minute.
- ◆ Collect healthful recipes that can be fixed quickly. Keep them close at hand.
- ◆ Use the microwave oven in new ways. It does more than heat foods.
- ◆ Make use of one-dish meals. Some are easier to prepare than separate dishes.

SECTION
11-2
Challenges in Meal Planning

FOCUS

MOTIVATORS

- Ask students to think about how many meals a week their families eat together. How do family schedules affect meal planning?
- Ask students to give a "thumbs up" or "thumbs down" as to whether they believe it would be easier or harder to plan meals for one. Ask several students to explain their reasoning.

VOCABULARY ACTIVITY

Pronounce the term listed under "Look for This Term." Have students find the term and its definition in the section.

STUDY SKILLS

- **Listening.** Invite a group of volunteers to each prepare an oral reading of a page of text from the section, while others follow along silently.
- Have students read the section and complete the appropriate part of the Chapter 11 Study Guide in the *Student Workbook*.

Section 11-2 Resources

◆ **Student Workbook,** pp. 83, 86
◆ **Teacher Resource Guide**
Lesson Plan 11-2 Organizer
Section 11-2 Quiz
◆ **Effective Instruction CD-ROM**
Exam*View*® *Test Generator*
◆ **Student Motivation Kit**
Reteaching Activities, p. 60
Enrichment Activities
Foods Lab Resources, pp. 45–46

TEACH

- *Multiple Roles*
- *Tips for Busy Schedules (text pages 321-322)*

Listing Activity

Discuss how planning meals at least a week in advance can help you save time. Then have students review the time-saving ideas listed on pages 321 and 322 of the text. After they have studied the list, ask them to write additional time-saving suggestions on the board.

Recipe Comparisons

Have students locate recipes that are ideal for families with busy schedules. Collect the recipes into a multi-page document, titled "Busy Life Cookbook." Give each student a copy. Then have students design a menu for a full week for a family of four based mainly on recipes in the document. L2

Debate

Have students form two groups for a debate. One group is to argue: "Hectic schedules make it impossible to plan family meals." The other is to argue: "Family meals are possible with good planning." Have the teams stage a debate in front of an impartial jury of their peers. L2

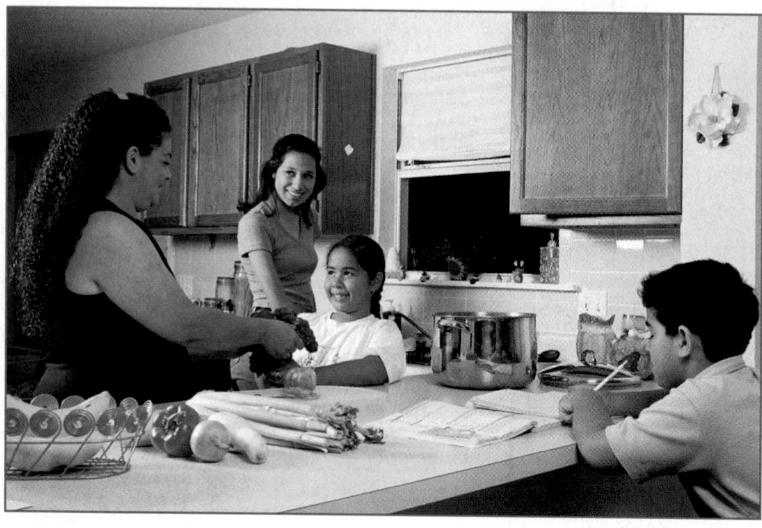

◆ A busy lifestyle can influence a person's cooking style. What are some ways in which the skills of teamwork and leadership can be used to help organize family chores in the kitchen?

- Look for ways to combine convenience foods with fresh foods in recipes and meals.
- Learn how to "cook for the freezer." When preparing a recipe, double or triple it and freeze the extra. Some families make cooking for the freezer a weekend project.
- Look for recipes with **versatility**—the capability of being adapted to many uses. For instance, Janice has a recipe for a basic seasoned meat-and-bean mixture, which can be used in a variety of recipes, such as chili, burritos, and taco salad. She prepares a large amount of the mixture and freezes it in recipe-size quantities to use in different ways.

Safety Check

Freezing extra portions of food is a good idea for people with busy schedules. Be careful, however, when thawing frozen food. The safest way to thaw it is slowly in the refrigerator. If you need the item in a hurry, thaw it in the microwave and cook it immediately.

INFOLINK

For more on changing a recipe in terms of its quantity, or yield, see Section 8-3.

Unpredictable Schedules

When family members have varied schedules, it's not always possible for everyone to sit down to a meal together. Here are some ideas for flexible meals:

- Plan meals that can be cooked early and refrigerated or frozen. Include instructions on how to assemble or reheat.
- Prepare one-dish meals in a slow cooker. Family members can help themselves as time permits.
- Set up a "breakfast bar" near the refrigerator with assorted cereals, bowls, spoons, and glasses. Keep milk, juice, and fresh fruit on one refrigerator shelf within easy reach.

HOME & COMMUNITY CONNECTION

Have students set up a "breakfast bar" at home based on the suggestion under the heading "Unpredictable Schedules" on page 322. Encourage students to use creative thinking, adding their own ideas to the "bar." After it is set up and utilized, students are to evaluate its usefulness based on their family's reactions. Have students report findings back to class. Ask: Did it help your family save time? Eat more healthfully? Eat breakfast when they normally skip it?

Meals for One

Shopping for food and preparing meals for one person is another challenge that requires thought, planning, and creativity. Most recipes provide four, six, or even eight servings, and not all can be decreased easily. Small sizes of packaged foods may be hard to find or expensive. Buying and preparing large quantities of food can result in a person eating the same food day after day.

One suggestion for getting around this problem is buying bulk foods in just the quantity needed. Another option is sharing large food packages—or even meals—with a friend. Still another is storing as many foods as possible in single-serving packages. For example, a pound of ground meat might be divided into four patties that can be separately wrapped and frozen.

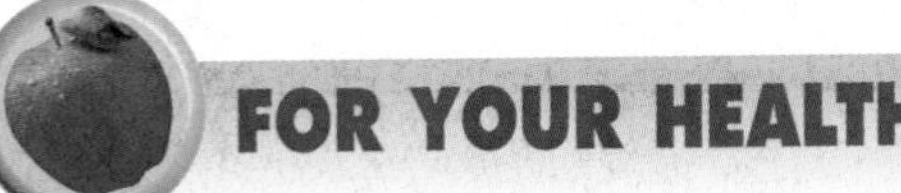

FOR YOUR HEALTH

Table for One

With increasing numbers of people marrying later or not marrying at all, more and more Americans are living "the single life." Is it possible to plan and prepare healthful meals for one person? The answer is yes. Here are some strategies for eating well and alone:

- To ensure that the foods you buy stay fresh, ask store managers for small packages of produce and meat items. For example, a whole watermelon could be cut in half or quarters.
- Consider buying small portions of salad ingredients at the supermarket salad bar if one is available. This option may seem more costly, but you'll have less waste.

Following Up

- Which of the strategies recommended above would also help a single person avoid the tendency to overeat? Explain your answer.

◆ **Simple one-dish meals such as arroz con pollo—a flavorful blend of seasoned rice and chicken—can save time. What are four other ways of working preparation into a busy schedule?**

Some singles slip into poor eating habits because they neglect to plan for and prepare nutritious meals. Cooking and cleaning up a meal may not seem worth the effort for just one person. Here again, management skills can help. The suggestions already given for busy lifestyles can help make meal preparation easier for single people, too.

Even when dining alone, singles should attempt to make mealtime special. Setting an attractive table and enjoying a relaxing meal can be a satisfying and healthful end to a busy day.

- *Meals for One*
- *When Plans Must Change (text pages 323-324)*

VISUAL LEARNING ***Using the Photograph*** Direct students to the photo of the teen holding up a platter of arroz con pollo. Provide cookbooks representing many different cultures to students. Have students identify dishes that can save time. Ask students to write their recipe name on a flagged push pin. Then, one by one, have students state their recipe name, provide a brief description of it, name the culture/country it represents, and then place the flagged push pin in the appropriate place on a world map on the bulletin board.

Group Meal Planning

Have student groups list foods that can be prepared early and frozen, for help with meals for unpredictable schedules. Suggest that liquids or sauces can be frozen in ice cube trays. Have each group share a copy of its list with all students. **L1**

Cooking Show

1. Have a team of six or seven students stage a live cooking show.
2. They are to begin by developing a "meal for one teen" recipe based on a class brainstorming session or questionnaire. One possible idea: pizza for one.
3. Group members are to assume roles. Some are to design a stage set, others are to do the preparatory work (setting up) in the lab, while still others are to write a script and prepare cue cards. One or two students are to serve as the TV chef(s) and prepare the food item.
4. If possible, videotape the show; air it on the school TV or computer network. **L3**

Extending Learning

Effects of Distractors on Eating— Weight-management programs often suggest that a person not watch television or read while eating—mainly to help prevent these activities from being associated with eating.

Alternatively, some experts suggest playing music or watching television while eating alone—to help improve the single person's meal enjoyment and help maintain good eating habits.

Have interested students develop experiments for either situation to test the effects of distractors on eating.

ASSESS

REVIEW

- Ask students to summarize the main ideas in this section.
- Have students complete the Section Review. (Answers appear below.)

EVALUATION

- Have each student pick a challenging meal planning situation out of a hat. Then have each prepare a short presentation on how to overcome their challenge.
- Have students take the quiz for Section 11-2. (Use the quiz in the *Teacher Resource Guide,* or construct your own with the **ExamView®** *Test Generator* on the *Effective Instruction CD-ROM.*)

RETEACHING

- Give students several menus for complete meals, some that can be prepared quickly and some that cannot. Have students practice identifying those that would be good choices for people with busy schedules or for emergencies when a quick meal is necessary.
- Refer to the *Reteaching Activities* booklet for the Section 11-2 activity sheet.

CLOSE

Prepare a class tip sheet on the options for eating nutritious meals at home when you need to plan for a busy household. Have one student enter tips onto a word processing software program and provide copies to each student.

When Plans Must Change

Life can be unpredictable. Sometimes it becomes necessary to change plans. You may not get home in time to prepare the meal you had planned. Illness or last-minute schedule changes can also disrupt meals.

To prepare for these times, keep a supply of "backup" foods on hand. Stock up on nutritious, quick-to-prepare foods that are shelf-stable or freezer-ready. Some basic items to consider are nonfat dry milk; canned chicken, tuna, and salmon; canned beans; and frozen portions of cooked dry beans, rice, and pasta. Set aside a few recipes or menus planned around your backup foods. If the unexpected happens, you'll be prepared.

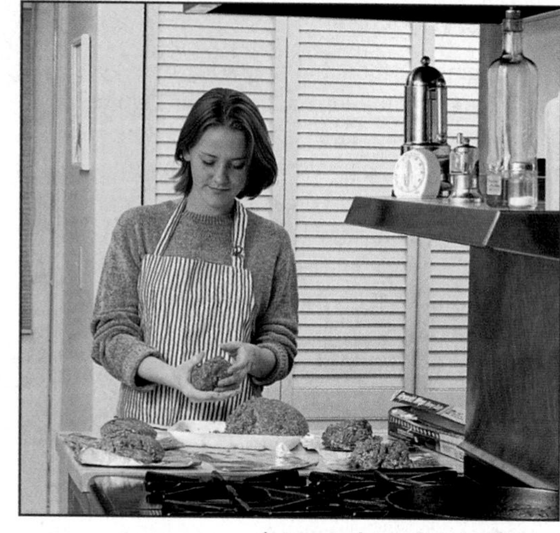

◆ Large packages of meat, which are often more economical to buy, can be divided for freezing. You can base the size of each smaller package on whether the meat will be used for a single-serving portion or a multi-serving dish.

INFOLINK

For more on shelf-stable foods and how to store them, see Section 7-4.

Section 11-2 Review & Activities

1. How do multiple roles affect people's lives? In what ways can management skills help?
2. What is meant by "cooking for the freezer"? How can it help families whose members lead busy lives?
3. Give three suggestions singles can use to plan and prepare meals.
4. **Applying.** Plan an "emergency" meal for you and your family using foods that can be kept on hand. Evaluate the meal for nutrition and appeal.
5. **Extending.** Find information on time management. Present what you learn to the class, including suggestions about how to manage time effectively.
6. **Applying.** Both parents in the Carter home are employed. Both teens in the family are also busy with school and church activities and coaching youth softball. Often by the time they all arrive home in the evening, they are too tired to cook and can't decide what to eat, so they grab something or go out. This routine is hard on the budget and their health. What suggestions would help the Carters?

Answers to Section 11-2 Review & Activities

1. They require that many duties fit a limited time; management allows you to plan, prioritize, and identify resources.
2. Preparing large quantities of a recipe and freezing excess. It saves time and fits unpredictable schedules.
3. Any three suggestions in "Meals for One," "For Your Health," page 323.
4. Answers will vary.
5. Answers will vary.
6. Answers may include: hold family meeting to assign food tasks; collect quick, nutritious recipes, especially one-dish meals; cook for freezer; keep supply of nutritious shelf-stable or frozen foods.

Recipe File

Fresh 'n' Fast Fried Rice

This tasty recipe combines fresh and convenience foods for families in a hurry.

Customary	Ingredients	Metric
3	Eggs	3
2 tsp.	Vegetable oil	10 mL
2 tsp.	Vegetable oil	10 mL
4 cups	Cooked rice, chilled	1 L
1 cup	Reduced-sodium chicken broth	250 mL
1 cup	Frozen green peas, thawed	250 mL
⅓ cup	Diced red pepper	75 mL
1 cup	Canned bean sprouts, drained	250 mL
⅓ cup	Chopped green onions	75 mL

Yield: Six 1-cup (250-ml) servings

Directions

1. In a small bowl, beat the eggs until well combined.
2. In a large, nonstick skillet or wok, heat 2 tsp. vegetable oil over medium heat. Add the eggs and cook, stirring occasionally, for 2 to 5 minutes or until eggs are set. Remove eggs to a bowl and set it aside.
3. Heat the remaining 2 tsp. oil over medium-high heat. Add the rice and stir-fry 5 minutes.
4. Add the remaining ingredients and the cooked eggs, and stir-fry a final 2 minutes.
5. Season as desired, or serve with sodium-reduced soy sauce.

Nutrition Information

Per serving (approximate): 207 calories, 8 g protein, 29 g carbohydrate, 6 g fat, 106 mg cholesterol, 188 mg sodium, 2 g fiber

Good source of: iron, vitamin E, vitamin C, B vitamins

Food for Thought

- Could you prepare this recipe for one person? Which ingredients would be the most difficult to divide by 6?
- Name at least two time-saving suggestions for preparing this recipe.

Recipe File

Fresh 'n' Fast Fried Rice

This recipe uses cooking strategies important for busy schedules, while providing nutrient-rich foods from four of the five food groups. Prior to assigning the lab, you may wish to have students review the portion of the text under the heading "Busy Schedules" on pages 321-322.

USING THE RECIPE

- Have students read the recipe and make sure they understand each step as well as the entire process.
- Review safety and sanitation procedures that apply to this recipe.
- Have each lab team fill out a work plan. (See the *Foods Lab Resources* booklet.)
- Have students check off the ingredients and equipment listed on the recipe worksheet as they gather each resource. Then have them prepare the recipe.
- Have students complete the evaluation and questions on the back of the recipe worksheet.

SEE ALSO...

The *Foods Lab Resources* booklet for the "Fresh 'n' Fast Fried Rice" recipe worksheet and other recipe alternatives.

Answers to Food for Thought

1. Yes, this recipe could be prepared for one person. The ingredients that would be most difficult to divide by 6 are diced red pepper and chopped green onions.
2. Two time-saving suggestions: (1) Thaw frozen green peas overnight in the refrigerator; (2) Dice red peppers and chop green onions at the same time using the same knife and cutting board.

SECTION
11-3
Food Costs and Budgeting

FOCUS

MOTIVATORS

- Ask students if they think food spending varies from family to family and why. List responses on the chalkboard. Later, compare students' responses with those listed in the text.
- Ask students to imagine it is the future and they are living on their own. What factors would they use to decide how much to spend each week for food?

VOCABULARY ACTIVITY

Pronounce the two terms listed under "Look for These Terms." Prior to looking in the text, ask students to suggest what they think the acronym *WIC* represents. Have students find the terms and their definitions in the section.

STUDY SKILLS

- **Outlining.** Have students read the section and outline it by copying the headers on paper and leaving space after each one. Students are to write a sentence in their own words, summarizing the content under each header.
- Have students read the section and complete the appropriate part of the Chapter 11 Study Guide in the *Student Workbook*.

SECTION
11-3
Food Costs and Budgeting

Objectives

After studying this section, you should be able to:

- Identify reasons food spending varies from family to family.
- Describe how using a food budget can help control spending on food.
- Identify programs that offer food assistance to individuals and families in need.

Look for These Terms

budget

WIC program

One day at the supermarket, Myra overheard a couple talking about the price of food. "Food has gotten so expensive. Many of the foods our family likes just cost too much anymore." Myra started to wonder how the cost of food fits into her own family's food budget.

Why Budget?

A **budget** is a plan for managing your money in order to cover the costs of life's necessities. Budgeting involves looking at your income and deciding how much money to set aside for food, housing, clothing, transportation, health care, savings, and other uses.

Food expenses make up a significant portion of most family and personal budgets. For example, an average middle-income family spends about 15 percent of the family income on food. A lower-income family may spend a greater percentage on food simply because the total income amount is less. The challenge for any family is meeting nutrient needs without spending more than the budget allows.

Factors Affecting Food Expenditures

The amount of money spent on food varies according to your personal or family resources, goals, and priorities. Other factors that affect the amount of money a family spends on food include:

- Total family income.
- The number of family members. The larger a family is, the more it will need to spend.
- The age of family members. It costs more to feed growing teens than other members. By the same token, it costs less to feed aging relatives who may be part of the household.

Section 11-3 Resources

◆ **Student Workbook**, pp. 84, 87
◆ **Teacher Resource Guide**
Lesson Plan 11-3 Organizer
Section 11-3 Quiz
Chapter 11 Test
◆ **Effective Instruction CD-ROM**
Exam*View*® *Test Generator*
◆ **Student Motivation Kit**
Reteaching Activities, pp. 61–62
Enrichment Activities

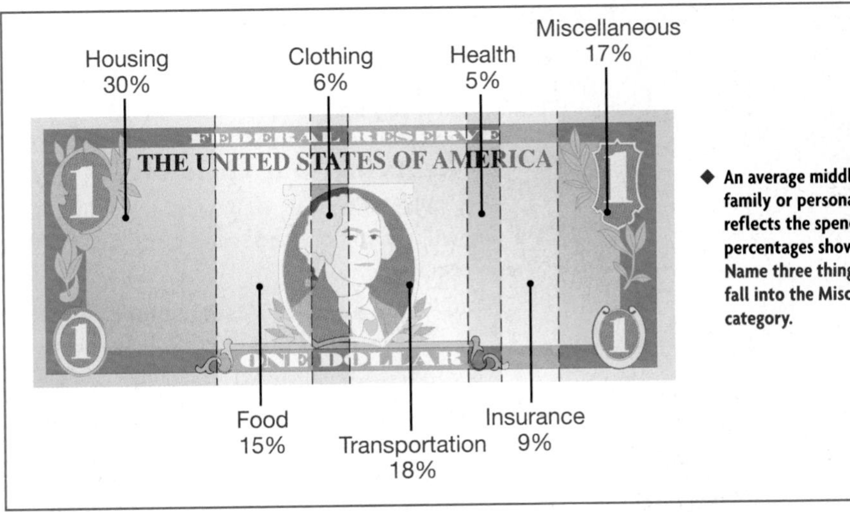

◆ **An average middle-income family or personal budget reflects the spending percentages shown here. Name three things that would fall into the Miscellaneous category.**

- Food prices in your area at various times of the year.
- The amount of food eaten away from home.
- Time and skills available for food preparation.
- The amount of food wasted. Food waste may occur if a food was not stored or prepared properly.

If someone in your family enjoys cooking, you might spend less money by eating more home-prepared meals. However, if busy schedules make convenience a family priority, you may spend more money on convenience foods. Every family has different priorities, so food budgets will vary.

Using a Food Budget

Whether you spend a little or a lot, you can benefit from following a food budget. It can show you whether you may be wasting money—or spending it wisely. It can also help you think about your food choices and determine whether they are wise ones.

Keeping a Spending Record

Setting up a food budget is simple. To begin, analyze how much you spend on food now. Keep a record of all the food you buy for two typical weeks. Divide your record into food bought at the food store and food eaten out. Food eaten out includes take-out food, delivered food, and foods bought from vending machines. Do not include nonfood supplies in your list, such as paper products, even if you buy them at the supermarket.

Add up the expenses for groceries and foods eaten out for the two weeks. Divide the total by two to get the average you spend per week.

Setting a Budget Amount

Use the information from your spending record when you plan your budget. What percentage of your income are you spending on food? Are you comfortable with the amount you are currently spending? If so, plan to spend a similar amount in future weeks. If you want to plan on spending less, set an amount that's slightly lower. Be realistic. If you set an amount

TEACH

- *Why Budget?*
- *Using a Food Budget (text pages 326-329)*

Interview

Ask students to interview a grandparent or other older adult about how food expenditures have changed since he or she was a young adult. Students should write articles relating their findings to modern food budgets. These should be compiled into a class newsletter. **L1**

Budget Project

Suggest students work with their families to keep a record of all food bought at the supermarket and food eaten out by all family members for two weeks. Remind students not to include nonfood supplies in their records. Have students add up the expenses for groceries and foods eaten out for the two weeks. Then divide the total by two to get the average their family spends per week. Have students share results with their family, along with suggestions for reducing the budget, if necessary. **L2**

Product Comparison and Taste Test Activity

Set up a blind taste-test display of three name-brand products and their less expensive, generic or store-brand counterparts. Products may include cereals, crackers, and pretzels. Have students rate the products in terms of taste, appearance, and overall appeal. Then share with students the price of the products. Discuss how price and ratings compared.

Technology TIE-IN

Before the development of modern packaging methods, food arrived at a grocery store in large barrels and boxes. The grocer scooped out the quantity the customer wanted.

Today, an increasing number of supermarkets and food stores feature "bulk foods sections." Customers can scoop out any quantity they want of certain foods from large containers.

Offering bulk foods is more than just nostalgia. It allows customers to control the quantity of foods they want and helps control their budgets.

TEACH cont.

- *Using a Food Budget (text pages 327-329)*

Supermarket Survey & Recipe R & D

Ask students to find and record prices for several lower cost foods from each of the food groups at the supermarket. Using their compiled lists, have students plan a one-day budget menu for a family of four with breakfast, lunch, and dinner. Ask them to create at least one original recipe for one of the meals. Then have them total up the food cost for the day, and for each meal, based on the percentage of each product used. L2

Substitution Activity

Note that Americans historically have spent more for meat than for any other part of the meal. Add that the USDA and Department of Health and Human Services are trying to "beef up" awareness of less expensive and more healthful non-animal protein sources such as dry beans and peas. Invite volunteers to form two task groups. One group is to browse through cookbooks in the classroom library, choose recipes containing meat, and develop non-animal protein variations (e.g., bean loaf for meat loaf). The other group is to create recipes that use dry beans or peas to begin with. Encourage groups to prepare samples of their creations.

◆ **Keeping track of your food spending for a period of time helps you decide on a realistic amount for your food budget. Why is it important to set a realistic food budget?**

that's unrealistically low, you'll find it hard to stay within your budget.

Evaluating the Food Budget

The amount you budget for food is your spending limit, so continue keeping records of food expenses in order to stay within the limit. Amounts will vary weekly since many items are not regular purchases.

After several weeks, examine your spending record. Did you budget the right amount, or do you need to make an adjustment? Consider cutting back in a different expense category if you want to increase the food budget. If you tend to spend too much on food, look at changing your spending habits. Planning and money management can help you reduce spending. If you spend wisely enough to have leftover money, you could add the amount to an emergency fund or savings account.

Reducing Your Spending

Planning meals with your budget in mind will get you on the savings track. Several tips can help.

- **Supermarket advertisements.** Newspaper ads and flyers show sale prices. Compare prices among stores.
- **Economical main dishes.** Since meat is a costly part of meals, try serving more beans with grains and other plant-based protein foods. Meat, fish, and poultry could be served in smaller amounts.
- **Food waste.** When planning meals, think about the number of servings needed and prepare just that amount. When serving food, practice portion control. Leftovers can be safely stored for future use.
- **Simple meals at home.** Homemade meals often cost less than convenience meals or foods eaten out. Taking extra time to prepare meals at home can be worthwhile. To cut down on preparation time and bring family members closer together, prepare meals together.
- **Flexible planning.** An unexpected sale price is a good reason to change your meal plans. Some people shop for food bargains first and then plan meals around them later.
- **Less expensive foods.** Compare prices for fresh, frozen, canned, and dried foods to find the best buy. Lower cost doesn't mean lower nutritional value or less flavorful food.

Extending Learning

Computing Percentages—A quick way to determine the percentage of monthly income spent on food is to use the following formula, which you may wish to share with students:

- Total the amount spent on food over the course of the month.
- Divide this result by the monthly income.
- Multiply by 100 to convert the decimal to a percentage.

Food Legislation and Policies

The strength of a nation depends on the strength of its people. That's why federal laws are aimed at helping people get the proper nutrition they need for good health. When individuals and families have limited income due to retirement, illness, or joblessness, they can get assistance through a number of programs. Many are based on federal legislation and administered at the state and local levels. Private organizations also help people who cannot afford nutritious food.

The public policies that promote nutrition and health, whether federal, state, or local, build stronger families. When families have the nutritious foods they need, they are better able to manage their lives and be productive citizens. Some of the programs that support this aim are described here. Details about these and other programs in your area can be found by calling local government agencies, such as social services and public health nursing services.

- **Food Stamp Program.** The Food Stamp Act governs the Food Stamp Program. This federal legislation was first enacted in 1964 and has undergone many legislative modifications over the years. A major aim of the law is to improve levels of nutrition among low-income households. Depending on income and family size, some households qualify for assistance in the form of food stamps or an Electronic Benefits Transfer (EBT) card. The USDA issues both. These forms of assistance are limited to essential food purchases. They cannot be used for non-food items, tobacco, or alcohol. They also can't be used for restaurant meals, take-out foods, and pet foods.
- **School Breakfast Program.** Through this federal program, the Child Nutrition Act of 1966 ensures that all children have access to a healthy breakfast at school to promote learning readiness and healthy eating behavior. Nutritionally balanced breakfasts are low-cost or free for children who are eligible.
- **National School Lunch Program.** This program is provided under the National School Lunch Act, first enacted in 1946. Low-income students may qualify for free or reduced-price meals. Nonprofit

◆ Food stamps and nutrition programs for the elderly, such as meals-on-wheels, are two examples of food assistance programs.

- *Food Assistance Programs (text pages 329-330)*

Field Trip

Take a field trip to a local soup kitchen or food bank. If possible, arrange ahead of time to have students volunteer during the trip by helping to serve meals at a soup kitchen or by repacking foods at a food bank. Back in class, ask each student to write a brief entry in his or her Wellness Journal discussing what was learned from this experience.

Group Research

Divide the class into groups. Assign each group to research one of the food assistance programs listed in the text. Ask groups to give a presentation to the class on the history of the program, persons eligible for assistance, and where to get information about the program locally. L1

COMPUTER ACTIVITY
Electronic Benefits Transfer

Under your supervision, have students contact the USDA online (www.usda.gov) to find out more about Electronic Benefits Transfer. Have students determine what other forms of funds transfer use a similar technology and whether future innovations are envisioned where this type of card will be usable from the individual's home. Have students share their findings.

Reinforcing Key Skills

Present the following problem to student groups. Allow time for them to discuss and compare their responses.

Communication—An older adult on your block lives alone. You're pretty sure he cannot afford the food to create well-balanced, nutritious meals. Community organizations have offered assistance, but the man refuses "out of pride." How could you help this man—tactfully—to get enough food and to have nutritious meals? What information would you share?

ASSESS

REVIEW

- Ask students to summarize the main ideas in this section.
- Have students complete the Section Review. (Answers appear below.)

EVALUATION

- Give students a spending record for a hypothetical family. Ask them to create a realistic food budget for that family and to explain how they would evaluate it.
- Have students take the quiz for Section 11-3. (Use the quiz in the *Teacher Resource Guide,* or construct your own with the **Exam***View*® *Test Generator* on the *Effective Instruction CD-ROM.*)

RETEACHING

- Provide students with index cards on which various nutritious foods are shown. Have students develop a one-day menu, then a shopping list, based on those foods, keeping budget considerations in mind. Have students share the total price of their shopping list. Note that typically a week's plan is suggested, but students are planning just one-day due to class-time constraints.
- Refer to the *Reteaching Activities* booklet for the Section 11-3 activity sheet.

CLOSE

Have students in class name specific and realistic ways they can reduce food spending for themselves.

food services in elementary schools, secondary schools, and residential child care centers receive government surplus foods and some cash to provide for children in need. In some areas, the Summer Food Service Program provides breakfast and lunch during summer vacation.

- **Child and Adult Care Food Program.** The National School Lunch Act also authorizes this program. It provides healthful meals and snacks to eligible children in various care settings and to eligible older adults in adult care centers.
- **Women, Infants, and Children Program (WIC).** Although first implemented in the early 70s, this federal program is now under the Healthy Meals for Healthy Americans Act of 1994. The WIC program aims to improve the nutrition and health of low-income pregnant and breast-feeding women, infants, and children up to five years of age. Supplemental foods, nutrition education, and access to health services are provided. Participants receive vouchers to use at retail food stores for specified nutrient-rich foods.
- **Elderly Nutrition Program (ENP).** In 1965 the Older American's Act was passed. In 1972 the Elderly Nutrition Program was initiated under this federal act. The program provides grant money for meals served to aging citizens. Meals are served to the homes of qualifying individuals, community centers, and care facilities for the aging population.
- **Soup kitchens and food banks.** These local services—run by religious groups as well as private organizations—provide food for people in need of meals or food assistance. Often these programs need volunteers. Helping can be a rewarding experience.

Section 11-3 Review & Activities

1. Identify four factors that affect how much families spend on food.
2. What is the benefit of keeping a food budget?
3. Give five suggestions for reducing food spending through wise meal planning.
4. **Interpreting.** Why do you think some people spend more for food than they intend to spend?
5. **Extending.** Federal laws and policies pertaining to health and nutrition apply across the country. Among state and local communities, however, laws and policies may vary. Investigate how people in your state and local area are helped with their food and nutrition needs. How do the programs work, and where are they located? Who is allowed to participate?
6. **Applying.** Imagine that you have only $7 to spend on a meal for a family of four. Choosing foods from newspaper ads and store flyers, plan the meal and compute the cost.

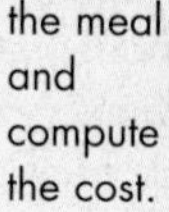

Answers to Section 11-3 Review & Activities

1. Any four: family income; family size; ages; local food prices; amount of food eaten out; food preparation time and skills; amount of food wasted.
2. It can show whether you're spending money wisely; make you think about food choices.
3. Any five: look for ads; make economical dishes; reduce food waste; make simple meals at home; allow flexibility in plans; choose less costly food forms.
4. Answers may include: they don't plan meals, make a budget, compare ads, or store leftovers.
5. Answers will vary.
6. Answers will vary.

Career Wanted

Social Service Assistant

"Asking for help is just the first step."

Marilyn Lakota

Education and Training
- Degree in sociology, social work, or related field
- Completion of supervised internship

Qualities
- Interest in helping others
- Communication skills
- Management skills

Q. Marilyn, what is your job specifically?

A. I work with low-income families. I help them learn what programs they're eligible for, like food assistance, and then apply for help. I also follow up to see that they're using the program as intended.

Q. What's your goal as you work with clients?

A. I want to teach resourcefulness. A consumer-oriented society like ours doesn't stress thriftiness. Some people were never taught how to budget or manage money. There's a great sense of accomplishment when they see that they can take control of their lives in this way. It starts a positive cycle. As they gain control, they gain confidence.

Q. What's your best asset, working in social service?

A. Strange as it may seem, it's two opposite qualities. First, I can put myself in my clients' shoes. I treat them the way I'd want to be treated. At the same time, I can distance myself and be objective when it's best for them.

Related Career Opportunities

Entry Level
- Soup kitchen volunteer
- Group home cook
- Home health aide

Technical Level
- Teacher assistant
- Social research assistant
- Dietetic technician

Professional Level
- Head Start teacher
- Social service policy maker
- Legislative lobbyist

Making Career Connections

CAREER INVESTIGATION. Choose a social service agency, such as a food bank or energy assistance program. Arrange to visit the agency and explore the role of social service workers. What specialized knowledge or background is needed? What are the earnings and job outlook? Share findings in class to get an overview of opportunities.

Career Wanted

Social Service Assistant

Thinking About the Career

Have students think of other questions they would like to ask Marilyn Lakota about being a social service assistant. (Examples: How do you deal with runaway teens? Do you ever visit clients' homes? In what specific ways does your organization help children who look like they're starving?)

Ask student volunteers to tell what they think would be the most exciting part of being a social service assistant.

Have students brainstorm specific ways a social service assistant can help babies get a better start on life.

Career-Building Opportunities

Ask students to determine the difference between the coursework and the opportunities available for those who major in social work compared to psychology. Suggest interested students research college bulletins to help identify which direction they may want to take.

For More Information

For additional information about careers in the social health field, have students contact:

- The National Health Council
  1730 M St., NW
  Washington, DC 20036
  www.nhcouncil.org
- The National Association of Social Workers
  750 First Street, NE, Suite 700
  Washington, DC 20002-4241
  www.naswdc.org
- National Organization for Human Service Education
  www.nohse.com/index.html

REVIEW

- Have students complete the Chapter Review. (Answers appear below.)

EVALUATION

- Ask students to create a practical menu for one week for a family of four. Assume that every member of the family has a busy schedule, and that none of the schedules are the same. Further assume that the family is on a limited income.
- Have students take the test for Chapter 11. (Use the chapter test in the *Teacher Resource Guide,* or construct your own with the **Exam***View®* *Test Generator* on the *Effective Instruction CD-ROM.*)

ANSWERS

Checking Your Knowledge

1. Some foods, such as fruits and vegetables, are seasonal, so they may not be available all year; a food store may not carry the items you need for a special recipe.
2. Any four: Color; shape and size; flavor and aroma; texture; temperature.
3. Answers will vary. Examples: Work around the recipe that takes the longest to prepare; prepare some foods ahead if you can do so safely.
4. Answers will vary. Examples: Plans of family, foods already on hand, foods that are on sale.
5. Any three: Start a collection of nutritious recipes that fit your lifestyle; use the microwave oven; make one-dish meals; look for ways to combine convenience foods with fresh foods in recipes and meals; cook for the freezer; look for versatile recipes.

Chapter 11 Review & Activities

Summary

Section 11-1: Basic Meal Planning

- When you plan meals, consider nutrition, eating patterns, individual needs and preferences, and your resources.
- Meals should appeal to all the senses.
- Having a work plan and schedule for preparing a meal allows you to have all the foods ready at the same time. Good management skills are also important.
- Weekly meal planning can help you use your resources wisely.

Section 11-2: Challenges in Meal Planning

- Many individuals and families in today's fast-paced society face challenges in meal planning.
- A variety of solutions are available for meeting the challenges of preparing meals for families with busy schedules or for one person.
- On days when plans change at the last minute, a supply of "backup" foods can be helpful.

Section 11-3: Food Costs and Budgeting

- Food expenses make up a significant portion of most family and personal budgets.
- The amount of money spent on food depends on the family's situation and composition.
- A spending record and food budget can help you determine whether you are making wise food-buying choices.
- Planning and money management can help reduce food spending.
- A number of food assistance programs are available to help people with low or limited incomes.

Checking Your Knowledge

1. How do food choices and availability affect meal planning?
2. Name four elements of meal appeal.
3. Give two suggestions for deciding the sequence in which to prepare the foods in a meal.
4. Name three things you should find out before preparing a weekly meal plan.
5. Give three suggestions to help families with busy schedules plan meals.
6. List two suggestions to help single people avoid buying larger quantities than they need.
7. Give three examples of foods to keep on hand for meals when plans change at the last minute.
8. What is the first step in setting up a food budget?
9. How can flexibility in meal planning help you save money?
10. What services are provided by the WIC Program? For whom are they provided?

Review & Activities Chapter 11

Thinking Critically

1. Determining Accuracy. Gilberto is planning to buy his aunt a cookbook for her birthday. In the cookbook section of a bookstore, he sees a book with a colorful, eye-catching cover and the title *The Anything Goes Guide to Cooking.* The preface to the book states that "Cooking should first and foremost be fun. Forget all that stodgy advice about shopping lists and preliminaries. Just go into the kitchen and let your creativity be your guide! That's what the best chefs do." What would you advise Gilberto to do before he decides whether or not to buy this book? Explain.

2. Recognizing Stereotypes. You overhear a student in your school saying that people who use food assistance programs are simply too lazy or stupid to get decent jobs to support themselves. How do you respond?

Working IN THE Lab

1. *Foods Lab.* Prepare a work plan and schedule for a simple meal. Use them when preparing the meal in the foods lab. Evaluate how well your schedule worked. What would you change before preparing the same meal again?

2. *Foods Lab.* Write the menu for a meal that you might purchase from a restaurant or supermarket deli. Find or create recipes to prepare these foods yourself. Estimate the price difference between the purchased meal and the homemade meal. If possible, prepare the meal and compare it with the purchased version.

Reinforcing Key Skills

1. Management. The main ingredients of your family's favorite chicken-rice casserole are cooked rice, diced chicken, cream soup, and shredded Swiss cheese. Usually it is served with dinner rolls and with pie for dessert. You want to increase the meal's nutritional value and appeal. Before you can adapt the meal, what information would you need to have?

2. Communication. Delaine and her parents do most of the family's meal planning and preparation. She would like to get her seven-year-old brother and ten-year-old sister interested and involved as well. What solutions can you propose to Delaine?

Making Decisions and Solving Problems

You know that one family in your neighborhood is on a very strict budget and has been skimping on food to make ends meet. You would like to help, but you don't want to offend them.

Making Connections

1. Social Studies. Using library or online resources, prepare a report on meal planning in other cultures, such as Asian or Middle Eastern. How do cultural differences (family structure, tradition, available foods, and so on) affect how and when meals are prepared and served?

2. Math. Keep a record of your spending for one week. Figure out what percentage of your weekly spending goes toward food. Combine your findings with those of your classmates to find the average percentage for the class.

ANSWERS cont.

6. Any two: Buy bulk foods in just the quantity needed; share foods that come in large packages; ask meat and produce managers for small packages of fresh foods; store foods in single-serving packages; buy small portions of salad ingredients at a supermarket salad bar.
7. Answers will vary. Examples: nonfat dry milk; canned chicken, tuna, salmon; frozen portions of cooked dry beans, rice, and pasta.
8. Keeping a spending record.
9. It allows you to take advantage of seasonal or sale prices on some food items.
10. Provides supplemental foods, nutrition education, and access to health services; available to low-income pregnant and breast-feeding women, infants, and children up to five years of age.

Thinking Critically

1. Answers will vary. One suggestion: Advise Gilberto to determine his aunt's cooking skills first. If she is not experienced in the kitchen and she needs to follow an exact plan and directions, the purchase of the cookbook would not be advised.
2. Answers will vary. Students should understand that, especially in times of economic hardship, some people have no choice. They may lose their jobs and be unable to find new ones, for example.

Reinforcing Key Skills

1. Answers will vary. Before adapting the meal, you need to know: the original recipe, family's likes and dislikes, foods available, budget available to purchase more foods, time available to prepare meal, equipment available, preparation and skills of the family cook.
2. Answers will vary. Ask her brother and sister what they like and incorporate some of their suggestions in meal planning. Also, encourage them to get involved in basic parts of meal preparation.

CHAPTER

12

Shopping for Food

Advance Planning Guide ☑

- Prepare a short questionnaire on food consumer habits.
- Arrange a field trip to a supermarket, warehouse store, and farmer's market.
- Develop a disorganized, problem-ridden shopping list of 50 (mostly food) items.
- Plan a week's menu.
- Gather eight foods with prices and coupons.
- Arrange the purchase of two different brand-name vegetable soup cans.
- Purchase five boxed cereals, one of which is high in fiber.
- Purchase three cans of a fruit: a generic, store, and name brand.
- Purchase chicken breasts with and without bones.
- Arrange with an elementary school principal to have students teach a lesson on food shopping to elementary school students.
- Invite a consumer specialist to speak to the class.
- Invite a speaker to discuss "green shopping."

CHAPTER

12

The food you buy is the foundation for the meals you prepare. Wise food shopping can save time and money and ensure nutritious meals.

In this chapter, you will learn how to be a successful food shopper. Learning the basic logic behind food labels, as you will discover, is one of the keys.

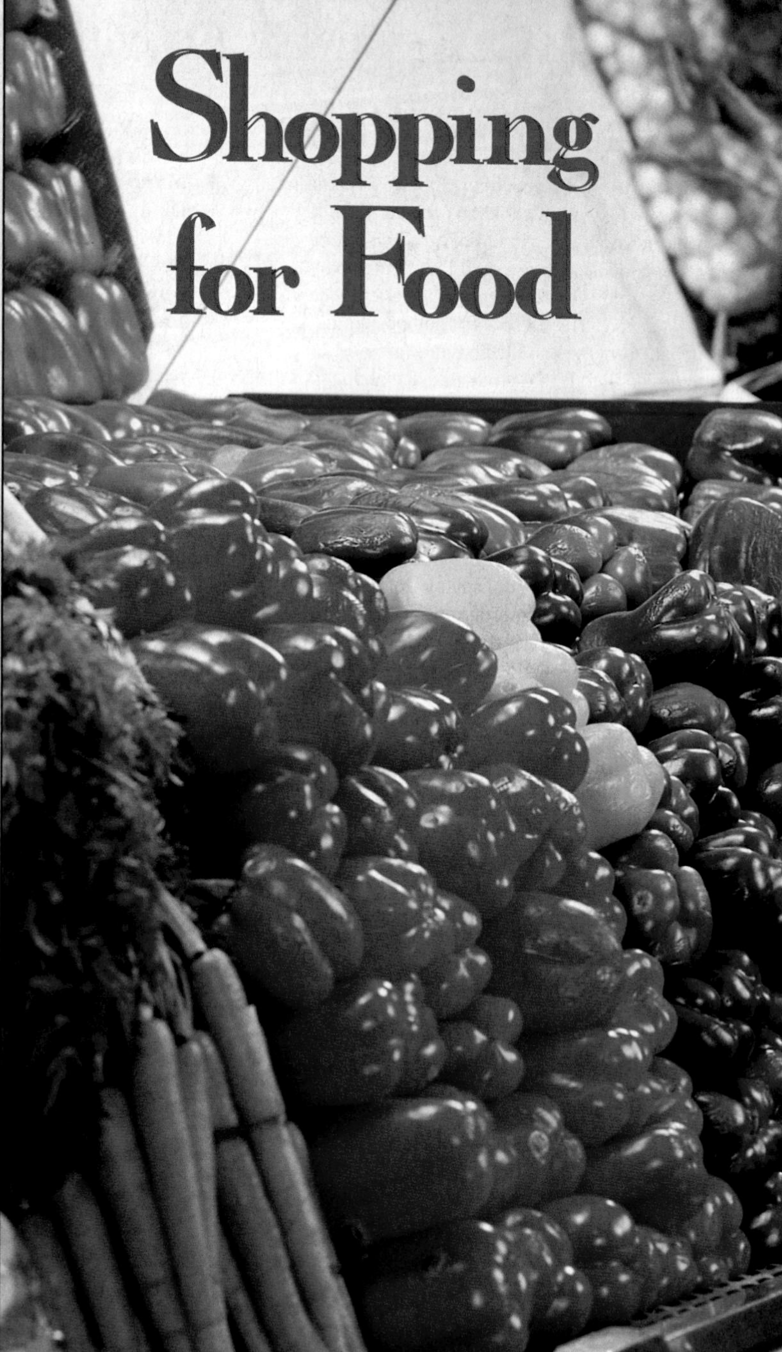

MEETING DIVERSE NEEDS

Celebrating Cultural Diversity. If there are students within the class who are first- or second-generation residents of the United States, ask them to provide a class presentation about the type of food specialty store unique to their culture. If possible, have these students bring to class a few food products or ingredients purchased from this type of store. Compile a list of specialty store names and locations and brief descriptions of foods available.

SECTION
12-1

Objectives

After studying this section, you should be able to:

- Give guidelines for planning where and when to shop.
- Explain the benefits of preparing a shopping list.
- Discuss ways to make the best use of coupons.

Look for These Terms

food cooperatives

impulse buying

staples

rebate

Before You Shop

Like many other activities, successful food shopping begins with planning. As an informed consumer, you need to ask yourself these questions: Where should I shop? When is the best time to go? Should I make a shopping list? Although these questions may seem basic and obvious, answering them, as you will see, is an important decision-making process.

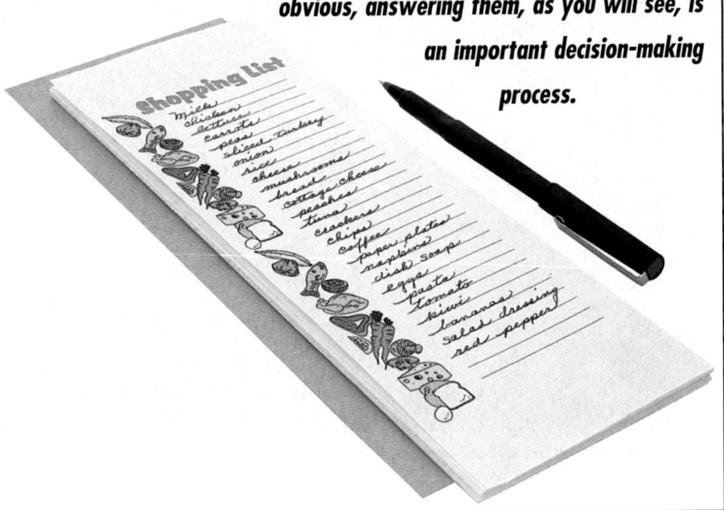

Where to Shop

You can buy food at several kinds of food stores. Each has its pluses and minuses. Your choice will depend on your own needs and wants.

- ◆ **Supermarkets.** Large stores that sell not only food but also many other items and services. Some have as many as 20,000 different food items. Most supermarkets offer a variety of customer services. In a large, busy supermarket, you may find it difficult to buy just a few items in a hurry.
- ◆ **Warehouse stores.** Offer basic items with few customer services. As a result, prices are lower than in most supermarkets. Although most warehouse stores are large, they have a limited variety of items. Items are usually displayed in cartons rather than on shelves. Shoppers must bag their own groceries and carry them out.
- ◆ **Food cooperatives.** Another low-cost option. **Food cooperatives** are food distribution organizations mutually owned and operated by a group of people. Members buy food in quantity and do the sorting, unloading, and other work themselves.

SECTION
12-1
Before You Shop

FOCUS

MOTIVATORS

- Have students identify non-food services offered in stores that sell food (pharmacy, photo developing, etc.). Write their answers on the chalkboard. Discuss the pros and cons of such arrangements.
- Provide students with a short yes-no questionnaire about food-buying practices (e.g., "If you were the primary food buyer in a family, would you use a shopping list?" "Would you use coupons?") Compare answers as a lead-in to a discussion of the advantages of yes answers.

VOCABULARY ACTIVITY

Pronounce the four terms listed under "Look for These Terms." Have students find the terms and their definitions in the section. Have them classify each term as a noun, verb, or other part of speech, and use each in an original sentence.

STUDY SKILLS

- **Listening.** Invite a group of volunteers to each prepare an oral reading of a page of text from the section, while others follow along silently.
- Have students read the section and complete the appropriate part of the Chapter 12 Study Guide in the *Student Workbook*.

Section 12-1 Resources

◆ **Student Workbook,** pp. 89, 91
◆ **Teacher Resource Guide**
Lesson Plan 12-1 Organizer
Section 12-1 Quiz
◆ **Effective Instruction CD-ROM**
Exam*View*® *Test Generator*
PowerPoint® Slide #26
◆ **Transparency Package,** CT-26
◆ **Student Motivation Kit**
Reteaching Activities, p. 63
Enrichment Activities

TEACH

- *Where to Shop (text pages 335-337)*

Field Trip

Arrange a field trip to three places to food shop: a supermarket, a warehouse store, and a farmer's market, for instance. Ask students to take notes about food choices available as you tour each aisle of each store. Have them write a report noting similarities and differences among the three types of store. Conclude with a discussion of what to look for when you are choosing a place to shop.

Store Survey

Have students visit a convenience store and health food store. Record observations of food choices and list the services each store offers, such as photo developing, delivery, etc. In the classroom, have students analyze these services, identifying their advantages or disadvantages for the customer. Have students discuss foods available at either of these stores that are not available at a supermarket. L1

Categorizing

Ask students to identify places to shop for food in the local community. Have them categorize the places listed by type of store. L1

◆ **Outdoor markets like this one are cost-effective alternatives to shopping in more conventional settings. What priorities besides cost need to be considered when shopping for food?**

Doing these things helps keep costs down. Some cooperatives are licensed to sell to the public as well as to members.

- **Health food stores.** Offer a wide range of foods, including items seldom found elsewhere. Foods are likely to be more expensive, however, than in other stores.
- **Specialty stores.** Limited to specific items, such as fish, meat, baked goods, delicatessen foods, or ethnic foods. Prices are usually higher than in supermarkets. In return, customers may get personal attention and fast service. Specialty stores may also carry food items, such as ethnic staples, not readily found elsewhere.
- **Convenience stores.** Give fast service and usually open early and close late. Some stay open around the clock. Their small size makes it easy to shop quickly, but they do not carry a full line of groceries. Prices are generally higher than in supermarkets.
- **Farmer's markets.** Also known as greengrocers. Specialize in fresh fruits and vegetables. The selection depends on the area and the season. You may find locally grown foods that are fresher and less expensive than those in the supermarket. Some markets are closed during cold-weather months.

Technology TIE-IN

Some food stores offer a shop-at-home service. Customers place their orders over the telephone, and the store delivers the items for an extra charge. In some cases, orders can be placed using a fax machine. Another option is ordering groceries by computer, over the Internet.

Ask students to consider these new ways of shopping for food. Discuss the advantages and disadvantages of each.

How to Decide

What should you consider when choosing a place to shop? First, be sure the store is clean. Next, consider your priorities. What kinds of food do you shop for most often? How far will you travel to shop? Are you willing to give up some services in exchange for lower prices?

If time is a priority, you may want to do most of your shopping at one store. That way, you can become familiar with the location of the items and spend less time shopping.

Some stores use promotions, such as giveaways, special prices, or discount clubs for frequent shoppers, to attract customers. When choosing a place to shop, consider whether these promotions will actually save you money. You may find you can save as much or more by shopping at a store with low everyday prices.

Safety Check

A safe shopping experience begins with a clean store. Here are some important qualities to consider:

- Check for cleanliness not just on the floor but also on the grocery shelves, in display cases, and in the checkout aisles.
- Self-serve areas, including bulk bins and salad bars, should be clean and, in some cases, covered.
- Fresh produce should look fresh—a sign of quality.
- Raw meat, poultry, and fish should look fresh, too. If you detect an odor when you pass by the seafood section, something's "fishy" about the freshness.
- Cold foods should be cold. Freezer sections should house solidly frozen foods, without signs of ice crystal formation or thawing.

When to Shop

The issue of when to shop involves answering three questions:

- **How often should you shop?** The answer depends on several factors. One is the storage space you have, including the size of your refrigerator-freezer. Over half of all American families do their shopping once a week.
- **Which days should you shop?** Be aware that many stores advertise in newspapers on Wednesdays. Special prices may start on Thursdays and be valid through the weekend. The days may vary depending on the area.
- **What time of day should you shop?** One time of day *not* to shop is right before mealtimes (or any time you are hungry). Studies show that people spend as much as 15 percent more on food when they shop on empty stomachs. Other times to steer clear of are early evenings and weekends—when stores are generally the most crowded. Shopping when the store is free of crowds can save you time. You are also more likely to make better choices when you are not feeling pressured.

A Shopping List

A well-thought-out shopping list can save you both time and money. It helps you speed up your shopping time and saves you from making special trips for forgotten items. A shopping list can also help you avoid **impulse buying**—buying items you didn't plan on purchasing and don't really need. Impulse buying can ruin any food budget.

- *Where to Shop*
- *When to Shop*
- *A Shopping List (text pages 335-339)*

Blueprint Activity

If there are students in the class with an interest in art or design, invite them to design poster-size floor plans for the supermarket of the future. Urge students to depict colorfully where and which foods and other products would be found. Ask them to provide a presentation to the class about their design.

Sharing Tips

Ask students to think of a precaution that they would observe when making the decision regarding when to shop. Then ask students to turn to a partner and share their responses. Ask several pairs to share their responses with the class. L1

USING Safety Check

Have interested students act as "health inspectors." Have them first prepare a checklist of qualities of a safe and clean supermarket. With their checklists, ask them to inspect their favorite supermarket. Have them report findings back to class. If they have any major findings, encourage "inspectors" to share them with a store manager.

Reinforcing Key Skills

Present the following problem to student groups. Allow time for them to discuss and compare their responses.

Critical Thinking—On the chalkboard write: "A recent poll of American families reveals that average annual grocery bills are higher as children grow older." Ask students to give reasons for this statistic and to ask questions. For example, how might such averages be determined? What factors influence an individual family's expenditures?

TEACH cont.

- *A Shopping List (text pages 337-339)*

Problem Identification Activity

Provide students with a "mock" shopping list of 50 (mostly food) items. The list should be disorganized with respect to amounts, and specific information should be missing. Have students review the shopping list and record all problems identified. Then have them rewrite it in an organized, useful format.

Brainstorming Activity

Ask students to define the term *impulse buying.* Ask students to brainstorm items that are likely to be bought on impulse in the supermarket. Write responses on the chalkboard. Then have students decide which ten items teens most often buy on impulse.

Home Survey

Ask students to survey their home kitchen food storage areas for staples. Have students discuss and compare their lists in class. What are common staples found on most lists? Are any unique to just one or two students? Discuss why. L1

Making a Shopping List

Once you get in the habit of making a shopping list, you'll find it can be done quickly and easily. The first step is to plan the meals you will serve for that shopping period. Be sure to check the newspaper ads to see what's on sale—perhaps you can include some of those items in your meal plan.

Next, check your menus and recipes to see what ingredients you need to purchase. Be sure to include the amount or quantity of each item needed, increasing the number if you plan to cook for the freezer.

From time to time you will want to check your supply of these basic items:

- **Staples**, items you use on a regular basis, such as flour, honey, and nonfat dry milk.
- Foods you keep on hand for emergencies: frozen dinners, canned foods, and other shelf-stable items.
- Cleaning supplies and paper products.

Many people keep a shopping reminder list handy in the kitchen. Whenever they notice that items are running low, they jot down a reminder to add those items to the shopping list.

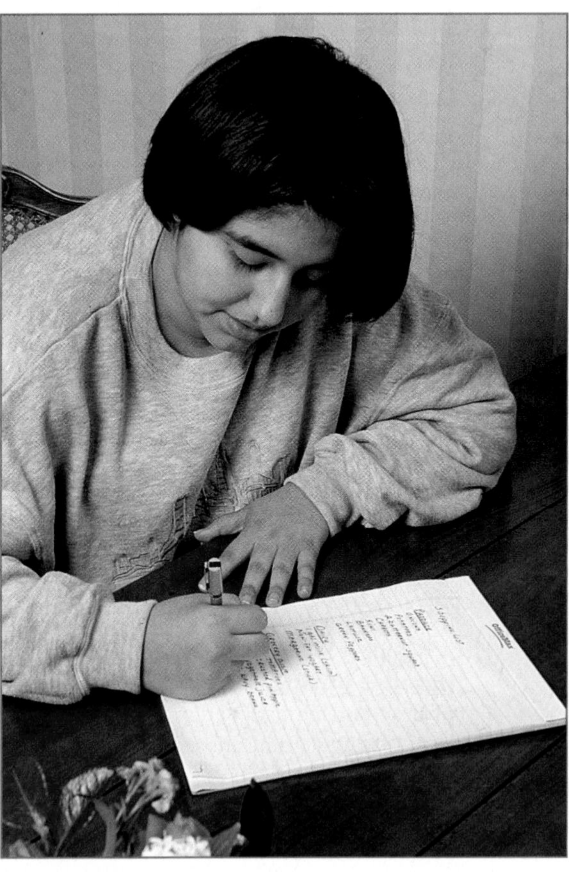

INFOLINK

To learn more about the steps involved in meal planning and cooking for the freezer, see Sections 11-1 and 11-2.
For more on shelf-stable foods and methods for proper storage, see Section 7-4.

◆ **A well-organized shopping list makes it easier to find needed items once you get to the store. What is the most logical order in which to shop for groceries? Explain your answer.**

Technology TIE-IN

The self-service grocery store began in parts of the United States as early as the 1920s. Consumers purchased food from a bakery, butcher, fish market, corner fruit store, and even a milk wagon. The only shopping choices were fresh foods, canned foods, and maybe a few frozen foods.

Today, supermarkets carry many items besides food. There may also be a pharmacy, optical center, and banking center. Some supermarkets offer nutrition information centers, too.

Organizing Your List

Organizing your list will help you shop more efficiently. When writing out your list, group items that are found in the same area of the store, such as dairy foods, meats, and frozen foods. This will help you avoid making several trips to the same area.

If you shop at one store regularly, make out your shopping list according to the way the store is arranged. Some stores provide a map or directory sheet showing which items are found in each aisle. Most have overhead signs above each aisle telling which foods are found there.

Some people keep copies of a basic shopping list that has the items they usually buy, arranged in the order those items are found in the store. Each week, they circle or check off the basic items they need and add any others. Alicia has her mother's basic shopping list stored in her computer. When her mother finishes the week's menus, Alicia adds the needed foods to the basic list and prints out the final one.

Coupons

Another consideration before you go shopping is whether you will use coupons. Coupons offer savings on the price of a specific product. Coupons are found in newspapers, magazines, product packages, and mailed advertisements. In some stores, a checkout computer automatically prints out coupons for future use on the basis of the purchases you have just made.

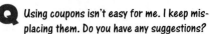

Using coupons isn't easy for me. I keep misplacing them. Do you have any suggestions?

Getting organized will help. A plain envelope is fine for storage if you save only a small number of coupons. To store a larger number, you might want to buy a special partitioned envelope that is tabbed to sort coupons by food type. Two other ways to sort coupons are alphabetically and by store aisle. Go through your coupon collection regularly to pull out those that will expire soon. That way you'll remember to use them. Throw away any that are outdated. Some people arrange their coupons according to expiration dates, which works best when you save only a small number of them.

There are two basic types of coupons:

- **Cents-off coupons.** These offer reduced prices on specific items. You present the coupon to the cashier when you make the purchase. The face value is subtracted from the total price of your purchases. Some stores will double or triple the amount of some coupons.
- **Rebate coupons.** A **rebate** is a partial refund from the manufacturer of a purchased good. You pay the regular price at the store. Later you fill out the rebate coupon and mail it, along with the required proof of purchase, to a specified address. The proof of purchase might be part of the package or a cash register receipt or both. A check for the coupon's face value is mailed to you.

- *A Shopping List*
- *Coupons*
- *Ready to Shop (text pages 337-340)*

Interviews

Ask students to interview the food shopper(s) in their families to find out whether that person makes a food shopping list. If so, how is it prepared? In class, have students share and discuss their findings. L1

List Making

Hand out a week's menu to each student and ask the students to make out an organized shopping list. Have several student volunteers share their lists with the class. How complete are they? Are they all organized the same way? Is one way better than another? L1

Math Activity

Set up a grocery display with eight food items priced and paired with a discount coupon. Ask students to compute the amount they would save by using coupons. How much would they save on "double coupon" days? Assuming that they could save that amount on grocery purchases every week, what would their yearly savings be?

Reinforcing Key Skills

Present the following problem to student groups. Allow time for them to discuss and compare their responses.

Management—Have students debate the issue: Grocery Bags—Paper, Plastic, or Cloth. What are the advantages and disadvantages of each choice? Challenge students to make arguments for reuse of these resources (for example, plastic bags can be easily crumpled and carried in a jacket pocket to the store for future use).

ASSESS

REVIEW

- Ask students to summarize the main ideas in this section.
- Have students complete the Section Review. (Answers appear below.)

EVALUATION

- Give students a meal plan for a seven-day week. Ask students to determine which type of food store(s) they will go to and then prepare a shopping list based on the meal plan.
- Have students take the quiz for Section 12-1. (Use the quiz in the *Teacher Resource Guide,* or construct your own with the **Exam***View*® *Test Generator* on the *Effective Instruction CD-ROM.*)

RETEACHING

- Give students a well-planned shopping list. Ask students to identify characteristics that make it "well-planned."
- Refer to the *Reteaching Activities* booklet for the Section 12-1 activity sheet.

CLOSE

Lead a class brainstorm session on the advantages of making a shopping list before you make the trip to the store. Challenge the class to identify at least twenty advantages.

Using Coupons

Clipping and sorting coupons takes time. For some people, the money saved is well worth the effort. Others may find that they can save just as much by buying less expensive products without coupons.

Here are some suggestions for using coupons:

- ◆ Be choosy. Collect coupons only for items you usually buy or want to try. Otherwise, you may be tempted to buy an unnecessary item just because you have a coupon.
- ◆ Read coupons carefully. Some are good only on a certain size of a product or only in a specific store. Most coupons have a time limit. Stores cannot accept coupons after the expiration date printed on them.
- ◆ Swap coupons. Some families and friends have coupon exchanges—they exchange coupons they won't use for ones they will.

Ready to Shop

Now that you've planned your shopping, you're ready to go to the store. Take along your shopping list and your coupons.

Remember the environment, too. If you use cloth shopping bags or have paper or plastic bags to return to the store, take those with you.

Consider any errands you might want to do during your shopping trip. Do them before you shop for food. That way, you can bring food home immediately so that it can be properly stored.

◆ **Cloth shopping bags conserve resources because they are reusable.**

Section 12-1 Review & Activities

1. What is an advantage of shopping in a warehouse store? Name two drawbacks.
2. Give two guidelines for choosing a time of day to shop.
3. How can preparing a shopping list help you save money?
4. **Analyzing.** Angelina clips every coupon in the Sunday paper and then tries to use them all. What might be some drawbacks of this approach?
5. **Evaluating.** Is it always wrong to buy on impulse? When is it most likely to be a problem?
6. **Applying.** Identify three to five places to buy food in or near your community. Note the type of shopping establishment for each one. Record your findings in a "Shopping Guide" that also contains recommendations from this section. Publish your guide on the classroom computer.

Answers to Section 12-1 Review & Activities

1. Lower prices; drawbacks will vary (example: food stacked high in crates may be hard to reach).
2. Any two: Don't shop when you're hungry; shop on days when store specials are in effect; avoid shopping when stores are crowded.
3. By discouraging impulse buying.
4. It takes time, and you may spend money on food you won't use or don't need.
5. Answers will vary. Not always; when you make too many unhealthy choices or spend too much money.
6. Answers will vary.

SECTION
12-2

Food Labels

Imagine going to the supermarket and discovering that the packaged foods have no labels. What important information would be missing?

In addition to helping you identify the contents of the package, food labels are valuable tools for making wise food choices. This section will help you learn what to look for on labels.

Objectives

After studying this section, you should be able to:

- Identify information on food labels.
- Explain how to interpret nutrition information found on food labels.
- Explain what is meant by product dating.

Look for These Terms

net weight
Daily Value (DV)
open dating
code dating
UPC

Basic Information

You may not be able to tell a book by its cover, but you can tell what's in a food product by its label. Certain basic information found on all food labels answers these questions:

- ◆ What food is in the container? Does it contain baked beans or chicken pot pie?
- ◆ How much food is in the container? The amount may be a volume measurement, such as 2 liters, or a **net weight**, the weight of the food itself, not including the package. Net weight includes liquid in canned food.
- ◆ Who manufactured, packed, or distributed the food? Where is the company located?
- ◆ What ingredients are in the food (assuming the food has more than one ingredient)? The ingredients are listed in order from largest to smallest amount by weight. To avoid certain ingredients, such as a food substance you are allergic to, read the ingredients list carefully.

The U.S. Food and Drug Administration (FDA) regulates much of the information on most food labels. The aim is to make sure consumers have complete, useful, and accurate information about the foods they buy and eat. Regulations are detailed and cover ingredients, quantities, and nutrition data.

Section 12-2 Resources

◆ **Student Workbook,** pp. 90, 92
◆ **Teacher Resource Guide**
Lesson Plan 12-2 Organizer
Section 12-2 Quiz
◆ **Effective Instruction CD-ROM**
Exam*View*® *Test Generator*
◆ **Student Motivation Kit**
Reteaching Activities, p. 64
Enrichment Activities
Food Science Resources, pp. 46–49, 53–55

SECTION
12-2
Food Labels

FOCUS

MOTIVATORS

- Ask students to recall and list the types of information found on food labels. Help students stretch their thinking by suggesting they visualize different types of food products. Ask students to save their lists and add to them as you study food labels.
- Ask students to bring six food labels to class—each one representing one category of the Food Guide Pyramid. Encourage them to include labels from fresh foods, frozen foods, refrigerated foods, canned foods, and dehydrated foods. Use the food labels as a source of information throughout this section.

VOCABULARY ACTIVITY

Pronounce the terms listed under "Look for These Terms." Have student volunteers find each of the terms and read their definitions to the class.

STUDY SKILLS

- **Guided Reading.** Have students look at the headings within Section 12-2 to preview the concepts that will be discussed.
- Have students read the section and complete the appropriate part of the Chapter 12 Study Guide in the *Student Workbook*.

TEACH

- *Basic Information*
- *Nutrition Information (text pages 341-343)*

VISUAL LEARNING ***Using the Photograph*** Have students study the Nutrition Facts panel on page 342, noting the information contained. Have students locate and identify the same types of information on actual food labels. Ask: What is the purpose of including Daily Values? How can you use this information to make more healthful food choices?

Display Activity

To emphasize the importance of all information on food labels, use products and their labels in the following variations:

- Set up a display of two brand-name vegetable soup cans with their labels removed. Ask students to name the food products. Ask if either soup contains monosodium glutamate. Discuss the importance of a label.
- Do the same with the Nutrition Facts panels, asking about sodium and vitamin C content.
- Restore both labels to the products. Review other information provided, including weight, preparation instructions, etc.

Nutrition Information

In addition to basic information, food labels are sources of helpful nutrition information. Nearly all packaged foods carry a standardized "Nutrition Facts" panel like the one shown below. Each panel contains the same types of information in a standard format, making it easy to find what you need. The information includes serving size, calories, nutrient amounts, and percent of Daily Values.

◆ **Food labels provide a variety of helpful information. What is the net weight of the canned item expressed in metric terms?**

Serving Size

Near the top of the panel, you will see "Serving Size" and "Servings Per Container." The serving size is based on the amount of food customarily eaten at one time. The FDA has established standard amounts for various types of food.

Nutrition Facts
Serving Size ¼ cup (40g)
Servings per Container about 9

Amount per Serving	
Calories	130
	% Daily Value*
Total Fat 0g	**0%**
Saturated Fat 0g	**0%**
Cholesterol 0mg	**0%**
Sodium 10mg	**0%**
Potassium 310mg	**9%**
Total Carbohydrate 31g	**10%**
Dietary Fiber 2g	**9%**
Sugars 29g	
Protein 1g	

Calcium 2% • Iron 6%

Not a significant source of calories from fat, vitamin A and vitamin C.

* Percent Daily Values are based on a 2,000 calorie diet. Your daily values may be higher or lower depending on your calorie needs.

	Calories:	2,000	2,500
Total Fat	Less than	65g	80g
Sat Fat	Less than	20g	25g
Cholest	Less than	300mg	300mg
Sodium	Less than	2,400mg	2,400mg
Potassium		3,500mg	3,500mg
Total Carbohydrate		300g	375g
Dietary Fiber		25g	30g

◆ **The Nutrition Facts panel provides easy-to-read nutrition information on the spot. How many calories are contained in this product?**

The rest of the nutrition label information, including calories and nutrient amounts, is based on one serving size. If you eat a larger or smaller serving than is listed on the label, you need to take that into account when reading the rest of the nutrition panel. For example, if you normally eat twice as much as the serving size shown on the label, you would need to double the amounts shown for calories and nutrients.

Calories

The label lists total calories per serving as well as the number of calories from fat per serving. You can use this information to keep track of the number of total calories and calories from fat you eat throughout the day. It also helps you determine fairly quickly which foods derive the recommended one-third or less of their calories from fat.

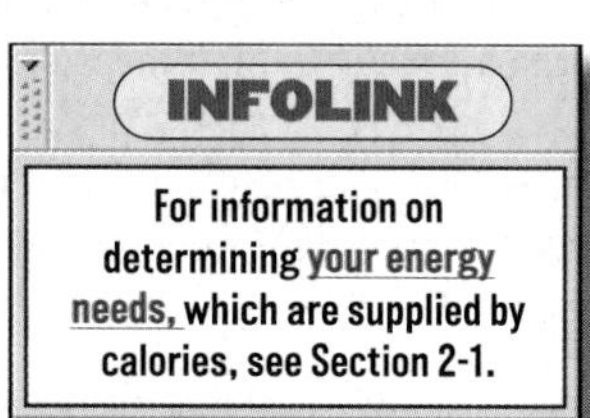

INFOLINK
For information on determining your energy needs, which are supplied by calories, see Section 2-1.

Extending Learning

Food Labels—The current food label rules established by the Food and Drug Administration (FDA) meet the provisions of the Nutrition Labeling Education Act of 1990 (NLEA). The Act requires nutrition labeling for most foods, defines health- and nutrient-related terms, and limits the use of health claims. The Act called for new labels on all affected products by 1994.

According to the guidelines, all chemicals added to preserve or enhance foods must be listed.

◆ **Label claims such as "High in Fiber" can't be used unless the product conforms to specific guidelines. What other types of information are found on this product?**

Nutrient Amounts and Daily Values

The nutrition panel gives information about some of the nutrients that are most important in a healthy eating plan. Amounts (in grams or milligrams) are given for total fat, cholesterol, sodium, total carbohydrate, dietary fiber, sugars, and protein.

For most of these nutrients, the label also lists "% Daily Value." Expressed as a percentage, **Daily Value (DV)** is a specific nutrition reference amount recommended by health experts. DVs are designed to help you put information about nutrient content into perspective. Two DVs—those for cholesterol and sodium—are the same for every adult. Others, including those for fat, saturated fat, total carbohydrate, and fiber, depend on how many calories you need daily.

For fat, saturated fat, cholesterol, and sodium, the DV listed is an upper limit. In other words, a person's goal is to consume no more than that amount each day. For total carbohydrate, fiber, vitamin A, vitamin C, calcium, and iron, the DV is a minimum. In this case, a person's goal is to take in at least that amount each day.

- *Nutrition Information (text pages 342-343)*

VISUAL LEARNING ***Using the Photograph***
Ask students to examine the photo on page 343, noting that the girl is reading the food label on a box of breakfast cereal. If possible, bring a box of this or another high-fiber cereal to class. Ask students to explain what they would look for on its food label to determine if they will purchase the product. Display the box alongside several other boxes of breakfast cereal. Ask: Which contains the highest amount of dietary fiber? How do the percentages of this nutrient compare over the range of products displayed?

Healthful Attitudes

Divide the class into small groups. Give each group food labels from at least two similar products (but ones which show nutritional differences, such as low-fat and regular cookies). Have students compare the products and draw conclusions. Urge students to present their conclusions to the class. **L1**

Reinforcing Key Skills

Present the following problem to student groups. Allow time for them to discuss and compare their responses.

Critical Thinking—The FDA regulations define standard serving sizes. Ask students why this was necessary. How is it helpful?

TEACH cont.

- *Label Language (text page 344)*

Survey

Have students create a questionnaire based on label language. The questions may be in true-false or simple fill-in form. Have them administer the questionnaire to students in the school, family members, and/or people in the community. Have students graph their results. Ask: Is the FDA getting its message across to the American consumer? Why or why not? If not, what recommendations can you make to help people interpret these claims? L1

Guidelines Activity

Invite students to use the classroom computer or another to publish their own set of "Label Language Guidelines." Have them tour retail establishments in the community—including food stores—to ask if they can leave copies of their helpful pamphlets in visible places as a courtesy.

Research and Debate

Ask students to visit supermarkets to compare the health claims on various food products. Then have students research the health claim controversies between the federal government, nutritionists, and consumer alert groups. Ask them to have an open debate on the question of whether food manufacturers should be permitted to print more health claims on food labels. L2

Q ***If I am supposed to eat no more than 30 percent fat per day in my eating plan, does that mean I should stay under 30 percent Daily Value for fat?***

A No, because 100 percent Daily Value for fat represents 30 percent fat for a 2,000-calorie eating plan. So, if you need about 2,000 calories per day, you can have up to 100 percent Daily Value for fat; if you need about 1,500 calories, then allow 75 percent Daily Value for fat; for a 2,500-calorie diet, allow 125 percent Daily Value for fat.

Label Language

In these health-conscious times, many food labels promise "reduced calories," "good source of fiber," or some similar claim. What do these claims mean? Here are the legal definitions of some of the most common ones:

- **"Low- . . ."** The terms *low- . . .* and *low in . . .* can be used on food labels if the food could be eaten frequently without exceeding recommended amounts of the indicated nutrient. Generally, these terms are used in conjunction with *fat, saturated fat, cholesterol, sodium,* or *calories.*
- **"Reduced . . .," "Less . . .," or "Fewer . . ."** To display these terms, the product must have at least 25 percent less of something (such as fat or calories) than a comparable food. The term *reduced* is used when the product has been nutritionally altered. For example, reduced-fat cheddar cheese has at least 25 percent less fat than regular cheddar cheese. Look for a specific comparison on the label.
- **"High in . . ."** This means that one serving of the food provides at least 20 percent of the Daily Value for the specified nutrient. For instance, an orange juice label might state "High in vitamin C."
- **"Good source of . . ."** This means that one serving of the food contains 10 to 19 percent of the Daily Value for a particular nutrient.
- **". . . -Free."** A food package that uses this claim has an amount of the ingredient in question so small that it is not likely to affect your body. The term *fat-free,* for example, indicates that the product has no fat or an insignificant amount of fat.
- **"Organically grown."** This and a similar claim, "organically produced," both describe the manner in which a fresh or processed food was grown or produced—typically, without synthetic pesticides or fertilizers. To display this claim, a processed food must be at least 95 percent organically produced. The term *natural,* however, can mean whatever the food processor wants it to mean.

The purpose of these and other definitions is to ensure that food manufacturers do not use terms in ways that will mislead consumers. Remember, if you're not sure what a label term means, read the "Nutrition Facts" panel. It will give you the specific amounts of nutrients and calories.

Health Claims

If foods meet specific requirements, health claims might appear on their labels. Such claims are regulated by the FDA and must be supported by a significant portion of the scientific community. They are limited to relationships between the food or nutrient and a particular disease or health condition. For instance, a health claim might link calcium and osteoporosis or fats and cancer.

FOOD SCIENCE

Health Claims

Health claims on food labels are supported by scientific evidence and might link the following: Calcium **and** osteoporosis; fat **and** cancer; fruits and vegetables **and** some cancers; fiber-containing grain products, fruits, and vegetables **and** cancer; saturated fat and cholesterol **and** heart disease; fruits, vegetables, and grain products that contain fiber **and** heart disease; sodium **and** high blood pressure; folate **and** neural tube birth defects.

Have students bring one food product that states a health claim.

Product Dating

Product dating is a voluntary, industry-wide system. Except for infant formula and some baby food, the federal government does not require food manufacturers or processors to provide this information. Some food packagers use **open dating**, a practice in which a date is stamped directly on the product for the benefit of the consumer. The exact meaning of the date varies, depending on the product and the wording:

- **"Sell by" date.** This type of date indicates the last day the product should remain on the store shelf. It allows a reasonable amount of time for home storage and use after the date. Dairy products and cold cuts are among the foods that often carry "sell by" dates. The package may state "Sell by (date)" or "Best if purchased by (date)."
- **"Use by" date.** Some packages state "Best if used by (date)." The product may still be safe to eat after the date has passed. However, the quality will start to go down. If a date alone appears on baked goods, such as breads and rolls, it is usually a "use by" date.

Dates are helpful to ensure a product's freshness; however, a package date does not guarantee quality. That depends on the manufacturing and the handling of the product.

Code dating refers to a series of numbers or letters that indicates where and when the product was packaged. It is used by manufacturers for products with long shelf lives. If a recall is necessary, the products can be tracked quickly and removed from the marketplace. Federal law requires code dating on most canned food.

Other Information

You will find many other types of helpful information on food labels. For example, some products carry grades on their packaging, such as "U.S. Grade A." Grading is a voluntary program for identifying the quality of foods. You will learn more about food grades as you study specific foods in Unit Four.

Some label information is required only for certain products. For example, beverages that contain juice must list the percentages of juices.

The label often includes a picture of the product. If the product is not shown exactly as it appears in the package, the photo must be labeled "serving suggestion."

You may see directions on the label for using the product. If the product requires special handling, you will find instructions on the label, such as "Refrigerate after opening" or "Keep frozen."

◆ The date stamped onto this milk carton provides critical information. What does it tell you?

- *Product Dating*
- *Other Information*
  (text pages 345-346)

Discussion Activity

Ask students to explain the significance of a "use by" date on a food product. Ask students to explain the purpose of code dating. Ask students to discuss other information that is available on food labels.

Label Reading Activity

Provide students with empty food packages that have open dating. Have students group the food packages according to the type of dating. Discuss the different types of product dating.

Letter-Writing Campaign

While analyzing food labels, encourage students to think of other information that they believe needs to be on the label, or current information that seems to be confusing or misleading that they feel should be changed. Have students consider how they might go about getting their ideas heard and considered. One possibility would be a letter-writing campaign to elected officials or an area FDA official. Have representative students draft and send letters on behalf of the class. L3

Extending Learning

Kosher Symbols—Some consumers follow "Kosher" practices. In Hebrew, this term means "fit" or "proper." Food products that meet "Kosher" standards will display a symbol that means the food has met additional standards of a Jewish food inspector. One of a few different symbols may be displayed on a Kosher food. Two types are "K" within a circle and "K" within a star. A "P," or the word "Pareve," next to this Kosher symbol means the item contains neither dairy nor meat products.

ASSESS

REVIEW

- Ask students to summarize the main ideas in this section.
- Have students complete the Section Review. (Answers appear below.)

EVALUATION

- Provide students with the class collection of food labels and ask them to explain each part of the label.
- Have students take the quiz for Section 12-2. (Use the quiz in the *Teacher Resource Guide,* or construct your own with the **Exam***View®* *Test Generator* on the *Effective Instruction CD-ROM.*)

RETEACHING

- Provide students with just the front of a can label—no Nutrition Facts panel and no ingredients list. Have each student state why he or she would or would not purchase the product based on the available information.
- Refer to the *Reteaching Activities* booklet for the Section 12-2 activity sheet.

CLOSE

Have each student come to the chalkboard and write one way that food labels can help a person follow a healthful eating plan.

UPC

You have probably noticed a pattern of black stripes similar to the one shown here on most products. This symbol, the **UPC**—or Universal Product Code—is a bar code that can be read by a scanner. Below the UPC is its numeric equivalent. The first five digits of this number identify the manufacturer; the second five, the product size and flavor (if relevant).

The UPC has specific uses. Many store checkout counters are equipped with electronic scanners that can read UPCs, thereby allowing the cashier to determine the correct price for a product automatically. It also enables the store to keep an automatic inventory of the product.

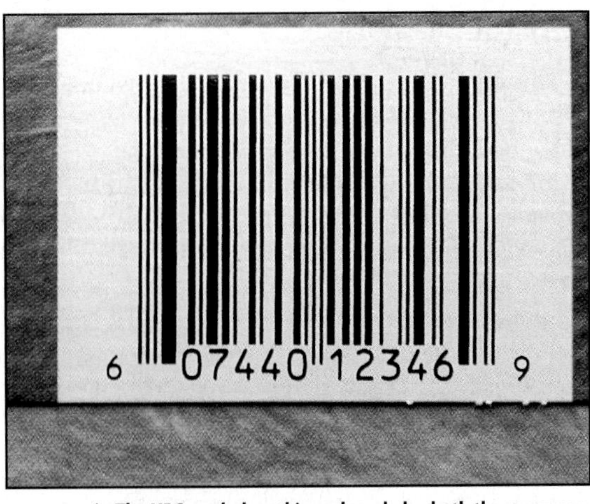

◆ **The UPC symbol on this package helps both the consumer and the merchant.** Explain how.

Section 12-2 Review & Activities

1. Identify three pieces of basic information found on all food labels.
2. Why is it important to consider serving size when reading a "Nutrition Facts" panel?
3. What is the purpose of the "% Daily Value" information on a "Nutrition Facts" panel?
4. What are the differences between "sell by" dates and "use by" dates? Why are such dates not a guarantee of quality?
5. **Synthesizing.** Why do you think it is difficult to define *natural* as a label term?
6. **Evaluating.** If an apple is organically grown, does it mean it's more nutritious than a nonorganic apple? Why or why not? Would you spend more money on organically grown produce? Why or why not?
7. **Applying.** Bring to class "Nutrition Facts" panels from two different foods. Use the panels to identify each food's nutritional pluses and minuses. Develop a rating system that can be applied to all foods—for example, a food with a DV for dietary fiber that is at least double that for fat and/or sodium rates a 10. Share your system with classmates.

Answers to Section 12-2 Review & Activities

1. Any three: type of food; amount; name and location of manufacturer, packer, or distributor; ingredients.
2. The rest of the nutrition information is based on the serving size.
3. To help consumers understand the product's nutrient information, to put nutrients into daily perspective, and to provide a basis of comparison.
4. Answers will vary. See page 345.
5. Answers will vary. See page 344.
6. Answers will vary. Organically grown produce is not necessarily more nutritious.
7. Answers will vary.

SECTION
12-3

Objectives

After studying this section, you should be able to:

- Describe ways of getting the most for your money when food shopping.
- Explain how to choose and handle food to preserve nutrition, quality, and safety.
- Give guidelines for courteous shopping.

Look for These Terms

bulk foods

comparison shop

unit price

store brands

generic

In the Supermarket

When you walk into a supermarket, you are faced with hundreds of items displayed in an eye-catching fashion. Consumer skills can help you pinpoint foods that combine good nutritional value and quality at the best price. In this section, you will learn how to apply these skills.

How Stores Are Organized

Some stores are so big they may seem like food mazes. Understanding how they are organized can help you navigate through them.

Most of the space in a supermarket is taken up by aisles lined with shelves stacked with shelf-stable foods in cans, jars, bottles, boxes, and packages. You might also find the following specific departments or sections:

- A produce department, where fresh fruits and vegetables are sold.
- A meat, poultry, and fish department.
- A refrigeration section. Often taking an entire aisle, this is where you will find dairy products, eggs, cured luncheon meats, and fresh pasta.
- A freezer section. Here you will find a variety of convenience foods and products meant to be consumed in their frozen state, such as ice cream.

Still other departments you might find include a meal center, delicatessen, salad bar, or bakery where you can buy fresh prepared foods. Some stores feature a department that specializes in **bulk foods**—shelf-stable foods that are sold loose in covered bins or barrels.

Section 12-3 Resources

◆ **Student Workbook**, pp. 90, 94
◆ **Teacher Resource Guide**
Lesson Plan 12-3 Organizer
Section 12-3 Quiz
Chapter 12 Test
◆ **Effective Instruction CD-ROM**
Exam*View*® *Test Generator*

◆ **Student Motivation Kit**
Reteaching Activities, p. 65
Enrichment Activities
Food Science Resources, pp. 59–61
Skills for Making Food Choices, pp. 29–30

SECTION
12-3
In the Supermarket

FOCUS

MOTIVATORS

- Ask someone who has lived in or traveled to another country to explain how food shopping is done there. What are the similarities and differences?
- Ask each student to think of a way to get the most for your money when food shopping. Ask each student to share his or her idea with the class.

VOCABULARY ACTIVITY

Pronounce the terms listed under "Look for These Terms." Before students find the terms' definitions in the section, ask them to project the meaning of each of the terms. Then have students read the section and find the terms and their definitions.

STUDY SKILLS

- **Outlining.** Have students read the section and outline it by copying the headers on paper and leaving space after each one. Students are to write a sentence in their own words, summarizing the content under each header.
- Have students read the section and complete the appropriate part of the Chapter 12 Study Guide in the *Student Workbook*.

TEACH

- *How Stores Are Organized*
- *Comparison Shopping (text pages 347-350)*

Group Lesson

Ask for four small groups of volunteers with an interest in teaching. Assign each group to prepare a lesson on one of the following topics:

- The basic departments in supermarkets
- What bulk foods are
- The differences between unit price and cost per serving
- The differences between store brands and generic items

Student "teachers" are to expand on and simplify the information in the text. Have the groups present their lessons to students in an elementary school. **L1**

Guest Speaker

Invite a consumer specialist to discuss ways beyond those described in the text to save money at the supermarket. Prior to the presentation, have students prepare questions to ask the speaker.

Math Activity

Set up a display of four or five cereals with their total price. Have students play "The Price Is Right" by determining the unit price or cost per serving of the displayed cereals to find the best buy. Have students work in teams or individually.

You place as much food as you want in a plastic bag, tie it, and attach a tag or sticker to the bag so that the checkout clerk can identify the contents. Foods that may be sold in bulk include grain products, nuts, dried fruits, dry beans and peas, snack foods, flour, sugar, herbs, and spices.

Departments with higher-profit items are usually located at the front of the store. These might include the floral department, bakery, deli, meal center, and produce department. The pleasant aromas and eye appeal of these departments are carefully designed to encourage the customer to spend money on these items.

◆ **Most stores provide the unit price on a shelf tab for the convenience of consumers. How is this helpful to the consumers?**

Comparison Shopping

No matter what size your food budget, getting the most for your money should be one of your goals when shopping. Yet, when faced with so many choices—different types of products, brands, and sizes—how can you spot the best bargain? The answer is to **comparison shop**, that is, to match prices and characteristics of similar or like items to determine which offers the best value. Among the methods used in comparison shopping are calculating unit price, computing cost per serving, and trying store brands or generic items.

Unit Prices

Which is a better buy, a 12-ounce jar of spaghetti sauce for \$1.32 or a 16-ounce jar for \$1.52? To find out, you need to know the **unit price**, an item's price per ounce, quart, pound, or other unit. In many stores, the unit price is shown on the shelf tab below the item, next to the total price. This gives you a quick and easy way to compare prices. If the unit price is not shown, you can calculate it yourself by dividing the total price of the item by the number of units.

In the example given before, the smaller jar of spaghetti sauce costs 11 cents per ounce (\$1.32 ÷ 12). The larger jar costs 9.5 cents per ounce (\$1.52 ÷ 16), so it is a better value.

Cost Per Serving

Sometimes the unit price is not the best basis for comparison, particularly when you are shopping for fresh meat, poultry, or fish. These foods are best compared by the cost of a serving. Suppose you were trying to decide between fish fillets on sale at \$1.80 per pound (500 g) and a whole broiling chicken at \$1.06 per pound. At first, the chicken might seem like a better bargain. However, because the chicken includes bones, skin, and fat, there is less usable meat. Even though the fish has a higher unit price, you would need less fish to feed the same number of people served by the chicken.

Extending Learning

Supermarket Organization—Foods in the grocery section of a supermarket are arranged according to basic categories, aisle by aisle. They include canned fruits; canned meats, poultry, and fish; salad dressings; mustard and catsup; grain products; dry beans and peas; shelf-stable microwavable foods; and baking ingredients and mixes. This section may also have special aisles for ethnic foods.

Ask students to compare costs of specialty foods to their American brand counterparts.

A first step to finding the cost per serving is determining how many servings a given amount will provide. (See the chart below.) Divide the price for that amount by the number of servings it will provide. The result will be the cost per serving. In the example on page 348, the cost per serving of fish fillets would be 45 cents. ($1.80 ÷ 4 servings). The cost per serving of a pound of chicken with bones, meanwhile, is 53 cents. ($1.06 ÷ 2 servings).

You can use cost per serving to help you in meal planning and budgeting. For instance, you could find the cost per serving of a homemade recipe by adding the cost of the ingredients and dividing by the recipe yield. You could find the cost per serving of a packaged food by dividing the total price by the number of servings indicated on the label.

Store Brands and Generics

A third strategy for saving money is to buy and try items other than commercial name-brand items. **Store brands** (also called private labels) are brands specially produced for the store. They are generally equal in quality to name brands but less expensive. **Generic** items, items produced without a commercial or store brand name, are usually even less expensive. The labels of generic products aren't as eye-catching as those of name brands, but your taste buds may not know the difference. Finding out which store brands and generics are good quality may take some experimenting, but the savings can make the effort worthwhile.

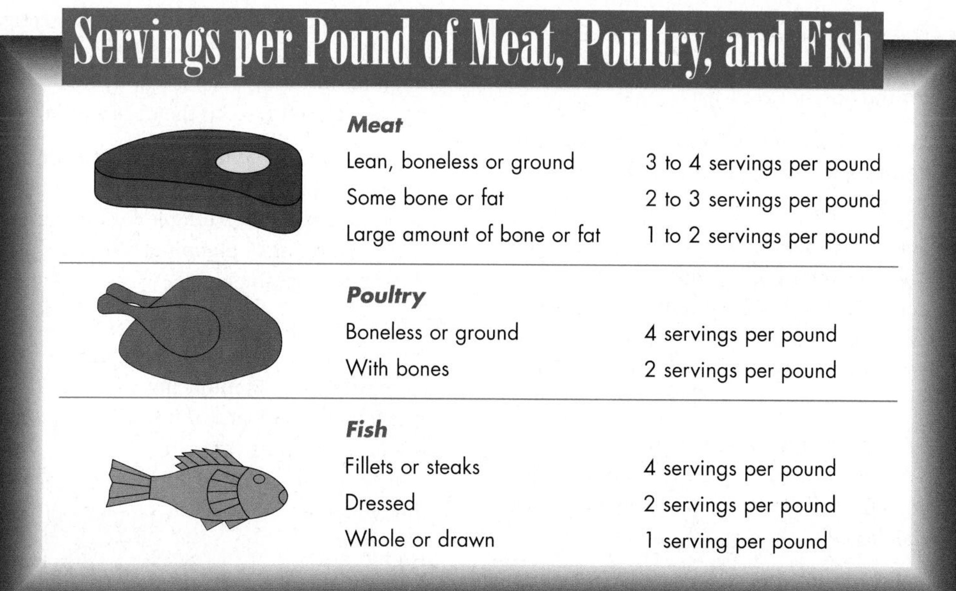

Servings per Pound of Meat, Poultry, and Fish

Meat	
Lean, boneless or ground	3 to 4 servings per pound
Some bone or fat	2 to 3 servings per pound
Large amount of bone or fat	1 to 2 servings per pound
Poultry	
Boneless or ground	4 servings per pound
With bones	2 servings per pound
Fish	
Fillets or steaks	4 servings per pound
Dressed	2 servings per pound
Whole or drawn	1 serving per pound

- *Comparison Shopping (text pages 348-350)*

Product Comparison

1. Set up a "blind" display consisting of three cans of the same fruit—a generic brand, a store brand, and a name brand—minus their labels. (Make sure you know which is which!)
2. Students are to rate the three products for color, size, shape, flavor, texture, and amount of liquid.
3. Have students share their results. Ask: Which fruit would you choose? Why?
4. Tell students which product is the generic, store, and name brand.

Provide and discuss the price, nutrition information, and intended use for each. Have students tell if they would still choose the same fruit based on this information. Why? **L3**

VISUAL LEARNING ***Using the Chart***
Direct students' attention to the servings-per-pound chart on this page. Point out the difference between 1 pound of chicken breast with bones and 1 pound without bones. Give students the price per pound for each based on a current newspaper flyer for a local supermarket. Then proceed to cut the bone out of an actual bone-in chicken breast and weigh it. Ask: Which is a better bargain based on edible portion?

Extending Learning

Supermarket Departments—The produce department is usually located near the front of the store in a corner. There is generally more space in corners than in aisles.

The dairy department is usually located against a wall, as are other refrigerated sections. They are closer to the refrigerated storage space behind the wall, and the shelves can be refilled easily.

The meat, poultry, and fish departments are usually next to each other, in the back of the store. The space on the other side of the wall is usually the butcher shop.

- *Comparison Shopping (text page 348-350)*

Exit Poll

Ask students to conduct an exit poll at a local supermarket, asking volunteers to identify money-saving ideas they use when food shopping. Back in class, students are to brainstorm ideas of their own and compile the ideas in a booklet titled "A Shopper's Guide to Saving Money." The booklets may be printed at school or at home. Suggest that students provide copies to the food purchasers within their households. L1

Student Demonstrations

Assign pairs of students to different parts of a food label, such as the ingredients list, the net weight, and the serving size. Have students work in pairs to demonstrate and discuss how to understand their part of the food label. Ask student pairs to bring in their own food labels to use for demonstration. L1

◆ **Many stores offer a choice between store brands and name brands. Identify two factors to consider when deciding which to buy.**

Other Money-Saving Ideas

Here are some additional suggestions for saving money at your food store:

- Use your shopping list, but be flexible. Look for sale items that you can substitute for the ones on your list.
- When using coupons, be sure you are really getting the best buy. Another brand may be less expensive even without a coupon.
- Join a shoppers' club if your store offers one. Customers are given an identification card that entitles them to reduced prices on certain items. Without the card, they would have to pay full price. Unadvertised specials are also available to club members.
- Periodically recheck the unit price of products you buy regularly. Manufacturers sometimes keep the same price but reduce the amount in the package.
- Consider bulk foods. They cost less because they are not prepackaged. In addition, you can buy just the amount you want.
- Don't buy more food than you can store properly, or more than can be used before spoiling.
- Be aware of strategies designed to encourage impulse buying. Don't be tempted by small, high-profit items, such as candy and magazines, placed next to the checkout lanes.
- Take advantage of the many customer services provided by the store. You may find a coupon rack, for example, or brochures with tips on meal planning, food budgeting, and shopping.
- Surf your supermarket's Web site, if one's available. Doing so enables customers with computers to communicate with the store. Customers can learn of future sales, send their suggestions through e-mail, print out coupons, and in some cases, order groceries.

Technology TIE-IN Some stores now have computerized systems that can actually fill out a customer's check. A printer at the checkout counter fills in the name of the store and the amount due. All the customer is required to do is sign the check. This system helps stores avoid costly customer errors such as transposed digits.

Some stores also have systems that allow customers to purchase groceries using debit cards from local banks.

Nutrition, Quality, and Food Safety

Shopping involves more than looking for low prices. To get the most value for your money, you must also pay attention to nutrition, quality, and food safety.

Remember to read labels carefully. Be sure you're getting the product and amount you want. Check the date on the package. Use the "Nutrition Facts" panel (explained in Section 12-2). Also look for additional nutrition information on shelf tags or signs.

Avoid packages that are dirty, rusty, leaking, or damaged in any other way. Harmful bacteria may have gotten into the food. If packages of meat, poultry, and fish leak, the juices can contaminate other foods with harmful microorganisms. To be safe, put meat, poultry, or fish packages in plastic bags so that they won't drip onto other foods in your cart—and, later, in your shopping bag.

When buying frozen foods, avoid packages that are frosted with ice. The frost means the package may have thawed a little and was then refrozen. This can affect food quality and possibly contribute to foodborne illness.

◆ Safety is an important factor when shopping for food. Identify the warning signs of each of these foods.

Keep fragile items in one part of your cart. As you add heavier items, move the fragile ones up so that they are always on top and won't be crushed.

Plan your route through the store. The freezer section and the meat, poultry, and seafood department should be your last stops. This plan ensures that your food stays at safe temperatures.

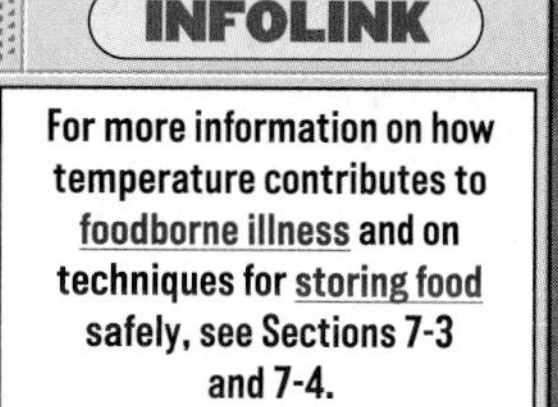

For more information on how temperature contributes to foodborne illness and on techniques for storing food safely, see Sections 7-3 and 7-4.

Courtesy When Shopping

Be considerate of other shoppers. Although there are no "supermarket police" to give traffic tickets, obey the same rules you would when driving. Don't race your cart through the store (especially around corners), and keep to the right side of aisles. If you bump into someone or have to pass another shopper, excuse yourself. Avoid blocking the aisles or other busy areas.

Any food that is damaged by shoppers is wasted. Consumers pay for the damage in the long run—the cost is added to the price of food. Remember:

- ◆ Do not open containers to look at or sample contents.
- ◆ Return a product to its proper place if you decide not to buy it.
- ◆ Handle produce gently. Do not squeeze it or throw it back into a bin.
- ◆ When you buy bulk foods, use the scoop or tongs provided. Do not taste the food or touch it with your hands. Close the bin or barrel when you are through.

- *Nutrition, Quality, and Food Safety*
- *Courtesy When Shopping*
- *Finishing Your Shopping (text pages 351-352)*

Guidelines

Ask students to develop a set of guidelines that they can follow to ensure that the foods they buy are safe and of high quality. Have students use the guidelines on a shopping trip for their family. **L1**

Writing

Have students write letters to "The Etiquette Expert" to ask questions about courtesy when shopping for food. Have students exchange letters with a partner and then write a response to the partner's letter. Ask volunteers to read their letters and responses. **L1**

Video Shoot

If students have access to a video camera, encourage several volunteers to create an original video on common courtesy when shopping. The video should highlight mistakes that a person might make without thinking. Prior to taping, students should obtain the store manager's permission and possibly even interview the manager. **L2**

Guest Speaker

Invite a speaker to discuss the impact food shoppers can have on the environment through their food purchases. As a follow-up, have students make a poster of "green shopping" techniques.

HOME & COMMUNITY CONNECTION

Have students draw a diagram of the supermarket where their family shops most often. On the diagram, have students identify the departments of the store. In class, ask students to draw the route they would take through the store when shopping for a week's groceries. Discuss students' routes.

ASSESS

REVIEW

- Ask students to summarize the main ideas in this section.
- Have students complete the Section Review. (Answers appear below.)

EVALUATION

- Ask students to sketch the various sections in a local supermarket, numbering the departments to show the order in which they would visit each to keep foods at their best quality.
- Have students take the quiz for Section 12-3. (Use the quiz in the *Teacher Resource Guide,* or construct your own with the **Exam***View*® *Test Generator* on the *Effective Instruction CD-ROM.*)

RETEACHING

- Provide students with simple cost-per-serving and unit cost problems to build their confidence in calculating these costs.
- Refer to the *Reteaching Activities* booklet for the Section 12-3 activity sheet.

CLOSE

Hold a "Round Robin" session on tips to save money at the supermarket.

Finishing Your Shopping

When you've selected all your items, it's time to head for the checkout lane. If you choose an express lane, be sure you have the right number of items. Don't choose a cash-only line if you intend to pay by check.

Watch the display as the prices are rung up. The clerk could make a mistake. If the store has computerized checkouts, the incorrect price might have been entered into the computer. If you think you are being charged incorrectly, politely ask the clerk to check the price for you.

◆ **Courtesy is important when shopping. Name three signs of a courteous shopper.**

Food stores vary regarding what forms of payment they will accept. To pay by check, you may need a store check-cashing card. Some supermarkets also accept credit cards or automated banking cards. Don't let the ease of using a card tempt you to go over your food budget.

Take your purchases home right away, and store them properly. Put frozen foods away immediately so that they don't thaw. Store refrigerated foods next, and finally, shelf-stable ones. Remember to repackage bulk foods in airtight, durable containers.

If you come home and discover a food you selected is spoiled or of poor quality, return it to the store as soon as possible. Do the same if you have any other problems with your purchases. Take the store receipt with you. Stores are interested in keeping their customers and will do their best to satisfy you.

Section 12-3 Review & Activities

1. What is the formula for calculating unit price?
2. Give three examples of ways to save money when shopping.
3. Why is it important to avoid buying food in damaged containers?
4. **Evaluating.** Do you think it is fair of stores to pass the cost of carelessness and mishandling of food by shoppers along to other customers? What solutions can you recommend to prevent shoppers from mishandling food?
5. **Synthesizing.** Some people will not buy store brands or generic items. Why do you think this is so? What might you say to such people?
6. **Applying.** Working in pairs, write and perform a skit demonstrating at least three poor shopping strategies. Have the rest of the class identify them.

Answers to Section 12-3 Review & Activities

1. Total price ÷ number of units = unit price.
2. See pages 348-350.
3. It may have been contaminated by microorganisms and be unsafe to eat.
4. Answers will vary. Food stores lose money because of food loss and raise food prices to counterbalance the cost of food mishandling. Stores can be proactive by posting signs.
5. Answers will vary. Some people believe the quality or flavor is inferior. People should try these items before passing judgment.
6. Skits will vary.

Career Wanted

Consumer Advocate

"Everyone deserves a level playing field."

Alana Burch

Education and Training
- Degree in law or government
- Familiarity with particular consumer area, such as nutrition, health care, or finance

Qualities
- Communication skills
- Networking skills
- Leadership

Q. How does a person train as a consumer advocate, Alana?

A. My background is in the law. My first position as a lawyer was with a firm that did a good deal of pro bono work—at no charge—for clients who couldn't afford a lawyer. It opened my eyes to how much people need an advocate when dealing with corporations and the legal system.

Q. What's the biggest obstacle people face in the marketplace?

A. People don't recognize their power as consumers and voters. They don't have to put up with an unfair or unsafe situation. They need to speak up and not wait until someone "important" notices their problem. Legislators and companies listen to me only because I'm backed by the voices of many individual citizens.

Q. What advice would you give someone interested in consumer advocacy?

A. Learn to write and speak persuasively. Always start by assuming the best about the people you're dealing with. Be patient, but persistent. Let them know that you're not going away.

Related Career Opportunities

Entry Level
- Town or city council member
- Law library clerk
- Police officer

Technical Level
- Mediator
- Paralegal
- Legal secretary

Professional Level
- Hearing officer
- Legislative assistant
- Occupational health and safety specialist

Making Career Connections

ACTION PLAN DEVELOPMENT. Imagine you've been asked to represent consumers in a dispute. Choose the issue and devise and outline an action plan for getting results. State the dispute clearly. What information do you need, and where can you find it? To what authority will you bring the case? What outcome would be fair and workable?

Career Wanted

Consumer Advocate

Thinking About the Career

As a class, have students discuss possible organizations for which a consumer advocate may work. If possible, students should interview an advocate to learn more about this career. Questions to be asked might include: In what way do you need to be assertive? What types of volunteer opportunities besides working with the Red Cross or a local hospital may help prepare someone for a career as a consumer advocate? What management skills are most useful?

Career-Building Opportunities

Have students choose one of the "Related Career Opportunities." Using the Internet, ask them to find out about organizations in which people in these careers may have membership.

For More Information

For additional information about careers as a consumer advocate, encourage students to contact:

- American Bar Association
  750 N. Lake Shore Drive
  Chicago, Illinois 60611
  www.abanet.org
- National Federation of Paralegal Associations
  P. O. Box 33108
  Kansas City, Missouri 64114-0108
  www.paralegals.org
- Public Voice for Food & Health Policy
  1101 14th St., SW
  Washington, D.C. 20005
  www.capitalresearch.org/publications/advocacyguide/Groups/pubvoice.html
- FindLaw
  Law and Legal Resources
  www.findlaw.com

REVIEW

- Have students complete the Chapter Review. (Answers appear below.)

EVALUATION

- Ask students to write a short essay describing the steps a person should take before, during, and after a trip to the supermarket.
- Have students take the test for Chapter 12. (Use the chapter test in the *Teacher Resource Guide,* or construct your own with the **Exam***View*® *Test Generator* on the *Effective Instruction CD-ROM.*)

ANSWERS

Checking Your Knowledge

1. Supermarkets are generally less expensive and carry a greater variety of products. However, specialty stores may carry a greater variety of the products in which they specialize.
2. Plan the meals you will serve; check your menus and recipes to see what foods and ingredients are needed; write those you don't have on your shopping list, along with the amounts needed; check your supply of basic items and add any you need to the list.
3. A cents-off coupon is redeemed at the checkout counter of the store; with a rebate coupon, you must pay full price and then send in the proof of purchase with the coupon for a partial rebate of the purchase price.
4. The weight of the food itself, not including the package.
5. The Daily Value for sodium is an upper limit; the Daily Value for vitamin C is a recommended minimum.
6. The food can be eaten frequently without exceeding daily recommended amounts of fat.

Chapter 12 Review & Activities

Summary

Section 12-1: Before You Shop

- A well-planned shopping trip begins with deciding where and when to shop.
- You can buy food from a number of types of stores. Which type you choose depends on your priorities.
- Preparing a shopping list helps prevent impulse buying.
- Collecting coupons is another money-saving strategy.

Section 12-2: Food Labels

- All food labels must include certain basic information.
- Nearly all food labels also include a "Nutrition Facts" panel to help you decide how well the product meets your nutritional needs.
- The use of certain terms and health claims on food labels is regulated by law.
- Open dating can help consumers judge how long products will remain safe.

Section 12-3: In the Supermarket

- Shopping skills can help you find nutritious, high-quality foods at the best price.
- Comparison shopping is easier if you know how to find the unit price and the price per serving.
- Choose quality foods and handle them carefully to help maintain nutritional value and safety.
- Food purchases should be taken home right away and stored properly.

Checking Your Knowledge

1. How do supermarkets and specialty stores compare in terms of foods sold, services offered, and price?
2. List four basic steps in making a shopping list.
3. What is the difference between a cents-off coupon and a rebate coupon?
4. What does *net weight* mean?
5. In what way is the Daily Value for sodium on a "Nutrition Facts" panel different from that for vitamin C?
6. What does "low-fat" on a food label tell you about the fat content of the food?
7. What kinds of health claims does the FDA allow on food products?
8. Describe the procedure for buying bulk foods.
9. Why is it helpful to calculate the cost per serving when buying fresh meat, poultry, or fish?
10. Name five signs that tell you a package of food may be unsafe.

Working IN THE Lab

1. ***Foods Lab.*** Make up a basic shopping list that could be stored on the computer. Explain how you would use the list.
2. ***Taste Test.*** Compare the taste, texture, and appearance of store brands or generic items with their name-brand equivalents. Compare a variety of types of foods, such as canned vegetables, breakfast cereals, and frozen juices. What conclusions can you draw?

Thinking Critically

1. **Comparing and Contrasting.** One of the items on Miguel's shopping list today is breakfast cereal. When he reaches the cereal aisle of his supermarket, he notices a large banner advertising double value on store coupons every Wednesday. Among the newspaper coupons he has clipped and brought with him is a rebate that returns one-third of the cost of any size package of this particular cereal as long as the coupon is mailed before December 31. What factors does Miguel need to take into account before he decides which coupon will give him the most value for his food dollar?
2. **Recognizing Assumptions.** Rhoda and her son Mark are shopping for a large turkey for a family gathering. All the bigger birds in the supermarket's meat case have ice crystals clinging to them. When Rhoda begins to reach for one of the birds, Mark reminds her that her shopping list specifies "fresh turkey." "This one is fresh," his mother replies. "See the sign?" She is pointing to a sign over the meat counter that states: "All our poultry is fresh, all the time." How might you respond if you were Mark?

Reinforcing Key Skills

1. **Directed Thinking.** Compare the prices of at least four different foods with those of their nutritionally modified equivalents (for example, cheddar cheese with reduced-fat or fat-free cheddar cheese). What are some possible reasons for the price differences?
2. **Leadership.** Devise a plan for increasing consumer awareness of food safety issues in food stores in your community. Put your plan into effect. Include a suggestion box, and use any responses received to assess the usefulness of your campaign.

Making Decisions and Solving Problems

While buying milk, you notice some cartons marked "Reduced for quick sale." You see the "sell by" date is the day after tomorrow. You wonder whether you should buy one of the reduced-price cartons.

Making Connections

1. **Social Studies.** Using library or online resources, find information about how people in other cultures do their food shopping. How are their shopping practices similar to and different from those in your own culture?
2. **Math.** Suppose you need chicken for a party for eight people. Check the prices and selections of different forms of chicken at the supermarket. Use the "Servings per Pound of Meat, Poultry, and Fish" chart on page 349 to determine which form offers the most value. What other factors would affect your decision?

ANSWERS cont.

7. Those that relate a food or nutrient with a disease or health condition.
8. Using the scoop or tongs provided, place the desired amount of the food in a plastic bag, tie it, and attach an identifying tag or sticker to the bag; close bin; do not taste the food or touch it with your hands.
9. These foods may contain bones and other parts that are not edible; the unit cost includes these parts, but cost per serving does not.
10. Any five: Dirty, bulging, dented, rusty, leaking, damaged.

Thinking Critically

1. Answers will vary. He needs to decide which size package he will be purchasing and needs to take into account the cost of the stamp to mail the rebate.
2. Responses will vary. Mark may respond by telling his mom that the sign may be misleading since the ice crystals indicate the turkey may have been frozen. Mark may suggest they purchase their turkey elsewhere, where the turkey has no signs of ice crystal formation.

Reinforcing Key Skills

1. Answers will vary. A higher cost for a modified food may be related to supply and demand or to the extra cost of manufacturing or advertising the product.
2. Answers will vary. Possible plan: Provide brochures that explain how to keep food safe while you are shopping.

CHAPTER 13

The Food Supply

Advance Planning Guide ☑

- Obtain orange juice in aseptic packaging, orange juice in a regular carton, and extra orange juice for a display.
- Create a list of foods that have to be inspected by a U.S. federal agency.
- Obtain recent articles about the safety of our food supply; copy them.
- Obtain foods with artificial sweeteners or fat substitutes for a taste test.
- Gather a variety of food products; copy their food labels.
- Invite an agriculture teacher or extension agent to speak to the class.
- Create a scrapbook of photos, pictures, and articles representing developing nations' food supplies.
- Set up a display of major staple foods of the world.
- Prepare soil mixtures that represent dominant soil types in developing countries.
- Obtain colored flags for map identification.
- Invite an agriculture specialist, food researcher, or nutritionist to speak to the class on the development of new food sources.

CHAPTER 13

André leaned back from his homework. Looking out his window, he could see huge snowflakes falling. He reached across the kitchen table for a favorite snack, an orange. As he peeled it, he noticed a sticker indicating that the orange came from California. André thought: This food has traveled farther than I ever have in seventeen years.

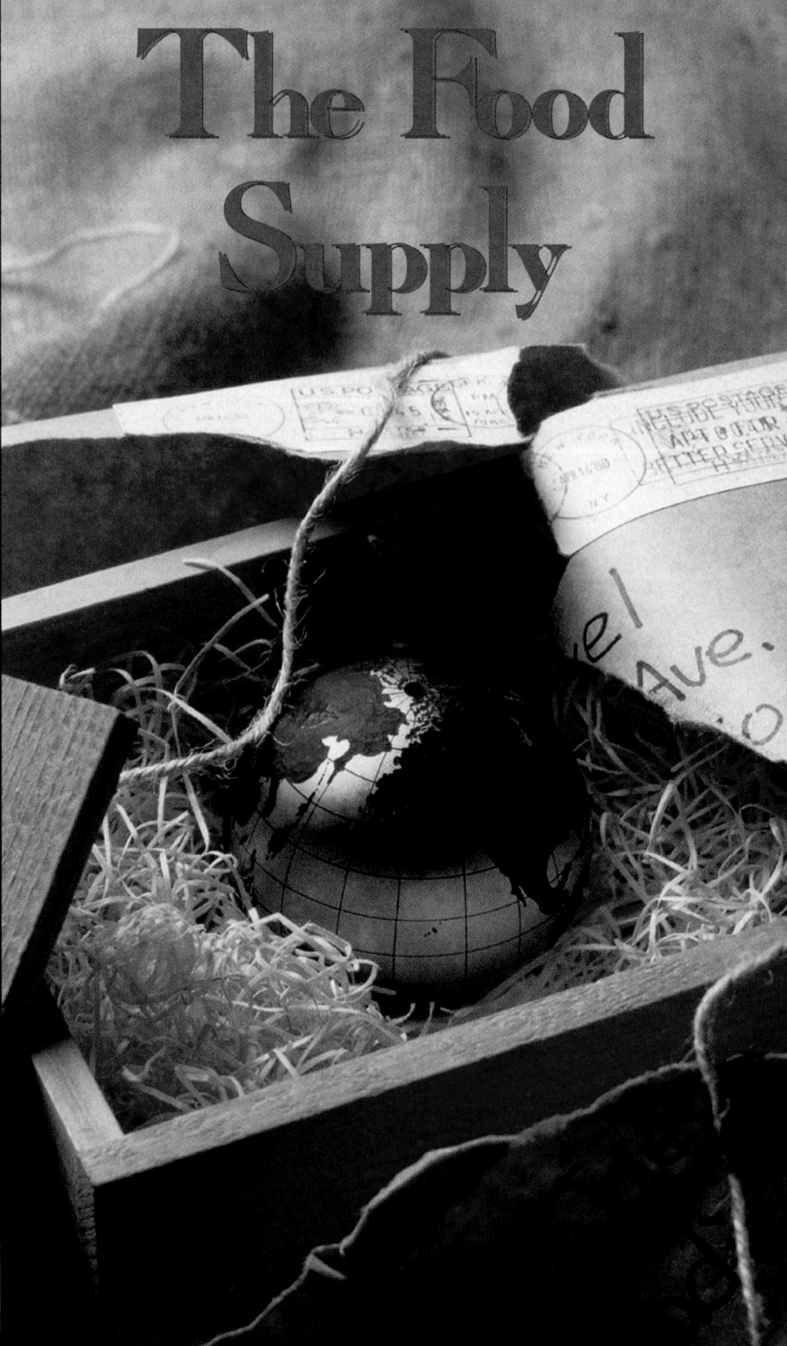

MEETING DIVERSE NEEDS

Multiple Intelligences: Naturalistic Learners. If there are students in the class who enjoy gardening and have an interest in food science, invite them to try a hydroponic gardening experiment to grow herbs, such as basil, or vegetables, such as tomatoes. If possible, have them create the garden on school property. Ask these students to share with the class the steps they took and ingredients or products used to start their hydroponic garden.

SECTION 13-1

Where Does Food Come From?

Objectives

After studying this section, you should be able to:

- Trace the route food takes from farm to marketplace.
- Describe innovative farming, processing, and packaging techniques.
- Identify factors that influence food prices.

Look for These Terms

sustainable farming

hydroponic farming

aquaculture

Like André's snack, most of the foods on your table at home have traveled hundreds or thousands of miles. In this section, you will learn about that journey and about the professionals through whose hands every food passes at various steps.

From Farm to Marketplace

Most food begins its journey on farms where it is grown. Farmers in the United States and Canada produce enough food not only for their own countries but also for sale elsewhere.

The Farmer

In recent years, several concerns have prompted a search for new farming technologies. One is the impact of traditional farming methods on the environment. Traditional methods rely on the use of potentially harmful chemicals in fertilizers and pesticides.

Among the alternative methods are the following:

- **Sustainable farming** is the cutting back on, or elimination of, chemicals in farming. In this method, animal manure replaces chemicals as a fertilizer. Nonchemical measures are also used to get rid of pests and weeds. One of these—integrated pest management—uses "good" bugs to destroy "bad" ones.
- **Hydroponic** (hy-druh-PAH-nik) **farming** is a method of growing plants without soil. Various materials, such as water, gravel, or sand, can be used to hold the plants.

SECTION 13-1

Where Does Food Come From?

FOCUS

MOTIVATORS

- Divide the class into small groups and have each group select five processed foods. Ask groups to list the steps each basic food underwent between field, orchard, or farm and purchase.
- Ask students to bring one empty food package to class, preferably one that they believe is unique or technologically advanced. Have students display their packages and describe the use of each. Then set up a package display with all these packages.

VOCABULARY ACTIVITY

Pronounce the terms listed under "Look for These Terms." Have students read the section and find the terms and their definitions in the section.

STUDY SKILLS

- **Listening.** Invite a group of volunteers to each prepare an oral reading of a page of text from the section, while others follow along silently.
- Have students read the section and complete the appropriate part of the Chapter 13 Study Guide in the *Student Workbook.*

Section 13-1 Resources

◆ **Student Workbook,** pp. 95, 97
◆ **Teacher Resource Guide**
Lesson Plan 13-1 Organizer
Section 13-1 Quiz
◆ **Effective Instruction CD-ROM**
Exam*View®* *Test Generator*
PowerPoint® Slide #27
◆ **Transparency Package,** CT-27
◆ **Student Motivation Kit**
Reteaching Activities, p. 66
Enrichment Activities
A Global Foods Tour, p. 159

TEACH

- *From Farm to Marketplace (text pages 357-360)*

Chart Making

Ask students to make a chart, either freehand or on the computer, listing six methods that are used to preserve perishable foods. In each category, students are to list as many foods as they can. Display the charts for the duration of study of this section. L1

Continuum Activity

The amount of processing that food undergoes varies greatly. Have students make continuums on sheets of paper with a minus sign at one end, a plus at the other, and a vertical dividing line at the approximate center. They are then to write the names of foods that exemplify minimal (–), moderate (centerline), or maximum (+) processing. Would the amount or type of processing affect their food choices? How and why?

Flow Charts

Have students research and make flow charts of the curing process. Is the process of curing growing or diminishing as a preservation process? What are the ingredients used in the curing process? What are their functions? What are advantages and disadvantages of the curing method? L1

Nutrient-enriched water provides food for the plants. Hydroponic lettuce, cucumbers, and tomatoes are currently available in many supermarkets.

- **Aquaculture** is a method of growing fish or seafood in enclosed areas of water. Fish farms may be areas located near the shore that are closed off with special nets, or they may be special ponds. Aquaculture is one of the fastest-growing industries in the world. The U.S. Department of Commerce predicts that by 2010, aquaculture will provide over a third of all fish eaten in this country.

The Processor

Once food is harvested, it is shipped to processors. The specific type of processing facility to which it travels depends on the type of food and the form in which it ultimately will be sold.

Processing ranges from very simple to complex. Fresh produce, for instance, needs minimum processing. It may just need to be cleaned, packaged, and shipped to the marketplace.

As part of the processing, many perishable foods are preserved to prevent spoilage and lengthen shelf life. Some commercial preservation methods include:

- **Canning.** Foods are sealed in airtight metal or glass containers and heated to destroy harmful microorganisms.
- **Freezing.** Foods are quickly frozen to slow down the growth of harmful bacteria.
- **Curing.** Ingredients such as salt, spices, sugar, sodium nitrate, and sodium nitrite are added to the food. This method is widely used in processing meats such as ham, bacon, and corned beef. It is also used to preserve fish, pickles, and some vegetables.

◆ **Farmers are continually on the alert for ways to produce more and better quality food.** Name some technological advances in farming during the past fifty years.

Reinforcing Key Skills

Present the following problem to student groups. Allow time for them to discuss and compare their responses.

Management—Most farmers still practice traditional farming methods using chemical fertilizers and pesticides. However, many are beginning to change to sustainable farming. Ask students: Aside from the pressure of consumer demand for foods grown without chemicals, what reasons might the farmers have for reducing their use of chemicals?

◆ **Milk goes through various amounts and types of processing before it is ready to be delivered to stores. Research the processing of milk and outline the process.**

◆ **Drying.** Moisture, needed by harmful microorganisms, is removed from the food. Drying is used for foods such as grains, dry beans, milk, and fruit.

◆ **Freeze-drying.** Food is first frozen and then dried. More flavor, texture, and nutrients are retained than with drying alone. Freeze-drying is used for foods such as instant coffee, dried soup mixes, strawberries, and mushrooms.

◆ **Controlled atmosphere storage.** Food is held in a cold area where the amounts of nitrogen, oxygen, and carbon dioxide in the atmosphere are controlled. This helps extend the shelf life of some foods, especially fruits.

Packing Technology

Several recent developments in packaging have enabled food manufacturers and processors to expand the kinds of products they offer. Here are some examples:

◆ **Aseptic** (ay-SEP-tick) **packages.** Also known as "juice boxes." Are made of layers of plastics, paperboard, and aluminum foil. The food and the package are sterilized separately, and the package is filled under sterile conditions.

◆ **Plastic cans and trays.** Are used for shelf-stable foods that can be heated in a microwave oven. Some trays also can be used in a conventional oven.

◆ **Packaging methods are continually being updated to keep up with technology and the needs and wants of consumers. Which of the types of packages shown do you use? What others do you use?**

• *From Farm to Marketplace (text pages 357-360)*

Poster Project

Have students create a poster that traces the steps in the processing of a food product from harvest to store. Remind them of the variety of processing methods and packaging procedures used. L1

In the Supermarket

Ask students to visit a supermarket and randomly pick one perishable food product from at least six different sections or aisles. They are then to record the name and a description of both the product and the method of preservation and packaging technology used. Ask student volunteers to share their findings with the class. How often did the same preserving technique emerge in a random activity? What conclusions, if any, can students draw? L1

Lab Experience Activity

Set up a room temperature display of an unopened juice box with aseptic packaging; an unopened juice in a small, regular carton; and a glass of juice. Ask students to anticipate how long each juice will stay fresh. After several days, compare the products with regard to color and smell. Caution students against tasting the products. Discuss how packaging affects freshness.

Extending Learning

Food Distribution—Many supermarket chains are so large that they have their own distribution systems, either nationwide or regional. They can afford to buy huge quantities of food direct from food processors or distributors and keep it in their own warehouses until needed. This saves money for the large chains and allows them to offer lower prices than smaller chains or independent stores. Use the names of large and small chains/independent stores in the area for discussion.

- *From Farm to Marketplace*
- *Food Prices*
  (text pages 357-361)

Student Mime

Have student pairs pantomime how a careless consumer can damage a particular food. Possibilities include squeezing bread or produce for freshness, and accidentally knocking a breakable container from a shelf while reaching for an item on a higher shelf. Discuss how such accidents can be prevented. L1

Creating a Game

Have groups of students write the steps in processing and distributing a food on index cards. Have groups exchange cards and arrange the steps in order. After the cards are in order, students should give a fact about each step. L1

Brainstorm Activity

Using the package display set up in the classroom, students are to brainstorm ideas on how to cut down on packaging of selected food packages. Discuss the idea of edible packaging.

USING CONNECTING FOOD AND HEALTH

Ask students to bring lists to class of at least five names of foods with packages that can be easily recycled. Compile a master list for students to use with their families for shopping.

- **Modified atmosphere packaging.** A mixture of carbon dioxide, oxygen, and nitrogen is inserted into the package before it is sealed. The gas mixture slows down bacterial growth. With this method, foods such as fresh pasta, prepared salads, and cooked meats can be kept, refrigerated, up to four weeks.

For information on canning, freeze-drying, and other methods for preserving food at home, see Section 24-5.

The Distributor

Once food is processed and packaged, it is shipped to the distributor. Distributors are the link between food processors and retailers (the stores where you buy food). There are many different kinds of distributors, depending on the food involved. Generally, the food is shipped to large warehouses, where it is stored before being sent to the retailer.

The Retailer

From the distributor, food is shipped to the many different kinds of food retailers. Supermarkets, which offer a wide selection of products, are the most popular type of retail food outlet in this country. Others are described in Section 12-1.

A primary job of the retailer is to present food to the consumer. In an effort to satisfy consumers, food processors and manufacturers constantly develop new products. Some stores review as many as 100 new products a week. Because shelf space is limited, they cannot accept every new product. If new products are accepted but do not sell well, they are removed from the shelves.

Connecting Food and Health

Waste Not

Food processors have begun developing packages that are more "environment-friendly." As a consumer, you can also do your part for the environment.

- Use "convenience" packaging only when absolutely necessary. For meals eaten at home, avoid using juice boxes and single-serving packages.
- Learn which resources are recyclable and which are not. When you have a choice, buy food in packages that can be recycled.
- Be a leader and set a good example for friends and family members, especially younger brothers and sisters. Help them follow the motto "Waste not, want not."

Think About It

- Make an inventory of food packages in your home pantry and refrigerator. Note which foods come in recyclable packages and which do not. Share your inventory with your family, and discuss ways to make responsible shopping choices.

Food Prices

For every dollar a consumer spends on food, between 3 and 25 cents goes to the farmer. The rest of the money covers processing, packaging, advertising, and distribution. Generally, the more a food is processed, the more it will cost the consumer. Food prices tend to go up or down for other reasons as well.

Ask students to interview food retailers in their area and ask them how food prices are determined in their retail operations. Suggest students ask what factors affect when and how a food price is increased. Have student volunteers share interview findings with the class.

- **Supply and demand.** If consumer demand for a food is greater than the supply, the price will go up. If supply is greater, as it is when crops reach their peak growing seasons, prices are low. Other foods, offered in limited supply, are high-priced.
- **Natural disasters.** Storms, earthquakes, floods, and droughts affect the price of food. For example, a severe freeze in California or Florida can damage orange trees, reducing the supply for the whole season. The reduced supply results in higher prices.
- **Consumer damage.** Careless consumers sometimes damage food when they shop. The damaged items may have to be thrown out by the store. Such losses are added to the prices consumers pay.

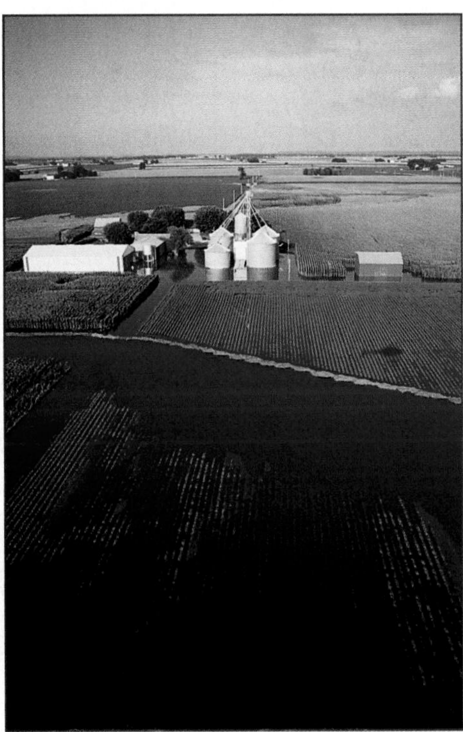

◆ **Floods and similar natural disasters can destroy crops and drive up the price of food. Identify two other factors that affect the prices of food.**

Section 13-1 Review & Activities

1. Name the four parts of the food supply network.
2. How and why is food preserved?
3. What factors affect food prices?
4. **Analyzing.** Why do you think there is a need for finding new farming technologies?
5. **Comparing and Contrasting.** What foods on your table at home or school might be grown or processed within 100 miles of your home? Which foods do you think travel the greatest distance to reach your local stores?
6. **Applying.** Interview a parent or another relative who shops for food regularly. Ask that person to think of any food or beverage products he or she used to buy at the supermarket but can no longer purchase there. Why might the product no longer be stocked? Has the person found a different brand of the product? Compile a class list of discontinued products.

ASSESS

REVIEW

- Ask students to summarize the main ideas in this section.
- Have students complete the Section Review. (Answers appear below.)

EVALUATION

- Ask students to draw a simple diagram describing the processes by which food goes from the farmer to the retailer.
- Have students take the quiz for Section 13-1. (Use the quiz in the *Teacher Resource Guide,* or construct your own with the **Exam***View*® *Test Generator* on the *Effective Instruction CD-ROM.*)

RETEACHING

- Using canned or packaged foods, students are to describe the processing methods that were used to process each food.
- Refer to the *Reteaching Activities* booklet for the Section 13-1 activity sheet.

CLOSE

Have students, one by one, reclaim the food packages they originally brought for the classroom display. Ask students if they will continue to use this product, or if they will search for a less processed food or a similar product with different packaging.

Answers to Section 13-1 Review & Activities

1. Farmer, processor, distributor, and retailer.
2. Through different forms of food processing; to prevent spoilage and lengthen shelf life.
3. Supply and demand, natural disasters, and consumer damage.
4. Answers will vary. New farming technologies are needed for several reasons: (1) due to the growing consumer demand for less chemical, fertilizer, and pesticide use and (2) to produce better quality or more nutrient-rich foods.
5. Answers will vary.
6. Answers will vary.

SECTION

13-2

A Safe Food Supply

FOCUS

MOTIVATORS

- Ask students to write a paragraph describing what they think makes a food safe to eat. Ask several student volunteers to read their paragraphs aloud.
- On the chalkboard list the following terms: calcium propionate, lactic acid, potassium sorbate, sodium nitrate, spices, sugar, and vitamin C. Ask students which ones they think are food additives. Circle each item as it is named—then circle the items not named. Proceed to the section reading.

VOCABULARY ACTIVITY

Pronounce the terms listed under "Look for These Terms." Have students read the section and find the terms and their definitions in the section.

STUDY SKILLS

- **Guided Reading.** Have students look at the headings within Section 13-2 to preview the concepts that will be discussed.
- Have students read the section and complete the appropriate part of the Chapter 13 Study Guide in the *Student Workbook*.

SECTION

13-2

Objectives

After studying this section, you should be able to:

- Explain how the government helps ensure the safety of the food supply.
- Identify and discuss food safety issues.

Look for These Terms

food additives

recall

irradiation

genetic engineering

tolerance levels

contaminants

A Safe Food Supply

When Brittany was shopping for cucumbers at the store, she noticed they were all shiny but felt a bit sticky. She asked the produce clerk why. He explained that they were coated with a wax to prevent loss of moisture and improve their appearance. He assured her that this process met government regulations for food safety.

Safeguarding the Food Supply

Government and industry make every effort to provide a safe food supply. In doing so, they face a number of challenges. One is testing food additives to be sure they will cause no harm. **Food additives** are chemicals added to food to preserve freshness or enhance color or flavor.

Another challenge is seeing that foods are handled properly on their way to the marketplace so that harmful microorganisms do not reach dangerous levels. A third challenge is staying on top of new food technologies and taking steps to ensure that harmful chemicals do not get into food accidentally.

Government Agencies

In the United States, several federal agencies are responsible for monitoring the safety of the country's food supply:

◆ **Food Safety and Inspection Service (FSIS).** This section of the United States Department of Agriculture (USDA) is responsible for the inspection and safety of meat, poultry, and eggs.

Section 13-2 Resources	◆ **Student Workbook**, pp. 95, 99 ◆ **Teacher Resource Guide** Lesson Plan 13-2 Organizer Section 13-2 Quiz ◆ **Effective Instruction CD-ROM** **Exam***View*® *Test Generator* PowerPoint® Slide #28 ◆ **Transparency Package,** CT-28	◆ **Student Motivation Kit** Reteaching Activities, p. 67 Enrichment Activities Food Science Resources, pp. 56–58, 113–115 Skills for Making Food Choices, pp. 31–32

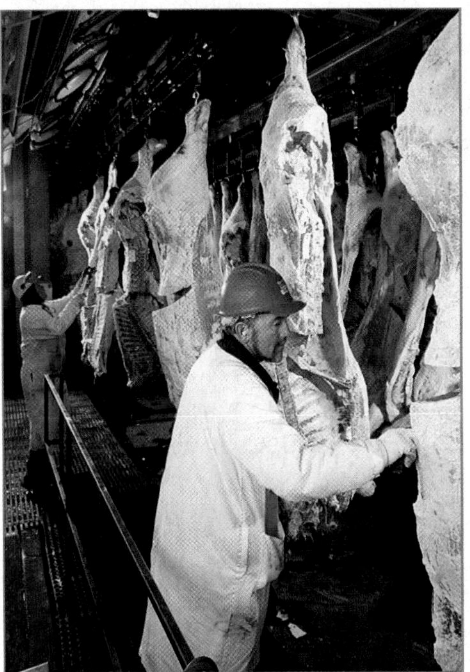

◆ **Inspectors from various government agencies work to protect the food supply. Choose one agency and explain the work it does.**

◆ **Food and Drug Administration (FDA).** The FDA is responsible for the general safety of food other than meat, poultry, and eggs. It enforces laws that regulate additives, food purity, packaging, labeling, and new foods and processing methods.

◆ **National Marine Fisheries Services.** This agency within the Department of Commerce offers a voluntary inspection program to fish processors.

◆ **Environmental Protection Agency (EPA).** The EPA registers pesticides and sets legal limits for pesticides in food. It also regulates disposal of hazardous wastes.

What happens if tests or consumer complaints show that a food is unsafe? The FDA may first ask the manufacturer to withdraw the product voluntarily. If the manufacturer refuses, or if the situation is a life-threatening one, the FDA will order a **recall**—the immediate removal of the product from store shelves and notification of the public through the media. The brand name and package code numbers are announced. Consumers who have purchased any of this food are asked to return it to the store.

Food Safety Issues

Many issues related to food safety are controversial. It is important to understand the facts as well as the opinions on both sides of each issue.

Food Additives

When you think of additives, you probably think of ingredients on food package labels with long, hard-to-pronounce names. Did you know, however, that spices are additives? Currently, some 3,000 additives are in use.

FDA approval for additives can be a lengthy process. An additive is first tested extensively. If it proves to be safe, the FDA approves it and sets regulations for its use. Additives with a long history of safe use are classified by the FDA as "Generally Recognized as Safe" (GRAS). Additives on the GRAS list can be used by food processors without further approval from the FDA. However, even these substances must be retested as standards change.

Even though additives are approved by the FDA, consumers sometimes raise questions about their safety. In some cases, the FDA undertakes a process of study and review.

TEACH

• *Safeguarding the Food Supply (text pages 362-363)*

Categorizing Activity

Ask students to list federal agencies responsible for food safety in the United States. Then provide students with a list of foods that are inspected in the United States. Ask them to categorize the foods with the appropriate agencies on their lists.

Reading Activity

Provide students with copies of recent newspaper or news magazine articles about the safety of our food supply. Ask each student to summarize his or her article. What questions about food safety does the article address? How often does the same issue arise in the news?

Research

Have several volunteers research the histories of the federal agencies responsible for food safety. Among questions to be answered are

- Why was the agency established?
- What is its role in ensuring food safety?
- What major contributions has the agency made to food safety?
- What are the agency's limitations?

Allow time for students to share and compare the agencies they have learned about. L1

Extending Learning

Specific Additives—Antioxidants can be used in foods as additives. They are preservatives that keep fats and oils from spoiling and keep other foods from losing color, flavor, or texture.

Monosodium glutamate, also known as MSG, is an additive that used to be common in prepared foods, especially Chinese cuisine. It is still used as a flavor enhancer in some foods.

Sodium nitrate is found in some processed meat. It helps prevent spoilage, preserve color, and inhibit the growth of botulinum bacteria.

- *Food Safety Issues (text pages 363-366)*

GRAS Activity

Invite students to contact the FDA or perhaps visit its web site under your supervision to learn more about the GRAS list. Challenge students to find out answers to the following questions and make posters or pamphlets with their findings: Which additives are currently on this list? Which were removed in the past 20 years and why? Who at the agency is ultimately responsible for deciding whether an additive is GRAS?

Taste Test

Have students sample and evaluate foods that contain artificial sweeteners or fat substitutes. Have them compare these foods with versions containing natural sweeteners and fat, as well as versions made with sweet spices and less fat (for example, roasted versus fried chips). Discuss the reactions.

Product Comparison Activity

Ask students to research additives and develop an annotated list of ten with their functions. Then hand out copies of food product labels. Tell students to read the label, identify the additives present, and determine the function of each. What effect will this have on future food choices?

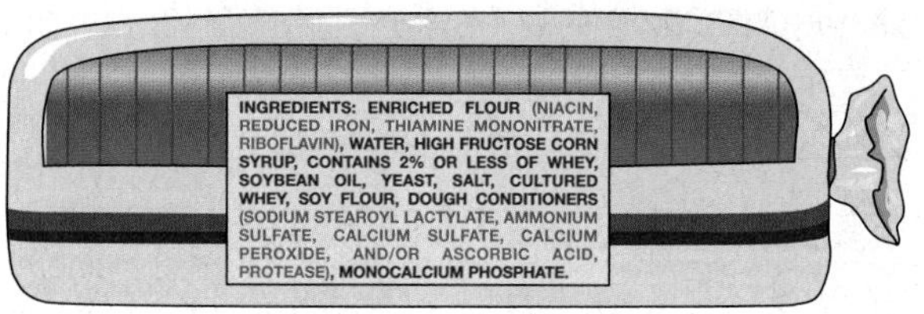

◆ **Additives are used in many foods to improve the quality or lengthen the shelf life. What is the meaning of the acronym "GRAS"?**

Consumers who are concerned about particular additives can avoid foods that contain them by reading ingredients lists carefully.

Sugar Substitutes

Sugar substitutes sweeten food while adding few or no calories. They can benefit people who must restrict the amount of sugar they eat, such as those with diabetes. Critics are not certain how helpful they may be for weight loss. Common artificial sweeteners include *aspartame* (ASS-pur-tame), *acesulfame-K* (ay-see-SULL-fame—KAY), and saccharin (SACK-uh-ruhn).

Some controversy has surrounded sugar substitutes. For example, saccharin was banned in 1977 after studies linked it with cancer in laboratory animals. By public demand, the ban was later lifted. The new rule allows products containing saccharin to be sold if a warning appears on the label and in the store.

Fat Substitutes

Fat substitutes are natural or artificial substances that replace fat in processed foods such as fried foods, baked goods, and ice cream. They are also used in reduced-fat foods, such as low-fat cheeses.

Some natural fat substitutes are based on proteins from ingredients such as nonfat milk or egg whites. Others are based on carbohydrates from sources such as cornstarch and oat bran. Natural substitutes are considered safe.

Artificial fat substitutes have also been developed. Since they do not break down during digestion, they add no fat or calories to the foods containing them. Specific FDA approval is required for artificial fat substitutes. One such substitute, *olestra* (oh-LESS-truh), was approved in 1996. However, some studies of this additive claim it removes some fat-soluble nutrients and phytochemicals from the body. The studies also indicate that olestra may cause mild digestive problems in some consumers. Because of these studies, the FDA requires that a warning label be on all packages of food that contain olestra, alerting consumers to these possible health risks.

INFOLINK

For more information on phytochemicals and their perceived role in fighting disease, see Section 2-4.

◆ **Olestra, a synthetic fat, was first approved by the FDA for public consumption in 1996. Compare and contrast the advantages and disadvantages of a product like olestra.**

Reinforcing Key Skills

Present the following problem to student groups. Allow time for them to discuss and compare their responses.

Critical Thinking—Imagine that you are waiting at a bus stop adjacent to a newsstand and your eye catches this headline: "FDA Bans Additives." What impact would this have on any foods you ate prior to learning details of the story? Explain your reaction.

Some experts are concerned that fat substitutes will not help people learn healthful eating habits. An eating plan heavily weighted toward fat-free treats may lack the proper balance of foods from the Food Guide Pyramid.

◆ **Irradiation plants use a conveyor system to move foods along. Explain the purpose of irradiation.**

Rods of cobalt-60

Main chamber has thick concrete walls.

Food is exposed to gamma rays.

Packaged food is loaded on conveyor belt.

Computer controls conveyor speed and amount of radiation.

Food after irradiation

Irradiation

Irradiation is the process of exposing food to gamma rays to increase its shelf life and kill harmful microorganisms. Irradiation does not make foods radioactive. It can, however, cause minor changes in flavor and texture and slight vitamin loss.

Those in favor of irradiation mention its potential to improve food safety. It could reduce food-borne illness and eliminate the need for dangerous pesticides.

Critics of irradiation point to other concerns. They claim that irradiation produces harmful by-products that can lead to cancer and birth defects. They also fear that the radioactive chemicals used in irradiation plants pose a danger to workers and the community.

The FDA first approved the use of irradiation for spices. It has also been approved for fruits, vegetables, poultry, ground beef, and seafood. Irradiated foods must be identified with the symbol shown at the top of this page.

Genetic Engineering

Genetic engineering is a method of enhancing specific natural tendencies of plants and animals. This is done by altering genes, tiny segments of matter that pass hereditary traits on from one generation to the next. Scientists have already used genetic engineering to produce new, hardier varieties of tomatoes, squash, and potatoes. They are working to develop other plants that are easier to grow and process, stay fresh longer, and have more nutrients.

Some critics have questioned the safety of foods that have been genetically altered. The FDA has developed guidelines for assessing the safety of such foods as they become available to consumers. It has also considered the question of product labeling. As with all foods, labeling is required if the product contains a substance that could trigger an allergic reaction or if the nutritional content has been altered.

- *Food Safety Issues (text pages 363-366)*

Debate

Divide the class into two teams. Have students stage an informal debate on the benefits and risks posed by genetically engineered foods. Prior to the debate, allow time for students to research their team's position. **L2**

Discussion Activity

Ask students to identify several improvements that have been made in the field of plant biotechnology. Ask students to define the term *biodiversity*. In what way might biotechnology pose a threat? Discuss sources of chemical residues in food.

Technology TIE-IN

In 1992, the first irradiation plant opened in Mulberry, Florida. More than 1000 pounds (500 kg) of strawberries were irradiated and shipped to a retailer. They sold quickly and consumers were pleased with the flavor and appearance of the strawberries.

In 1997, the FDA approved irradiation for fresh and frozen meats, including poultry, beef, and lamb, as a means to protect these foods from contamination by salmonella and Escherichia coli 0157: H7.

TEACH cont.

- *Food Safety Issues*
- *What Consumers Can Do (text pages 363-367)*

Guest Speaker

Invite an agriculture teacher or extension agent to speak to the class on the use of biotechnology to improve food products. Discuss the potential advantages and disadvantages of genetically engineered foods.

USING Safety Check

Have a volunteer read aloud the Safety Check on this page. Ask students to record any disposal instructions they can find from one household chemical product that they have at home (or can find in a supermarket). Do any package directions differ from the advice in the text feature? If so, how?

Some people are concerned that genetic engineering could result in a food supply that is dependent on a few specifically designed plants. If so, unforeseen problems, such as a sudden change in climate, could endanger the entire food supply. Others, however, see genetic engineering as a way to increase the diversity of the world's crops.

This much is certain: Genetic engineering raises issues that have never had to be dealt with before. They will probably be debated for years to come.

Illegal Chemical Residues

In recent years, concern about chemical residues in food has increased. These residues are substances left behind in food after processing. Chemical residues have the potential to cause health problems, some of which can be serious.

Chemical residues can come from a variety of sources. In meat and poultry, they are usually from drugs used to improve animal health or from pesticides in animal feed. Residues gather in animal tissues. In plant foods, including grains, fruits, and vegetables, pesticides are usually the main residues.

Government agencies establish **tolerance levels**—maximum safe levels for certain chemicals in the human body. It is illegal for foods to contain more of a chemical than the tolerance level set for it. Government agencies test food samples regularly for illegal residue levels.

Safety Check

Never dump household chemicals down the drain or on the ground. The chemicals could contaminate the water and food supply. Follow package directions for proper disposal, or call your local sanitation department.

Contaminants

Contaminants are harmful substances that accidentally get into food as it moves from the farm to the table. One type of contaminant is chemical pollutants. Hazardous chemicals from industries, farms, or careless consumers can easily get into water supplies. Plants drawing on polluted water can become contaminated. Fish and other animals are also affected.

Microorganisms are another source of contamination. Salmonella bacteria, for example, can contaminate eggs and chickens, causing foodborne illness. *Aflatoxins* (AF-luh-TOCK-sunz) are poisonous substances produced by certain types of mold. They can sometimes be found in grains, milk, cheese, and peanuts.

As with illegal residues, various government agencies test food for contaminants to ensure the safety of the food supply.

◆ **Although pesticides serve an important purpose, they also pose a health threat. Explain the threat.**

Extending Learning

Water Pollution—Dumping of chemical residues has compromised not only food products but one of our most precious nutrients, water. The view that the world's water reserves were so vast that there was plenty of fresh water to go around prompted industry, agriculture, and private citizens to abuse much of the planet's fresh water resources through several forms of pollution:

- the dumping of raw sewage or industrial waste.
- the use of products that contain harmful chemicals.
- oil spills.

What Consumers Can Do

Contradictory reports regarding the safety of the food supply can be confusing to consumers. For reliable information, turn to a reputable consumer group concerned with food safety. Many such groups serve as watchdogs of both government and industry. Before you accept facts presented by a consumer group, however, be sure you know how it is funded. Some are merely agents for food and chemical industries.

Here are some additional suggestions for promoting a safe food supply:

◆ Support consumer groups that reflect your views.

◆ Avoid buying products from companies whose policies you do not support.

◆ Keep track of any laws that are being introduced relating to food. Write to your representatives. Tell them how you feel about any aspect of food safety.

◆ **Writing to your representatives in government is constructive action you can take to ensure a safe food supply. What food safety issue interests you? Try writing a letter that expresses your concerns.**

Section 13-2 Review & Activities

1. Name four government agencies responsible for food safety.

2. What is a recall? Why are recalls important?

3. What is a food additive? Give two examples.

4. How might irradiation improve food safety?

5. Extending. The federal government monitors food safety, but state and local governments do too. Investigate laws and policies that address food safety in your state and local community. County and state health departments have information. Check the government pages in the telephone directory for listings.

6. Extending. On the Internet, find out how the National Association of City and County Health Officials (NACCHO) supports local public health agencies.

7. Comparing and Contrasting. Learn more about genetic engineering. What information supports the different points of view on this topic? What is your opinion?

ASSESS

REVIEW

- Ask students to summarize the main ideas in this section.
- Have students complete the Section Review. (Answers appear below.)

EVALUATION

- Ask students to present a brief report on the effects of technology on food supplies and safety.
- Have students take the quiz for Section 13-2. (Use the quiz in the *Teacher Resource Guide,* or construct your own with the **Exam***View®* *Test Generator* on the *Effective Instruction CD-ROM.*)

RETEACHING

- Have pairs of students list federal and state agencies that regulate food safety. Present partners with several situations regarding food safety and ask them to choose the agency to contact in each case.
- Refer to the *Reteaching Activities* booklet for the Section 13-2 activity sheet.

CLOSE

Remind students of the first motivator for this section. Would they change their answers now? What makes foods safe or unsafe?

Answers to Section 13-2 Review & Activities

1. See pages 362-363.

2. The immediate removal of product from stores and notification of public; they protect consumers from unsafe products.

3. A chemical added to food to preserve freshness, enhance color or flavor. Examples include sugar, salt, spices, other ingredients.

4. It reduces foodborne illness, eliminates need for dangerous pesticides.

5. Answers will vary.

6. Generally, group provides information and other resources; researches and implements programs on various health-related issues.

7. Answers will vary.

SECTION
13-3
The Global Food Supply

FOCUS

MOTIVATORS

- Ask students to identify reasons the world's food supply varies from year to year. (Examples: droughts, floods, or other natural disasters; amount of land in cultivation.)
- Gather pictures, photos, and articles for a scrapbook that tells a story of the food supply issues of developing nations. Share the scrapbook with students; compare the developing nations' food supplies to our food supply.

VOCABULARY ACTIVITY

Have students define *industrialized* and *developing*. Compare and contrast these definitions. Then pronounce all the terms listed under "Look for These Terms." Have students read the section and find the terms and their definitions in the section.

STUDY SKILLS

- **Outlining.** Have students read the section and outline it by copying the headers on paper and leaving space after each one. Students are to write a sentence in their own words, summarizing the content under each header.
- Have students read the section and complete the appropriate part of the Chapter 13 Study Guide in the *Student Workbook*.

SECTION 13-3

The Global Food Supply

In a perfect world, everyone would have plenty to eat. In the real world, many individuals and families go to bed hungry every night.

What accounts for the differences in the amounts and types of food available to different regions? This section will provide some answers.

Objectives

After studying this section, you should be able to:

- Explain why staple foods differ around the world.
- Identify the causes of food shortages.
- Discuss the possible ways to remedy global food problems.

Look for These Terms

industrialized nations
developing nations
staple foods
famine
subsistence farming

The Global View

One reason for differences in the food supply around the world is differing economic conditions. Countries are often categorized according to their economic progress. The **industrialized nations**, also called developed countries, are the richest. These are countries that rely on sophisticated, organized food industries to supply their citizens with food.

Developing nations are countries that are not yet industrialized or are just beginning to become so. People in such places cannot afford to buy food and must grow their own.

Some countries rank between industrialized and developing countries. As they progress economically, they are able to provide more food for their people.

Staple Foods

The food supply in any region also depends on what foods can be grown there. Only certain foods can be grown in each region. These **staple foods** are foods that make up the region's basic food supply. Several factors determine the staple foods for a given area:

- **Geography.** Food is most easily grown in areas where the soil is rich, such as valleys or plains. In mountainous areas, farming is more difficult. Animals that can live on rocky slopes, such as goats, may be raised.

Section 13-3 Resources

◆ **Student Workbook**, pp. 96, 100
◆ **Teacher Resource Guide**
Lesson Plan 13-3 Organizer
Section 13-3 Quiz
Chapter 13 Test
◆ **Effective Instruction CD-ROM**
Exam*View*® *Test Generator*

◆ **Student Motivation Kit**
Reteaching Activities, p. 68
Enrichment Activities
A Global Foods Tour, pp. 147–160

- **Climate.** Moderate temperatures make it possible to grow a wide variety of food. In some climates, temperatures vary and food can be grown only during the warm months. Extreme temperatures, either high or low, limit the kinds of food that can be grown.
- **Rainfall.** Some crops thrive in areas that receive a lot of rainfall annually. Little, if any, food can be grown in dry areas such as deserts.

In many parts of the world, grains are the main staple foods. This is especially true in developing countries. Each type of grain, such as wheat, rice, corn, and rye, is best suited to a particular climate. For example, rice grows in warm, wet climates.

Grain is also fed to animals used for food. However, animals are inefficient in converting grain to meat. With cattle, for example, it takes about 8 to 10 pounds (3.6 to 4.5 kg) of grain to produce 1 pound (500 g) of meat.

Food Shortages

It's estimated that about 700 million of the world's people don't have enough to eat. For some, that means going hungry for several days at a time. The most severe form of diminished food supply is **famine**—food shortages that continue for months or years. Many die of starvation during periods of famine.

The problem of world hunger is a complex one. Some of the basic causes are economics, inefficient farming methods, fuel shortages, overpopulation, wars and politics, and natural disasters. These factors may affect food production, or they may cause problems in distributing or using the food.

Economics

In many developing countries, most people are too poor to buy food and live instead on very meager meals consisting of home-grown foods. This practice of maintaining a small plot of land on which a family grows its own food is known as **subsistence farming**.

Some farmers have enough land to grow crops they can sell, or *cash crops*. However, when cash crops are exported, local food shortages often occur. Also, world food prices change so frequently that cash-crop farmers cannot depend on steady incomes.

In developing countries, good roads are rare. Villages are separated, with no modern transportation to connect them. As a result, it's difficult to distribute food. One area may have a surplus of food while a few miles away, people have nothing to eat. During famine, poor distribution keeps food aid from reaching starving people.

◆ **Rice paddies like this one provide supplies of the staple grain throughout much of Southeast Asia. Investigate other foods that play a role in the diet of people in Cambodia or Vietnam.**

TEACH

- *The Global View (text pages 368-369)*

Making Comparisons

Have students make Venn diagrams by drawing two large intersecting circles on a sheet of paper. In the overlapping portion, they are to list characteristics that industrialized and developing nations have in common. In the nonoverlapping areas, they are to note differences. Discuss the effects of economic conditions on food supply based on factors included in diagrams. L1

Display Activity

Display on a table in the classroom foods that represent the major staple foods of the world. Using colored flags to represent each staple food, volunteers are to select a food and identify the parts of the world in which it is a staple. Discuss factors that influence the basic food supply of different parts of the world.

Finding/Developing Recipes

Have students research staple foods (particularly protein sources) of developing nations. Ask: What determines the staple foods in an area? Discuss the factors that limit the types of food that can be grown in an area. Then have students find or develop recipes that could be prepared within a developing nation. Ask students to compile these into a "Developing Nation Cookbook." L1

FOOD SCIENCE

Soil Fertility Experiment

Prepare soil mixtures that represent the dominant soil types in various developing countries. Ask a science teacher to help you with the percentages of components. Provide seeds for three or four staple foods that grow in the United States. Have students try to grow each food in each soil type and report on their results. Remind students that the climate will have an effect on the results of the experiment. Have interested students repeat the experiment, adjusting the "climate" to simulate conditions in various areas of the world.

- *Food Shortages (text pages 369-371)*

Discussion Activity

Ask students to define *subsistence farming*. Ask students to explain what a cash crop is and to list problems that developing countries have with cash crops. Discuss the various factors that contribute to food shortages.

Reading

Have students bring to class newspaper or magazine clippings about food crises around the world. Discuss the circumstances that created specific crises. What relief efforts are being undertaken? L1

Lab Experience

Have students conduct an energy efficiency experiment to see how long it takes water to boil in glass, earthenware, aluminum, and stainless steel utensils. Ask students to relate their findings to fuel shortages in underdeveloped and developing countries. L1

Writing

Ask students to write a paper based on the question under the heading "Overpopulation" on page 370: Will the food supply keep up with the increase in population? Have students supply pro as well as con input. L1

◆ **Subsistence farming relies on simple tools powered by people or animals.** Why is modern machinery not used for these tasks?

Inefficient Farming Methods

Subsistence farming makes use of ancient methods. Animals, instead of gas-powered machinery, supply the power. Farm tools are simple, having designs that date back hundreds of years. With such outdated tools and methods, food production is low. However, modern farming equipment and methods are costly and not always suited to the crops and conditions in developing countries.

Fuel Shortages

Most food must be cooked before being eaten, which means that fuel for cooking is essential. In developing countries, wood is the most common cooking fuel. Unfortunately, many areas are experiencing serious shortages of wood. Without fuel for cooking, people may go hungry.

Overpopulation

The world population, which has been growing steadily, could increase to 15 billion people by 2010. The most rapid increase has been in developing countries. As population grows, so does the demand for food. At the same time, more land is taken for housing, leaving less land for farming. When people clear forests to get more farmland, they destroy their source of fuel.

Will the food supply keep up with the increase in population? Some experts think not.

Wars and Politics

Wars can have a devastating effect on food supplies. Animals are killed and crops destroyed. People are forced to abandon their farms. Fighting disrupts food distribution systems.

Extending Learning

Alternative Fuel Sources—Solar energy is an inexpensive alternative in many countries in which wood is in short supply. Various models of solar appliances can meet the needs of most regions.

Camels are the main means of transportation in hot desert areas. A small refrigerator can be strapped to the camel's back and a solar panel mounted on top. The solar panel converts the sun's rays into energy that runs the refrigerator. This technology opens possibilities for food storage.

Food is also used as a political weapon. Opposing parties may interfere with food distribution or manipulate supplies. Food aid may never reach the needy because it is stolen and sold on the black market.

During the 1900s, millions of people in Africa died of starvation because of civil wars in many countries.

Natural Disasters

Natural disasters, such as floods and earthquakes, can destroy a region's food supply. Crops may be damaged and animals killed. If soil erosion occurs or roads are destroyed, food supplies can be affected for many years. Prolonged drought, especially in developing countries, can result in famine and starvation.

What Can Be Done?

Many efforts are being made to increase the global food supply. The most common goal is to teach people in developing countries how to help themselves. Where modern farm machinery and methods are not affordable, programs must help people within the means available to them.

The United Nations, government agencies such as the Peace Corps, and private nonprofit organizations, such as the American Friends Service Committee and Oxfam International, are involved with the education process. They show farmers how to improve farming methods and equipment and how to increase water supplies. In Ethiopia, for instance, food production increased as a result of broadening the tiny steel blade on the crude wooden plows used by farmers.

The Role of Technology

Technology is a vital part of the search for ways to feed a growing world population. Using current knowledge and scientific methods, scientists continue to improve food production and preparation techniques.

Solar energy offers much hope as a solution to the problem of fuel shortages. It has great potential where the climate is sunny and dry most of the year. Several types of solar cookers are available, including one made inexpensively from cardboard, aluminum foil, and a plastic bag. These cookers can be used for most meal preparation tasks, such as simmering rice, baking potatoes, cooking casseroles and stews, and even pasteurizing milk. The solar

◆ **Solar cookers are handmade as well as manufactured in different shapes and sizes. You'll find many other examples on the Internet.**

- *What Can Be Done? (text pages 371-372)*

Posters

Ask students to research at least one product that is being developed to increase the food supply, particularly in developing nations. Have students compile the main points of their research onto posters with drawings (if possible) of the identified, potential food products. **L2**

Guest Speaker

Invite an agriculture specialist, food researcher, or nutritionist to speak to the class on the development of new food sources. How can these help solve global food shortages? If possible, have them bring a basic solar cooker and demonstrate its use.

Discussion Activity

Discuss problems that could result from trying to introduce modern farming machinery and methods in developing nations.

Computer Research

Using the Internet, have students find out how to get involved with one program, such as the Peace Corps, that helps people in developing countries and works to solve food crises. Have representative students share findings with the class on several of the programs. **L1**

Reinforcing Key Skills

Present the following problems to student groups. Allow time for them to discuss and compare their responses.

Management—Why do you think there is so much food wasted in this country? What could be done to prevent food waste?

Leadership—What would you do if a flood, earthquake, or other natural disaster affected a large portion of your neighboring community's food supply?

ASSESS

REVIEW

- Ask students to summarize the main ideas in this section.
- Have students complete the Section Review. (Answers appear below.)

EVALUATION

- Have students write a short essay explaining the reasons for food shortages and what can be done about them.
- Have students take the quiz for Section 13-3. (Use the quiz in the *Teacher Resource Guide,* or construct your own with the **Exam***View*® *Test Generator* on the *Effective Instruction CD-ROM.*)

RETEACHING

- Using a world map, help students identify areas of the world in which food shortages are likely to occur (developing countries).
- Refer to the *Reteaching Activities* booklet for the Section 13-3 activity sheet.

CLOSE

List five world shortage issues in columns on the chalkboard. Then have each student come to the chalkboard and list one thing people in the United States can do about one of the issues. Discuss the students' listed comments.

cookers are being used in various areas, including India, China, Africa, Central America, and the southwestern United States.

Nutritionists from nonprofit organizations teach area residents how to use solar cookers. They also teach the basics of good nutrition.

In their work with foods, scientists use technology to produce tougher varieties of grains and other plant foods that can resist disease and pests. They are also developing foods that tolerate drought and poor soil. For example, if a particular type of wheat can be made to grow where it never could before, a new food source becomes available in some areas of the world.

Nutritious food products are also sought. Because people in some developing countries cannot easily digest milk or milk products, an alternative is now possible. After making a paste from ground leaves, the paste is used as the basis for a highly nutritious crumbly cake.

Technology offers many ideas for the future. A growing world population is likely to depend on them for survival.

CLOSE-UP ON SCIENCE: PHYSICS

Solar Cookers

A well-designed solar cooker, often called a solar box cooker, can achieve very good results when cooking food. The cooker's dark bottom absorbs heat, and a glass panel traps it. Thin but well-insulated walls lined with reflective foil deflect heat to the cooking chamber. Using dark-colored pots directs more heat to the food. Under the best conditions—long periods of strong sunlight—temperatures inside a cooker can reach 300°F (150°C). When conditions are less than ideal, cutting foods into smaller pieces and starting the cooking earlier help the cooking process along.

Section 13-3 Review & Activities

1. What is meant by the term *staple foods*? Name two factors that determine the staple foods found in a given place.
2. Identify five causes of food shortages.
3. Name two ways in which technology is improving the global food supply.
4. **Analyzing.** Put the following statement in your own words: "To learn about hunger, you need look no farther than your own backyard." What accounts for the problem indicated by this statement?
5. **Extending.** What problems could result from trying to introduce modern farming machinery and methods in developing nations?
6. **Applying.** Find information about regions that are experiencing famine. Write a one-page report about one such locality, along with any ideas you have for dealing with the problem.

Answers to Section 13-3 Review & Activities

1. Foods that make up a region's basic food supply; any two: geography, climate, and rainfall.
2. See pages 369-371.
3. See page 371.
4. Answers will vary. One possibility: People are starving right here in the United States; an unequal distribution of wealth in a democracy.
5. Students should identify the problems that may arise as a result of inadequate training (accidents) as well as support (product maintenance).
6. Answers will vary.

Career Wanted

Food Safety Inspector

Education and Training
- Degree in food science or related field
- Experience in food industry
- Testing and certification

Qualities
- Attention to detail
- Communication skills
- Management skills

"Food safety is everyone's business, but especially mine."
Louis Panopolous

Q. How do you monitor food safety, Louis?

A. I inspect both the processor and the product. I check that the plant is sanitary and that workers handle food properly. I talk to the manager about any concerns and take food samples for analysis. When I get the results, I can write and file my report. I also respond to specific complaints.

Q. What do you see as the biggest challenge to a safe food supply?

A. The increase in global trade presents some concerns. The more food travels, the greater the chance for contamination. International cooperation and communication will be increasingly important. Also, the long-term effects of newer technologies are still unclear.

Q. What do you like best about your job?

A. I feel I'm performing an essential service, not only by inspecting foods, but also by educating food handlers. That's very rewarding. I also enjoy learning about advances in food science that may lead to increased food safety, especially for developing countries. That's very exciting.

Related Career Opportunities

Entry Level
- Cafeteria worker
- Produce grader
- Lab assistant

Technical Level
- Lab technician
- County health inspector
- Quality assurance technician

Professional Level
- Microbiologist
- Public health administrator
- Consumer safety officer

Making Career Connections

CAREER EXPLORATION. Use library and Internet resources (possibly FDA and USDA sites) to write an article about a typical day at work for a fictional food safety inspector. Include locations and products inspected, special equipment used, and the person's authority to investigate and start proceedings against violators.

Career Wanted

Food Safety Inspector

Thinking About the Career

- Ask students to read and briefly summarize the job of a food safety inspector. Students are then to develop and seek answers to questions relating to a career in this field—for example: How do you go about getting a job with the FDA? How does an inspector check for violations? What are examples of violations?
- Ask students to brainstorm what they think would be the most exciting part of being a food safety inspector.

Have students discuss the responsibilities inherent in a career in food safety inspection.

Career-Building Opportunities

Students planning a career in consumer and food safety should check with local food laboratories for volunteer and employment opportunities.

For More Information

For additional information about careers in food safety or sanitation, encourage students to contact:

- The Food Safety Network
  www.foodsafety.gov
- Center for Food Safety and Applied Nutrition
  U.S. Food and Drug Administration
  5100 Paint Branch Pkwy.
  College Park, MD 20740-3835
  www.cfsan.fda.gov
- Food Safety and Inspection Service
  United States Department of Agriculture
  Room 1175-S
  1400 Independence Ave. SW
  Washington, DC 20250-3700
  www.fsis.usda.gov

REVIEW

- Have students complete the Chapter Review. (Answers appear below.)

EVALUATION

- Divide the class into two teams. Each team should brainstorm questions about Chapter 13. Then allow the teams to take turns asking each other questions. At the end of the questioning period, the team with the most correct answers wins.
- Have students take the test for Chapter 13. (Use the chapter test in the *Teacher Resource Guide,* or construct your own with the **Exam***View*® *Test Generator* on the *Effective Instruction CD-ROM.*)

ANSWERS

Checking Your Knowledge

1. The use of animal manure and integrated pest management.
2. Any four: canning, freezing, curing, drying, freeze-drying, controlled atmosphere storage.
3. If consumer demand for a food is greater than the supply, the price will go up, and vice versa.
4. Food and Drug Administration and Food Safety and Inspection Service; the FDA is responsible for food other than meat, poultry, and eggs—the very foods that FSIS *is* responsible for.
5. Those with a long history of safe use.
6. Substances left behind in food after processing. In meat and poultry, they are usually from drugs used to improve animal health or from pesticides in animal feed. In plant foods, pesticides are usually the main residues.

Chapter 13 Review & Activities

Summary

Section 13-1: Where Does Food Come From?

- Most food begins its journey to the consumer as a farm product.
- New farming technologies have been developed that do not use fertilizers or pesticides, which can harm the environment.
- From the farm, food is sent to a processor, where it is prepared for its final use.
- The processor sends food to the distributor, who sells it to the retailer. The retailer then sells the food to the consumer.
- The price consumers pay for the food depends on many factors.

Section 13-2: A Safe Food Supply

- In the United States, the federal government monitors the safety of the nation's food supply. Various government agencies inspect food for contamination and regulate food processing, packaging, and labeling.
- Food safety issues that are a source of concern include the use of food additives, food irradiation, genetic engineering, chemical residues from food processing, and contaminants that threaten the food supply.

Section 13-3: The Global Food Supply

- The basic food supply, or staple foods, of a region depends on geography, climate, and rainfall.
- Food shortages are caused by a number of factors that affect food production and distribution.
- International agencies and scientists are working to increase the food supply in developing countries.

Checking Your Knowledge

1. Give two examples of sustainable farming practices.
2. List four commercial preservation methods.
3. How does supply and demand affect food prices?
4. Identify what *FDA* and *FSIS* stand for. What types of food is each agency responsible for keeping safe?
5. What types of food additives are found on the GRAS list?
6. What are chemical residues? How do they get into food?
7. How does food production differ in industrialized nations and developing nations?
8. Explain the problems associated with growing cash crops in developing countries.
9. Explain the relationship between the growing population, food supplies, and fuel supplies.
10. How can genetic engineering be used to help increase the world's food supply?

Working IN THE Lab

1. ***Taste Test.*** Cook or heat equal amounts of two forms of the same vegetable. Compare for taste, texture, appearance, price per serving, and convenience.
2. ***Food Science.*** Conduct an experiment using two loaves of bread—one homemade and the other a store brand with preservatives. Place one slice of each on a plate, uncovered. Wrap another slice of each in plastic wrap. After two, five, and seven days, compare for mold and other signs of spoilage. What conclusions can you draw?

Thinking Critically

1. **Identifying Ambiguous Statements.** Brad had just bought a package of crackers from the school vending machine. He was about to take a bite when Serena, a classmate, stopped him. "I'm doing you a huge favor," she said. "Those crackers are loaded with additives. If you want a safe snack, I have an extra apple in my backpack. I'll be happy to give it to you." On the basis of information provided in the chapter, how would you advise Brad to respond? Explain.
2. **Determining Credibility.** Imagine that a respected scientist testifies before the FDA that a certain pesticide is safe and effective. Later it is discovered that the university where the scientist teaches receives large donations from the company that makes the pesticide. How does this affect your opinion of the scientist's findings?

Reinforcing Key Skills

1. **Communication.** You are grocery shopping for the family dinner. When you reach the produce department, you find that most of the fruits and vegetables are bruised, wilted, or otherwise damaged. Knowing that this drives prices up, decide whom you would speak to and what you would say. Write out the text of your message.
2. **Leadership.** A friend tells you that, unless you are a scientist or politician, there is nothing you can do to increase the world's food supply. You want to prove him wrong by reducing food waste and helping the hungry in your community. Tell what action you would take.

Making Decisions and Solving Problems

Your friend wants to lose weight. She tells you that her weight-loss plan is based mainly on low-calorie foods and beverages made with artificial sweeteners and fat substitutes. She asks for your opinion. What do you say to her?

Making Connections

1. **Language Arts.** Using library or online sources, investigate the history of a food additive that has been in use for at least 100 years. Write a short autobiography, in which you take the point of view of the additive. Discuss the reason you were "born" (your original purpose), what kind of popularity you have enjoyed, and any controversies that might lead to your untimely demise. Your autobiography may be humorous, but keep it informative. Read your work aloud to classmates.
2. **Social Studies.** Using library sources, locate five farming regions on at least three different continents. For each region, identify the main crops, describe the geography and climate conditions that make the crops successful, and tell what products they are used in. Share your findings in a brief report.

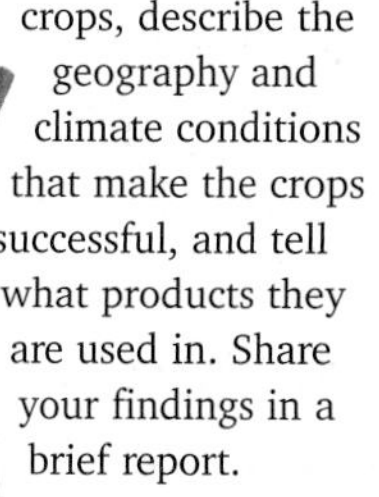

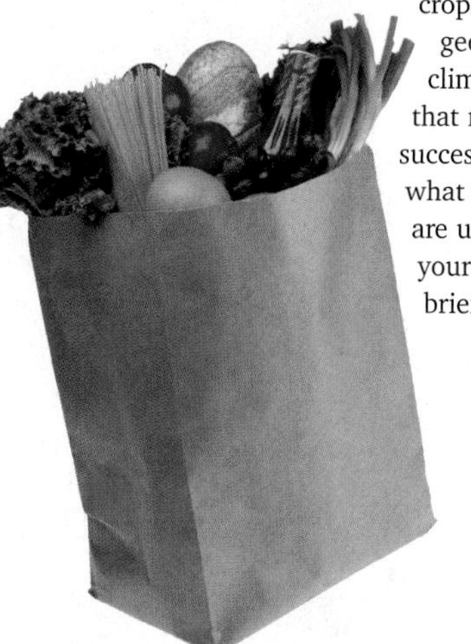

ANSWERS cont.

7. In industrialized nations, people have the technology and other resources to create and use modern equipment and rely on sophisticated, organized food industries to supply their citizens with food. In developing nations, people cannot afford the equipment or the food; they must grow their own food; they often use inexpensive solar cookers for preparation.
8. Local food shortages can occur, and world food prices fluctuate so much that cash-crop farmers cannot depend on steady incomes.
9. As the population grows, so does the demand for housing, leaving less land for farming; as people clear away trees to create farmland, they destroy sources of fuel.
10. Scientists hope to produce varieties of grains and other plant foods that are resistant to drought and other environmental problems.

Thinking Critically

1. Answers will vary. Brad may respond as follows: Thanks for offering, but I prefer crackers right now. The crackers are processed more than your apple, but the additives that are in them actually help keep the crackers fresh —they're not in there to harm me. Some additives actually make products safer and more nutritious.
2. In spite of his impeccable credentials, the scientist may have been biased.

Reinforcing Key Skills

1. Answers will vary.
2. Answers will vary. Students should demonstrate initiative in their answers as well as an understanding of the leadership skill for food choices.

CHAPTER 14

Buying for the Kitchen

Advance Planning Guide ☑

- Obtain copies of a consumer magazine that rates a particular appliance.
- Gather appliance warranties.
- Gather empty packaging for small appliances that have product information, warranty, etc., on the outside of the package.
- Obtain a variety of consumer magazines that compare the same appliance.
- Obtain catalogs, brochures, and other promotional materials for a flatware categorizing activity.
- Obtain cookware catalogs.
- Arrange a class field trip to a kitchen planning center.
- Obtain or gather kitchen storage devices; create a display.
- Invite a panel of experts on planning an efficient, comfortable, and attractive kitchen.
- Invite at least one speaker with a physical challenge that has adapted his or her kitchen.
- Gather floor plans of kitchens of several different designs.

CHAPTER 14

Buying for the Kitchen

Shopping for a new refrigerator took Shasta's family to several different appliance stores. Using information she had learned in her family and consumer sciences class, Shasta helped her parents compare features on different models.

Some day you may be making a purchase like this for your own home. In this chapter, you will learn what you need to know.

MEETING DIVERSE NEEDS

Visual/Spatial Learner. Invite students with an art aptitude to develop a miniature three-dimensional model display of a "dream" kitchen plan that they believe would be functional/ideal for a family in 2025. After completion, have class "artists" explain how their design is functional and how it's different from kitchen plans today. Encourage the class to listen carefully.

SECTION
14-1

Objectives

After studying this section, you should be able to:

- Describe the decisions that must be made before shopping for kitchen equipment.
- List four important shopping guidelines that can help you make wise kitchen purchases.

Look for These Terms

credit
principal
interest
annual percentage rate (APR)
finance charge
warranty
EnergyGuide label
service contract

Consumer Skills

Buying equipment for a kitchen can vary from shopping for a mixing spoon to buying a major appliance. No matter what you plan to buy, using consumer skills will increase your chances of making a smart purchase.

Before You Shop

Have you ever bought an article of clothing that ended up unworn in a drawer or closet? Before you buy anything, you need to think about your reasons for making that purchase. This step is particularly important when you are making a major purchase.

Begin by asking yourself these questions. If you are updating an item you already have, will the replacement be enough of an improvement to justify its cost? If you are buying a new item, will you use it? How much can you afford to spend? How will you pay for the item? Shasta's family asked themselves these questions. The refrigerator they ended up buying cost less than they initially planned to spend!

Paying for Your Purchase

Most people pay cash for small items. Some save so that they can pay cash for larger purchases, too. Many people, however, use credit for at least part of the cost of major purchases.

Section 14-1 Resources

◆ **Student Workbook,** pp. 101, 103
◆ **Teacher Resource Guide**
Lesson Plan 14-1 Organizer
Section 14-1 Quiz
◆ **Effective Instruction CD-ROM**
ExamView® *Test Generator*
◆ **Student Motivation Kit**
Reteaching Activities, p. 69
Enrichment Activities

SECTION
14-1
Consumer Skills

FOCUS

MOTIVATORS

- Ask students to identify the least used kitchen equipment in their homes. What is the item's intended purpose? Why is it seldom used? What can be done to prevent the purchase of such items in the future?
- Identify a kitchen appliance that the class foods lab might need to replace soon. Ask students to identify the features they think the new appliance should have, considering space, need, and cost. Pass out copies of a consumer magazine with ratings on the appliance. Ask students to select the appliance they would recommend buying.

VOCABULARY ACTIVITY

Pronounce the terms listed under "Look for These Terms." Have students read the section and find the terms and their definitions in the section.

STUDY SKILLS

- **Guided Reading.** Have students look at the headings within Section 14-1 to preview the concepts that will be discussed.
- Have students read the section and complete the appropriate part of the Chapter 14 Study Guide in the *Student Workbook*.

TEACH

- *Before You Shop (text pages 377-378)*

Discussion Activity

Ask students to explain the terms *principal* and *interest*. Ask: What other fees may be included in finance charges? Discuss the problems with using credit. How can they be avoided?

VISUAL LEARNING ***Using the Art*** Ask students to examine the credit statement on this page and suggest fees other than the purchase price and APR that Gregory Ledsma will need to pay. Discuss how interest charges and late fees can add up if Mr. Ledsma continues paying the minimal amount due and paying late. Ask students to act as "credit counselors" and provide suggestions to Mr. Ledsma. If desired, give students calculations based on this statement.

Math Activity

Ask students to assume they have purchased a range that cost $695. With a down payment of $100 and a 14% annual percentage rate on the remainder, how much interest would you have to pay in one year? (*$83.30*) Suppose you pay the remainder at the end of one year. How much did you actually pay for the range? (*$778.30*)

Buying on Credit

Credit is money you borrow from a lender. The lender may be a bank, as is the case with most credit cards, or it may be a different kind of financial institution. Buying on credit is more expensive than paying cash, but it allows you to use the item while you pay for it.

Credit has a vocabulary of its own. The money you borrow is the **principal**. The lender charges you interest. **Interest** is a fee for the loan, expressed as a percentage of the amount you borrow. Interest rates vary. By law, they must be stated in terms of **annual percentage rate (APR)**, which gives you the yearly cost of a loan.

When considering credit, look carefully at the **finance charge**—the total amount you will pay for borrowing. It includes interest and other costs, such as service charges and credit-related insurance premiums. Monthly payments are usually computed by dividing the total cost (principal + finance charge) by the number of months of the loan.

For major purchases, you may have several financing options. Many stores offer financing. Loans are available from institutions such as banks and finance companies. Credit cards can also be used.

Shop for credit as carefully as for your purchase. Ask each lender for the APR and finance charges so that you can compare the cost of borrowing. The differences in total cost may surprise you.

One problem with using credit is that you may be tempted to spend more than you can afford. Failure to make monthly payments on time can cause significant problems. The items you purchased can be taken away from you, and you may find it difficult to get credit in the future. You can avoid these problems by deciding on a price range you are comfortable with and sticking to it.

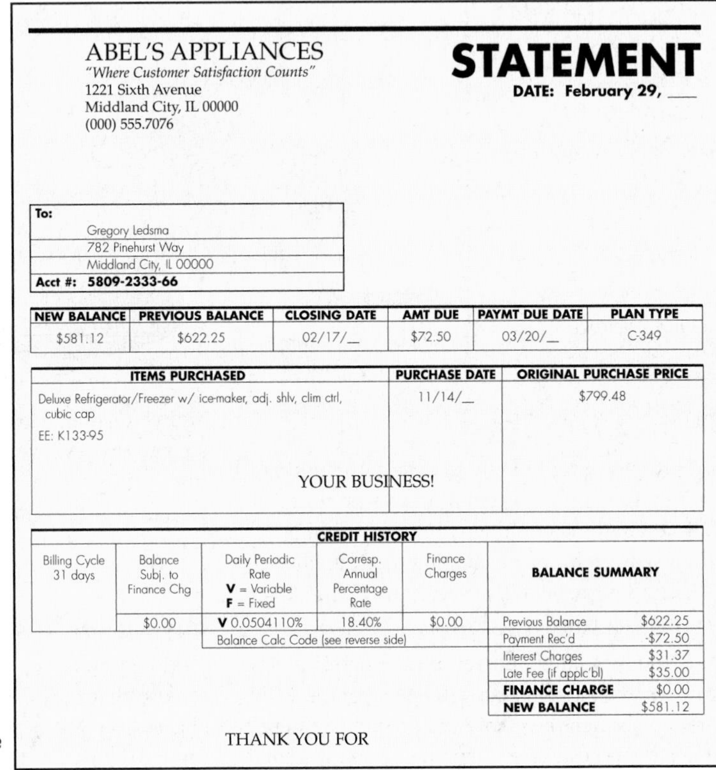

ABEL'S APPLIANCES
"Where Customer Satisfaction Counts"
1221 Sixth Avenue
Middland City, IL 00000
(000) 555.7076

STATEMENT
DATE: February 29, ___

To:
Gregory Ledsma
782 Pinehurst Way
Middland City, IL 00000
Acct #: 5809-2333-66

NEW BALANCE	PREVIOUS BALANCE	CLOSING DATE	AMT DUE	PAYMT DUE DATE	PLAN TYPE
$581.12	$622.25	02/17/__	$72.50	03/20/__	C-349

ITEMS PURCHASED	PURCHASE DATE	ORIGINAL PURCHASE PRICE
Deluxe Refrigerator/Freezer w/ ice-maker, adj. shlv, clim ctrl, cubic cap EE: K133-95	11/14/__	$799.48

THANK YOU FOR YOUR BUSINESS!

CREDIT HISTORY

Billing Cycle 31 days	Balance Subj. to Finance Chg	Daily Periodic Rate **V** = Variable **F** = Fixed	Corresp. Annual Percentage Rate	Finance Charges
	$0.00	**V** 0.0504110%	18.40%	$0.00
	Balance Calc Code (see reverse side)			

BALANCE SUMMARY	
Previous Balance	$622.25
Payment Rec'd	-$72.50
Interest Charges	$31.37
Late Fee (if applc'bl)	$35.00
FINANCE CHARGE	$0.00
NEW BALANCE	$581.12

◆ **People who buy on credit periodically receive bills that look something like this. What is the annual percentage rate on this loan?**

Extending Learning

Credit—Failure to make monthly payments on time can have serious consequences. These can include:

- Late payment fees.
- Loss of good credit rating. This may prevent future borrowing.
- Repossession. With large purchases, this means losing all the money already paid, as well as the item itself.

Anyone having a problem making payments should tell the lender immediately. Often a new payment plan can be worked out until finances improve.

◆ Some consumer publications are run by not-for-profit organizations that permit them to conduct unbiased tests on goods and products. How can you determine which publications rely on these types of tests?

Buying Guidelines

Following a few simple shopping guidelines can help you make wise choices when buying for the kitchen. Any item you plan to keep a long time should be chosen with special care.

Consider Your Needs and Wants

Begin by identifying the characteristics and features most important in the item you plan to buy. For instance, if you're buying a new appliance, write down the measurements of the space where it must fit. If your new dishes must be microwave-safe, note that.

Also write down the features you would like the item to have. Rank your wants from most to least important. Setting priorities is helpful because you may not be able to find an item within your price range that has all the features you want.

Gather Information

Well-informed shoppers are usually happy with the items they purchase and often get a good price. Many sources of information are available. Look for advertisements and articles in magazines and newspapers. Some consumer magazines conduct unbiased tests to compare similar items from different manufacturers. You can also contact manufacturers directly for up-to-date information.

The reliability of the store is also important, especially for major purchases. Check with the closest Better Business Bureau to see whether the business has had complaints from consumers and whether the complaints have been settled satisfactorily.

Look for Consumer Safeguards

As you shop, look for consumer safeguards. Government agencies, manufacturers, and dealers have provided means for ensuring the quality of products.

Seals of Approval

Seals of approval are given by nonprofit testing agencies to show that a product meets certain standards for safety and performance.

- ◆ On gas appliances, look for the *American Gas Association* seal. It indicates that a gas appliance's design, performance, and reliability have been tested and certified.

- *Buying Guidelines (text pages 379-381)*

Hypothetical Situation Activity

Tell students to imagine a hypothetical situation in which they are responsible for purchasing a new microwave oven for their home. Ask students what type of information they should gather before making the purchase. On the chalkboard, record a list of students' suggestions.

Display Activity

Ask students to bring to class a seal of approval found on a large or small kitchen appliance at home. Have students draw the seal. Set up a class display of the seals. Discuss the seals and the types of products that have these seals.

Product Comparisons Activity

1. Have students work in small groups to compare the features available for one type of kitchen appliance.
2. Have them pick from a hat which type of equipment to compare.
3. Ask groups to identify situations when certain features might be considered needs, and others when the same features might be wants.
4. Have each group report its findings to the class. L1

HOME & COMMUNITY CONNECTION

Ask students to interview the person in their family responsible for the purchase of kitchen equipment in their home. Have students make a list of the decision-making steps that go into the person's purchase of equipment. Also, suggest students ask about equipment problems that have occurred, if any, and how the person handled the problems. Have a few student volunteers share results of their interviews with the rest of the class.

TEACH cont.

- *Buying Guidelines (text pages 379-381)*

Rating Activity

Bring to class sample warranties from appliances. Have students work in groups to rate the warranties in terms of coverage and limitations. Have students share their ratings; discuss how useful to the consumer each warranty might be. In what way are some warranties designed to protect the manufacturer more than the consumer?

> **Appliance Store Survey**
>
> Ask students to visit an appliance store and compare the EnergyGuide information on refrigerator-freezers and dishwashers. Ask students to compare the operating costs for each appliance. **L1**

Discussion Activity

Ask students to describe the documents that usually accompany an appliance when you buy it. Ask students why people should fill out and return the registration card that comes with most warranted items.

> **VISUAL LEARNING** ***Using the Photograph***
>
> Ask students to research the cost of electricity in their area. Then, with students' results, recalculate as a class the actual yearly energy cost for the refrigerator if it were their own, based on the EnergyGuide label on this page.

◆ **The EnergyGuide label gives the appliance's estimated energy cost. Why is this information important?**

Based on standard U.S. Government tests
ENERGYGUIDE
REFRIGERATOR-FREEZER
WITH AUTOMATIC DEFROST
WITH TOP-MOUNTED FREEZER
WITHOUT THROUGH-THE-DOOR-ICE SERVICE
AMANA APPLIANCES
TR21V2
CAPACITY: 20.6 CUBIC FEET
Compare the Energy Use of this Refrigerator with Others Before You Buy
This Model Uses
665 KWH/YEAR
Energy use (kWh/year) range of all similar models
Uses Least Energy 555
Uses Most Energy 767
kWh/year (kilowatt-hours per year) is a measure of energy (electricity) use.
Your utility company uses it to compute your bill. Only models with 20.5 TO 22.4 cubic ft and the above features are used in this scale.
Refrigerators using more energy cost more to operate.
This model's estimated yearly operating cost is:
$58
BASED ON A 1995 U.S. GOVERNMENT NATIONAL AVERAGE COST OF 8.67¢ PER KWH FOR ELECTRICITY. YOUR ACTUAL OPERATING COST WILL VARY DEPENDING ON YOUR LOCAL UTILITY RATES AND YOUR USE OF THE PRODUCT.
Part No. 12395311

- On electrical appliances, look for the *Underwriters Laboratories* seal. It indicates that an electrical appliance design is reasonably free from the risk of fire, electric shock, and other hazards.

Other seals of approval may be found on a product or a package. Find out more about who issued the seal and what it means. Don't assume that every seal comes from a reliable product-testing agency.

Warranties

A **warranty** is a manufacturer's guarantee that a product will perform as advertised. If you have problems with the product, the manufacturer promises to replace it or repair it. A warranty often has limits on the length of time it is in effect and what is covered.

◆ **Looking for seals of approval is one consumer skill that can help you make an informed decision. Describe two other skills.**

EnergyGuide Labels

An **EnergyGuide label** gives information to help you estimate the energy costs of an appliance. Such labels are required for most major appliances. A dollar figure tells the average yearly cost for that model. You can compare the costs for different models. You can also project your own energy expenses based on the cost of gas or electricity in your area.

Extending Learning

Solving Appliance Problems—If problems show up in an appliance, call the dealer or service agency. Keep a written record of all the calls you make. If the dealer fails to help, call the manufacturer. Look for a toll-free number in the owner's manual or on the product's packaging. If you are not satisfied by the responses to your phone call, write a letter to the manufacturer's consumer office. Include a copy of your receipt. Keep a copy of your letter. If you can't get help from the manufacturer, call the Better Business Bureau and your local office of consumer affairs.

Service Contracts

A **service contract** is repair and maintenance insurance purchased to cover a product for a specific length of time. It is usually sold by the store that sells you the product. Service contracts often don't cover the total cost of repairs and parts. They may duplicate the protection received free with the warranty. Service contracts are often expensive and are only as good as the company that issues them.

Be an Active Shopper

While shopping, don't just look. Think about how the product will perform and last.

- Keep written notes. Making a list of your likes and dislikes as you shop can help you make a final decision.
- Consider accident prevention. Look for a seal of approval. Check carefully for potential hazards as well as features that protect against accidents.
- Handle tools, cookware, and appliances. Do they seem comfortable to use and durable?
- Look at the warranty and owner's manual. What exactly does the warranty cover? Will the item be easy to use and care for?
- Compare prices. More features and better quality usually mean a higher price. Some brands are generally more expensive than others. Sometimes, however, lower-priced items are a better buy.
- Ask the dealer about additional costs. Are there separate charges for delivery and installation?

Connecting Food and Health

Let the Seller Beware

Suppose you *do* buy something that doesn't work. What recourse do you have as a consumer? Here are some places you can turn for help:

- **Department of Consumer Affairs.** These offices exist at the municipal level. They are staffed by people trained to know local regulations and procedures. You can find the number in your local telephone directory.
- **Media action programs.** More than 100 newspapers and 50 radio and TV stations across the nation offer action or hot line services for consumers who need help.
- **Government agencies.** The Consumer Product Safety Commission (CPSC) and Federal Trade Commission (FTC) are just two of many federal agencies that protect your interests and rights.

Think About It

- Gather information at your local library, online, or from your local telephone directory about specific services in your community that aid consumers. Use a computer to make a guide to these services; explain the type of services each offers and how to contact each organization. Make copies of your guide available in your school and community.

HOME & COMMUNITY CONNECTION

Suggest students search all available boxes or warranty files of any recently purchased appliance at home. If they find any registration cards, have them encourage adults in the household to fill these out and send them to the manufacturer. Also, encourage all students to share information with their families on why it is important to send in registration cards for appliance purchases.

- *Buying Guidelines*
- *When You Get Your Purchase Home*
(text pages 379-382)

USING CONNECTING FOOD AND HEALTH

Have students review all consumer action guides prepared in accordance with the "Think About It" section of the feature and compile these guides into a "Superguide."

Interview

Ask students to be on the alert for advertisements for appliance outlets and in particular for their "motto." (You may want to refer students back to the fictional art on page 378 and to the motto for this store.) Have students choose a store with a motto and either write or visit a manager, equipped with the suggestions listed under the heading "Be an Active Shopper" on this page. Ask students to pay close attention to the salesperson's or manager's "non-verbal" cues—including facial expressions and body language—during their conversation. Does the person's behavior and demeanor seem to support the store motto? If not, what does this suggest about advertising come-ons? L1

Lists

Ask students to list additional suggestions for becoming an active shopper. Have them create the list, using a computer software program, with lively, action text and computer art. Encourage students to share the lists with their families. L1

ASSESS

REVIEW

- Ask students to summarize the main ideas in this section.
- Have students complete the Section Review. (Answers appear below.)

EVALUATION

- Ask volunteers to investigate online offers of credit cards and easy payment plans. They should report to the class how much variation there is among these offers.
- Have students take the quiz for Section 14-1. (Use the quiz in the *Teacher Resource Guide,* or construct your own with the **Exam***View*® *Test Generator* on the *Effective Instruction CD-ROM.*)

RETEACHING

- Provide empty packages for small appliances that have product information, warranty, etc., on the outside of the package. Have pairs of students compare the various appliances and record their findings.
- Refer to the *Reteaching Activities* booklet for the Section 14-1 activity sheet.

CLOSE

Moderate a student discussion; have students develop a "top ten" list of responsibilities of the consumer in purchasing appliances and other items.

Q ***What should I do if I need to return a defective product?***

A First take the item to the customer service department in the store of purchase. If the problem isn't resolved, ask to see a manager. You can also contact the manufacturer's customer relations department. The Better Business Bureau helps with some unresolved cases. This private group works to ensure fair business practices by helping settle disputes. For all contacts, be positive and reasonable, without accusing or attacking. Explain the problem politely and be specific about what you want—a refund or an exchange, for instance. Use proper grammar and correct spellings, and give all needed information, including copies of receipts. Most companies genuinely want to keep customers happy and will work with you to resolve a problem.

When You Get Your Purchase Home

You will probably bring home some important documents with your purchase, especially if it's an appliance. You may have your receipt, a warranty, and an owner's manual. Keep these documents together in a safe place. If a warranty registration card is provided, you can fill it out and send it in. Doing so verifies your warranty if you misplace the original purchase documents. Also, the manufacturer can notify you if a danger or defect in the product is discovered. You may also receive other product information.

Read the owner's manual before you use the product. Then test the product to make certain it works. If it doesn't, return it to the store or call the dealer.

Section 14-1 Review & Activities

1. What are two questions to consider before shopping for kitchen equipment?
2. What is credit? What is interest?
3. List the four guidelines to follow when shopping for the kitchen.
4. What should you do when you get your purchase home?
5. **Synthesizing.** What are some ways the choice of kitchen equipment affects how a family plans and prepares meals?
6. **Extending.** Review the definition of *impulse buying,* introduced in Chapter 12 (page 337). Do you think someone who buys on impulse should apply for a credit card? Explain your answer.
7. **Applying.** Collect magazine and newspaper advertisements for different brands of a major kitchen appliance. Make a chart that compares the various features that are available.

Answers to Section 14-1 Review & Activities

1. See page 377.
2. Money you borrow from a lender; a fee for the loan, expressed as a percentage of the amount you borrow.
3. Consider your needs and wants, gather information, look for consumer safeguards, be an active shopper.
4. See text at the top of this page.
5. Answers will vary.
6. Answers will vary.
7. Answers will vary.

SECTION 14-2

Choosing Kitchen Equipment

Just what kinds of equipment are included in a kitchen depends on budget, space, and personal preference. Equipping a kitchen can be an expensive process. Most people start with the basics and then add equipment over the years.

Objectives

After studying this section, you should be able to:

- Give examples of choices available in appliances, small equipment, and tableware.
- Discuss features to look for when buying items for the kitchen.

Look for These Terms

self-cleaning

continuous-cleaning

Buying Appliances

Appliances can take up a major portion of your kitchen equipment budget. That's why it pays to shop carefully.

Refrigerator-Freezers

Today there are more options than ever before in refrigerator-freezers. The freezer may be placed at the top, side, or bottom. Some models defrost the freezer automatically. Manual-defrost models must be emptied, thawed, and cleaned regularly.

◆ **Some refrigerator-freezers have adjustable shelves for more flexibility. Name two other special features. What are their advantages and disadvantages?**

Section 14-2 Resources

◆ **Student Workbook,** pp. 101, 105
◆ **Teacher Resource Guide**
Lesson Plan 14-2 Organizer
Section 14-2 Quiz
◆ **Effective Instruction CD-ROM**
Exam*View*® *Test Generator*
◆ **Student Motivation Kit**
Reteaching Activities, p. 70
Enrichment Activities
Skills for Making Food Choices, pp. 33–34

SECTION 14-2

Choosing Kitchen Equipment

FOCUS

MOTIVATORS

- Ask students to make three lists of appliances—those found in a typical kitchen of the 19th century, in a 1950s kitchen, and in a kitchen of today. What changes in the lifestyle, buying habits, and disposable income of American families have encouraged this rapid transformation of our kitchens?
- On the chalkboard, list twelve small kitchen appliances, such as a toaster, a blender, and an ice cream maker. Have students suppose that they need to stock a new apartment and have only enough money for one such item. Which would they choose and why?

VOCABULARY ACTIVITY

Pronounce the two terms listed under "Look for These Terms." Have students read the section and find the terms and their definitions in the section. Ask students why both of these words are hyphenated.

STUDY SKILLS

- **Listening.** Invite a group of volunteers to each prepare an oral reading of a page of text from the section, while others follow along silently.
- Have students read the section and complete the appropriate part of the Chapter 14 Study Guide in the *Student Workbook.*

TEACH

- *Buying Appliances (text pages 383-385)*

Product Comparison

Bring to class different consumer magazines that compare the same appliance. Ask pairs or small groups to analyze the same appliance in more than one magazine. How do the test procedures and criteria differ? Have students decide which brand of the appliance they would select on the basis of each report and list their reasons. **L3**

Discussion Activity

Ask students to describe various types of cooktops that are now available. Ask students to explain how an induction cooktop works. Ask students to explain the difference between a self-cleaning oven and a continuous cleaning oven. Moderate a class discussion on which types of cooktops and ovens students would choose and why?

Group Decision-Making

Have students work in small groups to make a list of essential appliances for a 20-year-old single adult who lives alone. Have groups share their lists and explain each selection. **L1**

- Ten percent of the electricity used in the average home is used for refrigeration.

Special features add not only to convenience but also to cost. Decide which features are most important and within your budget. In the refrigerator, choices include adjustable shelves, temperature- and humidity-controlled compartments for vegetables and meat, and special areas for tall or large items such as milk and soda. You will also find automatic ice makers and doors with ice and chilled water dispensers on the outside.

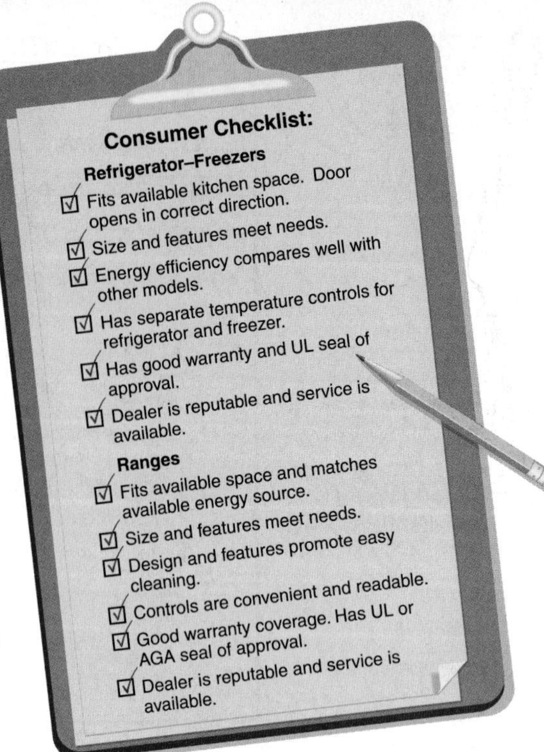

Consumer Checklist:
Refrigerator–Freezers
☑ Fits available kitchen space. Door opens in correct direction.
☑ Size and features meet needs.
☑ Energy efficiency compares well with other models.
☑ Has separate temperature controls for refrigerator and freezer.
☑ Has good warranty and UL seal of approval.
☑ Dealer is reputable and service is available.
Ranges
☑ Fits available space and matches available energy source.
☑ Size and features meet needs.
☑ Design and features promote easy cleaning.
☑ Controls are convenient and readable.
☑ Good warranty coverage. Has UL or AGA seal of approval.
☑ Dealer is reputable and service is available.

Ranges, Cooktops, and Ovens

When buying a major cooking appliance, you'll have to make some basic decisions first. Are you looking for an all-in-one range, a countertop oven, or separate built-in cooktop and oven units? Do you want a gas or an electric model? If you are replacing appliances in an existing kitchen, these decisions may already be determined. If you are remodeling or planning a new kitchen, your options are probably more open.

Cooktops

Although traditional gas burners or electric coils are still most typical, many new choices in cooktops are available. For example:

- **Sealed gas burners.** Have no visible flame and no pilot light. This feature adds safety and aids cleanup.
- **Smooth cooktops.** Are easy to clean. They include induction cooktops, which use electromagnetic energy. Heat is generated when a pan made of a magnetic metal is placed on the induction cooktop.
- **Modules.** Units that allow greater flexibility. A grill, griddle, or other accessory can be substituted for standard surface units.

INFOLINK

For more on cooktops and the advantages and limitations of the different types, see Section 9-1.

Ovens

Shopping for an oven—as a separate unit or as part of a range—begins with the choice of conventional, convection, or microwave models. You may prefer a range with two ovens—one below the cooktop and a smaller one at eye level. Another option is an oven that combines two or more cooking methods in a single unit, such as a microwave-convection oven. As noted in Chapter 9, convection ovens use a fan to circulate the heated air and reduce cooking time.

Extending Learning

Refrigerator-Freezer Features—Some refrigerator-freezers offer advanced features, such as:

- Pull-down counter for serving snacks.
- Electronic monitors to alert you to any problems.
- Adjustable humidity levels that can be set for different foods.
- Tempered glass shelves that wipe up easily and prevent foods from dripping to lower shelves.
- Adjustable storage and wider door shelves that offer more efficient use of space.

Conventional and convection ovens are available with easy-clean options. A **self-cleaning** oven has a special cleaning cycle that uses high heat to burn off food stains. A **continuous-cleaning** oven has special rough interior walls that absorb spills and splatters. Soil residue can be easily wiped off.

Microwave ovens have many features. Some come equipped with a turntable. Others have a rack, which increases the capacity of the oven. Another feature is electronic programming, which can be used to cook food automatically. Browning units improve the appearance of microwaved foods. Temperature probes allow heating to a specific temperature.

Small Appliances

From sandwich makers to automatic bread machines, the list of small appliances available seems endless. Small electrical appliances can save time, money, and energy. However, having too many can cause storage problems. Before you buy, consider whether the appliance will be helpful enough to justify the cost and space required. Will you use it, or will you just store it in the back of a cabinet?

As with any other kitchen equipment, look for features that promote safety, comfort, ease of use, and ease of care. Doing research ahead of time will help you learn what to look for and which features you may want or need. For example, if you are shopping for a food processor, you will want to consider models that include a safety lock, a food pusher, and an overload switch—all these are important safety features.

Buying Other Equipment

Equipment needs don't end with major and small appliances. Kitchens also need cookware, bakeware, and tools.

Cookware and Bakeware

As discussed in Chapter 9, utensils used for cooking and baking can be made from a variety of materials, depending on their intended use. Each material has advantages and disadvantages.

Both cookware and bakeware are available as sets or by the individual piece. Keep in mind that both are major investments that should last for years. Consider these purchasing guidelines:

- Look for materials and finishes that are strong and durable enough to withstand daily use. Edges should be smooth. Handles should be heat-resistant.
- Choose high-quality items. Look for seamless construction. Metal should be heavy enough to resist warping.
- Check the balance of each piece. Look for flat bottoms and secure lids.

◆ Many small appliances serve just one specific function, such as making toasted sandwiches, automatically baking bread, or making ice cream. What factors do you need to evaluate before making such a purchase?

- *Buying Appliances*
- *Buying Other Equipment (text pages 383-386)*

Categorizing

Ask students to bring in appliance advertisements that include ranges, cooktops, and ovens. Have students work in groups to compare features and prices of a range, cooktop, or oven. Ask students to report their findings to the class in categories: least expensive, moderately priced, expensive. Compare findings. L1

Computer Brochure Development

1. Have students create a sales brochure for a small appliance. They should include information about features, safety, care, and use.
2. Have them use a computer software program of choice and use computer art to create their sales brochures.
3. Within their sales brochure, students should include a healthful recipe that can be prepared using their appliance. L1

Checklists

Ask students to create a checklist of guidelines to follow when purchasing cookware or guidelines to follow when purchasing kitchen tools. Encourage students to use a computer for development of the checklists. L1

Technology TIE-IN

Science and technology have greatly improved the characteristics of gas ranges. Lighting a gas burner or oven requires igniting the gas released when the unit is turned on. Early ranges required use of a match. Then small, continuously burning flames called "pilot lights" were developed. This increased convenience but wasted energy.

Today, pilotless ignition electrically generates a spark when the burner is turned on. This method is both safe and energy-efficient.

TEACH cont.

- *Buying Other Equipment*
- *Buying Tableware (text pages 385-387)*

Cost Comparisons

Ask students to visit a store that sells cookware or consult a cookware catalog. Have them compare and report on the cost of four 10-inch skillets made of different materials. L1

Display Activity

Have students make a display of photos showing place settings for various formal and informal occasions. The place settings should use a variety of the types of tableware available. Point out the advantages and disadvantages of each.

Categorizing

Have students work in small groups to examine catalogs, brochures, and other promotional materials and compare the characteristics and cost of stainless steel, silver plate, and sterling silver flatware. Have students categorize the flatware by characteristics and/or cost. Encourage students to share categorized lists. L1

USING Safety Check

Ask students to find out how to determine if tableware or cookware contains lead. Are there lead-testing kits to order or hotline phone numbers to call?

INFOLINK

For more on specific items of cookware and bakeware and the materials used in their construction, see Section 9-1.

Tools

As explained in Chapters 8 and 9, dozens of hand tools are available to make the process of preparing food faster and more convenient. Many of these tools are designed for specific tasks. Others can be used for several different jobs. Follow these guidelines when selecting kitchen tools:

- Choose tools that fit a real need. Avoid buying ones you will seldom use.
- Well-designed, high-quality tools are easy to use and will last for a long time. Knives, for example, should have sturdy handles that are firmly attached to the blades. Look for at least two rivets (fasteners) through the handle and the blade. Higher-quality knives have three.
- Tools used for hot foods should be heat-resistant.
- Keep storage in mind. If you can't store the tool in a convenient place, you probably won't use it very often.

Buying Tableware

The term *tableware* refers to any item used for serving and eating food, including dinnerware, flatware, glassware, and linens. The amount, type, and formality of tableware people choose vary. Some people have one set; others have two or more.

◆ **Look for quality kitchen tools when stocking essential items. Which of these knives would you be most likely to buy? Explain your answer.**

Reinforcing Key Skills

Present the following problems to student groups. Allow time for them to discuss and compare their responses.

Management—You have been asked to create a concept for a small appliance of the future. Students are to use their knowledge of small appliances to envision needs of consumers in the future. They are then to sketch and describe their new appliance.

Communication—What would you do if your family has been using pottery bowls to eat cereal from, and you suspect that they may contain lead?

Dinnerware, flatware, and glassware are available with many different designs, or patterns, on them. Remember, however, that patterns in tableware do not have to match. You can mix and match pieces that complement one another.

Most tableware is priced and sold by the place setting—the pieces used by one person to eat a meal. Sometimes you can buy sets for a number of people. Serving pieces may be sold individually or grouped as a set. Some tableware is also sold as open stock, meaning you can buy each piece separately.

Prices for tableware vary widely depending on quality and brand name. Fine china, crystal glassware, and silver flatware are the most formal and most expensive choices. Most people who have these items use them only for special occasions. For everyday use, there are many less costly, easy-to-care-for, yet attractive options. These include stainless steel flatware, informal glassware, and dishes made of stoneware, glass-ceramic, or plastic. Microwave-safe dinnerware and dishwasher-safe tableware are practical choices.

Safety Check

Lead is a toxic metal that can travel from a container into food. It may be present in tableware and cookware made from pottery. Lead crystal glassware also contains lead. Do not use lead crystal regularly or store beverages in lead crystal for more than a few hours.

Section 14-2 Review & Activities

1. Give four examples of options available in range cooktops.
2. List three things to look for when buying cookware and bakeware.
3. What does buying tableware as open stock mean? What is another way tableware may be sold?
4. **Extending.** Suppose you and a friend decided to share an apartment while in college. What considerations might determine how you go about equipping a kitchen effectively?
5. **Analyzing.** Why should the observation "You get what you pay for" be the motto of anyone furnishing a home kitchen?
6. **Applying.** Choose a large or small kitchen appliance. Using magazines or other resources, make a list of the special features that are available.

ASSESS

REVIEW

- Ask students to summarize the main ideas in this section.
- Have students complete the Section Review. (Answers appear below.)

EVALUATION

- Ask students to outline the factors to consider before buying kitchen equipment.
- Have students take the quiz for Section 14-2. (Use the quiz in the *Teacher Resource Guide,* or construct your own with the **Exam***View*® *Test Generator* on the *Effective Instruction CD-ROM.*)

RETEACHING

- Ask students to look through cookware catalogs and decide what type of cookware they would buy if they were in the market for these items. Ask them to state reasons for their choices.
- Refer to the *Reteaching Activities* booklet for the Section 14-2 activity sheet.

CLOSE

Have several students act as salespeople who are trying to sell to buyers, portrayed by other students. Items for sale are large and small appliances and kitchen tools. Encourage the sellers to describe the special features of the appliances and tools. Encourage the buyers to ask questions about the features that interest them.

Answers to Section 14-2 Review & Activities

1. Sealed gas burners, solid cast iron disks, smooth cooktops, modules.
2. Materials and finishes that are strong and durable enough to withstand daily use, quality, and balance.
3. You can buy each piece separately; by the place setting, either individually or grouped as a set.
4. The size of the kitchen and each person's interests.
5. If you pay for cheaper appliances and designs, the quality may not be as good.
6. Answers will vary.

SECTION
14-3
Designing a Kitchen

FOCUS

MOTIVATORS

- Ask students to describe in writing or sketch their vision of the kitchen of the future. Ask volunteers to read their descriptions aloud. Discuss reasons kitchens of the future might differ from those today.
- Have students think of one feature of their home kitchen that they don't like or that is inconvenient and one that they like and feel is well-planned. Have students share their thoughts.

VOCABULARY ACTIVITY

Ask students to name the two terms that can be considered geography terms. (*peninsula, island*) Ask students to compare the geographic definitions with the way the terms are used in this section.

STUDY SKILLS

- **Outlining.** Have students read the section and outline it by copying the headers on paper and leaving space after each one. Students are to write a sentence in their own words, summarizing the content under each header.
- Have students read the section and complete the appropriate part of the Chapter 14 Study Guide in the *Student Workbook*.

SECTION
14-3

Objectives

After studying this section, you should be able to:

- Discuss considerations in kitchen design.
- Explain how the floor plan and other elements of a kitchen can affect safety and convenience.
- Give examples of barrier-free kitchen designs.

Look for These Terms

work flow
peninsula
island
grounding
task lighting
life-span design

Designing a Kitchen

As Jenna approached Taylor, she noticed that her friend was reading a magazine on home improvements. "Why are you reading that?" Jenna asked.

"We're planning to remodel our home kitchen," Taylor replied. "I'm reading up on remodeling to help my mom make a checklist of things to think about."

Kitchen Design Basics

Taylor and her mom are smart! If you are remodeling a kitchen or moving to a new home, knowing something about kitchen design can help you evaluate how convenient and accident-free a kitchen is. This knowledge can also come in handy if you're ever in a position to plan a totally new kitchen. Even if you're not planning to remodel, you can use the information to find low-cost ways to improve your kitchen. Finally, knowing basics of kitchen design can open the door to some exciting career possibilities.

Planning a successful kitchen begins with recognizing the lifestyle of the people who will use it. Following well-researched principles of kitchen design helps ensure efficiency.

Considering Lifestyle

Taylor and her mother live alone. Their kitchen needs are different from those of a larger family. Some questions to think about when considering the design of a kitchen are:

- What activities, besides cooking, will take place in the kitchen? Will it be used, for example, for eating? For entertaining?

Section 14-3 Resources

◆ **Student Workbook,** pp. 102, 107
◆ **Teacher Resource Guide**
Lesson Plan 14-3 Organizer
Section 14-3 Quiz
Chapter 14 Test
◆ **Effective Instruction CD-ROM**
Exam*View*® *Test Generator*
PowerPoint® Slide #29
◆ **Transparency Package,** CT-29
◆ **Student Motivation Kit**
Reteaching Activities, p. 71
Enrichment Activities

- How much kitchen equipment and food must be stored?
- Will more than one person at a time generally work in the kitchen?
- What are the needs and preferences of those who will use the space?

Designing for Efficiency

An efficient kitchen starts with a well-designed floor plan. It should provide enough space for working but also keep walking to a minimum. It should also optimize the **work flow**, that is, the recurring patterns of activity and repetitive tasks associated with any type of job routine. In a kitchen, these tasks revolve around food preparation—food is removed from storage, washed if necessary, prepared, and served—and involve moving from one place in the kitchen to another.

The Work Triangle

As noted in Section 7-1, the sink, cooking, and cold storage centers are the three major kitchen work centers. They make up the primary path of work called the "work triangle." In this common design, each work center is located at a point in the triangle. For an efficient work flow, the legs of the triangle should total between 12 and 22 feet (3.6 and 6.7 m).

When only one person works in the kitchen, the work triangle is an efficient arrangement. However, today's kitchens are often used by several people at once. Additional work space and duplicate work centers help avoid traffic jams. For example, a second sink or a separate microwave oven can give space for two cooks. The kitchen may then have adjacent or overlapping work triangles.

The kitchen should be arranged so that people going from one room to another do not pass through the work triangle. Such traffic can cut efficiency and may cause accidents.

◆ **Kitchen design should be based on how the space and appliances will be used. Identify two other factors that need to be considered.**

TEACH

- *Kitchen Design Basics (text pages 388-389)*

Discussion Activity

Ask students to define *work flow* and give an example of a work flow in a kitchen. Ask students to define *work triangle* and to give a situation in which the traditional work triangle would not be the most efficient layout for a kitchen.

Class Survey

Based on their own family needs, have students write answers to the lifestyle questions on pages 388 and 389. Ask several student volunteers to read aloud their responses. Discuss how variations in lifestyle might affect kitchen design. L1

Observation Activity

Ask students to observe someone preparing a meal and record the person's movements about the kitchen, including how many steps approximately the entire activity required from start to finish. Have students suggest ways of turning negatives into positives within the confines of their current kitchen layouts.

Extending Learning

Efficiency Engineering—Have students review or examine the term *ergonomics,* which appears both in Chapter 1 and the Glossary. Reveal that a subset of ergonomicists today are people with the job description of efficiency engineers. These are management experts who examine a process or situation and seek ways of minimizing steps or time involved to carry out a given operation.

Invite interested volunteers to learn more about this line of work and ways in which efficiency engineers might be called upon to make kitchens more useful.

TEACH cont.

- *Basic Kitchen Plans (text pages 390-393)*

Art

Ask students to draw floorplans of their home kitchens on small sheets of poster board. Students are to label their floorplans in terms of the type of kitchen. They should draw red lines to show the work triangle. Post the floorplans around the classroom. L1

Field Trip

Arrange a class field trip to a kitchen planning center to see first-hand examples of various types of kitchens. Ask the sales consultant to discuss trends, new products and technology, and costs. Prior to the trip, ask students to prepare a list of potential questions to ask the sales consultant. After the trip, ask students to identify one interesting fact they learned from the trip that is worth sharing with family members at home.

Debate

Ask students to hold a general, open-format debate on the advantages and disadvantages of different types of basic kitchen plans. Nominate two students to record the main points from the debate. One is to list advantages, the other disadvantages. Tally the number of each for each kitchen plan to determine which plan is favored by most students. L1

Basic Kitchen Plans

Kitchens are often categorized by the location of the cabinets and major appliances. These common types have certain characteristics:

- **One-wall.** All three work centers are on one wall. One-wall kitchens tend to be small, with limited storage and counter space.
- **Corridor.** The work centers are located on two parallel walls. This pattern is efficient for one cook. However, efficiency is lessened if the corridor is a traffic lane through the kitchen.
- **L-shaped.** The work centers are on two connecting walls. No through traffic interrupts work.
- **U-shaped.** This efficient plan has work centers on three connecting walls, forming a U shape.

These basic kitchen plans may be modified by the addition of a peninsula or an island. A **peninsula** is an extension of a countertop. An **island** is a freestanding unit, often in the center of the kitchen. Both can include storage space below the countertop. They can be equipped with a sink or cooktop, or they may serve as an eating area.

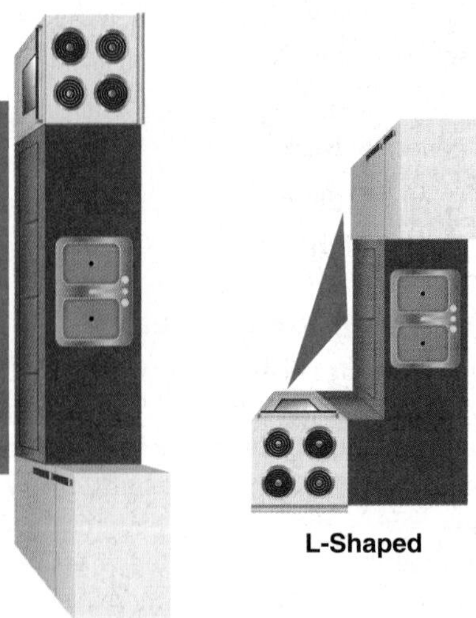

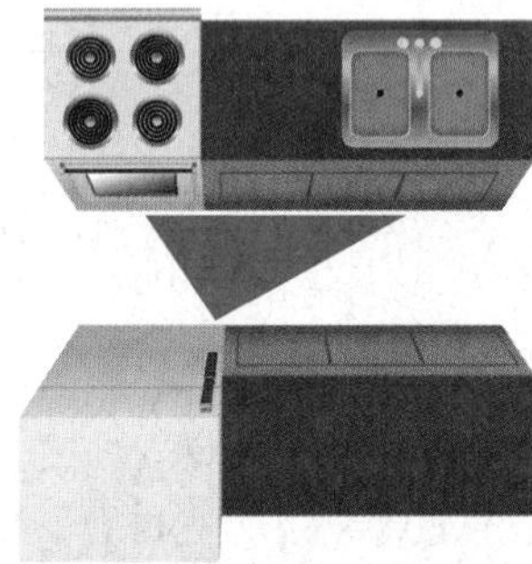

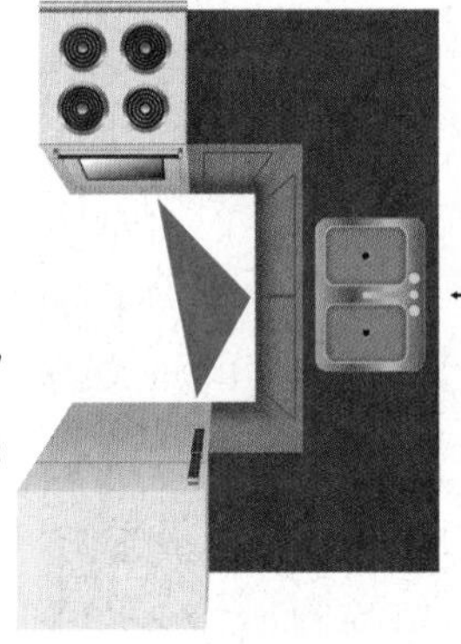

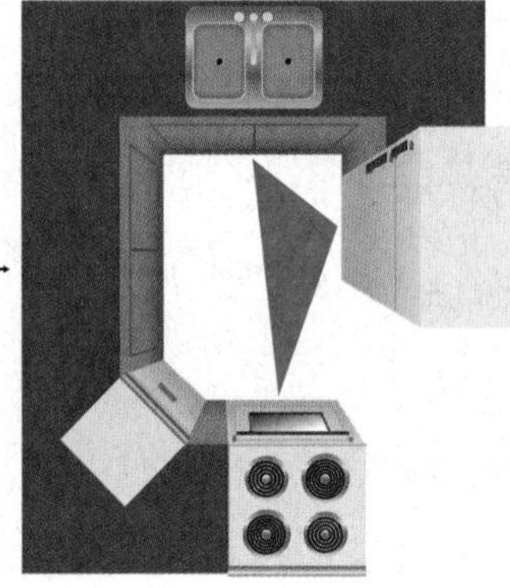

◆ **In basic kitchen designs, the sink, cooking, and cold storage centers are seen as forming three points of a "work triangle." What particular needs are served by each of the basic plans shown? What other considerations would affect which kitchen plan a family might choose?**

Reinforcing Key Skills

Present the following problem to student groups. Allow time for them to discuss and compare their responses.

Management—Discuss how time spent organizing a kitchen can result in time savings when the kitchen is in use. Ask students to explain why this is an example of good time management. What other resources are being managed in this example?

Storage and Work Space

The amount of storage and counter space in the kitchen also affects how pleasant and efficient it is to work in.

Storage

Few kitchens have the storage space that people want. When building or remodeling, a plan for storage helps. In existing kitchens, storage can often be improved inexpensively.

Kitchen cabinets include base cabinets that rest on the floor and are generally 36 inches (91 cm) high and 24 inches (61 cm) deep. Wall cabinets, which vary in size, are attached to the wall above the countertop. Floor-to-ceiling cabinets are another cabinet type.

Storage aids can be ordered as part of new cabinets and often added to existing cabinets. Roll-out shelves provide easy access, as do pop-up shelves that hold mixers or other appliances in base cabinets. Vertical dividers for baking sheets and trays are a handy cabinet option. Pull-out ventilated baskets hold such produce as potatoes and onions.

Cabinets are made of wood, plastic laminate, and other materials. Units should be well made, with durable hardware. Durability counts since cabinets receive more use than most furniture in a home.

Safe and Sanitary Storage

To store tools and equipment safely in kitchen cabinets, try to plan specific spaces for them. When space is limited, store seldom-used items outside the kitchen to keep from overloading shelves. Placing large, heavy equipment in lower cabinets limits overhead lifting and reaching. If stacking items, place the heaviest on the bottom, and limit stacking heights. Stack glass items as little as possible, paying attention to weights. Small portable shelves can be placed on existing shelves to separate items. Tools with sharp or pointed parts should be placed in drawers where they can easily be found. Knives belong in wooden blocks.

◆ **Different kitchen storage solutions exist.** What are some space-saving storage options for a small kitchen?

For good sanitation, be sure to clean tools and equipment before storing them. Cupboard shelves and walls should be washed occasionally to keep storage spaces clean. Special shelf lining papers that wipe off easily can be purchased for quick cleaning.

Counter Space

Each work center needs its own counter space. Additional counter areas are needed for preparing and mixing food.

Work space can be improved in an existing kitchen without remodeling. A cart, a table, or an island can provide additional work space. So can a flip-down shelf, a pull-out breadboard, or an adjustable cutting board that fits over the sink.

- *Basic Kitchen Plans (text pages 390-393)*

Kitchen Type Survey

Have students conduct a survey in their community of kitchen types. One way of handling this project is to ask individuals on the street which of the illustrations on page 390 is most like their home kitchen. Have students compile their findings as a bridge to a discussion of which types are most prevalent, with reasons for their findings (for example, they live in a development where all the houses were built by a single builder around the same time). 

Demonstration

Create a display of kitchen storage devices, including stackable and nested storage containers, and demonstrate how the devices are used. Ask students when and why stretching storage space in the kitchen is important. Lead a discussion on other ways to stretch storage space in the kitchen.

Product Development Activity

Ask students to brainstorm original ideas for new storage aids. Have students draft their idea in words, pictures, or both and to share these with the class. Moderate a class discussion on the practicality of these ideas.

Extending Learning

Designing a Kitchen

- Standard counter height is 36 inches (about 1 m). For tasks such as kneading dough and mixing, 30 inches (76 cm) is more comfortable for most people.
- An island should not interrupt the work triangle, and its placement should not cause overly narrow traffic lanes within the kitchen.
- Reaching deep inside base cabinets can result in strained muscles. To reduce the risk of injury, install pull-out racks that glide easily.

TEACH cont.

- *Basic Kitchen Plans (text pages 390-393)*

Demonstration

Ask students to explain why grounding is so important, not just with kitchen appliances but any electrical appliances. Then demonstrate the correct way to provide grounding for a three-prong plug when an outlet only has two holes. Have one volunteer student search all outlets in the classroom to make sure all are being used correctly.

Discussion Activity

Ask students to explain why task lighting is important in some areas of a kitchen. Ask students to describe factors to consider when buying flooring for a kitchen.

Panel of Experts Activity

Invite a panel of experts to discuss how to plan an efficient, comfortable, and attractive kitchen. Prior to the presentation, have students develop a list of potential questions to ask the panel. After the presentation, ask students to write a summary of what they have learned. Have a few student volunteers read their paragraphs.

Countertops should be durable and easy to clean. Plastic laminates are the most common material. Solid surfacing is seamless and easier to clean than laminates. It is also more expensive. Ceramic tile is attractive but requires more care.

The Kitchen Environment

Cabinets and major appliances are the primary elements of a kitchen. Other components, however, also make up the kitchen environment. Some of these are essential but operate behind the scenes. Others make the kitchen comfortable and attractive.

The Electrical System

Much of the electrical usage in a home comes from the kitchen. Small appliances, many large appliances, and lighting all depend on electrical power.

If you are planning a new kitchen or remodeling an old one, providing adequate electricity should be a priority. This means having enough electric power coming into the kitchen, sufficient outlets, and a grounded electrical system. **Grounding** is a method of minimizing the risk of electrical shock by providing a path for current to travel back through the electrical system, rather than through your body. The National Electrical Code requires that new homes have grounding wires as part of their wiring systems. Outlets with three holes usually indicate the wiring is grounded. (Check with an electrician to be certain.) These outlets accept three-pronged plugs from grounded appliances. For a grounded system with two-hole outlets, you can use special adapters to plug in grounded appliances.

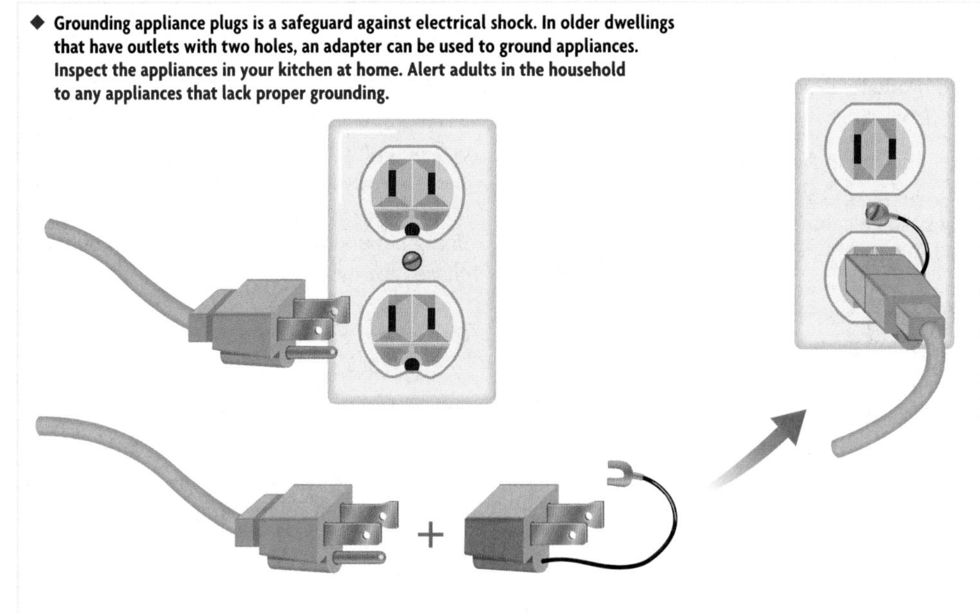

◆ **Grounding appliance plugs is a safeguard against electrical shock. In older dwellings that have outlets with two holes, an adapter can be used to ground appliances. Inspect the appliances in your kitchen at home. Alert adults in the household to any appliances that lack proper grounding.**

Technology TIE-IN Ask students to pick one topic related to the kitchen environment—electrical system, lighting, ventilation, plumbing, or walls and floors—and research technological advances currently being developed to help improve the kitchen environment. This may include slip-free floor covering and solar kitchen lighting. Ask students to write reports of their research.

The power in my kitchen often goes out when I am using several appliances. What can I do about this?

A You may have an overloaded circuit or have tripped a breaker. Have a qualified electrician check out the electrical system. The condition you describe is one symptom of inadequate wiring, which can cause fires. Other telltale signs of a problem include lights dimming when an appliance goes on, appliances taking a long time to heat up, mixers and motors slowing down, and needing to use extension cords regularly with appliances.

Lighting

Good lighting is essential in a kitchen for both comfort and safety. General lighting, usually from lighted ceiling panels or a ceiling light fixture, provides overall light. During the day, natural light from windows may also help light the room. Modern kitchen design also frequently makes use of **task lighting**—bright, shadow-free light over specific work areas. Task lighting is usually used over the countertops, sink, and range. Spotlights or fluorescent fixtures are often mounted beneath overhead cabinets to light countertop areas. Recessed spotlights or track lights on the ceiling can also be positioned to light specific locations. Dimmer switches allow adjustment of the light to any level of brightness.

Ventilation

Cooking produces moisture, heat, grease, and odors. Good ventilation is needed to clear these from the kitchen. Windows, exhaust fans, and range hoods can all provide ventilation. Some cooktops and grills have built-in ventilation systems called downdraft systems.

Plumbing

The plumbing system brings water to the kitchen and takes away waste water. With the addition of a garbage disposal, most food waste can also be carried away.

Sinks are the most visible parts of the system. Alternatives to traditional sinks include ones mounted without rims and ones that are part of the countertop itself. In addition, there are many bowl shapes, sizes, and combinations.

Walls and Floors

Wall coverings and flooring must look good and be durable and easy to clean. Options are available at varying price levels:

- **Wall covering.** May be paint or wallpaper. Look for "scrubbable" types. Kitchen walls have to be cleaned frequently, especially near the sink and range.
- **Flooring.** Should be durable and easy to clean, as well as comfortable to stand on. Ceramic tile has excellent durability but can be uncomfortable after long periods of standing. Vinyl or hardwood floors are resilient and easier on the feet. Choose flooring that does not have to be waxed or polished.

Barrier-Free Kitchens

Because food preparation is a basic activity, kitchen designers are working to make it easier for everyone. Their efforts are part of a movement known as **life-span design**. This is a design approach in which living space is adapted to the needs of people of various ages and degrees of physical ability. Life-span designs incorporate wider doorways and aisles in the kitchen to accommodate wheelchairs or walkers.

- *Barrier-Free Kitchens (text pages 393-394)*

Discussion Activity

What is the purpose of the movement among kitchen designers known as "lifespan design"? Ask students to describe characteristics of life-span designs. Write characteristics named on the chalkboard during the discussion.

Guest Speaker

Invite an individual who is physically challenged to visit the class and explain how he or she has adapted his or her kitchen to meet personal needs. If possible, have this presenter demonstrate at least one adaptation device or bring a photo of one such adaptation. Prior to the presentation, ask students to research this topic online or use print resources so they can be an attentive audience.

Inquiry

Have students write to or search relevant web sites of organizations concerned with adapting kitchen workspaces to accommodate individuals with special needs. Two organizations students might contact are the Association of Home Appliance Manufacturers and the American Foundation for the Blind. Have students report their findings to the class. L2

HOME & COMMUNITY CONNECTION

Suggest to students that some older adults have limited physical abilities. Some may just have less stamina and strength for common kitchen tasks. Have each student visit an older relative or person in the community to determine if the person's kitchen is barrier-free. Have a few volunteers share their experiences. Encourage students to provide suggestions to older citizens for creating barrier-free kitchens, when applicable.

ASSESS

REVIEW

- Ask students to summarize the main ideas in this section.
- Have students complete the Section Review. (Answers appear below.)

EVALUATION

- Have students write a list of guidelines for designing a kitchen.
- Have students take the quiz for Section 14-3. (Use the quiz in the *Teacher Resource Guide,* or construct your own with the **ExamView®** *Test Generator* on the *Effective Instruction CD-ROM.*)

RETEACHING

- Provide floor plans of kitchens of several different designs. Have students practice identifying each type of kitchen plan.
- Refer to the *Reteaching Activities* booklet for the Section 14-3 activity sheet.

CLOSE

Divide the class into two groups. Have groups nominate one person to record and number students' suggestions. Hold a five-minute contest to see which side can come up with the most ways to update a kitchen inexpensively and to make it safer and more efficient. Compare and discuss recorded lists.

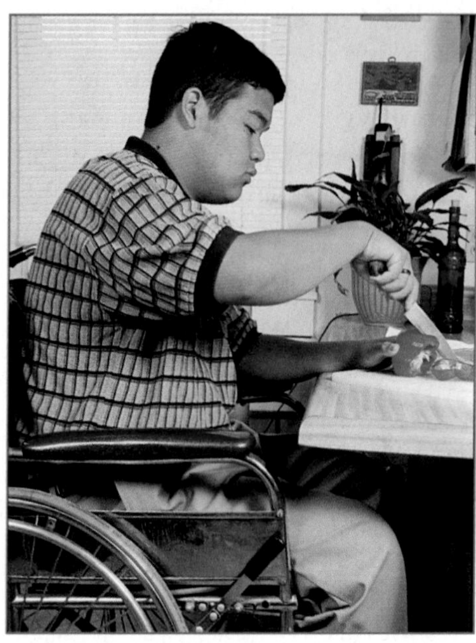

◆ **Barrier-free kitchen design makes it easier for everyone to use the kitchen. What specific features would make a kitchen convenient for this young man?**

Work surfaces are placed at various heights so that preparation can be done sitting or standing. Open shelving and drawers, rather than closed cabinets, provide easier access.

Kitchens can also be designed, remodeled, or adapted to meet specific physical challenges. For example, cabinet knobs can be replaced with easy-to-grasp handles. Braille controls can be added to appliances. Kitchen designers, appliance manufacturers, and support organizations are good sources of information about designs for people with special needs.

Section 14-3 Review & Activities

1. List three questions to consider when planning the design of a kitchen.
2. Give two guidelines for evaluating the efficiency of a kitchen floor plan.
3. When storing tools and equipment, how can you ensure good sanitation?
4. What is meant by the term *life-span design*? Give an example.
5. **Applying.** Could any work center in your kitchen at home use some reorganizing? Choose one center and list the tasks performed there. Also list any stored foods and tools in the center. What changes would you make to improve efficiency?
6. **Extending.** Look through a kitchen-remodeling book or magazine, or visit a kitchen cabinet showroom. What cabinet colors, styles, and features do you like best? Compare costs of different materials. What would you choose to fit varying budgets?
7. **Applying.** Explain how you would safely store the following items: an iron skillet; a large mixer with bowls; delicate crystal glasses; a bread knife; and a set of four casserole dishes of different sizes. Include reasons for your storage ideas.
8. **Analyzing.** Many families find that the kitchen is the center of activity, even when guests are in the home. Why do you think this is true? What kitchen design features might entice people to spend time in the kitchen?

Answers to Section 14-3 Review & Activities

1. Any three from pages 388–389.
2. Any two: has enough workspace; minimizes walking; optimizes work flow.
3. Clean tools before storing; wash shelves and walls; use easily cleaned shelf liners.
4. Approach to design that adapts living space to people of various ages and physical abilities. See pages 392–393.
5. Answers will vary.
6. Answers will vary.
7. Answers may include: skillet—low cabinet; mixer—cart or low shelf; glasses—upper shelf, not stacked; knife—separate place in drawer; dishes—eye-level shelf.
8. Answers will vary.

Career Wanted

Kitchen Design Consultant

"Utility plus beauty equals success."

Leigh Smith

Education and Training
- Degree from accredited art and design school
- Knowledge of design trends and materials

Qualities
- Creativity
- Communication skills
- Analytical skills

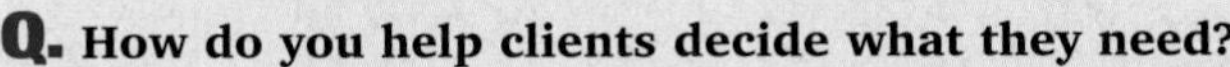

Q. Leigh, what does a kitchen design consultant do?

A. I act as a link between the client, architect, and builders. I learn my clients' needs and submit sketches for their approval. When they choose one, I coordinate with the architect and different contractors—plumbing, lighting, and so on—to make it a reality.

Q. How do you help clients decide what they need?

A. I try to develop a family profile—how many people, their ages and abilities, how they use the kitchen. I also have a budgeting worksheet to help them decide how much they can spend, based on income and what work they can do themselves. I explain other factors that affect costs, too.

Q. How close does the real kitchen come to the client's dream kitchen?

A. That's an interesting question. "Dream" designs are often overloaded with features and gadgets. I keep people focused on what they really need and can afford, and what will work. With this approach, most people are satisfied that the kitchen they get is the best one possible.

Related Career Opportunities

Entry Level
- Home improvement center sales consultant
- Appliance store sales consultant
- Carpenter

Technical Level
- Cabinetmaker
- Real estate agent
- Drafter

Professional Level
- Architect
- Interior designer
- Lighting design consultant

Making Career Connections

CAREER EXPLORATION. Visit the Web sites of kitchen design consultants and home-building organizations. Compare the background, experience, and philosophies of different consultants. Based on these profiles, do you think you would enjoy this career? Write a one-page explanation of your observations.

Career Wanted

Kitchen Design Consultant

Thinking About the Career

Prior to reading the feature, ask students to note the career of Leigh Smith and to brainstorm a list of qualifications and prerequisites they believe someone in this line of work would have.

After reading, ask students what other skills might be helpful for a kitchen design consultant. Why?

Career-Building Opportunities

Students interested in careers in design should check with schools or centers in the community that offer art or design courses; record a list of the courses. Have students share their lists with other interested students.

For More Information

For additional information about careers in kitchen design or architecture, encourage students to contact:

- The American Institute of Architects (AIA)
  1735 New York Ave., NW
  Washington, DC 20006
  www.aia.org
- National Kitchen and Bath Association (NKBA)
  687 Willow Grove Street
  Hacketstown, NJ 07840
  www.nkba.org

REVIEW

- Have students complete the Chapter Review. (Answers appear below.)

EVALUATION

- Describe various lifestyles for students and have them design a kitchen plan to suit each lifestyle.
- Have students take the test for Chapter 14. (Use the chapter test in the *Teacher Resource Guide,* or construct your own with the **Exam***View*® *Test Generator* on the *Effective Instruction CD-ROM.*)

ANSWERS

Checking Your Knowledge

1. Advantage: It allows you to use the item while you pay for it. Disadvantage: It's more expensive.
2. A label that gives information to help estimate energy costs of an appliance. It helps you compare costs for different models and project your own energy expenses based on the cost of gas or electricity in your area.
3. Any four: keep written notes; consider accident prevention; handle tools, cookware, and appliances before buying; look at the warranty and owner's manual; compare prices; ask the dealer about additional costs.
4. Any three: adjustable shelves; temperature- and humidity-controlled compartments for vegetables and meat; special areas for tall or large items such as milk and soda; automatic ice makers; doors with ice and chilled water dispensers on the outside.
5. Any three: whether the appliance will be helpful enough to justify the cost and space required; safety, comfort, ease of use, ease of care; any special features you may want or need.

Chapter 14 Review & Activities

Summary

Section 14-1: Consumer Skills

- Before you buy any kitchen equipment, be sure you need and will use it.
- People who decide to buy on credit need to investigate the costs of borrowing.
- When you shop for equipment, consider your needs and wants.
- Look for consumer safeguards, and consider your purchase carefully.

Section 14-2: Choosing Kitchen Equipment

- It is easier to shop for appliances, cookware, bakeware, tools, and tableware when you are familiar with some of the basic options you will find. A wide range of choices is available.
- Some features are essential for safety and quality, while others depend on personal needs and preferences.

Section 14-3: Designing a Kitchen

- A kitchen should be planned for efficient use by everyone.
- The floor plan should allow an uninterrupted work flow.
- Storage units and counter space should be adequate, accessible, and durable.
- Electricity, lighting, and plumbing should provide safety and convenience.
- Life-span design helps make the kitchen easier to use for people of various ages and degrees of physical ability.

Checking Your Knowledge

1. Name one advantage and one disadvantage of buying on credit.
2. What is an EnergyGuide label? How can it be helpful when you are shopping for appliances?
3. List four ways of being an active shopper.
4. Identify three special features that may be found in refrigerator-freezers.
5. List three things to consider when buying small appliances.
6. Describe two signs of quality construction in knives.
7. List four basic kitchen floor plans.
8. In kitchen design, how does a peninsula differ from an island? What is the purpose of both?
9. Why is good lighting important in a kitchen?
10. Identify three features of good flooring.

Working IN THE Lab

1. ***Demonstration.*** With one or two classmates, role-play an appliance shopping trip. One member of the group is to be a customer interested in buying one of the appliances in the foods lab. Another is to be the salesperson. Identify the points to consider when buying appliances.
2. ***Foods Lab.*** Design an efficient kitchen floor plan. Include the location of large appliances and the dimensions of the work triangle.

Review & Activities Chapter 14

Thinking Critically

1. **Analyzing Decisions.** One evening, you and your family go shopping for a microwave oven. At the first store you visit, the salesclerk shows you a model that has most of the features you want and is on sale. When you say that you would like to shop a little further, the clerk informs you that the sale ends that day. Do you think your family should go ahead and make the purchase? Why or why not?

2. **Comparing and Contrasting.** James is helping his father shop for appliances for the kitchen in their new apartment. Using newspaper ads, they are comparing models. Some of the ads show appliances with extra features that James and his father might not use very often. Other ads show models that lack some of the features they would like. What are the pros and cons of buying an appliance that fits each of these descriptions? Which choice do you think you would make? Why?

Reinforcing Key Skills

1. **Communication.** Sources of information about a product could include advertisements, reports in consumer magazines, and comments from salespeople. Which do you think would be the most accurate and reliable? Explain.

2. **Leadership.** Conner's family plans to buy a new refrigerator. His sister likes the ice cube dispenser in one model. The self-defrosting freezer appeals to his father, and the adjustable shelves, to his mother. The list of available features is very long, and each person prefers a different combination. The only refrigerator that pleases everyone is well beyond the budget. Conner has an idea to help his family choose. Describe what you think it is.

Making Decisions and Solving Problems

A new student in your foods lab group uses a wheelchair. The appliances, storage areas, and work space are sometimes difficult for him to use. The two of you have been asked to suggest long-range and short-range solutions to the problem. What recommendations would you make?

Making Connections

1. **Math.** Visit an appliance showroom in your community, and compare the EnergyGuide labels on three different models of the same appliance. Calculate the cost of using each for one week, one month, and one year. Determine the difference in energy costs, and rank the appliances from least to most expensive to use.

2. **Art.** Plan and sketch an attractive, efficient kitchen design for a small apartment. Point out the features that make the kitchen efficient (either on the drawing or in a separate written description). Use colored pencils, paint chips, or wallpaper samples to show the color scheme. Display your finished design in an in-class "gallery."

ANSWERS cont.

6. Sturdy handle that is firmly attached to the blade by at least two rivets.
7. One-wall, corridor, L-shaped, U-shaped.
8. A peninsula is an extension of a countertop; an island is a free-standing unit, often in the center of the kitchen. Both can provide added storage and work space.
9. It provides comfort and safety.
10. Any three: Durable, easy to clean, comfortable to stand on, does not have to be waxed or polished.

Thinking Critically

1. Answers will vary. Encourage students to demonstrate skills for food choices, including critical thinking, in devising solutions to the problem.
2. Answers will vary.

Reinforcing Key Skills

1. Answers will vary. Students should recognize that consumer publications distributed by not-for-profit organizations are probably the most reliable source of information.
2. As a leader, Conner might emphasize the importance of working cooperatively to discover a solution that benefits everyone as much as possible.

UNIT 4 Foods for Meals and Snacks

INTRODUCING UNIT 4

Prior to class, prepare two decks of index cards—one with names of foods covered in the unit (such as lima bean, egg, chicken), the other a brief description of a preparation technique that doesn't identify the food (for example: "Wash four large _____ and remove their cores. Fill the resulting cavities with sugar, cinnamon, and butter or margarine…") Shuffle the decks one at a time and have students randomly choose a card from each deck. Have them read their "recipes" aloud, inserting the name of the food they drew. Afterwards, discuss why the jumbled recipes were so ridiculous. Point out that it is not enough to understand preparation methods but the use of the *right* method for a particular food.

UNIT

Foods for

KEY TO ABILITY LEVELS Each section of the text contains skill-building activities. Each activity has been labeled for use with students of various learning styles and abilities.

L1 **Level 1** activities are basic activities and should be within the range of all students.

L2 **Level 2** activities are average activities and should be within the range of students working at average and above-average levels.

L3 **Level 3** activities are challenging activities designed for the ability range of above-average students.

Meals and Snacks

UNIT 4 PROJECT

Have students set up a Classroom Information Center for the unit. This center—which may take the form of a bulletin board, a loose-leaf notebook with blank pages on a desk or table, or a folder on the classroom computer—is to contain facts and data provided by students on shopping for and preparing ingredients for foods, meals, and snacks. Among the types of information students might add are the following: addresses and hours of operation of food stores in the community, with brief reviews (e.g., Jordan's Market carries hard-to-find ingredients at fair prices, but the lines at the cashier are always long); taste-tempting, teen-friendly recipes involving the food groups and categories covered in the unit; and nutrition or food science facts left over from research students have done. Each student is to provide at least 2 pieces of information per chapter. All are invited to make free use of this information during work on Unit 4.

PROJECT FOLLOWUP

At the end of work on the unit, ask students to evaluate their Information Center for range of coverage, accuracy, and overall usefulness to members of the class. Discuss with them ways of improving a facility of this kind. Ask: What other kinds of information could be shared in the type of format they have chosen for the project? Would taxpayers' money be well served if the city or community established such centers at strategic locations around town? Whom would these most benefit?

FCCLA Projects

Illustrated Talk. Students explain and show how a food of interest is produced, also covering its nutritional value and any special features. They demonstrate how to select and prepare the food, and how to prepare a recipe that uses it. Samples of the food and/or recipe are offered for tasting.

Community Service. Students plan, prepare, and serve a luncheon for nursing home residents or clients in an eldercare program. They confer with facility or agency supervisors to learn what foods may be served and how to prepare them. An activity or other entertainment is included in the event.

CHAPTER

15

Convenience Foods

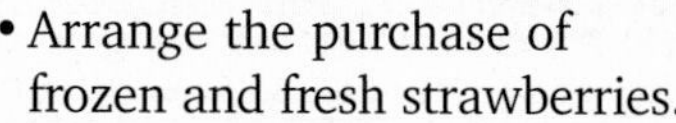

Advance Planning Guide ☑

- Arrange the purchase of frozen and fresh strawberries.
- Arrange a field trip to a large supermarket.
- Purchase convenience and non-convenience forms of the same foods for a taste test.
- Obtain empty packages from several convenience foods.
- Arrange the purchase of dry and canned white beans; soak the dry beans prior to demonstration.
- Arrange the purchase of four different dried foods.
- Invite a local caterer or restaurant chef to speak to the class and provide a demonstration on pre-preparation.
- Obtain a recipe with more than ten ingredients; copy for all students.
- Prepare a homemade mix, such as herb dressing; gather food items and implements for student preparation using the mix.

CHAPTER 15

Convenience Foods

Section 15-1
Choosing Convenience Foods

Section 15-2
Cooking with Convenience

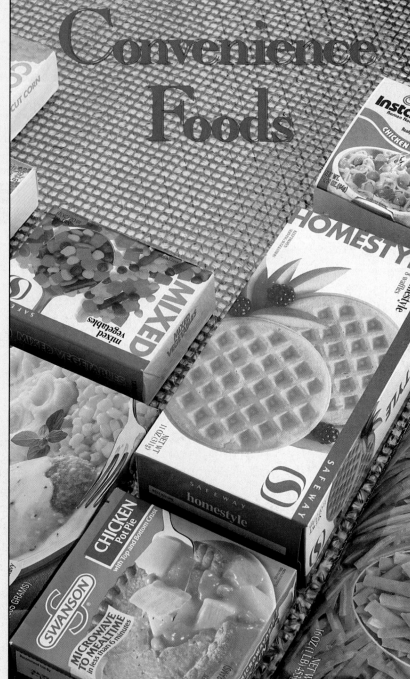

What does the term *convenience foods* mean to you? To Joanne, it means foods that are easy to cook and require little cleanup. Ricco thinks of packaged mixes that save time. Chantel uses the term to describe any ready-to-eat foods.

No matter how you define the term, convenience foods can be part of a healthful eating plan. In this chapter, you will find out how.

MEETING DIVERSE NEEDS

Intrapersonal Learner. If there are self-starters among the students, ask one or two to create a concept for an original line of convenience foods. Guide these students by having them ask themselves: What age group will the product be targeted at? How will it be marketed? Advertised? After students have completed their convenience food concept, have them give a thorough presentation to the students, who are to act as "company representatives."

SECTION
15-1

Objectives

After studying this section, you should be able to:

- Identify different types of convenience foods and their uses.
- Discuss the pros and cons of using convenience foods.

Look for These Terms

manufactured food

analogues

formed product

Choosing Convenience Foods

Through technology, we live in an age of instant communication. Is it any wonder that people want food the minute they feel hungry? The demand for on-the-spot meals has given rise to a new generation of convenience foods.

Convenience Foods

In general, a convenience food is one that has been commercially processed to make it more convenient to store or use. Some convenience foods have been around for such a long time that they have become staples in the American food supply. You might not think, for example, of packaged sliced bread or bottled salad dressing as convenience foods. When they first appeared, though, these products were viewed as time-saving innovations.

Convenience foods include items that have been processed for a longer shelf life. Nonfat dry milk can be stored without refrigeration and kept for a longer time than fluid milk.

Another purpose of convenience foods is to reduce meal preparation time. Food that is partially prepared when purchased—cheese that is already shredded or vegetables that are already washed and cut up—can save time in the kitchen. Some foods are combined and packaged for specific uses, such as a mixture of frozen stew vegetables. Dry mixtures are available for everything from macaroni and cheese to salad dressing to baked goods. Often you need only add one or two ingredients and complete a few simple steps to prepare the food.

Of course, convenience can go even further. You can buy snacks, main dishes, side dishes, desserts, and even complete meals that are already prepared. Some need only be thawed

SECTION
15-1
Choosing Convenience Foods

FOCUS

MOTIVATORS

- Have students list two convenience foods their families use. Tally students' answers. Which types of convenience food were mentioned most often?
- Set up a display of frozen strawberries and fresh strawberries. Have students taste a sample from each and answer the questions in the caption to the photograph on page 402. Discuss responses.

VOCABULARY ACTIVITY

Have students find the terms listed under "Look for These Terms" and write a paragraph using them all.

STUDY SKILLS

- **Listening.** Invite a group of volunteers to each prepare an oral reading of a page of text from the section, while others follow along silently. Preparation should include mastering the pronunciation of unfamiliar words and a grasp of essential concepts.
- Have students read the section and complete the appropriate part of the Chapter 15 Study Guide in the *Student Workbook*.

Section 15-1 Resources

◆ **Student Workbook,** pp. 109, 111
◆ **Teacher Resource Guide**
Lesson Plan 15-1 Organizer
Section 15-1 Quiz
◆ **Effective Instruction CD-ROM**
Exam*View*® *Test Generator*
PowerPoint® Slide #30
◆ **Transparency Package,** CT-30
◆ **Student Motivation Kit**
Reteaching Activities, p. 72
Enrichment Activities
Food Science Resources, pp. 36–39, 53–55

TEACH

- *Convenience Food (text pages 401-403)*

Discussion Activity

Discuss reasons people use convenience foods (longer shelf life, reduce meal preparation time). Divide the class into two groups. One group is to brainstorm convenience foods that fit the first description, the other convenience foods that fit the second. Share and discuss foods named.

Research

Have students learn more about manufactured foods, including analogues, egg substitutes, and formed products. Suggest they begin their research by examining the packaging of such products at local food stores or on the Internet. Have the class reconvene to share general information on cost and nutritional content. What future manufactured products are currently in development? L1

Field Trip

Take a field trip to a large supermarket that has several convenience sections. Ask the store manager to explain the growth in available convenience foods, which food products are best sellers, and what are the store's plans to incorporate more convenience foods. Have students write a summary of the field trip experience.

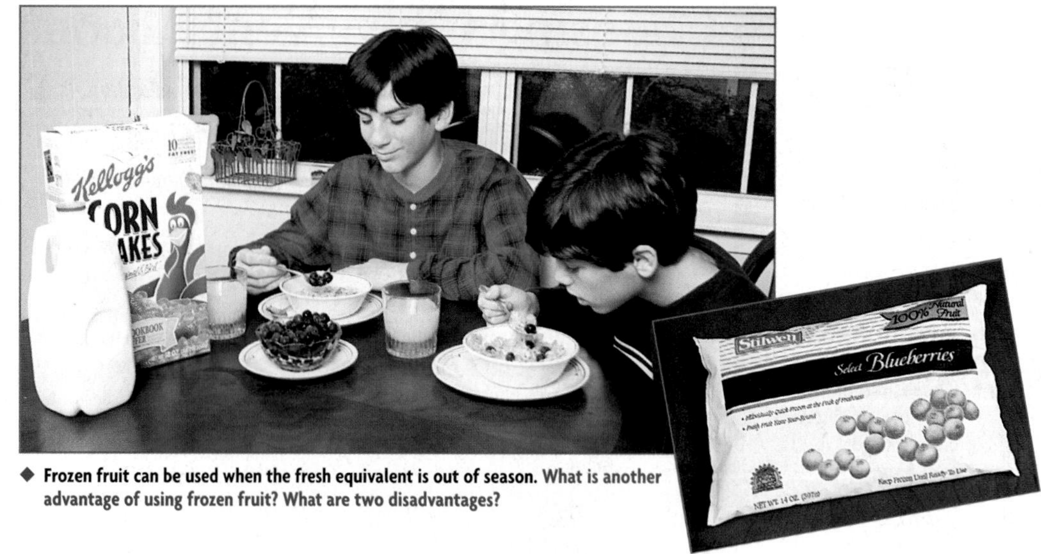

◆ **Frozen fruit can be used when the fresh equivalent is out of season. What is another advantage of using frozen fruit? What are two disadvantages?**

or heated. Others are ready to eat right out of the package.

Manufactured Foods

Have you sampled a meatless burger? Known by several different names, vegetable patties are one example of a **manufactured food**—a product developed to serve as a substitute for another food. Many manufactured foods have been developed to meet special nutritional needs or to provide low-cost alternatives. There are several types of manufactured foods:

- **Analogues.** **Analogues** (AN-uh-logs) are foods made from a vegetable protein and processed to resemble animal foods. They can be made from textured soy protein (TSP), tofu, vegetables, or grains. When flavored and processed, they are made into foods such as breakfast links, meatless burgers, pot pies, and hot dogs. These products are generally low in fat and cholesterol. TSP can also be purchased as granules so that you can make your own meatless dishes.
- **Egg substitutes.** These manufactured foods are usually made from egg whites with other ingredients added. Because they have no yolks, they have little or no saturated fat and cholesterol. They are usually sold in the freezer or refrigerator sections of the supermarkets. You can also buy ready-to-cook and ready-to-eat foods made with egg substitutes.
- **Formed products.** A **formed product** is a food made from an inexpensive food source processed to resemble a more expensive one. An example is *surimi* (soo-REE-mee)—white fish flavored and shaped to resemble lobster or crab. The prices of imitation foods are lower than the prices of the foods they replace. Such foods must be labeled "imitation" and can't be called by the name of the food they replace.

Sometimes manufactured foods are substituted for more expensive ingredients in convenience products. For example, "blueberry waffles" often do not contain real blueberries.

Technology TIE-IN

One of the results of food science research in recent years has been new technology for food processing. Aseptic packages are replacing cans and jars. This process has allowed food products like fluid milk to be shelf-stable.

Ask students to research and report on these new methods. How do processing time and temperature differ? What is the effect on the finished product? Are there nutrient losses?

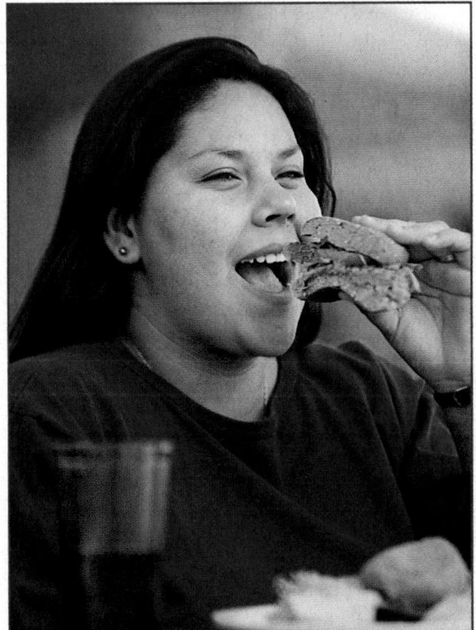

◆ **Vegetable patties like this one are a manufactured substitute for red meat. Visit a local supermarket and examine the package label of a product like this one. In your Wellness Journal, note both advantages and disadvantages of using such products.**

Instead, blueberry "buds"—a manufactured food consisting of sugar, oil, artificial flavor, salt, dyes, and other additives may be used.

Pros and Cons of Convenience Foods

Every day, about 30 new convenience foods appear in the marketplace to meet the growing demand. These foods can be a blessing to today's busy families. Yet, as a smart consumer, you need to be aware of the downside of using convenience foods.

Cost

Convenience can be costly. Every additional step in processing adds to the price of a food. At the supermarket, for example, a ready-to-cook meat loaf costs more than twice as much as regular ground beef. Similarly, the cost per serving of cut-up chicken pieces is usually higher than that of a whole chicken.

Before buying any convenience food, evaluate the per-serving cost against other factors, such as time. Would you save money if you cut up the chicken yourself?

Nutrition

Processing usually destroys some nutrients. Heat, for example, destroys vitamin C. When grains are processed, much of the fiber and some of the nutrients are lost. Many convenience foods also tend to be high in added sodium, sugar, and fat.

What can you as a consumer do? Here are several suggestions:

- Look for convenience foods that are low in sodium, fat, and sugar. With the increasing awareness of good nutrition, such convenience foods are becoming more common. Instead of canned fruit packed in heavy sugar syrup, for example, look for fruit packed in water or its own natural juice.

◆ **Formed foods, such as surimi products, can be a good value. Think of other ways in which formed foods might be used.**

- *Pros and Cons of Convenience Foods (text pages 403-404)*

Taste Test

Divide the class into four groups. Have groups conduct taste tests to compare convenience and non-convenience forms of the same foods. For example, arrange for samples of cooked ground beef and cooked ground beef containing a high percentage of TSP, or scrambled eggs and scrambled egg substitutes. Have students rank the flavor, color, and texture of competing samples. Can students make inferences about the flavor of these products served in fairly simple form versus combined with a lot of other ingredients?

Nutritional Comparison

Have students use Nutrition Facts panels to compare the nutrients in fresh and convenience products. Based mainly on nutritional comparisons, have students discuss the question "Is fresh always best?" L1

Price Comparison

Have students compare the prices of different forms of the same food, such as fresh, canned, frozen, and dried peaches. Have students chart the prices of each. What is the cost differential? Are convenience foods invariably more expensive? Are frozen berries, for example, more expensive than fresh berries out of season? What accounts for these differences? L1

Extending Learning

Convenience Foods

- Frozen vegetables can have higher levels of nutrients than fresh vegetables because they are frozen immediately after harvest.
- Convenience products commonly labeled as "sandwich steaks" may contain beef that has been chopped, shaped, and thinly sliced. Some may contain no beef at all.
- If commercial convenience foods cost less than homemade ones, it's often because they contain less of an expensive ingredient or lower quality ingredients.

ASSESS

REVIEW

- Ask students to summarize the main ideas in this section.
- Have students complete the Section Review. (Answers appear below.)

EVALUATION

- Have students create a Degrees of Convenience scale. The scale might have a range of 1 to 3, where 1 is least convenient and 3 is most convenient. Have students use the scale to rate every food sampled and discussed in the section.
- Have students take the quiz for Section 15-1. (Use the quiz in the *Teacher Resource Guide,* or construct your own with the **Exam***View*® *Test Generator* on the *Effective Instruction CD-ROM.*)

RETEACHING

- Bring empty packages from several convenience foods to class. Have students practice reading the labels to discover nutrient contents and ingredients common to these foods.
- Refer to the *Reteaching Activities* booklet for the Section 15-1 activity sheet.

CLOSE

Lead a discussion on the role convenience foods play in today's society. Ask students to complete this statement: "The main advantages of convenience foods are . . ." Then ask them to complete this statement: "The main disadvantages of convenience foods are . . ."

- Choose frozen plain vegetables over those in cans. Unlike their canned counterparts, which usually have some salt added, frozen vegetables contain no added sodium, sugar, or fat.
- Use ready-to-cook and ready-to-eat foods sparingly. These often contain high amounts of sodium and fat. Ready-to-eat take-home food is the biggest culprit of all in terms of fat content.

Meal Appeal

Processing affects the flavor, color, and texture of food. Often, additives are used to make the final product resemble its fresh counterpart. The flavor and appearance of certain convenience foods may not compare with similar foods that are homemade.

◆ **Whether you choose convenience foods or the homemade versions, you make tradeoffs. When would you heat and serve a purchased frozen lasagna? When would you make it from scratch? What reasons support each choice?**

Section 15-1 Review & Activities

1. What is a manufactured food? What is an analogue?
2. In what three areas are there potential downsides to using convenience foods?
3. Identify two ways to make the most of convenience foods from a nutrition perspective.
4. **Comparing and Contrasting.** Convenience foods have changed greatly over the years. Interview an older adult who can tell you about those changes. Ask what and how many products were available in stores. How did they taste? What explains any of the changes described? What does the person think about these changes? Report what you learned to the class.
5. **Analyzing.** Some people like the taste of frozen dinners and some don't. How would you explain this difference in tastes?
6. **Analyzing.** With today's busy schedules, many people consider convenience foods essential and use them regularly in meals. What might be some effects of this trend?
7. **Comparing and Contrasting.** Compare the cost and nutrition of at least three different convenience forms of a food. For example, you might compare canned prepared, boxed mix, and frozen spaghetti. Which form might be the best choice? Why?

Answers to Section 15-1 Review & Activities

1. See page 402.
2. Cost, nutrition, meal appeal.
3. Any two: use those low in sodium, fat, and sugar; choose frozen plain vegetables over canned; use ready-to-cook and ready-to-eat foods sparingly.
4. Answers will vary.
5. Answers may include: they have negative emotional associations with dinners; ate dinners before new techniques improved flavors; might prefer dinners if seldom experienced home-prepared foods.
6. Answers may include: nutrition may suffer; less time together making meals; food makers may develop more nutritious varieties.
7. Answers will vary.

SECTION
15-2

Cooking with Convenience

You may have heard the saying, "Variety is the spice of life." One of the easiest ways people on the go can add variety to their meals is by using convenience foods. Besides being versatile and easy to prepare, these foods can be part of a healthful eating plan.

Objectives

After studying this section, you should be able to:

- Give suggestions for planning healthful meals around convenience foods.
- Describe general methods for preparing basic convenience foods.
- Discuss the benefits of making your own convenience foods.

Look for This Term

reconstitute

Planning Meals with Convenience Foods

Meals that use convenience foods can be nutritious and help you meet your daily food needs. Here are some guidelines for making daily food choices when you use convenience foods:

- If you use convenience products for one part of the meal, plan the rest of your choices carefully. Make other parts of the meal from fresh or frozen foods that can be prepared quickly. These include fresh or frozen plain fruits and vegetables, whole-grain breads and cereals, and low-fat dairy products. The FDA allows plain frozen fruits and vegetables to be labeled "healthy" if they meet certain requirements.
- When using dry mixes to make main dishes, side dishes, and sauces, reduce the amount of fat called for in the directions. Use fat-free milk or water instead of whole milk.
- Use quick-cooking grains as a side dish to add variety to meals. These include rice, bulgur, millet, kasha, and couscous.
- Keep shelf-stable or frozen main dishes and meals on hand for emergencies, but try to avoid using them regularly for meals.

SECTION
15-2
Cooking with Convenience

FOCUS

MOTIVATORS

- Ask students to describe their family's favorite convenience food meal. When is this meal most likely to be prepared? Who prepares it?
- Put a pot of dry beans on the cooktop. Tell students how long the beans were soaked, and how long the beans will need to cook (based on package instructions); turn on the burner. Discuss the inconvenience of this length of preparation. Then open one or two large cans of white beans; rinse and drain them. Discuss the convenience of this preparation, noting that the dry beans are still not close to being ready.

VOCABULARY ACTIVITY

Pronounce the term listed under "Look for This Term." Have students find the term and its definition in the section.

STUDY SKILLS

- **Guided Reading.** Have students look at the headings within Section 15-2 to preview the concepts that will be discussed.
- Have students read the section and complete the appropriate part of the Chapter 15 Study Guide in the *Student Workbook*.

Section 15-2 Resources

◆ **Student Workbook**, pp. 109, 113
◆ **Teacher Resource Guide**
Lesson Plan 15-2 Organizer
Section 15-2 Quiz
Chapter 15 Test
◆ **Effective Instruction CD-ROM**
Exam*View*® *Test Generator*

◆ **Student Motivation Kit**
Reteaching Activities, p. 73
Enrichment Activities
Foods Lab Resources, pp. 47–48
Food Science Resources, pp. 53–55
Skills for Making Food Choices, pp. 35–36

TEACH

- *Planning Meals with Convenience Foods*
- *Preparing and Using Convenience Foods (text pages 405-407)*

Guideline List

Ask students to create a list of guidelines for planning daily food choices using convenience foods. Explain that the nutritional content of the specific foods must be considered in planning. Urge students to share their guidelines with family and community members. L1

Commandments

Ask students to create "10 Commandments of Precaution" that need to be taken when handling certain convenience foods. Have students post their lists in prominent places in the classroom and on the inside of a kitchen cabinet at home for easy reference. L1

Students Demonstrations

Provide four student groups with four different dried foods. Ask students to demonstrate and explain how to reconstitute their dried food. L1

Recipe Compilation Activity

Ask students to bring to class a copy of a recipe that uses at least one convenience food. Invite volunteers to review the recipes and gather the best of them into a "Convenience Food Cookbook" for use in the classroom.

◆ **Macaroni and cheese can be the centerpiece of a meal that provides needed nutrients. What fresh foods would you serve to balance this main dish?**

INFOLINK

For more information on the steps in planning meals, see Section 11-1.
For more on the nutrients in grains of various kinds, see Section 17-1.

Preparing and Using Convenience Foods

Most convenience foods have directions for use on the package. Always read the directions carefully, even if you have used the product before. Manufacturers sometimes change the ingredients or the preparation methods.

If you want microwavable convenience foods, check the package directions before buying. Not all convenience foods can be successfully microwaved.

Here are some general guidelines for using common convenience foods. You'll also find information about specific convenience foods in later chapters.

- **Canned foods.** Many canned foods are ready to eat or need little preparation other than heating. Some canned soups must be mixed with water or milk. Once canned foods are opened, any leftovers must usually be refrigerated.
- **Frozen foods.** Some frozen foods may need only to be thawed. Others must be cooked without thawing. Check the package for special directions, such as "Do not heat in toaster oven."
- **Chilled foods.** Use the same care in handling chilled convenience foods—fresh pasta and sauces, for example—that you do when preparing the same foods from scratch. Keep them refrigerated until you are ready to use them. Use a chilled food product by the date shown on the package, or check to see if it can be frozen. As an alternative, consider using it in a recipe that can be frozen.
- **Dried foods.** Many dried foods, such as nonfat dry milk, need to be reconstituted. To **reconstitute** means to add back the liquid that was removed in processing.

FOOD SCIENCE

Dried Foods

Have students research the methods used to dry convenience foods and devise an experiment to determine the best way for the average person to dry foods. Ask students to write a report of their research. Select a few reports to share with the class. If possible, allow the students whose reports were selected to carry out their experiments for the class.

- **Dry mixes.** Most mixes contain the dry ingredients needed to prepare the food. You add other ingredients, such as liquids. Along with the basic directions, the package may have suggestions for variations.

Safety Check

Before opening canned goods, wipe the top of a can with a clean, wet dishcloth. Doing so will keep dirt and harmful microorganisms from getting into the food.

HEATING INSTRUCTIONS

MICROWAVE OVEN:
Microwave ovens vary. Heating time may require adjustment.
- Remove dinner from carton.
- Cut and remove film cover from fruit compartment only.
- Cut a slit in center of film cover over main entree.
- Heat on HIGH 6 to 7 minutes or until hot, rotating dinner once.
- Let stand in microwave oven 1 to 2 minutes.
- Stir main entree before serving.

When heating TWO dinners, follow instructions above, heating approximately 12 to 14 minutes or until hot, rotating once.

CONVENTIONAL OVEN:
Preheating oven is not necessary.
- Remove dinner from carton.
- Cut and remove film cover from fruit compartment only.
- Cut a slit in center of film cover over main entree.
- Heat at 350°F on COOKIE SHEET in center of oven 30 to 35 minutes or until hot.
- Remove dinner from oven on COOKIE SHEET.
- Let stand 1 to 2 minutes before serving.

Temperatures above 350°F AND/OR failure to use a COOKIE SHEET may cause damage to the plastic tray, food, and/or oven.

NOTE: When removing cover, be careful to avoid steam burns.
Do not prepare in toaster oven.

◆ **Many convenience food packages today include two sets of heating instructions. Follow them exactly for best results. What cautions are given on the package directions shown here?**

Ready-to-Eat Food

One category of convenience foods that needs special attention is ready-to-eat take-home foods. Although these foods are piping hot when you buy them, they may cool by the time you get them home, allowing harmful bacteria and microorganisms to grow. Before serving any such food, test the temperature with an instant-read thermometer. If it is not at least 160°F (72°C), reheat the food until it reaches the proper temperature. Remember to refrigerate or freeze any leftovers.

Making Your Own Convenience Foods

Even though people are busy, they may be concerned about the cost or nutritional quality of convenience foods. Some solve the problem by making their own convenience foods. Homemade convenience foods have several advantages:

- You decide on the kind and quality of ingredients to put into the product.
- You can control the amount of sodium, sugar, and fat used.
- Homemade convenience foods often cost less to prepare than commercial ones.
- They have few or no additives.
- You enjoy meals with a homemade appearance and flavor.

On the next three pages are some ideas for making your own convenience foods.

- *Making Your Own Convenience Foods (text pages 407-408)*

USING

Ask for a student volunteer to demonstrate the safe way to open a canned good while the other students observe.

Menu Planning

Have students work in small groups to plan three meals around one or more convenience foods, including those that are homemade. Remind students to incorporate nutrient-rich foods from several food groups into each meal. Have groups share menus with the class. **L2**

Lab Experience

1. Have students prepare one meal featuring one or more convenience foods.
2. Emphasize the importance of reading and following package directions carefully.
3. Students should develop a rating scale for convenience products, including savings in time, ease of preparation, cost, nutrition, and taste.

After the meal, moderate a class discussion. Ask what ratings students gave the meal for each category. Would they eat these convenience foods again? Why or why not? **L1**

Reinforcing Key Skills

Present the following problem to student groups. Allow time for them to discuss and compare their responses.

Management—You had several purchases to make, including postage stamps from the post office, fresh fruit from the farmer's market, and a ready-to-eat meal for dinner from a restaurant. Does it make a difference what order these errands are run? If so, what would be the best order?

TEACH cont.

- *Making Your Own Convenience Foods (text pages 407-408)*

Cooking Call-In

If there is a cooking show in the area that takes call-ins (or if the school's locality receives "The Food Network" on cable TV), have a volunteer call in with a recommendation for making one's own convenience foods or pre-prepared ingredients. Prior to placing the call, the student speaker should prepare a statement on the advantages of both these helpful tips. L2

Recipe R & D

Have students work in groups to develop a recipe in which all ingredients can be pre-prepared. Suggest students use recipe books for guidance. Have students write their recipe in standard format and share copies with the class. L3

Guest Speaker

Invite a local caterer or restaurant chef to come to class to speak with students about the importance of pre-prepared ingredients as a time saver in the food preparation industry. Have the speaker demonstrate a few time-saving pre-preparation techniques that he or she uses often.

Pre-prepared Ingredients

Perhaps there are some basic ingredients that you often use in recipes. You can save time by preparing a quantity of these foods ahead of time and refrigerating or freezing them.

- **Sautéed chopped vegetables.** Many recipes call for sautéed chopped garlic, onions, celery, or green pepper. Chop and sauté the vegetables or combinations you use most often. Freeze them in recipe-size quantities, such as ¼ cup (50 mL). You can also freeze chopped vegetables without sautéing them, as long as you plan to cook them. Freezing softens crisp vegetables.
- **Dry beans and grain products.** Cook dry beans and grain products, such as rice and pasta, in quantity. Freeze them in 1-cup (250-mL) portions. Use them for salads, casseroles, soups, and side dishes.
- **Cubed or shredded cheese.** Cube or grate the kind of cheese you use frequently, such as cheddar or mozzarella. Store in a container with a tight-fitting cover, and keep refrigerated or frozen until used.
- **Bread crumbs or cubes.** Cut bread into cubes and dry them. For crumbs, grind dried bread slices in a blender or food processor. You can also crush them with a rolling pin between two pieces of waxed paper or in a large, sealed plastic bag. Store the crumbs or cubes in an air-tight container in the refrigerator or freezer. For added flavor and fiber, use whole wheat bread.

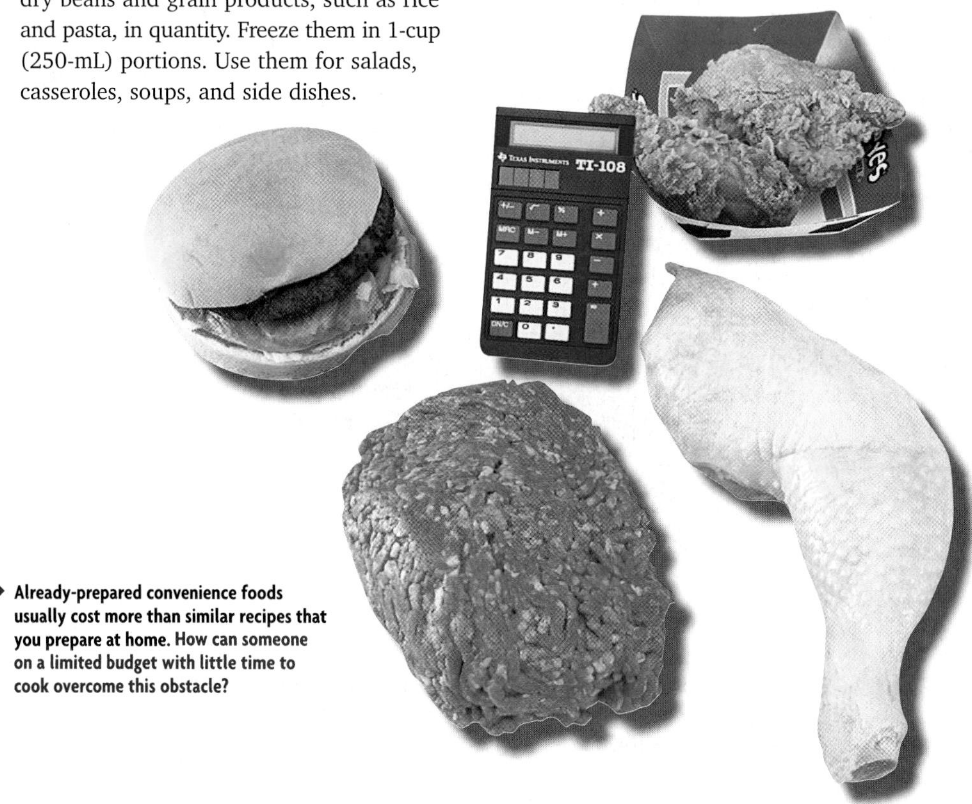

◆ **Already-prepared convenience foods usually cost more than similar recipes that you prepare at home.** How can someone on a limited budget with little time to cook overcome this obstacle?

Extending Learning

Home Meal Replacements—Home Meal Replacements (HMRs) are the current trend in convenience foods. HMRs are primarily homestyle, take-out foods that are ready-to-eat. Many commercial venues (i.e. supermarkets) and noncommercial venues (i.e. colleges and hospitals) have established their own HMR operations due to their revenue generating potential. The number of HMR venues is expected to continue growing.

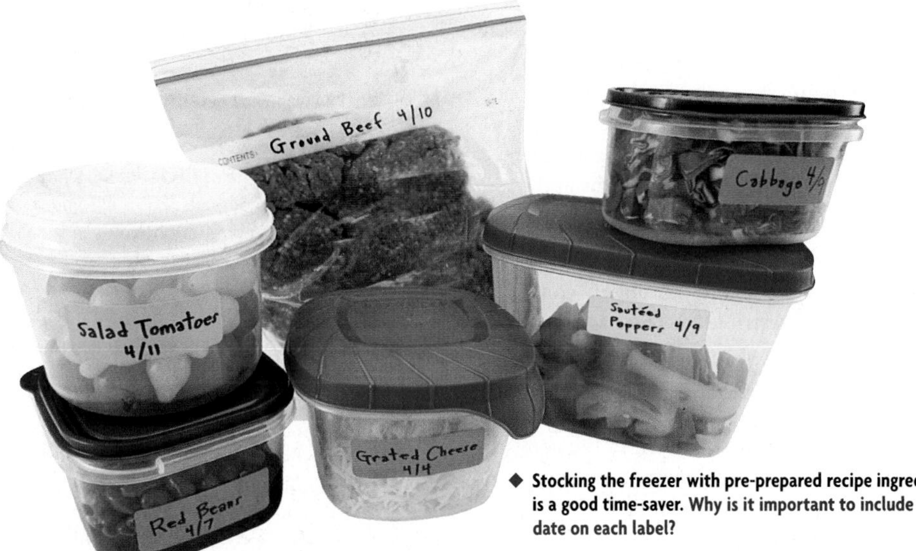

◆ **Stocking the freezer with pre-prepared recipe ingredients is a good time-saver. Why is it important to include the date on each label?**

Frozen Main Dishes

Although it may sound time-consuming to cook your own meals and freeze them, doing so can save you time and money in the long run. The advantages may be worth the extra time it takes.

Some busy people set aside one or two weekend days to cook for the freezer. They prepare as many of their favorite recipes as they can and then freeze them. Karen's mother gets the entire family involved in the "cooking weekend." They have a large freezer and can prepare and store enough main dishes to last about two months. Because everyone is involved, it has become a fun activity the family enjoys.

Others cook for the freezer regularly by preparing more than they need whenever they cook. The leftover food is frozen for future meals. One particularly handy tip is to freeze extra broth and other clear soups in ice cube trays. Once frozen, the cubes can be transferred to a plastic freezer bag for future microwaving to make a quick meal or to add to other recipes.

Storing Frozen Main Dishes

When packaging the food, consider how it will be used. If family members eat at different times, freeze the food in single-serving packages.

When labeling the packages, include any instructions needed to serve the food. For example, if the recipe is to be served over rice, write that on the package so that the rice can be thawed at the same time as the other foods.

For more information on packaging and freezing foods, see Section 7-4.

- *Frozen Main Dishes*
- *Homemade Mixes*
  (text pages 409-410)

Categorizing Activity

Provide students with a recipe with more than ten ingredients. Ask students to categorize recipe ingredients into groups. Ingredient groups may be as follows: (1) can be pre-prepared and stored in the freezer, (2) can be pre-prepared but not frozen, and (3) cannot be pre-prepared. Discuss categorized results.

VISUAL LEARNING ***Using the Photograph***

Ask students for what type of recipes these frozen foods might be used. Create a list on the chalkboard. (For instance: sautéed peppers for quick accompaniment with steak or as a sandwich topping.)

Demonstration

As a demonstration, prepare a homemade mix. Then have students work in groups to prepare a variety of food using the mix as a base. For instance, the homemade mix may be an herb mix. The students might make (1) herb dressing with oil and vinegar, (2) herb dip with low-fat mayonnaise, (3) herb-coated baked French "fries," and (4) herb-coated baked chicken. What conclusions can they draw about the versatility of this type of ingredient? What other types of prepared mixes can students adapt to two or more recipes?

HOME & COMMUNITY CONNECTION

Ask students to create a recipe for homemade mix or create a homemade frozen dinner. Ask the students to have another family member re-heat and eat the frozen dinner or use the mix for recipe preparation with the next family meal. Have students ask for family member feedback on convenience, flavor, and more. Encourage students to continue creating this or other homemade mixes or frozen dinners for themselves and their families.

ASSESS

REVIEW

- Ask students to summarize the main ideas in this section.
- Have students complete the Section Review. (Answers appear below.)

EVALUATION

- Have students create an outline of the topics covered in this section. Students may use section headings for main topics, but subtopics should be in their own words.
- Have students take the quiz for Section 15-2. (Use the quiz in the *Teacher Resource Guide,* or construct your own with the **Exam***View*® *Test Generator* on the *Effective Instruction CD-ROM.*)

RETEACHING

- Bring to class packages from several commercially packaged convenience foods. Have students analyze the contents and discuss how a similar convenience food could be prepared at home.
- Refer to the *Reteaching Activities* booklet for the Section 15-2 activity sheet.

CLOSE

Hold a class debate on the relative advantages of buying convenience foods and making your own.

Homemade Mixes

You can make your own mixes for foods that you prepare regularly, such as quick breads or beverages. Seasoning mixes are great time-savers because you handle just one container instead of many different jars of herbs and spices.

The secret of making a successful mix is to be sure the ingredients are thoroughly combined and evenly distributed. Then, when you measure out the quantity you need, you will be sure to get the right amount of all the ingredients. Some ingredients may be heavier than others and may settle down in the container. Before measuring the amount you need, mix well to be sure the ingredients are evenly distributed.

You may not be able to store homemade mixes as long as commercial ones, which usually have preservatives added to extend the shelf life. Therefore, make only the quantity you think you will use before the mix has a chance to spoil.

Q ***What convenience mixes for different foods could I make at home?***

A You can make mixes for everything from main dishes to desserts. For a creamy pasta dish, combine dry noodles, dry milk, salt, pepper, and other seasonings. Store the mixture in a tightly sealed container and add boiling water when you need a quick main dish. If you like, stir in tuna or add ground beef and tomato sauce for a beef noodle casserole. Plain and flavored hot cocoa mixes can be made from dry milk, unsweetened baking cocoa, powdered sugar, and powdered nondairy "creamer." Spice mixes can be used to give meat or fish a new taste. Why not develop your own blend? If a recipe for muffins or cake combines dry ingredients before adding the moist ones, you can make a convenience mix. Simply combine the dry ingredients, store them, and add the other ingredients when you're ready to bake. When time is limited, all of these mixes add "convenience" to cooking.

Section 15-2 Review & Activities

1. List three tips for healthfully using convenience foods in meals.
2. Why is it important to read the directions on convenience foods even if you have used the product before?
3. Name two guidelines for using chilled convenience foods.
4. **Synthesizing.** Gloria's homemade pumpkin bread has long been a family favorite. Recently, Gloria discovered a mix that produces a result fairly close to her own, in addition to being less expensive. What reasons could you give Gloria for continuing to make her pumpkin bread from scratch?
5. **Synthesizing.** How might you and your family use homemade convenience foods? What types of foods would be most helpful?
6. **Applying.** Plan an entire dinner or lunch menu that combines a main dish convenience food with easy-to-prepare fresh foods as side dishes. Evaluate the meal for nutrition, cost, and appeal.

Answers to Section 15-2 Review & Activities

1. See bulleted list on page 405.
2. Manufacturers may have changed the ingredients or the preparation methods.
3. Keep them refrigerated until you are ready to use them; use a chilled food product by the date shown on the package.
4. See bulleted list on page 407.
5. Answers will vary. Assess answers for clarity of thought and application of material from the section.
6. Answers will vary.

Recipe File

Whole Wheat Quick Bread Mix

Homemade convenience mixes can save time and money in the kitchen. Compare the "Favorite Wheat Pancakes" recipe on the next page to other recipes you may have tried made with purchased convenience mixes.

Customary	*Ingredient*	*Metric*
6 cups	Whole wheat flour	1500 mL
3 cups	All-purpose flour	750 mL
1½ cups	Instant nonfat dry milk	375 mL
1 Tbsp.	Salt	15 mL
1 cup	Sugar	250 mL
½ cup	Wheat germ	125 mL
¼ cup	Baking powder	50 mL

Yield: About 12 cups (3 L) baking mix

Directions

1. Combine all ingredients in a large bowl.
2. Place the baking mix in a large container with a tight-fitting cover. Label with the name of the mix and the date.
3. Store baking mix in the refrigerator. Use within 12 to 14 weeks.

Note: Mix well again before measuring to use in recipes.

Recipe File

Whole Wheat Quick Bread Mix
Favorite Wheat Pancakes

These convenience food recipes are both prepared using homemade mixes. Prior to assigning the lab, you may wish to have students review the portion of the text under the heading "Homemade Mixes" on page 410.

USING THE RECIPE

- Have students read both recipes and discuss the steps for each.
- Review safety and sanitation procedures that apply to each recipe. For the Whole Wheat Quick Bread Mix, check that the storage container is airtight.
- Have each lab team fill out a work plan. (See the *Foods Lab Resources* booklet.)
- Have students check off the ingredients and equipment listed on the recipe worksheet and prepare the recipe.
- Have students complete the evaluation and questions on the recipe worksheet.

SEE ALSO...

The *Foods Lab Resources* booklet for the "Whole Wheat Quick Bread Mix" and "Favorite Wheat Pancakes" recipe worksheets and other recipe alternatives.

Recipe File

Favorite Wheat Pancakes

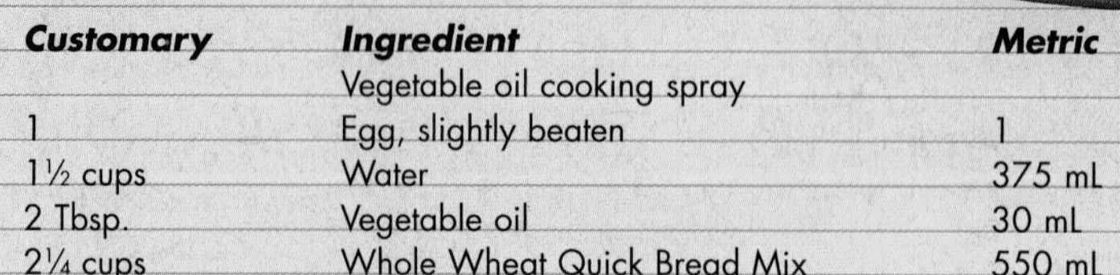

Customary	Ingredient	Metric
	Vegetable oil cooking spray	
1	Egg, slightly beaten	1
1½ cups	Water	375 mL
2 Tbsp.	Vegetable oil	30 mL
2¼ cups	Whole Wheat Quick Bread Mix	550 mL

Yield: About 15 4-inch (10-cm) pancakes
Equipment: Non-stick skillet
Temperature: Medium-high

Directions

1. Spray skillet with vegetable oil cooking spray. Preheat.
2. Combine egg, water, and oil in medium bowl.
3. Stir in Whole Wheat Quick Bread Mix just until moistened.
4. For each pancake, ladle ⅓ cup batter into skillet. Tilt skillet slightly to spread batter into rounds.
5. Cook until top of pancake is speckled with bubbles. Turn and cook on the other side until golden brown, about 3 or 4 minutes.
6. Serve hot with syrup, sliced bananas or berries in season, if desired.

Nutrition Information

For each 3-pancake serving: 244 calories, 8 g protein, 39 g carbohydrate, 7 g fat, 43 mg cholesterol, 259 mg sodium
Good source of: potassium, iron, vitamin E, B vitamins, calcium, phosphorus

Food for Thought

- In what way were the pancakes different from others you have tasted that were prepared from a mix? Were they better? Explain.
- What other foods could be made from the Whole Wheat Quick Bread Mix? Where could you find recipes for these foods?

Answers to ***Food for Thought***

1. Answers will vary. They might have a fresher, more "homemade" taste. They might be darker and nuttier-flavored due to the whole-wheat flour in the mix.
2. Answers will vary. Whole-wheat quick bread, rolls, or buns, or whole-wheat muffins (with or without fruit). Recipes could be found in baking cookbooks.

Career Wanted

Food Processing Plant Worker

Education and Training
- High school diploma
- On-the-job training

Qualities
- Attention to detail
- Concentration
- Safety conscious

"People appreciate our work whenever they enjoy a good meal."
Carl Coran

Q. Carl, what does your job involve?

A. I sort ears of corn for a frozen foods company. As the corn passes on a conveyor, I inspect for defects or damage and pull off any that don't meet standards. The rest are frozen and packaged.

Q. What are your working conditions like?

A. It takes some getting used to. Because the machinery is noisy, we wear special ear protection. We're required to take breaks every 20 minutes to help us stay alert. That's important for comfort and safety. Even jobs that you wouldn't think of as dangerous can cause repetitive stress injuries.

Q. Are there chances to advance in your job?

A. Oh, yes, and I plan to. I'm leader of my work unit's quality assurance team and hope to make line supervisor. I signed up for computer classes, too, because the advanced machinery is all computerized. I've known people who took mechanical training and became machine repairers. The key is staying open to learning new skills.

Related Career Opportunities

Entry Level
- Food batchmaker
- Farm worker
- Restaurant grader

Technical Level
- Produce department manager
- Agricultural inspector
- Quality control technician

Professional Level
- Purchasing manager
- Industrial engineer
- Sanitarian

Making Career Connections

CAREER EXPLORATION. Research the process used to make one convenience food. What tasks are involved? What machinery and skills are needed? What provisions are made for workers' health and safety and for advancing in the plant or company? Report your findings, discussing advantages and disadvantages of this career.

Career Wanted

Food Processing Plant Worker

Thinking About the Career

Have students read the feature, then seek out additional information on careers in a food processing plant. Using this information, as well as job facts provided by Carl Coran in his interview, have students prepare dramatic presentations titled "A Day in the Life of a Food Processing Plant Worker." In their dramatizations, students should answer the following questions: What machines does a person in this line of work use? What happens to bruised or defective ears of corn that are not removed from the conveyer system? What other foods are processed at this type of facility? How does this job differ from that of a machine operator?

Ask students to brainstorm types of products that are processed at processing plants.

Career-Building Opportunities

Students who are interested in food processing or production careers should check employment opportunities at local food processing or production plants.

For More Information

For additional information about food processing or production careers, encourage students to contact:

- Personnel offices of local food production plants
- Local chapters of the United Food and Commercial Workers International Union (AFLCIO)
- American Frozen Food Institute
  2000 Corporate Ridge, Suite 1000
  McLean, VA 22102
  www.affi.com
- Food Processing Machinery and Supplies Association
  200 Daingerfield Road
  Alexandria, VA 22314-2800
  fpmsa.org
- National Food Processors Association
  1350 I Street, NW, Suite 300
  Washington, DC 20005-3305
  www.nfpa-food.org

REVIEW

- Have students complete the Chapter Review. (Answers appear below.)

EVALUATION

- Provide a list of well-known convenience foods or make a display of packages. Have students write menus for nutritious, home-cooked meals using the foods.
- Have students take the test for Chapter 15.(Use the chapter test in the *Teacher Resource Guide,* or construct your own with the **Exam***View*® *Test Generator* on the *Effective Instruction CD-ROM.*)

ANSWERS

Checking Your Knowledge

1. It can be stored without refrigeration and kept for a longer time.
2. To meet special nutritional needs or to provide low-cost alternatives to other foods.
3. It is short for *textured soy protein*; it is used to make foods such as breakfast links, meatless burgers, pot pies, and hot dogs.
4. Any two: Processing usually destroys some nutrients; when grains are processed, fiber and nutrients tend to be lost; many convenience foods are high in added sodium, sugar, and/or fat.
5. To add back liquid that was removed in processing.
6. Any three: Sautéed chopped vegetables; dry beans and grain products; cubed or shredded cheese; bread crumbs or cubes.
7. Setting aside one or two weekend days to cook for the freezer; regularly preparing more than they need when they cook.
8. No—they lack preservatives.

Chapter 15 Review & Activities

Summary

Section 15-1: Choosing Convenience Foods

- Convenience foods are items that have been processed for longer shelf life, ease of preparation, or both.
- Manufactured foods are developed to serve as substitutes for other foods.
- Although convenience foods can save time and energy, they may be more costly, less nutritious, and less appealing than home-prepared or fresh foods.

Section 15-2: Cooking with Convenience

- With careful planning, convenience foods can be part of a nutritious meal.
- Prepare convenience foods according to the package directions.
- You can make your own convenience foods by pre-preparing ingredients, freezing main dishes, and making homemade dry mixes.

Checking Your Knowledge

1. In what way is nonfat dry milk more convenient than fluid milk?
2. Name two reasons why manufactured foods have been developed.
3. What is TSP? How is it used?
4. Identify two nutritional disadvantages of some convenience foods.
5. What does the term *reconstitute* mean?
6. Identify three types of recipe ingredients that you can pre-prepare.
7. Describe two practices many people use to make and freeze main dishes.
8. Do homemade dry mixes last as long as commercial varieties? Explain.

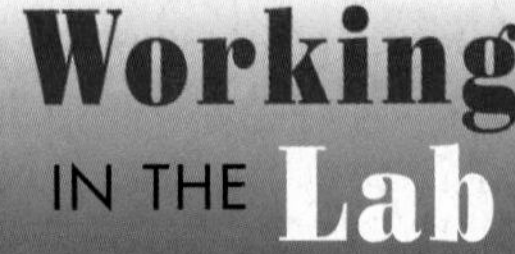

1. ***Food Preparation.*** Prepare a ready-to-cook entrée or side dish and a similar recipe from scratch in the foods lab. Compare them for meal appeal and nutritional value.
2. ***Food Science.*** Using a recipe from this book or another source, prepare a dry mix. Store it and a similar commercial variety under identical conditions. Check both mixes regularly for texture and appearance. Prepare recipes, using the mixes at regular intervals. How does time affect the quality of each mix?
3. ***Foods Lab.*** Prepare a commercial dry mix according to the basic package directions. Prepare another batch, using a variation suggested on the package or one of your own creation. Compare the two recipes for taste, texture, appearance, and nutritional value.

Thinking Critically

1. **Identifying Ambiguous Statements.** Peter comes from a family that enjoys preparing meals in the kitchen from scratch. His friend Simon comes from a family where everyone is so busy with activities outside the home that the term *home-cooked meal* has come to be synonymous with heating a convenience food in the microwave. How is each of the friends likely to react to an advertisement for a new food product that promises a "great home-made flavor"? Explain your answer.
2. **Recognizing Stereotypes.** Hattie and two friends were hungry after hockey practice and agreed to stop for a bite to eat. "I don't know exactly what I'm in the mood for," Hattie said. "Hey, how about the new pizza restaurant that opened on Maple Street?" Rita suggested. "Count me out!" Heather said pointedly. "I was walking by there yesterday and I saw a microwave oven on the counter. That's a sure sign that the food is awful!" What stereotype is reflected in this conversation? What logical flaw, if any, can you find in the argument?

Reinforcing Key Skills

1. **Management.** Emilia forgot to shop earlier in the week for the family dinner she was supposed to cook tonight. She had planned to make a shrimp and crab pasta entrée, salad, and fruit salad for dessert. Use information from the chapter to help Emilia organize her dinner plan—which includes sticking to a modest budget.
2. **Directed Thinking.** You are preparing your family's dinner when some old friends of the family drop by. You would like to invite them to stay for the meal, but you aren't sure you have enough food. Explain how to use convenience foods to stretch the recipes.

Making Decisions and Solving Problems

Your family uses convenience foods every day. You are worried about the effect on the family's health and on the budget. What would you do?

Making Connections

1. **Social Studies.** Trace the history of convenience foods. What were some of the first commercially sold convenience foods? What technologies make them possible? How has their use affected family life? Present your findings in an illustrated time line.
2. **Math.** Prepare a homemade convenience food. Calculate the cost per serving. Compare this with the per-serving cost of a similar commercial variety. Express the price difference in dollars and cents and as a percentage.

ANSWERS cont.

Thinking Critically

1. Answers will vary. Peter's possible reaction: "I doubt it can be as good as what I'm used to." Simon's possible reaction: "I can't wait to try it."
2. Stereotype: All microwaved food does not taste good. Flaw: Can't apply stereotype to ALL foods.

Reinforcing Key Skills

1. Answers will vary. Among options students might suggest are using surimi in place of the shellfish and buying the salad and cut-up fruit from the salad bar at the supermarket.
2. Answers will vary. One possibility, depending on the recipe, is the addition of TSP.

CHAPTER

16

Vegetables and Fruits

Advance Planning Guide ☑

- Purchase a variety of vegetables and fruits for various activities throughout Chapter 16.
- Gather Nutrition Facts panels from cans of fruit packed in water and fruit packed in syrup.
- Arrange a field trip with the manager or produce manager of a local supermarket. If permission slips will need to be issued, make sure to do this ahead of time.
- Prepare lists of plant parts that can be eaten as vegetables.
- Arrange with a local caterer, chef, or other professional who handles food in his or her line of work to speak to students and demonstrate techniques for attractively cutting produce.
- Purchase apples, pears, bananas, oranges, cantaloupes, or other available seasonal produce for the Food Science Lab on page 426.
- Buy ascorbic acid tablets (375 mg) for the Using the Food Science Lab on page 426.

CHAPTER

16

Not only are vegetables and fruits some of nature's most delicious foods, they also are packed with important nutrients. In this chapter, you'll learn how to select fresh produce and other forms of vegetables and fruits. You'll also learn strategies for making the most of these foods once you get them home.

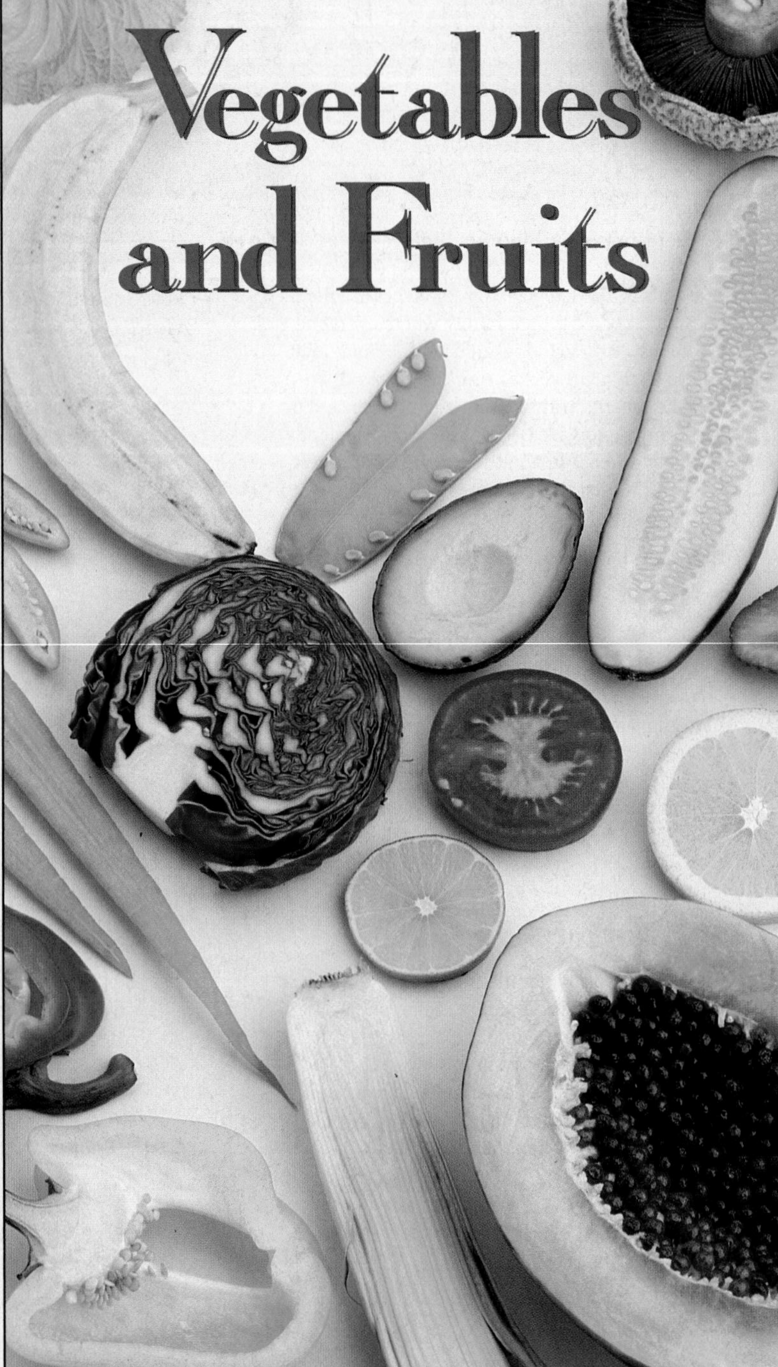

MEETING DIVERSE NEEDS

Naturalistic Learners. If there are students in the class who enjoy gardening and have raised vegetables and/or fruits, invite a panel to speak to the class about this activity. Suggest that the speakers explain important concepts such as the distinction between plants that grow from seed versus ones raised from seedlings, noting which vegetables and fruits fit each description. Encourage the class to listen carefully, and allow time after the presentation for questions and answers.

SECTION
16-1

Choosing Vegetables and Fruits

Picture yourself at a picnic, biting into an ear of tender, sweet corn. Imagine the crunch and tart, juicy goodness of a crisp, ripe apple. Vegetables and fruits appeal to all the senses. They are also an excellent source of many of the nutrients your body needs.

Objectives

After studying this section, you should be able to:

- Identify the nutrients found in vegetables and fruits.
- Recognize qualities to look for when buying vegetables and fruits.
- Discuss guidelines for storing fresh produce.

Look for These Terms

cruciferous vegetables
tuber
mature fruits
ripe fruits

Nutrients in Vegetables and Fruits

Fresh vegetables and fruits are low in fat and sodium and have no cholesterol. At the same time, they are high in carbohydrates. They are also chock-full of important micronutrients, including antioxidants—substances that may lower the risk of some cancers and heart disease. Among the antioxidants that vegetables and fruits provide are

- ◆ **Vitamin C.** Many people, when they think of vitamin C sources, think of citrus fruits. However, many other vegetables and fruits are rich in this vitamin, including kiwifruit, strawberries, cantaloupe, cabbage, and potatoes.
- ◆ **Vitamin E.** Apples and warm-weather fruits such as apricots, nectarines, and peaches are good sources of vitamin E. So are **cruciferous** (kroo-SIH-fur-uhs) **vegetables**—vegetables in the cabbage family. These include bok choy, broccoli, brussels sprouts, cauliflower, collards, kale, kohlrabi, mustard greens, rutabagas, and turnips and their greens.
- ◆ **Beta carotene.** The body uses this phytochemical—a health-promoting substance found in foods from plants—to make vitamin A. It is found in yellow or orange vegetables and fruits, as well as in cruciferous vegetables.

Section 16-1 Resources

◆ **Student Workbook,** pp. 115, 117
◆ **Teacher Resource Guide**
Lesson Plan 16-1 Organizer
Section 16-1 Quiz
◆ **Effective Instruction CD-ROM**
Exam*View*® *Test Generator*
PowerPoint® Slides #31, 32
◆ **Transparency Package,** CT-31, 32
◆ **Student Motivation Kit**
Reteaching Activities, p. 74
Enrichment Activities
Food Science Resources, pp. 36–39, 66–68

SECTION
16-1
Choosing Vegetables and Fruits

FOCUS

MOTIVATORS

- Have students read the week's newspaper advertisements. If they were shopping, which vegetables and fruits would they buy? Why? Are all advertised fruits "good buys"?
- Review with students changes in fresh produce that have occurred during the history of the United States. What factors have been responsible for these changes? How have consumers benefited?

VOCABULARY ACTIVITY

Direct students' attention to "Look for These Terms." Pronounce aloud the word *cruciferous.* Ask a volunteer to investigate the meaning of the root *cruci(f)-* (cross-shaped). Ask students to examine one such vegetable to see if they can understand the meaning of the name.

STUDY SKILLS

- **Listening.** Invite a group of volunteers to each prepare an oral reading of a page of text from the section, while others follow along silently.
- Have students read the section and complete the appropriate part of the Chapter 16 Study Guide in the *Student Workbook*.

TEACH

- *Nutrients in Vegetables and Fruits*
- *Types of Vegetables*
- *Types of Fruits*
  (text pages 417-419)

Discussion Activity

Discuss with students which specific nutrients are found in which vegetables and fruits. Emphasize that, in general, vegetables are high in a given nutrient and low in calories. Expand the discussion to other non-plant foods noted in Chapter 2 that provide some of the same micronutrients. Ask interested volunteers to devise "power" recipes—tasteful blends of vegetables and non-plant foods rich in nutrients. How could these be made part of a regular eating plan?

Research Activity

Have students investigate the most recent scientific claims regarding the role of cruciferous vegetables in lowering the risk of certain lifestyle diseases. Direct students to reputable sources of information, including online government sites. Have students report their findings to the class.

- In a recent year, Americans ate twice their weight in fresh fruit.
- Although the terms *yam* and *sweet potato* are used interchangeably, the two actually belong to different plant families.

◆ **Fresh vegetables and fruits appeal not only to the sense of taste but to sight, smell, touch, and even sound. Choose two fruits or vegetables. For each one, give a word describing its appeal to each of the five senses.**

For more on antioxidants and their role in reducing the risk of certain diseases, see Section 2-4.

FOR YOUR HEALTH

Vegetable and Fruit Serving Equivalents

According to an old saying, you can't add apples and oranges. You *can,* however, substitute equivalent servings of fruits and vegetables depending on your tastes and preferences. Knowing this can help you get the daily servings of fruit and vegetables the Food Guide Pyramid recommends. If you don't like snacking on raw carrot sticks, try a glass of chilled tomato juice instead. Single-serving cans or packs of applesauce are an easy and tasty way to get a serving of fruit. The Food Guide Pyramid, on page 98, contains other suggestions.

Following Up

1. Which items might be best to take along on a weekend camping trip? Which might make a great appetizer at dinner? Explain your choices.
2. Think about specific foods you enjoy eating that equal one serving of fruits or vegetables. Maintain a list of these in your Wellness Journal. Refer to the list often.

Types of Vegetables

Do you know what tomatoes and cucumbers have in common? If you answered that both are often used as salad ingredients, you are right. Another and perhaps more surprising link is that both are really fruits, not vegetables. Strictly speaking, a fruit is any part of a plant that holds the seeds.

Types of Fruits

Most supermarkets carry a wide variety of fruits. Some may be from neighboring areas; others may come from across the country or halfway around the world. Here are some you might find in your supermarket:

- Many kinds of melons, from cantaloupe to casaba.
- Citrus fruits, including grapefruit, oranges, and tangerines.
- A bounty of berries—raspberries, strawberries, blueberries, and more—as well as grapes.
- Many kinds of apples and pears.
- Cherries, plums, peaches, apricots, and other drupes (fruits with a central pit enclosing a single seed).
- Tropical fruits, including bananas, pineapple, papayas, kiwifruit, carambola (star fruit), and mangoes—the list is endless!

Extending Learning

Tomatoes—Point out to students that early names for the tomato, which include *mala insana*—or "unhealthy apple"—reflect the widespread belief that the fruit was poisonous. Add that the tomato is native to Peru and was first brought to Europe by explorers, most likely the Spanish, during the 1500s.

Discuss with students possible reasons why early people may have assumed certain plants to be poisonous.

What Is a Vegetable?

Vegetables can come from many different edible plant parts. They are all vegetables, but they may also be stems, fruits, or even flowers!

Look and Learn:

How might the nutrient content of a vegetable be related to the part of the plant that it comes from?

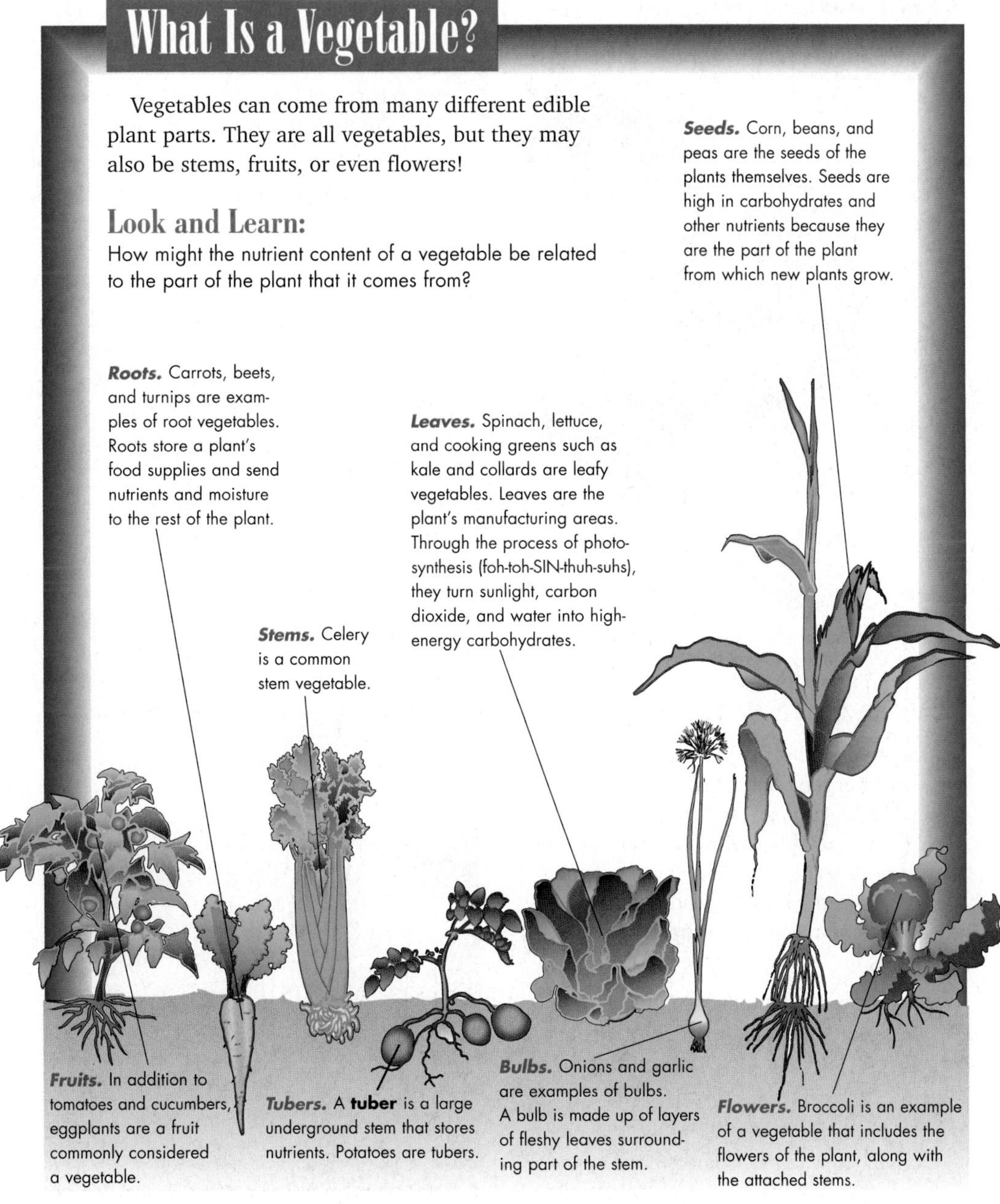

Seeds. Corn, beans, and peas are the seeds of the plants themselves. Seeds are high in carbohydrates and other nutrients because they are the part of the plant from which new plants grow.
Roots. Carrots, beets, and turnips are examples of root vegetables. Roots store a plant's food supplies and send nutrients and moisture to the rest of the plant.
Leaves. Spinach, lettuce, and cooking greens such as kale and collards are leafy vegetables. Leaves are the plant's manufacturing areas. Through the process of photosynthesis (foh-toh-SIN-thuh-suhs), they turn sunlight, carbon dioxide, and water into high-energy carbohydrates.
Stems. Celery is a common stem vegetable.
Fruits. In addition to tomatoes and cucumbers, eggplants are a fruit commonly considered a vegetable.
Tubers. A **tuber** is a large underground stem that stores nutrients. Potatoes are tubers.
Bulbs. Onions and garlic are examples of bulbs. A bulb is made up of layers of fleshy leaves surrounding part of the stem.
Flowers. Broccoli is an example of a vegetable that includes the flowers of the plant, along with the attached stems.

- *Types of Vegetables*
- *Types of Fruits (text pages 418-419)*

Categorizing Activity

Have students form brainstorming groups in an effort to list as many fruits as they can. Have groups share their lists, writing a master list on the board. Share with students the information in the "Food Science" box at the bottom of this page. Then challenge students to come to the board and identify each of the fruits listed, by writing one of the following letters in front of it: *P* for temperate, *S* for subtropical, and *T* for tropical. Instruct them to research any fruits they cannot categorize.

Product Comparison

Provide small groups of students with Nutrition Facts panels from each of several cans of fruit packed in water and several packed in syrup. Have groups compare the nutritional information in order to arrive at hypotheses regarding differences in the number of calories, DVs of key nutrients, etc. L2

VISUAL LEARNING — *Using the Illustration*

Ask students to extend the information in "What Is a Vegetable?" by researching other vegetables that fit into each category listed. Have students make charts on sheets of poster board that indicate the name of each vegetable, category it belongs to, and nutrient(s) it supplies.

FOOD SCIENCE — Horticulture Science

Horticulturists—scientists who study the growth of plants—define vegetables as "the edible products of herbaceous plants." Explain the herbaceous plants are those which have stems that are softer than the stems of shrubs and trees.

Horticulturists classify fruits based on the temperatures they require for growth:

- *Temperate fruits* include common fruits such as apples and peaches.
- *Subtropical fruits* include citrus fruits as well as dates and figs.
- *Tropical fruits* include bananas, pineapples, and mangoes.

TEACH cont.

- *Buying Fresh Produce (text pages 420-421)*

Supermarket Survey

Have students visit one supermarket and record the convenience forms of fruits and vegetables available (such as ready-to-eat carrot and celery sticks). Permit time for them to discuss and compare their findings. L1

Field Trip

Take a field trip to the produce department of a supermarket or to a farmer's market. Ask the produce manager to point out signs of quality and to give buying tips for fresh produce. Ask the manager to explain how vegetables and fruits are priced and how price is affected by season. Have students look for examples of produce that is loose, packaged, and "unitized" (held together with a rubber band or plastic tie). Ask: Which vegetables are priced per pound? By the package? By unit?

- On August 21, 1959, the United States went from last place to first place as a worldwide producer of pineapples. On that date, Hawaii was admitted to the Union.

◆ **There are several types of fruit in this photo. Choose different fruits for variety and good nutrition. Try a fruit you have never eaten before and give your reaction to it.**

Buying Fresh Produce

Produce is sold many ways, including loose or in a bag or a plastic-covered tray. Some items, like broccoli, are sometimes sold in bunches held together with a rubber band or plastic tie. If you want less of a prepackaged item, ask a clerk to open it and repackage the amount you want. Here are some other guidelines for buying produce:

- ◆ Inspect produce carefully. Stains on the package or an unpleasant odor may be a telltale sign that the item is damaged or spoiled.
- ◆ Avoid produce that looks wilted, shriveled, bruised, or decayed. Some produce may have natural blemishes, which do not affect quality. Grapefruit and oranges, for instance, may have brownish surface areas.
- ◆ Buy by weight, when possible. Except for leafy vegetables, vegetables and fruits should feel heavy for their size. Buy top-quality vegetables and fruits. They will give you more nutrients for your money and will last longer.
- ◆ Buy only what you can store and use. Most high-quality vegetables and fruits last about a week in the refrigerator.
- ◆ Remember that some vegetables, such as greens, cook down from their original volume. For example, 1 pound (500 g) of raw mustard greens yields 1½ cups (350 mL) of the cooked vegetable.

Seasonal Produce

Some vegetables and fruits, such as spinach, broccoli, bananas, apples, and grapes, are available the year round. Others—asparagus, peaches, and plums, for example—have a specific growing season. During this season, when the vegetable or fruit is plentiful, prices drop and quality goes up. When shopping, look for year-round favorites and items that are in season. Seasonal produce is often available during the off-season months but tends to cost more then.

◆ **When you can, buy produce by weight. The next time you are at the supermarket, weigh an average sized vegetable or fruit that is sold loose. Note this in your Wellness Journal for future reference.**

Technology TIE-IN Point out that having fresh fruit the year round in non-growing regions is a development of only the last 100 years or so. Note that bananas, today a staple fruit in local supermarkets, were a rarely encountered delicacy in the United States as recently as 1870. Have interested students work in small teams to create pictorial timelines of technological advances that have led to the current rich assortment of fruits we find in the produce department.

◆ **Washing produce before storing it speeds up decay. Name two steps you *should* take when storing produce.**

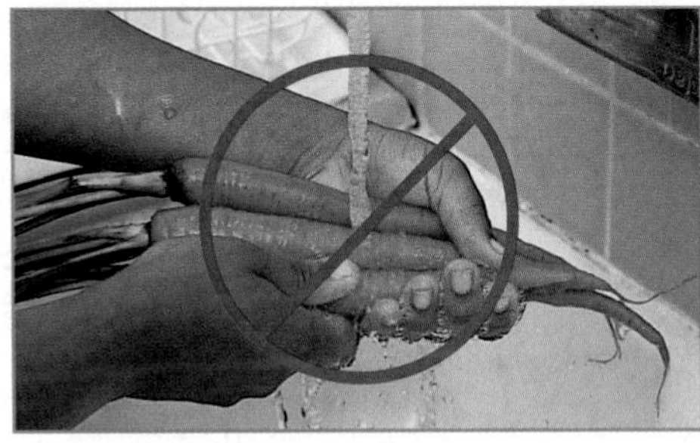

Ripeness

Vegetables and fruits are usually harvested when they are mature. **Mature fruits** are fruits that have reached their full size and color. However, fruits are not always ripe when harvested. **Ripe fruits** are fruits that are tender and have a pleasant aroma and fully developed flavor.

As shown in the chart below, some fruits continue to ripen after they are harvested. Buy these fruits at the stage of ripeness you want—ripe, if you plan to use them right away, or less ripe, if you plan to use them several days later. Some fruits are naturally green when they are ripe, such as many varieties of apples and pears. However, avoid other fruits that are green (except bananas), since they will not ripen well.

Test for Ripeness

To test for ripeness on most fruits, press very gently. Ripe fruit will give slightly under the pressure. Don't press so hard that you damage the fruit.

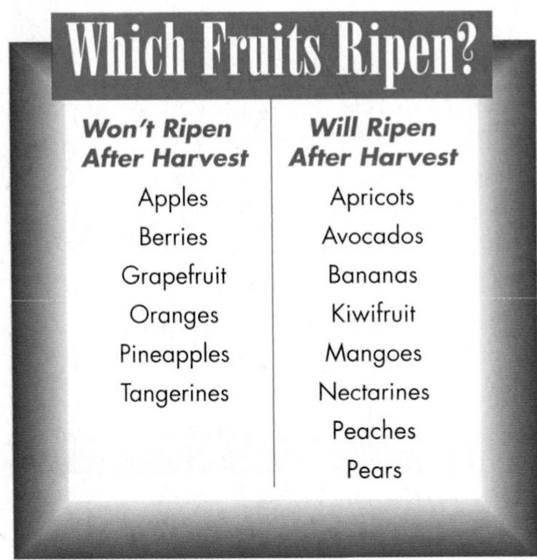

Which Fruits Ripen?

Won't Ripen After Harvest	Will Ripen After Harvest
Apples	Apricots
Berries	Avocados
Grapefruit	Bananas
Oranges	Kiwifruit
Pineapples	Mangoes
Tangerines	Nectarines
	Peaches
	Pears

Storing Fresh Produce

Unless produce is dirty, it should not be washed until you are ready to use it. Added moisture will speed up the action of bacteria, causing spoilage. Moisture remaining on produce can also cause mold to grow. If you need to wash produce before storing it, be sure it is thoroughly dry.

- **Storing unripe fruits.** For faster ripening, place them in a brown paper bag at room temperature. For slower ripening, refrigerate. As you need ripe fruit, take it out of the refrigerator and let it ripen at room temperature.
- **Storing potatoes, sweet potatoes, and onions.** Store in a cool, dark, dry place. They will keep longest at a temperature of about 45°-50°F (7°-10°C). If you must store potatoes and onions at room temperature, buy only what you can use in a short time. If refrigerated, onions and sweet potatoes will mold and decay, and the flavor of potatoes will change as their starch turns to sugar.
- **Storing other vegetables and fruits.** Refrigerate in the crisper section or in brown paper bags. If you use plastic bags, punch holes in them so that some of the moisture can escape. Don't line the bottom of the crisper with paper towels; they get soggy and cause the produce to decay or turn moldy.

- *Storing Fresh Produce (text page 421)*

Checklists

Have students develop a checklist of guidelines for storing fresh vegetables and fruits. Have students use the checklist to examine the storing of vegetables and fruits at home and in the foods lab. Any improper storing should be shared with family members at home. L1

COMPUTER ACTIVITY: Creating a Pamphlet

Have students create pamphlets that summarize in a lively text format tips on storing produce. Have students speak with managers of local food stores, produce markets, greengrocers, and supermarkets about leaving copies of the booklet available as a public service to customers.

USING Safety Check

See "Safety Check" on page 422. Have interested students research solanine to find out in what ways it is harmful and why it appears when potatoes are exposed to light. Ask students to report their findings to the class. Emphasize that refrigerator storage is not recommended because this causes sugar to build up and the potatoes to discolor during cooking due to the Maillard reaction, which is discussed in Chapter 9 (page 279).

FOOD SCIENCE: Ethylene and Ripening

Explain that as fruit ripens it gives off the gas ethylene, which acts as a ripening agent. Add that scientists know that ethylene produced by a ripe fruit can stimulate ethylene production in underripe fruit, thereby speeding up the ripening process.

Ask students to discuss ways in which this knowledge might be applied in their own homes and lives. Have them write down hypotheses on what might happen if ripe and unripe fruits are stored in the same enclosure. Allow them to test their hypotheses with fruit in the class foods lab.

TEACH cont.

- *Convenience Vegetables and Fruits (text pages 422-423)*

Debate

Have students form two groups for a debate. One group is to argue the benefits of convenience foods, the other the challenges. Each team is to start by reading the points made in the chart on this page and then expanding on these by brainstorming and, as necessary, doing independent research. For example, students from the "Challenges" group might note that canned fruits often provide less fiber than fresh fruit, while the "Benefits" team might argue that certain convenience foods are fortified with added micronutrients and may provide more of some vitamins and minerals than even fresh fruit. L1

Letter-Writing Campaign

After sharing the information about wax in "Extending Learning" at the bottom of this page, encourage students to visit the FDA web site to learn more about the chemical composition of this wax. Have students then consider how they might go about raising public awareness of the harmlessness of this coating through a letter-writing campaign. Letters might be written to government officials on the civic or state level, as well as to government health agencies. Have representative students draft and send their letters. L3

Safety Check

Potatoes that are exposed to light sometimes develop a greenish color. This color indicates that the potato may contain a harmful, bitter-tasting compound called solanine. Solanine may also be found in potato sprouts. Cut away green portions and sprouts before using potatoes. Discard potatoes that have a bitter taste.

Convenience Vegetables and Fruits

Convenience forms of vegetables and fruits can be a real help in today's busy families. Canned and frozen vegetables and fruits can be stored longer than fresh produce and can be prepared quickly. They often cost less than fresh produce, yet provide similar amounts of vitamins and minerals.

Juices are also convenient and refreshing. You can buy vegetable and fruit juices in bottles, cartons, cans, or as frozen concentrate. Read the label carefully when you shop. If the label says "juice," the product is 100 percent juice. Products that are not pure juice must be called by another name, such as "fruit drink."

Quick and Easy Convenience Fruits

Canned, frozen, and dried fruits offer convenient choices. Here are tips for using them:

- For a quick, low-fat dessert, purée canned fruit in a blender and serve over angel food cake.
- To serve frozen fruits, thaw only partially. The ice crystals that remain will help the fruit stay firm.
- Dried fruits are sweet and chewy—a concentrated form of energy. They can be eaten as snacks, cooked, or used in recipes.

Buying Convenience Vegetables and Fruits

Challenges	*Solutions*
Canned fruits are often high in added sugar.	Look for fruits packed in natural juice instead of sugar syrup.
Canned vegetables are often high in sodium.	Look for low-sodium varieties. Drain the liquid from high-sodium vegetables before heating.
Some frozen vegetables are relatively expensive.	Buy frozen vegetables in bags. They cost less than those in boxes. Buy plain vegetables without sauces and other extras. Add your own special touches, such as a sprinkling of herbs.

Extending Learning

Wax on Fruit—Some produce that you buy in the store has been waxed. This wax replaces the natural protective coating that is removed when produce is washed after harvest. It also adds to the "eye appeal" of the produce and helps prevent moisture loss.

All waxes have been approved by the FDA. However, some people have voiced concern over whether consumers are being given enough information about the types of wax found on the produce they buy.

◆ **Convenience forms of vegetables and fruits give consumers more options. Which of the items pictured have been used in your home?**

Section 16-1 Review & Activities

1. Name three nutrients found in fresh vegetables and fruits. Identify specific vegetables and fruits that contain these nutrients.

2. What are three qualities to look for when buying fresh produce?

3. Identify similarities and differences between mature and ripe fruit. Under what circumstances would you buy one or the other?

4. Why should produce be stored unwashed?

5. **Analyzing.** Twenty-five years ago, supermarkets and produce stands did not offer as great a variety of vegetables and fruits as many do today. What are the reasons for this change? From a nutritional standpoint, how does this change benefit consumers?

6. **Synthesizing.** The supermarket where Chet shops is having a sale on bananas. Most of the bananas are green. What information would you need to know before you could advise Chet on how much of the fruit to buy?

7. **Applying.** Use the information from this section to create a Produce Storage Checklist. Armed with your checklist, inspect the state of produce storage in your home. Discuss any problems you encounter with adults in the family, and clarify any myths or misinformation that may exist.

ASSESS

REVIEW

- Ask students to summarize the main ideas in this section.
- Have students complete the Section Review. (Answers appear below.)

EVALUATION

- Display a variety of fruits and vegetables in various stages of maturity, ripeness, and quality. Number each fruit or vegetable. Have students write a short summary of each fruit's state of maturity and ripeness, noting damage and flaws.
- Have students take the quiz for Section 16-1. (Use the quiz in the *Teacher Resource Guide,* or construct your own with the **Exam***View*® *Test Generator* on the *Effective Instruction CD-ROM.*)

RETEACHING

- Provide students with a list of plant parts that can be eaten as vegetables. Have students write an example of each, along with storage methods for that vegetable.
- Refer to the *Reteaching Activities* booklet for the Section 16-1 activity sheet.

CLOSE

Have students complete this statement: "The single most important point when it comes to the proper storage and handling of produce is _____." Allow time for students to compare their responses.

Answers to Section 16-1 Review & Activities

1. See bulleted list on page 417.
2. See bulleted list on page 420.
3. See page 421. Always buy mature fruit, but ripeness depends on your personal needs.
4. Added moisture will speed up the action of bacteria, causing spoilage.
5. Answers will vary. Possibilities: There is a greater interest in exotic vegetables and fruits; high-speed transportation allows items to be brought from around the world.
6. Answers will vary. Possible answer: How soon the fruit will be used.
7. Answers will vary.

SECTION
16-2
Preparing Raw Vegetables and Fruits

FOCUS

MOTIVATORS

- Ask students to name a food that is tasty, eaten raw, and easily prepared in minutes. How many students named fresh vegetables and fruits? Which ones were named?
- Demonstrate a variety of ways to cut fresh produce to create interesting shapes.

VOCABULARY ACTIVITY

Pronounce the term under "Look for This Term." Ask whether any students know the root from which the first word is derived (enzyme). Have students find the term and its definition in the section.

STUDY SKILLS

- **Guided Reading.** Have students look at the headings within Section 16-2 to preview the concepts that will be discussed.
- Have students read the section and complete the appropriate part of the Chapter 16 Study Guide in the *Student Workbook*.

SECTION
16-2

Preparing Raw Vegetables and Fruits

Objectives

After studying this section, you should be able to:

- Describe how to wash fresh produce.
- Give suggestions for healthful and attractive ways to prepare and serve raw vegetables and fruits.

Look for This Term

enzymatic browning

Fresh raw vegetables and fruits are one of nature's convenience foods. They take almost no time to prepare. In minutes, you can have slices of sweet pepper to scoop up your favorite dip. Even when time is short, you can add zip to your morning cereal—and important nutrients to your eating plan—with fresh strawberry or peach slices.

Washing Fresh Produce

Before you eat or cook any fresh vegetable or fruit, you need to wash it. Washing removes pesticide residues, dirt, and pathogens. Even vegetables that are going to be peeled need to be washed first to prevent transferring pesticides and dirt to the edible parts. For tender vegetables and fruits, wash thoroughly in cool, clear water. Be sure to remove all visible dirt. For thicker-skinned produce, such as winter squash, scrub with a stiff brush. Also scrub potatoes and other vegetables that tend to have a lot of dirt. To minimize nutrient loss, do not soak produce in water.

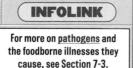

For more on pathogens and the foodborne illnesses they cause, see Section 7-3.

Safety Check

Never use detergent when washing produce. The produce can absorb the detergent, which can make people ill if it's swallowed. Detergent sometimes reacts with pesticides and waxes found on the produce. The chemicals that result from such reactions can be harmful to humans.

Section 16-2 Resources

◆ **Student Workbook,** pp. 115, 119
◆ **Teacher Resource Guide**
Lesson Plan 16-2 Organizer
Section 16-2 Quiz
◆ **Effective Instruction CD-ROM**
Exam *View® Test Generator*
PowerPoint® Slide #33
◆ **Transparency Package,** CT-33
◆ **Student Motivation Kit**
Reteaching Activities, p. 75
Enrichment Activities
Foods Lab Resources, pp. 49–50
Food Science Resources, pp. 113–115

◆ The raw vegetables pictured are easy to chew and digest, making them great snacking options. In your Wellness Journal, record two interesting ways of making these or other raw vegetables a part of your meals and snacks.

Cutting Fresh Produce

After it is washed, some produce needs to be peeled—for example, potatoes and oranges. Other produce, such as jicama, may need to be pared. Inedible parts, including the seeds of sweet peppers, the stems of fruit, and any soft spots or damaged areas, also need to be removed.

For more nutrients and fiber, eat edible skins rather than paring them away. However, if you're concerned about removing wax and residues, pare the produce. Even though some nutrients will be lost in paring, most will remain.

Cutting vegetables and fruits into pieces makes them easier to eat and adds eye appeal. Keep the chunks fairly large when cutting, and serve them as soon as possible. That way, you retain the nutrients. Vegetables and fruits can be cut into dozens of interesting shapes. Sweet peppers, carrots, and zucchini can be presented as strips. Carrots can be sliced crosswise; so can kiwifruit and bananas. Tomatoes and peaches can be cut into wedges. One eye-catching way to present fresh fruits is to cut them into bite-size shapes and serve them with wooden picks. You can also use a melon baller or small scoop to make balls of soft-fleshed fruits, such as cantaloupe.

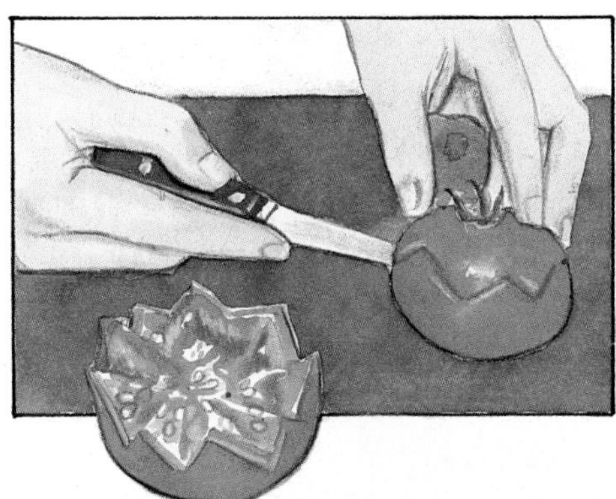

◆ Some raw produce, such as a tomato, can be cut in a decorative shape to make it more visually appealing. Name two other types of raw produce that might be cut into creative shapes.

TEACH

- *Washing Fresh Produce*
- *Cutting Fresh Produce (text pages 424-427)*

Demonstration

Demonstrate how to wash fresh vegetables and fruits to remove pesticide residues, dirt, and germs. Show how to use a vegetable brush. Point out that soaking produce in water causes nutrient loss. Emphasize the point made in the "Safety Check" feature that produce should never be washed in detergent. Have interested students investigate what specific chemicals in detergents are responsible for this chemical reaction.

Student Demonstrations

Have students work in pairs to demonstrate how to cut fresh vegetables and fruits. Discuss reasons to avoid paring produce with edible skins. Have students demonstrate different ways to cut vegetables and fruits. L1

Guest Speaker

Invite a local caterer, restaurant chef, or other food professional to come to class to speak with students about "eye appeal" in cutting foods. If possible, this professional might demonstrate techniques for attractively cutting and arranging raw produce.

FOOD SCIENCE

Chemicals to Treat Fruit

Explain that some fruits are treated with chemicals to maintain quality and increase storage time. Add that fungicides, bactericides, ripening inhibitors, and coloring agents may be added as well. Invite students to visit pre-screened Web sites that offer information on the names of these agents. After students have shared their findings with the class, conclude with a discussion of how these chemicals are similar to and different from the additives used to preserve the shelf life of foods.

- *Cutting Fresh Produce*
- *Serving and Storing Cut Produce (text pages 426-427)*

Taste Test

1. Ask for approximately 10 volunteers to take part in a blind taste test.
2. Feed the volunteers pieces of fruit of each type left over from the Food Science Lab. Make sure the rest of the class knows which samples are which.
3. Have volunteers raise their hand when they believe they have tasted a piece of browned fruit.

When the experiment has concluded, discuss the results. Ask whether students feel the experiment proves that we eat with our eyes as much as we do our taste buds.

USING THE Food Science LAB

Observe that food professionals often use methods other than those used by the general public to achieve certain reactions. Amplify on this by providing students with 375-mg ascorbic acid tablets. Have them repeat the activity, this time crushing one tablet and using it in place of the lemon juice in the third bullet under "Conclusions." What difference, if any, does this make in flavor? Appearance?

Point out that the lab calls for a glass plate, noting that glass is a non-reactive compound. Ask: What do you think this means?

Preventing Cut Fruits from Darkening

Some fruits turn dark after they are cut. This discoloration, which results from the exposure of a fruit's flesh to the air, is called **enzymatic** (EN-zih-mat-ik) **browning**. Although oxygen in the air will eventually cause any fruit to turn brown, the reaction occurs more quickly in fruits that contain a certain enzyme.

An easy way to avoid enzymatic browning is to coat the fruits with some form of ascorbic acid (vitamin C) as soon as they are cut. You might, for example, dip the pieces of cut fruit in lemon juice. Another option is to buy ascorbic acid powder to mix with water and sprinkle on cut fruit.

◆ Lemon juice can keep banana slices from turning dark. Would you need to use lemon juice on any other fruits in this salad? Why or why not?

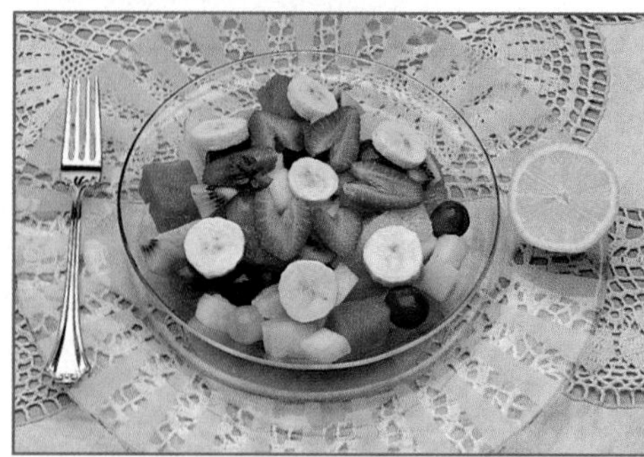

Food Science ◆ LAB ◆

How Quickly Do Different Fruits Darken?

If you were preparing a fruit salad, how would you keep one fruit from darkening while you prepared the others? To answer, you need to know which fruits undergo enzymatic browning and at what rate of speed.

Procedure

1. Working with four classmates, simultaneously cut an apple, a pear, a banana, an orange, and a cantaloupe into small cubes. Place the cubes on a glass plate.
2. Carefully inspect each fruit for discoloration at 2-minute intervals. At the first sign of browning, note how long it took for enzymatic browning to begin.

Conclusions

- ◆ Which fruits underwent enzymatic browning? Which didn't?
- ◆ How can this information help you when preparing an entire meal?
- ◆ Repeat the experiment, this time coating the pieces of fruit with lemon juice after they are cut. Then taste the fruit. How does the juice affect the fruit's flavor?

ASSESSING PERFORMANCE IN THE LAB

Have students create a rubric that evaluates group performance during the Food Science Lab. Explain that the rubric is to have the form of a grid with four or five different categories of competence for each criterion covered. Suggest that at the low end of the rubric, criteria might include "Failed to follow directions" and "Worked poorly as a team, chaotic."

Once the rubric has been completed, groups should assess their work. Each student should then write in his or her Wellness Journal a paragraph recommending ways of improving in these areas.

Unlike fruits, the majority of vegetables do not turn brown when cut. If they are allowed to stand for several days, however, they may begin to darken.

Serving and Storing Cut Produce

An assortment of cut-up raw fruits and vegetables can be a healthful touch when entertaining. Instead of just heaping the fruits and vegetables on a plate or in a bowl, use your imagination. You'll have more fun preparing the food, and the people you are serving will appreciate the extra effort. You might arrange different kinds of produce in ever-widening rings or in wedges like a pie. Keep in mind that color contrast makes a pleasing display.

If you don't plan to serve the produce immediately, cover your arrangement tightly with plastic wrap. Squeeze out as much air as possible, and refrigerate until serving time. You might want to serve the produce with a tasty low-fat dip, possibly one made with yogurt.

Try keeping cut-up vegetables in the refrigerator as handy snacks. Store them in a tightly sealed plastic bag or on a plate covered with plastic. Again, squeeze out as much air as possible to keep nutrients from being destroyed by oxygen.

Section 16-2 Review & Activities

1. Why is it important to wash produce before eating it?
2. Explain enzymatic browning in your own words. Explain how it can be prevented.
3. **Analyzing.** Why is keeping cut-up fruits and vegetables on hand as snacks a good idea from a nutritional standpoint?
4. **Extending.** Identify ways in which the presentation of cut vegetables and fruits might be used to increase young children's interest in these foods. Sketch possible fun shapes that would be easy to prepare. If possible, try presenting these foods to a toddler and record his or her reactions.
5. **Applying.** With a small group of classmates, discuss ways of communicating to teachers and students in your school that vegetables and fruits are the ultimate convenience food. For example, you might create a public service announcement or series of original posters. Assess the effectiveness of your campaign by randomly interviewing members of the school community in the days and weeks following.

ASSESS

REVIEW

- Ask students to summarize the main ideas in this section.
- Have students complete the Section Review. (Answers appear below.)

EVALUATION

- Tell students you are going to prepare a vegetable and fruit snack tray, pausing at each step so that students can decide if you have followed proper procedure for washing and cutting produce. Section an orange without first washing the skin, slice an apple that is conspicuously dirty, etc. Be sure to mix proper procedures in with the erroneous ones.
- Have students take the quiz for Section 16-2. (Use the quiz in the *Teacher Resource Guide,* or construct your own with the **ExamView®** *Test Generator* on the *Effective Instruction CD-ROM.*)

RETEACHING

- Display pictures of various fruits. Have students identify the fruits and describe at least one way each could be prepared.
- Refer to the *Reteaching Activities* booklet for the Section 16-2 activity sheet.

CLOSE

Lead a brainstorming session to list a variety of occasions for which fresh fruits and vegetables might be appropriate.

Answers to Section 16-2 Review & Activities

1. It removes pesticide residues, dirt, and pathogens.
2. Exact wording, which will vary, should tell that this is a discoloration that results from the exposure of a fruit's flesh to the air; by coating the fruits with ascorbic acid.
3. These provide more of the nutrients the body needs than do other snack foods, such as chips, cookies, and candy.
4. Answers will vary. Possibilities include cutting familiar shapes and/or characters to heighten interest.
5. Answers will vary.

SECTION

16-3

Cooking Vegetables and Fruits

FOCUS

MOTIVATORS

- Provide students with fresh and cooked samples of a fruit. Have students compare texture, tenderness, color, and flavor. What effect did cooking have on the fruit?
- Prepare two or three vegetables that may be unfamiliar to students (for example, artichoke, eggplant, pea pods) or prepare familiar vegetables in different ways. Have students sample the vegetables and describe their reaction. What qualities of the dish led to this reaction?

VOCABULARY ACTIVITY

Direct students' attention to "Look for This Term." Ask if anyone knows what this substance is or what color it is associated with. Have a volunteer locate the bold-face entry in the section and read the definition.

STUDY SKILLS

- **Outlining.** Have students read the section and outline it by copying the headers on paper and leaving space after each one. Students are to write a sentence in their own words, summarizing the content under each header.
- Have students read the section and complete the appropriate part of the Chapter 16 Study Guide in the *Student Workbook*.

SECTION

16-3

Objectives

After studying this section, you should be able to:

- Identify the effects of heat and cooking on vegetables and fruits.
- Describe methods for cooking vegetables and fruits.

Look for This Term

chlorophyll

Cooking Vegetables and Fruits

If given a choice, would you rather eat vegetables that look bright and colorful, or ones that look discolored and washed-out? It probably isn't a difficult choice to make.

This visible difference relates to how the vegetables were cooked. Paying close attention to cooking methods can affect not only the look but also the flavor and even the feel of a vegetable or fruit.

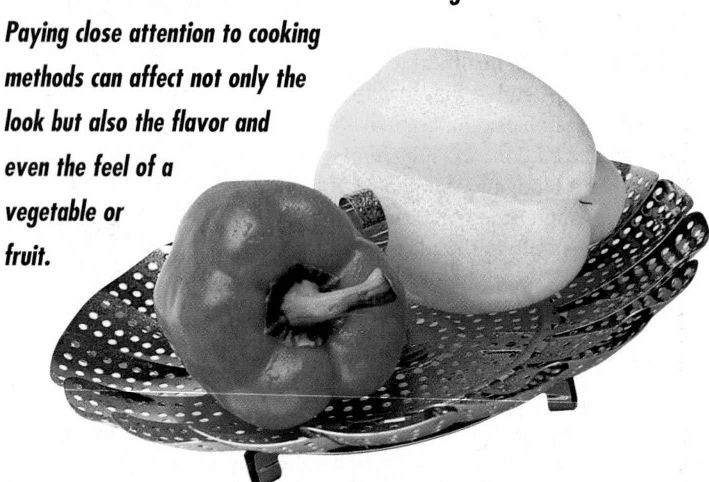

Effects of Cooking on Vegetables and Fruits

Cooking causes changes in vegetables and fruits. One of the most important changes is not observable to the human eye. It is a loss of vitamin C and other nutrients. You can minimize these losses when cooking by:

- Keeping vegetables and fruits whole or in large pieces.
- Cooking them quickly, using methods that require only a small amount of water—for example, steaming, simmering in a tightly covered pan, or microwaving.
- Serving cooked vegetables and fruits with the cooking liquid whenever possible.

◆ **The amount of water used when cooking vegetables has impact. Why is it better to cook them in a small quantity of water?**

Section 16-3 Resources

◆ **Student Workbook,** pp. 116, 121
◆ **Teacher Resource Guide**
Lesson Plan 16-3 Organizer
Section 16-3 Quiz
Chapter 16 Test
◆ **Effective Instruction CD-ROM**
Exam*View*® *Test Generator*
PowerPoint® Slide #34
◆ **Transparency Package,** CT-34

◆ **Student Motivation Kit**
Reteaching Activities, p. 76
Enrichment Activities
Foods Lab Resources, pp. 11, 51–58
Food Science Resources, pp. 40–45, 62–65, 101–103
Skills for Making Food Choices, pp. 37–38

Sensory Changes in Cooked Vegetables and Fruits

In addition to nutrient loss, cooking results in changes to the texture, color, and flavor of vegetables and fruits.

- **Texture.** Heat softens the cell walls, making vegetables and fruits more tender. Many vegetables, such as green beans and winter squash, must be cooked to be edible. Starchy vegetables are easier to digest when cooked. If overcooked, vegetables and fruits become mushy.
- **Color.** When properly cooked, vegetables and fruits retain pleasing colors. Green vegetables get their color from **chlorophyll** (KLOR-uh-fil), the chemical compound that plants use to turn the sun's energy into food. If overcooked, green vegetables can turn an unpleasant olive green.
- **Flavor.** The heat of cooking releases flavors, making them more noticeable. Fruit flavors mellow somewhat and taste less acid. Herbs, spices, or other foods can be added during cooking, allowing their flavors to mingle with the natural flavor of the vegetable or fruit. When overcooked, vegetables and fruits lose their flavor or may develop an unpleasant flavor.

How can you prevent discoloration when cooking vegetables?

Adding a small amount of an acid food, such as vinegar or lemon juice to the cooking water, will stop red cabbage and beets from discoloring. To retain the color of green vegetables, steam them. If you boil them, don't add baking soda, as some people recommend. The chemical reaction that takes place destroys phytochemicals and other nutrients, and creates a mushy texture.

Cooking Fresh Vegetables

Fresh vegetables can be cooked by several different methods. The timing and method depend on the tenderness of the vegetable and the size of the pieces into which it has been cut.

Steaming Vegetables

Steaming is one of the most healthful ways to cook vegetables. Fewer precious nutrients are lost because the vegetables are not cooked in water. Because steaming takes a little longer than some other methods, be sure to build ample time into your meal preparation plan.

To steam vegetables, place a steamer basket in a saucepan with a tight-fitting lid. Add water to a depth just below the bottom of the steamer. Cover the pan and bring the water to a boil. Add the vegetables to the steamer basket and cover. Reduce the heat slightly, but not so much that the water stops boiling and producing steam. Steam the vegetables until tender.

Simmering Vegetables

Vegetables can be simmered in a covered pan in a small amount of water. Be sure to use a pan made of stainless steel, enamel, or glass. Do not use aluminum or copper. These minerals react with sulfur compounds in vegetables, resulting in a loss of vitamin C, folic acid, and vitamin E. They can also create unpleasant odors and flavors in foods.

Allow about ½ cup (125 mL) of water for four servings of vegetables. Pour the water into a medium-size saucepan, cover, and bring to

TEACH

- *Effects of Cooking on Vegetables and Fruits (text pages 428-429)*

Discussion Activity

Discuss with students the differences in texture, color, and flavor between a vegetable that is overcooked and one that has been cooked just long enough. Ask which of these properties individuals feel is the most important and why.

Recipe R & D

Divide students into pairs or small groups. Have them imagine they have been hired by a test kitchen to do research and development on recipes using the liquid left over from cooking vegetables or fruits. Groups are to find and modify existing recipes to use this liquid, or they may create new recipes. Groups are to write their recipes in standard format with a brief introduction explaining the nutritional importance of preserving cooking liquid. L3

VISUAL LEARNING *Using the Photograph*

Direct students to the photo of two pots of cooked vegetables on page 428. Ask: Which vegetables look more appealing? What could have been done to the other vegetables to improve their appearance? Discuss the adjectives that students choose to describe the vegetables in each pot.

Reinforcing Key Skills

Present the following problem to student groups. Allow time for them to discuss and compare their responses.

Resources—Latitia is preparing dinner for friends. The chicken dish she will be serving has just finished cooking when she remembers she forgot to boil the string beans she planned to serve alongside. Latitia is concerned that the chicken will dry out if she leaves it in the oven, but she can't serve raw beans. What would you advise her to do?

TEACH cont.

- *Cooking Fresh Vegetables (text pages 429-431)*

Recipe Comparisons

Have students locate recipes for preparing a single vegetable. Collect the recipes into a multi-page document. Give each student a copy, then ask all students to complete the following questions for discussion: By what methods may the vegetable be prepared? Which recipes retain the vegetable's natural nutritional advantages? Which recipes add fat to the vegetable? Which cooking methods require the longest cooking times? L2

Demonstration

Have students view a demonstration of cooking vegetables in the microwave oven. Review guidelines for using the microwave oven (Section 9-4) and discuss the advantages of microwave cooking.

Research Activity

Have students find a picture of a vegetable steamer in Chapter 9. Explain that you don't need a special steaming pot to enjoy the flavor and nutritional benefits of steamed vegetables. Have students find alternatives to steaming pots by searching the Internet (key words: "Steaming vegetables") or by speaking with local home cooks. Set aside class time to discuss these alternatives.

a boil. Add the vegetables, cover, and bring to a boil again. Then lower the heat until the water just simmers. Cook, covered, until vegetables are tender.

FOR YOUR HEALTH

Low-Fat Flavor Alternatives

Vegetables are naturally low in fat. Yet when butter, mayonnaise, cheese, or rich sauces are added, the fat content soars. Is it possible to add zip to vegetables without adding the fat grams? Here are some ways:

Instead of . . .	Try . . .
• Sour cream	• Plain, nonfat yogurt
• Mayonnaise or salad dressing	• Low-fat or fat-free dressing
• Butter or margarine	• Butter flavoring

You might also like to flavor vegetables with herbs or lemon juice. Try a flavored vinegar—ordinary vinegar that has been allowed to steep with fresh herbs or even fruit added to it.

Following Up

1. Examine the nutrition labels of sauces or toppings that you or people you know put on vegetables. How many grams of fat per serving does each contain? What percentage of your Daily Value for fat does this amount represent?
2. Experiment with flavored mustards and other lower-fat alternatives to dressing up vegetables. Write about your findings in your Wellness Journal.

Microwaving Vegetables

Microwaving cooks vegetables quickly using only a small amount of water. As a result, the vegetables lose few nutrients and keep their color, texture, and flavor.

Remember, larger pieces will take longer to cook than smaller ones. Keep in mind, too, that pieces the same size will cook more evenly. If parts of a vegetable are less tender than others—for example, the stems of broccoli and asparagus—arrange the tender parts toward the center and the less tender ones toward the edge of the baking dish.

When cooking whole vegetables that have a skin, such as potatoes or squash, pierce the skin with a fork. This will keep the vegetables from bursting. Always be sure to cover the container to keep in moisture. Follow the directions in the owner's manual or cooking guide for cooking times, power settings, and any special instructions.

Baking Vegetables

Vegetables with a high moisture content can bake in the dry heat of an oven. Vegetables of this type include winter squash, potatoes, and sweet potatoes.

Winter squash is usually cut in half, the seeds removed, and the halves placed on a baking sheet. Squash usually bakes at 350°F (180°C) for 30 minutes or longer, until it is tender. The time depends on the variety and size of the squash.

Potatoes baked in the skins are usually placed right on the oven rack. They can bake at any temperature between 300°F (150°C) and 450°F (230°C). The baking time will depend on the temperature. This flexibility in temperatures makes it possible to bake potatoes with other foods that need more exact temperatures. For example, you can bake muffins at 375°F (190°C) and still bake potatoes at the same time.

FOOD SCIENCE

Conventional Vs. Microwave Cooking

See the *Food Sciences Resources* booklet for the "Cooking Vegetables by Conventional and Microwave Cooking Methods" teaching guidelines and student experiment worksheet. This experiment compares the effects of both cooking method and time on the color, texture, and flavor of broccoli.

Sweet potatoes can also be baked with the skin on. Put them in a shallow pan in case juices begin to run out. They bake best at 400°F (200°C).

Pared whole vegetables such as carrots, onions, and potatoes can be baked in the same pan with a roast. This method adds fat to the vegetables, but it also browns them nicely and gives them a tasty crust.

Frying Vegetables

Some vegetables, including onion, garlic, celery, and sweet pepper, are sometimes chopped and sautéed before they are used in recipes. Sautéing brings out the flavor of the vegetables. Stir-frying and deep-frying are other popular methods of cooking. Except for potatoes, deep-fried vegetables are usually covered with a batter before frying.

Keep in mind that frying in even a small amount of oil adds fat and calories to vegetables. This is especially true when the vegetables are deep-fried.

◆ **Vegetables stir-fried with other foods use just a small amount of added fat.** **In a print or online source, learn about one different culture that makes use of stir-frying. Share your findings with the class.**

Connecting Food and Social Studies

Vegetables: A Bird's-Eye View

If the frozen food section of your supermarket sometimes feels as cold as the Arctic, perhaps that is no accident. Clarence Birdseye—the scientist without whose pioneering work there might be no frozen food—wouldn't have it any other way!

Birdseye was born in 1886 in Brooklyn, New York. Before graduating from college, he was offered a job as a biologist for the United States government. While on assignment to the Arctic, he discovered that the extreme cold temperatures would flash-freeze fish placed on the ice. When cooked later, the fish tasted almost the same as if it had been caught fresh. Birdseye went on to conduct further experiments. By 1930, he had perfected the freezing of vegetables, fruits, fish, and meats. Thus, the frozen food industry was born.

Think About It

- Using print or online resources, learn more about Birdseye's contributions to a related industry—the refrigerated shipping of foods. In a brief report, explain how refrigerated shipping has allowed us to enjoy fruits and vegetables once unknown to this part of the world.

- *Cooking Fresh Vegetables (text pages 429-431)*

Discussion Activity

Discuss the nutritional advantages of vegetables. What can cause normally low-fat vegetables to become high-fat items? How can vegetables be flavored without adding fat during cooking or at the table?

Finding Recipes

Have students look for recipes for baking or frying vegetables. Ask students to compare the recipes on the basis of added fats, cooking time, and nutritional value of the food after cooking. L2

Lab Experience

Divide the class into two sets of lab groups. One set of groups is to prepare the same fresh vegetable in several different ways. The other set of groups is to do the same thing with convenience forms of the vegetable. Groups are to note the following for the food they cook: cooking time, cost, and nutrition information, if available. Have the class reconvene for a taste test of the various preparations. Conclude with a class discussion of the results. L2

HOME & COMMUNITY CONNECTION

Ask students who have microwave ovens at home to check the owner's manual or other cooking references for instructions on cooking a baked potato. Students are to record this information, along with the oven's manufacturer and model number. (Students who do not have microwave ovens in their homes may consult manufacturers' Web sites or may visit an appliance dealer.) Have students note differences that they find from brand to brand. What conclusions can be drawn from this comparison?

TEACH cont.

- *Cooking Fresh Fruits (text pages 432-433)*

Cooking Show

Have a team of students stage a live cooking show.

They are to begin by posing the question asked in the first sentence under the heading "Fruit Sauces" to other students in the school.

Team members are then to extend invitations to interested students to attend a live cooking program in the class foods lab.

Group members are to assume roles. Some members are to design a stage set, others are to do preparatory work (setting up) in the lab, while still others write a script and prepare cue cards. One or two students are to serve as the TV chef(s) and prepare different fruit sauces. (Chefs are to try out the sauces in a test run before the show.)

If possible, videotape the show and air it on the school TV network. **L3**

Lab Experience

As an introduction to the portion of the text under the heading "Fruits Sauces," have students prepare homemade applesauce, with some students adding sugar before cooking the apples, others after the apples are cooked. Have the class compare the two sauces. What conclusions can they draw about when the sugar should be added? Have them explain their reactions. Then have them read the relevant portion of the text. **L2**

Cooking Fresh Fruits

Cooking fruits is a nice alternative for adding variety to your food choices. Cooked fruits can be served hot or chilled. They may be eaten as part of the main course, as dessert, or as a snack.

Like vegetables, fruits can be cooked by several different methods. These include poaching, turning them into a fruit sauce, baking, and microwaving.

Poaching Fruits

Poaching, or stewing, is the cooking of fruit in enough simmering liquid to cover it. The goal is to retain the shape of the fruit as it cooks.

Fruits that can be poached include plums, berries, apples, and pears. Small fruits, such as berries, are left whole. Apples and pears may be cooked whole or cut into large pieces.

Add sugar at the beginning of the process. The sugar is not just for sweetness but to help the fruit keep its shape during cooking by strengthening the cell walls. For more flavor, you can also add lemon or orange rind, a cinnamon stick, or vanilla. Simmer, uncovered, just until the fruit is tender.

Fruit Sauces

You have almost certainly eaten applesauce, but have you ever tried peach sauce, plum sauce, or pear sauce? All these fruits can be made into sauce. Different fruits can even be combined in a sauce to create tasty, new flavors.

Fruit sauces are made by cooking the fruit in a liquid. Unlike poaching, however, the goal when making a fruit sauce is to break down the texture. Sugar, therefore, is not added until after cooking.

To make a fruit sauce, pare the fruit and cut it into small pieces for faster cooking. Add water to a saucepan to a depth of about ¼ inch (0.6 cm), and place the fruit in the pan. Bring to a boil, lower the heat to simmer, and cover. Cook, stirring occasionally, until the fruit has broken down. The time will vary, depending on the kind of fruit and the size of the pieces. Sweeten as desired with sugar, honey, or syrup. Spices or other flavorings may also be added.

◆ **Poaching adds flavor to fruit while retaining the shape for an attractive presentation. Some contemporary chefs flavor fruits with pepper. Identify two other spices that might give fruits an interesting taste.**

ASSESSING PERFORMANCE OF THE COOKING SHOW

Instruct students who took part in the cooking show to devise a questionnaire to be filled out by audience members before they leave the foods lab. The questionnaire should ask audience members to rate the production in terms of its clarity, informational content, and overall enjoyment level. Group members are to use the ratings to launch a discussion on how they could improve this type of group effort in the future and what features they would retain.

Baking Fruits

When you bake fruits, you need to take care to avoid overcooking them. Best results are obtained with firm fruits—such as apples, pears, and bananas—that are whole or in large pieces.

Apples are probably the most popular baked fruit. They are easy to prepare and make a delicious ending to any meal. Use a variety of apples suited to cooking, such as Rome Beauty. Before cooking, core the apples, and cut a thin strip of skin from around the middle. This will allow the apples to expand as they cook, so that they won't burst. You can fill the cavity with raisins and sweet spices such as cinnamon and nutmeg. Place the apples in a baking dish and pour hot water around them to a depth of ¼ inch (0.6 cm). Bake at 350°F (180°C) until tender, about 45 to 60 minutes.

Microwaving Fruits

Fruits are easy to prepare in the microwave oven. They cook quickly and keep their fresh flavor and their shape. Because they are so tender, however, they can easily overcook. Watch the timing carefully.

Cover fruits when microwaving them, but leave a small opening for excess steam to escape. If you are cooking whole fruits, such as plums, pierce them with a fork in several places to keep them from bursting.

The basic steps in poaching, making a fruit sauce, and baking fruit are similar for microwave and conventional cooking. Power level and cooking time will vary, so check the owner's manual or a microwave cookbook.

Section 16-3 Review & Activities

1. Name three undesirable changes that can occur if vegetables or fruits are overcooked.
2. Explain in a step-by-step fashion two methods for cooking vegetables.
3. Choose one cooking method that is used for both vegetables and fruits. Identify similarities and differences in the method's application to the two types of produce.
4. What are some of the ways in which cooked fruits can be used?
5. **Analyzing.** How can a knowledge of the nutritional impact of cooking on vegetables and fruits benefit an individual shopping for produce?
6. **Synthesizing.** A saying popular in professional kitchens is that people "eat with their eyes." How does this saying apply to the cooking of fruits and vegetables?
7. **Applying.** Write an article for the food page of a newspaper. In your article, provide ideas for cooking vegetables that help retain nutrients, appearance, texture, and flavor. If your local newspaper has a food page, send the article to the paper.

ASSESS

REVIEW

- Ask students to summarize the main ideas in this section.
- Have students complete the Section Review. (Answers appear below.)

EVALUATION

- Have students make a list in their Wellness Journal of ways of using the information covered in this section to cook vegetables and fruits for family members at home. Encourage students to follow up with a description of the family's reaction. Which dishes did they like? What long-term changes in eating habits at home may result?
- Have students take the quiz for Section 16-3. (Use the quiz in the *Teacher Resource Guide,* or construct your own with the **ExamView**® *Test Generator* on the *Effective Instruction CD-ROM.*)

RETEACHING

- Have pairs of students gather recipes for vegetables and fruits. Ask the partners to classify the recipes according to cooking method.
- Refer to the *Reteaching Activities* booklet for the Section 16-3 activity sheet.

CLOSE

Remind students that cooking methods affect the look and flavor of cooked fruits and vegetables as well as the texture. Ask which vegetables and fruits they think are most difficult to cook. Explore different options for cooking these items.

Answers to Section 16-3 Review & Activities

1. They can become mushy, have an unpleasant color, and lose their flavor.
2. Answers can include any of the procedures described on pages 429-431.
3. Answers, which will vary, should be comprehensive.
4. They can be served hot or chilled and eaten as part of the main course, as dessert, or as a snack.
5. Answers will vary but should note the likelihood of making a more informed choice.
6. Answers will vary. Students should note the importance of the color of cooked fruits and vegetables.
7. Answers will vary.

Recipe File

Herbed Vegetable Combo

This recipe uses the cooking method of simmering vegetables. Prior to assigning the lab, you may wish to have students review the portion of the text under the heading "Simmering Vegetables" on pages 429-430.

USING THE RECIPE

- Have students read the recipe and make sure they understand each step as well as the entire process.
- Review safety and sanitation procedures that apply to this recipe.
- Have each lab team fill out a work plan. (See the *Foods Lab Resources* booklet.)
- Have students check off the ingredients and equipment listed on the recipe worksheet and prepare the recipe.
- Have students complete the evaluation and questions on the recipe worksheet.

SEE ALSO...
The *Foods Lab Resources* booklet for the "Herbed Vegetable Combo" recipe worksheet and other recipe alternatives.

Recipe File

Herbed Vegetable Combo

This quick and easy dish combines several colorful, nutritious vegetables of summer. If you like, experiment with other seasonings, such as basil or lemon juice.

Customary	*Ingredient*	*Metric*
2 Tbsp.	Water	30 mL
1 cup	Thinly sliced zucchini	250 mL
1 cup	Thinly sliced yellow summer squash	250 mL
½ cup	Green pepper strips	125 mL
¼ cup	Diced celery	50 mL
¼ cup	Chopped onion	50 mL
½ tsp.	Caraway seed	3 mL
⅛ tsp.	Garlic powder	0.5 mL
1 medium	Tomato, cut into wedges	1 medium

Yield: 4 servings
Equipment: Large nonstick skillet with cover

Directions

1. Heat water in skillet over medium heat.
2. Add vegetables. Cover and cook until vegetables are tender-crisp, about 4 minutes.
3. Sprinkle seasonings over vegetables. Top with tomato wedges.
4. Reduce heat to low. Cover and cook about 2 minutes, or just until tomato wedges are heated.
5. Serve hot.

Nutrition Information

Per serving (approximate): 24 calories, 1 g protein, 5 g carbohydrate, trace of fat, 0 mg cholesterol, 12 mg sodium
Good source of: vitamin C

Food for Thought

- How much time would you allow for pre-preparation tasks for this recipe?
- Why is this a healthful method for cooking vegetables?

Answers to ***Food for Thought***

1. Pre-preparation time would vary, depending on the cutting, slicing, and chopping skills of the cook. A professional chef could prepare the raw vegetables for cooking in about 5 minutes, and a skilled cook in less than 10. A less experienced cook should allow more time to complete these tasks.
2. Because it uses no added fat and cooks the vegetables only to tender-crisp. Nutrient loss is minimized.

Career Wanted

Wholesale Produce Buyer

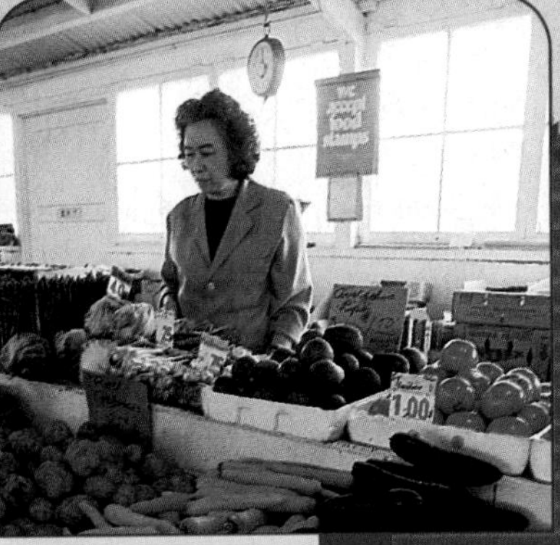

"I can get Hawaiian pineapples to people in Alaska."

Lian Yang

Education and Training

- Experience in sales or food industry
- Courses in business or economics
- Ability to use computer databases

Qualities

- Management skills
- Communication skills
- Flexibility

Q. Lian, where does a wholesaler fit in the food industry?

A. We're a main link in the distribution chain. We buy produce from the farm or processor and sell it to the retailer—the restaurant or supermarket, for example. Shipments from all over the world come and go on our docks.

Q. How do you keep track of everything and everyone?

A. Computers are our lifeline. I can contact sellers and buyers, compare prices, learn about auctions, and track shipments. Of course, we have our own Web site so people can find us. The job can be hectic. I sometimes feel like a juggler, with four balls in the air at once. That's why I'm proud of our reputation for getting buyers the quality food we promise, at a fair price and on time.

Q. What's the biggest issue faced by food wholesalers today?

A. As the market becomes increasingly global, we have more business opportunities but also more questions about food safety. We must also consider impacts on the environment and workers.

Related Career Opportunities

Entry Level

- Produce sorter
- Shipping clerk
- Salad maker

Technical Level

- Processing plant supervisor
- Sales representative

Professional Level

- Market analyst
- Produce farm manager
- Food packaging designer

Making Career Connections

CAREER INTERVIEW. Contact a wholesale food buyer or someone with this knowledge. Ask what affects produce availability. How is produce quality maintained in transit? What are a wholesaler's responsibilities to sellers and buyers? What are advantages and disadvantages of using a wholesaler? Write a paper describing a career in wholesale.

For More Information

For additional information about careers in wholesale buying and selling, encourage students to contact:

- Association of Sales & Marketing Companies
  1010 Wisconsin Ave., NW, Ninth Floor
  Washington, DC 20007
  www.asmc.org

Career Wanted

Wholesale Produce Buyer

Thinking About the Career

Read or paraphrase the following to students: Some cities, communities, and localities are noted for one particular type of commerce or industry. Learn whether the area you live in fits such a description, or—if you already know about local industry—investigate the flow of goods and services in this industry. Find out by interviewing a factory worker, executive, or other individual who works in the field. What aspect of work in this industry corresponds to being a wholesale buyer? What jobs are done by this individual? How does the job description compare and contrast with that of a wholesale grocery buyer?

Ask students to list other questions they might ask someone in Lian Yang's position about the nature of the job. (Examples: How many hours a week do you usually work? In what way is your job competitive? How much math do you need to know?)

Career-Building Opportunities

Choose one of the "Related Career Opportunities." Using help-wanted ads in your local newspaper or online resources, learn more about the relationship between these two careers. How does someone advance from an entry-level position to the next level? What skills beyond educational requirements are useful?

REVIEW

- Have students complete the Chapter Review. (Answers appear below.)

EVALUATION

- Divide the class into two teams. Each team is to brainstorm questions about Chapter 16. Then allow the teams to take turns asking each other questions. At the end of the questioning period, the team with the most correct answers wins.
- Have students take the test for Chapter 16. (Use the chapter test in the *Teacher Resource Guide,* or construct your own with the **Exam***View*® *Test Generator* on the *Effective Instruction CD-ROM.*)

ANSWERS

Checking Your Knowledge

1. Any three: bok choy, broccoli, brussel sprouts, cauliflower, collards, kale, kohlrabi, mustard greens, rutabagas, turnips and their greens; they contain carotene, which the body uses to make vitamin A.
2. They store a plant's food supply and send nutrients and moisture to the rest of the plant.
3. Prices are lower and quality is just as high.
4. To prevent transferring pesticides and dirt from skin to the edible parts.
5. When you want to prevent the fruit from turning brown after it has been cut.
6. In a tightly sealed plastic bag or on a plate covered with plastic; as much air as possible should be squeezed out to keep nutrients from being destroyed by oxygen.

Chapter 16 Review & Activities

Summary

Section 16-1: Choosing Vegetables and Fruits

- Vegetables and fruits are sources of nutrients vital to the body.
- Shop carefully for the best quality and value on in-season and year-round produce.
- Some fruits can be ripened after purchase.

Section 16-2: Preparing Raw Vegetables and Fruits

- Fresh produce should be washed just before use.
- To retain the most nutrients, keep paring and cutting to a minimum.
- Adding ascorbic acid (vitamin C) will prevent cut fruits from turning dark.

Section 16-3: Cooking Vegetables and Fruits

- Cooking affects the nutrient value, texture, color, and flavor of produce.
- Overcooking can result in discoloration and loss of texture, flavor, and nutrients.
- Fresh vegetables and fruits can be cooked in a variety of ways.
- Deep-frying vegetables adds fat and should be done sparingly.

Checking Your Knowledge

1. Give three examples of cruciferous vegetables. What is a possible health benefit of eating them?
2. Why are the roots in vegetables an excellent source of phytochemicals?
3. Why is it best to buy fresh produce in season?
4. Why is it important to wash produce, even if you are going to peel it before eating?
5. Under what circumstances might you buy ascorbic acid powder, mix it with water, and sprinkle it on fruit?
6. How should cut produce be stored?
7. How can you minimize vitamin C loss when cooking vegetables and fruits?
8. Explain the process of simmering vegetables.
9. Give three suggestions for microwaving vegetables.
10. What characteristic makes some fruits better for baking than others?

Working IN THE Lab

1. ***Food Science.*** Select two similar potatoes. Store one in a cool, dry, dark place. Store the other in the refrigerator. After at least one week, bake the potatoes. Compare their taste and texture. What caused the difference?
2. ***Food Science.*** Based on what you know about the effects of lemon juice on cut fruit, make a prediction about the action of other juices on cut fruits. Test it by conducting a brief experiment. Was your prediction correct? Why or why not?
3. ***Food Preparation.*** Select any vegetable or fruit, and prepare it using three of the methods detailed in the chapter. Compare the results for appearance, taste, texture, and convenience. Identify when you might want to use each method.

Review & Activities Chapter 16

Thinking Critically

1. Distinguishing Between Fact and Opinion. While out with three friends, Nadine revealed her plan to eat only fruit from now on. Each friend had a different response, as follows: (a) "Eating that much fruit would be boring." (b) "Fruits have a lot of nutrients, but they don't have all the nutrients you need." (c) "Out-of-season fruits taste awful." Evaluate each response. For any that are opinion, restate the same or a similar idea in a way that gives factual information.

2. Determining Credibility. While standing in the supermarket checkout line, Margot notices a tabloid headline that states, "New Scientific Study Shows Eating Fried Vegetables Reduces Disease Risks." Next to this article is a story about a woman who claims she is married to a Martian. What would you advise Margot about the reliability of the article on fried vegetables? Why? How could she find out more about the study mentioned in the headline?

Reinforcing Key Skills

1. Directed Thinking. Rae's supermarket has just expanded its produce section. Before Rae fills her shopping cart with exotic produce, what questions should she ask the produce clerk? What questions should she ask herself about the storage capabilities of her home pantry?

2. Management. Elio is preparing the family meal tonight. He plans to include a tossed salad along with the main course, and assorted fresh fruit for dessert. Before you could advise Elio about meal preparation plans, what other information about the fruit would you need to have? About the meal as a whole?

Making Decisions and Solving Problems

Adam understands the health benefits of eating two to four servings of fruits each day, but he has a small appetite. By the time he has finished his sandwich at lunch or main course at dinner, he is often too full to eat fruit. What could Adam do?

Making Connections

1. Math. By using newspaper ads or visiting a local supermarket, compare the per-serving costs of fresh, frozen, and canned versions of a specific fruit or vegetable. Use package labels or cookbooks to compare the preparation time for each form. Show your findings with two bar graphs: one for price and one for preparation time.

2. Social Studies. Using cookbooks, food magazines, or online sources, learn about a vegetable or fruit widely used in another culture. In that culture, how is the vegetable or fruit purchased and stored? Is it eaten raw or cooked? What methods are used in its preparation? Share your findings with the class in the form of an illustrated report.

ANSWERS cont.

7. By keeping them whole or in large pieces; cooking them quickly using methods that require only a small amount of water; and serving the cooking liquid whenever possible.
8. Allow about ½ cup (125 mL) of water for four servings; pour the water into a medium-size saucepan, cover, and bring to a boil; add the vegetables, cover, and bring to a boil again, then lower the heat until the water just simmers; cook, covered, until vegetables are tender.
9. Any three: cut pieces small and in equal sizes; arrange the tender parts toward the center and the less tender ones toward the edge of the baking dish; pierce the skin with a fork; cover the container to keep in moisture.
10. Firm fruits, cooked whole or in large pieces, give the best results.

Thinking Critically

1. Response B is factual, while responses A and C are opinion. Restatements: (for A) If you eat too much of the same fruit, it can become boring, which is why variety is emphasized in the *Dietary Guidelines for Americans.* (for C) When fruits are purchased out of season, they often must be shipped from alternative points of origin from where they are usually derived and, therefore, may taste unusual. Therefore, choosing produce in season makes sense.
2. It is probably unreliable because of the sensationalistic headline that appears on the same page. She could consult reputable print or online resources.

Reinforcing Key Skills

1. Answers will vary but might include knowing which kinds of fruits she plans to serve since this will determine when they should be cut and/or whether she should use an ascorbic acid source to retard enzymatic browning.
2. Answers will vary. One possibility would be making fruit sauce.

CHAPTER

17

Grains, Legumes, Nuts, and Seeds

Advance Planning Guide ☑

- Purchase a variety of grains, legumes, nuts, and seeds for various activities throughout Chapter 17.
- Prepare small bowls containing different varieties of uncooked grain.
- Prepare a variety of simple grain products for students to taste.
- Purchase a variety of packaged grain products that include preparation instructions.
- Purchase various types of rice; obtain directions for preparing them and prepare.
- Purchase six packages of breakfast cereal—three that are high in fiber and three that are not.
- Purchase regular, quick-cooking, and instant oatmeal.
- Purchase five types of dry legumes and a few cans of beans; bring legume package labels and bean cans to class.
- Purchase ingredients for the Recipe File on page 458.

CHAPTER

17

Grains, Legumes, Nuts, and Seeds

Among the earliest crops raised by humans for food, grains remain a staple in many cultures around the world. In this chapter, you will learn about choosing and using grains in a healthful eating plan.

MEETING DIVERSE NEEDS

Celebrating Cultural Diversity. If there are students in the class who came from other countries, ask them to bring to class or, if possible, prepare grain-, legume-, nut-, or seed-based dishes that are native to their culture. As an alternative, these students might simply share recipes for these specialties. In this case, have students compile their recipes and provide copies to all students.

SECTION
17-1

Choosing Grains and Grain Products

Grains have been the most important staple in the world's food supply for thousands of years. How many grains and grain products do you eat? How many can you name? After reading this section, you may become familiar with some different grains and grain products.

Objectives

After studying this section, you should be able to:

- Describe the nutrients in grains and grain products.
- Identify different grain products and their uses.
- Give guidelines for buying and storing grain products.

Look for These Terms

germ
endosperm
bran
whole grain
enrichment
fortification

What Are Grains?

Grains are the seeds of plants in the grass family. Common grains in North America include wheat, rice, corn, buckwheat, oats, rye, triticale (trih-tih-KAY-lee), barley, and millet.

Every seed, or kernel, of grain is composed of three main parts:

◆ **The germ.** The **germ** is a tiny embryo in a seed that will grow into a new plant.

◆ **The endosperm.** The **endosperm** is the food supply for a seed's embryo, made up of proteins, starches, and other nutrients. It takes up most of the inner part of the grain.

◆ **All three parts of the grain kernel are nutritious. What is the function of each part?**

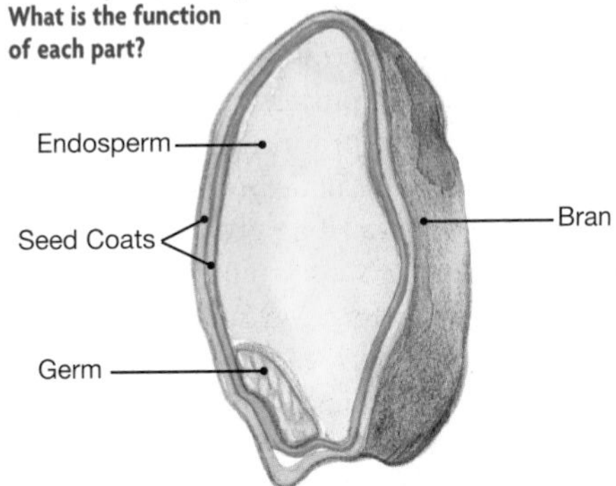

◆ **The bran.** The **bran** is the edible, outer protective layers of a seed.

SECTION
17-1
Choosing Grains and Grain Products

FOCUS

MOTIVATORS

- Pass around small bowls containing different varieties of uncooked grain for students to identify by sight and touch. Ask students to identify the grains and name products made from them. Discuss ways grains were prepared by early peoples. Identify modern methods of preparing grains.
- Have students taste-test a variety of simply-prepared grain products. Which have students eaten before? Which do they think are most and least nutritious? Why?

VOCABULARY ACTIVITY

Pronounce the terms listed under "Look for These Terms." Have students find the terms and their definitions in the section.

STUDY SKILLS

- **Note Taking.** Have students read the section independently. While they are reading, they are to take notes on the important concepts discussed within the section.
- Have students read the section and complete the appropriate part of the Chapter 17 Study Guide in the *Student Workbook*.

Section 17-1 Resources

◆ **Student Workbook,** pp. 123, 125
◆ **Teacher Resource Guide**
Lesson Plan 17-1 Organizer
Section 17-1 Quiz
◆ **Effective Instruction CD-ROM**
Exam*View*® *Test Generator*
PowerPoint® Slides #35–37
◆ **Transparency Package,** CT-35–37
◆ **Student Motivation Kit**
Reteaching Activities, pp. 77–78
Enrichment Activities
Skills for Making Food Choices, pp. 39–40

TEACH

- *What Are Grains?*
- *Nutrients in Grains (text pages 439-440)*

Listing Activity

Ask students to write down the definition of *grains* and list several grains that they have eaten. Have students exchange lists. Ask: Are there any grains listed that you have never tried? That you have never heard of?

Fact Identification Quiz

Write on the board a number of boldfaced terms and headings from the section (for example, *fortified, long-grain, short-grain*). Point out to students that these terms are commonplace, yet a mystery to the vast majority of people who eat them on a regular basis. Have students demonstrate this point for themselves by creating a short quiz, either true-false or some other format, on grain facts. They are to administer the quiz to individuals in their family and community and report the findings. What are some ways of making these important facts better known? L1

Categorizing

Bring a variety of packaged grain products to class. Have the students classify the products into two groups: whole-grain and processed. Discuss reasons for choosing one type of product over another. Ask: What are some ways of maximizing the nutrient benefits of a grain food that is processed? L1

Nutrients in Grains

Grains get a lot of attention in health news because they are naturally packed with nutrients. The endosperm is high in complex carbohydrates and proteins, with just a small amount of vitamins and minerals. The bran is rich in fiber, B vitamins, and some trace minerals. The germ provides B vitamins, vitamin E, iron, zinc, and other trace minerals; some protein; and a small amount of saturated fat.

Grain Processing

Before consumers can use them, all grains must be processed. This begins with the removal of the outer husk, a natural fibrous material, which exposes the kernel. What happens from that point on will affect the nutrient value of the grain or grain product.

When the **whole grain**—the entire edible grain kernel—is used, the resulting product contains most of the kernel's original nutrients. Examples of whole-grain products are whole wheat flour and whole-grain breakfast cereals.

Very often, the bran and germ are removed during processing—along with the grain's fiber and many of its nutrients. White flour and many breakfast cereals are products made in this fashion. Usually, these products undergo **enrichment**, a process in which some nutrients lost as a result of processing are added back to the product to near original levels. Some products may also undergo **fortification**, a process of adding 10 percent or more of the Daily Value for a specific nutrient to a product by the manufacturer. Most fortified foods supply about 25 percent of the Daily Value for one or more nutrients. Some have 100 percent of many nutrients.

The Food Guide Pyramid recommends eating 6 to 11 daily servings of enriched or whole grains and grain products. Typical servings include one slice of bread; ½ cup (125 mL) cooked cereal, rice, or pasta; or 1 ounce (30 g) of ready-to-eat cereal.

INFOLINK

For more about the benefits of including fiber in your eating plan, see Section 2-2. For more on Daily Value (DV) and how to use this important information to improve your eating habits, see Section 12-2.

◆ Enriching grain products restores some of the nutrients lost in processing. Explain fortification.

Reinforcing Key Skills

Present the following problem to student groups. Allow time for them to discuss and compare their responses.

Communication—A grandparent or other older adult has joined your family for dinner. When offered brown rice, the person declines, noting that as a youth he or she was always told that the whiter a grain product is, the better it is for you. How do you respond to this?

Buying Grains and Grain Products

When you buy grains and grain products, keep nutrition in mind. Choose whole-grain products as much as possible. Aim for at least three of your grain servings from whole grains each day. If a product you choose does not provide whole grains, be sure it is enriched. Look for products low in fat, added sugar, and sodium, too. Try different grains for variety.

When buying, read the labels to make certain you get the product you want. If the grain is visible in the package, inspect it carefully to be sure you are getting good quality. Pasta, for example, should not appear to be cracked or broken.

Which grains should you buy? That's a matter of personal taste, as well as knowing what's available.

Rice

Several different varieties of rice are grown. You can choose rice with short, medium, or long grains.

- **Short grains.** The grains are almost round. When cooked, the rice is moist and the grains stick together. Short-grain rice is a good choice for creamy dishes and for molded rice rings, or if you plan to eat with chopsticks.

◆ **The type of rice you choose may depend on how you plan to use it. What else would you consider when buying rice?**

Connecting Food and Social Studies

Graham for Graham

The ideas that we should eat a variety of foods and that different foods provide different nutrients may seem new. However, these ideas can be traced back at least 150 years —to an American religious leader by the name of Sylvester Graham.

Graham was an early supporter of whole wheat bread. However, he felt that the whole wheat flour sold commercially at the time was not "pure" enough. Graham came up with his own recipe for a coarsely ground wheat flour, which he called "Graham flour." Graham used his flour in a special flat bread, which he served to the guests of Graham boarding houses. These were health clinics located throughout the country in the early 1800s. Whether the bread relieved stomach pains, as Graham claimed, most people who tasted it fell in love with it. Today, we know Graham's invention better as the graham cracker.

Think About It

- Using library or online resources, research two other nineteenth-century "health food" pioneers—Dr. John Henry Kellogg and Dr. Charles Post. In a brief report, identify how the two men (who knew each other) were connected and what food innovations each was responsible for.

- *Buying Grains and Grain Products (text pages 441-445)*

Art

Have students draw diagrams of different types of grains and identify the parts of each. Have students share their diagrams with the class. Then moderate a student discussion on why it is beneficial to eat the whole grain products drawn in many of the students' diagrams? L1

Independent Research

Ask students to select one of the grains mentioned in the lesson or in discussion that they have never heard of and/or sampled. Students are to investigate that grain, noting where it is grown, its nutrient content, and how it is processed and used. Have select students share their reports with the class. L2

USING CONNECTING FOOD AND SOCIAL STUDIES

Ask students to bring in a copy of an original or cookbook recipe using Graham flour or Graham crackers. Make sure they record the source of the recipe, if it's not original. Compile all recipes into a "Graham Cookbook."

HOME & COMMUNITY CONNECTION

Ask students to identify and list all the types of grains and grain products available in their kitchen storage cabinets. Next to each type, have students list at least one way each grain or grain product can be used. Have students bring their lists to class. Have two students create a master list of all the grains and grain products and their uses. Copies can then be given to all students to share with their families for more variety with grain preparation.

TEACH cont.

- *Buying Grains and Grain Products (text pages 441-445)*

Display

Ask students to bring to class the food label (with Nutrition Facts panel) of one grain or grain product that they use at home. Have students work as a group to arrange the packages on a table or other classroom surface in descending order of fiber content per serving. Discuss the differences in flavor, mode of preparation, and other nutrient values of the various foods. Urge students to present the findings in a database, chart, or other useful form. L1

Taste Test

Show students raw and cooked examples of long-grain, medium-grain, and short-grain rice, both white and brown. What visual differences can students find? Have students compare the taste and texture of the cooked rice. If possible, supply wooden chopsticks to have a student demonstrate the use of them when eating short-grain rice in Asian meals.

Direction Comparisons

Provide students with directions for preparing brown rice, white rice, converted rice, and instant rice. Have students compare directions for preparing each. What are the main differences? Why are there differences? L2

◆ **Oats are a versatile grain. Rolled oats, the basis of oatmeal, can also be used in baked goods, meat loaf, and other recipes.** In what other forms are oats sold?

- **Medium grains.** The grains are plump, tender, and moist. They stick together, but not as much as short-grain rice.
- **Long grains.** When cooked, the grains are fluffy and stay separated.

Rice can vary in the way it is processed. *Brown rice* is the whole-grain form of rice. Only the outer, inedible hull has been removed; the bran, endosperm, and germ still remain. *White rice* has had the bran and germ removed. *Converted rice* has been parboiled (briefly boiled) to save nutrients before the hull is removed. *Instant rice* has been precooked and dehydrated. It takes only a few minutes to prepare.

The fiber content of rice also varies—mostly as a result of the removal of the bran for white rice. The fiber content of brown rice is about three times higher than that of white rice.

How does wild rice fit in with the other types of rice? It's actually the seed of water grass, not a grain at all.

Other Grains

In addition to rice, many other types of grains can be creatively cooked and served as side dishes. Cooked grains are also popular as hot breakfast cereals. Some can be used in baking or other recipes. Here are some types of grains you may have eaten or may want to try:

- **Barley.** Mild-flavored, hardy grain. Usually used in soups and stews.
- **Brans.** The ground bran of oat, rice, or wheat can be purchased to use as a hot cereal or in baking. All are high in fiber. For instance, 1 ounce (30 g) of wheat bran has about 13 grams of fiber.
- **Bulgur.** Wheat kernels that have been steamed, dried, and crushed. Tender with a chewy texture. Used in main dishes, salads, and as a side dish. A popular use for bulgur is in tabbouleh, a Middle Eastern salad flavored with mint and parsley.

FOOD SCIENCE

Converted Rice

Converted rice retains more nutrients than other types of rice, although it takes longer to cook. When a food is parboiled, it is cooked partially by boiling for a brief period of time. When rice is parboiled, the intense heat drives the nutrients from the hull and the bran into the endosperm, so that they remain in the rice when the hull and bran are removed.

- **Cornmeal.** Coarsely ground dried corn. Available in yellow or white types. Used as a breakfast cereal and in baked goods.
- **Couscous** (KOOS-koos). Steamed, cracked endosperm of wheat kernel. Has a nutty flavor. Used as a cereal, in salads and main dishes, or sweetened for dessert.
- **Cracked wheat.** Crushed wheat berries with a very tough and chewy texture. Often added to bread.
- **Grits.** Coarsely ground endosperm of corn. Used as a breakfast cereal or side dish.
- **Kasha** (KAH-shuh). Roasted buckwheat that is hulled and crushed. Has a pleasant, nutty flavor. Used as a breakfast cereal or side dish.
- **Millet.** Small, yellow grains with a mild flavor. A staple in Europe, Asia, and northern Africa. Used in breads and as a breakfast cereal or side dish.
- **Oats.** Often eaten as a hot cereal or used in baked goods. Quick-cooking types are available.
- **Quinoa** (KEEN-wah). A small, ivory-colored, ricelike grain, quinoa cooks much faster than rice and is an excellent source of protein—higher than any other grain. Its neutral flavor makes it a perfect addition to side dishes, soups, meat loafs, and more.
- **Triticale** (trih-tuh-KAY-lee). A cross between wheat and rye, with more protein than wheat. Can be used in cereals and main dishes and combined with other cooked grains.
- **Wheat berries.** Whole, unprocessed wheat kernels. Can be cooked as a cereal or used in grain-based dishes.

Ready-to-Eat and Instant Cereals

Breakfast cereals are among the largest-selling foods in the United States. Each year Americans spend close to $1 billion on these products.

Besides tasting good, dry breakfast cereals can fit into a healthful eating plan. Just read the "Nutrition Facts" label on the box or bag to make sure you know what you're buying. Look for a product that is high in complex carbohydrates and fiber. It's not necessary for a cereal to provide 100 percent of the nutrients you need in a day. In fact, you can get a nutritious product often at a lower cost by buying cereals that are not highly fortified.

When eating a breakfast cereal in milk, keep in mind that some vitamins and minerals were added in the form of sprays and thus will dissolve in the milk. These nutrients are not lost as long as you finish the milk in the bowl along with the cereal.

Another ready-to-eat grain product is wheat germ. It has a pleasant, nutty flavor and is an excellent source of protein, vitamins, and minerals, along with a small amount of unsaturated fat. It also is a good source of fiber—more than 4 grams of fiber per ounce. Wheat germ can be added to yogurt, cereals, and other foods for a nutritional boost, and for extra crunch.

Some of the hot cereals already described, such as oats and grits, are also available in instant forms. Cooking time is shorter. Often sugar and other flavorings have been added.

- *Buying Grains and Grain Products (text pages 441-445)*

Finding Recipes

Using library or online cooking resources, have students find a recipe or recipe idea that uses cereals or other grains in an interesting way or a way that's new to them. Have students share recipes or recipe ideas. **L2**

Research and Poster Presentation

Divide students into pairs. Assign each pair one of the grains listed on pages 442-443. Ask pairs to research and prepare a grain poster for their assigned grain. Each poster should include: (1) the name of the grain; (2) different types, if applicable; (3) origin; (4) where it's grown today; (5) uses; (6) uncooked sample; and (7) any other interesting facts (including popular misconceptions). Display all posters in a prominent location where all students can benefit during coverage of the chapter. **L2**

DID You Know?

- Technically, couscous is a form of pasta, not a grain.
- Maize is the only grain that originated in America; the others were developed in Europe, Asia, and Africa.
- The word *cereal* is derived from Ceres, the Roman goddess of grains and agriculture.

Extending Learning

Quinoa—A staple food of the Incas in ancient times, quinoa (KEEN-wah) was called "the mother grain." Although it has been around for a long time, quinoa is relatively new to many Americans. It is a unique grain since it appears to be a complete protein. Quinoa is rice-like since it is prepared similarly to rice and can be used in place of rice, but it takes about half the time to prepare and expands more than regular rice. In fact, quinoa expands to nearly four times its original size.

- *Buying Grains and Grain Products (text pages 441-445)*

Store Survey

Have students survey the cereal section of a grocery store to compare regular, quick-cooking, and instant hot cereals and ready-to-eat cereals, completing a checklist that includes the following questions:

- Which are most and least expensive per serving?
- Which are most and least nutritious?
- Which contain the most fiber?
- Which are high in fat, sugar, and sodium?

Ask students to note the location of sugar-added cereals on the grocery shelves. What conclusions can they draw? (Reminder: "Sugar" on the Nutrition Facts panel refers to all sugars, including sugar naturally found in dried fruits and milk.) L1

USING THE Food Science LAB

Ask students to conduct the Food Science Lab on a parent or older adult. In class, ask students: Are the conclusions the same or different from those arrived at by students? If so, how, and to what factors do students ascribe the difference?

Connecting Fiber and Flavor in Cereals

Some people believe that high-fiber, whole-grain cereals may not be as tasty as low-fiber cereals made from processed grains. Is this always the case?

Procedure

1. Blindfold a classmate for a blind taste test.
2. Pour out ¼-cup (50-mL) portions of three cereals that are high in fiber (at least 5 grams of fiber per serving) and three that are not (2 grams of fiber or less per serving).
3. Have your subject taste each sample and record his or her reactions. Products are to be assigned a rating of 1 or 2, where 2 is high-fiber and 1 is low-fiber.
4. Compare the ratings for each cereal with the actual fiber content on the Nutrition Facts panel for the product.

Conclusions

- How did your subject's rankings compare with the actual fiber content of each cereal?
- How can this information help in your future purchases of cereal?
- How does cost correlate with flavor or fiber content?

Pasta

Did you know that *pasta* is the Italian word for "paste"? Like paste, pasta dough is made from flour and water. After it is rolled thin, pasta dough can be formed into hundreds of different shapes. Examples include spaghetti, corkscrews, bow ties, and macaroni.

Both enriched and whole wheat pastas are available. Whole wheat pasta has almost three times as much fiber as traditional, enriched pasta. Some pastas are flavored and colored with carrots, spinach, tomatoes, or other foods. Noodles are pasta made with eggs. Noodles can also be made without egg yolks, which makes them lower in fat and cholesterol than regular noodles.

Packages of dried pasta are found in the grocery section with other shelf-stable foods. You may find fresh pasta in the refrigerated section.

Choosing pasta can be fun. Selecting a variety of pasta shapes and sizes can add appeal to many meals.

For more about creating **meal appeal**, see Section 11-1.

Reinforcing Key Skills

Present the following problems to student groups. Allow time for them to discuss and compare their responses.

Management—Dave likes sweet-tasting cereal in the morning, but there's none left. All that's available is a hi-fiber bran cereal with no added sugar. What recommendation might Dave's parent make?

Leadership—What would you tell a young child who refuses to finish the milk leftover in his or her cereal bowl?

◆ **Pasta comes in an almost endless variety of shapes and colors.** What ingredient do you think gives green pasta its color?

Breads

Breads range from enriched white bread to whole wheat and mixed whole grains. They come in assorted flavors, shapes, and sizes, including individual rolls.

Leavened (LEV-uhnd) breads are made with a leavening ingredient, such as yeast or baking powder, which causes the bread to rise. Unleavened, or flat, breads, like tortillas, are made without leavenings. Pita bread is a flat bread that can be split horizontally to make a pocket and then filled with a variety of foods.

When buying bread, read the label carefully. *Whole wheat* means the product is made from the whole grain. If only the word *wheat* is used, it usually means some part of the grain has been removed, or unbleached white flour has been used. Some dark breads are made with white flour with caramel or molasses added for color.

Storing Grains and Grain Products

To maintain the quality of grains and grain products, follow these storage guidelines:

- Store whole grains and whole-grain products in the refrigerator if you plan to store them for a couple of weeks or more. Because they contain oil, they can spoil at room temperature if not used quickly.
- Refrigerate fresh pasta.
- Store other uncooked grains and grain products, such as white rice and dried pasta, in a cool, dry place in tightly covered containers.
- Store breads at room temperature for short-term storage. Otherwise, freeze them. Hard-crusted bread gets stale faster when refrigerated. However, in humid weather, refrigerate bread to prevent mold from growing.
- Store cooked grains in the refrigerator if they will be used within a few days. For longer storage, freeze.

- *Buying Grains and Grain Products*
- *Storing Grains and Grain Products (text pages 441-446)*

VISUAL LEARNING ***Using the Photograph*** To demonstrate the variety of pasta shapes, ask students to bring in a single sample of dried pasta. Provide students with a large colored poster board and glue to create a chart of all the different shapes of pasta with the pasta names underneath each shape. Ask: Which pasta could you use to dress up a plate of roasted chicken?

Pasta Timeline

Have students research the origins and spread of pasta as a food. Have them convert their findings into a timeline that shows when this food was first introduced into the United States. Students are to annotate their timelines with facts about pasta consumption in selected years. L2

Student Presentation

Ask students to bring to class a sample of one piece of bread, any type. Have each student show the class their bread, name the type (including whether it's "wheat" or "whole wheat"), state how they like to use it in meals, and how it is best stored. L1

Extending Learning

Wheat Gluten—People following vegetarian eating plans find the use of wheat gluten helpful as a protein-rich alternative to meat. The most common food made from wheat gluten is seitan. Found in the refrigerated section of health food stores, Asian markets, and other specialty food stores, seitan is meatlike, providing a mild flavor and chewy texture. It's often used as an ingredient in place of ground or chopped chicken, turkey, or meat.

ASSESS

REVIEW

- Ask students to summarize the main ideas in this section.
- Have students complete the Section Review. (Answers appear below.)

EVALUATION

- Have students each create a list of at least ten grains or grain products. Next to each, they are to note the nutrients contained in that food.
- Have students take the quiz for Section 17-1. (Use the quiz in the *Teacher Resource Guide,* or construct your own with the **Exam***View*® *Test Generator* on the *Effective Instruction CD-ROM.*)

RETEACHING

- Tape or glue samples of various types of grains to the front of separate index cards. On the back of each card, write the name of the grain. Have students work in pairs to drill each other on the names of the grains.
- Refer to the *Reteaching Activities* booklet for the Section 17-1 activity sheet.

CLOSE

Refer to the grain taste test (the second motivator activity for this section). Have students reevaluate their answers. Now which grains do they think are most and least nutritious?

Q ***How can I add whole-grain products to my diet?***

A Asking this question shows you value the healthfulness and good taste of whole grains. Try these ideas. Make toast with heavy whole-wheat bread. Replace some of the white flour in recipes with whole-wheat flour. In supermarkets, look for pasta packages marked "whole wheat." Choose air-popped popcorn for a good crunchy snack. Try oven-toasted oats instead of nuts in baked goods. Add two or three spoons of oats to vanilla yogurt and top with sliced fruit and a little chocolate syrup for a great snack or dessert. Add wheat germ to cookie recipes, and use it as part of the crumb topping on a casserole. Substitute barley or brown rice for white rice in your recipes, remembering to increase the cooking time. Be open to ethnic foods. Bulgur, for instance, is popular in Mediterranean cooking. By sharing ideas like these with others, you can expand your whole-grain horizons even more.

◆ **Breads can be either leavened or unleavened. What is the difference?**

Section 17-1 Review & Activities

1. Identify the three parts of a grain kernel and the nutrients found in each.
2. Name four grains that can be cooked and eaten as side dishes.
3. What should you look for when choosing a nutritious ready-to-eat cereal?
4. **Synthesizing.** One teen typically limits grain foods in her diet to white bread, white rice, and pasta made with white flour. What health consequences may she be at risk for later in life as a result of her choices?
5. **Analyzing.** What qualities have made grain products so popular around the world?
6. **Applying.** Find three recipes that use different grains or grain products. Make a chart that identifies the grains and describes their nutritional value.

Answers to Section 17-1 Review & Activities

1. See pages 439-440.
2. See bulleted list on pages 442-443.
3. Cereals that are high in complex carbohydrates and fiber.
4. Answers will vary. These highly processed foods lack some nutrients and fiber found in whole grains. She may be at higher risk for some cancers, heart and digestive diseases.
5. Answers may include: they are inexpensive, widely available, easily prepared and stored, and nutritious.
6. Recipes and answers will vary.

SECTION 17-2

Preparing Grains and Grain Products

Objectives

After studying this section, you should be able to:

- Explain the general principles of cooking grains.
- Describe how to prepare rice and other grains, pasta, and breakfast cereals.

Look for This Term

al dente

Properly prepared, grains can be a nutritious, flavorful part of any meal, from breakfast to dinner. You can serve them plain or top them with vegetables, seasonings, and sauces. You can even serve some as desserts by adding sweeteners or fruits.

Principles of Cooking Grains

Because they are dry, grains need to be prepared in liquid—usually plain or salted water. Many grains can also be simmered in broth or stock. Even though most grains are cooked in a similar way, cooking methods and times vary. Always follow package or recipe directions.

Unless package directions state otherwise, do not rinse enriched grains prior to cooking. Rinsing can cause a loss of added B vitamins.

Microwaving grains is not always practical. Because grains need time to absorb liquid to soften, microwaving does not usually save time. Pasta, for instance, takes just as long in the microwave as it does to cook conventionally. Nevertheless, go ahead and check the package for microwave directions.

◆ **Biryani—a delicious blend from India of basmati rice, meats, raisins, nuts—is a healthful way of satisfying several nutrient requirements. Consult cookbooks or online resources for other rice-based one-dish meals. Share your findings with the class.**

Section 17-2 Resources

◆ **Student Workbook,** pp. 124, 127
◆ **Teacher Resource Guide**
Lesson Plan 17-2 Organizer
Section 17-2 Quiz
◆ **Effective Instruction CD-ROM**
Exam*View*® *Test Generator*

◆ **Student Motivation Kit**
Reteaching Activities, p. 79
Enrichment Activities
Foods Lab Resources, pp. 59–68
Food Science Resources, pp. 108–109

SECTION 17-2

Preparing Grains and Grain Products

FOCUS

MOTIVATORS

- Have student groups prepare and taste test grains with which they are not familiar, such as grits, hominy, barley, kasha, millet, quinoa, and amaranth. How do the taste and texture of these grains compare with those of more familiar varieties?
- Have students compare the package directions for preparing several different grain products. Ask students to develop a set of general principles that would apply to most grain products.

VOCABULARY ACTIVITY

Pronounce the term listed under “Look for This Term.” Have students find the term and its definition in the section. Point out that the term *al dente* is Italian and means "to the tooth."

STUDY SKILLS

- **Guided Reading.** Have students look at the headings within Section 17-2 to preview the concepts that will be discussed.
- Have students read the section and complete the appropriate part of the Chapter 17 Study Guide in the *Student Workbook*.

TEACH

- *Principles of Cooking Grains*
- *Preparing Rice and Other Grains (text pages 447-448)*

Discussion Activity

Ask students to explain why microwaving grains is not a timesaving technique. Ask students to explain why long-grain rice should be stirred only if necessary while cooking.

Meal Planning

Assign a grain type to students and ask them to plan an entire, well-balanced meal around it. Discuss foods they would include to round out their protein needs. Would the meal include meat? Would it need to? **L2**

Finding Recipes

Have students find recipes that use rice and other grains. Classify the dishes as main dishes, side dishes, and desserts. Discuss with students how different grains or grain products are associated with ethnic foods or specific cultures or countries. **L1**

Preparing Rice and Other Grains

Rice is usually simmered, using just the amount of liquid that the grain can absorb. Bring the liquid to a boil, add the rice, cover, and bring to a boil again. Then reduce the heat so the rice simmers gently.

Package directions may tell you to stir the rice at intervals as it cooks. Do not stir long-grain rice unless necessary. Stirring can scrape off starch, making the grains stick together.

Near the end of cooking time, check the rice for doneness. It should be moist and tender but firm. There should be no liquid left in the pot. If any liquid remains, continue cooking without the cover until the excess liquid is absorbed or evaporates. Instant rice requires a slightly different cooking method. Follow package directions.

Barley, grits, kasha, and many other grains are cooked in much the same way. One that is not is bulgur, which is "cooked" by pouring boiling water over the dry grain and letting it stand 30 minutes.

Preparing Pasta

Unlike rice and some other grains, pasta is cooked uncovered in a large amount of boiling water. Pasta is one of very few foods that must be boiled. The boiling helps circulate the pasta so that it cooks evenly.

Check the package for the amount of water to use. With dry spaghetti, for example, use about 1 quart (1 L) of water for every 4 ounces (120 g) of spaghetti. Be sure the pot is large enough for the amount of water used and the boiling action of the water.

Grain Measurements and Cooking Times

Grain (1 cup, or 250 mL, dry)	*Amount of Liquid*	*Cooking Time*	*Cooked Yield (approximate)*
Barley (pearl)	2½ cups (625 mL)	40 minutes	3 cups (750 mL)
Cornmeal	4 cups (1 L)	25 minutes	3 cups (750 mL)
Grits (regular)	4 cups (1 L)	25 minutes	3 cups (750 mL)
Kasha	2 cups (500 mL)	20 minutes	2½ cups (625 mL)
Millet	2½ to 3 cups (625 to 750 mL)	35-40 minutes	3½ cups (875 mL)
Rice (long- or medium-grain)	2 cups (500 mL)	45 minutes (brown) 15 minutes (white)	3 cups (750 mL)
Bulgur	2 cups (500 mL)	None	2½ cups (625 mL)

FOOD SCIENCE

Rice Preparation Comparison

Have students prepare ½ cup (125 mL) long-grain rice according to the directions on the package. Direct half of the students to stir the rice as little as possible and the other half to stir every five minutes. Have students compare the appearance, texture, and taste of the sample. What conclusions can students draw?

◆ **Never rinse pasta after cooking. Doing so washes away valuable nutrients. Give two tips for preserving the flavor and nutrient value of pasta.**

After cooking, drain the pasta in a colander or strainer. Never rinse pasta after cooking it—this removes nutrients. To keep cooked pasta hot, set the colander or strainer over a pan of hot water and cover.

If you have leftover cooked pasta, freeze it. First, stir 1 teaspoon (5 mL) cooking oil into the drained pasta to keep it from sticking. Freeze in serving-size portions.

Dry pasta is generally cooked to a doneness stage known as **al dente** (ahl DEN-tay), firm to the bite. Cooking time varies from 5 to 20 minutes, depending on the thickness of the pasta. If the pasta is to be further cooked in a recipe (such as lasagne), cook it for a shorter time so that it is slightly more firm. Unless directions state otherwise, fresh pasta will cook in a fraction of the time needed by dry pasta.

 ***How can I keep pasta from sticking together during or after cooking?***

 Start by using plenty of water. Bring the water to a rapid boil, then add pasta slowly so that the water continues boiling. Stir frequently. After cooking, if the pasta still seems to be sticking together, toss it with 1 teaspoon (5 mL) of cooking oil per portion.

Dry Pasta Quantities

Type of Pasta	*Dry Weight*	*Dry Volume*	*Cooked Yield (approximate)*
Small pasta shapes—macaroni, shells, spirals, twists	4 ounces (120 g)	1 cup (250 mL)	2½ cups (675 mL)
Long, slender pasta strands—spaghetti, angel hair, vermicelli	4 ounces (120 g)	1-inch (2.5-cm) diameter bunch	2 cups (500 mL)

- *Preparing Pasta*
- *Preparing Cereals (text pages 448-450)*

Demonstration

Demonstrate how to cook dry pasta, having students taste and compare textures of the pasta at the "al dente" stage and when the pasta is overcooked. Emphasize the points listed in the Q & A.

Finding Recipes

Have students brainstorm ways to serve cooked pasta. Then, using library or online cooking resources, students are to find additional nutritious pasta recipes. Note the versatility of pasta. L1

Product Comparison

Have students prepare and taste test regular, quick-cooking, and instant oatmeal. Have students create a chart to record product comparisons along the following dimensions: ease of preparation, time required for preparation, appearance, texture, taste, and cost. Then have students rank the three types in each area, where 1 means "most preferred" and 3 is "least preferred." Encourage students to share their results. L1

Extending Learning

Draining Pasta—Point out to students that draining pasta requires special care because of the weight of the pot and the high temperature of the cooking water.

- Have the strainer or colander ready in an empty sink with the drain open.
- Lift the pot or kettle carefully with both hands, using potholders.
- Be sure the path to the sink is clear before carrying the pot there.
- Pour out the pasta and water slowly to avoid splashing.

ASSESS

REVIEW

- Ask students to summarize the main ideas in this section.
- Have students complete the Section Review. (Answers appear below.)

EVALUATION

- Have students prepare ½ cup (125 mL) dry pasta to the "al dente" stage. Observe the procedure and safety techniques they use and evaluate the final product.
- Have students take the quiz for Section 17-2. (Use the quiz in the *Teacher Resource Guide,* or construct your own with the **Exam***View*® *Test Generator* on the *Effective Instruction CD-ROM.*)

RETEACHING

- Have students prepare an instruction guide outlining the steps in cooking top-quality pasta.
- Refer to the *Reteaching Activities* booklet for the Section 17-2 activity sheet.

CLOSE

Lead the class in a one-day menu plan development session, using grains in various ways throughout the menu. Make sure the menu plan includes at least six servings of grains, of which at least three are whole grains.

Preparing Cereals

A bowl of steaming hot cereal can really jump-start your body on a cold morning. Even if you live in a region that has mild temperatures year-round, a bowl of oatmeal or other hot cereal makes a tasty breakfast.

Some hot cereals can be prepared with either water or milk. Check the package directions. Instant hot cereals usually require only that you add boiling water. Some ready-to-eat cereals can be microwaved to serve hot.

Whether hot or cold, have your cereal with milk, especially if you don't drink much milk otherwise. You will get one of the servings that a growing teen needs from the Food Guide Pyramid. For natural sweetness and added nutrients, try adding fresh or dried fruit, such as strawberries, raisins, dried apricots, or sliced bananas.

◆ **Cereal is often eaten for breakfast, but it also makes a good snack and even a quick dinner when you're in a hurry. Some people combine two or more cold cereals for taste variety. How can you add nutritional value to a bowl of cold cereal?**

Section 17-2 Review & Activities

1. Why shouldn't you rinse grains before cooking them?
2. Does microwaving grains save time? Explain.
3. How can you tell when rice is properly cooked?
4. **Extending.** Are there advantages to using fresh pasta instead of dry pasta? If yes, what are possible advantages?
5. **Synthesizing.** When preparing grains at home, what are some creative ways you can use them with your meals?
6. **Applying.** Find recipes for a variety of pasta sauces. Which appear to be low in fat and high in fiber? How might you reduce the fat in the other recipes? How might you increase the fiber?

Answers to Section 17-2 Review & Activities

1. Rinsing washes off added B vitamins.
2. No, because the grains need a certain amount of time to absorb water.
3. It should be tender but firm, and there should be no water left in the pot.
4. Yes. Fresh pasta can be prepared more quickly. This also means less electric or gas resources are used.
5. Answers will vary.
6. Recipes and answers will vary. Reducing fat—use evaporated fat-free milk or fat-free milk in place of some or all creams, decrease butter or oil, or use lower-fat cheeses. Increasing fiber—add vegetables or beans.

SECTION 17-3

Legumes, Nuts, and Seeds

Legumes have been eaten all over the world for more than 10,000 years. Legumes include dry beans, peas, and lentils. All these foods come in different shapes, sizes, and colors. No matter what form or shape, they are packed with flavor, nutrition, and meal appeal.

Objectives

After studying this section, you should be able to:

- Identify the nutrients in legumes, nuts, and seeds.
- Give guidelines for buying, storing, and preparing legumes, nuts, and seeds.

Look for This Term

legumes

Nutrients in Legumes

Technically, **legumes** are plants whose seeds grow in pods that split along both sides when ripe. They are excellent sources of complex carbohydrates (especially fiber), proteins, B vitamins (including folate), iron, calcium, potassium, and some trace minerals. Nearly all are low in fat. In addition, their use has been linked to reduced risk of heart disease, some cancers, and other lifestyle diseases.

Because of their rich concentration of plant proteins, legumes are grouped along with other protein sources—including meat, poultry, and fish—in the Food Guide Pyramid. Health experts urge eating dry beans, peas, or lentils instead of meat at least twice a week. When totaling your servings, count ½ cup (125 mL) of cooked dry beans as 1 ounce (28 g) of lean meat. Legumes can also do double duty as a vegetable serving.

Legumes and Grains

Legumes and grains work perfectly as a team. Each has the amino acids (building blocks of proteins) the other lacks. By eating both any time during a day, you can get all the essential amino acids needed for good health. The soybean is the only legume that naturally contains all the building blocks of proteins necessary for health. Grains and legumes make up about two-thirds of the proteins eaten by people all around the world.

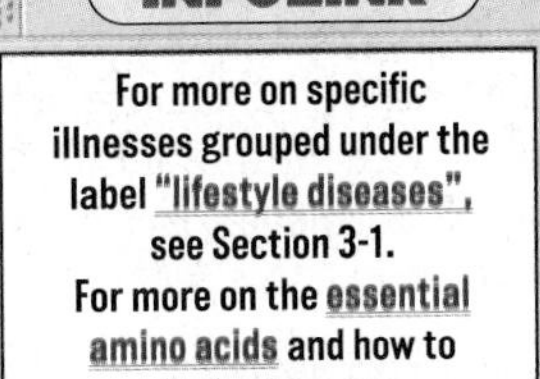

INFOLINK

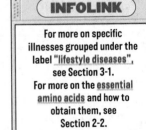

For more on specific illnesses grouped under the label "lifestyle diseases", see Section 3-1.
For more on the essential amino acids and how to obtain them, see Section 2-2.

SECTION 17-3

Legumes, Nuts, and Seeds

FOCUS

MOTIVATORS

- Have students work in small groups to review recipes from different cultures to identify ways legumes, nuts, and seeds are used. Have groups identify the types of legumes, nuts, and seeds used in the recipes they found. Also have them describe the types of dishes. Point out that legumes are considered to be the second most important food in the world, after grains.
- Have students identify favorite foods that combine grains with legumes, nuts, or seeds.

VOCABULARY ACTIVITY

Pronounce the term listed under "Look for This Term." Have students find the term and its definition in the section.

STUDY SKILLS

- **Outlining.** Have students read the section and outline it by copying the headers on paper and leaving space after each one. Students are to write a sentence in their own words, summarizing the content under each header.
- Have students read the section and complete the appropriate part of the Chapter 17 Study Guide in the *Student Workbook*.

Section 17-3 Resources

◆ **Student Workbook,** pp. 124, 128
◆ **Teacher Resource Guide**
Lesson Plan 17-3 Organizer
Section 17-3 Quiz
Chapter 17 Test
◆ **Effective Instruction CD-ROM**
Exam*View*® *Test Generator*
PowerPoint® Slide #38
◆ **Transparency Package,** CT-38
◆ **Student Motivation Kit**
Reteaching Activities, p. 80
Enrichment Activities

TEACH

- *Nutrients in Legumes*
- *Buying and Storing Legumes (text pages 451-453)*

Discussion Activity

Ask a volunteer to find and define the word *legume*. Follow with a discussion of the nutrients commonly found in legumes and what to look for when you buy legumes.

Multiple Question Activity

Invite students each to use information in the section to prepare an answer that can have more than one question (for example, the word "Soup" could be the answer to the question "What can you cook with dry peas?" and "What can you cook with black beans?") Have students write down the questions, then exchange answers with another student. Work until all questions have been identified.

Calculations

Have students compare the nutrients in legumes with those in grains. What are the advantages of eating dry beans, peas, or lentils at least twice a week instead of meat? L1

◆ **Legumes are considered "crossover" foods. They can be grouped with meats, poultry, and fish in the Food Guide Pyramid, but they can also be grouped with vegetables. How would you classify red beans served as a main-dish casserole?**

Buying and Storing Legumes

Because legumes continue to dry out when stored, a good rule of thumb is to buy only as much as you will use within six months. The drier they are, the longer they will take to cook.

If legumes are visible in the package, inspect them carefully. Look for bright color, no visible damage, and uniform size. Mixed sizes result in uneven cooking, since smaller ones cook faster than larger ones.

Store dry legumes in a cool and dry place. Once the package has been opened, transfer the remainder to a tightly covered container.

◆ **This lasagne combines pasta sheets with cooked dry beans. What are the advantages of using legumes as a protein source?**

Extending Learning

Legumes—Legume pods usually grow above ground on vines or small bushes. The legume has a seed coat, or skin, to protect the interior. The inside of a legume is called the *cotyledon* (cat-uhl-LEAD-uhn). The *hilum* (HIGH-lehm) is a tiny spot where the seed was attached to the pod. It absorbs water through this area.

Types and Uses of Legumes

Type of Legumes	*Uses*	*Popular Recipes*
Black beans (turtle beans) Black skin, cream-colored inside, sweet flavor.	Soups, stews, Latin American and Asian dishes	Cuban rice and beans
Black-eyed peas Actually beans, not peas. Small, oval, with black "eye" on one side.	Main dishes with ham or rice, curries	"Hoppin' John," a Southern recipe
Dry peas Available whole or split, green or yellow.	Soups	Split-pea soup
Garbanzo beans (chickpeas) Round, roughly shaped, nutlike flavor, firm texture. Hold their shape when cooked.	Dips, main dishes, salads, roasted as a snack	Hummus, a Middle Eastern dip
Lentils Thin, tiny, disc-shaped. Come in colors ranging from grayish brown to green to reddish orange.	Soups, stews, salads, curries, side dishes	Main ingredient in East Indian dish, dal
Lima beans White, flat beans in assorted sizes. Baby limas are smallest with mild flavor. Butter beans are largest with a rich, buttery flavor.	Soups, casseroles, salads, side dishes	Succotash
Pink and red beans Vary in size, flavor, and intensity of color. Kidney beans are largest, with a hearty flavor.	Stew, mixed bean salads, Latin American main dishes	Chili con carne
Pinto beans Pink and white, speckled. Similar in flavor and texture to pink and red beans.	Chili, stew, Mexican rice and beans	Refried beans
Soybeans Distinct flavor. High in protein and fat. Difficult to digest.	Soy products—tofu and soy milk	Some meatless burgers, tofu
White beans Vary in size and flavor, but all have a firm texture. Great Northern are largest. Navy beans are medium in size.	Soups, casseroles, mixed dishes	Boston baked beans

Cooked legumes can be stored in the refrigerator if you plan to use them within three days. For longer storage, freeze them. When putting the beans in freezer containers, add enough cooking liquid to cover them so that they will not dry out. Frozen cooked beans can be thawed in a microwave oven or in the refrigerator.

- *Buying and Storing Legumes (text pages 452-453)*

Display Activity

Set up an unlabeled, numbered display of at least five of the legumes from the chart on this page. Have students write the numbers down on a blank piece of paper, view the display, and record the type of legumes next to its corresponding number. Review with students the varying shapes, sizes, and colors of the legumes. Ask students to share their favorite ways to eat these legumes.

Finding Recipes

Using library or online cooking resources, ask students to create another column entitled "My recipe suggestions," to add to the chart on this page. Ask them to try to find at least one recipe for five of the legumes. They can record the name of the recipe in their chart. Have students share the recipes with other students. Encourage students to prepare the recipes at home. **L1**

Extending Learning

Lentils—Lentils have a mild, distinctive flavor. After preparation, they can be served whole in a variety of ways or puréed and used as a meat extender. Cooked lentils can be frozen for future use.

Lentils were one of the first crops to be cultivated. Legend has it that lentils were introduced into the United States in the early 1900s by a German minister. Traveling in the state of Washington, he gave a farmer a small amount of lentil seeds. Currently, most of the lentils in the United States are grown in Idaho and Washington.

- *Preparing Legumes (text pages 454-456)*

Discussion Activity

Read students the following three statements for class discussion: (1) Explain why it is important to sort and rinse dry legumes carefully, (2) Describe the procedure for rinsing legumes, and (3) Explain the advantage of soaking beans before cooking them.

Small Group Discussion Activity

Have students work in small groups to review cooking instructions on the labels of dry legumes. Ask them to discuss these and other questions: Why should legumes be sorted before cooking? Why should beans be soaked? Why should the soaking water be changed several times? Why should fresh water be used for cooking?

Label Reading

Have students read the ingredients and Nutrition Facts panels on convenience forms of beans. Have them compare their findings with the ingredients and Nutrition Facts panels on dry beans. Have students record similarities and differences. Discuss students' findings as a means ultimately to a master list that can be stored for future reference in a classroom resource folder. L1

Preparing Legumes

Like grains, legumes are versatile and easy to prepare. They tend to pick up the flavor of bay leaf, onion, or other seasonings you add to the cooking water. Just be sure to give them time to absorb water until they are soft enough to eat.

Once cooked, beans and other legumes can be served whole, mashed, or puréed, as a side dish, or as a main ingredient in casseroles, soups, stews, chilis, burritos, and salads. Dry peas and lentils are tasty in soups and stews. To be really creative, try a lasagne made with beans or a lentil loaf instead of a meat loaf.

Sorting and Rinsing

Before cooking, sort legumes carefully. Pick out foreign material such as pebbles and stems. Also discard any legumes that are damaged, are smaller than others, or have a greenish tint.

Rinse the legumes carefully by placing them in cool water. Drain, then rinse again. Repeat, if necessary, until the water is clear.

Soaking Beans

Dry beans normally take from one to two hours to cook. Soaking before cooking can cut down on cooking time by 15 to 30 minutes. Dry peas and lentils do not have to be soaked.

To soak dry beans, use a large pot. For every pound (500 g) of any kind of beans, sorted and washed, add about 10 cups (2.5 L) hot water. Simmer for two to three minutes; then turn off the heat and cover the beans. Let them soak for at least an hour. The longer beans soak, the less cooking time they need. If beans have been soaked, drain and rinse them before proceeding with the recipe.

◆ **Sorting legumes is an important step in the cooking process. Describe the next two steps.**

FOOD SCIENCE

Using Legumes as Thickeners

Have students choose a recipe that calls for a thickener such as flour or cornstarch. Have some students prepare the recipe as it is written. Have other students prepare the recipe but substituting puréed legumes (puréed in a blender) for the thickener. (Note: A larger amount of legumes will be needed, compared to the amount of flour or cornstarch.) Compare the two dishes. Ask students to evaluate the substitution in terms of taste, texture, and appearance.

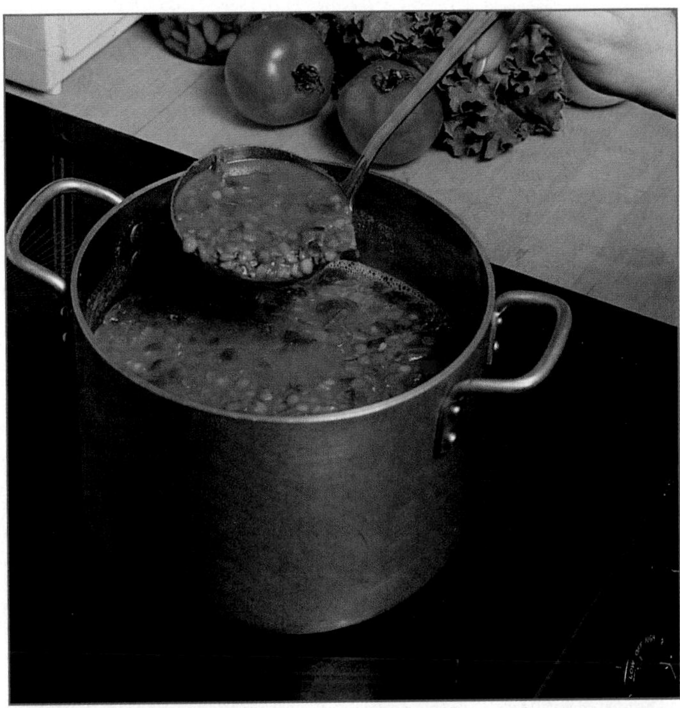

◆ **Soups based on legumes make for hearty, cold-weather fare. What would you serve with this lentil soup to help balance your daily nutrient intake?**

are a bit firmer. If you plan to mash them, cook longer so that they are a little softer.

When done, the beans should have a little cooking liquid left. Although beans retain most of their important nutrients, serve the cooking liquid with the beans—it contains small traces of B vitamins. If you plan to use only the beans, save the liquid for soups, sauces, or broth.

Simmering Beans

Place the beans in a large pot—they double in volume as they cook. Add water, using the amount specified on package directions. More water may be needed if the legumes are old and dry. If you like, you can spice up the cooking water by adding chopped onions, garlic, or dried herbs.

Cover the pot and bring the water to a boil. Then lower the heat to a simmer. Follow package directions for cooking time. For best results, start checking at the minimum cooking time specified. If the beans are not tender enough, continue cooking. If the beans are used in a salad or for further cooking in a recipe, cook them a shorter time so that they

Other Methods

A convenient way to cook beans is with a slow cooker. Do not presoak them. Check the slow cooker owner's manual for exact directions. In general, the beans are combined with boiling water in the cooker. Mix well, cover, and cook on the high setting. This method generally takes three to eight hours, depending on the kind of beans.

Beans also can be cooked in a pressure cooker. Again, follow the directions in the owner's manual.

Legumes can be cooked in the microwave, too. It takes about the same amount of time as conventional cooking.

- *Preparing Legumes (text pages 454-456)*

Demonstration

Using legumes, perform several brief demonstrations that ask the question "What is wrong with this picture?" For instance, you might show students a small saucepan filled more than half way with dry beans. Use the demonstrations as a bridge to a discussion of the issues raised (e.g., always choose a large pot when cooking beans). Ask students to describe two ways to cook beans, other than simmering on a stovetop.

Making a Chart

Have students make charts showing the proper steps to cooking dry beans. Invite them to post their charts in locations at home where they can be accessed for quick reference. L1

Lab Experience

Have different students work in small groups to cook soaked, dry beans by different methods, including simmering on the range top, in a slow cooker, in a pressure cooker, and in a microwave oven. (Reminder: Dry beans will take at least an hour to cook. If time constraints exist, begin the cooking process for the students prior to class.) Compare the results. Ask: What factors might influence a person's choice of method? L2

Extending Learning

Beans and Gas—Suggest that some people might complain about gas formation after bean consumption. Tell students that there are several products on the market that, when used along with beans, have the effect of reducing gas in the digestive system. Have interested students find out more about these products and how they work.

TEACH cont.

- *Nuts and Seeds (text pages 456-457)*

Recipe R & D

Tell students to create a pamphlet titled "101 Nutty Ideas." The pamphlet is to consist primarily of quick, easy, and nutritious recipe ideas using nuts. As a prologue to the recipes, ask students to develop five simple suggestions for incorporating nuts into a healthful eating plan. L1

Nutrient Comparison Activity

Have students compare the nutrients in nuts and seeds with those in grains and legumes. In which nutrients are nuts and seeds high? What is considered a serving size of nuts and seeds; to which food group do they belong?

Supermarket Survey

Have students survey a local supermarket to make a list of the nuts and edible seeds available. In what forms are nuts and seeds available? What are the advantages and disadvantages of buying these foods in each form? L1

- Americans eat 250,000 tons of peanut butter each year.

Q ***How can I prevent the beans I cook from being either hard or turning to mush?***

A Tough beans sometimes get that way when the recipe calls for salt or an acid food, such as vinegar or tomatoes. If your recipe does, add these ingredients near the end of the cooking time. To prevent beans from getting mushy or having the skins break, cook them gently, leaving the lid slightly ajar. One more tip: If you don't have time to cook dry beans, don't let that stop you from using them in meals. Use canned beans—they're a time-saver.

Nuts and Seeds

Like legumes, nuts and seeds are included in the Meat Group of the Food Guide Pyramid. Nuts and seeds are high in protein and B vitamins. They're also high in fat, though not the saturated kind. When eaten in moderation, they can be a beneficial part of a heart-healthy eating plan.

Among the wide assortment of nuts available are almonds, filberts, cashews, and Brazil nuts. Even though peanuts are legumes, people use them as they do other nuts. The same is true of walnuts, which are actually seeds. Other popular edible seeds include sunflower, pumpkin, squash, and sesame seeds.

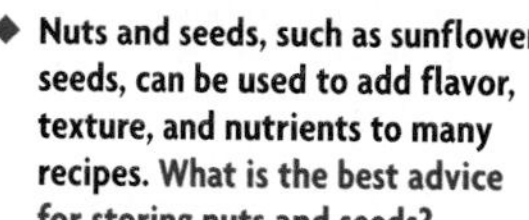

◆ **Nuts and seeds, such as sunflower seeds, can be used to add flavor, texture, and nutrients to many recipes. What is the best advice for storing nuts and seeds?**

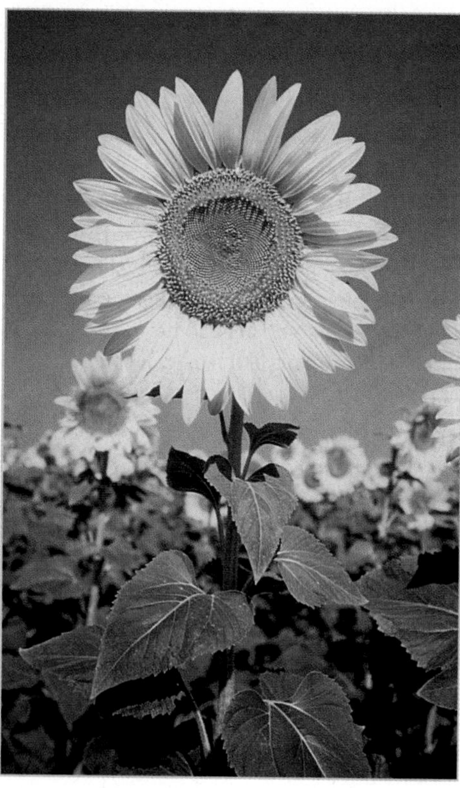

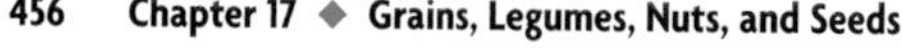

Extending Learning

Nuts and Seeds—Unlike peanuts, nuts grow on trees. Because trees mature slowly, the supply of nuts is limited.

Nuts have a hard outer shell and a tender, chewy inside. Seeds have a hard outer shell that can be easily removed before eating.

Many seeds, such as safflower, are used mainly for the oils they contain.

Buying and Storing Nuts and Seeds

Nuts and seeds are sold both with and without the shell. Many varieties are available raw or roasted—either in oil or dry roasted, a special process in which no oil is added.

Nuts and seeds can be ground into a thick, spreadable paste. The most common example is peanut butter. Tahini (tuh-HEE-nee), a spread made from ground sesame seeds, is popular in Middle Eastern cooking.

When buying nuts and seeds, avoid those in shells that are cracked or broken. Harmful pathogens may be present in the edible parts.

If you're not planning on using them quickly, store nuts and seeds in the refrigerator. Because they contain oil, even in their raw state, they can spoil at room temperature over time.

Using Nuts and Seeds

You can enjoy nuts and seeds in a variety of ways. Chopped or ground nuts and seeds add flavor and texture to baked goods, salads, cereal, and yogurt. They can also be used in meatless baked dishes for added protein. Nut butters and spreads can be used in sandwiches or recipes.

When using nuts and seeds in low-fat cooking, first toast them in the oven or on the range. Toasting enhances flavors, so you can use less and still get the same full flavors.

Section 17-3 Review & Activities

1. Name five nutrients supplied by legumes.
2. Within how many months should dry legumes be used? Why?
3. What are the three basic steps in preparing dry beans?
4. **Evaluating.** Since nuts and seeds are high in fat, how can you include them in a healthful eating plan? List at least three examples.
5. **Analyzing.** What characteristics of legumes do you think explain their long history as staples in the world food supply?
6. **Applying.** Look through cookbooks to find recipes that use legumes in each of the following: a vegetarian main dish, a main dish with meat or poultry, a soup, and a salad. Be prepared to discuss how the recipe directions relate to the preparation principles you have learned in this section.

ASSESS

REVIEW

- Ask students to summarize the main ideas in this section.
- Have students complete the Section Review. (Answers appear below.)

EVALUATION

- Have students develop two tip sheets, including tips to choose, prepare, and store (1) legumes and (2) nuts and seeds.
- Have students take the quiz for Section 17-3. (Use the quiz in the *Teacher Resource Guide*, or construct your own with the **Exam***View*® *Test Generator* on the *Effective Instruction CD-ROM.*)

RETEACHING

- Using the display of various types of legumes, help students identify each type and explain how they might use the legume in a meal or recipe.
- Refer to the *Reteaching Activities* booklet for the Section 17-3 activity sheet.

CLOSE

Have students name one new way they might include legumes, nuts, or seeds in their weekly meal plans.

Answers to Section 17-3 Review & Activities

1. See page 451.
2. Six months; because the legumes continue to dry out while they are being stored.
3. Sorting and rinsing, soaking, and simmering (cooking).
4. Answers will vary. Use them sparingly as snacks, toast them to use less for the same full flavor in baked goods, sprinkle small amounts on salads for flavor and crunch.
5. Answers will vary. They are easy to grow, abundant, easy to prepare, and high in protein.
6. Recipes and answers will vary.

RECIPE FILE

Western Beans and Rice

This recipe demonstrates a tasty way to create a main dish with convenient, canned beans.

USING THE RECIPE

- Have students read the recipe and make sure they understand each step as well as the entire process.
- Review safety and sanitation procedures that apply to this recipe.
- Have each lab team fill out a work plan. (See the *Foods Lab Resources* booklet.)
- Have students check off the ingredients and equipment listed on the recipe worksheet and prepare the recipe.
- Have students complete the evaluation and questions on the recipe worksheet.

SEE ALSO...

The *Foods Lab Resources* booklet for the "Western Beans and Rice" recipe worksheet and other recipe alternatives.

RECIPE FILE

Western Beans and Rice

This recipe combines legumes and rice to provide complete proteins. It also combines conventional and microwave cooking techniques with convenience forms of rice and legumes. Serve this dish with a tossed salad, fruit, and milk for a complete meal.

Customary	*Ingredient*	*Metric*
(See package directions)	Brown rice	(See package directions)
(See package directions)	Water	(See package directions)
1 Tbsp.	Vegetable oil	15 mL
1 cup	Chopped onion	250 mL
1 cup	Diced celery	250 mL
3 cups	Canned pinto beans, drained and rinsed	750 mL
1 8-oz. can	Reduced-sodium tomato sauce	224-g can
½ cup	Water	125 mL
¼ tsp. (or to taste)	Hot pepper sauce	1 mL (or to taste)

Yield: 6 1-cup servings
Equipment: Saucepan; 1-qt. (1-L) microwave-safe dish with cover
Power level: 100%

Directions

1. Prepare instant brown rice in saucepan according to package directions, using amount of rice and water to make 3 cups cooked rice.
2. While rice is cooking, combine onion, celery, and oil in microwave-safe dish. Cover.
3. Cook onion and celery at 100% power for 2 minutes, stirring after 1 minute.
4. Stir in beans, tomato sauce, ½ cup water, and hot pepper sauce. Cover.
5. Cook mixture at 100% power for 5 to 8 minutes, stirring after 4 minutes.
6. Let stand 1 minute.
7. Serve over hot, cooked rice.

Nutrition Information

Per serving (approximate): 250 calories, 9 g protein, 46 g carbohydrate, 4 g fat, 0 mg cholesterol, 531 mg sodium
Good source of: potassium, iron, vitamin E, B vitamins, phosphorus

Food for Thought

- What foods provide the most protein in this recipe?
- If you were preparing this recipe to serve as a side dish, what foods could you serve it with?

Answers to **Food for Thought**

1. (1) Pinto beans (most), (2) brown rice, and (3) tomato sauce.
2. Answers will vary. Serve a tossed salad, fruit and milk, plus a main entrée of grilled chicken or fish.

Career Wanted

Health Food Store Nutritionist

Education and Training
- Bachelor's degree in dietetics, foods and nutrition, or related area
- Experience in retail

Qualities
- Communication skills
- Analytical skills
- Enjoy meeting people

"You can't have 'health' without the 'foods.'"

Margery Kleinerman

Q. Margery, why do people shop at health food stores?

A. Some customers like our organically grown produce; some are vegetarians who buy our meatless items. Those who have food allergies appreciate our gluten- and dairy-free foods. We also carry kosher foods.

Q. Do you have credentials as a nutritionist?

A. Yes, I have a degree in dietetics. I can't plan a diet for a particular client, but I can explain nutrition facts and suggest other resources. Our quarterly newsletter, for instance, has tips and recipes.

Q. How did you get into this business?

A. My grandfather actually started the store. He was a Russian immigrant who sold imported foods. I became interested in the health aspect of ethnic foods. Russian cooking, for instance, uses a lot of whole grains.

Q. What's in the future of health foods?

A. Well, "nutraceuticals," foods that could fight illness, may have potential. Business-wise, we're looking for a sales boost with online marketing.

Related Career Opportunities

Entry Level
- Sales associate
- Agricultural commodity grader
- Community garden volunteer

Technical Level
- Dietetic technician
- Food importer
- Master beekeeper

Professional Level
- Dietitian
- Research chemist
- Chef in ethnic restaurant

Making Career Connections

INVENTORY SELECTION. Visit a health food store or online seller. Examine the products offered. Choose ten items that you would stock if you were a health food store manager. Explain why you chose each item. Compare your inventory with those of classmates.

Career Wanted

Health Food Store Nutritionist

Thinking About the Career

Have students think about what other opportunities might exist for someone with a dietetics degree. Also, have students think about how a dietetics background helps in a career as a health food store nutritionist.

Ask students to describe why they might visit a health food store. Then discuss the role a health food store nutritionist might have played to help them with their needs or purchases.

Career-Building Opportunities

Ask students to visit a specialty or health food store in their community and ask if a nutritionist works there. When possible, have interested students interview the nutritionist about his or her educational background, plus educational recommendations he or she has for students interested in a career as a nutritionist.

For More Information

For additional information about careers in nutrition, encourage students to contact:

- The American Dietetic Association
  216 W. Jackson Boulevard
  Chicago, IL 60606-6995
  www.eatright.org
- Society for Nutrition Education
  9202 N. Meridian St., Suite 200
  Indianapolis, IN 46260
  www.sne.org

REVIEW

- Have students complete the Chapter Review. (Answers appear below.)

EVALUATION

- Divide the class into two teams. Each team is to brainstorm questions about Chapter 17. Then allow the teams to take turns asking each other questions. At the end of the questioning period, the team with the most correct answers wins.
- Have students take the test for Chapter 17. (Use the chapter test in the *Teacher Resource Guide,* or construct your own with the **Exam***View*® *Test Generator* on the *Effective Instruction CD-ROM.*)

ANSWERS

Checking Your Knowledge

1. Whole-grain products use the whole wheat grain (germ, endosperm, and bran). Enriched products have usually had some parts of the grain removed by processing, and are enriched with nutrients to make their nutritional value similar to what it was before processing.
2. *Couscous:* steamed, cracked endosperm of wheat kernel; used as cereal, in salads and main dishes, or sweetened for dessert. *Kasha:* roasted buckwheat that is hulled and crushed; used as breakfast cereal or side dish. *Triticale:* cross between wheat and rye; used in cereals and main dishes and combined with other cooked grains.
3. Whole grains or grain products, fresh pasta, bread only for short time if humidity is high.
4. Because they are dry.
5. Long-grain rice; because stirring scrapes off the starch and makes the rice grains stick together.
6. *Al dente;* firm when you bite into it.

Chapter 17 Review & Activities

Summary

Section 17-1: Choosing Grains and Grain Products

- Grain kernels are made up of the germ, endosperm, and bran.
- Grains are generally high in complex carbohydrates, proteins, fiber, vitamins, and minerals. However, the nutritional value of grains depends on how they are processed.
- Cooked grains are popular as side dishes and breakfast cereals; grain products include instant and ready-to-eat cereals, pasta, and breads.
- Look for nutrition and quality when buying.
- Store grains and grain products properly to maintain their quality.

Section 17-2: Preparing Grains and Grain Products

- Grains must be cooked before eating.
- Although cooking methods for many grains are similar, always check the package directions.
- Rice and many other grains are simmered in only as much water as they can absorb.
- Pasta is boiled in a large amount of water and then drained.
- Breakfast cereals are served hot or cold, often with milk and fruit.

Section 17-3: Legumes, Nuts, and Seeds

- Legumes are high in protein, fiber, and other nutrients. Most are low in fat.
- The many types of legumes can be used in main dishes, side dishes, and salads.
- Dry beans require long cooking in water. Soaking them first decreases the cooking time.
- Nuts and seeds are high in protein and unsaturated fat. In moderation, they may be eaten plain or added to baked goods and other dishes.

Checking Your Knowledge

1. What is the difference between whole-grain and enriched products?

2. Describe the following grain products and tell how they are used: couscous, kasha, and triticale.

3. Name three specific instances when grains or grain products should be refrigerated.

4. Why must grains be cooked before they are eaten?

5. What type of rice should not be stirred during cooking? Why?

6. What term is used to describe properly cooked pasta? What does it mean?

7. Describe the following legumes and tell how they are used: chickpeas, lentils, soybeans.

8. Give three guidelines for buying legumes.

9. Briefly describe how to cook beans.

10. What nutrients are found in nuts and seeds?

Review & Activities Chapter 17

Thinking Critically

1. **Drawing Conclusions.** Hallie, an aging adult with gastric problems, has been advised by her health professional to avoid using whole-grain products. What might be the reason for this advice? Why might the advice be sound, even though non-whole-grain products often lack the bran and germ, and hence, are less nutritious?
2. **Recognizing Assumptions.** A friend of yours who wants to lose weight tells you she plans to avoid pasta because it is fattening. Do you agree? Explain your answer.
3. **Identifying Cause and Effect.** Saril has found a recipe for a stew that includes lentils, tomatoes, and onions. He says, though, that the last time he cooked lentils, they came out tough and chewy. What are some possible explanations for this result? What precautions should Saril take when preparing the recipe?

Working IN THE Lab

1. ***Food Preparation.*** Prepare a variety of different grains, such as couscous, bulgur, and millet. Compare them for taste, texture, and appearance. Decide what types of dishes or recipes each grain might be used in. Give reasons for your answers.
2. ***Food Preparation.*** Prepare a dessert dish using rice or pasta. What nutritional value does rice or pasta add to the dessert?

Reinforcing Key Skills

1. **Communication.** Imagine that you work as a media consultant. A company that manufactures and sells pasta has come to you, asking you to develop a campaign to increase public awareness about the goodness and nutritive values of their product. Make a list of the facts to include in your campaign.
2. **Management.** Sean cooked too much rice for his family's dinner. He wonders what to do with all the extra rice. Help Sean find a solution.

Making Decisions and Solving Problems

Your family relies mostly on processed grain products and eats very few whole grains. You would like to introduce more whole grains to make your family's meals more nutritious. You have had limited success introducing new foods in the past.

Making Connections

1. **Social Studies.** Using library sources, write a report on a grain product that is popular in a specific culture. How was the grain introduced in that country? Why is it popular? How is it used? What percentage of the population is employed in growing and processing the grain?
2. **Math.** Draw a graph comparing the cooking times of various grains and legumes. If available, use a computer to develop the graph. Post your graph in a high-visibility location near the classroom foods lab for quick reference.

ANSWERS cont.

7. *Chickpeas (garbanzo beans):* round, roughly shaped with a nutlike flavor; used in appetizers, salads, main dishes. *Lentils:* thin, disc-shaped, come in several colors; used in soups, stew, salads, side dishes. *Soybeans:* have a distinct flavor and provide all the amino acids needed for health; used in soy products —tofu, soy milk, some veggie burgers.
8. Bright color, no visible damage, uniform size.
9. Sort and rinse them; add hot water and simmer for two or three minutes; then turn off heat and soak for at least an hour; drain and rinse beans; simmer beans in fresh water until done.
10. They are high in protein and B vitamins.

Thinking Critically

1. Whole grains are high in fiber, which can aggravate digestive problems.
2. Pasta itself is a low-fat food. When heavy sauces rich in fats are added, however, it can become a high-calorie food, especially when consumed in large portions.
3. Answers will vary. Saril needs to make sure the lentils have cooked long enough to absorb their liquid, and he needs to avoid adding the tomatoes until the end of the recipe, since doing so can toughen legumes.

Reinforcing Key Skills

1. Answers will vary. Allow time for students to share and compare efforts.
2. Answers will vary. Encourage creative answers.

CHAPTER

18

Dairy Foods and Eggs

Advance Planning Guide ☑

- Create a bulletin board entitled "Milk Power."
- Purchase fat-free milk and butter for a demonstration.
- Purchase a variety of cheeses for a cheese-tasting party.
- Purchase fat-free dry milk for a demonstration.
- Purchase raw vegetables, dip mix (vegetable soup mix), sour cream, and yogurt for the Lab Experience on page 468.
- Purchase five frozen dairy desserts for the "For Your Health" activity on page 469.
- Purchase yogurt and obtain cheesecloth and strainer for a demonstration; prepare one batch of "yogurt cheese."
- Prepare a list of problems that can occur during preparation with milk, yogurt, and cheese.
- Purchase the necessary ingredients for the Recipe File on page 474.
- Purchase a variety of eggs for various activities throughout sections 18-3 and 18-4.
- Purchase fresh mushrooms and other necessary ingredients for the Recipe File on page 481.
- Create a bulletin board entitled "Egg-citing Eggs."
- Obtain a recipe for hard meringue.

CHAPTER

18

Dairy Foods and Eggs

Todd had worked up a big thirst during football practice. He went straight to the refrigerator and poured himself a tall, cold glass of milk. Like many teens, Todd knows milk tastes great. In this chapter, you will learn about the many benefits of milk, other dairy foods, and eggs.

MEETING DIVERSE NEEDS

Verbal/Linguistic Learners. If there are students in the class who enjoy telling or writing stories, ask them to compose original stories about the travels of milk, butter, or ice cream from the cow to the table, from the point-of-view of the food. The stories should be based on fact, but be entertaining. Have these students read their stories to the class, or provide copies of the stories to the other students for their own reading pleasure.

SECTION 18-1

Objectives

After studying this section, you should be able to:

- Identify nutrients in milk and other dairy foods.
- Describe the types of dairy foods available.
- Give guidelines for buying and storing dairy foods.

Look for These Terms

pasteurized
homogenization
cultured
ripened cheese
unripened cheese

Broguiere's
"Milk So Fresh . . . The Cow Doesn't Know It's Missing"
Broguiere's Farm Fresh Dairy
Montebello, California

Choosing Dairy Foods

Dairy foods include milk and the many products made from milk, such as yogurt and different kinds of cheeses. Daily servings of milk and other dairy foods provide many nutrients that promote good health.

Nutrients in Milk

Milk has been called an almost perfect food. It is especially high in proteins, vitamin A, riboflavin, vitamin B_{12}, calcium, phosphorus, magnesium, and zinc. When fortified, it is an excellent source of vitamin D. The Food Guide Pyramid recommends two to three servings a day of milk or other dairy foods.

◆ **Milk and milk products are loaded with important vitamins and minerals. Name three micronutrients found in milk.**

SECTION 18-1
Choosing Dairy Foods

FOCUS

MOTIVATORS

- Create a bulletin board entitled "Milk Power." Show a personified glass of milk with large muscles. List the nutrient content of milk and equivalent servings of other dairy products.
- Host an in-class cheese-tasting party. Provide a variety of ripened and unripened cheeses for students to taste. Discuss the consistency, shape, color, texture, and flavor of the cheeses.

VOCABULARY ACTIVITY

Pronounce the terms listed under "Look for These Terms." Ask a volunteer to look up *culture* in the dictionary and explain what buttermilk and cultured pearls have in common.

STUDY SKILLS

- **Guided Reading.** Have students look at the headings within Section 18-1 to preview the concepts that will be discussed.
- Have students read the section and complete the appropriate part of the Chapter 18 Study Guide in the *Student Workbook*.

Section 18-1 Resources

◆ **Student Workbook,** pp. 129, 132
◆ **Teacher Resource Guide**
Lesson Plan 18-1 Organizer
Section 18-1 Quiz
◆ **Effective Instruction CD-ROM**
Exam*View*® *Test Generator*
PowerPoint® Slides #39–41
◆ **Transparency Package,** CT-39–41
◆ **Student Motivation Kit**
Reteaching Activities, pp. 81–82
Enrichment Activities

TEACH

- *Nutrients in Milk (text pages 463-466)*

Demonstration

Using fat-free milk and butter, demonstrate the fat content of milk. Start with an 8 ounce glass of fat-free milk; add ½ teaspoon butter (represents low-fat milk); add another ½ teaspoon butter (represents reduced-fat milk); add another one teaspoon of butter (represents whole milk). Note: One teaspoon of butter provides 4 grams of fat. Discuss how the differences in fat content add up when consuming three servings a day.

Discussion Activity

Ask students to explain what UHT milk is. What might be some uses for UHT milk?

Class Survey Activity

Survey the class to find out how many students get the recommended two to three servings a day of dairy products. Discuss typical servings of various dairy foods.

- Humans are the only species who drink the milk of another mammal.

Types of Milk

Although whole milk contains some saturated fat and cholesterol, lower-fat and fat-free forms are available. These products, which appear in the chart on the right, also have less cholesterol than whole milk.

Fresh whole milk contains about 87 percent water and 13 percent solids, some of which are milk fat. The other solids, which are fat-free, contain most of the protein, vitamins, minerals, and lactose (milk sugar) found in milk. These fat-free milk solids are also found in reduced-fat, low-fat, and fat-free milk.

Fat in Milk

Type of Milk	*Amount of Fat*
Whole milk	8 g fat per 8-oz. (250-mL) serving
Reduced-fat milk	5 g fat per 8-oz. (250-mL) serving
Low-fat milk	2.5 g fat per 8-oz. (250-mL) serving
Fat-free milk	Trace of fat

Processing of Fluid Milk

When shopping, look for milk that has been **pasteurized**. To help ensure food safety, milk is heat-treated to kill enzymes and harmful bacteria. Enzymes in milk can make it spoil quickly. Sometimes milk is ultra-pasteurized, heated to a higher temperature than in pasteurization. This permits it to be kept longer in the refrigerator. When exposed to even higher temperatures—as in the case of UHT (ultra-high temperature) processing—milk becomes a shelf-stable product that can be packaged in aseptic containers.

◆ **Is one of these products used in your household? Identify the fat content of each product by percent.**

FOOD SCIENCE

Lactobacillus Acidophilus

A small percentage of Americans have a condition called lactose intolerance; they cannot digest the "milk sugar" lactose. Some others may develop lactose maldigestion; they cannot digest milk properly. One way to make milk easier to digest is to add a healthful bacteria, lactobacillus acidophilus.

Acidophilus milk looks and tastes very similar to regular cow's milk. It is found in whole to fat- free forms. The label must state that the milk contains the acidophilus bacteria.

◆ **Milk comes in a variety of forms. Which of these products are used in cooking? Which are used as a beverage? Which serve both functions?**

Milk fat is lighter than other milk fluids and easily separates, rising to the top of the milk. **Homogenization**, the process whereby fat is broken down and evenly distributed in the milk, prevents this from happening. When fat is removed from milk, most of the vitamin A is removed along with it. By law, any vitamin A removed during the process must be replaced. In addition, most manufacturers voluntarily fortify milk with vitamin D. You can also buy milk with added calcium.

INFOLINK

For more on shelf-stable foods and guidelines for storing them, see Section 7-4. For more on aseptic containers—"juice boxes"—and what they are made of, see Section 13-1.

Other Types of Milk

Besides plain fluid milk, various flavored milks and convenience milk products are available:

- **Buttermilk.** Has a tart, buttery flavor and smooth, thick texture. These properties are a result of its having been **cultured**—fermented by a harmless bacteria added after pasteurization. Other familiar cultured dairy products are yogurt and sour cream.
- **Kefir** (kuh-FEER). A cultured beverage similar in flavor to yogurt. The authentic Middle Eastern product is made of fermented camel's milk. In the United States, kefir is made from cultured cow's milk.
- **Chocolate milk.** Has chocolate or cocoa and sweetener added.

- *Nutrients in Milk (text pages 463-466)*

Demonstration

Demonstrate how to reconstitute fat-free dry milk to make fluid milk. Have students sample it. Refrigerate and have students sample again the next day. Compare the taste of the reconstituted milk with the taste of other milks. Discuss cost, nutritive value, taste, and use.

Supermarket Survey

Have students visit a supermarket and make a list of the types of milk available. Suggest students review the photograph on this page for a guide to milk variety. Which products are cultured? Which are flavored? Which are shelf-stable? How do fat-free dry milk and evaporated milk compare nutritionally with whole or fat-free milk? L1

USING Safety Check

Set a glass of milk out in an area that students will notice. Don't mention it; wait until a student comments about it. If needed, encourage students to note the concern with the milk being left out at room temperature. Before the class is over, try pouring it back into the original container; students should stop you.

Extending Learning

BST—Bovine somatotropin (BST), is an FDA-approved, genetically-produced, protein hormone that is injected into dairy cows to increase milk production by approximately 25 percent. BST is also a naturally-occurring protein hormone made by cows. With or without BST supplementation, flavor and BST and nutritional levels in milk are the same. BST has no effect on humans in the amount found in milk.

TEACH cont.

- *Other Dairy Foods (text page 466-470)*

Nutrient Comparison

Ask students to bring in an empty container of regular or frozen yogurt. In small groups, have students study the Nutrition Facts panels and ingredient list. Then have them make a graph of their findings. Discuss the differences. L1

Recipe Development

Ask students to create a recipe or recipe idea using yogurt. Ideas may include a parfait (layers of yogurt, fruit, and cereal in a parfait glass) or potato topping (yogurt, chives, and bacon bits.) Have students record their recipes or ideas and share them with other students. If possible, ask interested students to prepare their recipes for the class. L1

USING THE CLOSE-UP ON SCIENCE: CHEMISTRY

Ask students to research: What dairy products are made by turning proteins into curds? Discuss students' findings in class.

- **Fat-free dry milk.** A powdered form of fat-free milk. When reconstituted, fat-free dry milk needs to be handled like liquid milk, which includes refrigeration. The instant variety of fat-free dry milk mixes easily with water. The powder may also be added directly to recipes to increase nutrients, especially protein and calcium, without adding fat.
- **Evaporated milk.** Canned whole or fat-free milk that contains only half the amount of water as regular milk. Evaporated fat-free milk is used as a cream substitute in beverages.
- **Sweetened condensed milk.** A concentrated, sweetened form of milk, used to make candy and desserts.
- **Lactose-free or reduced-lactose milk.** Available for people with lactose intolerance.

Other Dairy Foods

Many dairy products that start off as milk reach the market in other forms. Among these are yogurt, cheeses, cream, butter, and frozen dairy desserts.

Yogurt

Yogurt is made by adding a harmless bacteria culture to milk. The result is a thick, creamy, custardlike product with a tangy flavor. Yogurt is available plain or with added flavorings, such as vanilla and fruits. For an added nutrition boost, as well as a tasty and refreshing snack, try adding fresh sliced fruit, such as a banana or kiwi, to plain yogurt.

A concentrated form of milk, yogurt is higher in calcium than liquid milk. One cup (250 mL) of fat-free yogurt has 452 milligrams of calcium, compared with 302 milligrams in the same quantity of fat-free milk. Yogurt can also have a fat content as low as, or lower than, that of comparable fluid milk. Consider that a serving of nonfat yogurt has 1.5 grams or less of fat per serving and a serving of low-fat yogurt has between 1.5 and 5.7 grams of fat. To get the least fat, carefully read the label on the container before making your purchase.

Safety Check

After pouring milk, return the container to the refrigerator immediately. Do not pour milk that has been sitting out in a serving pitcher back into the original container. Instead, if the milk has been at room temperature less than two hours, refrigerate it in a separate container and use it soon. Discard milk that has been left at room temperature more than two hours.

CLOSE-UP ON SCIENCE: CHEMISTRY

Coagulating Milk Protein

Milk contains many different proteins, but two major ones are involved in making milk products such as yogurt and cheeses. The two proteins are casein (KAY-seen) and whey. When an acidic food or milk-clotting enzymes such as rennin (REH-nuhn) are added to milk, the two proteins separate. Casein clumps together into solid groups called curds, as in cottage cheese. The whey is a thin, bluish liquid that remains after the curds clump. Many different dairy products are made by turning proteins into curds.

Reinforcing Key Skills

Present the following problems to student groups. Allow time for them to discuss and compare their responses.

Leadership—Mrs. Murray decided to add chocolate to milk as a good way to entice her 5-year-old daughter, Janet, to drink milk. Do you feel this is a sensible idea? Why or why not?

Management—Your 13-year-old cousin doesn't drink milk. How can your cousin meet dairy recommendations without drinking milk?

Cheeses

When you want to add zip to a sandwich or a tangy touch to pasta, say "Cheese!" Cheese is a natural food made from milk curds with the whey drained off. There are two basic categories of cheeses:

- **Ripened cheese.** Also called aged cheese. Made from curds to which ripening agents —bacteria, mold, yeast, or a combination of these—have been added. The cheese is then aged under carefully controlled conditions. Aging time depends on the kind of cheese. The result is a cheese that can be stored for a relatively long time. The texture of ripened cheeses ranges from soft to very hard. In between is a wide range of textures, including semisoft, semihard, and hard.
- **Unripened cheese.** Made from curds that have not been aged. Most unripened cheeses will keep only a few days in the refrigerator.

Specialty cheeses are created by combining several ripened cheeses by either cold or hot processing methods. *Cold pack cheese* is a blend of ripened cheeses processed without heat. Flavorings and seasoning are often added. *Pasteurized process cheese* is a blend of ripened cheeses processed with heat. Examples are process American cheese, cheese spread, and cheese food.

Types of Cheese

		Appearance	Texture and Flavor
Ripened Cheeses	Blue Cheese	White cheese with a blue vein.	*Semisoft.* Tangy flavor.
	Brick	Light yellow color.	*Semisoft.* Sweet, mild but pungent flavor.
	Brie (BREE)	White, edible crust with a creamy, yellow interior.	*Soft.* Mild to pungent flavor.
	Camembert (KAM-ehm-behr)	White, edible crust with a creamy, yellow interior. Similar to Brie.	*Soft.* Mild to pungent flavor.
	Cheddar	White to orange color.	*Hard.* Mild to sharp flavor.
	Colby	Similar to cheddar, but moister.	*Hard.* Mild to sharp flavor.
	Edam (EE-duhm)	Creamy, yellow Dutch cheese with red wax coating.	*Semihard.* Mild, nutlike flavor.
	Feta (FAY-tuh)	White, crumbly cheese.	*Semihard.* Salty, pickled flavor.

- ***Other Dairy Foods (text pages 466-470)***

Student Display

Ask students to bring one dairy food of choice to class for a display. Have students identify the fresh and convenience forms of the dairy foods. Using the Nutrition Facts panels, have students compare the nutrients in the foods. Which has the most calcium? Do any provide fiber? Which has the most fat? What is the serving size? **L1**

Categorizing Activity

Ask students to name the two basic categories of cheeses and to explain the general differences between them. Record a list of the differences on the chalkboard.

Taste Test

Set up a numbered, blind taste test display of one ripened and one unripened cheese, such as feta and mozzarella. Have each student taste a small cube of each and note the flavor and record the name of the numbered cheese. Then have each student view the cheeses, note the appearance, and record the names of the numbered cheese. How did students do? Were both their flavor and appearance results the same?

FOOD SCIENCE

Separating Fat from Cream

Emphasize that invisible fat can be made visible by demonstrating how agitation of cream will cause the fat globules to separate from the liquid. Proceed by pouring a half-pint container of heavy cream into a glass jar with a tight lid. Add a clean glass or ceramic marble to the jar and shake vigorously. Drain the liquid into a glass, and put the solid on a small plate or dish. Ask students to taste the samples, noting what you have created (i.e., buttermilk and butter).

TEACH cont.

- *Other Dairy Foods (text pages 466-470)*

Nutrition Research

Using Nutrition Facts panels, a nutrition software program, or a combination, ask students to record the total fat content for one serving of each type of cheese listed in the chart on pages 467-468. Have them list the cheeses in order from highest fat to lowest fat. Have them repeat this activity for calcium contents. Have students share and compare findings. **L2**

Information Share

Have students research the history, production, characteristics, and uses of one type of cheese. Invite students to present their findings to the class in the form of an oral report, a poster, or some other medium that communicates information. **L1**

Lab Experience

Have students prepare dips using regular sour cream, plain yogurt, and blended cottage cheese. Serve with raw vegetable dippers. Have students compare the calories and fat in the dips, as well as the taste. What conclusions can students draw? In what other recipes could you substitute yogurt or cottage cheese for sour cream? For which dairy product might you choose a low-fat or fat-free alternative? **L1**

Types of Cheese (cont'd)

		Appearance	Texture and Flavor
Ripened Cheeses (cont'd)	Gouda (GOO-duh)	Creamy, yellow cheese with red wax coating. Similar to edam, but higher in fat.	*Semihard.* Mild nutlike flavor.
	Monterey Jack	Creamy, white cheese with tiny cracks.	*Semisoft.* Mild flavor.
	Muenster (MUHN-stir)	Orange exterior and white interior.	*Semisoft.* Mild flavor.
	Parmesan (PAHR-muh-zahn)	Creamy, white, granular cheese.	*Very hard.* Tangy, robust flavor.
	Provolone (proh-vuh-LOH-nee)	Creamy, golden yellow, plastic-like cheese.	*Hard.* Bland to sharp, smoked flavor.
	Romano (roh-MAH-noh)	Creamy, white cheese. Similar to parmesan.	*Very hard.* Rich, tangy flavor.
	Swiss	Creamy, white cheese with holes in it.	*Hard.* Nutlike flavor.
Unripened Cheeses	Cottage Cheese	Moist, soft cheese with large or small curds.	Bland flavor, but flavorings such as chives may be added. May be creamed.
	Cream Cheese	Smooth, spreadable, white cheese.	Mild, slightly acid flavor. Flavorings such as strawberry may be added.
	Farmer's Cheese	Firm and dry. Similar to cottage cheese.	Bland flavor.
	Mozzarella	Creamy, white, plastic-like cheese.	*Semisoft.* Mild flavor.
	Ricotta	Moist, white cheese.	Mild, sweet flavor.

Cream

Cream is a liquid separated from milk. Several types, which vary as to fat content, are available. Heavy cream, the highest in fat, whips easily. Light cream, which is not as high in fat, is often used in coffee. Half-and-half is a mixture of milk and cream. Sour cream, made by adding lactic acid bacteria to cream, is thick and rich with a tangy flavor. It's also relatively high in fat and calories. Add it sparingly to your baked potato, or select a reduced-fat or fat-free sour cream product. Another alternative is using thickened yogurt. You'll learn how to make thickened yogurt in Section 18-2.

FOOD SCIENCE

Lactose Maldigestion

Have students find out more about lactose maldigestion and intolerance and what causes these conditions. How do incidences of these conditions vary by country? How does lactose maldigestion differ from lactose intolerance? Why can people with lactose maldigestion consume some dairy products but not others?

◆ Long ago, milk was sold with a layer of thick, sweet top cream. Sometimes a ladle-like spoon came with the milk to use to remove the top cream. Because of its high fat content, heavy cream should be used sparingly. Identify some lower-fat alternatives to cream.

Butter

Butter is made from milk, cream, or a combination of the two. Because it's high in saturated fat and also contains cholesterol, the most healthful choice is to use it in moderation.

Butter is graded for quality by the USDA. *Grade AA* is superior in quality. It has a delicate, sweet flavor and a smooth, creamy texture, and it spreads well. It may be purchased salted or unsalted. *Grade A* butter is very good in quality and has a pleasing flavor with a smooth texture. *Grade B* butter is made from sour cream and has a pleasing flavor.

Frozen Dairy Desserts

Several different types of frozen desserts are available. They differ in fat content and ingredients. All come in a variety of flavors. Here are some examples:

- **Ice cream.** A whipped, frozen mixture of milk, cream, sweeteners, flavorings, and other additives. In addition to regular ice cream, you can buy reduced-fat, low-fat, fat-free, and no-sugar-added versions.
- **Frozen yogurt.** Similar to ice cream, but with yogurt cultures added. Low-fat and fat-free varieties are the most popular.
- **Sherbet.** Made from milk fat, sugar, water, flavoring, and other additives. It generally has less fat and more sugar than regular ice cream.

As an occasional treat on a hot summer's day, a frozen dairy treat can be just the thing. Just be cautious in choosing a product. As an alert consumer, you need to go beyond the

FOR YOUR HEALTH

The Scoop on Frozen Dairy Desserts

What's in a name? When it comes to frozen dairy desserts, the answer is "a whole lot!" All of the products in the list below vary in terms of fat, sugar, and calorie content. None, however, could be described as a low-calorie treat. Use the following information when choosing a frozen dairy dessert. Numbers of calories and fat grams are based on a ½-cup (125-mL) serving.

	Calories	Fat (grams)
Premium ice cream	175	12
Regular ice cream	135	7
Low-fat ice cream	92	3
Sherbet	135	2
Low-fat frozen yogurt	125	3

Following Up

- Think about some of the ways frozen dairy treats are served—for example, in sundaes. Investigate how various toppings and other additions affect the total fat and calorie content. What strategies can you think of for increasing the nutrient value of frozen treats?

- *Other Dairy Foods*
- *Buying and Storing Dairy Foods (text pages 466-470)*

FOR YOUR HEALTH

Have students conduct taste tests of five frozen dairy desserts of the same flavor. Cover the containers and color-code. Dip small samples into mini paper baking cups the same colors as the container labels. Have students compare taste, texture, and price. Have students try to identify which color matches each of the five frozen dairy desserts.

Product Comparison

Ask students to bring in an empty frozen dairy dessert package. Have students compare Nutrition Facts panels from frozen dairy desserts, including regular ice cream, low-fat ice cream, frozen yogurt, and fruit sherbet. Which provides the most calcium? Vitamin A? Which are highest and lowest in fat and calories? L2

Listing Activity

Review with students the tips for storing dairy foods. Ask students to brainstorm and list other guidelines for storing dairy foods. Ask a volunteer to compile the list on the classroom computer so that copies can be furnished to each member to take home and share with families.

FOOD SCIENCE

Effects of Gelatin Experiment

You may wish to present or have students complete Experiment 12 in the *Food Science Resources* booklet, which examines the effects of gelatin on frozen desserts. The experiment tests the appearance, texture, flavor, and melting characteristics of adding gelatin to a frozen dessert.

ASSESS

REVIEW

- Ask students to summarize the main ideas in this section.
- Have students complete the Section Review. (Answers appear below.)

EVALUATION

- Have students write a short essay describing what they have learned about the various types of dairy products available.
- Have students take the quiz for Section 18-1. (Use the quiz in the *Teacher Resource Guide,* or construct your own with the **ExamView**® *Test Generator* on the *Effective Instruction CD-ROM.*)

RETEACHING

- Ask students to write a newspaper article on choosing dairy foods based on nutritional value.
- Refer to the *Reteaching Activities* booklet for the Section 18-1 activity sheet.

CLOSE

Have students participate in the creation of a large chart showing the various types of dairy products available, the nutrients in each, and ways to include these products in a weekly menu.

name and descriptions on the label. Above all else, pay attention to portion size. Remember, even fat-free ice cream can have up to 300 calories per cup!

Buying and Storing Dairy Foods

When buying dairy products, look for the date on the package. Most milk products can safely be used for up to five days beyond the "sell by" date if they have been stored properly. Yogurt and some ripened cheeses may be stored for longer periods of time. Be sure containers are sealed tightly and have not been opened before you buy them.

Dairy foods are highly perishable. Store them immediately when you get home from shopping. Refrigerate all dairy foods in their original containers, if possible.

Here are some additional tips for storing dairy foods:

- Tightly close milk and cream containers. These products can pick up aromas from other foods and develop off-flavors.

◆ **Cheese can be frozen for later use in cooked dishes, such as this Mexican casserole of tortillas layered with chicken and tomatillos (green tomatoes). What other dishes do you like that have cheese in them?**

- Store milk away from light. Light destroys the riboflavin (a B vitamin) in milk.
- Keep cheeses tightly wrapped.
- Hard cheeses can be frozen, but the texture will change. Freeze in ½-pound (250-g) portions. Use crumbled, shredded, or in cooked dishes.
- Refrigerate butter up to several weeks. For longer storage, freeze up to nine months.
- Store ice cream tightly covered in the freezer.

Section 18-1 Review & Activities

1. Identify four nutrients in milk and milk products.
2. Why is milk pasteurized?
3. What is the difference between ripened and unripened cheese?
4. Give three tips for storing milk and milk products.
5. **Analyzing.** Make a chart of the shelf-stable dairy products detailed in the chapter. For each product, identify common uses as well as other situations in which it might be used.
6. **Evaluating.** Discuss the benefits of using fat-free yogurt over other dairy foods in cooking.
7. **Applying.** Use the chart "Nutritive Value in Foods," in Appendix B, to compare the nutrients in various dairy products. Which are highest in calcium? Which are lowest in fat?

Answers to Section 18-1 Review & Activities

1. See page 463.
2. To kill enzymes and harmful bacteria that make milk spoil quickly.
3. See bulleted list on page 467.
4. See bulleted list on page 470.
5. Charts and uses will vary. Fat-free dry, evaporated, sweetened condensed, and UHT milk should be included.
6. Answers will vary. Fat-free yogurt can give a very similar taste without adding the fat and calories.
7. Answers will vary. See the "Nutritive Value of Foods" chart in Appendix B.

SECTION 18-2

Preparing Dairy Foods

Objectives

After studying this section, you should be able to:

- Identify ways to prevent problems when cooking with milk.
- Discuss ways to use yogurt in recipes.
- Identify guidelines for preparing cheese.

Look for This Term

scalded milk

Ted was heating milk to make cocoa when the phone rang. He knew that if he left the milk to get the phone, the milk might boil over. So he let the answering machine take the call.

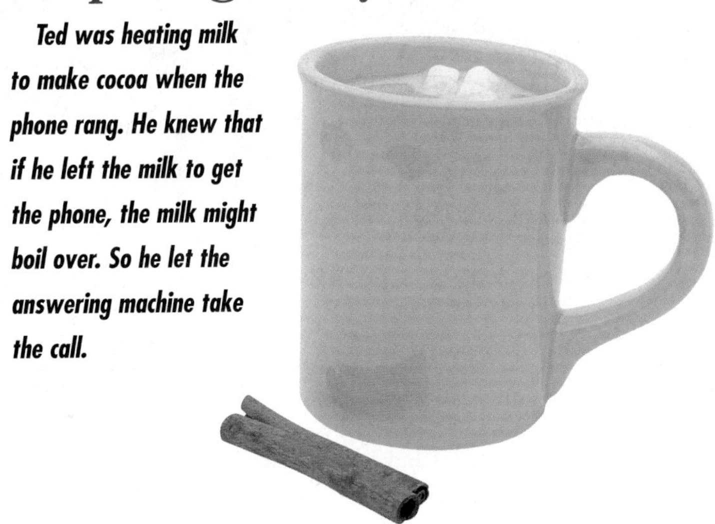

Cooking with Milk

Ted was aware that dairy foods are delicate proteins. They must be cooked carefully at moderate temperatures and for a limited amount of time.

Milk can be the base for preparing delicious cooked foods, including cocoa and soups. However, several problems can arise when you're cooking milk:

- **Forming a skin.** As milk cooks, protein solids clump together, forming a skin on the surface. The skin can make the milk bubble up and boil over. To keep a skin from forming, cover the pan or stir the mixture regularly. If a skin forms, use a wire whisk to beat it back into the mixture. Removing it removes nutrients.
- **Scorching.** When milk solids fall to the bottom of a pan, they stick and burn. To prevent milk from scorching, use low heat. Stir the mixture to keep the solids circulating. Cooking milk in a double boiler can help prevent scorching.

◆ **When milk-based recipes such as this corn chowder are cooked carefully, the result is smooth and flavorful. How did the person who cooked this chowder avoid scorching the milk?**

SECTION 18-2

Preparing Dairy Foods

FOCUS

MOTIVATORS

- Ask students if they know what causes a skin to form on the surface of milk as it cooks. What causes milk to scorch? What makes milk curdle when mixed with an acid food? What should you do if yogurt separates when it is stored? What happens if cheese is overcooked? Point out that the answers to these questions and more will be answered in this section.
- Ask students if they have ever encountered anything unusual or any problems when cooking with milk, yogurt, or cheese. What problems did they encounter?

VOCABULARY ACTIVITY

Pronounce the term listed under "Look for This Term." Have students find the term and its definition in the section.

STUDY SKILLS

- **Listening.** Invite a group of volunteers to each prepare an oral reading of a page of text from the section, while others follow along silently.
- Have students read the section and complete the appropriate part of the Chapter 18 Study Guide in the *Student Workbook*.

Section 18-2 Resources

◆ **Student Workbook**, pp. 129, 133
◆ **Teacher Resource Guide**
Lesson Plan 18-2 Organizer
Section 18-2 Quiz
◆ **Effective Instruction CD-ROM**
Exam*View*® *Test Generator*

◆ **Student Motivation Kit**
Reteaching Activities, pp. 83–84
Enrichment Activities
Foods Lab Resources, pp. 69–72
Food Science Resources, pp. 69–74
Skills for Making Food Choices, pp. 41–42

TEACH

- *Cooking with Milk*
- *Using Yogurt in Recipes*
- *Preparing Cheese (text pages 471-473)*

Discussion Activity

Name a dozen problems that can occur during preparation with dairy products. Have students suggest at least one way to prevent each problem from occurring.

Demonstration

Ask students to explain how to thicken yogurt. Demonstrate how to make "yogurt cheese" using a strainer and cheesecloth. Prepare one batch overnight. Have students compare the thickness differences between the "yogurt cheese" and regular yogurt. How do the two compare in flavor? For what purposes could students recommend using the thickened yogurt where higher-fat foods are normally used?

Lab Experience

Divide the class into lab groups. Have each group practice heating milk to scalding temperature on top of the range and in a microwave oven. Review each group's scalding techniques. **L1**

Categorizing

Ask students to list the names of cheeses and explain which should be served chilled, and which should be served at room temperature. Have students compare their cheese lists. **L1**

◆ **Cocoa is a favorite cold-weather beverage made with milk. Name two ways of preparing cocoa.**

◆ **Curdling.** When milk curdles, it has separated into curds and whey. Curdling may occur when milk is heated with acidic foods, such as vegetables and fruits. It can also be caused by salt or high heat. To prevent curdling, use low temperatures, stir the mixture, and combine milk with acidic foods gradually.

Some recipes call for **scalded milk**, milk that is heated to just below the boiling point. Use low heat and cook only until bubbles appear around the sides of the pan.

Milk and milk-based recipes can be prepared easily in the microwave oven. Be sure to use a large enough container in case the milk foams up.

Using Yogurt in Recipes

Yogurt can be a nutrient-dense substitute for sour cream, cream cheese, milk, and mayonnaise. You can use it in many recipes, from soups to main dishes to salads.

Here are some basic guidelines to remember when cooking with yogurt:

- ◆ Yogurt can be cooked, baked, or frozen. The active bacteria cultures may not survive, but the nutrients will still be the same.
- ◆ Whey may separate from the curd in yogurt when it is stored. Stir the whey back into the yogurt before you use it.
- ◆ Cook yogurt at moderate temperatures for only the time needed. Yogurt is just as delicate as other dairy foods. If overcooked, it will curdle.
- ◆ To keep yogurt from separating during cooking, blend 1 tablespoon (15 mL) cornstarch with a small amount of yogurt. Combine with the remaining yogurt, and use according to recipe directions.
- ◆ You can thicken yogurt by letting the whey drain off. Line a strainer with a double thickness of cheesecloth. Empty the yogurt into the strainer and set the strainer over a bowl. (The bowl should be a size and shape that prevent the strainer from touching the bottom.) Refrigerate up to 12 hours or until enough whey has drained off to give the desired thickness. If the yogurt is thick enough, you can use it as a cheese. Use the nutrient-rich whey in soups and casseroles, or substitute it for water, buttermilk, or milk in baking.

Q&A

Q ***When making cocoa, how can I cut down on fat and prevent problems—such as lumping and scorching—from occurring?***

A Use fat-free milk to reduce fat. To prevent lumping, mix the cocoa powder and sugar thoroughly. Gradually add a little liquid, stirring well to make a smooth paste. Then continue adding the rest of the liquid, stirring constantly. Use low heat to prevent scorching, or cook the cocoa in the microwave.

FOOD SCIENCE: Serving Temperature of Cheese

Ask volunteers to bring in approximately two ounces of ripened cheese; cut in half. Have these students prepare two cheese trays of ripened cheese. One of the trays is to be refrigerated, while the other is permitted to reach room temperature. Have students sample cheese from both trays. What conclusions can they draw about the effects of temperature on the flavor and texture of cheese?

You can also use yogurt as a salad dressing, dip, sauce, or dessert topping. For example, top cooked vegetables such as asparagus with plain yogurt; then sprinkle with chopped nuts and minced chives.

Preparing Cheese

Serve unripened cheeses, such as cottage cheese and cream cheese, chilled. Add seasonings and chopped vegetables to them to make zesty dips.

Ripened cheese tastes best when served at room temperature. Remove it from the refrigerator at least 30 minutes before serving. You can also bring it to room temperature by microwaving it. Follow the directions in the owner's manual.

Follow these guidelines when cooking cheese:

- Heat cheese just long enough to melt it. If overcooked, cheese gets stringy and tough.
- To speed up cooking time, shred, grate, or cut cheese into small pieces.
- Be careful when microwaving cheese—the fat in it attracts microwaves. The cheese may be hotter than the rest of the microwaved food.
- To lower the fat in recipes with cheese, choose sharp-flavored varieties. Since they have more flavor, you can use less cheese.

◆ **This zesty salad dressing was made by blending fresh herbs and plain, nonfat yogurt. What other ways can yogurt be used in cooking?**

Section 18-2 Review & Activities

1. List two ways to prevent milk from curdling.

2. How can yogurt be used as a substitute for cheese?

3. What happens to cheese if it is overcooked?

4. Extending. Ronit's six-year-old daughter doesn't like milk or cheese. What recommendations can you make for using milk and/or other dairy products in cooking that can help Ronit meet her daughter's nutritional needs?

5. Synthesizing. Would you try to dovetail other food preparation tasks with the cooking of dairy products? Why or why not?

6. Applying. Locate a recipe for homemade cream of tomato soup. Read through the directions carefully. What does the recipe recommend to prevent curdling? How might you improve upon the directions?

ASSESS

REVIEW

- Ask students to summarize the main ideas in this section.
- Have students complete the Section Review. (Answers appear below.)

EVALUATION

- Provide students with a list of problems that can occur during preparation with milk, yogurt, and cheese. Students will need to solve the problems and record their solutions.
- Have students take the quiz for Section 18-2. (Use the quiz in the *Teacher Resource Guide,* or construct your own with the **Exam***View*® *Test Generator* on the *Effective Instruction CD-ROM.*)

RETEACHING

- Have students create charts showing guidelines for preparing food items that contain cheese, milk, or yogurt.
- Refer to the *Reteaching Activities* booklet for the Section 18-2 activity sheet.

CLOSE

Have students all participate in the creation of a class guide entitled "Ten Steps to Dairy Food Preparation Success."

Answers to Section 18-2 Review & Activities

1. Use low temperatures, and combine milk with acidic foods gradually.
2. Thicken it, and use it as a topping for cooked vegetables.
3. It gets stringy and tough.
4. Answers will vary. Many foods that contain milk and dairy products do not taste like the milk or dairy product.
5. Answers will vary. Dairy products are very delicate and easily overcooked. It may not be a good idea to try to dovetail.
6. Answers will vary.

Recipe File

Easy Macaroni and Cheese

This recipe is prepared using several types of dairy products—process cheese spread, butter, and evaporated fat-free milk.

USING THE RECIPE

- Have students read the recipe and discuss each step. Note the importance of cooking the milk mixture over the indicated medium-low heat, not high heat.
- Review safety and sanitation procedures that apply to this recipe.
- Have each lab team fill out a work plan. (See the *Foods Lab Resources* booklet.)
- Have students check off the ingredients and equipment listed on the recipe worksheet and prepare the recipe.
- Have students complete the evaluation and questions on the recipe worksheet.

SEE ALSO. . .
The *Foods Lab Resources* booklet for the "Easy Macaroni and Cheese" recipe worksheet and other recipe alternatives.

Recipe File

Easy Macaroni and Cheese

Just about every home cook—and many professional ones, too—have a recipe for macaroni and cheese. Here's a version that's easy *and* good!

Customary	***Ingredients***	***Metric***
½ lb.	Elbow or corkscrew macaroni	250 g
4 oz.	Process cheese spread (sold in loaves)	125 g
½ cup	Green pepper, chopped	125 mL
¼ cup	Finely chopped onion	50 mL
1 tsp.	Butter or margarine	5 mL
1 cup	Evaporated fat-free milk	250 mL
¼ tsp.	Ground pepper	1 mL
½ cup	Dry breadcrumbs	125 mL
1 tsp.	Butter or margarine, melted	5 mL

Yield: 4 servings
Equipment: Saucepan; 1½ qt. (1.5 L) casserole
Oven Temperature: 350°F (180°C)

Directions

1. Cook macaroni according to package directions. Drain and set aside.
2. Preheat oven.
3. Cut cheese into cubes and set aside.
4. In a saucepan, sauté green pepper and onion over medium-low heat in 1 teaspoon (5 mL) butter or margarine, about 1 to 2 minutes, stirring constantly.
5. Stir in evaporated fat-free milk and cheese cubes.
6. Cook over medium-low heat, stirring constantly, until cheese is melted and mixture is well blended. Stir in pepper.
7. Combine milk and cheese mixture with macaroni in casserole. Mix gently.
8. Combine breadcrumbs and 1 teaspoon (5 mL) melted butter or margarine.
9. Sprinkle breadcrumb mixture over macaroni and cheese mixture.
10. Bake 20 to 30 minutes until hot and bubbly.

Nutrition Information

Per serving (approximate): 387 calories, 18 g protein, 57 g carbohydrate, 10 g fat, 19 mg cholesterol, 570 mg sodium
Good source of: potassium, iron, vitamin A, vitamin D, vitamin C, B vitamins, calcium, phosphorus

Food for Thought

- Why is the cheese cut into cubes before it is cooked?
- What are some low-fat foods you could serve with this dish to make a nutritionally-balanced menu?

Answers to Food for Thought

1. To speed up cooking time and help the cheese melt more evenly.
2. Answers will vary. Since it already has dairy and grains, serve it with fruits, vegetables, and meats. For instance, serve it with vegetable salad, lean ham steak, and fresh fruit juice.

SECTION
18-3

Objectives

After studying this section, you should be able to:

- Describe the structure of an egg.
- Identify the nutrients provided by eggs.
- Give guidelines for buying and storing eggs.
- Explain how to cook eggs by conventional and microwave methods.

Look for These Terms

albumen
chalazae
coagulate
shirred eggs

Egg Basics

Trudy watched in puzzlement as her father cracked eggs into a bowl and began to beat them. "Hey, Dad," she said. "Did you forget that it's dinnertime, not breakfast?" Trudy's dad knows that while many people enjoy eggs for breakfast, they can be featured in other meals as well. Eggs are an economical food source and can be prepared in a variety of ways.

Structure of an Egg

An egg's shell is lined with several membranes. A pocket of air lies between these membranes and the shell at the wide end. As the egg ages, the air pocket grows.

Inside the egg is the **albumen** (al-BYOO-muhn), a thick, clear fluid commonly known as the egg white. The yolk—the round, yellow portion—floats within the albumen. Anchoring the yolk in the center of the egg are **chalazae** (kuh-LAH-zuh), twisted, cordlike strands of albumen.

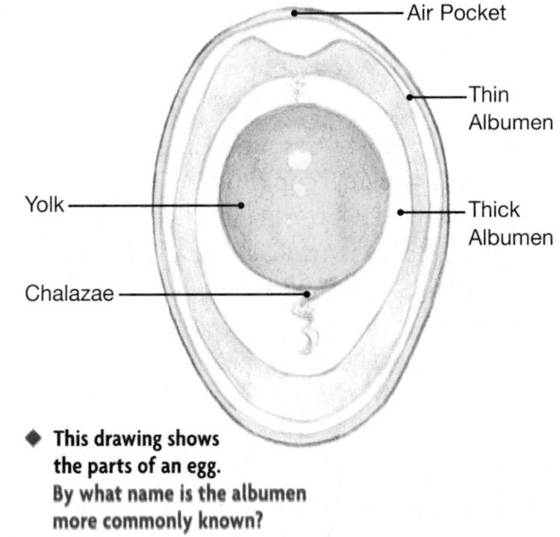

◆ **This drawing shows the parts of an egg. By what name is the albumen more commonly known?**

SECTION
18-3
Egg Basics

FOCUS

MOTIVATORS

- Ask students to name their favorite methods of preparing eggs. List the methods on the board in order of popularity from the most popular to least popular.
- Ask if any students have ever tried microwaving an egg in the shell and, if so, what happened? Explain that in this section, students will learn about precautions involving eggs.

VOCABULARY ACTIVITY

Pronounce the four terms listed under "Look for These Terms." Have students find the terms and their definitions in the section.

STUDY SKILLS

- **Outlining.** Have students read the section and outline it by copying the headers on paper and leaving space after each one. Students are to write a sentence in their own words, summarizing the content under each header.
- Have students read the section and complete the appropriate part of the Chapter 18 Study Guide in the *Student Workbook*.

Section 18-3 Resources

◆ **Student Workbook,** pp. 130, 134
◆ **Teacher Resource Guide**
Lesson Plan 18-3 Organizer
Section 18-3 Quiz
◆ **Effective Instruction CD-ROM**
Exam*View*® *Test Generator*
PowerPoint® Slide #42
◆ **Transparency Package,** CT-42
◆ **Student Motivation Kit**
Reteaching Activities, p. 85
Enrichment Activities
Foods Lab Resources, pp. 73–76
Food Science Resources, pp. 50–52, 75–81

TEACH

- *Structure of an Egg*
- *Nutrients in Eggs*
- *Buying Eggs*
- *Storing Eggs (text pages 475-477)*

Health Research

Ask students to research the health benefits of eggs for special populations, such as aging adults, or for all populations. Research might be carried out online under your supervision. Ask that students use the information to create a Nutrition Facts panel for eggs. They are to follow the model on other food packages. L2

Observation Activity

Have students hold an egg up to a strong light and observe the contents. Have them locate the air pocket at the wide end. They are then to break the egg onto a saucer and locate its parts: shell, membranes, albumen, yolk, and chalazae.

Demonstration

Break a Grade AA, Grade A, and Grade B egg onto three separate plates. Note differences in size, shape, and consistency.

USING Safety Check

Ask students to find out how much of a pasteurized egg substitute product can be used in place of one raw egg in a recipe.

Nutrients in Eggs

Eggs are an excellent source of protein, riboflavin (a B vitamin), and iodine. In addition, they are good sources of vitamin A, some other B vitamins, vitamin D, iron, and trace minerals. However, egg yolks also contain saturated fats and cholesterol.

On the Food Guide Pyramid, eggs are part of the Meat, Poultry, Fish, Dry Beans, Eggs, and Nuts Group. When counting servings, remember that a single egg counts as 1 ounce (30 g) of meat. However, because whole eggs are so high in cholesterol, health experts recommend eating no more than four egg yolks a week. There is no limit on the number of egg whites because they are cholesterol-free.

Buying Eggs

Eggs are sold according to grade and size standards set by the USDA. Both grade and size are clearly marked on the package.

Grade

The USDA grade shield on the package means that the eggs have been federally inspected for wholesomeness. The grade is determined by the inner and outer quality of the egg at the time it was packaged. It has nothing to do with the freshness of the egg or its size.

The three egg grades are AA, A, and B. There is no difference in nutritive value among them. However, there is a difference in appearance when cooked. Grade AA and A eggs have a thicker white and are used when appearance is important, such as with fried or poached eggs. Grade B eggs are used when appearance is not important, as in baked products or scrambled eggs. As a rule, grades AA and A are the grades most commonly found in supermarkets.

Size

The size of an egg is determined by the minimum weight for a dozen. The sizes most commonly sold are large and extra large. As a general rule, recipes assume that large eggs will be used.

Eggs are usually priced according to size and supply. Check the unit price to determine which size is the best buy. Be sure to open the carton and inspect the eggs. They should be clean and whole, without any cracks.

Storing Eggs

Eggs are highly perishable. Store them immediately when you get home from shopping. Refrigerate eggs in the original carton. Do not put them in the egg tray commonly found in the refrigerator door—the drop in temperature each time the door is opened may cause the eggs to lose quality. In addition, egg shells are porous and pick up aromas from other foods if stored uncovered. Do not wash eggs before storing—washing destroys the egg's natural protective covering.

Safety Check

Harmful bacteria in raw or undercooked eggs have caused foodborne illness. To be sure that eggs are safe to eat:

- Do not use eggs that are cracked or broken. They may contain harmful bacteria.
- Always cook eggs thoroughly—until the whites and yolks are firm.
- Serve cooked eggs and egg-rich foods right after cooking.
- Never eat raw eggs or any foods containing raw eggs, such as homemade eggnog, homemade ice cream, or raw cookie dough. Raw eggs in commercial products are usually pasteurized, which destroys harmful bacteria.

FOOD SCIENCE **Protein Coagulation Experiment**

In conjunction with this section, you may want to demonstrate or assign Experiment 13 in the *Food Science Resources* booklet. This experiment tests the effects of different cooking times on the coagulation of protein.

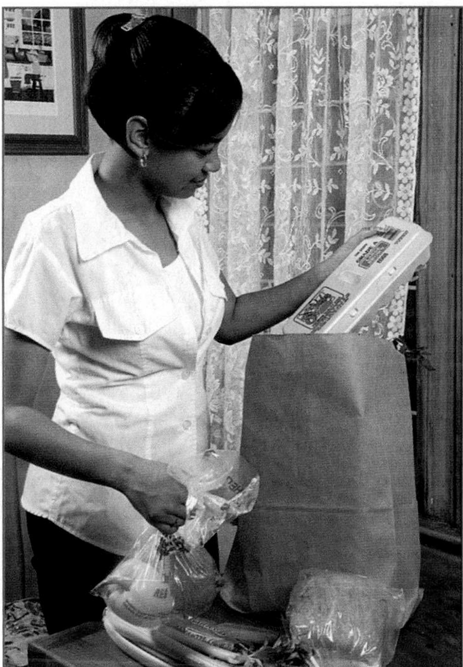

◆ **Knowing how to store eggs properly can make a difference when it comes to their quality and nutrient values. Name two things you should do and two things you shouldn't.**

Refrigerate leftover raw yolks or whites in a covered container if you plan to use them within two to four days. For longer storage, freeze them. Refrigerate cooked egg dishes immediately and use them within three days.

Preparing Eggs

Like dairy foods, eggs are delicate proteins. They must be cooked at moderate temperatures for a limited amount of time. When overcooked, egg whites shrink and become tough and rubbery. When egg yolks are overcooked, they toughen and turn gray-green on the surface.

Eggs can be cooked on top of the range, in the oven, or in the microwave oven. Depending on which method you use, there are a few differences in basic cooking principles. In conventional cooking, use medium to low heat. Time the eggs carefully to be sure they are thoroughly cooked. The whites will **coagulate**, or become firm, before the yolks do.

When eggs are cooked in a microwave oven, the yolks cook faster than the whites. That is because the fat in the yolks attracts more microwaves than the whites do. Remove eggs from the microwave oven while they're still moist and soft. Standing time will complete the cooking.

Eggs can be prepared in several basic ways: cooked in the shell, fried, baked, poached, or scrambled.

Q ***What's the best way to freeze eggs?***

A To freeze whole raw eggs, beat the eggs until well-blended and pour them into freezer containers. Three tablespoons (45 mL) of beaten whole egg equals one large egg. To freeze raw whites, place the white of one egg in each compartment of an ice cube tray. After freezing, put frozen cubes in a tightly sealed freezer container and use as needed. Two egg whites equal one large egg. Use frozen eggs only in dishes that will be thoroughly cooked.

Safety Check

Never microwave an egg in the shell. Steam builds up in the egg. When it can no longer be held in by the shell, the egg can burst and cause a serious injury.

- *Storing Eggs*
- *Preparing Eggs (text pages 476-480)*

Using Q&A

First ask students to describe proper storage for eggs. Then demonstrate how to freeze whole eggs and egg whites.

Discussion Activity

Ask students to do the following: Explain what happens to eggs when they are overcooked. Explain the difference in the way eggs cook in the microwave and in conventional cooking. Describe the procedure for cooking eggs in the shell.

Demonstration

Boil several eggs. Show how to peel a hard-cooked egg. Then have a few student volunteers give the same demonstration, while other students note if they're using proper techniques. Encourage students to practice at home.

USING Safety Check

Have students use cooking resources or cookbooks, specifically microwave cookbooks, to find an egg-based recipe that's prepared in the microwave.

Extending Learning

Egg Protein—Ovomucin is the protein that makes albumen thick. It does not coagulate as quickly as the other proteins in the egg white. When you begin to fry an egg, the thin albumen flows away from the egg; it coagulates first. The thicker the albumen, the longer it takes to coagulate. Chalazae is the thickest part of the albumen. It may only partially coagulate.

As the egg fries, the albumen coagulates first. The yolk proteins begin to set at a slightly higher temperature than the albumen.

TEACH cont.

- *Preparing Eggs (text pages 477-480)*

Lab Experience

Have lab groups each prepare three hard-cooked eggs. Simmer two eggs for 15 minutes; boil one for 20 minutes. Let one of the first two eggs cool at room temperature. Cool the others in cold water. Compare the results. Have students draw conclusions. L1

Discussion Activity

Ask students to describe the procedure for frying an egg. Ask students to explain the following: (1) why it is necessary to pierce the yolks before baking an egg in a microwave oven; (2) the difference between boiling and poaching eggs; (3) why it is important not to stir scrambled eggs constantly while they cook.

Guest Speaker

Have the chef of an area restaurant speak to the class about interesting ways to prepare eggs for different types of meals (breakfast, brunch, lunch, dinner). If possible, have the chef demonstrate his or her omelet preparation techniques.

Eggs Cooked in the Shell

When cooking eggs in the shell, place a single layer of them in a saucepan. Add water to a level at least 1 inch (2.5 cm) above the eggs. Cover the saucepan, and bring the water just to boiling. Turn off the heat. If using an electric range, remove the pan from the heating element. Let the eggs stand in the hot water, covered. If you want soft-cooked eggs, let them stand about 4 to 5 minutes for a safe doneness. For hard-cooked eggs, let stand about 15 minutes if you're using large eggs (about 18 minutes for extra-large eggs).

After cooking, immediately run cold water over the eggs to stop the cooking process. To serve soft-cooked eggs, break the shell with a knife and scoop the egg out of the shell into a serving dish. To remove the shell from a hard-cooked egg, gently tap the egg all over to crack the shell. Roll the egg between your hands to loosen the shell. Peel the shell away starting at the large end.

Fried Eggs

Eggs can be fried in a very small amount of unsaturated fat or in a nonstick skillet that has been coated with a vegetable-oil cooking spray. With this method, the excess fat is held to a minimum. To fry eggs healthfully:

1. Heat a skillet over medium-high heat until it is hot enough to sizzle a drop of water.
2. Gently break one egg at a time into a small bowl or custard cup. If the yolk breaks, save the egg for another use. Otherwise, gently slip the egg from the bowl into the heated pan.
3. Immediately reduce the heat to low. Cover the pan, and cook the eggs slowly until done.
4. Turn the eggs over to cook the other side.

Baked Eggs

Baked eggs, also known as **shirred eggs**, are easy to prepare and low in added fat. Begin by breaking the eggs into a small bowl, then slipping them into a greased, shallow baking dish or custard cup. You can use individual dishes or place several eggs in one dish. Top the eggs with a small amount of milk, if you like.

To bake conventionally, place in an oven preheated to 325°F (160°C). Bake until done—about 12 minutes for two eggs. To microwave, first pierce the yolks with the tip of a knife or a wooden pick so that steam can escape. Cover the baking dish with either waxed paper or cooking parchment, and vent it to allow steam to escape. Follow the power level and timing instructions in the owner's manual or in a recipe book.

INFOLINK
For more on covering food when cooking in the microwave oven, see Section 9-4.

Poached Eggs

Poaching is a method of cooking eggs, out of the shell, in simmering water. To poach eggs conventionally, bring the water to a boil in a saucepan or deep skillet; then reduce the heat to a gentle simmer. Break one egg at a time into a small dish. Hold the dish close to the surface of the water and slip in the egg. Simmer about 5 minutes or until done.

You can also poach eggs in a microwave oven. Follow the directions in the owner's manual or in a recipe book. Be sure to pierce the yolks first to let steam escape.

FOOD SCIENCE

Coagulation Temperature of Egg Yolks

Ask students if they know why it is technically impossible to fry eggs until the yolks are completely done. Explain that the egg white sets at about 149°F (65°C), but the yolk must be cooked to about 156°F (69°C) before it coagulates. This means that the white will become rubbery if the yolk is cooked beyond the point of being firm but tender.

◆ **Poached eggs are a healthful alternative to other forms of cooked eggs since they require no added fat. Here they are served over salmon patties.** **What are three points to remember when poaching eggs?**

After cooking, use a slotted spoon to lift the eggs out of the water and drain them. Serve the eggs in a dish or over toast.

Scrambled Eggs

When making scrambled eggs, beat the eggs together with water or milk. Use 1 tablespoon (15 mL) liquid for each egg.

To cook conventionally, melt a small amount of butter or margarine in a skillet, or use a vegetable-oil cooking spray. Pour the egg mixture into the hot skillet. As the mixture starts to thicken, gently draw a spatula across the bottom and sides of the pan. This forms large curds and allows the uncooked egg to flow to the bottom of the skillet. Continue this procedure until the eggs are thickened and no visible liquid remains. Don't stir the eggs constantly. They will get mushy.

To make scrambled eggs in the microwave oven, cook the egg mixture in a custard cup or other microwave-safe container. Follow the power level and timing instructions in the owner's manual or in a recipe book. Stir once or twice during cooking and again at the end of the cooking time. Let stand to complete the cooking.

◆ **Eggs are not just for breakfast. The centerpiece of this dinner is fluffy scrambled eggs accompanied by a broiled tomato, rice, grapes, and a green salad.** **How many food groups in the Food Guide Pyramid are represented in this meal?**

- *Preparing Eggs (text pages 477-480)*

Lab Experience

Divide the class into two work groups. Have members of one group fry several eggs, experimenting with various cooking times and temperatures. Have them compare the results for texture and appearance. The second group is to prepare eggs using other preparation methods discussed in the section. Have groups reconvene to share their findings. L1

Recipe Collection

Have students use the experiences from the previous activity to kitchen-test and compile a collection of recipes for preparing eggs. Which ones are students' favorites? Have students find the nutritional value of each recipe by using a nutrition software program or print publication. L1

Brainstorm Activity

Ask students to brainstorm ways to prepare eggs healthfully, such as with less fat.

HOME & COMMUNITY CONNECTION

Ask students to conduct a home cooking demonstration activity for their families, choosing one type of egg preparation. Throughout the demonstration, suggest students explain what they're doing and why. Have students obtain feedback from their families. Ask students to share their experiences.

ASSESS

REVIEW

- Ask students to summarize the main ideas in this section.
- Have students complete the Section Review. (Answers appear below.)

EVALUATION

- Assign a method for cooking eggs and have students prepare the eggs correctly.
- Have students take the quiz for Section 18-3. (Use the quiz in the *Teacher Resource Guide,* or construct your own with the **ExamView**® *Test Generator* on the *Effective Instruction CD-ROM.*)

RETEACHING

- Have students write a booklet giving step-by-step instructions for preparing eggs in different ways.
- Refer to the *Reteaching Activities* booklet for the Section 18-3 activity sheet.

CLOSE

Lead a discussion on the various methods of cooking eggs. On the board, record students' brainstormed comments for "Do's" and "Don'ts" of egg preparation.

Connecting Food and Health

Egg Color Confusion

Perhaps because brown eggs look more "natural," they've gained a reputation as being more healthful than white eggs. Actually, the only difference between brown and white eggs is the breed of chicken that lays them. White eggs are produced by white-feathered birds, and brown eggs, by red-feathered birds. In nutrition, flavor, and cooking qualities, the eggs are the same.

Because red hens are typically larger than white and eat more feed, brown eggs may be more expensive. Variations in egg yolk color are due to the chicken's diet. Those fed yellow cornmeal or marigold petals produce eggs with a deeper yellow yolk than those fed white cornmeal. Artificial color additives are not allowed in chicken feeds.

Think About It

- Some people think brown and white eggs have different tastes. Prepare eggs of both colors in exactly the same way and conduct a class taste test. What do you conclude?

Basic Omelet

A basic omelet, also called a French omelet, is made with beaten eggs, just as scrambled eggs are. However, you cook an omelet in a skillet without stirring the eggs. The result is shaped somewhat like a large pancake.

While cooking, occasionally lift the edge of the omelet to allow uncooked egg to flow to the bottom. When the omelet is almost done, you may add a filling, such as sautéed vegetables. Fold the omelet in half to serve.

There are many variations on omelets. In the next section, you'll learn how to make a puffy omelet using beaten egg whites.

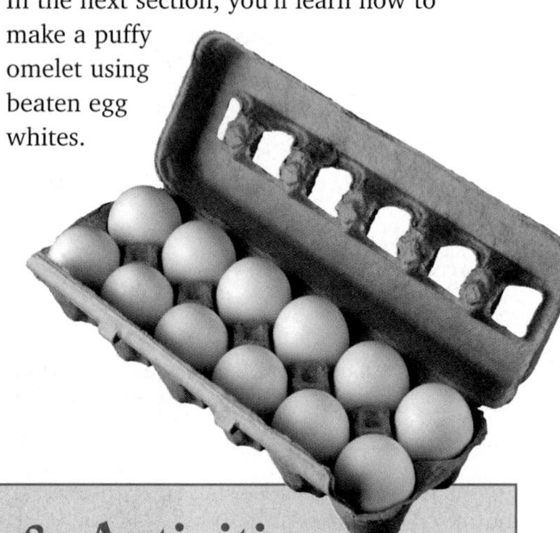

Section 18-3 Review & Activities

1. Describe the structure of an egg.
2. Name four nutrients found in eggs.
3. In what ways are eggs similar to and different from dairy foods?
4. Describe how eggs should be stored.
5. **Extending.** Did you ever crack an egg and notice a small red spot on the yolk? Find information that explains what this is, why it exists, and how it affects the edibility of the egg. How often do these occur? Report to the class.
6. **Analyzing.** Eggs have been called the most versatile food in the kitchen. Give reasons why this statement may have been made.
7. **Applying.** Design an advertisement to promote the use of eggs. You may want to focus on their versatility or nutritional value.

Answers to Section 18-3 Review & Activities

1. See page 475.
2. See page 476.
3. Both contain protein, riboflavin, and vitamin A, also saturated fat and cholesterol; require limited cooking at low temperatures; are highly perishable. Differences include flavor, use in recipes, food group.
4. See page 476.
5. This is a bloodspot, caused by rupture of vessels in yoke; has no effect on quality; occurs in less than 1% of all eggs.
6. Answers will vary.
7. Advertisements will vary.

Recipe File

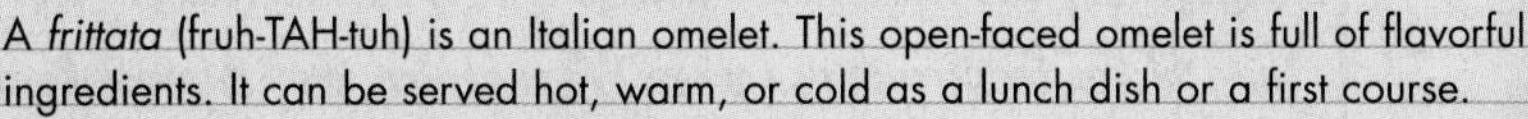

Italian Frittata

A *frittata* (fruh-TAH-tuh) is an Italian omelet. This open-faced omelet is full of flavorful ingredients. It can be served hot, warm, or cold as a lunch dish or a first course.

Customary	Ingredients	Metric
¼ lb.	Fresh mushrooms, thinly sliced	125 g
2	Green onions, minced	2
1½ Tbsp.	Butter or margarine	20 mL
6	Eggs	6
3 Tbsp.	Fresh parsley, chopped	45 mL
½ tsp.	Dried basil, crumbled	2 to 3 mL
¼ cup	Grated Parmesan cheese	30 mL
	Salt and pepper to taste	

Yield: 4 servings

Conventional Directions

Equipment: Large non-stick skillet with oven-safe handle
Oven Temperature: Broil

1. Sauté mushrooms and green onions in margarine or butter over medium heat until tender-crisp.
2. Preheat broiler.
3. Beat eggs in medium bowl.
4. Add parsley, basil, 2 tablespoons cheese, and salt and pepper to the eggs. Mix well.
5. Pour egg mixture over vegetables in skillet. Cook over medium heat, without stirring, until edges are lightly browned.
6. Sprinkle with remaining cheese.
7. Broil until top is golden brown.
8. Cut into wedges and serve hot.

Nutrition Information

Per serving (approximate): 227 calories, 13 g protein, 14 g carbohydrate, 17 g fat, 327 mg cholesterol, 424 mg sodium
Good source of: iron, vitamin A, vitamin D, vitamin E, B vitamins, calcium, phosphorus

Food for Thought

- How does the preparation method for this recipe differ from that for scrambled eggs?
- Name two ways you might reduce the amount of fat in the frittata.

Recipe File
Italian Frittata
This recipe demonstrates the versatility of eggs.

USING THE RECIPE

- Have students read the recipe and discuss each step. Caution students not to get the burner too hot while sautéing the mushrooms and onions to avoid being splattered with hot margarine or butter.
- Review safety and sanitation procedures that apply to this recipe.
- Have each lab team fill out a work plan. (See the *Foods Lab Resources* booklet.)
- Have students check off the ingredients and equipment listed on the recipe worksheet and prepare the recipe.
- Have students complete the evaluation and questions on the recipe worksheet.

SEE ALSO...
The *Foods Lab Resources* booklet for the "Italian Frittata" recipe worksheet and other recipe alternatives.

Answers to **Food for Thought**

1. The eggs are not stirred in this recipe as they are in scrambled eggs.
2. Answers will vary. Use a vegetable oil spray instead of margarine; use fat-free Parmesan instead of regular Parmesan cheese.

SECTION 18-4

Using Eggs in Recipes

FOCUS

MOTIVATORS

- Challenge students to see who can think of the most uses for eggs in cooking. Give a prize to the person who thinks of the most different uses.
- Create a bulletin board entitled "Egg-citing Eggs." Include illustrations of dishes that feature eggs, such as soufflé, meringue pie, omelet, and eggs Benedict. Point out that eggs can be prepared in more ways than fried, scrambled, hard or soft cooked, and poached.

VOCABULARY ACTIVITY

Pronounce the three terms listed under "Look for These Terms." Have students find the terms and their definitions in the section. Ask three student volunteers to find out from what language each of these terms is derived.

STUDY SKILLS

- **Guided Reading.** Have students look at the headings within Section 18-4 to preview the concepts that will be discussed.
- Have students read the section and complete the appropriate part of the Chapter 18 Study Guide in the *Student Workbook*.

SECTION 18-4

Objectives

After studying this section, you should be able to:

- Describe the difference between stirred custard and baked custard.
- Explain how to separate and beat egg whites.
- Identify uses of beaten egg whites.

Look for These Terms

quiche

soufflé

meringue

Using Eggs in Recipes

Have you ever heard the expression "wearing many hats"? It means performing many different functions—which is just what eggs do in recipes. They add richness and nutrients. They bind ingredients together. They thicken foods such as sauces. When beaten, they incorporate air and can help baked products rise.

Custards

One example of a recipe made with eggs is custard. Custard is a tender blend of milk thickened with eggs. It serves as a base for main dishes, such as **quiche** (KEESH)—a pie with a custard filling that contains foods such as chopped vegetables, cheese, and chopped cooked meat. Sweetened, flavored custard is a popular dessert.

There are two types of custard, stirred and baked:

- ◆ **Stirred custard.** Is cooked on top of the range and stirred constantly until it thickens enough to coat a spoon. It is also known as soft custard. Stirred custard is pourable and creamy. You can serve it as a pudding or as a sauce over cake or fruit.
- ◆ **Baked custard.** Is baked in the oven. It has a firm, delicate consistency. If you are preparing it in individual custard cups, set the cups in a pan of hot water to keep the mixture from overcooking. Bake the custard until a knife inserted in or near the center comes out clean. Baking time varies, depending on the size of the pans. If overbaked, the custard will curdle. If not baked long enough, it won't set.

Section 18-4 Resources

◆ **Student Workbook,** pp. 130, 136
◆ **Teacher Resource Guide**
Lesson Plan 18-4 Organizer
Section 18-4 Quiz
Chapter 18 Test
◆ **Effective Instruction CD-ROM**
Exam*View*® *Test Generator*
◆ **Student Motivation Kit**
Reteaching Activities, p. 86
Enrichment Activities
Food Science Resources, pp. 50–52, 75–77

◆ **Custard is a versatile combination of milk and eggs. It serves as a base for main dishes, such as quiche. Describe the difference between stirred and baked custard.**

Q&A

Q *Is there anything I can do to rescue a stirred custard that curdles and looks lumpy?*

A Pour the custard gradually into a blender or food processor and beat it. The sauce will be frothy instead of velvety. However, it will be usable unless it is very badly curdled.

Separating Eggs

Sometimes recipe directions call for only the yolk or white of the egg. In that case, you need to separate the egg. Eggs separate more easily when they are cold.

An easy, sanitary way to separate whites from yolks is to use an inexpensive egg separator. Simply break the egg carefully into the separator. The white will flow through, leaving the yolk in the separator.

◆ **Egg separators make it easy to separate whites from yolks. What is another benefit of these devices?**

TEACH

- *Custards*
- *Separating Eggs (text pages 482-484)*

Discussion Activity

Ask students to discuss the following: The difference between stirred custard and baked custard; how you can prevent curdling; how you can prevent overcooking.

Finding Recipes

Ask students to find custard or custard-based recipes. In class, have students note the similarities and differences in the recipes. Have them review the preparation techniques. Also, have them review how the recipes are served. L1

USING Safety Check

Show students an egg separator. Demonstrate how to easily and safely separate an egg using the egg separator.

Have students suggest other safety practices with eggs. Remind students of the risk of salmonella bacteria. Note: Although the risk of getting sick from eating soft cooked or underdone eggs is small, cooking eggs thoroughly is a wise precaution. This is especially true if the eggs will be served to children, aging adults, or individuals with health problems.

FOOD SCIENCE: Variables in Beating Eggs

Have students beat egg whites in bowls made of various materials. Compare results obtained using each type of bowl with and without cream of tartar. Point out that because plastic or wooden bowls tend to absorb grease from other foods, they should not be used for beating egg whites. An aluminum bowl causes dark egg whites; copper reacts with the whites and helps stabilize the foam. However, if cream of tartar is used with a copper bowl, the egg whites will turn green. Have students determine what causes these reactions.

TEACH cont.

- *Beating Egg Whites (text pages 484-486)*

Discussion Activity

Ask students to explain the purpose of beating egg whites. Then ask students to list guidelines for beating egg whites.

Demonstration

Demonstrate the soft-peak stage and the stiff-peak stage for egg whites. Have students note the differences between the stages. Ask students for what recipes stiff-peaks might be preferable. For what recipes soft-peaks might be preferable.

Demonstrate how to properly fold egg whites into other ingredients, such as a flour mixture. Have students note how the technique keeps the air and volume in the beaten egg whites. Ask why this is important.

Discussion Activity

Ask students to describe the procedure for making a puffy omelet.

Finding Recipes

Ask students to find recipes that require beaten egg whites. What types of recipes use beaten eggs most? L1

Safety Check

The traditional method for separating whites calls for passing the yolk back and forth from shell half to shell half. This method is no longer recommended. Bacteria may be present in the pores of the shell and could be picked up by the yolks and whites.

Beating Egg Whites

When egg whites are beaten, air is incorporated into them. Beaten egg whites can be used to add volume and lightness to baked products. For example, they can be used to prepare soufflés. A **soufflé** (soo-FLAY) is a dish made by folding stiffly beaten whites into a sauce or batter, then baking the mixture in a deep casserole until it puffs up.

Here are some guidelines for beating egg whites:

- When separating the yolks from the whites, be careful that no yolk mixes with the whites. Yolks contain fat, and even a drop of fat can keep whites from reaching full volume.
- Before beating, let egg whites stand at room temperature for 20 minutes. This will allow them to reach the fullest volume when beaten.
- Use beaters and bowls that are clean and completely free of fat. Plastic bowls tend to absorb fat, so use only glass or metal bowls.

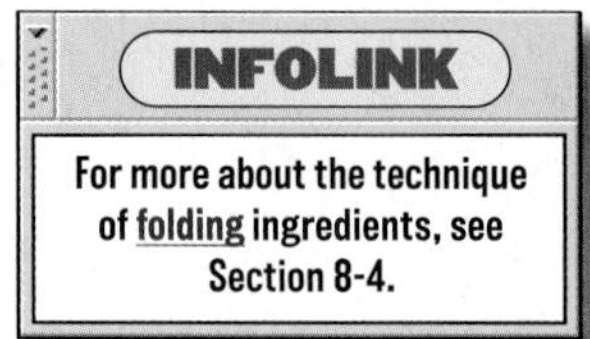

For more about the technique of folding ingredients, see Section 8-4.

Forming Peaks

As you beat egg whites, you will notice them turning white and foamy. Eventually, they begin to form peaks. There are two different stages of peaks that eggs can reach. The terms for these stages frequently appear in recipes involving beaten eggs.

- **Soft-peak stage.** The peaks bend over slightly when the beaters are lifted out of the whites.
- **Stiff-peak stage.** The peaks are glossy and hold their shape when the beaters are lifted out of the mixture.

Stop beating egg whites as soon as they reach the stage called for in the recipe. Never try to beat past the stiff-peak stage. If you overbeat the whites, they will turn dry and dull and begin to fall apart. Since they have lost air and moisture, they can no longer be used.

When using beaten egg whites in mixtures, fold them in. If stirred or beaten, the whites lose air and volume. To fold beaten whites into a mixture, add them to the bowl containing the mixture. Use a flat tool, such as a rubber spatula, for folding.

Puffy Omelet

You can use beaten egg whites to make a puffy omelet. A puffy omelet is made by separating the eggs and beating the whites and yolks separately. Fold the stiffly beaten whites into the yolks. Pour the mixture into a skillet with an ovenproof handle. Cook it first on top of the range until it is puffed and lightly browned on the bottom, about 5 minutes. Then bake it at 350°F (180°C) for 10 to 12 minutes or until a knife inserted in the center comes out clean.

Extending Learning

Omelets—A French or puffy omelet has a puffy texture and is baked in the oven. There are endless ways to fill the omelet.

- Chili, Sloppy Joe mixture, or taco filling.
- Drained, canned bean sprouts or water chestnuts.
- Yogurt, plain or mixed with fresh fruit.
- Macaroni and cheese or any heated leftover casserole.
- Grilled chicken or turkey.
- Stir-fried tofu and vegetables.

◆ **Besides lending themselves to a variety of fillings, puffy omelets are light in texture. Create a recipe for a puffy omelet that includes a nutrient-dense filling. Try preparing the dish and write about your experiences in your Wellness Journal.**

You can serve the omelet open-faced or folded. To serve the omelet folded, cut partially through the center of the omelet for ease in folding. Then fill the omelet with foods such as cheese, vegetables, or meats.

Meringues

A **meringue** (muhr-ANG), a foam made of beaten egg white and sugar, is used for desserts. There are two types of meringue, soft and hard. Soft meringue is used to top precooked pies and puddings. Hard meringue is used in the form of baked meringue shells that can be filled like a pie.

To make a meringue, beat the whites until they are foamy. Cream of tartar is sometimes added to the whites before beating to make the meringue more stable. When the whites are foamy, gradually beat in the sugar, one tablespoon at a time. Most soft meringue recipes call for 1 to 2 tablespoons (15 to 30 mL) sugar per egg white. A hard meringue may use 4 tablespoons (50 mL) sugar per egg white. Continue beating until the sugar is dissolved. To find out if the sugar is dissolved, rub a little meringue between the thumb and forefinger. If it feels gritty, not all the sugar is dissolved.

Soft Meringue

A soft meringue is made by beating egg whites to the soft-peak stage. Spread soft meringue over hot, precooked pie filling or pudding. On a pie, the meringue should touch the crust all around the edge. Otherwise, it may shrink during baking. Bake it in a preheated oven according to recipe directions until the peaks are lightly browned.

Sometimes a liquid accumulates between the meringue and pie filling, a condition known as weeping. This happens when the sugar is not completely dissolved or the meringue is not beaten to the soft-peak stage. Meringue weeps less when put on a hot filling.

- *Beating Egg Whites (text pages 484-486)*

Discussion Activity

Ask students to explain what a meringue is. Why is it better to put a meringue on a pie while the filling is still hot? Name various uses for soft meringue. What fillings could you use in a meringue shell?

Research

Have students find out how eggs are used in recipes in other parts of the world. Have students write a short report on their findings. Encourage students to write the report using a computer. Have a few select students share excerpts of their reports orally. L1

Recipe Analysis

Provide students with a hard meringue recipe. Ask students to perform a nutrient analysis of the recipe using a nutrition software program or other food values reference. Discuss students' results in class. (Note: The fat content of hard meringue is often very low, sometime fat-free.) L1

FOOD SCIENCE

Cleanliness of Equipment and Egg Whites

Remind students to use completely clean, fat-free materials when beating egg whites. Demonstrate the difficulties that can arise when even a trace of yolk or fat residue is permitted to come into contact with egg whites. Then demonstrate egg whites beaten under ideal conditions (i.e., at room temperature) in a clean bowl.

ASSESS

REVIEW

- Ask students to summarize the main ideas in this section.
- Have students complete the Section Review. (Answers appear below.)

EVALUATION

- Have students prepare a puffy omelet. Observe their procedure and evaluate the finished product.
- Have students take the quiz for Section 18-4. (Use the quiz in the *Teacher Resource Guide,* or construct your own with the **Exam***View*® *Test Generator* on the *Effective Instruction CD-ROM.*)

RETEACHING

- Have students draw pictures of beaten eggs at the three most commonly used stages.
- Refer to the *Reteaching Activities* booklet for the Section 18-4 activity sheet.

CLOSE

Refer students to the bulletin board motivator for this section. Ask students to think of other creative ways to prepare and serve eggs.

◆ **Lemon meringue pie is a classic dessert. Identify the type of meringue used to make the delicate fluffy topping.**

Hard Meringue

A hard meringue is made by beating egg whites to the stiff-peak stage. You can bake hard meringue on a baking sheet. Line the sheet with cooking parchment, waxed paper, or foil. Shape the meringue into individual or large shells using a spoon, spatula, or pastry tube.

A baked hard meringue is crispy. It must bake at a low enough temperature to dry out thoroughly but not overcook. Unless it dries well, the meringue may be sticky and chewy. Bake according to the time and temperature in the recipe directions. Turn off the oven and leave the meringue in it for at least another hour to dry out.

Section 18-4 Review & Activities

1. What is the difference between a baked custard and a stirred custard?
2. What is the safest way to separate egg whites from the yolks?
3. Name two dishes that use beaten egg whites.
4. **Evaluating.** Karl prefers to separate egg whites by breaking the egg into his bare hand and gently cradling the yolk, while the white slips between his fingers into a bowl. What problems, if any, can you see in this approach?
5. **Extending.** What might you fill baked meringue shells with?
6. **Applying.** Beat one egg white using ⅛ teaspoon (0.5 mL) cream of tartar. Beat another egg white without cream of tartar. Compare the results.

Answers to Section 18-4 Review & Activities

1. A baked custard is baked in the oven and has a firm consistency. A stirred custard is cooked on top of the range, is pourable, and has a creamy consistency.
2. Use an egg separator.
3. Answers will vary. Soufflés, puffy omelets, and meringues are three possible answers.
4. Answers will vary. His hands may be dirty; grease from his hands may keep beaten egg whites from reaching full volume; the egg yolk may slip easily off his hand into the bowl of whites.
5. Answers will vary.
6. Answers will vary.

Career Wanted

Agricultural Engineer

Education and Training
- Degree in agricultural science or engineering
- Familiarity with farming

Qualities
- Analytical thinking
- Creativity
- Communication skills
- Attention to detail

"It takes smart farming to feed the world's people."

Theo Hughes

Q. Theo, how do you combine engineering and farming?

A. Actually, they're perfect mates. Engineering is just applying math and science principles to solve problems, and farming has always been a scientific business.

Q. So what kinds of problems do you solve?

A. Anything that involves the use of technology is fair game. How do you build a tractor to resist tipping on inclines? Is there a more efficient way to deliver fertilizer to fields than spraying? Even improving one part of a machine can cut costs and make a job easier. To hit on the right designs, we work with many different professionals—farmers, biologists, marketing experts, feed mill operators, and mechanical engineers.

Q. Is this a career for people who like the outdoors?

A. You have to appreciate farm life. I work in a research lab now, but I still go out to the fields and dairy barns. Sometimes there's no substitute for getting a firsthand view of the situation.

Related Career Opportunities

Entry Level
- Farm worker
- Agricultural equipment salesperson
- Assistant ranch or farm manager

Technical Level
- Custom chemical applicator
- Hardware store manager
- Dairy herd manager

Professional Level
- Soil scientist
- County extension agent
- Feed sales consultant

Making Career Connections

FOOD PRODUCTION RESEARCH. Choose a favorite dairy food and learn how it is produced. Identify steps in the process that might involve agricultural engineering. Discuss your list in class. Compile classmates' lists to create an overview of how this profession contributes to food production.

Career Wanted

Agricultural Engineer

Thinking About the Career

Ask students to think about the obstacles that an agricultural engineer might have to cope with. For instance, how might the weather affect farming? Then have students think about what long-term effects might occur if an agricultural engineer doesn't manage obstacles, such as weather, properly. If possible, have students research how farms have overcome certain obstacles and report the findings to the class.

Career-Building Opportunities

Have students interview someone in any one of the careers noted in "Related Career Opportunities." Ask students to write a summary of the interview. Compile interviews into each career category and provide copies to interested students.

For More Information

For additional information about careers in agronomy, encourage students to contact:

- American Association for Agricultural Education www.aaaeonline.org
- American Society of Agricultural Engineers 2950 Niles Road St. Joseph, MI 49085-9659 asae.org
- American Society of Agronomy, 677 S. Segoe Road Madison, WI 53711 www.agronomy.org

REVIEW

- Have students complete the Chapter Review. (Answers appear below.)

EVALUATION

- Divide the class into two teams. Each team is to brainstorm questions about Chapter 18. Then allow the teams to take turns asking each other questions. At the end of the questioning period, the team with the most correct answers wins.
- Have students take the test for Chapter 18. (Use the chapter test in the *Teacher Resource Guide,* or construct your own with the **Exam***View®* *Test Generator* on the *Effective Instruction CD-ROM.*)

ANSWERS

Checking Your Knowledge

1. Whole: 48 percent; low-fat: 16 to 38 percent; fat-free: traces of fat.
2. Answers will vary. Yogurt, buttermilk, and cheese are all cultured products.
3. It is a blend of ripened cheeses that are processed with heat.
4. Protein solids clump together on the surface as liquid evaporates; prevent it by covering the pan or stirring regularly.
5. It contains many nutrients; use it in soups and casseroles, or substitute for water, buttermilk, or milk in baking.
6. Changes in temperature when the door is opened may cause eggs to lose quality; eggs may pick up aromas from foods.
7. Freeze in an ice cube tray or similar container.
8. Place single layer of large eggs in saucepan, add water to a level at least 1 inch (2.5 cm) above eggs, cover saucepan, bring to boil, turn off heat and remove from burner, let eggs stand in covered pan for 15 minutes.

Chapter 18 Review & Activities

Summary

Section 18-1: Choosing Dairy Foods

- Milk is high in protein, vitamin A, and B vitamins. A variety of milk products are available.
- Dairy products also include yogurt, cheese, cream, butter, and frozen dairy desserts.
- Dairy foods must be refrigerated or frozen.

Section 18-2: Preparing Dairy Foods

- When heating milk, avoid scorching, curdling, and skin formation.
- Yogurt is a healthy substitute for higher-fat dairy products.
- Unripened cheese should be served chilled; ripened cheese tastes best at room temperature.
- Avoid overcooking cheese.

Section 18-3: Egg Basics

- Eggs are good sources of protein, several vitamins, and iron. The yolks are high in fat and cholesterol.
- Eggs are sold by size and grade.
- Eggs should be refrigerated in their original cartons.
- Eggs may be cooked in the shell, fried, baked, poached, scrambled, or made into a basic omelet.

Section 18-4: Using Eggs in Recipes

- Eggs perform different functions in recipes.
- Custard serves as the base for both main dishes and desserts.
- Some recipes call for only egg yolk or white, requiring eggs to be separated.
- Egg whites can be beaten to add volume and lightness to recipes.

Working IN THE Lab

1. ***Food Science.*** Add 1 tablespoon (15 mL) lemon juice to 1 cup (250 mL) room-temperature milk. Let the milk stand for 10 minutes. Describe the results. What do you think is happening to the milk? What is this process called?
2. ***Food Preparation.*** Develop your own recipes for scrambled eggs. Experiment by adding seasonings and other ingredients. Evaluate the results for taste, appearance, nutritional value, and cost per serving.

Checking Your Knowledge

1. Identify the percentage of calories from fat in whole, low-fat, and fat-free milk.
2. Give two examples of cultured milk products.
3. How is pasteurized process cheese made?
4. What causes skin formation when milk is cooked? How can you prevent it?
5. Why should you save the whey from thickened yogurt? How can it be used?
6. Give two reasons why you should not store eggs in the egg tray on the refrigerator door.
7. Describe how to freeze leftover raw egg whites.
8. Briefly describe the procedure for making hard-cooked eggs.
9. Describe the characteristics of egg whites beaten to the soft-peak stage and the stiff-peak stage.
10. Identify two ways to keep meringue from weeping.

Review & Activities Chapter 18

Thinking Critically

1. Determining Accuracy. While standing in the checkout line at the supermarket, Delia is thumbing through a popular magazine and comes upon an article that explains how you can enjoy eggs, while still reducing the amount of cholesterol in your overall eating plan. She notices that the author of the article has the initials M.D. after her name in the byline, but the name itself is not one that Delia recognizes. Would you advise her to read the article or skip on to the next feature? Explain the factors that affect your recommendation.

2. Distinguishing Between Fact and Opinion. Chet receives an advertisement and a cents-off coupon in the mail for a new dairy dessert product. The ad claims that the product contains one-fifth the fat of regular full-fat ice cream and adds that a panel of qualified judges all agreed that the product was as rich and creamy as the leading brand of premium ice cream. How many of the claims made in the ad are fact and how many are opinion?

Reinforcing Key Skills

1. Communication. In the past, milk, other dairy foods, and eggs have been given a bad reputation by health care professionals. What information could you include in a press release aimed at reeducating the public about the advantages of including dairy foods and eggs in their eating plans?

2. Directed Thinking. Milk and other dairy foods are traditionally a part of the eating habits of cultures that raise herd animals, such as milk cows or goats. In other cultures, dairy foods are not a part of traditional eating styles. Use this and other information to answer this question: What impact do social influences have on food choices?

Making Decisions and Solving Problems

You offer to make a dip for a friend's party. You want to make it attractive and tasty but low in fat and cholesterol as well.

Making Connections

1. Math. Compare the per-serving price and nutritional value of sour cream and its lower-fat substitutes, including yogurt and reduced-fat sour cream products. Record your findings on a chart or bar graph. Also tell how each product's nutritional value affects your decision about which is the best buy.

2. Social Studies. Using print or online resources, write a report on the international origins of dishes mentioned in this chapter. Where and when did soufflés and meringues originate? What other international dishes use beaten egg whites?

ANSWERS cont.

9. *Soft-peak stage:* peaks bend over slightly when beaters are lifted out of whites; *stiff-peak stage:* peaks are glossy and hold their shape when beaters are lifted out of the mixture.
10. Dissolve the sugar completely; put the meringue on while filling is still hot.

Thinking Critically

1. I would advise her to read the article. An M.D. is a medical doctor —a recognized health authority —a fact which suggests that the information is likely based on sound science. Name recognition doesn't necessarily correlate with accuracy of information.
2. Fact: advertisement, coupon, ⅕th the fat. Opinion: judges agreeing.

Reinforcing Key Skills

1. Answers will vary. Milk and dairy advantages include: Protein, calcium (decreases osteoporosis risk) and lower fat varieties available. Egg advantages include: Protein, iron, variety of nutrients, egg whites are fat free, versatility.
2. Answers will vary. Family, media, and other environmental factors all have an impact on what people eat.

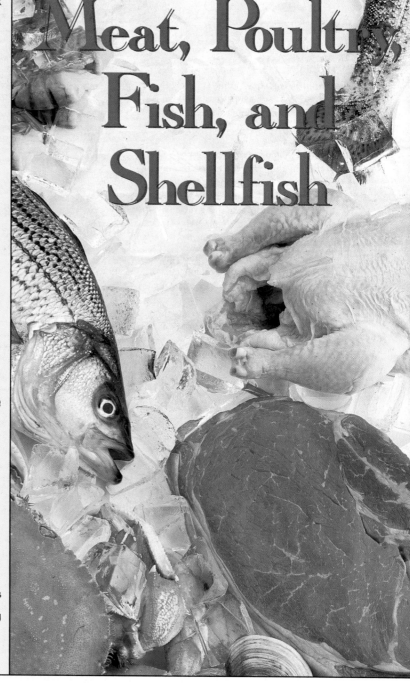

CHAPTER
19
Meat, Poultry, Fish, and Shellfish

Advance Planning Guide 

- Prepare samples of several types of ground poultry.
- Obtain copies of the school's lunch menus.
- Obtain bone shapes that can be used to identify cuts of meat.
- Purchase 6 oz. (168 g) loin cuts of beef, lamb, pork, and veal.
- Set up a display of at least three beef bones.
- Purchase prime, choice, and select grades of beef for an observation activity.
- Purchase a variety of processed meat.
- Purchase whole chicken for the Visual Learning Activities on pages 504 and 517 and Demonstration Activity on page 518.
- Purchase packages of ground poultry, giblets, and processed poultry.
- Purchase Grade A and Grade B poultry.
- Arrange a visit to the school cafeteria on a chicken preparation day.
- Purchase shoulder or chuck steak for the Food Science Lab on page 513.
- Purchase and cube meat, poultry, and firm fish and chop vegetables for Lab Experience on page 519.
- Purchase needed ingredients for the Recipe File on page 523.
- Purchase needed ingredients for the Recipe File on page 524.

CHAPTER
19

Meat, Poultry, Fish, and Shellfish

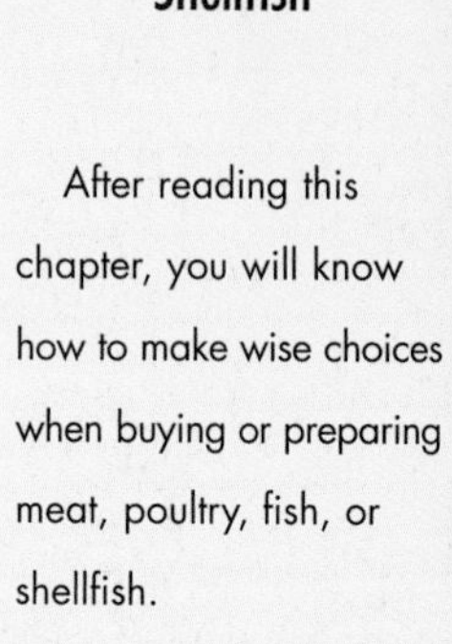

After reading this chapter, you will know how to make wise choices when buying or preparing meat, poultry, fish, or shellfish.

MEETING DIVERSE NEEDS

Physically Challenged Students. If there are students in the class who have a physical challenge related to manual dexterity, ask them to work with abled students at some of the more rigorous lab or demonstration activities. Arrange in advance for partners to discuss and delegate responsibilities, perhaps with one handling physical tasks, the other mental tasks.

SECTION
19-1

Looking at Meat, Poultry, Fish, and Shellfish

Objectives

After studying this section, you should be able to:

- Identify nutrients in meat, poultry, fish, and shellfish.
- Discuss factors that affect tenderness.
- Give guidelines for comparing costs of meat, poultry, fish, and shellfish.

Look for These Terms

cut

marbling

Most American meals are built around a main dish, often one containing meat. The meat might be a form of beef or pork. Families who favor poultry might sometimes choose turkey, duck, or goose instead of chicken. Fish and shellfish, lamb, and veal are other possibilities.

Cuts

A starting point when shopping for meat, poultry, fish, and shellfish is to recognize that each of these foods is sold in the form of fresh or frozen cuts. A **cut** is a particular edible part of meat, poultry, or fish. Cuts of meat, for instance, include steaks, chops, and roasts.

In addition to these raw cuts are numerous cured meat and poultry products, such as ham, bacon, cold cuts, and sausages. Many convenience forms are available as well.

How can you make wise decisions when shopping for meat, poultry, fish, and shellfish? Start by taking a look at how the different choices vary with regard to nutrition, tenderness, and cost.

INFOLINK

For more on the different types of convenience foods and how to make wise choices when shopping for them, see Section 15-1.

Nutrition

Meat, poultry, fish, and shellfish are all nutritious foods. They are excellent sources of complete protein. All provide B vitamins, phosphorus, and certain trace minerals. Meat and poultry are good sources of iron and zinc. Fish, especially fatty fish such as salmon and tuna, are good sources of omega-3 essential fatty acids.

SECTION
19-1

Looking at Meat, Poultry, Fish, and Shellfish

FOCUS

MOTIVATORS

- Hold a contest. Have students make a list of sources of meat, poultry, fish, and shellfish. The student who identifies the most sources wins.
- Ask students to identify recent nutritional or safety concerns related to meat, poultry, fish, and shellfish. How have these concerns affected their families' eating habits?

VOCABULARY ACTIVITY

Pronounce the two terms listed under "Look for These Terms." Have students find the terms and their meanings within the section. If possible, bring to class a piece of marble to demonstrate the meaning of marbling as it applies to meat.

STUDY SKILLS

- **Guided Reading.** Have students look at the headings within Section 19-1 to preview the concepts that will be discussed.
- Have students read the section and complete the appropriate part of the Chapter 19 Study Guide in the *Student Workbook*.

Section 19-1 Resources

◆ **Student Workbook**, pp. 137, 140

◆ **Teacher Resource Guide**

Lesson Plan 19-1 Organizer

Section 19-1 Quiz

◆ **Effective Instruction CD-ROM**

Exam*View*® *Test Generator*

PowerPoint® Slide #43

◆ **Transparancy Package**, CT-43

◆ **Student Motivation Kit**

Reteaching Activities, p. 87

Enrichment Activities

TEACH

- *Cuts*
- *Nutrition*
  (text pages 491-493)

Discussion Activity

Ask students to list the nutrients available in meat, poultry, fish, and shellfish. Review benefits of these nutrients. Then ask students to name two types of animal foods that are generally lower in fat content than other animal foods.

Supermarket Survey

Have students survey a local supermarket to identify the varieties of cuts of meat, poultry, fish, and shellfish available. In class, have students compile all the varieties in chart form. L1

Flash Cards

Have students make flash cards of cuts of meat, poultry, fish, and shellfish; students should draw or paste photos of cuts on one side and the name of the cuts on the other. Have students use the flash cards to practice identifying each of these. L1

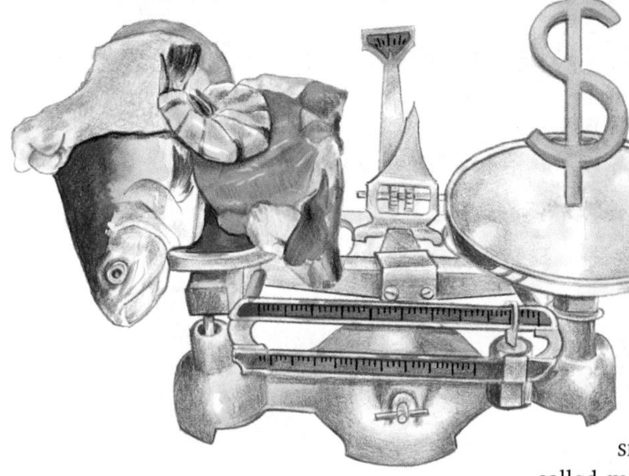

◆ **Cost is one of several factors that must be weighed when shopping for meat, poultry, fish, and shellfish. Name two other factors.**

The Food Guide Pyramid recommends two to three servings daily from the Meat, Poultry, Fish, Dry Beans, Eggs, and Nuts Group. A typical serving can be 2 to 3 ounces (56 to 84 g) of cooked lean meat, poultry, or fish.

Many Americans eat servings of meat, poultry, and fish that are larger than the recommended portions. That means they eat more protein than needed. The larger servings may also add more fat and cholesterol to daily food choices.

Fat and Cholesterol

Because they are animal foods, meat, poultry, fish, and shellfish all contain cholesterol. All animal muscle contains about the same amount of cholesterol per ounce, except for organ meats (such as liver), which have more.

Fat content varies. Most fish is low in fat. So is turkey breast meat. Other poultry and meat cuts generally have more fat, but the amount varies depending on the cut and the preparation method. Meat, poultry, fish, or shellfish that has less than 10 grams of fat in a 3½-ounce (98-g) serving is considered lean. It must also have less than 4 grams of saturated fat and less than 95 milligrams cholesterol.

Types of Fat

Meat and poultry contain both invisible fat—which is part of the chemical composition of the food—and visible fat. In meat, a layer of visible fat may surround the lean muscle portion of the cut. In addition, small white flecks of internal fat, called **marbling**, may appear within the muscle tissue of the meat. In poultry, most of the visible fat is located in the skin and in layers under the skin.

◆ **Visible fat occurs in two ways—as fat layers surrounding muscle sections and as marbling within muscle sections. Which type of fat contributes to a cut's tenderness?**

Extending Learning

Iron—Meat, poultry, fish, and shellfish provide iron, mostly in the form of heme iron. Heme iron is generally better absorbed than iron found in plant sources, non-heme iron. Iron content is one important nutritional factor to consider when selecting meat, poultry, fish, and shellfish.

- *Nutrition*
- *Tenderness*
  (text pages 491-495)

Comparing Fat and Cholesterol Content

Type of Food (3-oz. [84-g] serving)	Total Fat (g)	Saturated Fat (g)	Cholesterol (mg)
Fish and Shellfish			
Cod, cooked	1	0	45
Tuna, canned in water	1	0	35
Red salmon, canned	6	2	45
Mackerel, cooked	13	2	60
Shrimp, cooked	1	0	166
Poultry			
Chicken, light meat, without skin, roasted	2	1	70
Chicken, dark meat, without skin, roasted	7	2	80
Turkey, breast meat, without skin, roasted	1	0	55
Meat			
Beef, top round steak, trimmed, broiled	4	1	70
Beef, ground, regular, broiled	18	7	76
Beef liver, pan-fried	7	2	410
Pork loin, trimmed, roasted	6	2	65

◆ **The fat and cholesterol content of different meats, poultry, fish, and shellfish vary. Which item has the most saturated fat? Which has the least total fat? How many milligrams of cholesterol is contained in a 3-oz. serving of waterpack canned tuna?**

INFOLINK

For information on how to limit fat and cholesterol in your eating plan, see Section 3-1.

Tenderness

You've probably heard meat called "so tender it melts in your mouth" or "as tough as shoe leather." You can increase your chances of selecting a tender cut if you know a little about the makeup of meat, poultry, or fish. As you will see later on, the choice of cooking method can also be a factor in tenderness.

Menu Planning

Have students practice creating menus that would allow a family of four to enjoy meat, poultry, fish, and shellfish while limiting fat and cholesterol. Have a few select students share their menus with the class by recording them on the board. Discuss these menus. **L1**

VISUAL LEARNING

Using a Chart Have students compare the amounts of fat, saturated fat, and cholesterol in meat, poultry, fish, and shellfish. Then tell students to calculate and discuss if the fat, saturated fat, or cholesterol contents are nutritional concerns when consuming 6 oz. (168 g) per day of any one of the choices. If so, challenge students to explain why.

Research

Have students find out why dark chicken meat has more fat, saturated fat, and cholesterol than white chicken meat. Have students find out why beef liver has a higher cholesterol content than other items in the chart on this page. Have students write a brief report of their findings. Discuss students' findings in class. **L2**

Extending Learning

Aging Meat—Letting meat age improves flavor and tenderness, although the cost increases. There are three common ways to age meat: Dry aging, fast aging, and vacuum-pack or Cryovac aging. In dry aging, meat is stored at closely monitored, low temperatures that limit the growth of microorganisms. In fast aging, meat is held under ultraviolet lights at slightly higher temperatures and humidity levels. In Cryovac aging, the current trend, moisture- and air-proof plastic bags protect meat.

- *Tenderness (text pages 493-495)*

Discussion Activity

Ask students to list the types of tissue that may be present in meat, poultry, or fish. Then ask students the following questions: (1) What is the relationship between thickness of muscle fibers and tenderness? (2) What is the difference between collagen and elastin? (3) What methods can be used to tenderize each? (4) What is the relationship between marbling and tenderness?

FOR YOUR HEALTH

On the board, write a one-day, high-fat menu that contains (1) a large serving of high fat cuts of meat, (2) no legumes, and (3) fried poultry or shellfish. Have students conduct a menu makeover; write the healthier menu next to the high fat menu. Discuss several ways to enjoy meat, poultry, and fish while limiting fat and cholesterol.

Research

Have students find out the percentages of fat to muscle weight for various types of meat and develop a chart of their findings. L2

FOR YOUR HEALTH

Have Your Cut and Enjoy It, Too

There's no way to avoid fat and cholesterol completely when your eating style includes meat, poultry, fish, and shellfish. You can still enjoy these foods, however, while limiting fat and cholesterol.

- Keep serving sizes sensible. Follow recommendations in the Food Guide Pyramid.
- Cut down on amounts of meat, poultry, or fish, and increase intake of grains and vegetables.
- Substitute legumes for meats several times a week.
- Choose cuts with less fat.
- Trim fat layers from meat. Remove poultry skin before eating.
- Use low-fat cooking methods, such as broiling or roasting. Avoid frying and other cooking methods that add fat.

Following Up

- In your Wellness Journal, record everything you eat during the course of one day. Then make up a one-day menu that is low in fat and cholesterol. Compare the two menus. Then, if necessary, devise a strategy you could use to cut down on the amount of fat and cholesterol in your current eating plan.

Makeup of Meat and Poultry

Meat and poultry have very long, thin muscle cells (sometimes called muscle fibers). Some are as long as 12 inches (30 cm). They are thinnest in young animals and in parts of the animal that get little exercise, such as the back. As animals get older, the fibers thicken. They are thickest in those parts that get the most exercise—the legs, for example. As a rule, the thicker the muscle fibers, the tougher and coarser the cut.

Meat and poultry also have several kinds of connective tissue—protein material that surrounds cells. These, too, can affect tenderness.

- **Collagen** (KAHL-uh-juhn). A thin, white or transparent connective tissue. When meat or poultry is cooked using moist-heat methods, such as simmering in liquid, the collagen softens and turns into gelatin.
- **Elastin** (ee-LAS-tuhn). A very tough, yellowish connective tissue. It cannot be softened by heat. Other tenderizing methods—pounding, cutting, or grinding—must be used to break down elastin.

Fat content can also have an effect on tenderness. Meat that has more marbling is more tender. In addition, fat gives meat and poultry flavor and helps keep it juicy as it cooks.

 ***What is one way to make a less tender cut of meat easier to eat?***

 The lengthwise direction of the muscle cells is known as the grain. One solution for less tender cuts of meat is to cut across the grain. By doing this, you cut the long fibers into pieces, and the meat may be easier to chew. Most meats are generally cut this way for retail sale. It's also a good way to cut cooked meat and poultry for serving.

FOOD SCIENCE: Identifying and Comparing Animal Tissues

Have students use a hand lens to examine one sample of a tender meat cut and one tougher cut. Have them identify muscle tissue, connective tissue, fat, and bone. Define marbling, collagen, and elastin. Discuss the factors that affect tenderness. Compare the observed muscle tissues. Ask students to write a brief report of their findings.

Makeup of Fish

The muscles in fish are arranged differently from those in meat and poultry. Instead of the long fibers found in meat and poultry, fish have very short fibers that are arranged in layers. The layers are separated by sheets of very thin, fragile connective tissue. When heated, this connective tissue turns into gelatin. As a result, all fish and shellfish are very tender. When cooked, the flesh flakes, or breaks up into small pieces, because the muscle fibers are short.

Comparing Costs

When shopping, cost is an important point of comparison. Meats, poultry, fish, and shellfish are generally the most expensive part of the food budget. However, cuts can vary widely in cost.

Remember to compare the cost per serving of different cuts of meat, poultry, and fish. If you find a bargain that is not on your shopping list, consider changing your plans. You may save a considerable amount.

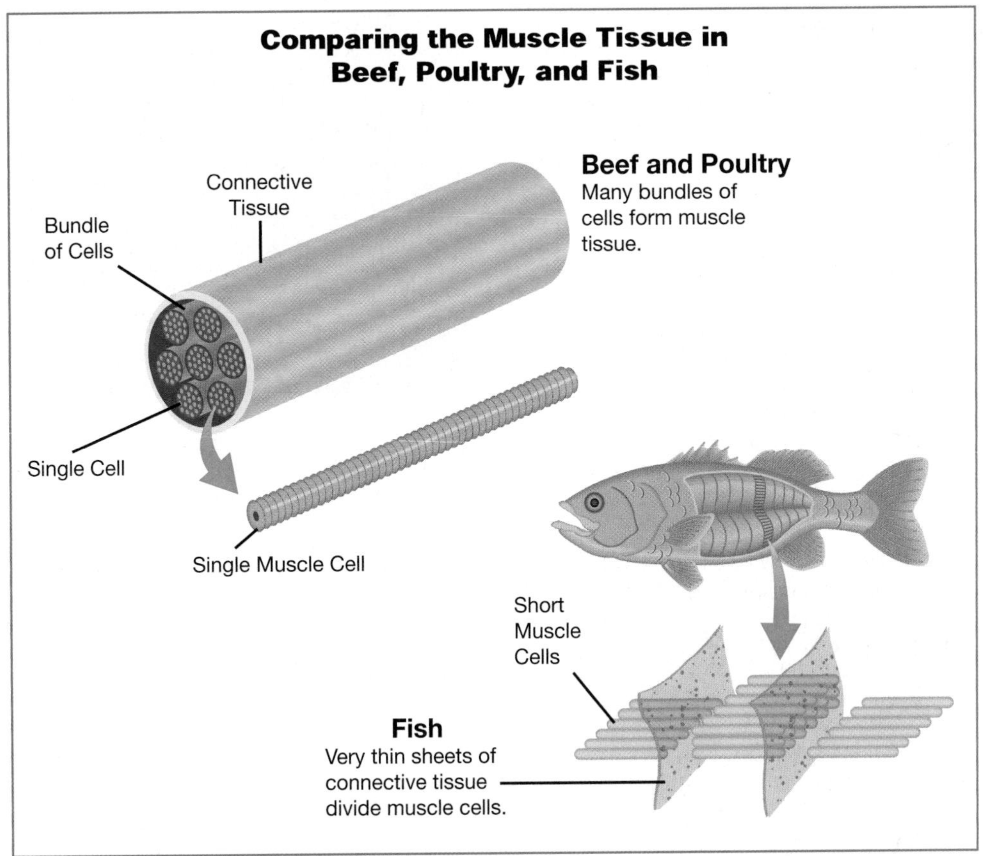

◆ **In beef and poultry, muscle tissue is held together in bundles by connective tissue. The thicker the fibers, the less tender the meat. Fish, by contrast, is made up of short muscle fibers and fragile connective tissue.** Explain the connection between the size of muscle tissue and cost of a product.

- *Comparing Costs (text pages 495-496)*

Comparing Cost per Serving

Ask students to collect package labels from a variety of meat, poultry, and fish. Have them arrange their labels from highest to lowest cost per pound and compare the cost per serving of the variety of cuts. Discuss factors that influence prices.

Have students compare the prices of several types of meat: boneless lean, boneless with fat, small bone, and bony meats. Determine price per serving. Make a comparison chart beginning with the lowest price per serving. L1

Lab Experience

Have students cook identical amounts of several types of ground poultry and thoroughly drain each sample. They should weigh the portions before and after to determine the percentage of weight loss and then recalculate the price per pound. Does higher-fat meat correlate to lower cost after preparation? Have them conduct a taste test and determine the best "taste" buy. L1

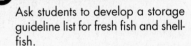

USING Safety Check

Ask students to develop a storage guideline list for fresh fish and shellfish.

Extending Learning

Bloom—The main pigment of animal muscles is myoglobin. It stores oxygen and is normally a bright red color. After the animal is slaughtered, myoglobin gets no oxygen and turns a purplish-red. However, when the meat is cut, the surface is exposed to air and turns a pinkish-red, known as "bloom." Consumers associate the pinkish-red with freshness. Therefore, retailers usually sell meat in packaging that allows oxygen to flow through, maintaining the bloom.

ASSESS

REVIEW

- Ask students to summarize the main ideas in this section.
- Have students complete the Section Review. (Answers appear below.)

EVALUATION

- Ask students to develop a ten question true or false quiz based on this section. Have them switch quizzes with another student and take his or her quiz.
- Have students take the quiz for Section 19-1. (Use the quiz in the *Teacher Resource Guide,* or construct your own with the **Exam***View*® *Test Generator* on the *Effective Instruction CD-ROM.*)

RETEACHING

- Have students prepare a poster that shows the differences in nutritional value and fat and cholesterol content of meats, poultry, fish, and shellfish.
- Refer to the *Reteaching Activities* booklet for the Section 19-1 activity sheet.

CLOSE

Provide students with copies of the school's lunch menus. Have students evaluate the meat, poultry, fish, and shellfish selections; moderate a class discussion of the evaluation.

Here are two general guidelines:

- Tender cuts are often more expensive than less tender cuts. Knowing how to cook less tender cuts can help you save money.
- Boneless meat and poultry are generally more expensive than cuts sold with the bone. You may be able to save money by removing the bones yourself. Remember, however, that boneless cuts yield more servings per pound. Be sure to check the cost per serving.

Safety Check

When shopping for meat, poultry, or fish, be sure the market or department smells fresh. Foul odors could indicate leaking packages or temperatures that may be too high for safety. The fish department may have a characteristic fishy aroma but should have no foul odors.

INFOLINK

For more on how to calculate cost per serving, see Section 12-3.

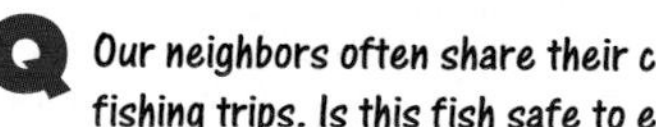

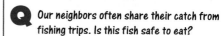

Q ***Our neighbors often share their catch from fishing trips. Is this fish safe to eat?***

A Like all living things, fish can absorb dangerous levels of pollutants from their environment. To reduce the risk of consuming these substances yourself, eat fish caught only in areas that are posted safe to fish by your state's environmental agency or local health department. Younger fish and those that feed on insects, such as bluegill, stream trout, and perch, are safest choices. "Bottom feeders," including carp and catfish, are more likely to ingest harmful substances. Since fat stores pollutants more readily than lean muscle, limit your intake of dark-fleshed, higher-fat fish. For this same reason, remove the fat, skin, and internal organs before preparing the fish. Choose a cooking method that allows fat to drip away, such as baking or broiling. Frying may seal in pollutants. Of course, you should follow all other safe food-handling practices as well.

Section 19-1 Review & Activities

1. List three nutrients found in meat, poultry, and fish.
2. Identify two factors that affect the tenderness of meat and poultry.
3. What is the most accurate way to compare the cost of different cuts of meat, poultry, or fish?
4. **Analyzing.** What factors might affect the price of meat, poultry, and fish?
5. **Evaluating.** Lonette is shopping for a cut of meat to broil. Having heard that fat adds flavor and tenderness, she is considering a cut with a broad band of fat around it. Do you agree with this choice? Why or why not?
6. **Applying.** In magazines and cookbooks, find at least six recipes for meat, poultry, or fish. Identify the cut and preparation method for each recipe. Why do you think some preparation methods are preferred for certain cuts?

Answers to Section 19-1 Review & Activities

1. See page 491.
2. See page 494.
3. By cost per serving.
4. Answers may include: availability; form (fresh, frozen, or canned); tenderness; presence of bone or other inedible parts.
5. No. Marbling within meat adds tenderness. Fat on edge adds only calories, may increase cost per serving.
6. Generally, preparation method is chosen to suit cut's tenderness or toughness.

SECTION
19-2

Meat Selection and Storage

Lee's family is on a tight budget. They shop carefully, check sale items, and try to get the most value for their money. Like Lee's family, the more you know about meat, the easier it will be for you to find the best buys. Even though there are many different cuts, an understanding of just a few basic guidelines can help you become a smart meat shopper.

Objectives

After studying this section, you should be able to:

- Describe the four basic types of meat.
- Identify tender and less tender cuts of meat.
- Identify processed meat products.
- Give guidelines for storing meat.

Look for These Terms

wholesale cuts

retail cuts

variety meats

Types of Meat

Each of the four basic types of meat has a distinct flavor and appearance. When shopping, look for color typical of the meat.

- ◆ **Beef.** Meat from cattle more than one year old. It has a hearty flavor. The cuts have bright red flesh. The fat is firm, with a white, creamy white, or yellowish color.
- ◆ **Veal.** Meat from very young calves, one to three months old. It has a mild flavor and light pink color with very little fat. "Special fed veal" has been fed a special milk-based diet. The flesh is more tender, with a grayish-pink color and white fat.
- ◆ **Lamb.** Meat from young sheep. It has a mild but unique flavor. Cuts are a bright pink-red color with white, brittle fat. The fat is sometimes covered with a *fell,* a colorless connective tissue.
- ◆ **Pork.** Meat from hogs. It has a mild flavor. Fresh meat is a grayish-pink color with white, soft fat.

Cuts of Meat

Meat is first divided into **wholesale cuts**. Also called primal cuts, these are large cuts for marketing. These wholesale cuts are further divided into **retail cuts**—the smaller cuts that you find in the supermarket. As an illustration, note that one of the wholesale cuts of beef is the chuck, from the shoulder area. Retail cuts from the chuck include blade roast and chuck short ribs.

SECTION
19-2

Meat Selection and Storage

FOCUS

MOTIVATORS

- Organize a visit to a meat processing plant where students can observe meat cutting, storage, packaging, and sanitation procedures.
- Display the bone shapes that can be used to identify cuts of meat. Ask students if they can identify the cut of meat from which each bone comes.

VOCABULARY ACTIVITY

Pronounce the three terms listed under "Look for These Terms." Have students find the terms and their definitions in the section. Ask them to create a word web that highlights the similarities and differences between the terms *wholesale* and *retail*.

STUDY SKILLS

- **Listening.** Invite a group of volunteers to each prepare an oral reading of a page of text from the section, while others follow along silently.
- Have students read the section and complete the appropriate part of the Chapter 19 Study Guide in the *Student Workbook*.

Section 19-2 Resources

◆ **Student Workbook,** pp. 137, 141
◆ **Teacher Resource Guide**
Lesson Plan 19-2 Organizer
Section 19-2 Quiz
◆ **Effective Instruction CD-ROM**
Exam*View*® *Test Generator*

◆ **Student Motivation Kit**
Reteaching Activities, p. 88
Enrichment Activities
Food Science Resources, pp. 59–61
Skills for Making Food Choices, pp. 43–44

TEACH

- *Types of Meat*
- *Cuts of Meat (text pages 497-500)*

Charts

Ask students to develop a titled chart on the computer. In the chart, students are to identify the four basic types of meat, the typical color of each, wholesale cuts, bone shapes, retail cuts, lean cuts, and the amount of fat that should be present around the cut. L1

VISUAL LEARNING *Using the Illustration*

Discuss the similarities and differences in the illustrations on this page of beef, veal, pork, and lamb wholesale cuts, while recording students' responses on the board in two columns: Similarities and Differences. For example, which has the most wholesale cuts? Where is the loin located in all four animals?

Product Comparisons

Ask students to collaborate to compare the price per pound of same cuts from the varying meats. Have students also compare nutritional values of each, utilizing a nutrition software program or print reference. Suggest students graph their findings and then draw conclusions. L1

◆ **Because of changes in breeding and feeding practices, the pork produced today is much leaner than in the past.** In a print or online resource learn about trichina (a microbe found in pork products in the past), the disease it caused, and measures that were taken to reduce this problem.

The price label on the meat package identifies the cut. The type of meat is listed first (beef, veal, pork, lamb). The wholesale cut is listed second. This tells you what part of the animal the meat comes from, such as chuck, rib, or round. The retail cut—for example, spareribs, chops, or steak—is listed third.

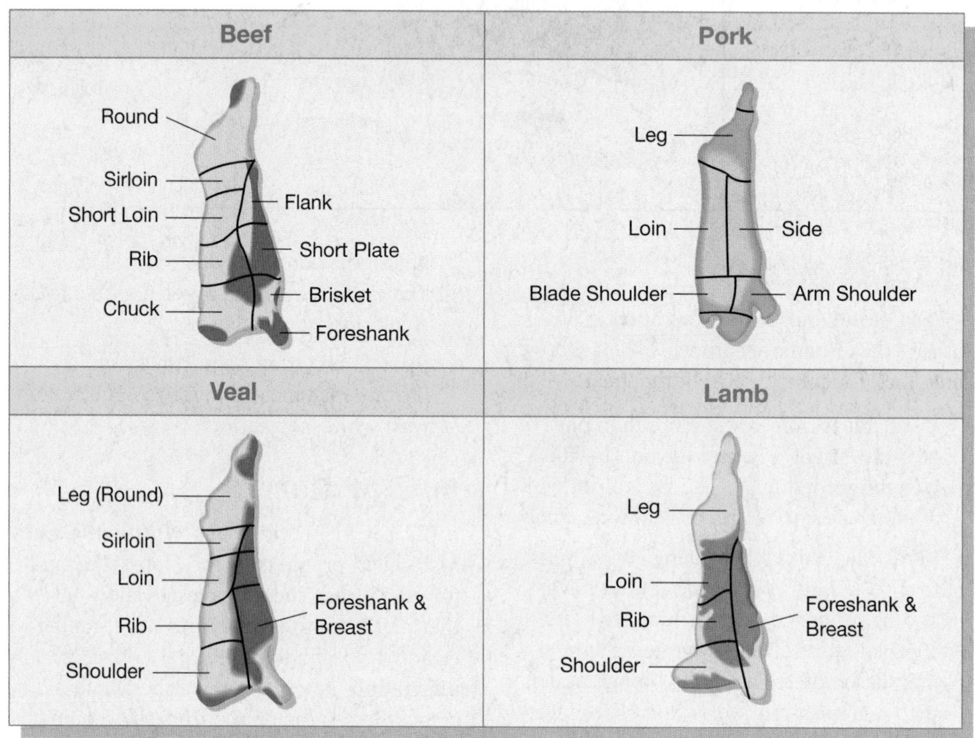

◆ **The wholesale cuts for the four types of meat animals are shown here.** Compare and give similarities and differences among the four types.

Reinforcing Key Skills

Present the following problems to student groups. Allow time for them to discuss and compare their responses.

Critical Thinking—Maureen wants to make chili. The recipe calls for pork leg meat. The food store has none available. What are Maureen's options?

Communication—A family of four in your neighborhood has been hit hard with medical expenses. They need to start budgeting. What advice would you give them about including meat?

Net Weight
Cost of Package
Unit Price
MEAT DEPARTMENT
WEIGHT Lb. Net 0.00
PAY $ 0.00
PRICE Per Lb. $ 0.00
BEEF TOP ROUND STEAK
Type of Meat
Wholesale Cut
Retail Cut

◆ **The label on a meat package can help you identify the retail cut.** Identify four other pieces of information provided on the label shown.

Bone Shape

Each wholesale cut has a distinctive bone shape that can be used to identify the meat cut. These shapes—which are nearly identical in beef, pork, lamb, and veal—are also clues to the tenderness of the cut. For example, the rib and T-shaped bones, both of which are part of the backbone, indicate meat that is tender. Knowing this can help you decide what cooking method to use.

TENDER
Wedge Bone (near round)
Flat Bone (center cuts)
Pin Bone (near short loin)
Sirloin Cuts
Back Bone (T-Shape) T-Bone
Loin or Short Loin Cuts
Back Bone and Rib Bone
Rib Cuts
Blade Bone (near rib)
Blade Bone (center cuts)
Blade Bone (near neck)
Shoulder or Chuck Cuts/ Blade Cuts
Shoulder or Chuck Cuts/ Arm Cuts
Arm Bone
TENDER
Leg, Round or Ham Cuts
Leg or Round Bone
Flank Cuts (no bones)
Short Plate
Brisket
Breast Cuts
Breast and Rib Bones

◆ **Bone shapes can help you decide how tender meat is and what cooking method to use. Notice the typical bone shapes for each part of the animal. An example of a retail cut is also shown for each wholesale cut.** From what part of the animal do the most tender cuts come?

• *Cuts of Meat (text pages 497-500)*

Taste Test

Show students 6 oz. (168 g) loin cuts from beef, lamb, pork, and veal. Ask them to record the appearance of each, including slight color differences. Then have four student volunteers prepare the four meats, all using the same cooking method. Have all students observe the appearance of each prepared meat, and then taste it. Discuss the differences in taste and appearance.

Display Activity

Set up a display of at least three beef bones. Refer students to the illustration on this page. Ask students to discuss the displayed bones, including name of cut, tenderness, and type of use associated with each bone.

Reading Labels

Ask students to bring to class more labels from different cuts of beef, veal, lamb, and pork. Point out that the type of meat is listed first, the wholesale cut is listed second, and the retail cut is listed third. Have students read each label and determine type, wholesale cut, and retail cut for each.

Reinforcing Key Skills

Present the following problems to student groups. Allow time for them to discuss and compare their responses.

Management—Ask students to work in groups to plan a one-day menu, including meat, for a family of four concerned about lowering fat intake. They should include an estimate of the fat intake per person for the day.

Leadership—Your nearby supermarket tends to have mostly high fat cuts of meat available. It never has beef round steak, but always carries beef chuck steak. Write a short letter to the store management.

TEACH cont.

- *Cuts of Meat*
- *Inspection and Grading (text page 497-501)*

Q&A Discussion Activity

Ask students to answer the following four questions: (1) What is ground meat made from? (2) What is the maximum percent fat by weight allowed by law in ground beef? (3)What is the definition of variety meats? (4) What are examples of variety meats? Moderate a class Q&A discussion.

Finding Recipes Activity

Have students identify organ meats available. Which organ meats are associated with regional or ethnic foods? Have students search cookbooks and/or Internet cooking resources for regional or ethnic recipes prepared with organ meat. Have students share recipe findings.

Store Survey

Have students survey the types of ground beef sold locally (ground chuck, ground round, etc.). Have students find the cost per pound and ask the meat cutter what the differences are, especially fat content. L1

Which Cuts Are Lean?

When shopping for meat, look for these lean choices (less than 10 grams of fat, less than 4 grams of saturated fat, and less than 95 milligrams of cholesterol in a 3½-ounce [98-g] serving):

- **Beef roasts and steaks:** round, loin, sirloin, chuck arm.
- **Pork roasts and chops:** tenderloin, center loin, ham.
- **Veal cuts:** all except ground veal.
- **Lamb roasts and chops:** leg, loin, foreshank.

Appearance is the best indicator of leanness. It is important, therefore, to inspect the package carefully. The fat that surrounds the cut should be trimmed to less than ¼ inch (0.6 cm). If there is more than that, you are wasting money by paying for excess fat.

Ground Meat

Ground beef is made from beef trimmings. By law, ground beef cannot have more than 30 percent fat by weight. Lean ground beef is available, although it may cost more.

You may also find packages of ground lamb, pork, and veal. If not, you can ask to have meat ground for you.

Organ Meats

Edible animal organs are usually called **variety meats**. Here are some examples.

- Liver is highly nutritious and tender, with a pronounced flavor.
- Lamb and veal kidneys are tender, with a mild flavor. Beef and pork kidneys are strong-flavored and less tender.
- *Chitterlings* usually refers to the intestines of pigs, but they may also come from calves. They are thoroughly cleaned and sold whole in containers.

Other organ meats are brains, heart, tongue, tripe (the stomach lining of cattle), and sweetbreads (thymus gland).

Inspection and Grading

Before it can be sold, meat has to be inspected by the USDA for wholesomeness. A round inspection mark is stamped on the meat with a harmless vegetable dye. The inspection mark is stamped in only a few places on the animal, so you will probably not see it on retail cuts.

Meat may also be graded. Grading is a voluntary program available to the meat industry, which pays for the service. Meat is graded according to standards that include amount of marbling, age of the animal, and texture and appearance of the meat.

These beef and bean burritos are just one example of the many uses for ground meat. When shopping, look for fat content on the label. Compute the fat content of a package of ground veal with the label "89 percent lean."

Extending Learning

Beef Cuts—The amount of fat in a beef cut varies, depending on the part of the animal. While the "Select" grade is generally lowest in fat, some cuts are proportionately higher in fat than others.

Some cuts in Select grade can be heavily marbled. In fact, lean cuts of Choice beef can have less fat than a marbled cut of Select. For example, a rib steak is more heavily marbled than a sirloin.

When buying meat, one should look carefully at the amount of visible fat and the marbling.

Following are the most common grades for beef:

- **Prime.** The highest and most expensive grade. The meat is well marbled with fat. It is very tender and flavorful.
- **Choice.** The most common grade sold in supermarkets. It has less marbling than prime but is still tender and flavorful.
- **Select.** Contains the least amount of marbling and is the least expensive. It is sometimes sold as a store brand.

Lamb and veal are also graded. The same grades are used as for beef, except that "Good" replaces "Select." Pork is not graded because the meat is more uniform in quality.

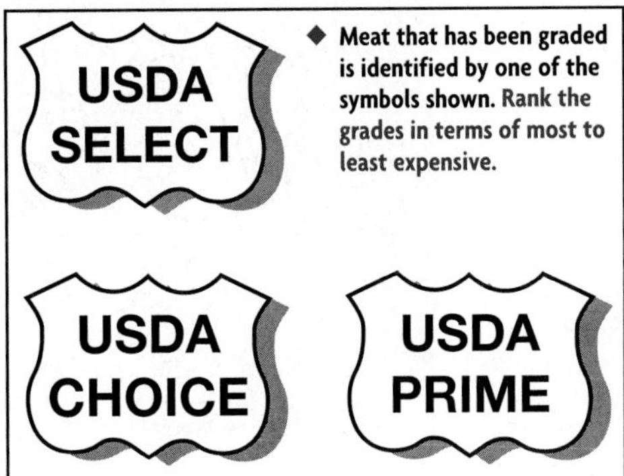

◆ **Meat that has been graded is identified by one of the symbols shown.** Rank the grades in terms of most to least expensive.

Processed Meats

About 35 percent of the meat produced in the United States is processed. Unlike other foods, which are processed mainly to extend shelf life, meats and other animal foods are processed to impart distinctive flavors. Typical processed meats include ham, bacon, sausage, and cold cuts.

The most common processing method is curing, placing the meat in a mixture of salt, sugar, sodium nitrate, potassium nitrate, ascorbic acid, and water. In addition to their function as preservatives, the nitrates also prevent the growth of botulin bacteria, a common cause of foodborne illness. The meat may be soaked in the solution, or the solution may be pumped into the meat.

Other processing methods include drying and salting, which help preserve meat, and smoking. Originally, smoking meant exposing the meat to wood smoke to preserve and flavor it. Today, only liquid smoke may be used for flavoring.

Often, more than one processing method is used. For example, bacon is cured and smoked. Chipped beef has been dried, salted, and smoked.

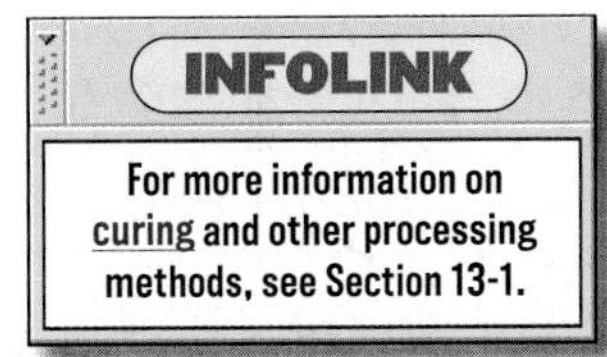

For more information on curing and other processing methods, see Section 13-1.

Using Processed Meats

Ham is meat from the thigh of a hog that has been cured and either smoked or canned. Check the label carefully for instructions. Some hams are precooked, but others must be cooked before eating. If the label does not specify, cook the ham.

Sausages are made from ground meat, often mixed with fat, salt, sugar, preservatives, seasonings, and other additives. Many different types of sausages are available. Some, such as fresh pork sausage, must be cooked before eating. Others are ready to eat, although they may be heated. Again, check the label carefully.

Cold cuts are processed meats that have been sliced and packaged. They are ready to eat. So are deli meats—processed meats sold fresh and sliced to order at deli counters in supermarkets and other food stores.

- *Inspection and Grading*
- *Processed Meats*
- *Storing Meat (text pages 500-502)*

Observation Activity

After describing prime, choice, and select grades, have students examine and try to identify the grades of beef cuts that are unlabeled. If time permits, have three lab groups pan-fry a thin piece of each and rank the samples by taste and tenderness. Do the results of the visual examination agree with taste test results?

Group Research

Have students work in small groups to research methods of processing meats. Which methods were used more in the past than today? Why have methods changed? Ask student groups to select one student to share research results with the class. Then moderate a class discussion on reasons processed meats should be eaten in moderation. **L1**

Taste Test

Purchase and simply prepare a variety of processed meats. Ask blindfolded students to try to identify the meat by taste and texture. Can students identify some of the spices added to the meats?

FOOD SCIENCE — Nitrates/Nitrites

Some studies have shown that nitrate/nitrite consumption can cause cancer. Have interested students research the nitrate/nitrite controversy and report their findings. Use the report to stimulate a class discussion on the merits of using nitrates/nitrites in meats. Or have students form debate teams, and allow each side five minutes to present its point of view, with a two-minute rebuttal after each presentation. Give the class 10 minutes to question the teams; then take a vote.

ASSESS

REVIEW

- Ask students to summarize the main ideas in this section.
- Have students complete the Section Review. (Answers appear below.)

EVALUATION

- Use a chart similar to the illustration on page 498, but without the labels. Have students identify the wholesale cuts.
- Have students take the quiz for Section 19-2. (Use the quiz in the *Teacher Resource Guide,* or construct your own with the **Exam***View*® *Test Generator* on the *Effective Instruction CD-ROM.*)

RETEACHING

- Show pictures or show a display of different bone types. Have students identify the cut of meat that has each bone type.
- Refer to the *Reteaching Activities* booklet for the Section 19-2 activity sheet.

CLOSE

Refer to the second motivator for this section. Ask students to describe how much more comfortable they are about identifying cuts of meat by looking at the bones.

FOR YOUR HEALTH

Go Easy on the Processed Meats

Cured meats are popular because of their wonderful smoky flavor. Unfortunately, the chemicals responsible for that flavor—nitrites and nitrates—have been linked with certain cancers. In addition, these meats are high in sodium, fat, or both. You can enjoy an occasional hot dog or deli sandwich, but remember to use these foods in moderation.

Following Up

- Approximately 35 percent of the nitrites and 13 percent of the nitrates in food are added during the manufacturing process. The rest occur naturally in certain vegetables—such as spinach, lettuce, and beets—and in baked goods. Discuss how this information might affect your eating style in the future.

Storing Meat

Meat requires cold storage. Use ground meat and variety meats within one to two days after storing them in the refrigerator. Other fresh meat will keep in the refrigerator for three to five days. For longer storage, freeze the meat.

INFOLINK

For more on cold storage temperatures of meats, see Section 7-4.

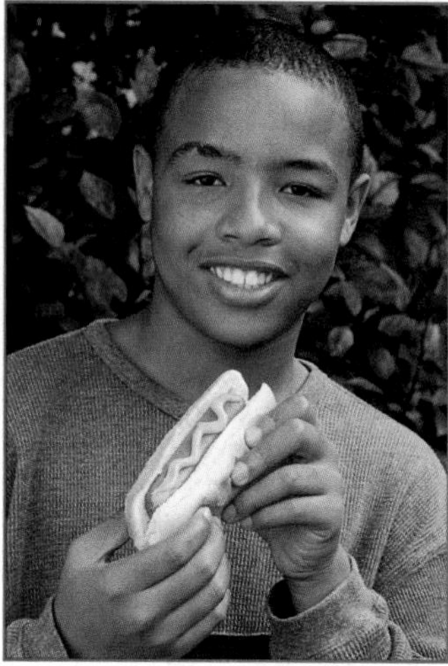

◆ **Because of the high fat and sodium content in conventional hot dogs, many people are switching to chicken and turkey franks, which are generally lower in both. Still, health experts advise eating such cured meat products only occasionally. How often do you eat processed meats? Should you make any changes?**

Section 19-2 Review & Activities

1. Name three wholesale cuts of beef that are considered tender.
2. Give four examples of processed meat products.
3. How long can fresh meat be stored safely in the refrigerator?
4. **Comparing and Contrasting.** How do beef, pork, veal, and lamb differ in color and flavor?
5. **Synthesizing.** How can processed meats be part of a healthful eating plan?
6. **Applying.** Bring to class several clean price labels from packages of meat. Using the information on the labels, identify the animal, wholesale cut, retail cut, unit price, and total price for the package. Calculate the cost per serving of each package. Which cuts are the most economical? The least?

Answers to Section 19-2 Review & Activities

1. Sirloin, loin, rib cuts.
2. Ham, bacon, sausage, cold cuts.
3. Ground and variety meats should be stored only one to two days; other meats, three to five days.
4. Beef is bright red; veal, light pink; lamb, bright pink-red; pork, grayish-pink. Beef has hearty flavor; others are mild.
5. They should be included in moderation due to use of nitrates and nitrites in curing and high sodium and fat content.
6. Answers will vary.

SECTION
19-3

Poultry Selection and Storage

The term poultry refers to any bird raised for food. Some poultry is relatively low in fat, which makes it a good choice for health-conscious consumers. Its mild flavor lends itself to many different recipes.

Objectives

After studying this section, you should be able to:

- Describe types and market forms of poultry.
- Give guidelines for buying and storing poultry.

Look for This Term

giblets

Types of Poultry

How do you want your poultry—whole, cut up, drumsticks only, boneless? Whether you want chicken, turkey, duck, or goose, you can buy different types of poultry in a wide variety of forms.

Chicken

Chicken has light and dark meat. The light meat is leaner and has a milder flavor than the dark meat.

The bird's age determines the tenderness of its meat and the cooking method to use. The terms used on the package label also give an indication.

- **Broiler-fryer chickens.** The most tender and most common. They can be cooked using almost any method.
- **Roaster chickens.** Raised to be roasted whole. They are slightly larger and older than broiler-fryers and yield more meat per pound.
- **Stewing chickens.** Older, mature birds. Since they are less tender than younger birds, they must be cooked in moist heat.
- **Rock Cornish game hens.** Young, small chickens of a special breed. They have less meat in relation to size than other chickens. One hen usually makes one serving. They can be broiled or roasted.

SECTION
19-3

Poultry Selection and Storage

FOCUS

MOTIVATORS

- Ask students to identify the types of poultry they have eaten. Which types do they like best? Least?
- Discuss reasons people are eating poultry more often now than in the past. Have students identify their families' favorite poultry dishes. Discuss the type of poultry used in each and the method of preparation.

VOCABULARY ACTIVITY

Pronounce the term listed under "Look for This Term." Have students find the term and its definition in the section.

STUDY SKILLS

- **Note Taking.** Have students read the section independently. While they are reading, they are to take notes in their own words of the important concepts within each heading.
- Have students read the section and complete the appropriate part of the Chapter 19 Study Guide in the *Student Workbook*.

Section 19-3 Resources

◆ **Student Workbook,** pp. 138, 142
◆ **Teacher Resource Guide**
Lesson Plan 19-3 Organizer
Section 19-3 Quiz
◆ **Effective Instruction CD-ROM**
Exam*View*® *Test Generator*
◆ **Student Motivation Kit**
Reteaching Activities, p. 89
Enrichment Activities

TEACH

- *Types of Poultry (text pages 503-506)*

Recall Activity

Ask students to recall the name of the five different types of chicken and three different types of turkey commonly available in supermarkets. With students, compare and contrast the different types. Moderate a session with students on mnemonic devices or other simple ways to remember the differences between these types. Ask students to list the various market forms in which broiler-fryers can be purchased.

VISUAL LEARNING ***Using the Illustration*** Demonstrate how to cut up a whole chicken, step-by-step, according to the illustration on this page. Compare the cost of buying a whole chicken with the cost of buying chicken parts or boned chicken.

Display Activity

Show students packages of ground poultry, giblets, and processed poultry. Discuss the terms used on the labels. Discuss several possible uses of each in cooking. If time permits, prepare small samples of each for students.

How to Cut Up a Whole Chicken

To cut up a whole chicken, follow the six steps shown below.

Look and Learn:

What are two advantages to buying a whole chicken and cutting it up yourself?

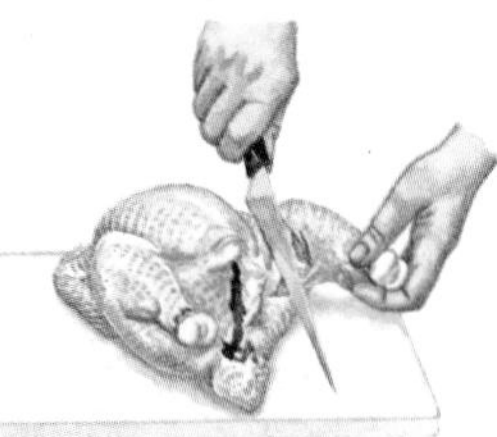

1. Slice the skin between one leg and the body.

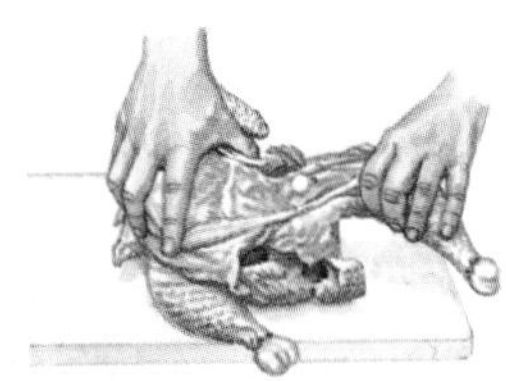

2. Bend the leg to crack the joint. Then cut through the joint and remove the leg. Repeat for the other leg and the wings.

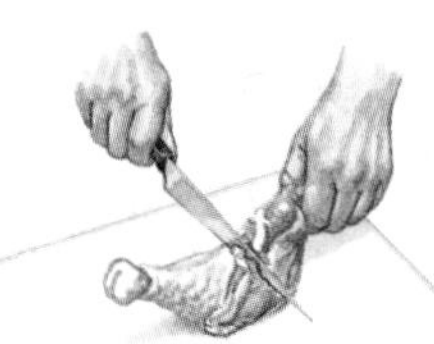

3. If desired, separate the drumstick from the thigh by cracking the joint and cutting through it.

4. Use kitchen shears to cut along the backbone on both sides, separating the breast from the back.

5. Hold the breast skin side down and snap it in two.

6. Cut the breast in half, leaving the breastbone on one of the halves.

- **Capons.** Desexed roosters under ten months old. Tender and flavorful, they are best roasted.

Poultry may be labeled in one of two ways, either fresh or frozen. *Fresh* poultry has never been chilled below 26°F (–4°C). *Frozen* means that the poultry has been chilled to below 0°F (–18°C).

Turkey

Turkeys are larger than chickens and have a stronger flavor. The light meat is leaner and more tender and has a milder flavor than the dark meat.

When buying a whole turkey, you have a choice of several types. They differ mainly in size. All are suitable for roasting, the most common method for cooking turkey.

FOOD SCIENCE **Substituting Ground Meat** Have students choose a recipe calling for ground beef. Have half the students prepare the recipe using ground beef, and the other half prepare the recipe using ground poultry instead. Have students compare the results in terms of taste, texture, and appearance. Ask students to write a brief report of their results.

- **Beltsville or fryer-roaster turkeys.** The smallest, with an average weight of 5 to 9 pounds (2.3 to 4.5 kg). They are not always available.
- **Hen turkeys.** Female. Weigh about 8 to 16 pounds (4 to 8 kg).
- **Tom turkeys.** Male. Can weigh up to 24 pounds (12 kg).

Whole turkeys are sold fresh or frozen. You can also buy turkey parts, such as drumsticks, thighs, and wings. Turkey breast is sold bone-in, boneless, or cut into tenderloins and cutlets.

Ducks and Geese

Ducks and geese have all dark meat, which is very flavorful but relatively high in fat. Usually, only whole, frozen ducks and geese are sold.

CLOSE-UP ON SCIENCE: BIOCHEMISTRY

Light and Dark Meat

Why does poultry have light and dark meat? The difference in color is due partly to the amount of exercise that different parts of the bird get. Muscles that get frequent, strenuous exercise need more oxygen than others. The oxygen is stored in a red-colored protein pigment called *myoglobin* (MY-uh-GLOW-bin). The amount of myoglobin in the muscle tissue determines the color. Dark meat is found in those parts of chickens and turkeys that get the most exercise, such as the legs. Because domesticated breeds of chickens and turkeys do not fly, their breast and wing muscles do not need as much oxygen to function. The tissue does not contain as much myoglobin, which makes breast meat lighter in color.

Ground Poultry

With the growing emphasis on healthful eating, ground chicken and turkey are found in many supermarket meat departments. When buying either product, read the label carefully. If it states "ground turkey breast" or "ground chicken," both the flesh and skin were used. As you may recall, most of the fat is in the skin. If the word *meat* is part of the description, such as "ground turkey breast meat" or "ground chicken meat," the poultry was ground without the skin. Poultry ground without skin is leaner.

You can use ground poultry in place of ground beef, but it results in a drier, blander product. Usually, you need to add a little more liquid and more seasonings to the recipe.

◆ **Chili made with lean ground turkey has a flavor and texture strikingly similar to chili made with red meat. Think of two other dishes made with ground red meat in which ground turkey or chicken might be substituted.**

- *Inspection and Grading*
- *Buying and Storing Poultry (text page 506)*

Grade Comparisons

Have students observe and compare Grade A and Grade B poultry. Have students record the differences and compare their observations with the text information. Then moderate a discussion on characteristics of poultry that is labeled "Grade A" and explanations of what to look for when buying poultry. L1

Research

Have students research poultry production, inspection, or marketing and prepare a one minute oral report for the class. Reports should include: How have they changed over time? What changes are expected in the future? L2

Cafeteria Visit Activity

On an appropriate date, take students to the school cafeteria to see the form in which chicken is purchased and how it is stored. If possible, have small groups of students watch chicken preparation for a school lunch. Have students note all observations. Was the chicken plump? Was the skin smooth and soft? What color was the flesh?

FOOD SCIENCE: Drugs in Poultry Feed

Have students research the pros and cons of using antibiotics and hormones in poultry and livestock feed. Ask students to make a list of the pros and cons. Compare lists in class. Are there more pros? Discuss the pros and cons.

ASSESS

REVIEW

- Ask students to summarize the main ideas in this section.
- Have students complete the Section Review. (Answers appear below.)

EVALUATION

- Have students list ten specific facts they learned from studying this section.
- Have students take the quiz for Section 19-3. (Use the quiz in the *Teacher Resource Guide,* or construct your own with the **Exam***View*® *Test Generator* on the *Effective Instruction CD-ROM.*)

RETEACHING

- Have students write a consumer information article on buying and storing poultry.
- Refer to the *Reteaching Activities* booklet for the Section 19-3 activity sheet.

CLOSE

Lead a discussion on the importance of choosing poultry carefully and storing it correctly. Record students' answers on the board and rank them in order of importance.

Giblets

Edible poultry organs are called **giblets** (JIB-luhts). Giblets are usually included in a package stuffed inside the whole, cleaned poultry. They include the liver, gizzard (stomach), and heart. Chicken livers and gizzards are also sold separately.

Processed Poultry

Turkey is also processed into products such as ham and bacon. Turkey and chicken are also processed into frankfurters and other types of sausage.

Inspection and Grading

Poultry is inspected and graded by the USDA. Grading is a voluntary program, just as it is with meat. The inspection and grade marks can appear on the label or on a wing tag attached to the bird.

Grade A is the grade of poultry most commonly found in supermarkets. It indicates the poultry is practically free of defects, has a good shape and appearance, and is meaty.

Buying and Storing Poultry

When buying poultry, look for plump, meaty birds. The skin should be smooth and soft. Color of the skin may vary from a creamy white to yellow, depending on the food eaten by the bird. Avoid poultry with tiny feathers or bruised or torn skin.

Use poultry that has been stored in the refrigerator within one to two days. For longer storage, freeze.

◆ **Processed chicken or turkey products, like this turkey bacon, may be lower in fat and sodium than processed meats. What precautions should be taken if turkey bacon is to become a part of every breakfast?**

Section 19-3 Review & Activities

1. What is the main difference among types of turkeys?
2. Why might ground chicken breast meat cost more than a product labeled "ground chicken breast"?
3. List three characteristics of good quality poultry.
4. **Analyzing.** Review the different forms of poultry. When might you prefer to buy each one?
5. **Evaluating.** Tell which cooking method is best for each of the following types of chicken: broiler-fryer, stewing chicken, capon. Explain your responses.
6. **Applying.** Make a list of as many different ways of using poultry in recipes as you can. Identify the type or form of poultry that might be used in each.

Answers to Section 19-3 Review & Activities

1. Their size.
2. "Ground chicken breast meat" does not contain lower cost skin, unlike "ground chicken breast."
3. Any three: Plump, meaty, smooth and soft skin; no tiny feathers; no bruised or torn skin.
4. Whole, cut up, or by the piece; answers will vary.
5. Broiler-fryer: almost any cooking method; stewing chicken: moist heat only; capon: roasted. Explanations will vary.
6. Answers will vary.

SECTION 19-4

Fish and Shellfish Selection and Storage

Objectives

After studying this section, you should be able to:

- Describe different types and market forms of fish.
- Identify different types and market forms of shellfish.
- Give guidelines for buying and storing fish and shellfish.

Look for These Terms

crustaceans

mollusks

Fish and shellfish have long been favorite foods of people living in coastal regions. Today, people almost everywhere can enjoy the nutrition and flavor of the many varieties of fish and shellfish that are available.

Types of Fish and Shellfish

What is the difference between fish and shellfish? Most fish have fins and a bony skeleton with a backbone. Shellfish have neither fins nor bones, but have a shell instead.

Some fish and shellfish come from freshwater lakes, rivers, streams, and ponds. They are known as freshwater varieties. Saltwater varieties, also known as seafood, come from oceans and seas. Today, some types of freshwater and saltwater fish and some shellfish are raised on fish farms.

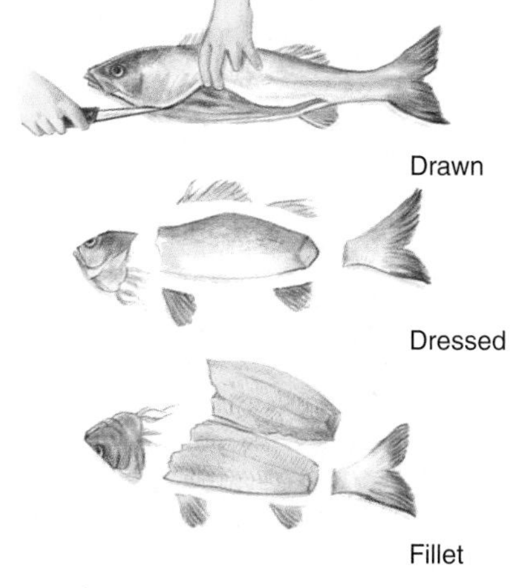

◆ You can purchase drawn or dressed fish, fillets, or steaks. Which would you choose if you wanted boneless fish?

SECTION 19-4

Fish and Shellfish Selection and Storage

FOCUS

MOTIVATORS

- Survey students to discover how many have eaten fish or shellfish in the last week. On the board, list the types of fish and shellfish students have eaten.
- Ask students how many have eaten fish they caught themselves. What benefits and drawbacks are there in catching fish to eat?

VOCABULARY ACTIVITY

Pronounce the two terms under "Look for These Terms." Then have students find the terms and their definitions in the section.

STUDY SKILLS

- **Outlining.** Have students read the section and outline it by copying the headers on paper and leaving space after each one. Students are to write a sentence in their own words, summarizing the content under each header.
- Have students read the section and complete the appropriate part of the Chapter 19 Study Guide in the *Student Workbook*.

Section 19-4 Resources

◆ **Student Workbook,** pp. 138, 143
◆ **Teacher Resource Guide**
Lesson Plan 19-4 Organizer
Section 19-4 Quiz
◆ **Effective Instruction CD-ROM**
Exam*View*® *Test Generator*
◆ **Student Motivation Kit**
Reteaching Activities, p. 90
Enrichment Activities

TEACH

- *Types of Fish and Shellfish (text pages 507-510)*

Nutrition Research

Have students identify as many fish choices as they can and explain the differences. Categorize the choices as light or dark in color. Have students research the total calorie, fat, saturated fat, cholesterol, iron, and calcium contents of two light and two dark choices. Ask students to compile all results into a comprehensive class reference. L2

Demonstration

Show students a whole fish. Discuss with them the concepts of drawn and dressed fish; then demonstrate both techniques. Explain how fish could be prepared once it is drawn or dressed. Finally, demonstrate how to cut steaks or fillets.

Writing

Have students find articles that warn about high levels of heavy metals, such as mercury and lead, in fish. Are there any current problems in this area? How can these problems be prevented? Ask students to each write a consumer action article on what consumers can do to help prevent these problems. L2

Types of Fish

There are dozens of varieties of fish. For cooking purposes, many are similar. If a specific fish isn't available, you can substitute a fish similar in flavor, color, and/or texture. The chart on the right gives some examples.

As you have learned, most fish are very low in fat. A few of the darker fish have a higher fat content.

Market Forms of Fish

You can purchase fish in several market forms. See the drawings on page 507. The most common are

- **Drawn.** Whole fish with scales, gills, and internal organs removed.
- **Dressed or pan-dressed.** Drawn fish with head, tail, and fins removed.
- **Fillets.** Sides of fish cut lengthwise away from bones and backbone. Usually boneless. Large fillets may be cut into smaller ones.
- **Steaks.** Cross sections cut from large, dressed fish. May contain bones from ribs and backbone.

Fish Choices

Fish with a light color, mild flavor, and tender texture:	*Fish with a dark color, more pronounced flavor, and firm texture:*
Catfish	Bluefish
Perch	Salmon
Sole	Tuna
Cod	Mackerel
Pike	Shark
Trout	Swordfish
Flounder	
Pollock	
Turbot	
Haddock	
Pompano	
Whitefish	
Halibut	
Red snapper	

Shellfish

Shellfish generally have a mild, sweet flavor. Almost all shellfish come from oceans and seas, but a few come from fresh water. There are two types of shellfish: crustaceans (krus-TAY-shuhns) and mollusks.

Crustaceans

Crustaceans are shellfish that have long bodies with jointed limbs, covered with a shell. They include crabs, crayfish, lobsters, and shrimp.

- **Crabs.** Have an oval shell, four pairs of walking legs, and two claws. Different varieties and sizes are available. Whole crabs are sold live, cooked, or frozen. Crab legs and claws are sold cooked and frozen. Cooked crabmeat is available refrigerated, frozen, and canned.
- **Crayfish.** Freshwater crustaceans. They are also called crawfish or crawdads. They look like small lobsters. Crayfish are sold whole, live, or cooked.
- **Lobsters.** Have a long, jointed body with four pairs of walking legs and two large claws, all covered with a hard shell. Average weight is from 1¼ pounds (625 g) to 2¼ pounds (1125 g). Maine lobster is the most popular. Fresh lobster is sold live.

Reinforcing Key Skills

Present the following problems to student groups. Allow time for them to discuss and compare their responses.

Critical Thinking—Have students compare and draw conclusions about the protein and calorie content of 3 oz. (84 g) of three kinds of fish, three cuts of beef, and three cuts of chicken.

Communication—Jevon wants to know why some types of mollusks vary so greatly in size. What would you tell him?

◆ **Shrimp.** Vary in size and color. They are usually sold frozen or previously frozen and thawed. You can buy raw shrimp, with or without the shell, as well as shelled, cooked shrimp.

Mollusks

Mollusks are shellfish with soft bodies that are covered by at least one shell. They include clams, mussels, oysters, scallops, and squid.

◆ **Clams.** Have two shells hinged at the back with edible flesh inside. Many varieties are available, from small to large. They are sold live (still in the shell) or shucked (removed from the shell).

◆ **Mussels.** Have a thin, oblong shell. Length varies from 1½ inches (3.8 cm) to 6 inches (15 cm). Shell colors also vary. The flesh is creamy tan and not as tender as that of oysters or clams. Mussels are sold live in the shell.

◆ **Oysters.** Have a rough, hard, gray shell. They come in various sizes. The flesh varies in color, flavor, and texture. Oysters are sold live or shucked.

◆ **Scallops.** Grow in beautiful, fan-shaped shells. Only the muscle that hinges the two shells is sold. Bay scallops are very tiny—about ½ inch (1.3 cm) in diameter—sweet, and tender. Sea scallops are larger—about 1½ inches (3.8 cm) in diameter—and not as tender as bay scallops.

◆ **Squid.** Also known as calamari (kah-luh-MAH-ree). It is sold fresh. Squid is popular in Asia and the Mediterranean area and has become popular in the United States.

◆ **Remember to look for signs of quality when buying fish and shellfish. How would you store the varieties shown here?**

• *Types of Fish and Shellfish (text pages 507-510)*

Supermarket Scavenger Hunt

Have students survey a supermarket to discover as many products as possible that contain processed fish. Suggest students search seafood sections, canned food, and frozen food sections. Set aside time for students to share and compare their findings. **L1**

USING Safety Check

Ask students to create a multicultural, educational poster that provides the information in the Safety Check on page 510. Suggest using drawings since people may not read English who need this information.

Research

Have students investigate current medical research on Omega-3 fatty acids and their relationship to cardiac health and disease. Ask students to write an abstract based on their collective research. **L1**

FOOD SCIENCE: Effect of Canning Liquid

Remind students that most of the darker fish are available in canned form. Point out that fish canned in water contains fewer calories than fish canned in oil. Provide samples of tuna canned in water and tuna canned in oil. Have students sample each one and evaluate for appearance, aroma, and taste. Using the labels from the cans, have students compare the nutritional information of each.

TEACH cont.

- *Inspection and Grading*
- *Buying Fish and Shellfish (text pages 510-511)*

USING CONNECTING FOOD AND SOCIAL STUDIES

Ask students to find and copy or rewrite a simple recipe using clams, oysters, and crabs that may have been part of a "potlatch" ceremony. Compile the recipes into a "potlatch" cookbook.

Quality Inspection Activity

Ask students to put on their health inspector "hats." Show two samples of fresh fish to students: one of good quality and one of poor quality. Have students "grade" each of the samples, noting specific reasons for the grades. Have students share and compare their findings.

Internet Search

Working under your supervision, students are to find and search the FDA and the National Marine Fisheries Service web sites to obtain information about the voluntary inspection and grading program for fish. Discuss the information students find. L2

Safety Check

People with certain types of health problems—including liver disease, diabetes, and immune disorders—should be careful never to eat raw or undercooked fish or shellfish. If they do, they risk serious illness or even death. The cause is harmful bacteria that may be present in the fish or shellfish. Thorough cooking kills the bacteria.

Processed Fish

Fish may be dried, pickled, smoked, or cured. Sometimes more than one method is used. For example, lox is a type of cured, smoked salmon. Cod is often salted and dried. Herring may be cut into chunks, pickled in vinegar and spices, and then packed in jars.

Canned fish and shellfish are ready to eat as is, heat, or use in recipes. To cut down on fat, look for fish packed in water instead of oil. If the fish is packed in oil, drain it well and rinse off the oil before using. Many other convenience forms of fish, such as frozen breaded fish fillets, are available.

Inspection and Grading

The Food and Drug Administration (FDA) has a modern food safety system for fish, known as Hazard Analysis and Critical Control Point, or HACCP (pronounced HAS-sip). All seafood processors, repackers, and warehouses—both domestic and foreign exporters to this country —must use it. The system focuses on identifying and preventing hazards that could cause foodborne illness.

A voluntary inspection and grading program is also carried on jointly by the FDA and the National Marine Fisheries Service of the U.S. Department of Commerce. The program attempts to focus on those parts of fish processing that may be risks to consumer

Connecting Food and Social Studies

Let's Potlatch!

In coastal regions today, the cost of fish and shellfish is much lower than elsewhere. At one time, these items were there for the asking. To the Native American people who inhabited the Pacific Northwest—the Tlingit, Kwakiutl, Haida, Tsimshian, and others—the clear, swift-flowing streams and rivers teemed with salmon and trout. The ocean offered an abundance of saltwater fish, and there were plenty of clams, oysters, and crabs.

With so many natural resources, there was much cause for celebration. The people became famous for their large gatherings, called *potlatches,* a word that in the Chinook language means "to give." Potlatch ceremonies were marked by the lavish distribution of gifts and food to guests from other clans, villages, and tribes.

Potlatches often lasted as long as two weeks. Wearing ceremonial dress and masks, each family performed its songs and dances. Then they feasted on the gifts the waters gave them.

Think About It

- In 1885, the Canadian government enacted a law making the potlatch ceremony illegal. Why do you think the government interfered in this way? How do you think this affected the lives of the people of the Northwest Coast? Investigate government regulations on fishing in the United States and what effect these laws have had on the supply of fish and shellfish.

Reinforcing Key Skills

Present the following problems to student groups. Allow time for them to discuss and compare their responses.

Critical Thinking—Morgan picks up a package of what she believes is crab meat, when, in fact, she has selected an imitation shellfish product. What differences do you think Morgan will find when the product is used?

Communication—Your favorite supermarket piles several layers of fresh fish on top of each other, all on ice. What information might you share with the unsuspecting customer standing nearby, inspecting the fish?

◆ **Fish that has been inspected carries this seal. Look for it on the package.** What other safeguards can help you select fish that is at its peak of flavor and safe to eat?

safety. Some state and local fish inspection services are also available.

Buying Fish and Shellfish

When you are buying fish, a fishy odor should make you suspicious. Fresh fish and shellfish that have gone bad will smell "fishy" or have an unpleasant ammonia odor. Here are some tips for buying fish and shellfish:

- ◆ Buy from a reliable source. Pay attention to the way fresh fish is displayed. If layers are piled on ice, the top layer may be too warm for safekeeping. Don't buy ready-to-eat fish that is piled next to fresh fish. Harmful bacteria from the fresh fish may have transferred to the ready-to-eat product.
- ◆ Use appearance, aroma, and touch to judge quality. Fresh fish should have shiny skin and a glistening color. Whole fish should have clear, full eyes and bright red or pink gills. Any fish should have a mild, fresh aroma, similar to that of cucumbers or seaweed. The skin should spring back when pressed.
- ◆ Some shellfish must be alive if bought fresh. Look for signs that they are alive, such as movement in lobsters. Mollusk shells should close when they are tapped.

Storing Fish and Shellfish

After you bring fish home, store it in the refrigerator or freezer immediately. Refrigerate live shellfish in containers covered with a clean, damp cloth. They need breathing space to stay alive. Do not put live saltwater shellfish in fresh water—they won't live.

Use fish stored in the refrigerator within one to two days. For longer storage, freeze.

Section 19-4 Review & Activities

1. Define the terms *crustacean* and *mollusk*. Give three examples of each.
2. List four signs to look for when buying fresh fish and shellfish.
3. How should live shellfish be stored?
4. **Comparing and Contrasting.** How are drawn fish and dressed fish alike and different?
5. **Evaluating.** Choose a fish from the list on page 508 or one of the following: amberjack, arctic char, mahimahi, or tilapia. Locate and report information about appearance, where it's found, flavor, and cooking uses.
6. **Applying.** Find recipes for fish and shellfish in magazines or cookbooks. Note whether each recipe calls for a light-colored fish, dark-colored fish, crustacean, or mollusk. Decide whether it would affect the finished product if you chose fresh, frozen, or canned fish. Which recipe would be most economical to serve to a group of six people?

ASSESS

REVIEW

- Ask students to summarize the main ideas in this section.
- Have students complete the Section Review. (Answers appear below.)

EVALUATION

- Ask students to draw a labeled diagram showing the characteristics to look for when buying fish or shellfish.
- Have students take the quiz for Section 19-4. (Use the quiz in the *Teacher Resource Guide,* or construct your own with the **Exam***View*® *Test Generator* on the *Effective Instruction CD-ROM.*)

RETEACHING

- Show students pictures of various types of shellfish. Ask students to identify the shellfish and its type (crustacean or mollusk).
- Refer to the *Reteaching Activities* booklet for the Section 19-4 activity sheet.

CLOSE

Lead a discussion on the characteristics of high-quality fish and shellfish. Record students' comments on the board. Then, based on students' discussion, circle the five most important quality characteristics.

Answers to Section 19-4 Review & Activities

1. Crustacean is shellfish with long body, jointed limbs, covered with shell. Any three: crab, crayfish, lobster, shrimp. Mollusk is shellfish with soft body covered by at least one shell. Any three: clam, mussel, oyster, scallop, squid.
2. Shiny skin; glistening color; mild, fresh aroma; skin springs back when pressed; clear, full eyes; bright red or pink gills.
3. In containers covered with a clean, damp cloth.
4. Both have scales, gills, and internal organs removed. Dressed fish have head, tail, and fins removed.
5. Answers will vary.
6. Answers will vary.

SECTION
19-5

Preparing Meat, Poultry, Fish, and Shellfish

FOCUS

MOTIVATORS

- Ask students if their families have changed the amounts of meat, poultry, fish, and shellfish they eat or the methods for preparing these foods in recent years. If so, what were their reasons? Discuss changes in recommendations from health experts regarding meat, poultry, fish, and shellfish.
- Survey students to identify the most popular preparation methods for meat, poultry, fish, and shellfish. Point out nutritional advantages and disadvantages of various methods.

VOCABULARY ACTIVITY

Pronounce the three terms listed under "Look for These Terms." Have students find the terms and their definitions in the section. Then ask students to determine if *marinating* and *marinades* have the same root.

STUDY SKILLS

- **Guided Reading.** Have students look at the headings within Section 19-5 to preview the concepts that will be discussed.
- Have students read the section and complete the appropriate part of the Chapter 19 Study Guide in the *Student Workbook*.

SECTION
19-5

Preparing Meat, Poultry, Fish, and Shellfish

Objectives

After studying this section, you should be able to:

- Explain how to select a cooking method for different cuts of meat, poultry, fish, and shellfish.
- Identify ways of preparing cuts for cooking.
- Tell how to test cuts for doneness.
- Give guidelines for cooking cuts by different methods.

Look for These Terms

marinating

marinades

doneness

Torey looked down at the supermarket's meat and poultry cases. "What should we have at the cookout?" he wondered. He pictured chicken breasts sizzling on the grill. Maybe thick swordfish steaks would be even better.

When it comes to cooking, meat, poultry, and fish have many similarities. Many of the same basic cooking methods can be used for each.

Cooking Meat, Poultry, Fish, and Shellfish

When cuts from animal foods cook, several changes occur in color, flavor, and texture.

- **Color.** The red color changes to brown. Beef, which is dark red, turns dark brown. Pork and the white meat of poultry, which are light pink, turn almost white.
- **Flavor.** Heat develops the flavor by creating chemical reactions within the cut.
- **Texture.** When heated, a cut loses fat and moisture. As a result, it shrinks. In addition, muscle fibers get firmer and connecting tissue becomes more tender.

When cooked in dry heat, animal foods lose some juices, carrying off some B vitamins. Some thiamin is destroyed by high temperatures. In general, however, few nutrients are lost unless the food is overcooked.

When a cut is overcooked in dry heat, it dries out and gets tough, stringy, and chewy. In moist heat, an overcooked cut gets mushy and loses its flavor. When overcooked in a microwave oven, the cut can get so hard that you can't chew it.

Section 19-5 Resources

- ◆ **Student Workbook,** pp. 139, 144
- ◆ **Teacher Resource Guide**
  Lesson Plan 19-5 Organizer
  Section 19-5 Quiz
  Chapter 19 Test
- ◆ **Effective Instruction CD-ROM**
  Exam*View*® *Test Generator*
  PowerPoint® Slide #44
- ◆ **Transparency Package,** CT-44
- ◆ **Student Motivation Kit**
  Reteaching Activities, p. 91
  Enrichment Activities
  Foods Lab Resources, pp. 12–14, 77–88

More than "Meats" the Eye

Is there more to cooking a cut of meat than just applying heat? You are about to find out by comparing several methods.

Procedure

1. Divide a piece of shoulder or chuck steak into three pieces. Place one piece in a mixture of lemon and ¼ teaspoon (1 mL) ground black pepper for 1 hour. Pound a second piece on both sides with a mallet to break down the muscle fibers.
2. Broil the two prepared pieces along with the untreated third piece for the same length of time. Be sure you know which piece was prepared by which method.
3. Taste all three pieces, noting the relative tenderness of the meat.

Conclusions

- Which piece was the most tender? The least tender?
- What generalizations can you make about the relative tenderizing effects of heat, acid, and pounding on a cut of meat?
- Which piece had the most flavor? What explanation can you offer?

Choosing a Cooking Method

The cooking method you choose depends on the tenderness of the cut. You can cook tender cuts—for example, some steaks, chops, and rib and loin roasts—using dry-heat methods such as broiling and roasting. Broiling, the faster of the two methods, cooks tender cuts in a matter of minutes. Other foods that take well to dry-heat cooking methods include ground meat, poultry, fish, and some shellfish.

Less tender cuts—such as blade roasts, arm steaks, stewing hens, and some shellfish—need to be tenderized. This can take place either during cooking, by using a moist-heat cooking method, or before, by marinating.

INFOLINK

For more on differences in cooking methods, including the use of dry versus moist heat, see Section 9-3.

Using Moist Heat

Applying moist heat to less tender cuts breaks down the collagen in them, making the meat tender. Moist-heat methods—simmering, stewing, and braising—all involve long, slow cooking that helps develop the meat's flavor.

TEACH

- *Cooking Meat, Poultry, Fish, and Shellfish (text pages 512-518)*

Discussion Activity

Divide the class into four groups for discussion. Assign one topic to each group, as follows. (1) List characteristics that change when animal foods are cooked. (2) List cuts that can be cooked using dry heat methods. (3) Explain how less tender cuts should be prepared in order to tenderize them. (4) Explain how much cooking time must be increased if the meat is cooked frozen and why. Have groups share their findings in a class-wide discussion.

Categorizing Activity

Have students categorize cooking methods as dry heat or moist heat methods. Relate appropriate cooking methods to the cut of meat, poultry, fish, or shellfish and its tenderness.

Using the Food Science Lab

Have students work together to find a recipe that uses shoulder or chuck steak. Have students decide if they would change preparation instructions based on lab results. Why or why not? If so, have them rewrite the directions accordingly. L1

Reinforcing Key Skills

Present the following problem to student groups. Allow time for them to discuss and compare their responses.

Management—Stanley came home and discovered that the meat for the evening meal was still in the freezer. Explore with students the options Stanley has, depending on the type of meat and cooking facilities available.

TEACH cont.

- *Cooking Meat, Poultry, Fish, and Shellfish (text pages 512-518)*

Student Demonstrations

Have selected students demonstrate ways of tenderizing less tender cuts of meat before cooking. Include mechanical methods such as grinding, pounding, and scoring; use of acids; and use of meat tenderizer. Remind students of safety procedures, such as the importance of not using marinades as a sauce once they have been in contact with raw meat. L1

Pop-quiz Activity

Conduct a pop quiz consisting of the following: (1) Describe two general measures of doneness. (2) Identify the minimum temperature to which meat and poultry should be heated, explaining why cuts should reach this temperature. (4) Explain why the meat may turn dark around the bones of some poultry when it is cooked. (5) Identify the internal temperatures for rare, medium, and well-done beef. Use student answers as a bridge to a discussion of these and related issues.

◆ **When properly cooked, meat is tender and flavorful and retains most of its nutrients. The cubes of lean meat on these skewers have been marinated for extra tenderness. What simple starch would you serve with these kebabs to add a serving from the grains group?**

Moist-heat methods also give you an opportunity to add seasonings, sauces, and other foods to the dish. You can create many different flavor combinations in this way. For this reason, you may sometimes choose to cook tender cuts in moist heat. If you do so, you should generally shorten the cooking time. Otherwise, the cut can easily be overcooked and fall apart.

Marinades

Marinating, or steeping in a liquid, is a method of tenderizing and adding flavor to foods before you cook them. **Marinades** (MAR-uh-nayds)—the flavorful liquids in which food is steeped—can turn less expensive cuts into tender, flavorful meals.

Most marinades contain three basic ingredients—oil, an acid, and seasonings. You can use any mild oil. The oil coats the outside of the food and keeps it from drying out as it broils or grills. The acid ingredient helps tenderize the food. Options include flavored vinegars, citrus juices, plain fat-free yogurt, and buttermilk. Seasonings add flavor. Try using herbs and spices or aromatic vegetables such as onions, peppers, garlic, and celery.

Pour the marinade ingredients into a large container, such as a reusable glass jar, and shake well. Place the food in a glass or plastic container, pour the marinade over the food, cover the container, and refrigerate. Occasionally turn or stir the food so that it marinates evenly. Do not marinate food in metal pans—the acid may react with the metal and give the food an unpleasant flavor.

Using Marinades

Marinating time depends on the food. Tender foods, such as fish, can marinate for an hour or less. Meat and poultry can marinate up to six or eight hours. Be careful not to over-marinate foods because they will get mushy. If you are marinating foods just for flavor, 30 minutes is usually long enough.

Before cooking, drain the food well. Discard marinade used for meat, poultry, fish, and shellfish, since it may contain harmful bacteria. If you want to baste with the marinade, make an extra batch to use for this purpose.

CLOSE-UP ON SCIENCE: CHEMISTRY

Meat Tenderizers

Enzymes are proteins that control chemical activity in living organisms. One use of enzymes is in meat tenderizers. Three enzymes that come from a fruit called the papaya are diluted with salt to form a dry powder called *papain* (puh-PAY-in). The enzymes in papain attack the connective tissue in muscle fiber. By breaking down the muscle fiber, they make the meat more tender to eat.

Extending Learning

Cooking Meat

- Do not salt a roast before cooking. The salt will draw out juices and nutrients.
- When roasting, keep the meat out of the drippings. If you do not have a roasting rack, improvise with several metal jar lids. Wash them in warm, soapy water and rinse. Punch holes in the tops so that heat and steam can flow. Place lids top side up on the bottom of the roasting pan and rest the meat on them.

Preparing to Cook

For best results, thaw frozen raw meat, poultry, and fish before cooking. If you don't thaw the cut, you will have to increase the cooking time. In general, increase the cooking time by about 50 percent. For example, if the normal cooking time is 40 minutes, the cooking time for frozen cuts would be about 60 minutes. However, the extra time needed depends on the size of the food and whether or not it was partially thawed.

Before cooking meat, poultry, or fish, be sure the cut is clean. Rinse it under cold water and pat dry with a paper towel. If you are cooking whole poultry, first remove the giblets and neck from the body and neck cavities. Rinse the cavities of whole poultry and drawn fish several times. Remove any foreign matter that may be present in the cavities.

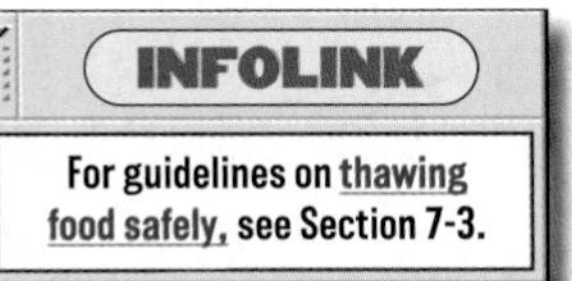

For guidelines on thawing food safely, see Section 7-3.

Trimming Fat

Before cooking meat and poultry, remove as much fat as possible. Trim visible fat from meat.

As you have learned, much of the fat in poultry is in or just under the skin. When cooking poultry in moist heat, remove the skin. However, when using dry-heat methods, leave the skin on to keep the poultry from drying out. Most of the fat will melt and drip away during cooking. Remove the skin before eating.

Judging Doneness

Doneness means having cooked a cut long enough for the necessary changes to take place so that a cut tastes good and is safe to eat. If any part is not cooked, there is a risk of foodborne illness.

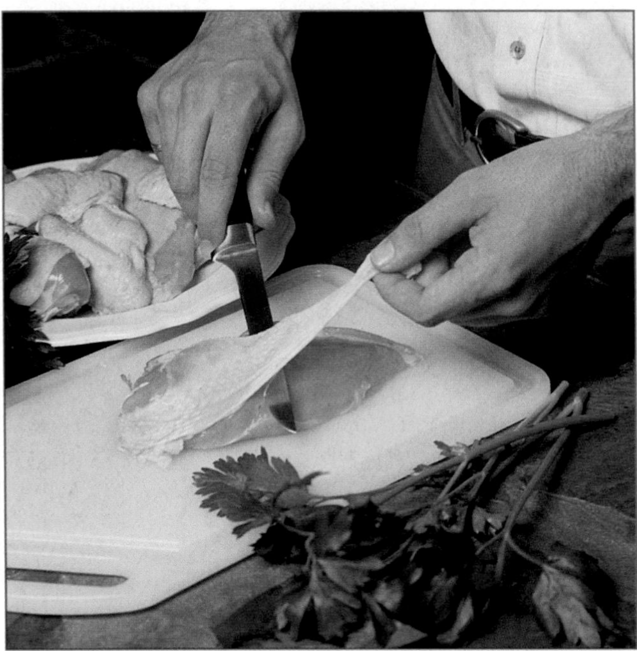

◆ **Remove the skin from poultry that will be cooked in moist heat to reduce the amount of fat in the finished dish. Explain why you should not remove the skin from poultry that is broiled until just before eating.**

- *Cooking Meat, Poultry, Fish, and Shellfish (text pages 512-518)*

Demonstration

Demonstrate methods for checking meat and poultry for doneness. Show how to use a meat thermometer to ensure accuracy. Refer students to the "Internal Temperatures for Meat and Poultry" chart on page 516. Discuss reasons to avoid eating undercooked meat, poultry, and fish. Demonstrate how to test fish for doneness. Explain how to use the "ten-minute rule."

VISUAL LEARNING ***Using a Chart*** Refer students back to the "Bacteria That Cause Foodborne Illness" chart on page 199 for more information about foodborne illness. How many of the bacteria in the chart are found in underdone cuts of meat, poultry, fish, or shellfish?

Lab Experience

Have groups of students cook small samples of the same inexpensive cut of meat in four different ways: slow cooker, dry heat, moist heat at low temperature, and moist heat at high temperature. Ask students to compare and rank the taste and tenderness of the cooked meats. Also have students compare the time it takes to cook the cut using each method. What can students conclude? L1

FOOD SCIENCE **Broiling Temperatures** Broiling is a modern name for the oldest cooking technique: roasting over an open fire or coals. All heat sources used in broiling emit visible light, which means they also emit intense infrared radiation. It is this infrared heat that does the cooking. The temperatures reached by broiler elements are much higher than those of an oven wall. The energy radiated by an element is proportional to the fourth power of the temperature. A broiler can radiate about 80 times as much energy as the wall of an oven set at 500°F.

TEACH cont.

- *Cooking Meat, Poultry, Fish, and Shellfish (text pages 512-518)*

VISUAL LEARNING ***Using a Chart*** Explain to students there are many ways to present information in graph form. Illustrate this point by recasting the "Internal Temperatures for Meat and Poultry" chart in an alternative format—for example, based on temperature categories rather than on food categories. Invite students to create still other graphic devices that contain the same information. (One possibility is an illustrated thermometer graph.) Allow time for students to share and compare their graphic representations.

Expanding the Chart Activity

Challenge students to expand on the information in the chart by creating another column for appearance. Ask why such a column would be useful in a pinch. Ask: What dangers might come from judging doneness in terms of appearance only?

Meal Plan Activity

Ask students to plan a balanced and varied one-day meal plan that centers on two of the items in the chart on this page. Allow students to share and compare their meal plans as a prelude to a discussion of the variety in meals that can be achieved through simple planning.

Internal Temperatures for Meat and Poultry

Food	Internal Temperature °F	°C
Beef		
Medium-rare (some bacterial risk)	145	63
Medium	160	71
Well-done	170	77
Pork, Lamb, Veal (Roasts, Steaks, Chops)		
Medium	160	71
Well-done	170	77
Poultry		
Whole chicken, turkey	180	82
Turkey breasts or roasts	170	77
Stuffing (cooked alongside bird)	165	74
Ham		
Fresh (raw) or shoulder	160	71
Precooked (to reheat)	140	60
Ground Meat and Poultry		
Turkey, chicken	170	77
Beef, veal, lamb, pork	160	71
Leftovers		
Meat in soups and stews (Bring soup and any grains to a rolling boil.)	165	74
Casseroles	160	71

Both meat and poultry are tested for doneness in the same general way. To be safe to eat, either should reach an internal temperature of at least 160°F (71°C).

Meat and poultry cooking times vary, depending on the method and the cut used. The cooking time given in the recipe is just a guide. Begin testing meat and poultry for doneness about 10 minutes before the end of the cooking time.

Testing Meat for Doneness

When roasting cuts more than 2 inches (5 cm) thick, don't rely on appearance alone as a test for doneness. Use a meat thermometer. This type of thermometer, usually made of metal, is inserted into the thickest part of the cut and left in place for the entire cooking period. Taking a reading in two or three different places yields an even more accurate sense of when a roast is done.

With other cooking methods or thinner cuts, use an instant-read thermometer. Do not use an instant-read thermometer in the oven while food is roasting. This type of thermometer is designed to be inserted into depths no greater than ½ inch (1 cm) and furnishes a reading within about ten seconds.

Technology TIE-IN Ask students to research the incidences of the foodborne illness salmonellosis, related to chicken and how it has increased or decreased over time. Ask students to pay special attention to how technology, such as irradiation or computerized inspection tools, might have affected the incidences. Have students develop a timeline based on research findings.

Testing Poultry for Doneness

When testing chicken, you may find the meat has turned dark around the bones. This is common in young broiler-fryers. Their bones have not hardened completely. During cooking, color pigment from the inside of the bone seeps out. The meat is safe to eat.

When testing cubes of poultry, pierce with a fork. If the fork slides easily to the bottom, the food is done.

How to Use a Meat Thermometer

A meat thermometer is an indispensable tool when cooking meat or poultry.

Look and Learn:

Explain the importance of inserting the thermometer into the thickest area of a cut or as close to the center as possible.

Ground Meat—Meat loaf

- ◆ Ground meat or poultry: Place the thermometer in the thickest part of the food.

Ham

- ◆ Roast: Insert the thermometer into the center of the thickest part, away from gristle, fat, and bone.

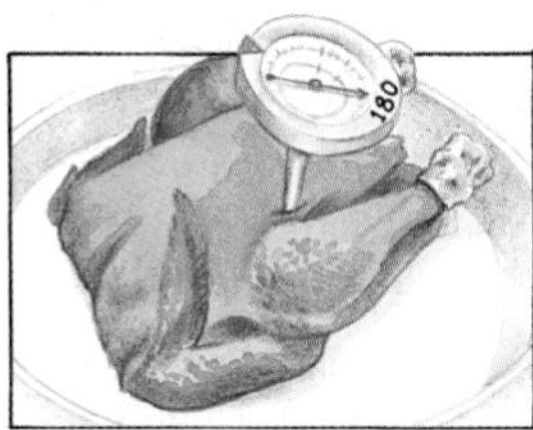

Whole Poultry

- ◆ Whole poultry: Insert the thermometer into the inner thigh, near the breast. It should not touch the bone. If the bird is stuffed, take a reading of the stuffing at the end of the cooking time.

- ◆ Casseroles: Insert the thermometer into the thickest portion. If the dish is shallow, check the temperature at the end of the cooking time with an instant-read thermometer. Insert it about ½ inch (1 cm) into the mixture.

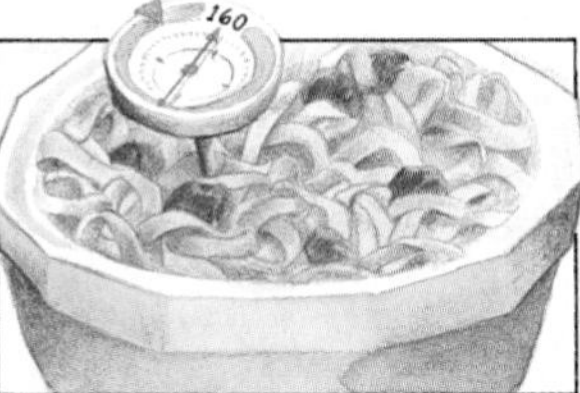

Casserole

Ground Meat—Burgers

- ◆ Thin pieces: Insert the instant-read thermometer sideways until the tip is in the center of the burger.

- *Cooking Meat, Poultry, Fish, and Shellfish (text pages 512-518)*

VISUAL LEARNING ***Using the Illustration***

Roast a whole chicken during class. Ask students to demonstrate the proper placement of a meat thermometer into the cooked, roasted chicken, according to the illustration on this page. Have students record the temperature. Review students' techniques and discuss the temperature range that the students should have recorded.

Lab Experience Activity

Chop the roasted poultry into pieces and have students test doneness with a fork. It should slide easily to the bottom. If possible, have students compare the cooked portion to a portion not thoroughly cooked to feel the differences.

USING Safety Check

Refer students to the feature on page 518. Ask students if they believe there is a way to salvage a meal that is half-cooked because an emergency dictates leaving the premises. Discuss students' ideas. Elicit that there is rarely a way of safely salvaging half-cooked meals.

HOME & COMMUNITY CONNECTION

Ask students to create a chart or brochure that explains how to determine doneness for meat, poultry, and fish. Suggest that the information format chosen be based on specific foods usually prepared by their families and based on the expertise level of family members that will be using it. Encourage students to make copies of their information sources to take home and share with family members.

TEACH cont.

- *Basic Cooking Methods (text pages 518-522)*

Poster Project

Have students work in groups to prepare posters listing the basic steps for roasting meat, poultry, and fish. Display posters around the classroom. L1

Demonstration

Demonstrate procedures for preparing whole poultry for roasting, with and without stuffing. Encourage student discussion on why it is better to tie the legs together and tuck tips of wings under back of a chicken before roasting or baking. Demonstrate how to truss poultry using metal skewers. Show how to baste the bird using a baster. Point out safety precautions for roasting whole poultry with stuffing.

Writing

Have students develop a brochure on "Preventing Holiday Hazards Involving Poultry." Have them include information on thawing, cooking, and storing cooked poultry. Suggest they use information other than just what is in this section; include information from previous chapters. L1

Safety Check

Once you start to cook a cut, regardless of the method, finish cooking it. Don't cook food partially and then complete the cooking later. Partial or interrupted cooking often produces conditions that encourage the growth of harmful bacteria.

Testing Fish for Doneness

Fish is very tender and cooks in a short time. When using conventional cooking methods, remember the "10-minute rule." Cook fish 10 minutes for every inch (2.5 cm) of thickness, as measured at the thickest part. However, there are a few exceptions. If fish is being baked in a sauce, add about 5 minutes to the total cooking time. Some moist-heat recipes may call for longer cooking times to allow flavors to blend. Remember to increase the cooking time if the fish is frozen.

Begin to check for doneness about 2 or 3 minutes before the cooking time is up. Fish is done when its flesh turns opaque. When gently lifted with a fork, the flesh flakes easily.

Basic Cooking Methods

You can use a number of different cooking methods for meat, poultry, fish, and shellfish. These include roasting, broiling, poaching, and microwaving.

INFOLINK
For more specifics on different cooking methods, see Sections 9-2, 9-3, and 9-4.

Roasting or Baking

When you are roasting or baking meat, poultry, or fish, it is usually not necessary to preheat the oven. However, follow recipe directions. The roasting temperatures in a conventional oven should be at least 325°F (160°C) to keep harmful bacteria from growing. Fish can bake at higher temperatures, such as 450°F (230°C).

The way you prepare meat, poultry, and fish for roasting or baking varies.

- **Large meat roasts.** Put the roast, fat side up, on a rack in a pan to hold the cut out of the drippings. Some rib cuts of meat form a natural rack. Insert the meat thermometer so that the tip is in the center of the roast. The thermometer should not touch bone, fat, or thick connective tissues.
- **Whole poultry.** Make the bird as compact as possible so that it cooks evenly. Tie the legs together. Tuck tips of wings under the back. Insert a meat thermometer deep into the thickest part of the thigh next to the body. Be sure it is not touching bone or fat. Do not stuff the bird, which can lead to cross-contamination. Instead, cook the stuffing in a separate pan.
- **Poultry pieces.** Place in a shallow pan, skin side up.
- **Fish.** Place the fish in a lightly oiled, shallow baking dish. If baking fillets, place them skin side down so that you can test for doneness. To keep the fish moist, brush with seasoned melted fat or sauce. You can also bread the fish. If so, dot the fish with a teaspoon (5 mL) of butter or margarine after breading.

Follow recipe directions for turning the food. Generally, large roasts, whole poultry, and fish do not have to be turned. Poultry pieces may need to be turned after half the cooking time. To reduce fat, use broth or juice for basting instead of drippings. Roast or bake for the time specified in the recipe.

FOOD SCIENCE

Barbecue Sauces for Chicken

Ask students if they have ever had home-barbecued chicken that was black-crusted and bitter. Explain that the primary cause is adding barbecue sauce too early. High heat burns sugar, a major ingredient of barbecue sauce. In addition, spices become bitter when scorched. To avoid this, do not brush on the sauce until 15 minutes before the chicken will be finished cooking. Also, keep the food four to six inches above the coals.

◆ **Tandoori chicken, a favorite in India, is marinated in a savory blend of yogurt and spices before grilling or broiling. In addition to adding an interesting flavor, what function does the yogurt serve in this dish?**

Broiling

Broiling is one of the quickest cooking methods. It is an ideal choice for families who are on the go but want to sit down together to a home-cooked meal.

To prepare meat for broiling, slash the fat around the edges. This will help keep the cut from curling. When broiling chicken, begin with the skin side down. Halfway through the broiling time, turn the skin side up. When broiling fish, which is lean, brush it lightly with melted butter or margarine to keep it from charring.

To add flavor to any broiled food, brush it with a sauce, such as barbecue sauce or salsa. For even greater variety, make kabobs. Thread cubes of meat, poultry, or firm fish onto skewers, alternating with tomato quarters, mushrooms, green pepper chunks, or other vegetables. Brush with melted butter or margarine, or a sauce, to keep the vegetables from drying out. Broil or grill, turning so that all sides are done.

Poaching

As noted in Chapter 9, poaching involves simmering whole foods in a small amount of liquid. Fish is one of the foods most commonly poached. Many people consider poached fish to be a delicacy, and it is often served in fine restaurants.

You may poach whole drawn fish, fillets, or steaks. The cooking liquid may be plain water, water with lemon or grapefruit juice, fish or vegetable stock, or milk. Usually, the liquid is seasoned to add more flavor to the fish. Try using herbs or spices—dill or grated fresh ginger, for example—and sautéed vegetables, such as onions and green peppers.

Poaching Fish Fillets

To poach fish fillets:

1. Pour the cooking liquid (seasoned as desired) into a large, deep skillet. Bring to a boil; then immediately reduce the heat to a simmer.
2. Place the fillets in a single layer in the pan. Add enough liquid, if necessary, to cover the fish by at least 1 inch (2.5 cm).
3. Cover the pan and simmer gently until the fish is just opaque throughout. Do not turn the fish while poaching.

- *Basic Cooking Methods (text pages 518-522)*

Creativity

Have students brainstorm ways to add visual meal appeal to broiled chicken. What are some simple measures that can add or enhance flavor? Have students compile a class list of all the ideas. Suggest that students try out their favorite ideas at home. Have students report back to class with results of any ideas tried. L1

Lab Experience

Have students practice broiling cubes of meat, poultry, or firm fish on skewers. Instruct students to alternate meat with pieces of vegetables such as tomato quarters, pieces of onion, and green pepper chunks. They are then to brush the foods with some form of fat or a sauce, to keep vegetables from drying out. Have students broil the skewers, turning so that all sides are done. L1

Finding Recipes

Have students find recipes for broiled or poached fish. Ask students to compare the nutritional value (at least calories and total fat) for each recipe. If time permits, have students poach fish in various liquids. Have students taste test each variety and write a short summary of their conclusions. L1

Reinforcing Key Skills

Present the following problem to student groups. Allow time for them to discuss and compare their responses.

Communication—Gabby was sent to the store by her mother to buy a holiday turkey. She is having a difficult time determining whether to purchase a fresh turkey that's pre-stuffed or one without stuffing. What advice might you offer?

TEACH cont.

- *Basic Cooking Methods (text pages 518-522)*

Discussion Activity

Ask students to explain why it is important to buy cuts of meat, poultry, fish, and shellfish that are uniform in shape and size if you intend to cook them in the microwave oven.

Listing

Ask students to list guidelines for microwaving meat, poultry, fish, and shellfish. L1

Demonstration

Demonstrate methods of adding visual appeal to light-colored meats cooked in a microwave. Show how a browning effect can be created using a dark-colored sauce, a browning dish or grill, or by broiling for a few minutes after cooking in the microwave oven.

Menu Planning

In groups, have students develop a one-day menu plan for a family of four that includes microwaved meat in one meal and microwaved poultry in another. Encourage students to be specific and creative. L1

Poaching Whole Fish

To poach whole drawn fish or fish steaks, first wrap the fish in cheesecloth. Allow enough length at the ends so that you can twist and knot them. Use the ends as handles to lower and raise the fish to prevent it from falling apart. Otherwise, follow the same procedure as for fillets.

If you like, you can serve hot poached fish with a sauce made from the cooking liquid. After removing the fish from the pan, boil the cooking liquid to reduce the amount of liquid and reach the desired flavor.

Poached fish may also be eaten chilled. You might serve cold poached fish with dill or cucumber sauce or use it in a salad.

◆ **Fish fillets poached in seasoned liquid emerge moist, tender, and flavored by the broth. Create your own recipe for poaching. Identify each step involved.**

Microwave Cooking

All types of meat, poultry, fish, and shellfish can be microwaved. When buying for microwaving, choose cuts that are uniform in size. Thaw frozen raw meat, poultry, fish, and shellfish completely before cooking in the microwave.

For best results, follow the directions in the microwave recipes exactly. Following are some general guidelines.

Microwaving Meat and Poultry

Remember that microwave ovens do not always cook evenly, even with a turntable. This is especially important to keep in mind when microwaving large cuts, such as meat roasts or whole poultry. Follow recipe directions exactly to be sure the meat or poultry cooks completely throughout.

When microwaving pork roasts, take special care to cook the meat thoroughly. Place the meat in a covered dish or in a loosely sealed, microwave-safe cooking bag. This will hold in moist heat to help ensure even cooking and tender, juicy meat. If you like, add a small amount of liquid, such as water, broth, fruit juice, or a sauce. You can also use a cooking bag for whole poultry.

FOOD SCIENCE: Microwave vs. Conventional Preparation

Have students prepare meat, poultry, or fish dishes in the microwave oven and by conventional methods. Have them compare cooking times and taste. Which methods do students most prefer? Least prefer? Ask students to be specific with their responses.

◆ A cooking bag can be used when microwaving roasts and whole poultry. Name two advantages of this method.

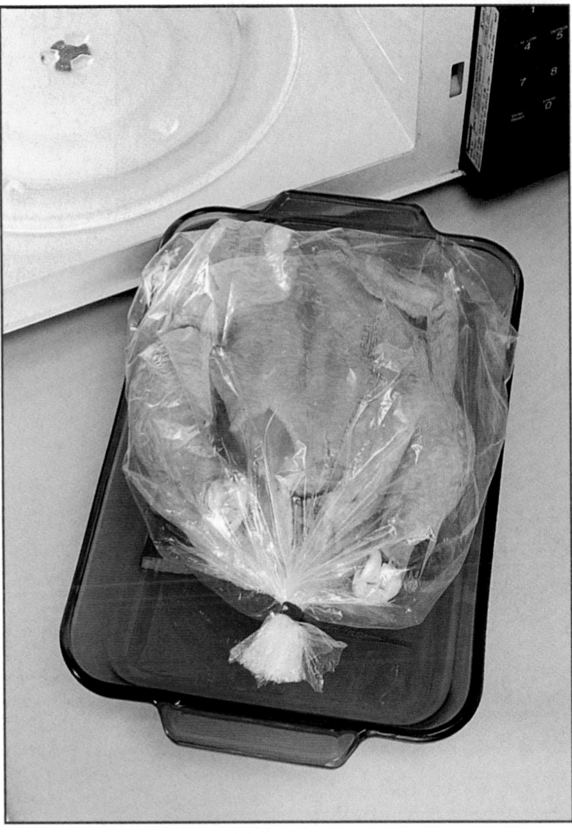

When microwaved, roasts and whole poultry are cooked at a lower internal temperature than with conventional cooking. This is because the internal temperature continues to rise during standing time. If the microwave oven has a temperature probe, you can program the oven to shut off when the food reaches the desired temperature.

During standing time, cover roasts loosely with foil to hold heat in. After standing time, check the meat or poultry in several spots with a meat thermometer to be sure it has reached the proper internal temperature throughout.

Light-colored cuts cooked in a microwave oven may look unappetizing because they have not yet browned. You may want to use one of the following methods to create a browned effect:

- Before cooking, brush or rub with a dark-colored sauce, such as barbecue, tamari, or Worcestershire.
- Use a browning dish or grill. These are specially made so that they become extremely hot. Press small cuts down against the bottom to brown them.
- After microwaving, put the cut in the broiler for a few minutes to brown it.

Microwaving Fish

When microwaving fish, allow about 3 to 6 minutes per pound (500 g) at 100 percent power. Thick fillets and whole fish take a little more time than thin ones.

Take care to avoid overcooking—fish is tender, and the microwave cooks quickly. Remove the fish from the microwave when it is still slightly underdone in the center. Let it stand for 5 minutes to complete the cooking; then test for doneness.

Shellfish cooks quickly, so be careful not to overcook it. If you do, it will get tough and rubbery.

- *Cooking Methods (text pages 518-522)*

Discussion Activity

Name common fried meat, poultry, and fish entrées. Ask students to explain why frying these foods results in a higher fat content than other cooking methods. Conclude by asking students to identify lower fat and/or more nutrient-dense alternatives of the dishes named.

Research

Have interested students research unusual methods used in other cultures for preparing meat, poultry, fish, and shellfish. One example is the exotic French method known as *salmis*, which involves roasting and braising game birds. If time permits, have students work in groups to arrange and prepare demonstrations of these cooking methods. L2

Finding Recipes

Ask students to find recipes that use as many different cooking methods as possible. Discuss the merits of each cooking method. L1

Extending Learning

Pan-frying Fish—Keep the following suggestions in mind.

- Before you fry fish, have paper towels ready for draining the fried food. Keep the towels away from the burner so that they do not catch fire.
- Use several layers of paper towels to drain fried fish. Have enough so that, as fat accumulates on the towels, you can replace them quickly. Don't use newspaper under a single layer of paper towels. It is loaded with chemicals that can transfer to the fish through the oil-soaked paper towels.

ASSESS

REVIEW

- Ask students to summarize the main ideas in this section.
- Have students complete the Section Review. (Answers appear below.)

EVALUATION

- Have students write a short essay about the cooking concepts covered in this section.
- Have students take the quiz for Section 19-5. (Use the quiz in the *Teacher Resource Guide,* or construct your own with the **Exam***View*® *Test Generator* on the *Effective Instruction CD-ROM.*)

RETEACHING

- Demonstrate how to determine when fish or shellfish cooked in the microwave oven is done, taking into account that further cooking will occur during standing time.
- Refer to the *Reteaching Activities* booklet for the Section 19-5 activity sheet.

CLOSE

Discuss preparation methods for meat, poultry, fish, and shellfish. Ask students to list new methods and/or foods they have discovered while studying this chapter.

Other Cooking Methods

You may pan-fry meat, poultry, and shellfish. Often the food is breaded or dipped in batter first. Remember that food absorbs fat as it fries. If you do choose to fry, use as little fat as possible—no more than 1 teaspoon (5 mL) of oil. You may use a vegetable-oil spray for sautéing small pieces of meat, poultry, fish, or shellfish.

Most meat (except veal) is marbled with fat and can be pan-broiled—cooked in a skillet without added fat—instead of fried. Just be sure to remove the fat that accumulates during cooking.

Some cooking methods—such as stewing, braising, and stir-frying—usually involve cooking several different foods together, such as meat and vegetables.

◆ **When microwaving fish, remove the fish before it has completely finished cooking. The fish should feel slightly firm when lightly pressed with a fork.** Check the manufacturer's instructions on a microwave oven in the foods lab or at home for any special tips on cooking fish. Record these in your Wellness Journal for future reference.

Section 19-5 Review & Activities

1. Name two specific cooking methods you might use for tender cuts and two you might use for less tender cuts.
2. Name three steps that might be involved in preparing raw meat or poultry for cooking.
3. Name two signs that fish is done cooking.
4. **Extending.** What would you do if you came home and found that the meat for the evening meal was still in the freezer?
5. **Evaluating.** What is the advantage of knowing basic guidelines for a number of different methods of cooking meat, poultry, and fish?
6. **Applying.** Choose one of the cooking methods discussed in this chapter. Write the name of the method vertically down the left-hand side of a sheet of paper. Next to each letter, write a sentence that begins with that letter and gives a fact about the cooking method.

Answers to Section 19-5 Review & Activities

1. Tender cuts—broiling, roasting; less tender cuts—any two: simmering, stewing, braising.
2. Thaw, clean by rinsing under cold water and patting dry with paper towel; rinse cavities; trim fat.
3. Flesh turns opaque; flesh flakes easily when lifted gently with a fork.
4. Answers will vary, depending on the type of meat and cooking facilities available. Students will probably mention thawing the meat in the microwave.
5. Answers will vary.
6. Answers will vary.

Recipe File

Pan-Asian Microwave Chicken Deluxe

The soy sauce gives this tangy main course a Chinese touch; the yogurt gives it a taste of India. The recipe is also great as kabobs—cut into chunks and skewered.

Customary	Ingredient	Metric
4	Boneless, skinless chicken breast halves	4
2 Tbsp.	Reduced-sodium soy sauce	30 mL
½ cup	Plain fat-free yogurt	125 mL
½ tsp.	Grated onion	3 mL
½ tsp.	Prepared mustard	3 mL
½ tsp.	Seasoned salt	3 mL
Dash	Ground pepper	Dash

Yield: 4 servings, ½ breast each
Equipment: Round microwave-safe dish with removable rack
Power level: 100% power

Directions

1. Brush chicken pieces with soy sauce.
2. Arrange chicken on rack close to edges of dish. Cover loosely with waxed paper.
3. Microwave at 100% power for 6 minutes.
4. Mix together yogurt, onion, and mustard in small bowl. Set aside.
5. Remove chicken pieces from rack. Turn pieces over and place in bottom of dish, arranging them in a circle around the edge.
6. Spoon yogurt mixture over each piece. Cover loosely with waxed paper.
7. Microwave at 100% power for about 6 minutes, or until fork can be inserted in chicken with ease.
8. Sprinkle with seasoned salt and pepper. Let stand, covered, 2 minutes before serving.

Nutrition Information

Per serving (approximate): 215 calories, 31 g protein, 3 g carbohydrate, 8 g fat, 84 mg cholesterol, 593 mg sodium
Good source of: B vitamins, phosphorus

Food for Thought

- Why is it important to arrange and turn the chicken pieces as specified in the recipe?
- What is the purpose of the soy sauce?

Answers to **Food for Thought**

1. So that it cooks evenly.
2. Answers will vary. The purpose is to give the effect of "browning" the chicken. It provides tangy "Chinese" flavor, too.

Recipe File

Pan-Asian Microwave Chicken Deluxe

This recipe uses the convenient cooking technique of microwaving to prepare a flavorful, low-fat chicken entrée. Prior to assigning the lab, you may wish to have students review the appropriate portion of the text under the heading "Microwave Cooking" on pages 520-521.

Using the Recipe

- Have students read the recipe and discuss each step.
- Remind students that waxed paper should cover the chicken only loosely, so that steam can be vented from the cooking chicken.
- Review safety and sanitation procedures that apply to this recipe.
- Have each lab team fill out a work plan. (See the *Foods Lab Resources* booklet.)
- Have students check off the ingredients and equipment listed on the recipe worksheet and prepare the recipe.
- Have students complete the evaluation and questions on the recipe worksheet.

See Also. . .

The *Foods Lab Resources* booklet for the "Pan-Asian Microwave Chicken Deluxe" recipe worksheet and other recipe alternatives.

Recipe File

Beef Patties with Herbs

This recipe uses the cooking method of broiling. Prior to assigning the lab, you may wish to have students review the portion of the text under the subheading "Broiling" on page 519.

USING THE RECIPE

- Have students read the recipe and discuss each step.
- Remind students that the small amount of fat can spatter and could cause severe burns. In addition, the spattered grease can be difficult to clean up from the kitchen surfaces.
- Review other safety and sanitation procedures that apply to this recipe.
- Have each lab team fill out a work plan. (See the *Foods Lab Resources* booklet.)
- Have students check off the ingredients and equipment listed on the recipe worksheet and prepare the recipe.
- Have students complete the evaluation and questions on the recipe worksheet.

SEE ALSO...
The *Foods Lab Resources* booklet for the "Beef Patties with Herbs" recipe worksheet and other recipe alternatives.

Recipe File

Beef Patties with Herbs

Building a better burger is a priority for many home and professional cooks. Here is a recipe that is more healthful and just as tasty as a pan-fried burger.

Customary	***Ingredients***	***Metric***
1 lb.	Extra-lean ground beef	500 g
½ tsp.	Ground pepper	3 mL
½ tsp.	Dried rosemary	3 mL
½ tsp.	Dried thyme	3 mL
4	Slices tomato	4
4	Thin slices onion	4
4	Crusty rolls, split	4

Yield: 4 servings, 1 sandwich each
Oven Temperature: Broil

Directions

1. Combine ground beef, pepper, and herbs until well blended.
2. Shape the ground beef mixture into four patties about ½ inch (1 cm) thick.
3. Place beef patties about 2 inches (5 cm) under the heat source. Broil 10 minutes, turning once after 6 minutes.
4. Serve patties with tomato and onion slices on crusty rolls.

Nutrition Information

Per serving (approximate): 351 calories, 28 g protein, 23 g carbohydrate, 16 g fat, 84 mg cholesterol, 313 mg sodium
Good source of: iron, B vitamins, phosphorus

Food for Thought

- If you substituted ground turkey meat for ground beef, what other changes might you need to make in the recipe? Why?
- What other serving suggestions could you make for these ground beef patties?

Answers to Food for Thought

1. Answers will vary; more seasoning/herbs may need to be used because turkey has a milder flavor than beef.
2. Answers will vary; serve Greek-style in a pita bread pocket with yogurt-cucumber sauce or serve Mexican-style in between two tortillas with salsa and avocado or grated cheese.

Career Wanted

Fish Production Technician

Education and Training
- On-the-job training
- Courses in biology, agriculture, and environmental studies

Qualities
- Observation skills
- Good physical health
- Enjoy working outdoors

"Raising fish is a real 'growth industry.'"

Troy Richter

Q. Troy, it's safe to say that most people have never heard of a fish production technician. What do you do?

A. I take care of food fish in a hatchery—catfish, specifically. I feed, record behavior, and control the environment. We raise fish like ranchers raise cattle, except instead of pasture and fences, we worry about pond depth, oxygen level, temperature, and velocity. Ranchers give injections to control disease. We flush the eggs with an antifungal solution.

Q. So the term "fish farming" is very apt.

A. It is. We share concerns with farmers as our industry grows, like the effect of fishpond waste on the environment, and the use of vitamins and animal products in feeds. Last year I helped tag our fish for biological research.

Q. Are you staying with this career?

A. I plan to. There are a lot of opportunities for the future, especially in teaching the technologies at a university level. I want to be here to help the industry grow responsibly.

Related Career Opportunities

Entry Level
- Seafood market worker
- Fishing vessel deckhand

Technical Level
- Biological science technician
- Fish hatchery manager
- Fishing vessel captain

Professional Level
- Hydrologist
- Wildlife inspector
- Marine biologist

Making Career Connections

CAREER INVESTIGATION. Write to these sources for information about fish-related careers: USDA; Environmental Protection Service; U.S. Fish & Wildlife Service; National Park Service; and U.S. Forest Service. Create a bulletin board display that shows opportunities.

Fish Production Technician

Thinking About the Career

Have students consider possible reasons that fish might be "tagged" for monitoring. Discuss these possibilities.

Ask students why people seem to be eating more fish nowadays. Do they expect fish consumption to keep increasing? Why or why not?

Have students brainstorm decisions that Troy Richter might have to make on a daily basis. What techniques might he use to make these decisions?

Career-Building Opportunities

Students interested in a career in the fishing industry may consider volunteering to help on small commercial fishing vessels. On a smaller scale, students may begin by studying about and taking care of fish in a home aquarium.

For More Information

For additional information about careers in the fishing industry, encourage students to contact:

- American Fisheries Society
  5410 Grosvenor Ln., Suite 110
  Bethesda, MD 20814-2199
  www.fisheries.org
- American Seafood Institute (ASI)
  25 Fairway Circle
  Hope Valley, RI 02832
  www.seafoodrus.org
- National Fisheries Institute
  1901 North Fort Myer Dr., Suite 700
  Arlington, VA 22209
  www.nfi.org
- International Game Fish Association
  300 Gulf Stream Way
  Dania Beach, FL 33004
  www.igfa.org

REVIEW

- Have students complete the Chapter Review. (Answers appear below.)

EVALUATION

- Divide the class into two teams. Each team is to brainstorm questions about Chapter 19. Then allow the teams to take turns asking each other questions. At the end of the questioning period, the team with the most correct answers wins.
- Have students take the test for Chapter 19. (Use the chapter test in the *Teacher Resource Guide,* or construct your own with the **Exam***View*® *Test Generator* on the *Effective Instruction CD-ROM.*)

ANSWERS

Checking Your Knowledge

1. Beef; fish.
2. A yellowish, very tough connective tissue in meat and poultry that cannot be softened by heat. It must be tenderized by other methods.
3. Beef—roasts and steaks (any two): round, loin, sirloin, chuck arm; pork—roasts and chops (any two): tenderloin, center loin, ham; lamb—roasts and chops (any two): leg, loin, foreshank.
4. Prime (highest and most expensive grade, meat well marbled with fat, tender and flavorful), choice (less marbling than prime, but still tender and flavorful), select (least expensive, least amount of marbling, sometimes sold as store brand).
5. Roasters, Rock Cornish game hens, capons.
6. Ground turkey was ground with the skin, so it contains more fat. Ground turkey meat was ground without the skin.

Chapter 19 Review & Activities

Summary

Section 19-1: Looking at Meat, Poultry, Fish, and Shellfish

- Meat, poultry, fish, and shellfish are sources of complete protein, B vitamins, and minerals. They also contain cholesterol and fat.
- Some cuts of meat and poultry are less tender than others.
- These foods are usually the most costly part of the food budget.

Section 19-2: Meat Selection and Storage

- You can identify cuts by the package label or by bone shape.
- The USDA inspects meat for wholesomeness.
- Some meats are processed by curing and other methods.
- Store meat properly to retain its quality.

Section 19-3: Poultry Selection and Storage

- Chicken and turkey may be purchased fresh or frozen, whole or in parts. Ducks and geese are usually available whole and frozen.
- Poultry is inspected and may be graded by the USDA.
- Poultry requires cold storage.

Section 19-4: Fish and Shellfish Selection and Storage

- Fish may be bought fresh or frozen in several market forms.
- Shellfish include crustaceans and mollusks. Many are sold live.
- Judge the quality of fish and shellfish by looks and aroma.
- Fish should be refrigerated or frozen.

Section 19-5: Preparing Meat, Poultry, Fish, and Shellfish

- Tender cuts can be cooked with dry-heat methods. Less tender cuts need moist-heat methods.
- Thaw, clean, and trim fat before cooking.
- You can test for doneness by using a meat thermometer.
- Basic cooking methods include roasting or baking, broiling, poaching, and microwaving.

Checking Your Knowledge

1. Of beef, pork, chicken, and fish, which generally has the most saturated fat? The least?
2. What is elastin? Why is it a factor in meat and poultry preparation?
3. Give two examples of lean cuts of each of the following: beef, pork, lamb.
4. List and describe three grades of meat.
5. Name three types of chicken suitable for roasting.
6. What is the difference between ground turkey and ground turkey meat?
7. What does the term *seafood* refer to?
8. What is the difference between fish fillets and fish steaks?
9. Describe how cuts from animal foods change in color, flavor, and texture when cooked.
10. Give three tips for broiling meat, poultry, or fish.

Review & Activities Chapter 19

Thinking Critically

1. **Identifying Cause and Effect.** Besides cost and tenderness, what other factors might affect your choice when buying meat, poultry, and fish?
2. **Making Generalizations.** Rona wants to try out a new recipe for pork roast that she glanced at in a magazine while waiting to get her hair cut. She has never cooked a roast. What specific information and techniques should she know about before attempting this recipe?

Working IN THE Lab

1. ***Taste Test.*** Compare the taste of different types of processed meat, poultry, or fish. Identify the processing method used, and tell what characteristics it gives the food.
2. ***Foods Lab.*** Choose a recipe calling for ground meat. Prepare it once using meat, and then using ground poultry instead. Compare the results.
3. ***Foods Lab.*** Poach a fillet of a firm-fleshed fish, such as salmon. Check the fish for doneness 2 or 3 minutes before the cooking time is due to end. When the fish is opaque and the flesh flakes easily, it is done.

Reinforcing Key Skills

1. **Management.** You would like to reduce the amount of money you spend on meat, poultry, and fish, while still providing your family with good-tasting, high-quality protein foods. What steps do you need to take before you can achieve this goal?
2. **Communication.** Elena refuses to try organ meats, giblets, or shellfish. She is sure she won't like them. Why might she feel this way? What might be some benefits of trying these foods? What arguments might you use to persuade Elena to give them a try?

Making Decisions and Solving Problems

You have just moved to a new town and would like to prepare dinner for some new friends. You choose a favorite recipe that calls for loin of lamb, but discover that none of the stores in your area carry it.

Making Connections

1. **Science.** Find information about meat processing methods. How were meats treated for preservation and flavoring in the past? How is this done today? What chemicals and chemical processes are involved? If possible, conduct an experiment or demonstration showing these principles at work.
2. **Math.** Compare the prices of similar forms of chicken and turkey in your area. Figure the cost per serving for each. Show the findings on a bar graph. List the possible reasons for any price differences.

ANSWERS cont.

7. Saltwater fish and shellfish; those that come from the sea or ocean (as opposed to freshwater fish and shellfish).
8. Fillets are skimmed from along the side of the fish and rarely contain bones. Steaks are cut across the fish and usually contain back and rib bones.
9. The red color changes to brown, and pink colors turn beige; flavors are developed; cuts shrink, muscle fibers get firmer, and connective tissue becomes more tender.
10. Any three: Slash the fat around the edges before broiling; when broiling chicken, begin with skin side down and turn when halfway through broiling time; brush fish lightly with melted butter or margarine to keep it from charring; brush broiled foods with sauce to add flavor.

Thinking Critically

1. Answers will vary. Nutritional value and fat or calorie content are possible answers.
2. Answers will vary. Possibilities include knowing about selecting cuts and how to gauge doneness, including proper use of a meat thermometer.

Reinforcing Key Skills

1. Answers will vary. First you need to determine how much money you will be able to spend. Then plan lower cost menus, making sure they're balanced and they provide appropriate amounts of good-tasting, high-quality protein foods. Finally, make a shopping list based on these menus.
2. Answers will vary. Elena might feel this way due to peer-pressure or the unusual/unfamiliar aroma or appearance. She might benefit due to nutritional value or she may like it, providing more variety in her eating plan. To persuade her, I would say, "You don't have to eat it, but you might like it. It tastes like (a similar-tasting favorite food)!"

CHAPTER

20 Food Combinations

Advance Planning Guide ☑

- Gather, obtain, or purchase all necessary ingredients for the following: Motivator, page 529; Sandwich Making, page 530; Taste Test, page 537; Visual Learning, page 538; Lab Experience, pages 539, 551, 552; Demonstration, pages 543, 545; Food Science Lab, page 545; Working in the Lab, page 556.
- Purchase all necessary ingredients for the Recipe File on pages 534, 541, 547, and 554.
- Create a bulletin board entitled "Salad School."
- Purchase cantaloupe and limes; prepare fruit soup for Section 20-3 Motivator.
- Arrange a flour, cornstarch, tapioca, potato, and legume display.
- Arrange convenience products to use as a soup base display.
- Obtain a basic microwave vegetable soup recipe.
- Set up a one-dish meal-related cookware and appliances display for Section 20-4 Motivator.
- Invite a chef to speak/demonstrate stir-fry techniques.

CHAPTER 20

Do you know people who have the same thing for lunch every day? Maybe you're one of those people. In this chapter, you'll learn some new, tasty twists on lunch and other interesting food combinations.

MEETING DIVERSE NEEDS

Interpersonal Learners. If there are students in the class who enjoy working in groups, invite them to collaborate on developing at least three healthful snacks. The recipes can be easy or difficult, one ingredient or several, but they all need to be healthful. The group will be responsible for writing the recipes in standard format, gathering ingredients, and producing a healthful snack "cooking show" for the class.

SECTION
20-1

Objectives

After studying this section, you should be able to:

- Describe how to make sandwiches using a variety of breads and fillings.
- Give suggestions for nutritious snacks.
- Explain how to pack an interesting, nutritious lunch and keep it safe to eat.

Look for These Terms

club sandwich

vacuum bottle

Sandwiches, Snacks, and Packed Lunches

You may think of the sandwich as an invention of Western culture. The truth is that people of many cultures, East and West, have been enjoying foods on bread for over 2,000 years.

What accounts for our fascination with sandwiches? How do they fit in with a healthful eating plan? In this section, you will find answers to both questions.

Sandwiches

No matter how you slice it, the sandwich is undoubtedly America's favorite lunchtime food. Different types of foods can be put together to make an endless variety of sandwiches.

Making Sandwiches

The foundation of any sandwich is bread. When constructing a healthful sandwich, start with a whole-grain product. As a change from sliced bread, make sandwiches with rolls, pita bread, taco shells, bagels, or tortillas. Toast the bread for added texture.

The variety of fillings is limited only by your imagination. Choose cooked lean meat, poultry, or fish; deli meats; mashed, cooked dry beans; egg, chicken, or fish salad; or low-fat cheeses.

Top the fillings with other foods. Try tomatoes, lettuce, pickles, onions, shredded carrots, sliced apples, cucumbers, and other fruits and vegetables. Add mustard or salsa for extra flavor.

Sandwiches can be heated easily in a microwave oven. Prepare the sandwich, omitting fresh vegetables and fruit, which will wilt during heating. Add those later. Wrap the sandwich in a paper towel and microwave it on 100 percent power for 30 seconds or until heated.

SECTION
20-1
Sandwiches, Snacks, and Packed Lunches

FOCUS

MOTIVATORS

- Make frozen fruit-bites for the students by freezing grapes prior to class. As students are enjoying the frozen fruit-bites, ask them to describe their favorite snacks. Differentiate between healthful snacks and those that are less nutritious.
- Create a class list of the most unusual sandwiches students have ever prepared or eaten. Would they eat them again?

VOCABULARY ACTIVITY

Pronounce the terms listed under "Look for These Terms." Have students find the terms and their definitions in the section. Ask a volunteer to explain how and why a vacuum bottle works.

STUDY SKILLS

- **Guided Reading.** Have students look at the headings within Section 20-1 to preview the concepts that will be discussed.
- Have students read the section and complete the appropriate part of the Chapter 20 Study Guide in the *Student Workbook*.

Section 20-1 Resources

◆ **Student Workbook,** pp. 145, 147
◆ **Teacher Resource Guide**
Lesson Plan 20-1 Organizer
Section 20-1 Quiz
◆ **Effective Instruction CD-ROM**
Exam*View*® *Test Generator*
PowerPoint® Slide #45
◆ **Transparency Package,** CT-45
◆ **Student Motivation Kit**
Reteaching Activities, p. 92
Enrichment Activities
Foods Lab Resources, pp. 89–96

TEACH

- *Sandwiches (text pages 529-530)*

Group Contest

Divide the class into four groups; have them nominate a group administrative executive to record group responses. Each group will have five minutes to list (and number) as many types of sandwiches as possible. Suggest students vary fillings and breads. After five minutes, compare groups' lists. Who came up with the most? Have that group's administrative executive read the list to the class. **L1**

Sandwich Making

Have students work in three groups to prepare small amounts of basic sandwich fillings (such as canned chicken with low-fat mayonnaise) and toppings (such as tomato and lettuce.) Have them use one of three varieties of breads to make small sandwiches for the class to compare and taste. **L1**

Recipe Reading

Have students find recipes for specialty sandwiches. Have students copy or rewrite the recipes, noting the source of the recipe. Discuss the variety of sandwiches. Which sandwiches are high in fat? How could you make those sandwiches more nutrient-dense? **L1**

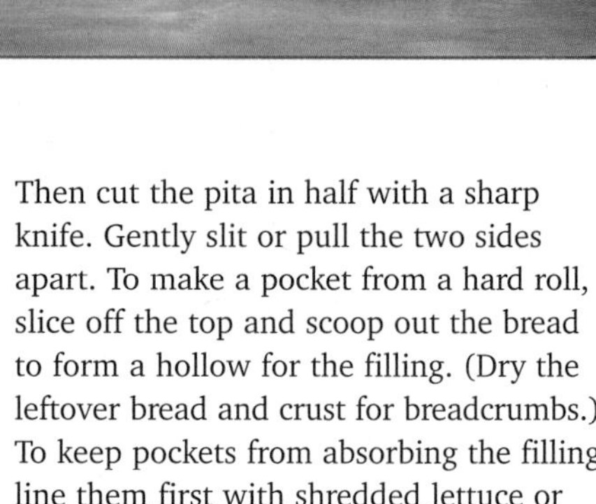

◆ **By using different breads, fillings, and flavorings, you can create an endless variety of sandwiches. Create a recipe for a favorite sandwich and bring a sample to class.**

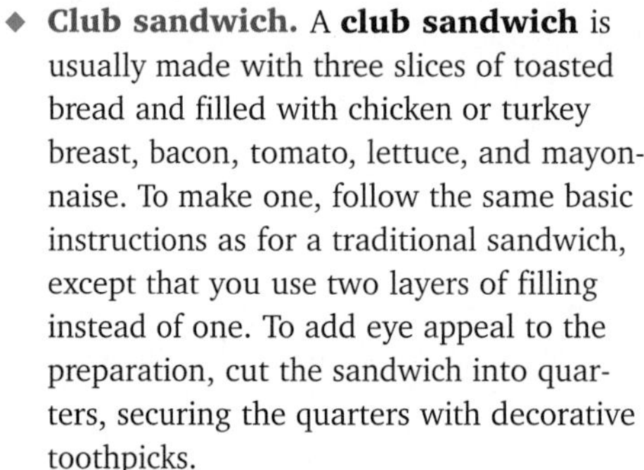

Specialty Sandwiches

Just as there is no end to the list of ingredients you can use to build a sandwich, so there are no constraints on the "architecture." Sandwiches can be flat, tall, round, or square. Here are some basic ways to make sandwiches:

- **Club sandwich.** A **club sandwich** is usually made with three slices of toasted bread and filled with chicken or turkey breast, bacon, tomato, lettuce, and mayonnaise. To make one, follow the same basic instructions as for a traditional sandwich, except that you use two layers of filling instead of one. To add eye appeal to the preparation, cut the sandwich into quarters, securing the quarters with decorative toothpicks.
- **Fancy sandwich.** Cut the bread into fun or fancy shapes with cookie cutters before or after you add the filling. Serve these sandwiches at formal events, on special occasions, or just for fun.
- **Filled pocket sandwich.** Make a pocket sandwich with pita bread, a hard roll, or a taco shell. To make a pocket from a pita, first warm the pita briefly in the microwave oven for easier handling. Then cut the pita in half with a sharp knife. Gently slit or pull the two sides apart. To make a pocket from a hard roll, slice off the top and scoop out the bread to form a hollow for the filling. (Dry the leftover bread and crust for breadcrumbs.) To keep pockets from absorbing the filling, line them first with shredded lettuce or cucumber slices.

Healthful Snacks

As noted earlier, snacks are as much a part of your daily eating pattern as meals, especially during the teen years when your nutrient needs are particularly high. There are many simple, nutritious ways to satisfy between-meal hunger. Enjoy fresh fruits and vegetables as quick snacks. You could also have a glass of fat-free milk, a small sandwich, or a cup of soup with whole-grain crackers. A creamy fruit smoothie could also fill the bill.

Extending Learning

Wraps—For an interesting sandwich, make a "wrap." Use a soft, flat bread, such as a tortilla, lavash, or chapati. Place it on a napkin or piece of foil. Spoon the filling down the center of the bread, leaving an even border on either side. Fold the bottom and side portions of the bread over the filling to create a cone which is open at one end, or simply roll it up tightly. Wrap a napkin or foil around the outside to prevent dripping.

◆ **Delicious refreshing fruit smoothies like the one shown here, made with fresh orange juice, can be made by blending fruit juice or fresh fruit with nonfat yogurt and ice cubes. What other combinations would make a great smoothie?**

Here are more ideas for healthful, tasty snacks:

- **Yogurt pops.** Pour flavored yogurt into a paper cup. Put a wooden ice pop stick or a plastic spoon in the center. Freeze the yogurt pop for at least an hour. The stick or spoon serves as a handle.
- **Frozen fruit bites.** Freeze whole berries or grapes to make frozen candy-like snacks.
- **"Un-chips."** Cut tortillas or pita bread into six or eight wedge-shaped pieces. Spread a single layer in a baking pan. Bake them in a preheated oven at 450°F (230°C) for about 5 minutes or until crisp. Serve with salsa or bean dip.

INFOLINK

For a review of eating patterns and the role snacks play, see Section 4-1.

FOR YOUR HEALTH

"Vegging" at Lunchtime

Many Americans fail to meet the minimum Food Guide Pyramid recommendation of three vegetable servings per day. One way to meet this requirement is to build a sandwich around vegetables. Here are some nutrition-packed vegetarian sandwich ideas:

- For a fresh and crunchy choice, top whole wheat bread with thinly sliced cucumber, diced green onions, fat-free cream cheese, and pepper.
- Instead of the usual grilled cheese, slip some sliced tomatoes in with low-fat cheese. You might also microwave cheese and tomato, open-face, on a bagel half.
- Place a mixed green salad or a grain salad, such as tabouleh, in a whole wheat pita pocket.
- Go Italian with mozzarella cheese, tomato, and fresh basil on Italian bread with a splash of flavored vinegar for a burst of flavor.
- Spread vegetarian refried beans, diced tomatoes, salsa, and shredded cheese on a tortilla. Roll up. Then heat and eat.
- Grill or roast your favorite vegetables. Then layer them on whole-grain bread and enjoy the natural taste of the veggies.

Following Up

- In the foods lab, create one of the sandwich ideas above, or invent one of your own. Cut the sandwich into bite-size pieces, insert a toothpick in each, and share the pieces with class members. Use their criticism as the basis for a campaign to educate people in your home on how to make healthful sandwich eating a part of the family's eating pattern.

- *Healthful Snacks (text pages 530-531)*

Categorizing

Have students make a list of twenty foods they have eaten as snacks within the past year. Then have them categorize their lists into two sections: nutrient-dense and non-nutrient-dense snacks. Have students compare choices within each category. L1

Finding Recipes

Have students work in small groups to find recipes for healthful snacks. Encourage student groups to share and discuss healthful snack recipes they find. L1

Snack Presentation

Ask students to bring to class one serving of a healthful snack that they enjoy. Have students prepare a brief presentation of their snack. Presentations need to include (1) food group(s) represented; (2) total calories, total fat, and any nutrient of which the food is a good source; (3) why the presenter enjoys the snack; and (4) how it's prepared. Encourage students to take notes about the healthful snack presentations. L2

HOME & COMMUNITY CONNECTION

Have students prepare a new, healthful snack food for their family, such as "yogurt pops" or "un-chips." Have them ask their family members for an evaluation of the snack. Suggest students prepare a different healthful snack if the first snack gets mixed reviews. Then encourage students to present a healthy snack-making seminar to their family to promote the continuance of healthy snack eating.

TEACH cont.

- *Packing a Lunch (text pages 532-533)*

Handout

Ask students to make a list of Do's and Don'ts for packing lunches. Have them combine their suggestions and prepare a computerized handout on packed school lunches. L1

Demonstration

Demonstrate how to preheat a vacuum bottle. Ask students what types of hot foods could be packed in the prepared vacuum bottle.

Brainstorm Session

Have students brainstorm other ways to reduce, reuse, and recycle items commonly used in packed lunches. Encourage students to share ideas—and practice the ideas. L1

USING Safety Check

Ask students to pack a "safe" lunch. Have students show their packed lunches, and discuss how/why it is "safe."

Packing a Lunch

It is estimated that about 30 percent of American workers carry a packed lunch. Their reasons vary from saving money to having better food choices. As you know, packed lunches can be taken to school, too.

With a little organization, packed lunches can be easy to assemble. Follow these simple guidelines:

- Remember that safety comes first. Keep hot foods hot and cold foods cold.
- To pack hot soup, chili, stew, or similar hot foods, use a wide-mouth **vacuum bottle** —a glass or metal bottle with a vacuum space between the outer container and the inner liner. Vacuum bottles do a better job of keeping foods hot than less expensive foam-insulated bottles. Before packing the vacuum bottle, preheat it—fill it with hot tap water and let it stand a minute or two. Empty the water, fill the bottle with piping hot food, and close tightly.
- Pack foods that are easy to handle. Avoid foods that are drippy or oily. If foods must be cut up, cut them before packing the lunch.
- To speed up lunch packing, set aside an area in the freezer, refrigerator, and a nearby cabinet for lunch foods and equipment.
- Make packing lunches a family affair. Take turns being the family's "designated lunch packer" for the day.
- Remember these three "R's"—reduce, reuse, and recycle. For example, plastic containers from yogurt, sour cream, and cottage cheese can be washed out and used to pack foods. Reuse plastic bags from the grocery store as lunch sacks. Save used aluminum foil if it can be recycled in your area. Try to avoid one-use containers and wraps. Use cloth napkins instead of paper ones. These tips will help you save time and money and cut down on waste.

Nutritious packed lunches should contain servings from several different groups on the Food Guide Pyramid. What food groups are represented by this lunch? How would you rate the lunch from a nutritional standpoint?

Extending Learning

Packed Lunches—These ideas feature complex carbohydrates:

- Large flour tortilla stuffed with refried beans, low-fat cheese, and lettuce.
- Large, round sourdough bread with insides scooped out; fill with chili and eat with scooped-out bread.
- Hummus with "Un-chips" or crackers.
- Pita bread sandwich filled with herb-seasoned cooked vegetables.

Add a salad or vegetable and round out with fruit, dessert, and milk.

Safety Check

Is brown-bagging the safest way to carry lunch to school? If you pack perishable food that's left at room temperature more than two hours, the risk of foodborne illness increases. It's especially important to remember this if you typically store your lunch in a stuffy locker.

For the safest bet, use an insulated lunch bag. You can also freeze sandwiches and juice boxes to help keep cold foods cold. The foods will be thawed by lunchtime. Use ice packs or chilled, insulated vacuum bottles to help keep foods cool. Pack nonperishable foods such as dried fruit, boxed juice, and peanut butter with crackers.

Assembling the Lunch

To prepare an interesting and nutrient-rich lunch, use a variety of foods, following the guidelines in the Food Guide Pyramid. Use your imagination. Think of leftover foods you enjoy eating cold—baked chicken, meat loaf, roast turkey, or pizza. Heat up leftover chili, stew, or soup to pack in a vacuum bottle.

If you take salads with greens, mix fruits and vegetables, but pack dressing separately. Drizzle on the dressing just before eating.

Bean dips and spreads make tasty sandwich fillings. Try using them as dips for fresh fruits and vegetables, too.

For a healthful lunch, be sure your food choices include whole grains as well as fresh fruits and vegetables.

What will you choose for a beverage? Milk and fruit juice are both flavorful and nutritious choices. Fruit juice can be frozen ahead of time. In addition to helping keep food cool, it will be a cool, refreshing drink.

Don't forget to include such nonfood items as forks, spoons, and napkins. Tuck in a wipe or a wet washcloth in a plastic bag to clean your hands and wipe up spills.

Section 20-1 Review & Activities

1. Name four kinds of bread that might be used to make a sandwich.

2. Identify two healthful snacks made with fruit.

3. Describe how to preheat a vacuum bottle.

4. Comparing and Contrasting. How do the snack suggestions in this section compare with those you choose at home in terms of nutrition, expense, and ease of preparation?

5. Synthesizing. A club sandwich is not traditionally a low-fat choice. How would you prepare a low-fat version of a club sandwich?

6. Applying. Draw a diagram showing how you would set up an ideal lunch-packing area in your kitchen at home. Explain the advantages of your plan. Share it with other family members who pack lunches for themselves.

ASSESS

REVIEW

- Ask students to summarize the main ideas in this section.
- Have students complete the Section Review. (Answers appear below.)

EVALUATION

- Have students prepare a menu for a packed lunch that is nutritious and appealing.
- Have students take the quiz for Section 20-1. (Use the quiz in the *Teacher Resource Guide,* or construct your own with the **ExamView**® *Test Generator* on the *Effective Instruction CD-ROM.*)

RETEACHING

- Show pictures of foods that are commonly used for lunch. Have students practice choosing nutritious, healthful lunches.
- Refer to the *Reteaching Activities* booklet for the Section 20-1 activity sheet.

CLOSE

Lead a discussion on the benefits of packing and eating a nutritious lunch every day. Then have the class plan an appealing, one-day meal plan that includes two healthful snacks, a packed lunch, and a sandwich.

Answers to Section 20-1 Review & Activities

1. Any four: Whole-grain sliced bread, rolls, pita bread, taco shells, bagels, or tortillas.

2. Any two: Fruit smoothie, frozen fruit bites, fruited yogurt pop, fresh fruit.

3. Fill it with hot tap water; let it stand a minute or two.

4. Answers will vary. Students can estimate expense.

5. Answers will vary. One example: three slices toasted whole-grain bread, chicken or turkey breast meat, tomato, green leaf lettuce, fat-free mayonnaise, and just one slice of bacon.

6. Answers will vary. Items will be in the same easy-to-reach vicinity, often on the same shelves.

Recipe File

Apple-Tuna Sandwiches

The ingredients in this sandwich recipe represent all five food groups.

USING THE RECIPE

- Have students read the recipe and discuss each step.
- Encourage students to be creative in making an attractive presentation of the sandwich.
- Review safety and sanitation procedures that apply to this recipe.
- Have each lab team fill out a work plan. (See the *Foods Lab Resources* booklet.)
- Have students check off the ingredients and equipment listed on the recipe worksheet and prepare the recipe.
- Have students complete the evaluation and questions on the recipe worksheet.

SEE ALSO...
The *Foods Lab Resources* booklet for the "Apple-Tuna Sandwiches" recipe worksheet and other recipe alternatives.

Recipe File

Apple-Tuna Sandwiches

This sandwich combines a variety of foods for a complex blend of flavors and textures. For variety, try serving this sandwich in whole-wheat pita halves or rolled in a tortilla.

Customary	***Ingredients***	***Metric***
7-oz. can	Water-pack tuna, drained and flaked	198-g can
½ cup	Chopped celery	125 mL
2 Tbsp.	Chopped onion	30 mL
½ cup	Plain, nonfat yogurt	125 mL
4	Lettuce leaves	4
4 slices	American cheese (optional)	4 slices
1	Apple, cored and thinly sliced (about 12 slices)	1
4	Whole wheat buns, split	4

Yield: 4 servings, one sandwich each

Directions

1. Combine tuna, celery, onion, and yogurt.
2. Cover the bottom of each bun with a lettuce leaf. Be sure leaves are dry.
3. Place a cheese slice (if desired) on top of the lettuce leaf.
4. Spread tuna mixture on top of lettuce or cheese on each bun.
5. Place 3 apple slices on top of tuna mixture.
6. Cover with top half of bun.

Nutrition Information

Per serving (approximate–sandwich with cheese): 277 calories, 22 g protein, 29 g carbohydrate, 8 g fat, 35 mg cholesterol, 675 mg sodium
Good source of: iron, B vitamins, calcium, phosphorus

Food for Thought

- Which food groups are represented in this sandwich?
- What ingredients might you add or subtract for a flavor variation?

Answers to **Food for Thought**

1. All five food groups: The Bread, Cereal, Rice, and Pasta Group; Vegetable Group; Fruit Group; Milk, Yogurt, and Cheese Group; and Meat, Poultry, Fish, Dry Beans, Eggs and Nuts Group.
2. Answers will vary. Use water-pack chicken instead of tuna; use pear instead of apple; use spinach leaves instead of lettuce leaves.

SECTION
20-2

Objectives

After studying this section, you should be able to:

- Describe how to select, wash, store, and serve several kinds of salad greens.
- Plan and assemble a salad using a variety of methods and ingredients.
- Identify ways to serve salads.

Look for These Terms

emulsion

base

body

Salads and Dressings

Salads can be as simple as assortments of greens or fruits, or they can be hearty main dishes. Fresh fruit salads can be refreshing desserts or snacks. Depending on the ingredients, salads can provide servings from each of the five food groups.

Ingredients for Salads

Almost any ready-to-eat food from the five food groups can be used in a salad. Some of the basic foods include:

- **Salad greens.** To most people *salad* is synonymous with *lettuce*—which, in turn, translates to "iceberg lettuce." Yet, a wide variety of types of lettuce exist, from romaine, bibb, and Boston, to red leaf and curly leaf. Besides waking up a salad, these other lettuces, especially the darker greens, are higher in nutrients, such as vitamin C and iron. Beyond lettuce, the world of salad greens also includes spinach, arugula (uh-ROO-gyah-luh), escarole, chicory, watercress, and radicchio (rah-DEE-kee-oh). To add interest and nutrition, try a blend of greens in a salad. You can also buy pre-washed greens, packaged and ready to use.
- **Other vegetables and fruits.** You can toss any fruits and vegetables, fresh, canned, or cooked, in salads. They can be sliced, dried, shredded, quartered, or cubed. Use red or green cabbage for coleslaw or mixed with other greens.
- **Cooked and chilled pasta, grains, legumes, meat, poultry, fish, or eggs.** Prepare hearty main dish salads by mixing these foods with fruits and vegetables. Try this salad: Combine leftover chilled rice

SECTION
20-2
Salads and Dressings

FOCUS

MOTIVATORS

- Create a bulletin board titled "Salad Center." Cut out pictures of various salad ingredients from magazines, or make your own illustrations from construction paper. Discuss how the ingredients could be combined to make salads.
- Purchase some potted herbs. Herbs thrive on a sunny windowsill. Discuss the nutrients and the flavor each will add to a salad.

VOCABULARY ACTIVITY

Pronounce the three terms listed under "Look for These Terms." Have students find the terms and their definitions in the section.

STUDY SKILLS

- **Listening.** Invite a group of volunteers to each prepare an oral reading of a page of text from the section, while others follow along silently.
- Have students read the section and complete the appropriate part of the Chapter 20 Study Guide in the *Student Workbook*.

Section 20-2 Resources

◆ **Student Workbook,** pp. 145, 148
◆ **Teacher Resource Guide**
Lesson Plan 20-2 Organizer
Section 20-2 Quiz
◆ **Effective Instruction CD-ROM**
Exam*View*® *Test Generator*
PowerPoint® Slide #46
◆ **Transparency Package,** CT-46
◆ **Student Motivation Kit**
Reteaching Activities, p. 93
Enrichment Activities
Foods Lab Resources, pp. 97–104
Food Science Resources, pp. 78–81

TEACH

- *Ingredients for Salads*
- *Salad Dressings (text pages 535-537)*

Nutrition Research

Have students select one salad green mentioned on page 535. Ask them to create a Nutrition Facts panel, based on one serving of their selected green, using nutrient research findings. Have students compare their panels. Discuss the nutrient comparisons. Which has the most vitamin C? Vitamin A? Fiber? L1

Cultural Research

Have students research one kind of green used in a salad in another part of the world. Have them attach a picture or make an appropriately colored drawing of the green and write a one page paper about the cultural use of it. L1

Display Activity

Display an assortment of five salad greens. Number each type. Have students practice identifying the greens. Discuss the differentiating features of the greens. What does the color of salad greens indicate?

◆ **Varying ingredients in salads, including lettuce, adds variety to your eating patterns. Find as many of the lettuces shown here as you can in your local supermarket and note the price of each. Which type(s) would you eat on a daily basis?**

and cooked dry beans, chopped onions, chopped tomatoes, seasonings, and greens. Sprinkle grated cheese as a topping. Serve with salsa or a splash of balsamic or cider vinegar.

Salad Dressings

Salad dressings not only add richness and flavor but also act as binding agents to hold salads together. There are several basic types of dressings:

- **Oil-based dressings.** Sometimes known as Italian or vinaigrette (vihn-uh-GREHT) dressings. Are a mixture of oil, vinegar, and seasonings. Typical vinaigrettes are made with 3 parts oil to 1 part vinegar. Oil-based dressings separate easily and must be mixed each time you use them.
- **Mayonnaise.** Made with oil, vinegar or lemon juice, seasonings, and eggs. Eggs create an **emulsion**—an evenly blended mixture of two liquids that do not normally stay mixed—which keeps the oil and acid from separating.
- **Cooked dressings.** Similar to mayonnaise, but use white sauce to replace some of the eggs and oil.
- **Dairy dressings.** Include ranch-type dressings. They usually have buttermilk, yogurt, sour cream, or cottage cheese as a main ingredient. Seasonings are added.

Low-Fat Dressings

Salad dressings are traditionally high in fat and calories—because of the oil used in making them. Today, however, many low-fat and

FOOD SCIENCE: Water Content in Lettuce

With just 8 calories per cup, lettuce is a staple to many calorie counters. The reason lettuce provides so few calories is that the leaves contain about 95 percent water by weight. Ask students to research and write about how this high water content gives crunch to a properly prepared salad, but makes lettuce leaves prone to drooping if mishandled. Students should explain how they as consumers can use this information to prevent lettuce from wilting.

Safety Check

Some salad dressings and mayonnaise preparations contain raw eggs, placing you at risk for foodborne illness. When making dressings that call for raw eggs, cook the eggs in their shells to the soft-cooked stage, as described in Chapter 18. Beat the eggs together with the liquid in the dressing until the dressing achieves the proper consistency. Commercially manufactured mayonnaise and other egg-based dressings are made with pasteurized eggs, which makes them safe to eat.

fat-free dressings are available. Check the fat content on the label when you are selecting bottled or packaged salad dressings. Remember, the nutrients listed on the label are for one serving of 2 tablespoons (30 mL). Many people use far more than that. To counter this habit, think in teaspoons, not tablespoons, when dressing your salad.

When making salad dressing at home, try using nonfat yogurt to make a flavorful, low-calorie dressing. Add your favorite herbs and spices, prepared mustard and honey, or a dry prepared mix to vary the flavor. You can also experiment with fruit juices and flavored vinegars for some or all of the oil in recipes.

Making a Salad

What kind of salad should you put your dressing on? First, you need to decide how you plan to serve it. *Appetizer salads* are small, tasty salads served at the beginning of a meal to stimulate your appetite—for example, a shrimp cocktail or small garden salad. An *accompaniment salad* is a small salad served with a meal. Coleslaw, fruit salads, and mixed green salads are examples. *Main dish salads* make up the main course of a meal. They've become very popular on lunch menus. They usually contain a protein-based food along with grains, fruits, and vegetables. For instance, a chef's salad is made with cooked meat, poultry, eggs, and cheese on a thick bed of assorted lettuce. A main dish salad is a great way to use leftovers. *Dessert salads* are usually made with fruit. Select a dessert salad for a sweet way to meet your daily requirement of at least two servings of fruit.

Preparing Salad Greens

If your salad has greens, you need to refrigerate them as soon as you get home from the supermarket. Greens grow close to the ground and thus may contain soil. Clean them before storing so that they will be ready to use.

CLOSE-UP ON SCIENCE: CHEMISTRY

Emulsification

There is much truth to the saying that oil and water don't mix. You can shake the two liquids together to combine them temporarily. As soon as you stop shaking, however, the tiny oil droplets produced by the agitation begin to combine with one another. Soon the oil and water are separate again.

The egg yolks in mayonnaise contain a natural substance that acts as an *emulsifying* agent. This agent coats the oil droplets and causes them to repel one another. It also reduces the ability of the vinegar (which is mainly water) to repel the oil. Therefore, the oil stays in small droplets that remain evenly mixed throughout the dressing.

- *Salad Dressings (text pages 536-537)*

USING Safety Check

Ask students to search recipe books or Internet recipes for salad dressings that contain raw eggs. Have students copy at least one recipe that contains raw eggs. Encourage students to share recipes they find to increase student awareness. What substitutions can students suggest to raw eggs? How can eggs be made safe for use in these dressings?

Taste Test

Have students compare the taste of traditional commercial salad dressings that are high in fat and calories with low-fat and fat-free dressings. Which products are most and least acceptable? Ask students to write a summary of their findings. Discuss how high-fat salad dressings can be included in a healthful eating plan.

Product Comparison

Ask students to bring to class a new or safely-packed bottle of a generic, name brand, or home-made salad dressing, attaching a cost label to the bottle. Have students compare the cost and taste of the various dressings. Which ones would they recommend? Why? L1

Extending Learning

Salads—Early salads consisted of greens and many fresh herbs, such as fennel, garlic, leeks, mint, onions, parsley, rosemary, and sage. These were washed, torn apart, and mixed with oil, salt, and vinegar. A 14th century English recipe said that even a plain salad should have at least 35 ingredients, including whole or candied flowers. A 19th century recipe book had only a summer and a winter salad. The winter salad had sliced hard-boiled eggs and beets but fewer greens.

TEACH cont.

- *Making a Salad (text pages 537-540)*

Group Activity

Using cookbooks and food magazines, students are to work in small groups to identify types of salads and salad ingredients that tend to be low in fat and nutrient-dense and those that tend to be high in calories and fat. Develop a class list of nutrient-dense salad ingredients. Then work together to create one class recipe for a 10+ ingredient nutrient-dense salad. You may want to invite students to invent a name for their salad. **L1**

Discussion Activity

Conduct a class Q & A discussion on the following: (1) Ask students to describe four ways in which salads can be used in a meal. (2) Ask students to explain how to prepare iceberg lettuce. (3) Ask students to describe ways of combining salad ingredients.

VISUAL LEARNING ***Using the Illustration***

As in the illustration on page 538, demonstrate how to core iceberg lettuce and separate the leaves. Demonstrate how to wash and prepare leafy greens. Ask students to comment on why it's important to perform these steps.

- **Iceberg lettuce.** Hold the head in your hands, core side down, as shown below. Hit the core on the counter once or twice to loosen it. Remove the core from the head. Let cold water run into the cavity for a minute or two until it pours out between the leaves. Place the head, core side down, in a colander and let it drain. Store the drained lettuce in a covered plastic container or in a plastic bag in the refrigerator.
- **Leafy greens.** Pull the leaves away from the core and wash them under cold running water. Place each leaf, stem side down, in a colander so that the water can drain off easily. You may also need to pat the greens dry before storage, but leave a little moisture to keep them crisp. Put the washed greens in a plastic container or in a large plastic bag, and refrigerate.
- **Premixed salad greens.** If you are using packaged premixed salad greens, don't assume they have been washed. Look for the words *washed* or *ready to eat* on the label. If they don't appear or if you're in doubt, wash the greens. Some mixed salad greens are sold in bulk in the produce section, where you use tongs to make your own selection. Always wash bulk mixed salad greens before using them.

Assembling the Salad

Salads are fun and easy to put together. Be creative: Choose a variety of textures and colors of greens, fruits, vegetables, or other foods for an attractive, healthful dish. The combinations are endless. So are the ways of presenting them. For an attractive touch, place a foundation of greens on the bottom of the salad bowl or plate—creating a **base** for

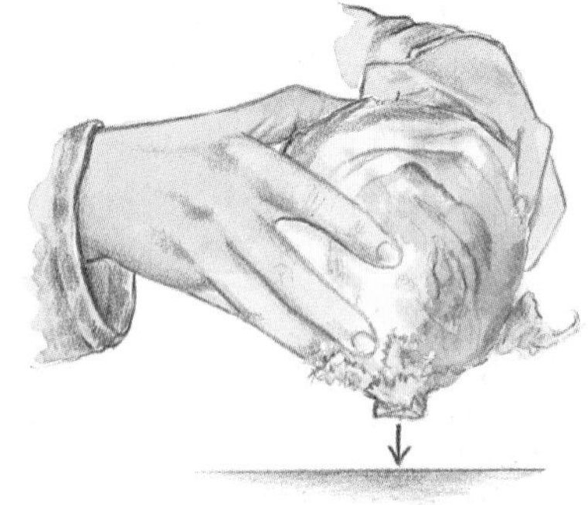

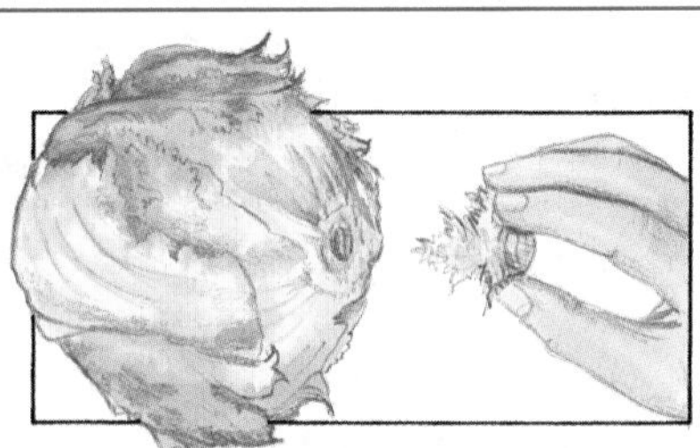

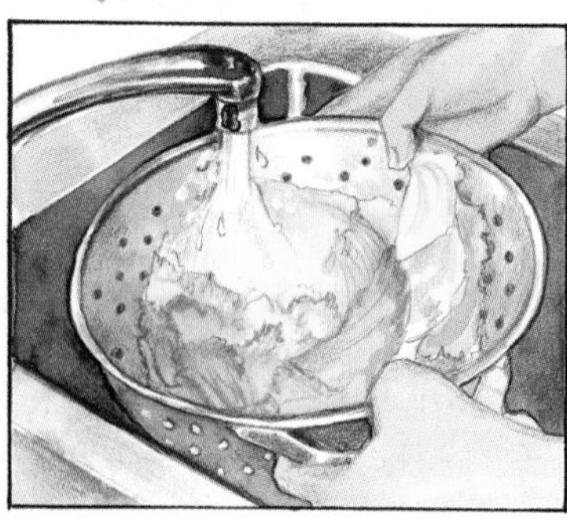

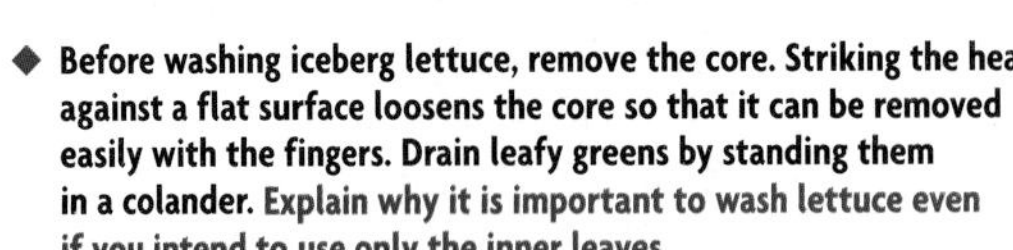

◆ **Before washing iceberg lettuce, remove the core. Striking the head against a flat surface loosens the core so that it can be removed easily with the fingers. Drain leafy greens by standing them in a colander. Explain why it is important to wash lettuce even if you intend to use only the inner leaves.**

HOME & COMMUNITY CONNECTION

Have students interview older adults, such as grandparents or elderly neighbors, about the types/descriptions of salads they typically ate as a teenager. Have students write a paper about how salads have evolved over time. Hold a class discussion on similarities and differences.

◆ **Making an arranged salad is an opportunity to develop your artistic skills. This refreshing fruit salad has been designed creatively. Make a design for an arranged salad. Try to include items from at least three different groups in the Food Guide Pyramid.**

your salad. Top with other salad ingredients to make up the **body**, or main part of the salad.

Here are a few hints, both plain and fancy, for presenting your salad creations:

- **Tossed or mixed salads.** This form of presentation includes the garden salad, a simple blend of greens and vegetables gently tossed with a dressing. For an attention-getting variation, present tossed salads in layers—for example, a layer of shredded greens, one of mashed cooked beans, and another of chopped tomatoes, all dressed with yogurt.
- **Arranged salads.** Salad ingredients can be arranged in one of a number of striking patterns, usually on a base of greens. One possibility is to fan fresh fruit slices around a mound of cottage cheese.
- **Molded salads.** Any salad mixture that holds its shape can be molded in a decorative container. Many molded salads are made with gelatin. Salads that contain a grain product, such as rice, and a binding agent, such as yogurt, also make attractive molded salads.

- *Making a Salad (text pages 537-540)*

Identification

Using cookbooks and food magazines, students are to work in groups to identify and analyze salad recipes. Ask students to identify the base, body, and dressing. Then have students categorize the recipes as tossed or mixed salads, arranged salads, or molded salads. Develop a written list of characteristics for each type of salad. L1

Lab Experience

Ask each student to bring in one food item of choice that can be added to salads, such as a red pepper, onion, orange, or avocado. Provide the greens and dressings and, if possible, the (potted) herbs. Have students prepare their salad ingredients for a salad bar. On paper plates, have each student arrange chosen ingredients in an appealing manner. Prior to enjoying their salads, have the class view the varying salad presentations. L1

Reinforcing Key Skills

Present the following problems to student groups. Allow time for them to discuss and compare their responses.

Management—Give students a description of leftover fruits, vegetables, or grain products and have them suggest ways to use the foods in salads.

Communication—Jean follows a low-fat eating plan. She's at a restaurant and plans to order a salad. The waiter arrives and she orders ____.

ASSESS

REVIEW

- Ask students to summarize the main ideas in this section.
- Have students complete the Section Review. (Answers appear below.)

EVALUATION

- Have students develop a basic recipe for a salad of their choice. The salad must be both nutritious and appealing.
- Have students take the quiz for Section 20-2. (Use the quiz in the *Teacher Resource Guide,* or construct your own with the **Exam***View*® *Test Generator* on the *Effective Instruction CD-ROM.*)

RETEACHING

- Prepare a salad or buy one from the school cafeteria. Have students determine the nutritional value of the salad.
- Refer to the *Reteaching Activities* booklet for the Section 20-2 activity sheet.

CLOSE

Refer students back to the "Salad Center" bulletin board. Ask students if they can add any other suggestions.

Serving Salads

Dress up your salads. Green salads often need the most help with their appearance. Arrange red pepper rings, grated carrots, sprouts, or other decorative vegetables on the greens. Then sprinkle with seeds, chopped nuts, or raisins. Add dressing just before serving. If dressing is added too early, the greens may wilt. Better still, serve the salad without dressing. Pass the dressing separately at the table so that people can add their own.

For added meal appeal and nutrition, nearly all salads can be served in edible "bowls," such as baked tortilla shells or hollowed-out fruits or vegetables. When in a rush, have your salad as a sandwich in a pita pocket.

◆ **Serving a mixed salad in a hollowed-out pineapple half makes a festive lunch main course. You begin by cutting the pineapple in half and carefully scooping out the fruit. Think of two other fruits or vegetables that could be used as edible "containers" for salad.**

Section 20-2 Review & Activities

1. Name three kinds of salad greens. How should they be stored?
2. List three methods for assembling salads.
3. When should salad dressing be added to a green salad? Why?
4. **Analyzing.** Discuss some suggestions for cutting down on fat and calories commonly found in salad dressings.
5. **Synthesizing.** In a salad, how would you use leftover (a) chili, (b) roast beef, (c) grilled vegetables? List at least one example for each.
6. **Applying.** Describe at least two ideas for turning a small tossed salad into a main dish salad. Try one of these ideas. Write about your findings in your Wellness Journal.

Answers to Section 20-2 Review & Activities

1. See page 535; in a covered plastic bowl or in a sealed plastic bag.
2. Tossed (or mixed), arranged, molded.
3. Just before serving; if dressed too early, the greens may wilt.
4. Answers will vary. See page 537.
5. Answers will vary. (a) Use it cold, mixed with lettuce, diced tomatoes, and low-fat shredded cheese in a baked tortilla bowl. (b) Slice and layer on greens to create a chef's salad. (c) Chop and mix with vinaigrette.
6. Answers will vary.

Recipe File

Garbanzo Salad with Honey-Mustard Dressing

Garbanzo beans, or chickpeas, provide valuable nutrients and fiber. They also combine well with other foods to create flavorful salads.

Customary	***Ingredients***	***Metric***
2 tsp.	Prepared mustard	10 mL
2 Tbsp.	Cider vinegar	30 mL
2 tsp.	Vegetable oil	10 mL
2 tsp.	Honey	10 mL
¼ tsp.	Celery seed	1 mL
8 leaves	Romaine lettuce	8 leaves
16-oz. can	Garbanzo beans, drained and rinsed	454-g can
1 large	Apple, cored and chopped	1 large
1 medium	Red or green pepper, chopped	1 medium
½ cup	Raisins	125 mL

Yield: 4 servings

Directions

1. In a small bowl, mix together mustard, vinegar, oil, honey, and celery seed. Set aside.
2. Tear lettuce into bite-size pieces.
3. In a large bowl, toss together lettuce, garbanzo beans, apple, pepper, and raisins.
4. Drizzle dressing over salad and toss.
5. Divide salad among four salad plates or bowls.
6. Serve immediately.

Nutrition Information

Per serving (approximate–salad with dressing): 233 calories, 7 g protein, 44 g carbohydrate, 5 g fat, 0 mg cholesterol, 459 mg sodium

Good source of: potassium, iron, vitamin A, vitamin E, vitamin C, B vitamins, phosphorus

Food for Thought

- Name one substitution you might make for each ingredient in the recipe.
- What could you do to keep the chopped apple from turning brown while you prepare the rest of the recipe?

Recipe File

Garbanzo Salad with Honey-Mustard Dressing

This recipe has meal appeal; it combines ingredients with a variety of textures, flavors, and colors.

Using the Recipe

- Have students read the recipe and discuss each step.
- Remind students to allow excess water to drain from the lettuce leaves before using them in the salad. Students may need to pat the lettuce dry, or use a salad spinner.
- Review safety and sanitation procedures that apply to this recipe.
- Have each lab team fill out a work plan. (See the *Foods Lab Resources* booklet.)
- Have students check off the ingredients and equipment listed on the recipe worksheet and prepare the recipe.
- Have students complete the evaluation and questions on the recipe worksheet.

SEE ALSO. . .

The *Foods Lab Resources* booklet for the "Garbanzo Salad with Honey-Mustard Dressing" recipe worksheet and other recipe alternatives.

Answers to Food for Thought

1. Answers will vary. Examples: Bibb lettuce, kidney beans, orange sections, jalapeño peppers, and cashews for the salad; vinaigrette dressing instead of the honey-mustard dressing ingredients.
2. Sprinkle it with lemon juice; use an ascorbic acid mixture.

SECTION
20-3
Soups and Sauces

FOCUS

MOTIVATORS

- Prepare a basic, cold fruit soup (puréed cantaloupe with a few drops of fresh lime juice); serve small samples to students. Ask students in what ways this motivator has broadened their definition of a soup.
- Put out samples of flour, cornstarch, tapioca, a potato, and a legume. Ask students to guess what common cooking purpose all of these foods serve.

VOCABULARY ACTIVITY

Pronounce the terms listed under "Look for These Terms." Have students find the terms and their definitions in the section. Ask students to name the terms that are French. Discuss the different pronunciations of French and English terms.

STUDY SKILLS

- **Outlining.** Have students read the section and outline it by copying the headers on paper and leaving space after each one. Students are to write a sentence in their own words, summarizing the content under each header.
- Have students read the section and complete the appropriate part of the Chapter 20 Study Guide in the *Student Workbook*.

SECTION 20-3

Soups and Sauces

What comes to your mind when you hear the word soup? Whether you picture a soup kettle simmering away for hours, a can of your favorite flavor, or a container from a supermarket deli, soup can be a delicious, nutritious meal.

Objectives

After studying this section, you should be able to:

- Describe how to prepare clear, vegetable, and cream soups.
- Explain how to make and use white sauce and gravy.
- Explain how to make lower-fat sauce or gravy alternatives.

Look for These Terms

aromatic vegetables
stock
bouillon
white sauce
roux
au jus

Making Soups

The first step in making most soups is to sauté **aromatic vegetables**, vegetables, such as onions, celery, and carrots, that add flavor to soups and other recipes. Sautéing vegetables before adding them helps develop the flavors. Use a stock pot and about 1 teaspoon (5 mL) of oil.

Next comes the liquid. Many soups start with **stock**, a clear, thin liquid made by simmering water flavored with the bones of meat, poultry, or fish, plus aromatic vegetables and seasonings. Many people today use canned convenience broths or bouillon cubes as a base for making soup. You can also combine broth with a seasoned vegetable juice for additional flavor and nutrients.

Taste the soup and correct the seasonings just before serving. This will help you avoid overseasoning the soup early in the cooking process.

Kinds of Soups

Soups are usually highly nutritious. Some B vitamins and vitamin C may be destroyed by heat, especially if the soup is cooked for a long time. Other water-soluble vitamins and minerals, however, remain in the liquid.

Section 20-3 Resources

◆ **Student Workbook,** pp. 146, 150
◆ **Teacher Resource Guide**
Lesson Plan 20-3 Organizer
Section 20-3 Quiz
◆ **Effective Instruction CD-ROM**
Exam*View*® *Test Generator*
PowerPoint® Slide #47
◆ **Transparency Package,** CT-47

◆ **Student Motivation Kit**
Reteaching Activities, p. 94
Enrichment Activities
Foods Lab Resources, pp. 15, 105–110
Food Science Resources, pp. 82–85
Skills for Making Food Choices, pp. 45–46

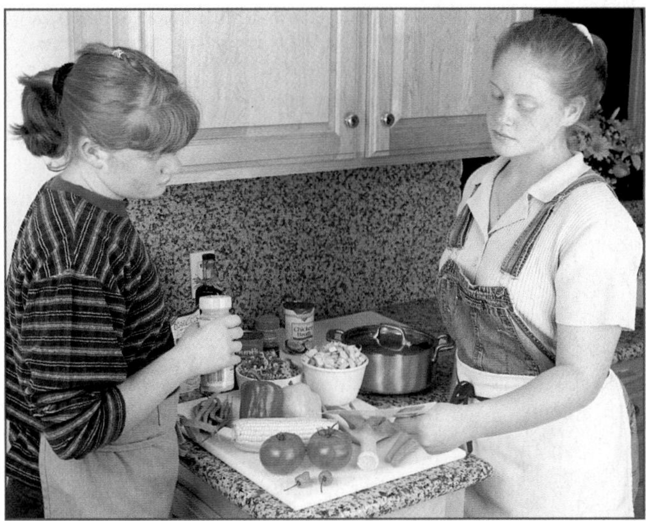

◆ Homemade soup doesn't have to take all day. Try starting with ready-made broth or vegetable juice. Add vegetables, grains, and leftover meat or poultry. What ingredients would you add to the ones shown to give your homemade soup a personal touch?

There are two main kinds of soups:

◆ **Clear soups.** These soups are usually based on unthickened, clear stock or broth. **Bouillon** (BOOL-yon) is a simple, clear soup without solid ingredients. Also called broth, the liquid is strained to remove any solids. Consommé (kahn-soh-MAY), the clearest broth, is rich and flavorful.

◆ **Thick soups.** Unlike clear soups, these soups are not transparent and they are thickened. One type, cream soup, is traditionally made with a **white sauce**—a milk-based sauce thickened with starch—plus cooked vegetables, poultry, or shellfish. Soups made this way can be high in fat.

Vegetable Soup

Vegetable soup, one of the most popular soups, is basically a clear soup with vegetables. Which vegetables are used is largely a matter of taste, although many recipes feature potatoes, tomatoes, peas, and corn, among others. Use at least three or four different vegetables for a rich flavor and colorful appearance.

When adding the vegetables, begin with those that take the longest to cook. Then add the remaining vegetables according to the time needed for cooking. Season the soup with herbs and spices. Cover and simmer the soup only until the vegetables are tender.

For variety, flavor, and more nutrients, add cooked legumes or grain products (pasta, rice, or barley). These foods contain starch and will thicken the soup. You can also add cooked leftover meat and poultry sliced in thin strips or cut into small cubes. Making soup can be fun—and a terrific way to use leftovers.

Purées

Purées, thick, low-fat alternatives to cream soups, are unique since they are naturally thickened by mashing or grinding one or more of their ingredients. Black bean soup, made from puréed black beans, is a well-known choice.

TEACH

- *Making Soups*
- *Kinds of Soups (text pages 542-544)*

Discussion Activity

Moderate a discussion of the following: (1) the three basic kinds of soup; (2) aromatic vegetables and how they are used (including why they are sometimes sautéed before being used); (2) how to make a cream soup lower in fat than traditional cream soups; (4) why care must be used when cooking milk-based soups in a microwave oven.

Display Activity

Display convenience products to use as a base for making soup. Have students identify other liquids that can be combined with the broth for added nutrition and flavor.

Demonstration

Demonstrate how to sauté aromatic vegetables to flavor soups. Discuss the purpose of sautéing the vegetables and why onions, celery, and carrots are considered aromatic.

Reinforcing Key Skills

Present the following problem to student groups. Allow time for them to discuss and compare their responses.

Critical Thinking—Roy has learned in his family and consumer sciences class that fat adds flavor to clear broths. He is visiting his aunt and notices that she trims excess fat off the meat before making broth. When Roy asks about this, his aunt shows him a recipe in a cookbook that suggests this. Should Roy assume that his aunt's book is wrong? If not, how do you explain this apparent discrepancy?

TEACH cont.

- *Kinds of Soup (text pages 542-544)*

Supermarket Survey Activity

Ask students to develop a list of varieties and forms of soups available in a supermarket. In class, discuss the nutritional and cost differences between commercial and homemade varieties. Ask how soup can help meet your nutritional needs. How might serving soup as the main dish help stretch the family's food budget?

Lab Experience

Provide students with broth and a basic microwave oven recipe for vegetable soup. Ask students to bring in a vegetable serving of choice. Have students work together in lab groups, combining a variety of the vegetables, to prepare the microwave vegetable soup. Have students comment on the flavor and preparation time. Discuss each group's recipe success. L1

Using Recipes

Have students locate recipes for fruit soups. If possible, have several students bring to class their prepared recipes for class members to sample. Ask all students to make menu suggestions for serving the soups. Discuss how to attractively serve the soup. L1

◆ **A hearty soup is almost a meal in itself. Broth or cream soup might be served as a first course. To make a complete meal, what foods would you serve with the soup shown here?**

Purées can be quick to fix, low in fat, and packed with nutrients. You can make a simple, low-fat purée using one or more puréed cooked vegetables, a starchy base, and enough stock or broth for desired consistency. Fat-free dry milk can be added, too.

You can vary the recipe by substituting different vegetables or dry legumes. Potatoes or cooked rice help thicken the soup and provide a starchy base. Purée all the cooked vegetables or legumes with the rice or potatoes for the smoothest, creamiest texture. Consider adding puréed rice or potatoes to other soups, too—for creaminess without adding cream or other high-fat products.

Cooking Soup in the Microwave Oven

Try making your own soup stock in the microwave oven. Microwaving can take less time than conventional cooking. Check a microwave cookbook for directions.

Vegetable soups can be prepared easily in the microwave oven. Chop the vegetables into uniform pieces, and add hot, lightly-seasoned water or broth. The hot liquid will help speed up the cooking process. Cook a larger quantity of soup in a covered, microwave-safe container to speed up cooking time. You may find, however, that larger quantities of soup take longer than on a conventional range.

Milk-based soups may foam during microwave cooking. Follow the directions in the owner's manual for the best results. Be sure to use a container that is the appropriate size.

Sauces and Gravies

Sauces and gravies are thickened liquids used to add flavor to cooked food. There are many different kinds of sauces and gravies. Most, however, are variations of a few basic types. Added ingredients and seasonings give each a distinct flavor.

Basic White Sauce

The most common sauce is white sauce. A white sauce begins with a **roux** (ROO), a blending of equal parts of flour and fat. The fat coats the starch granules to prevent them from lumping together when milk is added. Fat also adds richness to the sauce.

For a medium-thick sauce, use 2 tablespoons (30 mL) each of butter and flour for every 1 cup (250 mL) of milk. For a thinner sauce, use 1 tablespoon (15 mL) each of butter and flour.

Over medium to medium-high heat, melt the fat and whisk in the flour. Before the roux

Extending Learning

Soup Garnishes—To add meal appeal, it helps to serve soup with a garnish. Try these suggestions:

- Creamy potato soup: fresh chives.
- Tomato soup: fresh basil or teaspoon of pesto sauce.
- Cucumber soup: dollop of fresh, plain yogurt.
- Mexican chicken soup: avocado slice (dipped in lemon juice) or tortilla strips.
- French onion soup: toasted cheese croutons.
- Sweet potato or carrot soup: fresh herbs or edible flowers.

What's the Best Thickener?

Cornstarch and flour are the most common thickening agents in home kitchens. Which provides the best overall thickening?

Procedure

1. In each of two pots, simmer 1 cup (250 mL) milk.
2. In separate covered jars, mix equal parts cornstarch and cold water, and flour and cold water.
3. Whisk one of the liquefied thickeners into one pot, the other thickener into the other pot. Compare the results in terms of thickness, ease of incorporation, and texture.

Conclusions

- How do the textures differ? Which starch would give the best results when making a clear fruit sauce?
- Did either starch clump up? If so, how could this affect your recipe results? How do you think the results would differ if you blended each starch with warm water?
- Which starch had more thickening ability?

◆ **Cornstarch is a thickening agent. What else can be used to thicken?**

browns, stir in the milk gradually. Cook the mixture over low heat, stirring constantly until it thickens. Season the sauce as desired. The sauce should be thick enough to coat the back of a wooden spoon.

Q ***How can I rescue lumpy gravy or sauce?***

A If a few lumps occur, put the sauce or gravy through a strainer. Reheat the mixture, stirring constantly, and serve.

Pan Gravy

Pan gravy is made like white sauce, but with meat juices instead of milk. For traditional pan gravy, remove the meat from the pan and pour the juices that remain into a measuring cup. Skim off and reserve the fat. Measure the remaining broth. Use 2 tablespoons (30 mL)

- *Sauces and Gravies (text pages 544-546)*

Demonstration

First, ask students to describe the procedure for making a white sauce. Then demonstrate, step-by-step, the procedure for making basic white sauce. Have students test the final product by dipping a wooden spoon into the sauce to determine whether the sauce coats the back of it. Discuss how this procedure is different for preparing pan gravy. If time allows, demonstrate pan gravy preparation.

Discuss ingredients that can be used to thicken liquid to make white sauce or pan gravy.

Then, in lab groups, have students make a thin, medium, and thick white sauce. Have students compare the three sauces. How would they use each sauce?

FOOD SCIENCE **Creating Sauce Experiment**

See the *Food Science Resources* booklet for the "How Do You Make Sauces Smooth?" teaching guide and student experiment worksheet. The experiment determines which preparation method is best for producing a smooth sauce when flour is used as a thickener.

ASSESS

REVIEW

- Ask students to summarize the main ideas in this section.
- Have students complete the Section Review. (Answers appear below.)

EVALUATION

- Have students prepare a soup, sauce, or gravy according to a recipe you provide.
- Have students take the quiz for Section 20-3. (Use the quiz in the *Teacher Resource Guide,* or construct your own with the **Exam***View*® *Test Generator* on the *Effective Instruction CD-ROM.*)

RETEACHING

- Provide pictures of different types of soup. Have students practice identifying the type of soup.
- Refer to the *Reteaching Activities* booklet for the Section 20-3 activity sheet.

CLOSE

Lead a discussion on the various roles soups can play in preparing balanced meals and meeting Food Guide Pyramid recommendations. Then ask students to finish the sentence: Soups are versatile because ____. Discuss students' responses.

each of fat and flour for each cup (250 mL) of meat broth. Make a roux, and heat until it starts to brown. Gradually add the meat broth, and stir constantly until smooth and thickened. Scrape the bottom of the pan to loosen browned meat particles. This adds flavor to the gravy.

Lower-Fat Alternatives

White sauce and gravy are traditionally high in fat. Consider using seasoned nonfat yogurt in place of white sauce. Instead of serving roasts with gravy, try serving them **au jus**—with the pan drippings from which the fat has been skimmed. The easiest way to skim fat is to wait until the drippings have cooled. The fat, which will rise to the top, may be easily removed with a spoon.

To make lower-fat gravy, shake a mixture of 2 tablespoons (30 mL) flour or cornstarch and ¼ cup (50 mL) cold water in a covered container. Then add it to 1 cup (250 mL) of broth, and heat the mixture to boiling, stirring constantly. Cook the mixture until it thickens, about 1 minute.

◆ **Thickened, defatted pan drippings can add flavor to meat. Describe the steps involved in removing fat.**

Section 20-3 Review & Activities

1. What are aromatic vegetables? Why are they sautéed?
2. Describe how to make stock.
3. What is a lower-fat alternative to serving gravy with roasted meat?
4. **Comparing and Contrasting.** How would a white sauce that started with a roux be different from one in which flour was added by itself to a liquid?
5. **Analyzing.** How might a family's food budget be stretched by serving soup as a main dish?
6. **Applying.** Create a recipe for a vegetable soup that you can prepare in 1 hour. What pre-preparation tasks could you do to cut down on the cooking time?

Answers to Section 20-3 Review & Activities

1. Vegetables, such as onions, celery, and carrots, that add flavor to soups and other recipes; to develop the flavor.
2. See page 542.
3. Serve the roast au jus.
4. The one with the roux would be smoother and richer.
5. Answers will vary. Soups are filling and can stretch meat, poultry, and fish to cover more meals; they can be made with legumes, grains, and other low-cost ingredients; soup provides a good medium for using leftovers.
6. Answers will vary. Steam vegetables beforehand or use leftover vegetables.

Recipe File

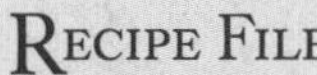

Creamy Potato Soup

This soup is a good source of calcium with less fat than traditional cream soups.

Customary	Ingredients	Metric
1 clove	Garlic, minced	1 clove
¼ cup	Chopped onion	75 mL
¼ cup	Chopped celery	75 mL
1 Tbsp.	Vegetable oil	15 mL
3	Potatoes, peeled and cubed	3
4 cups	Reduced-sodium chicken broth	1 L
½ cup	Nonfat dry milk	125 mL

Yield: 4 servings, one cup each

Directions

1. In a Dutch oven or a stock pot, sauté garlic, onion, and celery in oil.
2. Add potatoes and chicken broth. Bring to a boil.
3. Reduce heat and simmer until potatoes are tender, about 15 minutes.
4. Carefully purée the soup in a blender or food processor.
5. Return puréed soup to pot. Stir in dry milk.
6. Simmer until thoroughly heated.
7. Season to taste and serve hot.

Note: For a chunkier soup, purée only half the soup before stirring in the dry milk.

Nutrition Information

Per serving (approximate): 192 calories, 10 g protein, 27 g carbohydrate, 5 g fat, 2 mg cholesterol, 641 mg sodium

Good source of: potassium, vitamin E, vitamin C, B vitamins, calcium, phosphorus

Food for Thought

- What is used to thicken this soup?
- What other vegetables could you add to this soup for flavor and variation?

Recipe File

Creamy Potato Soup

This recipe is an example of a purée.

USING THE RECIPE

- Have students read the recipe and discuss each step.
- Remind students to use only the amount of oil recommended in the recipe to sauté the vegetables. Adding more than that will make the finished soup higher in fat and possibly a bit greasy.
- Review safety and sanitation procedures that apply to this recipe.
- Have each lab team fill out a work plan. (See the *Foods Lab Resources* booklet.)
- Have students check off the ingredients and equipment listed on the recipe worksheet and prepare the recipe.
- Have students complete the evaluation and questions on the recipe worksheet.

SEE ALSO...

The *Foods Lab Resources* booklet for the "Creamy Potato Soup" recipe worksheet and other recipe alternatives.

Answers to **Food for Thought**

1. Potatoes are the main thickening agent.
2. Answers will vary. Examples: Carrots or corn.

SECTION

20-4

Casseroles and Other Combinations

FOCUS

MOTIVATORS

- Ask students to name as many one-dish meals as they can. List their ideas on the board. Ask why one-dish meals are popular. What advantages do they offer?
- Display cookware and appliances that lend themselves to one-dish meals. Ask students to tell what these items have in common. Discuss how specialized cookware and appliances can aid in simplifying food preparation for busy people.

VOCABULARY ACTIVITY

Pronounce the two terms listed under "Look for These Terms." Have students find the terms and their definitions in the section. Ask students how the suffix *-er* changes the root of each term.

STUDY SKILLS

- **Note Taking.** Have students read the section independently. As they are reading, they're to take notes, in their own words, of important points within each heading.
- Have students read the section and complete the appropriate part of the Chapter 20 Study Guide in the *Student Workbook*.

SECTION 20-4

Objectives

After studying this section, you should be able to:

- Plan and prepare hearty one-dish meals using a variety of ingredients.
- Explain how to prepare low-fat one-dish meals.
- Explain several methods used to prepare one-dish meals.

Look for These Terms

extender

binder

Casseroles and Other Combinations

If you were to trace the history of food preparation to its earliest known roots, you would find a common link among the cooking habits of various primitive cultures. That link is the one-pot meal. In addition to its potential for providing servings from all five food groups, the one-pot meal—whether a stew, braised meat, stir-fry, or casserole—is a convenient solution for families with little time to cook.

Stews

Stewing is an efficient way to cook some less tender cuts of meat or poultry. Fish and shellfish stews are delicious, too.

Stews may be made with a variety of vegetables. Potatoes or other starchy vegetables can be added for thickness. Also consider using sliced apples, dried apricots, or other fruits.

Although water is the basic liquid in stew, try substituting broth or vegetable juice for part of the water. Tomato juice, for example, contains acid, which helps tenderize meat and adds flavor.

◆ A fish stew made with fresh cod is one example of a hearty main dish combination. What would you serve with it to make an appealing, nutritionally balanced meal?

Section 20-4 Resources

◆ **Student Workbook**, pp. 146, 151
◆ **Teacher Resource Guide**
Lesson Plan 20-4 Organizer
Section 20-4 Quiz
Chapter 20 Test
◆ **Effective Instruction CD-ROM**
Exam*View*® *Test Generator*
◆ **Student Motivation Kit**
Reteaching Activities, p. 95
Enrichment Activities
Foods Lab Resources, pp. 111–118

◆ Fresh or dried fruits can be included in stewed meat dishes to perk up the flavor and add nutrients. Consult the "Nutritive Value of Foods" table in Appendix B to determine the number of grams of food energy provided by adding a whole sliced apple to this stewed pork. How many grams of fat does the fruit add?

Cooking Time

The cooking time of a stew varies with the tenderness of the main ingredient. Fish stews, for example, take just enough time for the fish to flake and the flavors to become blended. Beef stew may need 2 or 3 hours to cook, while poultry may cook in 1 hour.

Cooking times also vary with the appliance used. A beef stew can cook in 30 minutes in a pressure cooker, 1 hour in a microwave oven, 2 to 3 hours on the range top or in a conventional oven, or about 9 hours in a slow cooker.

Vegetables and fruits may need different amounts of cooking times, depending on tenderness and the size of the pieces. Add them to the stew according to the amount of cooking time needed. Those that will take the longest to cook—chunks of fresh carrot, for instance —should be added early in the process. Items such as frozen peas or corn, which take less time to cook, can be added later. Canned vegetables or leftover cooked vegetables can be added near the end of the cooking time.

To stew meat on the range top, brown cubes of meat without added fat in a large pan. This creates a darker, more flavorful stew and helps the meat keep its shape. Remove the meat cubes to a clean plate. In the same pan, sauté aromatic vegetables in a small amount of fat; then return the browned meat to the pan. Add seasonings and enough liquid to cover the meat. Cover the pan and simmer until tender, adding the other ingredients during the cooking time, as explained above.

Before stewing poultry, cut it into parts or other large pieces. Remove the skin to reduce fat.

Braised Foods

Braising is used to cook large, less tender cuts of meat and poultry. It can also be used to give flavor to tender cuts. Fish, for example, is sometimes braised in a flavorful sauce.

Meat is often browned before braising; usually, poultry is not. Place the meat or poultry in a Dutch oven or other heavy pan. Add enough liquid to cover the bottom and create steam. Add onions, garlic, herbs, spices, and other seasonings. Cover the pan and bake at 350°F (180°C), or simmer on top of the range.

TEACH

- *Stews (text pages 548-549)*

Discussion Activity

Ask students to identify liquids that can be substituted for some of the water in stews. What is the advantage of doing this? Discuss flavor, color, and nutritional advantages.

Making Graphs

Ask students to identify typical cooking times for beef stew in different appliances. Then have them make a graph of the information. L1

VISUAL LEARNING *Using the Photograph*

Provide students with a copy of a high-fat beef stew recipe. Suggest to students that you want to adapt the recipe—making it lower in fat and more nutrient-dense. Ask students to evaluate and record appropriate, specific changes to the recipe and instructions, such as how the adding of the apples is done in the photo on this page. Discuss students' "beef stew makeovers" in class. Did anyone add both fruits and vegetables? Did anyone use poultry instead of beef?

FOOD SCIENCE Stewing Methods

Have students work in groups to prepare stew using different methods: pressure cooker, microwave oven, range top or conventional oven, or slow cooker. Compare the tastes and preparation times. Discuss situations in which each method would be a good choice.

TEACH cont.

- *Braised Foods (text pages 549-550)*

Writing Basic Instructions

Using the information in this section, have students write a very basic instructional guide for preparing braised foods. Encourage a numbering or other simplified system for the steps. Then discuss these basic instructions. L1

Finding Recipes

Have students use recipe books to find examples of food combinations appropriate for braised dishes, like the combinations suggested on this page. Have them record their combination findings and share them with other students. L1

Using Recipes

Have students use recipe books to study and record the cuts of meats, poultry, and fish that are typically braised. Have students record the number of times each cut is mentioned, too. Have students compile their findings and create a class list of most common cuts of meat, poultry, and fish to be braised. Discuss results. L1

Add other vegetables as the meat braises. Large items, such as halved or quartered potatoes and carrot halves, need to be added toward the beginning. Add peas, corn, or other quick-cooking vegetables near the end of the cooking time. Consider adding fresh or canned fruit for a different flavor. Some tasty combinations are pork with peeled and quartered fresh apples (or applesauce), poultry with pineapple or orange juice, fish with lemon or grapefruit juice, beef with prunes or dried apricots, and lamb with canned plums.

Check the food at frequent intervals to be sure enough liquid remains to cover the bottom of the pan. Add water as needed. To thicken the gravy, add a diced potato an hour before serving.

The total cooking time depends on the size and cut of the meat. Cook until the ingredients are tender and the flavors are well blended.

Stir-Fries

Stir-frying is a quick and easy way to make a flavorful, nutrient-rich dish. It can be low in fat if you choose your ingredients carefully.

The secret to successful stir-fried foods is to cut up all the ingredients and assemble them in the order they are to be cooked. Because stir-frying is fast, there's no time to stop and cut up foods while you're cooking. High heat is also essential to cook food quickly and keep vegetables crisp.

◆ **You can use almost any combination of protein foods, fruits, vegetables, seasonings, and sauces in a stir-fry. Why is it important to slice each type of food uniformly?**

HOME & COMMUNITY CONNECTION

Have students find out if the technique of braising is used to prepare any meal eaten at their home. If so, have these students write one of the recipes in standard recipe format on a computer and bring it to class. Compile all available braising recipes. Make copies for all students. Encourage students to practice their braising techniques at home using these recipes.

Pre-preparation

Cut raw meat or poultry across the grain into thin, narrow strips. Meat that has been chilled in the freezer will be easier to slice. Cubes or strips of tofu or cooked meat, poultry, or fish can also be used. Vegetables should be cut into pieces of uniform size to ensure even cooking.

Stir-Frying Basics

The wok is ideal for stir-frying. It has a rounded bottom and sits on a metal ring placed on the range. Electric woks are also available. If you don't have a wok, you can use a large non-stick skillet.

The pan is ready for cooking when a few drops of water sizzle and evaporate immediately. Heat 1 to 2 tablespoons (15 to 30 mL) of oil. Add garlic, ginger, or seasonings and cook for a few seconds to flavor the oil. Next, add the meat, poultry, or fish. Keep the pieces in motion constantly so that they don't burn.

When this main ingredient has finished cooking, transfer it to a clean plate and proceed to the vegetables. Cook dense, fibrous items, such as broccoli and carrots, first. (You can also precook them in the microwave oven.) Then cook the remaining vegetables. When they are done, return the cooked main ingredient to the wok or skillet.

If you like, you can complete your stir-fry with a sauce by adding a mixture of cornstarch and stock or light, reduced-sodium soy sauce. (If you plan on stir-frying often, you may want to keep a small jar of this premixed solution handy in the refrigerator.) Stir until the sauce begins to thicken.

As you stir-fry, avoid overloading the pan. Putting too much food in the pan at one time will result in vegetables that are steamed, not stir-fried.

Stir-Fry Suggestions

In additional to being flavorful and helping you meet daily nutrient needs from several food groups, stir-fries are easy to prepare and versatile.

- **Seasonings.** ¼ to ½ teaspoon (1 to 3 mL) grated raw ginger, pressed garlic, crushed, dried thyme or marjoram.
- **Protein.** 1 cup (250 mL) cubed tofu, meat, poultry, or fish.
- **Vegetables or fruits.** 3 cups (750 mL) of at least three bite-size vegetables and fruits.
- **Sauce.** Mix 1 tablespoon (15 mL) cornstarch with 1 tablespoon (15 mL) tamari sauce, soy sauce, or prepared mustard to make a paste. Add 1 cup (250 mL) canned broth, fruit juice, or vegetable juice, and mix well. (Since cornstarch is added, this sauce will thicken when thoroughly heated.)

Pizza

Pizza is a hearty main dish served on a crust. Traditional pizza calls for a yeast bread crust topped with a tomato-based sauce, cheese (generally mozzarella), and other toppings. However, numerous variations are possible.

To bake pizza at home, use any large shallow pan. Pick your favorite flavor combinations using the following list as a guide. Be sure to add your own innovative choices to the list.

- **Base.** One ready-made or homemade crust.
- **Seasonings.** A small amount of garlic, oregano, basil, marjoram, pepper, cayenne, cinnamon, nutmeg, or chili powder.
- **Sauce.** Canned pizza, pasta, taco, or chili sauce; salsa; puréed fresh or canned fruit.

- *Stir-Fries (text pages 550-551)*

Writing

Ask students to write a paragraph explaining why it is important to be organized and to know exactly what you are going to do, and in what order, when you stir-fry foods. L1

Guest Speaker

Invite a chef to give tips about stewing, braising, and stir-frying foods. If possible, have a chef from a Chinese restaurant demonstrate stir-frying techniques.

Lab Experience

Have students work in lab groups to prepare vegetables and meats and stir-fry several different dishes using a wok. Remind students to begin with the foods that take the longest. Have students prepare a stir-fry sauce and rice to serve with the dishes. L1

Extending Learning

Stir-Fry Combinations—An unlimited number of stir-fry combinations are possible. The following suggestions are tasty combinations:

- Sliced raw beef, garlic, beef broth, soy sauce, ginger, onion, green pepper, red pepper.
- Raw chicken breast, chicken broth, ginger, garlic, green onion, snow peas, water chestnuts.

- *Pizza*
- *Casseroles (text pages 551-553)*

Lab Experience

1. Divide students into lab groups for a "Create Your Own Pizza" Lab.
2. Have groups decide on pizza toppings of their choice. Encourage creativity and healthfulness, such as a Chinese stir-fry pizza or a dessert fruit pizza. (See Extending Learning on this page.)
3. Have students bring to class the needed ingredient toppings.
4. Provide students with pre-prepared pizza crusts. Students will need to top them and, if necessary, bake them.
5. Prior to eating, have each group view the other pizza creations. L1

Discussion Activity

Ask students to explain the purpose of the extender and the binder in a casserole. Have students work in groups to develop a list of bases, binders, and extenders, in addition to those mentioned in the text.

Recipe Analysis

Have students find recipes for casseroles and list the food groups contained in each. Have students compile a written list of well-balanced main-dish casseroles that sound appealing to them. L1

◆ Making pizza at home is easy and can be fun. These teens have come up with some combinations that feature a rice crust and vegetables as toppings. Plan a class pizza party. Have each person bring a different ingredient to include.

- **Toppings.** Chopped or sliced veggies; pineapple slices; cooked or canned meat, poultry, or fish.
- **Grated cheese.** Mozzarella, feta, gouda, cheddar, Swiss, or parmesan.

Pizza is generally baked in an oven preheated to 425°F (220°C). The cooking time may vary depending on the pizza size and the ingredients. Check a cookbook for cooking times.

Casseroles

A casserole is a tasty blend of cooked ingredients that are heated together to develop flavor.

There are three main parts to a casserole. The base of a casserole provides its main texture and flavor. It also needs an **extender**, a food ingredient that helps thicken a dish—for example, rice or pasta—and a **binder**, a liquid that holds the other ingredients together. Seasonings and aromatic vegetables give heightened flavor and added texture. Here are some suggestions for casserole combinations:

- **Base.** Cubed, cooked meat, poultry, or fish; browned, drained ground beef or poultry; grated or cubed cheese.
- **Vegetables.** Any cooked or canned vegetables.
- **Extenders.** Dry breadcrumbs; cooked, diced potatoes, pasta, rice, grits, or barley; cooked, mashed dry beans.
- **Aromatic vegetables.** Chopped celery or bell pepper; sautéed mushrooms, onions, or garlic.
- **Seasonings.** Dried, crushed oregano, basil, thyme, or marjoram; ground ginger, mace, cinnamon, chili powder, cayenne or black pepper. Start with ¼ teaspoon (1 mL). You can always add more to taste.
- **Binders.** Fat-free milk, broth, fruit juice, soup, eggs, or a thickened sauce.

Extending Learning

Pizza—You can bake pizza in any large, shallow pan. Try various shapes for variety. Try these combinations of ingredients:

- Tex-Mex: salsa, chili powder, ground beef and Mexican sausage, green pepper, onion, cheddar cheese.
- Polynesian: drained, crushed pineapple and applesauce; thinly-sliced cooked ham or chicken; mozzarella or Swiss cheese.
- Vegetarian: spaghetti sauce, basil, oregano, broccoli, zucchini, onions, red or green pepper, mozzarella and Parmesan cheese.

◆ **Casseroles like this spicy southwestern blend of corn, rice, beans, peppers, and other ingredients make interesting and varied one-dish meals. In what ways do casseroles save time and energy when planning and preparing meals?**

Cooking a Casserole

To make a casserole for four people, combine 1 cup (250 mL) of each ingredient choice (except for seasonings). Place the mixture in a 1½ quart (1.5 L) covered baking dish that has been coated with cooking oil spray. Bake the casserole about 30 minutes in an oven preheated to 350°F (180°C). Remove the cover after 20 minutes if the liquid needs to thicken.

To microwave a casserole, combine the ingredients in an ungreased baking dish with a cover. Cook the casserole at 100 percent power for 6 to 18 minutes, depending on the ingredients. Stir once or twice during cooking, and rotate the casserole halfway through the cooking time.

Casseroles can save you time and energy when planning and preparing meals. Enjoy the variety of food choices used to make casseroles —and all other combination dishes.

Section 20-4 Review & Activities

1. Stewing or braising is an ideal cooking technique for what types of meat? Give two examples.
2. Why must stir-fry ingredients be cut up and assembled before you start cooking?
3. Name three main parts of any casserole. Give an example of each.
4. **Analyzing.** Discuss reasons why combination foods, such as those detailed in this section, are good, economical choices for many families.
5. **Synthesizing.** How can stews be prepared for people who want low-fat meals? How can low-fat casseroles be prepared?
6. **Applying.** Develop a list of at least six ingredients that you could use in making three of the one-dish meals discussed in this section. What foods might you need to have on hand for "emergency" one-dish meals?

ASSESS

REVIEW

- Ask students to summarize the main ideas in this section.
- Have students complete the Section Review. (Answers appear below.)

EVALUATION

- Have students plan a one-day menu for a family of four that features pizza and a casserole. The menu should be nutritious as well as appealing.
- Have students take the quiz for Section 20-4. (Use the quiz in the *Teacher Resource Guide,* or construct your own with the **Exam***View*® *Test Generator* on the *Effective Instruction CD-ROM.*)

RETEACHING

- Ask students to create a poster that lists guidelines for stir-frying foods.
- Refer to the *Reteaching Activities* booklet for the Section 20-4 activity sheet.

CLOSE

Ask students to debate these questions: Are specialized small cooking appliances essential for busy people? Are casseroles and other combination foods generally not ideal for people who live alone?

Answers to Section 20-4 Review & Activities

1. Tougher cuts. Examples will vary.
2. Since foods cook so quickly, there isn't time to cut up or assemble foods once cooking starts.
3. See page 552.
4. Answers will vary. Many are one-dish meals; some are extended or based on grains (low in cost); some make use of tough cuts of meat (often cheaper).
5. Answers will vary. All require selecting your own ingredients, which can be low in fat. Choose lean meats, lower-fat dairy products, and little oil or added fat. Use additional fruits or vegetables.
6. Answers will vary. Examples: canned beans and vegetables, dry pasta, rice, garlic, dry herbs.

Recipe File

Whitefish Stir-Fry

This stir-fry recipe is ideal for people who like healthy, quickly-prepared food.

USING THE RECIPE

- Have students read the recipe and discuss each step.
- Caution students not to allow too much food to cook in the wok or skillet at one time to avoid steaming the food.
- Review safety and sanitation procedures that apply to this recipe.
- Have each lab team fill out a work plan. (See the *Foods Lab Resources* booklet.)
- Have students check off the ingredients and equipment listed on the recipe worksheet and prepare the recipe.
- Have students complete the evaluation and questions on the recipe worksheet.

SEE ALSO...

The *Foods Lab Resources* booklet for the "Whitefish Stir-Fry" recipe worksheet and other recipe alternatives.

Recipe File

Whitefish Stir-Fry

Stir-fried dishes can include an endless variety of ingredients. The combinations provide not only flavor, but texture and meal appeal, too.

Customary	***Ingredients***	***Metric***
1 Tbsp.	Cornstarch	15 mL
1 Tbsp.	Reduced-sodium tamari or soy sauce	15 mL
1 cup	Pineapple juice	250 mL
1 Tbsp.	Vegetable oil	15 mL
1 clove	Garlic, minced	1 clove
1 cup	Snow peas	250 mL
1 cup	Red or green pepper, chopped	250 mL
½ cup	Sliced water chestnuts	125 mL
1 cup	Pineapple chunks	250 mL
1 cup	Whitefish fillets, cooked and cubed	250 mL
	Hot cooked rice (optional)	

Yield: 4 servings, one cup each on rice

Directions

1. In a small bowl, combine cornstarch with tamari or soy sauce. Add pineapple juice and mix well. Set aside.
2. Heat oil in wok or a large, nonstick skillet. Add garlic and sauté a few seconds to flavor the oil.
3. Add snow peas, pepper, water chestnuts, and pineapple.
4. Cook, stirring constantly, until snow peas and pepper are tender-crisp.
5. Add cooked whitefish to vegetables.
6. Mix the sauce from Step 1 and pour it over the mixture.
7. Cook, stirring constantly, until mixture is thickened and fish is thoroughly heated.
8. Serve over hot cooked rice, if desired.

Nutrition Information

Per serving (approximate–stir-fry only): 169 calories, 15 g protein, 17 g carbohydrate, 4 g fat, 54 mg cholesterol, 202 mg sodium

Good source of: potassium, vitamin E, vitamin C, B vitamins, phosphorus

Food for Thought

- How could you cut the vegetables or fish to vary their appearance?
- How can you tell when the oil is hot enough for cooking?

Answers to ***Food for Thought***

1. Answers will vary. Cut the fish and vegetables in long strips or julienne-style.
2. A few drops of water should sizzle and evaporate immediately.

Career Wanted

Provisioner Kitchen Supervisor

Education and Training
- Degree in food management
- Background in business and food science

Qualities
- Management skills
- Communication skills
- Ability to handle stress

"I'd love to hear people say they pick an airline for its food."
Ivan Kai

Q. First, Ivan, what is a "provisioner"?

A. It's a company that supplies fully cooked meals in large quantities to other businesses. Our biggest clients are airlines, but we supply some colleges and civic centers, too.

Q. What does your job entail?

A. I oversee operations in the kitchen and make suggestions about the meals we offer, based on my technical knowledge. In our aim to improve airline food, we buy high-quality ingredients. Meals are vacuum-sealed, cooked using computer monitoring, and then flash frozen. This retains more flavor, as well as nutrients, and promotes safety. With so much time and distance in preparing, transporting, and serving, food safety is critical.

Q. What are other concerns for your company?

A. We need to appeal to many different tastes and diets, especially for international air carriers. We meet the safety standards of both the USDA and the EEC, the European Economic Community. Costs and business trends affect us like any other company.

Related Career Opportunities

Entry Level
- Food server
- Fast-food cook
- Produce grader

Technical Level
- Cafeteria manager
- Sauce cook
- Franchise restaurant owner

Professional Level
- Food technologist
- Purchasing agent
- Sales engineer

Making Career Connections

CAREER EXPLORATION. Learn about one step in provisioning, such as food preparation, processing, packaging, or distribution. Create a flow chart showing the process used in that phase. Combine your research with that of others to link the different areas in a larger chart. List some of the jobs in each area.

Career Wanted

Provisioner Kitchen Supervisor

Thinking About the Career

Think about what some obstacles may be to menu planning for airline meals. Have students search the Internet to determine the actual number of special meal options available to airline passengers.

Think about the skills that a provisioner may need to "beat" a competitor. Why are problem-solving skills important?

Career-Building Opportunities

Suggest interested students research, evaluate, and possibly consider part-time work in one of the entry level positions indicated in "Related Career Opportunities."

For More Information

For additional information about careers, encourage students to contact:

- Association of Sales & Marketing Companies
  1010 Wisconsin Ave., NW, Ninth Floor
  Washington, DC 20007
  www.asmc.org

REVIEW

- Have students complete the Chapter Review. (Answers appear below.)

EVALUATION

- Have students write a short essay describing the topics covered in this chapter.
- Have students take the test for Chapter 20. (Use the chapter test in the *Teacher Resource Guide,* or construct your own with the **Exam***View*® *Test Generator* on the *Effective Instruction CD-ROM.*)

ANSWERS

Checking Your Knowledge

1. A fancy sandwich uses bread cut into fun or fancy shapes; a club sandwich uses three slices of toasted bread.
2. Line them first with shredded lettuce or cucumber slices.
3. Any two: Use a freezer gel pack, insulated lunch bags, vacuum bottles; to keep bacteria from growing and to prevent food-borne illness.
4. An oil-based dressing separates easily whereas a mayonnaise dressing, which contains eggs as an emulsifier, does not.
5. Base: lining of greens on serving bowl or plate; body: main salad ingredients.
6. Both contain vegetables; vegetable soups are clear; purées are thick and not transparent.
7. By cooking the mixture over low heat and stirring it constantly.
8. To create a darker, more flavorful stew and to help the meat keep its shape.
9. Just enough to cover the bottom —for steaming, not stewing.
10. It keeps the vegetables crisp.

Chapter 20 Review & Activities

Summary

Section 20-1: Sandwiches, Snacks, and Packed Lunches

- Sandwiches can be as varied as the ingredients from which they are made.
- Nutritious snacks are part of a healthful eating plan.
- When packing lunches, keep hot foods hot and cold foods cold.

Section 20-2: Salads and Dressings

- Salads may include greens, fresh fruits or vegetables, cheese, and cooked grains, legumes, meat, poultry, fish, or eggs.
- Basic dressings include oil-based, mayonnaise, cooked, and dairy varieties. Many options for low-fat dressings exist.
- For appealing salads, find artful ways to make and serve them.

Section 20-3: Soups and Sauces

- There are two main types of soups: clear soups and thick soups.
- Soups often rely on aromatic vegetables for flavoring.
- You can use quick and easy methods to make low-fat soups.
- Sauces and gravies can add flavor to cooked foods. Keep sauces and gravies low in fat.

Section 20-4: Casseroles and Other Combinations

- One-dish meals can be healthful choices.
- Types of one-dish meals include stews, braised dishes, stir-fries, pizza, and casseroles.
- Combination dishes have variety and creativity in the kind and amounts of ingredients used.

Working IN THE Lab

1. ***Taste Test.*** Plan and prepare one or two sandwich fillings and toppings. Use a variety of breads to make up enough sandwiches so that each person can sample a piece of each sandwich. Discuss how these foods measure up to the recommendations of the Food Guide Pyramid.
2. ***Foods Lab.*** Plan and prepare a main dish salad that uses at least one ingredient from each of the five food groups. If possible, invite some teachers to a luncheon to share it.

Checking Your Knowledge

1. What is the difference between a fancy sandwich and a club sandwich?
2. How can you keep pocket sandwiches from absorbing moist fillings?
3. What are two ways to keep packaged lunches cold? Why is food temperature important?
4. What is the basic difference between an oil-based dressing and a mayonnaise dressing?
5. What are the base and body of a salad?
6. Name one way vegetable soups and purées are the same and one way they are different.
7. How can you keep a sauce made with flour from becoming lumpy?
8. Why is meat often browned before stewing?
9. When braising, how much liquid should you add to the pan?
10. Why is high heat essential for stir-frying?

Thinking Critically

1. Determining Accuracy. Compare the labels of several popular salad dressings, including some lower-fat varieties. Rate them in terms of fat and sodium content. How do their ratings compare with the claims or descriptions on the label?

2. Comparing and Contrasting. Examine a can of ready-made gravy, a package of gravy mix, and a can of cream soup, such as mushroom, that may be used for gravy. Using the same serving size for each, calculate the calories and fat. Which rates the highest and lowest in each category? How do your findings compare with the commonly held assumption that gravies are calorie-laden additions to meals?

Reinforcing Key Skills

1. Communication. Write a proposal to the administration of your school presenting concrete and persuasive arguments for adding a salad bar in the school lunchroom. In your proposal, point out the importance of excluding high-fat dressings and other high-fat toppings. Provide reasons for your statements.

2. Management. What specific planning and pre-preparation steps are required to prepare a soup of choice in 15 minutes or less? A stir-fry?

Making Decisions and Solving Problems

Your school sports team is leaving for an all-day tournament in the morning. The coach told each athlete to pack one meal to eat at noon and another to eat in the evening because there will be no stops along the way. What would you pack?

Making Connections

1. Social Studies. Use library references or cookbooks to find out what sandwiches are popular in other cultures. One possibility you might investigate is the *smørbrød* of Denmark. Report to the class on at least two different sandwiches. Include a description of each sandwich and a list of the ingredients in each one. If possible, prepare samples to bring to class.

2. Language Arts. Write a short essay on one of the following topics:

a. The sandwiches I ate as a child were memorable.

b. If I were a salad, I would be a [name a type of salad] because . . .

c. More than just a meal, soup may help you feel better when you're not well.

d. I recommend pizza for breakfast, lunch, dinner, and dessert.

ANSWERS cont.

Thinking Critically

1. Labels and answers will vary. In some cases, students may find sodium content increases as fat decreases.
2. Gravy choices and answers will vary. Students will likely find ready-made gravies that are low in fat or fat-free. Packages of gravy mix and canned cream soups can vary depending on individual preparation.

Reinforcing Key Skills

1. Answers will vary. Encourage students to share and compare their proposals, with an eye toward actually submitting one composite proposal to the administration.
2. Planning and pre-preparation steps will vary.

CHAPTER
21
Baking

Advance Planning Guide ☑

- Gather baked products for a display.
- Gather a variety of flours and liquids.
- Obtain four baking recipes with baking soda or powder; white-out the leavening agent; copy recipes for class.
- Create flash cards with various ingredients names on one side and purpose on the other.
- Gather pictures of quick breads for a display.
- Purchase or prepare several variations of one type of quick bread for Section 21-2 Motivator.
- Purchase all necessary ingredients for the following: Lab Experience, pages 569, 570, 575, 580, 582; Product Evaluation, page 581; Sections 21-2 and 21-3 Evaluation.
- Purchase all necessary ingredients for the Recipe File on pages 572, 577, 586.
- Obtain pictures (samples) of a variety of yeast breads.
- Obtain recipes for shortened and foam cakes.
- Obtain a popular chocolate chip cookie recipe.
- Purchase pie crust mixes and ready-to-use crusts for a display.

CHAPTER
21

How can a few ingredients make a moist, light cake or an apple pie with a flaky crust? The secret lies in the amounts of the ingredients used and how they are combined and baked. In this chapter, you will learn about ingredients and techniques used for baking.

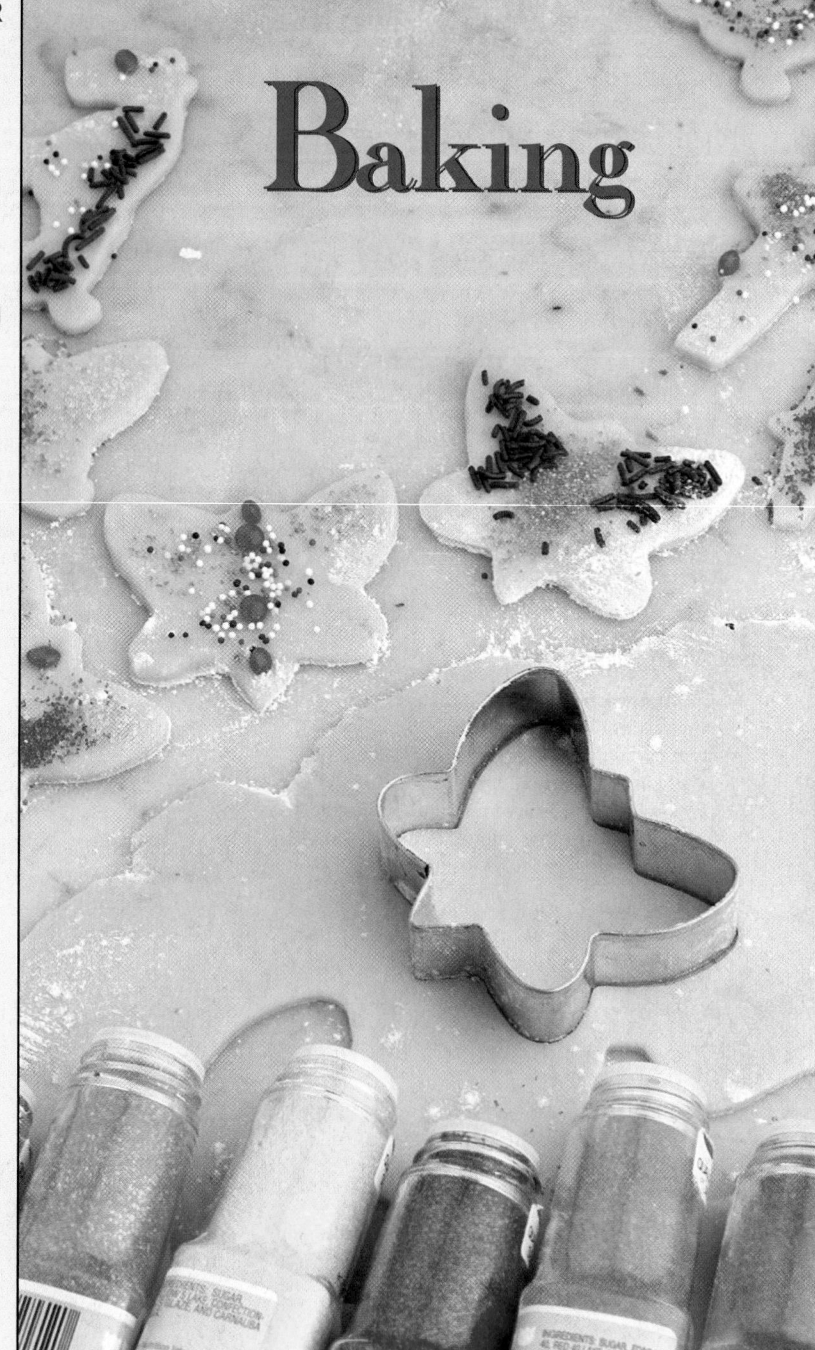

MEETING DIVERSE NEEDS

Physically Challenged Students. If there are students in the class who are physically challenged, partner them with able-bodied students. Partners should discuss responsibility for physical and other tasks so that there is an equitable division of labor. Ask both members of each such team to write an assessment of their work together.

SECTION
21-1

Objectives

After studying this section, you should be able to:

- Identify the basic ingredients in baking and the function of each.
- Explain how to select and prepare pans for baking.
- Compare conventional and microwave baking.

Look for These Terms

gluten

leavening agent

knead

Ingredients and Techniques for Baking

Have you ever passed a bakery and been lured in by the aroma of cookies, cakes, and other baked goods? Although it is hard to imagine, all these items start off with the same few basic ingredients.

Ingredient Basics

The ingredients common to all baking are flour, liquid, leavening agents, fat, sweeteners, eggs, and flavoring. Baked goods are generally nutritious, but many are high in fat, sugar, and calories.

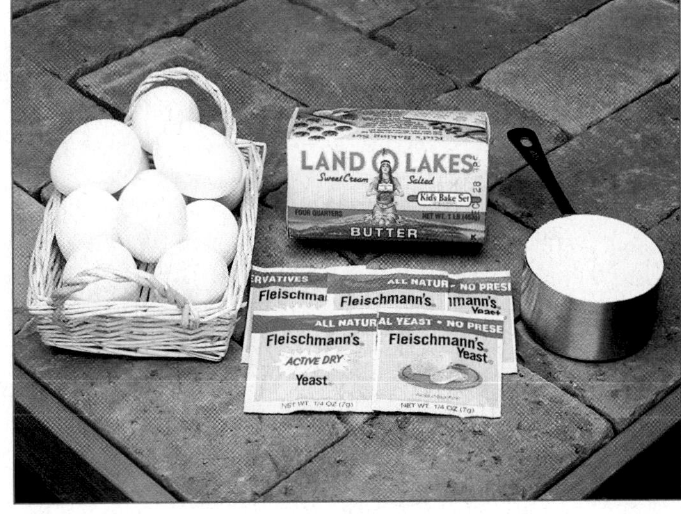

◆ **Ingredients such as these are common to many different baked goods. Identify the specific role each ingredient shown plays in baked goods.**

SECTION
21-1
Ingredients and Techniques for Baking

FOCUS

MOTIVATORS

- Ask students to identify ingredients they have used in baking. Point out that all baked products are made from just a few basic ingredients. The different products result from differences in amounts of ingredients, the order in which the ingredients are combined, how they are mixed, and how they are baked.
- Display several baked products. Have students point out the differences in the appearance and textures of the products.

VOCABULARY ACTIVITY

Pronounce the terms listed under "Look for These Terms." Have students find the terms and their definitions in the section. Have them attempt to devise a rule accounting for the differences in pronunciation of the letter combination *ea* in *leavening* and in *knead*.

STUDY SKILLS

- **Guided Reading.** Have students look at the headings within Section 21-1 to preview the concepts that will be discussed.
- Have students read the section and complete the appropriate part of the Chapter 21 Study Guide in the *Student Workbook*.

Section 21-1 Resources

◆ **Student Workbook,** pp. 153, 156
◆ **Teacher Resource Guide**
Lesson Plan 21-1 Organizer
Section 21-1 Quiz
◆ **Effective Instruction CD-ROM**
Exam*View*® *Test Generator*

◆ **Student Motivation Kit**
Reteaching Activities, p. 96
Enrichment Activities
Food Science Resources, pp. 50–52, 86–89, 93–96, 104–107, 116–120
Skills for Making Food Choices, pp. 47–48

TEACH

- *Ingredient Basics (text pages 559-563)*

Listing Activity

Ask students to list three liquids commonly used in baking. Ask students to list leavening agents used in baked products. Then create a class list of both on the board. Have students describe each liquid and leavening agent.

Discussion Activity

Discuss the various sweeteners available. Why is it important to read the manufacturer's directions when using artificial sweeteners? Ask students to discuss flavorings that are commonly used in baked goods.

Comparison Activity

Set up a flour and liquid display. The flour display is to include all-purpose, bread, cake, and whole-wheat flour. The liquid display is to include water, fat-free milk, and buttermilk. Have students record the differences among the products in each display, including the texture and color of flours and the nutritive value and leavening effect of liquids. Provide students with baked product recipes. Conclude with a discussion on the appropriateness of substituting these different types of flours and liquids in the recipes.

Flour

One ingredient you'll find in nearly every baked product is flour. The proteins and starch in flour make up most of a baked product's structure. **Gluten** (GLOO-ten), a protein that affects the texture of a baked product, helps determine how the product will rise. Starch helps absorb some of the liquid that is added in most baking recipes.

Types of Flour

There are many types of flours. All vary in gluten content.

- **All-purpose flour.** The most popular flour in American kitchens. It gives good results for most products.
- **Bread flour.** Has the highest gluten content and gives bread a strong structure.
- **Cake flour.** Contains less gluten and gives cakes a tender structure.

Whole-Grain Flour

Whole-grain flours have weaker gluten than all-purpose flour. Some whole-grain flours have no gluten at all. This explains why products made with only whole-grain flour rise less and have a heavy texture. Whole-grain flours include wheat, rye, and cornmeal.

To overcome this limitation, whole-grain flours are generally combined with all-purpose flour in equal proportions in recipes. Note that whole-grain flours need to be stirred rather than sifted—the particles are too large to go through a sifter.

Since they contain some fat, whole-grain flours should be stored in the refrigerator to keep them fresh. Store other flours in airtight containers in a cool, dry place.

Liquid

Liquids play a role in the many physical and chemical changes that occur during baking. Water and milk are the most common liquids used in baking. Milk adds flavor and nutrients, and helps baked goods brown better. To reduce fat in a recipe, use fat-free milk instead of whole milk.

Some recipes call for buttermilk, which gives a slightly tangy flavor. Buttermilk also makes the mixture more acid and affects the kind of leavening agent needed.

Leavening Agents

What is the difference between a cake that turns out flat and one that rises nicely? One answer is the use of a **leavening agent**, a substance that triggers a chemical action causing a baked product to rise. Leavening agents make most baked products less compact and give them a softer texture.

◆ Knowing the specific purpose of each of the many types of flour is central to becoming a versatile baker. Explain the differences among the three types of flour shown.

Extending Learning

Leavening Agents—Baking powder includes an ingredient to absorb moisture, such as cornstarch, so that it does not lose its leavening power. Because baking powder is highly perishable, it should be stored in a cool, dry place and used before the expiration date on the container.

Baking powder and baking soda both contain sodium. One teaspoon (5g) baking powder contains approximately 400 mg sodium; one teaspoon (5g) baking soda contains approximately 1370 mg sodium.

◆ **Leavening agents can be the difference in whether a cake rises like the top layer or the bottom layer as seen here. Identify three different leavening agents in the school foods lab.**

Types of Leavening Agents

Here is a list of leavening agents and a description of how each works:

◆ **Air.** Is trapped in mixtures as they are beaten. Creaming fat and sugar, sifting flour, and adding beaten egg whites all add air to a baked good. When the mixture is heated, the trapped air expands and the product rises. Angel food cake is leavened mainly by air in beaten egg whites.

◆ **Steam.** Leavens products that contain high amounts of water. As the product bakes, the water heats. Eventually, it turns into steam, which expands, causing the product to rise. Popovers and cream puffs use steam for leavening.

◆ **Yeast.** A microorganism that produces carbon dioxide gas as it grows. It needs food (such as flour or sugar), liquid, and a warm temperature to grow. Several forms of yeast are available. *Active dry yeast* and *quick-rising dry yeast* come as dry granules in a packet. The quick-rising type leavens the dough about twice as quickly. Both can be stored at room temperature. *Compressed yeast* comes in individually wrapped cakes and must be refrigerated. Use yeast before the expiration date on the package.

◆ **Baking soda.** Is used whenever the recipe calls for buttermilk, yogurt, sour milk, or other acidic liquid. When combined with this type of liquid, baking soda produces carbon dioxide gas.

◆ **Baking powder.** Is made of baking soda and a powdered acid such as cream of tartar. The most common type, double-acting baking powder, releases some carbon dioxide gas when it is first mixed with a liquid. The remainder is released when it is heated.

 ***I baked a cake that didn't rise. What went wrong?***

 One possible problem is the baking powder, which will work only if the ingredients in it are still active. You can test whether baking powder is fresh by mixing 1 teaspoon (5 mL) with ⅓ cup (75 mL) of hot water. If it bubbles quickly, it is still active.

- *Ingredient Basics (text pages 559-563)*

Problem-Solving Activity

Provide each student with copies of four recipes that call for baking powder or baking soda, first taking care that the leavening agent has been obscured on copies. Ask students to determine the missing leavening agent for each recipe and explain why they chose the agent they did. Discuss responses while displaying baking soda and powder.

Recipe Analysis

Ask students to bring to class copies of at least three baking recipes, each using a different leavening agent. Ask students to identify the leavening agent, the gas produced during baking, and other ingredients that make the leavening action possible in their recipes. Then have students practice this activity using other students' recipes. **L1**

Using 

Ask one volunteer to perform the baking powder freshness test for the class, using the baking powder created for the Foods Lab. What's the result?

Ask students to think of ways to help keep baking powder fresh. Why is it important not to use baking powder that is out-of-date or not fresh?

FOOD SCIENCE

Reaction Speed Experiment

See the *Food Science Resources* booklet for the "How Fast Do Chemical Leavening Agents Work?" teaching guide and students' experiment worksheet. The experiment tests the effects and reaction times of leavening agents mixed with liquids.

TEACH cont.

- *Ingredient Basics (text pages 559-563)*

Research

Assign students to three intense-sweetener groups. Have them research their assigned sweetener for use in baking. How can it be used in baking? How much can be used in place of sugar, if any? In what type of baked recipes does it work well? Ask students to find or develop at least one recipe appropriately using their sweetener in baking. Have each group give a presentation to the class on their sweetener research. If possible, have groups prepare their recipe and bring samples for the students to taste during their presentation. **L1**

VISUAL LEARNING ***Using the Photograph***

Ask students to work in groups to develop a chart of healthful substitutions that reduce fat in baked goods. Suggest that students research their substitutions and provide specific amounts whenever possible. Review students' charts. Encourage students to test their substitutions at home, bringing in samples of their prepared, "heart-healthy" baked goods, when possible.

Fat

Although it contributes calories to many baked products, fat adds richness, flavor, and tenderness. Fats can be solid or liquid.

Solid and liquid fats are not easily substituted for one another. In place of butter or shortening, you can use regular margarine, but do not use soft, whipped, or liquid margarine or spreads. They may contain air, water, or oil, which can affect the results. You can substitute solid shortening for butter or margarine. Any cooking oil may be used in baking, as long as it has a mild flavor.

Since fats play an important role in baked products, they usually can't be eliminated. However, they can often be reduced or partially substituted with other flavorful ingredients. Applesauce or puréed dried fruits are common substitutes.

Refrigerate lard, butter, and margarine. Store shortening and oils at room temperature unless the label directs otherwise.

Eggs

Eggs add flavor, nutrients, richness, and color to baked products. They also help form the structure of the baked product. When beaten, eggs add air to the mixture. To reduce fat and cholesterol, use two egg whites or ¼ cup (50 mL) liquid egg substitute in place of one whole egg.

Sweeteners

Sugar is the most commonly used sweetener. It helps make baked products tender, adds sweetness and flavor, and helps the crust brown. Granulated white sugar and brown sugar are used in many recipes. Other sweeteners include honey, corn syrup, molasses, and powdered sugar. Some sugar substitutes are suitable for baking, but others are not. Follow the manufacturers' recommendations.

Store most sweeteners in tightly covered containers in a cool place. Some sweeteners should be refrigerated after opening. Follow label directions.

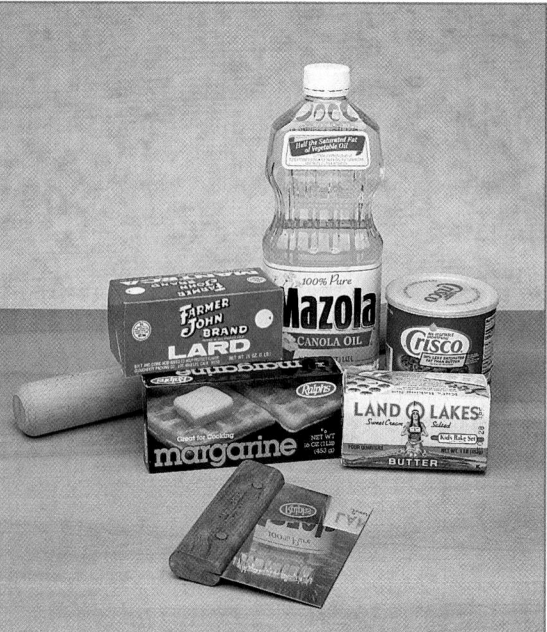

◆ **Fat adds richness, flavor, and tenderness to baked goods. List four guidelines for fat usage in baking and storage.**

For more on sugar substitutes, see Section 13-2.

Extending Learning

Fruit Purée—When replacing part of the fat in baked products, it's important to replace it with one or more ingredients that provide the same fat-like characteristics. Fruit purées have many of the same baking characteristics as fats. Prune purée, in particular, provides tender texture, moistness, and rich flavor. It enhances the flavors of cinnamon, orange, and chocolate. In general, replace ½ cup fat with ¼ cup prune or other fruit purée in baking.

Flavorings

Fruits, vegetables, and nuts add flavor, texture, and nutrients to baked goods. Herbs, spices, and extracts are used in small amounts to add flavor. Some sweet spices—for instance, cinnamon and nutmeg—can actually enhance the flavor enough to allow you to cut back slightly on sugar.

Extracts are flavorings in a liquid form. Vanilla and almond are two common varieties. Store herbs, spices, and extracts in tightly closed containers in a cool, dry area.

Combining the Ingredients

The success of a baked product depends on not only the ingredients used, but also the order in which they are combined. During the mixing process, changes take place that affect the texture of the finished product.

The Role of Gluten

When flour and liquid are mixed together, the gluten in flour develops, or becomes strong and elastic. It forms a network of tiny air cells. Air, steam, or gas produced by the leavening agent is trapped by these cells. When heated, the trapped gases expand and the product rises.

The longer the mixing time, the greater the extent to which gluten is developed. For example, ingredients for cakes and quick breads are mixed only long enough to combine them. As a result, the gluten is not strong. The cells remain small and the network stretches very little. This results in a fine, tender texture.

Yeast breads, on the other hand, are mixed much longer than cakes. The dough for yeast bread is worked with the hands to develop the gluten. As a result, the gluten is very elastic and expands easily. Larger air cells are produced, giving yeast breads a coarser texture.

Batters and Doughs

The amount of liquid in relation to the amount of flour determines whether a mixture is a batter or a dough, and affects how you handle the mixture. Batters have more liquid than doughs. There are four kinds of batters and doughs:

- **Pour batters.** Are thin enough to pour in a steady stream. They are used to make cakes, pancakes, and waffles.
- **Drop batters.** Are thick and are usually spooned into pans. They are used to make some quick breads and cookies.

◆ **Waffles are one baked product made from a batter. Identify the type of batter used to make each of the following: waffles, cookies, pancakes, quick breads.**

- *Combining the Ingredients (text pages 563-564)*

Discussion Activity

Ask students to write their responses for the following: (1) Explain why it is important to mix flour and liquid ingredients only as long as directed. (2) List and describe four types of batters and doughs. (3) What kneading is; explain its purpose. (4) Explain differences between batters and doughs; suggest uses for each. Discuss students' responses.

Student Demonstrations

Have students work in small groups to demonstrate procedures for creaming, beating, cutting in, folding, and kneading. Have each group define the technique they demonstrate. Discuss differences among the techniques. L1

Analyzing Recipes Activity

Provide students with recipes for a variety of breads. Have students study the mixing methods in each recipe and group those that use the same method. Have students list the general steps for mixing each group of similar recipes. Identify the methods as the standard mixing method, muffin method, one-bowl method, and pastry and biscuit method.

Extending Learning

Gluten

- Gluten holds baked goods together.
- When a product is heated, the air, steam, or gas expands and stretches the gluten. During baking, the proteins and starch in the flour set, giving the baked product its final shape.
- Methods of mixing and amounts of ingredients are determined partly due to the effect they have on gluten development.
- The person preparing the baked good has much control over the gluten development.

TEACH cont.

- *Preparing to Bake (text pages 564-565)*

Display Activity

Ask each of several volunteers to bring to class a different type of baking pan, and set up a display of the pans. While grouping similar materials in the display, discuss the effects of different types of baking materials on baked products.

Using Recipes Activity

Give students several recipes. Have them select appropriate pans and describe how the product should be prepared and placed in the oven.

Creating a Baking Demonstration

Ask students to develop a baking demonstration for an elementary classroom. In the presentation, they should instruct children how to prepare a cake mix, grease and flour the pan, and place the pan safely and correctly in the oven. L1

USING Safety Check

Tape at least three different papers—brown paper, waxed paper, and parchment paper—on the board and number them. On a blank piece of paper, have students correctly name each paper type, write a description of it, and suggest its use in baking.

- **Soft doughs.** Are soft and sticky but can be touched and handled. Rolled biscuits, yeast breads and rolls, and some cookies start with soft doughs.
- **Stiff doughs.** Are firm to the touch. Easy to work with and cut, they form the basis for piecrust and some cookies.

Methods of Mixing

There are several basic methods for combining ingredients. All will be explored later in this chapter. Use the method called for in the recipe you have chosen.

Unless the recipe directs otherwise, have all ingredients at room temperature before mixing. Thirty minutes is long enough to warm refrigerated items.

Kneading

After some dough is mixed, you may have to **knead** it, or work the dough with your hands to thoroughly mix ingredients and develop gluten. Kneading is a four-step process:

1. Turn the dough out on a very lightly floured surface.
2. With the heel of your hands, push down on the edge of the dough nearest you.
3. Fold the dough in half toward you and give it a quarter turn.
4. Continue pushing, folding, and turning for the time directed in the recipe.

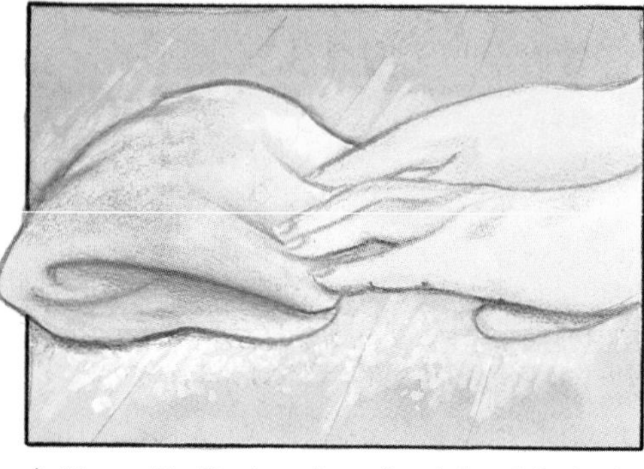

◆ **When making biscuits and yeast breads, knead the dough by pushing, folding, and turning it. Describe the steps in this process.**

Preparing to Bake

The baking pans you choose can affect the results of baking. Use the size and type of pan specified in the recipe. If the pan is too large or too small, the product will not bake properly.

The material the pan is made of is also important. Most recipes are developed for light-colored metal pans. If you use glass pans, lower the temperature by 25°F (14°C). Glass retains more heat than metal, and at the higher temperature, a dark, thick crust may result.

Dark pans also retain more heat than light ones and can create a thick crust. If you use dark metal pans, you may have to lower the oven temperature by about 10°F (6°C).

Glass bakeware or special microwave bakeware must always be used when baking in the microwave oven.

Reinforcing Key Skills

Present the following problems to student groups. Allow time for them to discuss and compare their responses.

Critical Thinking—Some cake recipes recommend that you grease and flour the bottom of the pan but not the sides. Ask students to discuss why this might be so.

Communication—Your cousin is baking a birthday cake in a glass pan. You walk into the kitchen as she is turning the oven temperature to the temperature stated on the recipe. What advice do you give her?

Pan Preparation

Baking pans must be properly prepared so that products can be easily removed from them at the end of baking. The pans should be prepared before the ingredients are mixed. Follow recipe directions carefully.

Here are several methods for preparing pans:

- **Grease and flour.** This means to lightly grease a pan with fat and dust it with flour. Use waxed paper to spread the fat. Sprinkle a little all-purpose flour into the pan. Tilt the pan to different angles until the flour is spread evenly. Turn the pan upside down over the sink, and tap it gently to remove any excess flour. Don't grease and flour pans for microwave baking—they become sticky.
- **Spray with a vegetable-oil cooking spray.** This is the easiest method, but it may not work with all products. Follow the directions on the label or in your recipe.
- **Line a pan with paper.** Begin by cutting a piece of cooking parchment the same shape and size as the pan bottom. Grease the pan and line the bottom with parchment paper. When the product is removed, peel the paper off the bottom. This method is used for rich cakes, such as fruitcake.

Note that some recipes required ungreased pans—otherwise the product will not rise properly. Be sure you know which method is required for your recipe.

Safety Check

The technique of lining a pan with paper requires parchment paper specially made for cooking and baking. Do not use brown paper or waxed paper. Brown paper contains chemicals that may be transferred to the food when it is heated. The wax in waxed paper may melt and possibly cause a fire.

Conventional and Microwave Baking

Most batters and doughs are baked. In a conventional oven, the dry heat creates desirable changes. The product browns, and depending on the ingredients, a crispy crust may develop. Because a microwave oven cooks with moist heat, baked products do not brown or develop a crust. They have more of a steamed texture and are very tender and moist.

Unless the recipe states otherwise, preheat the conventional oven. Before turning on the oven, be sure the oven racks are in the proper position. After you put the pans in the oven, set the timer. Begin checking the product for doneness about 5 minutes before the time is up.

Only certain kinds of cakes, quick breads, and cookies can be baked successfully in a microwave oven. Follow the directions in the owner's guide or in a microwave recipe.

◆ **In order to make the finished product easy to remove, you may need to prepare the pan for some recipes. Lining a pan with parchment paper is shown here. Why do you need to read a recipe carefully to determine whether it requires greasing the pan?**

- *Conventional and Microwave Baking*
- *Storing Baked Products (text pages 565-566)*

Discussion Activity

Hold a class discussion on the following: (1) why microwave ovens produce different baking results from those produced by a conventional oven; (2) why it is necessary to preheat a conventional oven before baking; (3) the use of cooling racks; (4) why most baked products should not be refrigerated; (4) why you should avoid opening the oven door while baking is in progress.

Adapting a Recipe

Have students adapt a conventional, basic cake recipe for the microwave oven. Then have half the students working in lab groups prepare the conventional recipe, the other half the adapted microwave recipe. Have students compare the products baked in a conventional oven with ones baked in a microwave oven. Discuss the advantages and disadvantages of microwave baking vs. conventional baking. **L1**

Extending Learning

Removing Baked Products from Pans

- Cake: Run a spatula around the inside of the pan to loosen the sides; place a cooling rack over the pan and turn both upside down. To turn the cake over, place another cooling rack over the bottom immediately and turn both so that the cake is now right-side up.
- Bread: Turn the pan on its side; using clean potholders, pull the hot loaf out of the pan and place it on a cooling rack.

ASSESS

REVIEW

- Ask students to summarize the main ideas in this section.
- Have students complete the Section Review. (Answers appear below.)

EVALUATION

- Have students write a short essay explaining the various ingredients used in baked products and the purpose of each.
- Have students take the quiz for Section 21-1. (Use the quiz in the *Teacher Resource Guide,* or construct your own with the **Exam***View*® *Test Generator* on the *Effective Instruction CD-ROM.*)

RETEACHING

- Create flash cards with various ingredient names on one side and the purpose of the ingredients on the other. Have pairs of students use the flash cards to help each other remember key baking ingredients.
- Refer to the *Reteaching Activities* booklet for the Section 21-1 activity sheet.

CLOSE

List common baking ingredients on the board. Have students brainstorm: What would happen if I forgot to add (ingredient) to my recipe? Record and discuss students' answers.

INFOLINK

For a review of proper pan placement in the oven during baking, see Section 9-3.
For an update on storing food to prevent spoilage and nutrient loss, see Section 7-4.

Removing Baked Products from Pans

Some baked products must be removed from the pans immediately when they come out of the oven. Others need to cool for a few minutes in the pans. Still others need to remain in the pans until they are completely cool. Follow the recipe directions.

Use cooling racks so that baked goods will cool faster and stay crisp. When baked goods are allowed to cool on a solid surface, such as a cutting board, moisture collects and the product can become soggy.

Storing Baked Products

Perishable baked products, including those with cream fillings or frostings, have to be refrigerated. Studies show that other baked products get stale quickly when stored at refrigerator temperatures. Store them at room temperature if they will be eaten within three days. To store them longer, freeze them in airtight freezer containers.

◆ **This carrot cake, which has a cream cheese icing, should be refrigerated. If this cake was unfrosted, what factors would need to be considered in deciding whether to refrigerate it?**

Section 21-1 Review & Activities

1. List the basic ingredients in baked products. Identify one function of each.
2. What is kneading? Briefly describe the four steps involved.
3. What are three ways of preparing pans for baking?
4. **Analyzing.** Pedro is considering cutting out half the sugar from a cake recipe to cut down on the calories. What might happen if Pedro goes through with his plan?
5. **Comparing and Contrasting.** Discuss the pros and cons of microwave baking versus conventional baking. When might you choose each?
6. **Applying.** Find a basic muffin recipe. Identify one function of each ingredient.

Answers to Section 21-1 Review & Activities

1. See pages 559-563.
2. See page 564.
3. Grease and flour; use vegetable-oil cooking spray, line the pan with paper.
4. The cake will not be as sweet, tender, flavorful, or brown.
5. Answers will vary. Conventional oven: Pros—browning, crisp crust; Cons—less tender and moist, may take longer. Use when brown, crisp crust is desired. Microwave oven: Pros—very tender and moist, may be quicker; Cons—no browning, no crisp crust, steamed texture. Use when browning and crust formation are not desired.
6. Muffin recipes and answers will vary.

SECTION
21-2

Objectives

After studying this section, you should be able to:

- Suggest several additions to quick breads that increase the nutritional value.
- Discuss the differences and similarities between the muffin method and the pastry and biscuit method of mixing.
- Describe the characteristics of properly mixed and baked muffins and biscuits.

Look for These Terms

cut in

rolled biscuits

drop biscuits

Quick Breads

As their name implies, quick breads are quick and easy to make. They don't require kneading, and most use baking powder as a leavening agent. Muffins, biscuits, pancakes, corn bread, and fruit breads are examples of quick breads.

Nutrients in Quick Breads

Quick breads can be a tasty way of getting some of the nutrients your body needs. They are good sources of carbohydrates, protein, B vitamins, and iron. Using whole grains adds fiber and trace minerals. Adding fruits, vegetables, and nuts packs in even more vitamins and minerals—as well as flavor and texture. Some quick breads are high in fat. By choosing wisely, however, you can use quick breads to add variety, flavor, and nutrition to your meals and snacks.

Muffins

Muffins are prepared using the *muffin method.* The most important part of this procedure is properly mixing the liquid and dry ingredients.

Muffin Method

Muffins that are properly mixed have a rounded, pebbly top with a coarse but tender texture inside. To mix ingredients for muffins:

1. *Sift* together or mix all dry ingredients (flour, sugar, baking powder, spices) in a large bowl. Using the back of a spoon, make a well in the center of the dry ingredients.

SECTION
21-2
Quick Breads

FOCUS

MOTIVATORS

- Display several pictures of quick breads, such as muffins, biscuits, pancakes, waffles, corn bread, and fruit bread. Ask students if they can identify each of the breads and tell what they have in common.
- Show students several variations of one type of quick bread, such as plain muffins, bran muffins, and banana muffins. Have students taste small samples of each and guess what changes were made to the recipe to make each variation.

VOCABULARY ACTIVITY

Pronounce the terms listed under "Look for These Terms." Have students find the terms and their definitions in the section.

STUDY SKILLS

- **Listening.** Invite a group of volunteers to each prepare an oral reading of a page of text from the section, while others follow along silently.
- Have students read the section and complete the appropriate part of the Chapter 21 Study Guide in the *Student Workbook*.

Section 21-2 Resources

◆ **Student Workbook,** pp. 153, 158
◆ **Teacher Resource Guide**
Lesson Plan 21-2 Organizer
Section 21-2 Quiz
◆ **Effective Instruction CD-ROM**
Exam*View*® *Test Generator*
PowerPoint® Slide #48
◆ **Transparency Package,** CT-48

◆ **Student Motivation Kit**
Reteaching Activities, p. 97
Enrichment Activities
Foods Lab Resources, pp. 16–17, 24–25, 121–122, 125–126
Food Science Resources, pp. 90–96

TEACH

• *Nutrients in Quick Breads (text pages 567-571)*

Brochure Development

Using a computer, students are to prepare an instructional brochure that lists steps in mixing muffins properly and outlines the following: (1) why it is important not to overmix the batter for muffins; (2) characteristics to look for when you check to see if muffins are done; (3) how to boost fiber and other nutrients in a muffin recipe. Suggest that students use illustrations in their brochures, where appropriate. L1

VISUAL LEARNING ***Using the Illustrations*** Have students copy the caption of the illustrations on page 568. Under each caption, students are to write why it's important to follow the step and what would happen if a step was omitted or not followed. Discuss students' responses.

Muffin Variations Activity

Have students identify ways to vary the flavor of muffins with different ingredients. Write a list of student suggestions on chart paper. Encourage one suggestion from each student.

◆ Quick breads, such as these muffins, can add nutrients and variety to meals. What are the common ingredients in quick breads?

2. *Beat* all liquid ingredients (eggs, milk or water, oil or melted fat, liquid flavorings) together in a small bowl until they are well blended.
3. *Pour* the liquid into the well you have made in the dry ingredients. Mix just enough to moisten the dry ingredients. A few floury spots can remain, and the batter should be lumpy.
4. *Fold* in such ingredients as chopped nuts and raisins with a gentle motion.

Take care not to overmix the batter. Overmixed muffins have peaks on top and are tough and heavy. The insides have long, narrow tunnels.

The Muffin Method

◆ Mix the dry ingredients and make a well in the center.

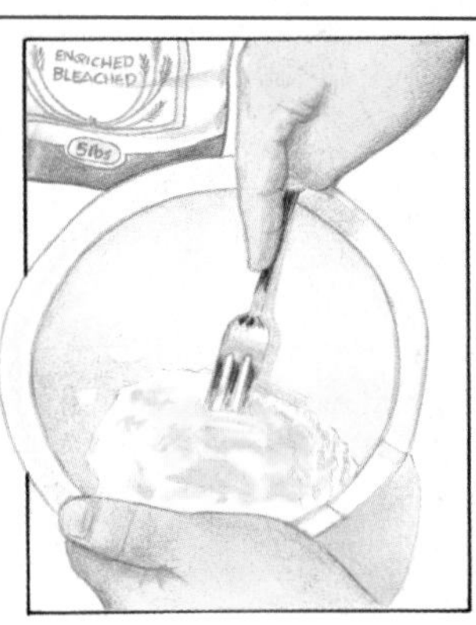

◆ Beat the liquid ingredients together.

◆ Add the liquids to the dry ingredients all at once. Stir briefly—do not overmix.

568 Chapter 21 ◆ Baking

Reinforcing Key Skills

Present the following problem to student groups. Allow time for them to discuss and compare their responses.

Communication—Kareem wants to include muffins in his lunches but doesn't know whether he should eliminate his sandwich or some other food that he normally eats. What would you tell Kareem? Explain your reaction.

Kinds of Muffins

The flavors of muffins can easily be varied with different ingredients. Fresh and dried fruits are often included. Try cranberries, blueberries, chopped dates, dried apricots, or your favorite combination. Muffin recipes may also include yogurt, tofu, shredded raw vegetables (zucchini or carrots), or cooked vegetables (such as sweet potatoes and winter squash). These ingredients add flavor as well as important nutrients. For a fiber boost, substitute ½ cup (125 mL) bran for an equal amount of flour in your muffin recipe.

◆ **Quick loaf breads have many of the same ingredients as muffins and use the same mixing method.** Name two foods that could be served with the loaf bread shown here.

Adding extra ingredients, such as fruit, to just any recipe may not work. Instead, start with a reliable recipe that already lists the ingredient you want.

Preparing and Baking Muffins

Instead of greasing muffin pans, you can line them with paper baking cups. Fill the cups only two-thirds full. If you add more than that, the batter will overflow and the muffins will have odd shapes.

When baking muffins, test them for doneness about 5 minutes before the end of the baking time. They are done when they are nicely browned. A wooden pick inserted in the center should come out clean. Muffins are best served warm.

Loaf Breads

Many quick loaf breads are mixed in the same manner as muffins. These simple cakelike breads even use many of the same basic ingredients. Cranberry-orange-nut bread is a holiday favorite. Other breads, including corn bread, are less sweet. Some loaf breads are flavored with vegetables and herbs.

Quick breads are generally baked in greased loaf pans. If the bread contains dried fruits and nuts, the bottom of the pan should be lined with parchment paper so that the loaf can be removed easily.

Check for doneness as you would with muffins. Don't be surprised if the top of the loaf cracks. That is typical for quick breads.

Biscuits

Biscuits are delicate, small breads. Properly made, they have a tender but crisp crust and are an even, light brown color. The inside is slightly moist and creamy white, and peels apart in tender layers.

There are two kinds of biscuits—rolled and drop. Both are made using the *pastry and biscuit method* of mixing.

- *Nutrients in Quick Breads (text pages 567-571)*

VISUAL LEARNING ***Using the Photograph*** Encourage students to suggest a variety of menus for meals that might include quick breads, such as muffins for breakfast or a carrot bread or other loaf bread as an accompaniment to a soup-and-salad lunch. Point out that quick breads can also be a dessert or snack. Have several volunteers write their meal plans on the board.

Lab Experiences

- Have a group of students demonstrate how to make muffins. Have students place half the muffin batter in greased muffin pans, the other half in paper baking cups. Have students demonstrate procedures for testing muffins for doneness. After students sample the products, lead a discussion on the advantages of each method.
- Have a group of students demonstrate how to make loaf breads. Have students grease one loaf pan and line another with parchment paper. Have students demonstrate how to check loaf breads for doneness. How did the different pan preparations affect the finished product? L1

FOOD SCIENCE **Cause of Tunnels in Muffins** Ask students if they can explain why overmixing muffins causes tunnels.

FOOD SCIENCE **Effects of Gluten Development Experiment** See the *Food Science Resources* booklet for the "Effect of Gluten Development on Muffins" teaching guidelines and student experiment worksheet. The experiment tests the effects of mixing methods on muffins.

- *Nutrients in Quick Breads (text pages 567-571)*

Listing Activity

Have students list all possible advantages of making biscuits ahead of time, freezing them, and re-heating them in the microwave oven. Discuss students' lists.

Lab Experience

Have students prepare biscuit dough to serve as a base for strawberry shortcake. Make sure each student has an opportunity to use a pastry blender. Have students bake the biscuits, cool them, and then split open a biscuit and top it with frozen, thawed strawberries for each serving. Conclude by asking what other fruits could be used to make shortcake. What toppings could be used in place of conventional whipped cream for a different taste and to reduce the fat content? L1

Food Design

Tell students that biscuits can be used in many creative ways. Have students brainstorm to develop the most creative food idea for using a biscuit. Have them draw their creation, name it, and present their idea to the class. (Possibilities might include a stuffed pizza biscuit or a banana split biscuit.) L1

◆ A pastry blender is a tool designed for cutting fat into flour. **Why is this tool preferable to using the hands when making baked goods?**

Pastry and Biscuit Method

In the pastry and biscuit method, the fat is cut into the flour. To **cut in** means to mix solid fat and flour using a pastry blender or two knives and a cutting motion. This technique leaves the fat in fine particles in the dough. During baking, the fat melts between layers of flour, giving a flaky texture.

Handle the dough as little as possible. If the shortening and flour are overmixed, the texture will be mealy, not flaky. Mixing ingredients for biscuits is easy.

1. Sift together or mix the dry ingredients in a large bowl.
2. Cut the shortening into the flour until the particles are the size of peas or coarse bread crumbs.
3. Make a well in the center of the dry ingredients, as in the muffin method, and add the liquids. Stir just until the ingredients are blended and form a soft dough.

Rolled Biscuits

Once you have mixed the dough, you can proceed with your recipe for either rolled or drop biscuits. **Rolled biscuits** are made by rolling out dough to an even thickness and cutting it with a biscuit cutter. If you don't have a biscuit cutter, you can use the rim of a water glass.

Begin by turning the dough out on a lightly floured board and kneading about ten strokes. Knead as much as possible with the tips of your fingers, since warmth from your hands may melt the shortening, causing the biscuits to be tough. Overkneading results in tough, compact biscuits.

Next, roll the dough out to a uniform thickness of about ½ inch (1.3 cm). Cut the biscuits out with a biscuit cutter that is lightly dusted with flour. Press the cutter straight down so that the biscuits have straight sides and even shapes. Do not twist the cutter. Otherwise, the dough might tear. You can reroll any leftover dough to make more biscuits.

Place the biscuits on an ungreased baking sheet, about 1 inch (2.5 cm) apart. Bake according to recipe directions.

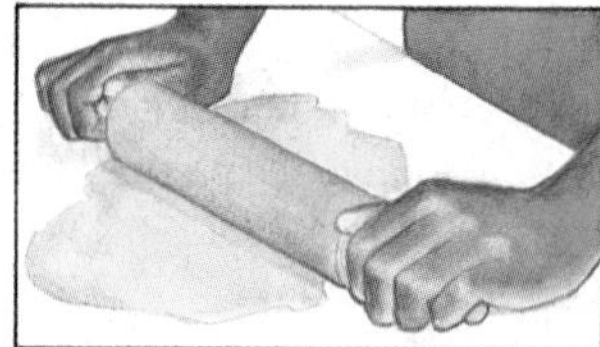

◆ For rolled biscuits, roll the kneaded dough out to an even thickness.

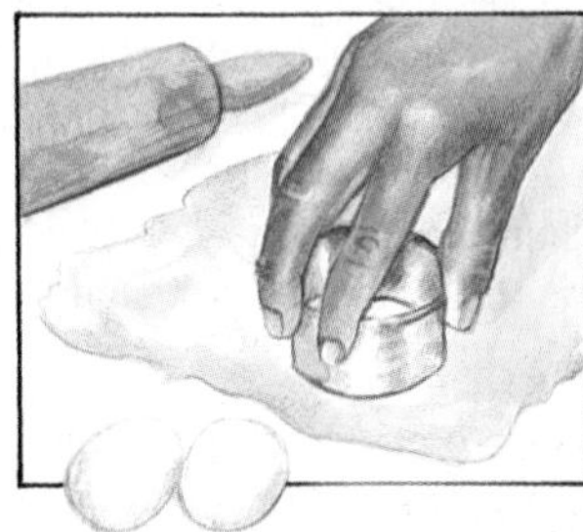

◆ Cut the biscuits out, being careful not to pull or tear the dough.

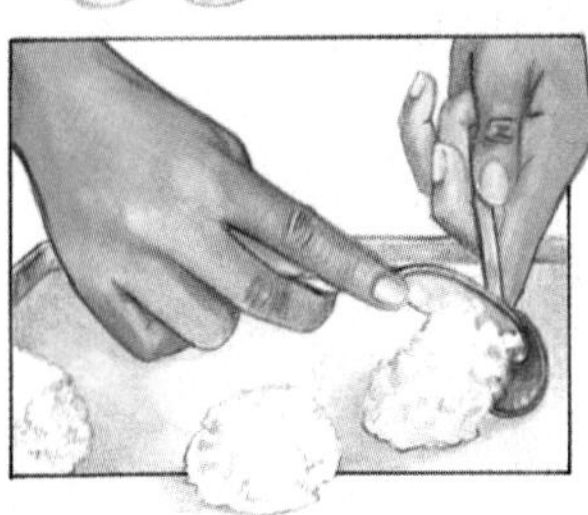

◆ For drop biscuits, just drop the batter from a spoon in mounds onto a greased cookie sheet. **How are rolled biscuits and drop biscuits similar? How are they different?**

FOOD SCIENCE: Types of Leavening for Biscuits

Have students experiment with different types of leavening using a basic rolled biscuit recipe. Variations might include baking powder, baking soda and buttermilk or sour milk, and baking soda and cream of tartar. Ask students to evaluate the results. How did the biscuits compare in flavor, texture, and color?

Drop Biscuits

Drop biscuits are made by dropping dough from a spoon. Since they contain more liquid than rolled biscuits, the batter is too sticky to roll. Although these biscuits have irregular shapes, they are just as flavorful and flaky as the rolled variety.

Mix the batter for drop biscuits using the same method as for rolled biscuits. Drop the batter in mounds on a greased cookie sheet about 1 inch (2.5 cm) apart. Bake according to recipe directions. You can also spoon drop biscuits onto a casserole as a topping.

Serving Biscuits

Biscuits are delicious when they are eaten warm, right out of the oven. Serve them with meals, or use them for sandwiches. For variety, they can be topped with gravy or sweet fruit and cream. Biscuits can be made ahead of time, frozen, and then reheated in the microwave oven.

◆ **Biscuits and muffins are usually served fresh from the oven or reheated. Which skill for food choices is used when planning hot biscuits as part of a meal?**

Section 21-2 Review & Activities

1. List five ingredients you can add to quick breads to increase the nutritional value.
2. Name two ways that the muffin method and pastry and biscuit method of mixing are similar. In what two ways are these methods different?
3. Describe the characteristics of a well-made muffin after baking.
4. **Evaluating.** Josh enjoys eating a variety of sandwiches made on biscuits. He has come up with the idea of baking the sandwich ingredients right in. Tell whether you think Josh's recipe is likely to succeed, giving reasons for your answer.
5. **Synthesizing.** Brainstorm ways that you can use quick breads to add variety to meals.
6. **Applying.** Find three recipes for quick breads. Identify the mixing method used in each.

ASSESS

REVIEW

- Ask students to summarize the main ideas in this section.
- Have students complete the Section Review. (Answers appear below.)

EVALUATION

- Have students prepare a quick bread according to a recipe you provide. Evaluate student procedures and results.
- Have students take the quiz for Section 21-2. (Use the quiz in the *Teacher Resource Guide,* or construct your own with the **Exam***View*® *Test Generator* on the *Effective Instruction CD-ROM.*)

RETEACHING

- Ask students to prepare posters showing the steps used to make rolled biscuits.
- Refer to the *Reteaching Activities* booklet for the Section 21-2 activity sheet.

CLOSE

Have students develop a one-day meal plan for themselves that includes a muffin, biscuit, and a slice of quick bread. Then have a few student volunteers write their menus on the board while you lead a class discussion about quick breads and how they can be used to help create a well-rounded meal.

Answers to Section 21-2 Review & Activities

1. Any five: Fruits, nuts, yogurt, sour cream, tofu, raw vegetables, cooked vegetables, bran.
2. Answers will vary. Similar: All dry ingredients are mixed together first. Liquid ingredients are all added in a well in dry ingredients. Different: Shortening is cut into flour for biscuits. Muffin batter is lumpy.
3. Nicely browned, with a rounded, pebbly top, and coarse but tender interior.
4. Answers will vary. The type of filling is a factor.
5. Answers will vary. Add variety of color, flavor, and texture; have a variety of uses.
6. Recipes and mixing methods will vary.

Recipe File

Low-Fat Cinnamon-Oatmeal Muffins

This recipe uses the muffin method technique. Prior to assigning the lab, you may suggest students review the section, "Muffin Method," on pages 567-568.

Using the Recipe

- Have students read the recipe and discuss each step.
- Remind students of the importance of not overmixing the batter.
- Review safety and sanitation procedures that apply to this recipe.
- Have each lab team fill out a work plan. (See the *Foods Lab Resources* booklet.)
- Have students check off the ingredients and equipment listed on the recipe worksheet and prepare the recipe.
- Have students complete the evaluation and questions on the recipe worksheet.

SEE ALSO...
The *Foods Lab Resources* booklet for the "Low-Fat Cinnamon-Oatmeal Muffins" recipe worksheet and other recipe alternatives.

Recipe File

Low-Fat Cinnamon-Oatmeal Muffins

Try serving these muffins with a fruit salad or use them as the bread in a sandwich.

Customary	*Ingredients*	*Metric*
¾ cup	Whole-wheat flour	175 mL
¾ cup	All-purpose flour	175 mL
1 cup	Uncooked rolled oats	250 mL
1 Tbsp.	Baking powder	15 mL
3 Tbsp.	Sugar	45 mL
½ tsp.	Ground cinnamon	3 mL
¼ tsp.	Salt	1 mL
1	Egg	1
1 cup	Fat-free milk	250 mL
¼ cup	Applesauce	50 mL

Yield: 12 muffins
Equipment: Muffin pan(s)
Temperature: 400°F (200°C)

Directions

1. Preheat oven.
2. Grease and flour muffin pan(s).
3. In a large bowl, combine flours, oats, baking powder, sugar, cinnamon, and salt. Mix well.
4. In a separate bowl, beat the egg.
5. Add milk and applesauce to egg. Stir well.
6. Add liquid mixture to flour mixture and stir until dry ingredients are just moistened. Do not overmix. (Batter should be lumpy.)
7. Fill muffin cups ⅔ full.
8. Bake 15 to 20 minutes or until a wooden pick inserted in the center comes out clean.

Nutrition Information

Per serving (approximate–per muffin):107 calories, 4 g protein, 21 g carbohydrate, 1 g fat, 18 mg cholesterol, 143 mg sodium
Good source of: B vitamins, phosphorus

Food for Thought

- What would happen if the muffin batter was mixed until no lumps remained?
- Why are the muffin cups filled only two-thirds full?

Answers to Food for Thought

1. Overmixed muffins will have peaks on the tops and be tough and heavy. The inside will have long, narrow tunnels.
2. If you add more than that, the batter will overflow and the muffins will have odd shapes.

SECTION 21-3

Objectives

After studying this section, you should be able to:

- Identify ways to simplify bread making.
- Describe the procedure for making yeast breads.
- Explain how to tell when yeast breads are done baking.

Look for This Term

quick-mix method

Yeast Breads and Rolls

Do you have a sandwich for lunch most days? If you do, it is probably made with a yeast bread. True to their name, yeast breads use yeast for leavening. The yeast also gives the bread a characteristic flavor and contributes to the wonderful aroma while the bread is baking.

Yeast Bread

Many people believe that bread baking is too time-consuming to fit in with today's fast-paced lifestyles. With a little organization, however, bread baking can be part of regular food preparation. Making yeast dough is a flexible process. The tasks can be timed to fit into the cook's schedule.

Time-Savers

Several appliances can help speed up the bread-making process. A microwave oven can be used to heat the liquid before adding it to the yeast, to bring refrigerated ingredients to room temperature, and to let the dough rise. Check the owner's manual for specific directions, which will vary depending on the oven's power and controls.

A heavy-duty mixer with a dough hook or a powerful food processor can be used to mix yeast dough quickly. These appliances will knead it in about 6 minutes compared with the 8 or 10 minutes required to knead it by hand. Bread machines will mix, knead, and bake yeast breads. They can be set to have bread baked in time for a meal.

◆ **As different as these breads appear, all use yeast for leavening. Do you know the name of the gas produced by yeast that causes breads like these to rise?**

SECTION 21-3

Yeast Breads and Rolls

FOCUS

MOTIVATORS

- Display several pictures or samples of yeast breads, such as white bread, sweet white bread, whole grain bread, batter bread, sourdough bread, rolls, and croissants. Ask students if they can identify each of the breads and tell what they have in common.
- Have students create a bulletin board showing some of the ways yeast dough can be shaped. You might select a few students to draw shapes as the rest of the students call out the shapes.

VOCABULARY ACTIVITY

Pronounce the term listed under "Look for This Term." Have students find the term and its definition in the section.

STUDY SKILLS

- **Outlining.** Have students read the section and outline it by copying the headers on paper and leaving space after each one. Students are to write a sentence in their own words, summarizing the content under each header.
- Have students read the section and complete the appropriate part of the Chapter 21 Study Guide in the *Student Workbook*.

Section 21-3 Resources

◆ **Student Workbook,** pp. 154, 159
◆ **Teacher Resource Guide**
Lesson Plan 21-3 Organizer
Section 21-3 Quiz
◆ **Effective Instruction CD-ROM**
Exam*View*® *Test Generator*
PowerPoint® Slide #48
◆ **Transparency Package,** CT-48

◆ **Student Motivation Kit**
Reteaching Activities, p. 98
Enrichment Activities
Foods Lab Resources, pp. 18, 26, 119–120
Food Science Resources, pp. 97–100

TEACH

- *Yeast Bread (text pages 573-574)*

Discussion Activity

Ask students to name three ways to use a microwave oven to speed tasks associated with making yeast bread. Ask how long yeast bread should be kneaded.

Studying Documentation

Ask students to read manufacturer's materials or instruction booklets to find out how automatic bread makers and similar appliances work. Have them write a report of their findings. Alternatively, have students research appliances currently available in the class foods lab or in their home kitchens for bread making. Have them write a comparison of the advantages and disadvantages of making yeast bread in a bread maker versus by hand. Have students report their findings to the class. L1

Demonstration

Demonstrate how to use the microwave oven and heavy-duty mixer with a dough hook to speed up breadmaking. Suggest students take notes about the demonstration.

Techniques in Making Yeast Breads

There are five important techniques that should be used when making yeast breads.

Look and Learn:

For each of the techniques shown, what would happen if it was not used properly?

Use a thermometer to check the temperature of the liquids.

After mixing the liquid and dry ingredients, use a spoon to beat in the additional flour. The amount needed will vary. It depends on the moisture content of the flour and even the humidity in the air that day.

Yeast goes to work during the rising time. Cover the dough to keep it from drying out.

Gently "punching" the dough after the first rising eliminates excess gas bubbles.

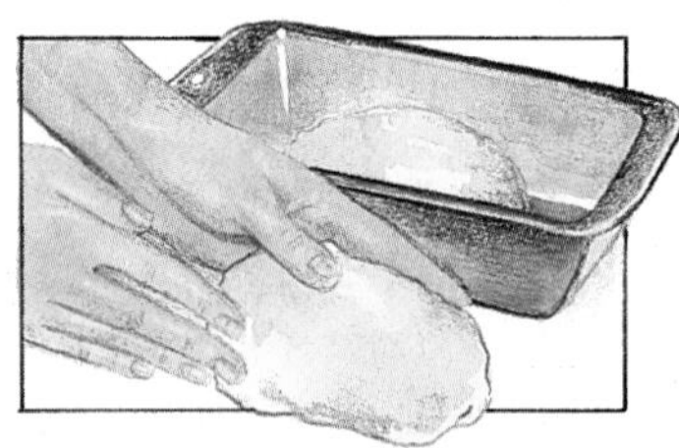

After shaping, bread dough is allowed to rise a final time in the pan.

FOOD SCIENCE

Yeast Experiment Have groups of students each prepare a small-necked bottle with varying amounts and kinds of yeast, water of varying amounts and temperature, and added ingredients, such as sugar and salt. Put a balloon over the mouth of the bottle and tie it with string. Note results at varying time intervals. Have students suggest reasons for variations in results.

Making Bread and Rolls

Yeast bread and rolls are both made by using the same simple five-step procedure. The steps include mixing the dough, kneading it, letting it rise, shaping it, and, finally, baking it.

Mixing the Dough

Most yeast breads are a simple mixture of flour, salt, sugar, liquid, fat, and yeast. Sugar provides food for the yeast so that it will grow. Salt controls the action of the yeast. Consult a recipe for the exact ingredients and amounts.

Although bread flour is ideal, most recipes for homemade bread call for all-purpose flour. It is more readily available than bread flour and makes a loaf with good texture. To add fiber and nutrients to recipes calling for all-purpose flour, substitute whole-grain flour for two-thirds of the total flour in the recipe. Keep amounts of other ingredients the same.

Before you begin, be sure the ingredients are at room temperature and the liquid is heated to the right temperature. Yeast will not grow if the liquid is too cold and will die if the liquid is too hot. When yeast is added to liquid at the proper temperature, the mixture becomes cloudy and begins to form a foamy layer within minutes.

Quick-Mix Method

The **quick-mix method** is a bread-making method that combines active dry yeast with the dry ingredients. A standard mixer will work for the first part of the mixing until the dough thickens and becomes too heavy for it. Beat the rest of the flour in with a wooden spoon.

1. Combine part of the flour with the undissolved active dry yeast, sugar, and salt in a large bowl.
2. Heat the liquid and fat to between 120°F and 130°F (49°C to 55°C).
3. Add the liquid to the dry ingredients, beating them with a mixer until they are well blended. At this point, the gluten is beginning to develop.
4. Beat in enough of the remaining flour to make the kind of dough specified in the recipe. You may need more or less flour than the recipe calls for. Some kinds absorb more liquid than others.

Kneading the Dough

Turn the dough out on a lightly floured surface. Knead the dough until it becomes a smooth, shiny ball, about 8 to 10 minutes. Use just enough flour to keep the dough from sticking to the work surface or to your hands. Too much flour will give a tough texture.

Don't be concerned if bubbles develop in the dough. They are a clue that gluten is developing. The cell walls are becoming elastic and expanding with carbon dioxide given off by the yeast.

Letting the Dough Rise

Shape the dough into a ball, and place it in a well-oiled bowl. Turn the ball in the bowl so that all sides are coated with oil. Place a piece of plastic wrap over the top of the dough to keep it from drying out; then cover the bowl with a clean dish towel. Set the bowl in a warm (not hot), draft-free place for about 1 to 1½ hours. The dough should rise to double its original size. Bread dough made with whole-grain flour will take longer to rise.

Once it has risen, punch the dough down by *gently* pressing your fist into the center. Gently pull the dough from the sides of the bowl toward the middle. These actions will eliminate the largest air bubbles.

- *Making Bread and Rolls (text pages 575-576)*

Taste Test

Ask volunteers to bring to class homemade or commercially prepared bread—white, whole wheat, or another type. Have students compare the taste of homemade yeast breads with commercially prepared yeast breads. Consider cost, nutrition, flavor, and texture. Ask: Which has the most fiber? Does flavor correlate with fiber? **L1**

Recipe Comparisons

Ask students to find recipes for making yeast bread and rolls. Have students compare the steps for making yeast bread and rolls. Based on these recipes, have students make a list of tips for success and a list of basic steps. **L1**

Lab Experience

Have students use store-bought refrigerated dough (such as crescent roll dough) to practice shaping breads and rolls. How many different shapes did students create? Have students share and compare shape ideas. **L1**

Extending Learning

Kneading Dough—Kneading affects the molecular structure of yeast dough, changing its texture and appearance. When the dough is first mixed, the protein molecules are long and coiled, forming a mass. As the dough is kneaded, the molecules begin to line up in a more orderly fashion. Coiled gluten molecules unwind and form layers in the dough. This firms the dough, giving it a satin-like surface.

Overkneading can break down the protein structure, and the dough will not rise properly.

ASSESS

REVIEW

- Ask students to summarize the main ideas in this section.
- Have students complete the Section Review. (Answers appear below.)

EVALUATION

- Provide a recipe for yeast bread and have students make the bread. Evaluate procedure and result.
- Have students take the quiz for Section 21-3. (Use the quiz in the *Teacher Resource Guide,* or construct your own with the **Exam***View*® *Test Generator* on the *Effective Instruction CD-ROM.*)

RETEACHING

- Demonstrate steps in making yeast bread. Have students observe the size, shape, and texture of the dough at each step.
- Refer to the *Reteaching Activities* booklet for the Section 21-3 activity sheet.

CLOSE

Have students complete the following sentence: "Even though I lead a busy life, I still can make yeast breads because _____." Discuss students' responses.

When the ball has doubled in size, the dough is ready for the fourth stage—shaping. To determine whether the dough is ready, push two fingers gently into the surface. If the finger indentations remain, the dough is ready to shape. If you aren't ready to shape the dough, you can let it rise again. You can also cover it and refrigerate it overnight. It will rise in the refrigerator and be ready to shape the next day.

◆ **Yeast dough can be shaped in many creative ways, such as this braided ring. What precautions do you think the baker took to ensure the evenly browned crust on this product?**

Shaping the Dough

Shape the dough into loaves or rolls, according to recipe directions. Use kitchen scissors or a sharp knife to cut the dough into pieces. Don't pull it apart. Place it in a greased pan or on a baking sheet. Cover and let the shaped dough rise again until it doubles in size.

Baking

Since baking times vary considerably, always bake as directed in the recipe. Bread and rolls have a nicely browned crust when done baking. Check loaves for doneness by tapping them with your finger. If they sound hollow, they are done.

Remove the bread or rolls from the pans, and place them immediately on a wire cooling rack. The rack prevents moisture from forming on the bottom crust and making it soggy. Let loaves stand about 20 minutes for easier cutting.

Section 21-3 Review & Activities

1. What appliances can help speed up the bread-making process? How do they save time?

2. What happens if the liquids in yeast breads are too hot or too cool?

3. How can you tell if dough is ready to shape and bake? How can you tell if a loaf of bread is done baking?

4. Extending. Why do you think dough should be cut, rather than pulled apart, to be shaped into rolls?

5. Comparing and Contrasting. Discuss the pros and cons of making yeast breads by hand versus using an automatic bread machine or commercial frozen bread dough.

6. Applying. Using cookbooks or other references, describe at least five different ways of shaping yeast breads other than in a loaf.

Answers to Section 21-3 Review & Activities

1. See page 573.
2. The yeast will not grow if the temperature is too cold; if the liquid is too hot, it will kill the yeast.
3. See pupil text above.
4. To prevent adverse shape characteristics.
5. Answers will vary. By hand—Cons: Longer preparation time, more possibility of mixing errors; Pros: Enjoyable, more control over process. Not by hand—Cons: Costlier, no creativity; Pros: More uniform dough, prevents mixing errors, saves time.
6. Answers will vary. Shapes can include braid, single or double knot, figure-eight, cloverleaf, wreath, and spiral.

RECIPE FILE

Honey Whole Wheat Bread

There is nothing like the aroma of freshly baked bread. The flavor is equally hard to beat, especially when the bread is served warm from the oven.

Customary	Ingredients	Metric	Customary	Ingredients	Metric
2½ to 3 cups	All-purpose flour	625 to 750 mL	1 cup	Fat-free milk	250 mL
3 cups	Whole wheat flour	750 mL	1 cup	Water	250 mL
2 tsp.	Salt	10 mL	¼ cup	Honey	50 mL
1 pkg.	Active dry yeast	1 pkg.	3 Tbsp.	Shortening	45 mL

Yield: 2 loaves
Equipment: Small saucepan; two 9 × 5 × 3 inch (23 × 3 × 8 cm) loaf pans
Oven Temperature: 400°F (200°C)

Directions

1. Mix 1 cup (250 mL) of each flour with salt and yeast in a large bowl. Set aside.
2. Combine milk, water, honey, and shortening in a small saucepan. Heat over low heat until warm, about 120°F (49°C). Shortening does not have to melt.
3. Add the heated liquid to the dry ingredients. Blend at low speed with a mixer about 2 minutes.
4. Add another ½ cup (125 mL) of each flour. Beat about 2 minutes at medium speed.
5. Stir in ¾ cup (175 mL) all-purpose flour and 1½ cups (375 mL) whole wheat flour with a wooden spoon until the mixture forms a soft dough. If necessary, add more all-purpose flour.
6. Place the dough on a lightly floured surface. Knead for 8 to 10 minutes until smooth and elastic.
7. Place the dough in a large, well-oiled bowl. Turn the dough to coat on all sides. Cover the dough with a piece of plastic wrap, and cover the bowl with a clean dish towel. Refrigerate overnight.
8. The next day, remove the dough from the refrigerator. Gently punch the dough down.
9. Turn the dough onto a lightly floured surface. Allow the dough to rest 10 to 15 minutes.
10. Divide the dough into two equal portions. Shape each portion into a loaf, and place each loaf in a well-greased loaf pan.
11. Cover the loaves with a clean dish towel, and allow them to rise in a warm place until double in size—about 1 hour, or until finger indentations remain.
12. Preheat the oven to 400°F (200°C). Bake the loaves for 25 to 30 minutes or until done.
13. Remove loaves from pans, and cool on a wire rack away from drafts.

Nutrition Information

Per serving (approximate–1/20 of loaf): 75 calories, 2 g protein, 14 g carbohydrate, 1 g fat, 0 mg cholesterol, 111 mg sodium
Good source of: B vitamins

Food for Thought

- Why do you suppose the flour is added a little at a time rather than all at once?
- What flavor does the honey impart to the loaf? What difference, if any, do you think would result if you used sugar instead? If you used molasses?

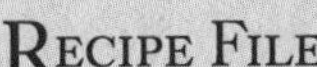

RECIPE FILE

Honey Whole Wheat Bread

This recipe uses the quick-mix method.

USING THE RECIPE

- Have students read the recipe and discuss each step.
- Review safety and sanitation procedures that apply to this recipe.
- Caution students to follow the directions carefully so that they don't accidentally miss a step. It is very important that the steps be done in the correct order when making bread.
- Have each lab team fill out a work plan. (See the *Foods Lab Resources* booklet.)
- Have students check off the ingredients and equipment listed on the recipe worksheet and prepare the recipe.
- Have students complete the evaluation and questions on the recipe worksheet.

SEE ALSO. . .
The *Foods Lab Resources* booklet for the "Honey Whole Wheat Bread" recipe worksheet and other recipe alternatives.

Answers to Food for Thought

1. Some types of flour absorb more liquid than others, so it's added a little at a time to prevent adding too much flour.
2. Sweet flavor; no significant difference when using sugar; molasses would create a pleasant, but slightly bitter, molasses-like flavor and darker color.

SECTION

21-4

Cakes, Cookies, and Pies

FOCUS

MOTIVATORS

- Write the word *cookie* on the board. Have students quickly name the flavors the word by itself conjures up. Do the same with the words *cake* and *pie*. Do students name the same kinds of cookies, cakes, and pies? Ask students to make generalizations about favorite baked desserts.
- Discuss with students the cookies, cakes, and pies they associate with holidays and special occasions. Have them include descriptions of their favorites.

VOCABULARY ACTIVITY

Pronounce the terms listed under "Look for These Terms." Have students find the terms and their definitions in the section. Ask a volunteer to look up the verb *shorten* in the dictionary and read aloud the definition that applies to baking.

STUDY SKILLS

- **Note Taking.** Have students read the section independently. While they are reading, they are to take notes, in their own words, on the important points within each heading.
- Have students read the section and complete the appropriate part of the Chapter 21 Study Guide in the *Student Workbook*.

SECTION 21-4

Cakes, Cookies, and Pies

Who doesn't like freshly baked cookies or a warm slice of homemade pie? Cakes, cookies, and pies are among the most popular baked goods. Unfortunately, treats like these are also traditionally high in fat, sugar, and calories. In this section, you will learn ways of eating your cake and having good nutrition, too.

Objectives

After studying this section, you should be able to:

- Describe types of cakes, cookies, and pies.
- Give guidelines for preparing cakes, cookies, and pies.
- Identify ways of reducing fat in cakes, drop cookies, and piecrust.

Look for These Terms

shortened cakes

foam cakes

Cakes

Although cakes are easy to make, accurately measuring ingredients is essential for good results.

Some cake recipes call for cake flour, which is low in gluten. If you do not have cake flour, substitute all-purpose flour, using 1 cup (250 mL) minus 2 tablespoons (30 mL) for each 1 cup of cake flour called for in the recipe.

There are two basic kinds of cakes—shortened cakes and foam cakes.

◆ **Treats like this, though tempting, are high in fat, sugar, and calories. Can desserts like these be part of a healthful eating plan? Explain.**

Section 21-4 Resources

◆ **Student Workbook,** pp. 154, 161
◆ **Teacher Resource Guide**
Lesson Plan 21-4 Organizer
Section 21-4 Quiz
Chapter 21 Test
◆ **Effective Instruction CD-ROM**
Exam*View*® *Test Generator*
PowerPoint® Slide #49
◆ **Transparency Package,** CT-49

◆ **Student Motivation Kit**
Reteaching Activities, p. 99
Enrichment Activities
Foods Lab Resources, pp. 19–23, 27–30, 123–124, 127–134
Food Science Resources, pp. 56–58, 104–107, 116–120

◆ **The one-bowl method saves time because there are fewer steps in mixing. How else might this method save time and personal energy?**

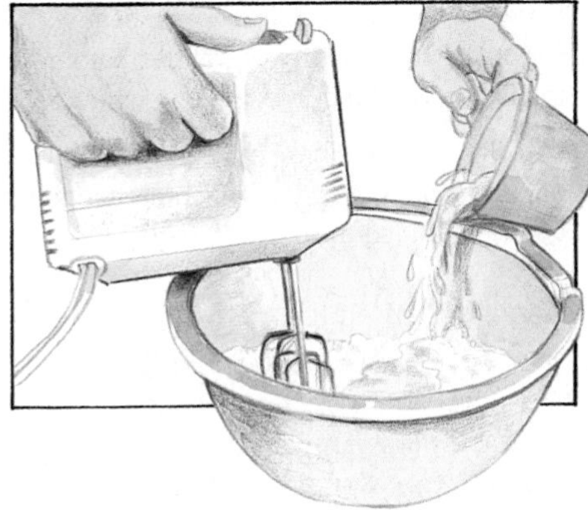

Shortened Cakes

Shortened cakes are usually made with a solid fat, though oil can also be used. The fat, which makes the cake rich and tender, is most often shortening, butter, or margarine. Shortened cakes can be made in a variety of flavors, including chocolate, lemon, and spice. Some contain chopped nuts or dried fruit.

Standard Mixing Method

Several methods can be used for mixing cakes. The most common for shortened cakes is the *standard method.* An electric mixer is helpful for creaming and beating the ingredients.

1. *Cream* the solid fat and sugar until the mixture is light and fluffy, as in whipped cream.
2. *Beat* the eggs into the mixture thoroughly, usually one at a time.
3. *Sift* the dry ingredients together.
4. *Mix* the liquids together.
5. *Add* the dry ingredients to the creamed mixture alternately with the liquid. Begin and end with the dry ingredients. This helps keep the fat from separating, which could affect the texture. Add the dry ingredients in fourths and the liquids in thirds. After each addition, beat the batter just enough to mix the ingredients.

One-Bowl Method

An alternative to the standard method for mixing shortened cakes is the *one-bowl method.* In this method, the dry ingredients are first combined by sifting and mixing. Solid fat, liquids, and flavorings are added and beaten with dry ingredients until well blended. The eggs are beaten in last.

Baking Shortened Cakes

You can bake shortened cakes in pans of many shapes and sizes, from individual cupcakes in muffin pans to large sheet cakes. Fancy molds can turn ordinary cakes into a masterpiece.

To check a shortened cake for doneness, insert a wooden pick in the center. If it comes out free of wet batter, the cake is done.

A shortened cake should have a slightly rounded top with a tender, shiny crust. When the cake is cut, it should have a fine, even grain and be moist and tender.

Foam Cakes

Foam cakes are cakes that are leavened with beaten egg whites, which give them a light, airy texture. Some foam cake recipes call for baking powder as well. Examples of foam cakes include:

- **Angel food cakes.** These cakes use only beaten egg whites for leavening. Because they contain neither egg yolks nor fat, they are good choices for low-fat desserts.

TEACH

- *Cakes (text pages 578-580)*

Discussion Activity

Have students write responses to the following: (1) Name the two basic types of cakes and list the characteristics of each. (2) Describe the standard method for mixing cakes. (3) Explain how to test a shortened cake and a foam cake for doneness. Allow students to read aloud their responses to initiate a discussion of these topics.

Recipe Idea Development

Ask students to develop and record ideas for lower calorie or nutrient-dense alternatives to traditional high-caloric frostings for cakes. Have students share and compare their ideas. L1

Fact Finding

Ask students to use either library resources or the Internet to research fun facts about cakes. Have them each create a list of at least 10 facts, such as the size of the largest cake ever made. Ask the following questions: What is the most popular cake flavor? What is a "cake walk"? Where did the expression "let them eat cake" originate? The expression "piece of cake"? What is the history of the "birthday cake"? L2

FOOD SCIENCE: Leavening Experiment

See the *Food Science Resources* booklet for the "How Do Shortened Cakes Rise?" teaching guidelines and student experiment worksheet. The experiment tests the effects of leavening agents on the appearance, texture, and flavor of shortened cakes.

TEACH cont.

- *Cakes (text pages 578-580)*

Recipe Comparison Activity

Provide students with a variety of recipes for shortened and foam cakes. Have students work in groups to separate recipes according to type and the mixing technique used. Read the descriptions for the standard and foam methods for mixing cakes. Have students check their recipes to see if they correctly categorized each recipe.

Brainstorm Activity

Some one-piece tube pans have fluted bottoms. Ask students to brainstorm ways to make it easier to remove the cake from this type of pan.

Lab Experience

Have students prepare shortened and foam cakes. Remind students that pan shape, size, and composition will affect baking time. Have students check the cakes for doneness using the appropriate technique. Have students evaluate the results according to shape, crust, grain, moistness, and tenderness. Conclude by leading a discussion on the similarities and differences between shortened and foam cakes. L1

- **Sponge cakes.** In these cakes, beaten egg yolks are added to the batter before the batter is folded into the egg whites.
- **Chiffon cakes.** These cakes include yolks, oil, and baking powder, which are blended and then folded into beaten egg whites.

Baking Foam Cakes

Foam cakes must be baked in ungreased pans. As the batter rises during baking, it clings to the sides of a pan. If the pan were greased, the cake would not be able to rise.

A tube pan is often used for foam cakes. If the pan is in only one piece, line the bottom with parchment paper so that the cake can be easily removed.

To test a foam cake for doneness, touch the top lightly. It should spring back.

Foam cakes are generally cooled upside down in the pan to keep them from losing volume or from falling. If the tube pan does not have legs to support it upside down, use an empty glass bottle with a slender neck or a large metal funnel turned upside down. Invert the tube pan over the neck of the bottle or funnel.

When the cake is cool, gently loosen the cake from the sides with a spatula. Turn the pan upside down to remove the cake. If the pan is in two parts and has a removable bottom, use a spatula to loosen the cake from the bottom.

Decorating Cakes

Cakes are often frosted. Since frostings are usually high in fat, sugar, and calories, you may want to try one of these alternatives:

- Make a glaze with confectioners' sugar and lemon, orange, or pineapple juice. Drizzle it over the cake, letting it flow down the sides. For added eye appeal, garnish with fruit twists.
- Sift a little confectioners' sugar over the top of the cake. Try putting a cutout paper design, such as a snowflake, on top before sifting the sugar.

Another low-fat option is to skip the icing and serve the cake with fresh or frozen fruit.

Foam cakes like these have a light texture and airy quality. What ingredient is responsible for these properties?

FOOD SCIENCE

Cooked Frosting The success of cooked frosting depends on achieving the right concentration of sugar and water. Concentration is related to the temperature at which a sugar-water solution will boil: the higher the concentration, the higher the boiling point. Emphasize to students that the accurate use of a candy thermometer when making cooked frosting will help ensure success.

◆ **These simple cake toppings are both easy to make and easy on the eye. Identify an advantage from a nutrition standpoint of these cakes over ones with frosting.**

Cookies

Cookies are easy to prepare. Many people consider homemade cookies well worth the time and effort they require. The main difference between cakes and cookies is that cookies have little, if any, liquid. This gives cookies a heavier texture than cakes.

Kinds of Cookies

Cookies vary in texture from soft to crisp. They can be made in assorted shapes and sizes, and can be decorated in many ways.

The thousands of cookie varieties can be divided into six basic kinds:

- ◆ **Bar cookies.** Are baked in square or rectangular pans and then cut into bars, squares, or diamonds. They can be made from a batter or a soft dough that is pressed into a pan. Textures vary from cakelike to chewy. Brownies are one popular example of bar cookies. Usually, bars are cooled in the pan and then cut.
- ◆ **Drop cookies.** Are made from a soft dough that is dropped from a teaspoon onto cookie sheets. During baking, the dough spreads out to make a thick cookie. Remember to allow enough space between cookies (about 2 inches [5 cm]) so that they can spread without touching. Most chocolate chip cookies are drop cookies. For reduced-fat drop cookies, replace some or all of the fat with applesauce, mashed bananas, puréed fruits, or canned pumpkin.

◆ **There are nearly as many methods for making cookies as there are flavors. Which type of cookies are the teens in the picture making?**

- *Cookies (text pages 581-582)*

Categorizing Activity

Ask students to turn a sheet of paper sideways and divide the sheet into six columns. At the top of each column, students are to list one of the six basic types of cookie. Then, using recipe resources, students are to copy names of recipes that fit into each of the cookie categories. Which category has the most recipes? The least?

Product Evaluation

Working in lab groups, students are to prepare and evaluate four types of chocolate chip cookies: ready-made, refrigerated dough, packaged mix, and homemade. Ask students to compare cost, preparation time, taste, texture, and appearance. Have the class discuss their findings in a round-table forum. **L1**

Recipe Development Activity

Using a popular chocolate chip cookie recipe, work together as a class to create versions of the recipe that are lower in fat and higher in micronutrients (for example, calcium). Discuss specifically how the recipes are more nutrient-dense. If time allows, prepare one of these more nutrient-dense versions.

Reinforcing Key Skills

Present the following problems to student groups. Allow time for them to discuss and compare their responses.

Management—Have students imagine they are making a batch of oatmeal drop cookies. When they take the first pan from the oven, the cookies have flattened and run together. What should they do before baking the rest of the cookies?

Communication—Danielle loves to make homemade cookies, but she needs time-saving tips. What might you recommend to her?

TEACH cont.

- *Cookies (text pages 581-582)*

Writing

Legend has it that cookies originated centuries ago when ovens had no thermostats and bakers baked by guesswork. To test the oven temperature, they put small amounts of cake batter on baking sheets. They could judge the oven temperature by the way the small cakes baked. Much to their surprise, the little cakes became popular. Ask students to research the history of cookies and write a colorful, nonfiction account of their findings. **L2**

Lab Experience

Have students make various kinds of cookies. Serve the cookies at a school function. **L1**

USING Safety Check

Using recipe resources, ask students to tally the number of cookie recipes that contain raw eggs, including those that just contain egg whites. Discuss students' tallies.

- **Cut-out cookies.** Also called rolled cookies. Are made from stiff dough that is rolled out and cut with cookie cutters.
- **Molded cookies.** Are formed by shaping the dough by hand into balls. These balls can be rolled in chopped nuts or other toppings before baking, or they can be flattened with a fork or the bottom of a glass. Peanut butter cookies are flattened with a fork, giving them their characteristic ridged appearance.
- **Pressed cookies.** Are made by pushing dough through a cookie press, which can create a variety of shapes. Spritz cookies are made this way.
- **Sliced cookies.** Sometimes called refrigerator or icebox cookies. Are made by forming a soft dough into a long roll and refrigerating it. When the roll is chilled and firm, the cookies are sliced and baked.

Baking Cookies

Most cookies are baked on cookie sheets—flat pans with only one edge. Let cookie sheets cool before baking more cookies. Otherwise, the warm pan will soften the dough and the cookies will lose their shape.

Bar cookies are done baking when they pull away slightly from the sides of the pan. A slight impression remains when they are tapped gently. Other cookies are done when the bottoms are lightly browned and the edges are firm.

Safety Check

Although you may be tempted to do so, don't eat raw homemade cookie dough. It nearly always contains raw eggs—which can contribute to foodborne illness.

Store cooled cookies in covered containers. Waxed paper between layers will keep them from sticking together.

Pies

One dessert that has a long tradition at holiday meals is pie. A pie is a flaky crust filled with either a sweet or a savory mixture. A sweet pie may contain a fruit, custard, or cream filling, and is generally served as a dessert. A savory pie, filled with a meat or a custard and vegetable mixture, is served as a main dish. Two examples are quiche and potpie.

Pies can have one or two crusts made with flour, fat, salt, and water.

Piecrust

The key to making the piecrust is proper technique. To mix the pastry, use the pastry and biscuit method described on page 570. For a flaky pastry, handle the dough as little as possible.

Use a lightly floured surface to roll out pastry dough. Roll the dough in a large, round circle about ⅛ inch (0.3 cm) thick and 2 inches (5 cm) larger than an inverted (upside-down) pie pan. If the dough cracks or tears, patch it with another piece of dough. Moisten the area to be patched with a little water; then press a piece of dough over it. Sprinkle some flour over the patched area, and continue to roll it with a rolling pin.

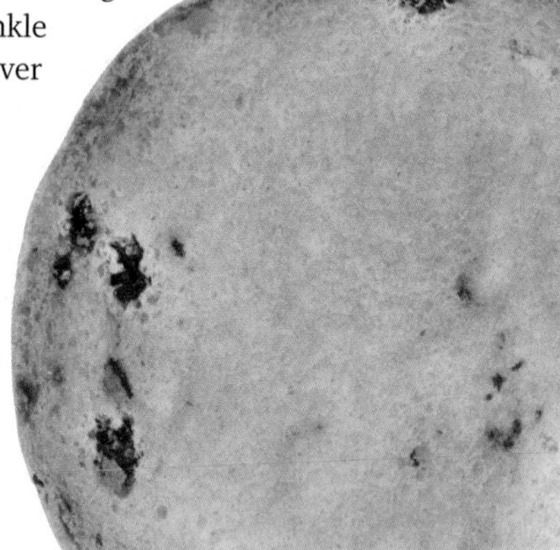

Extending Learning

Storing Cookies—When preparing cookies, make an extra batch to freeze. Most cookie batters and doughs freeze well, except for those made by the foam method. When freezing a batter, pour it into a freezer container and seal well. Doughs may be shaped into rolls and frozen. Thaw in the refrigerator.

Techniques in Preparing Pie Crust

There are four techniques that are important in successfully preparing the crust for a pie.

Look and Learn:

Will the pie in the drawings be a one-crust or two-crust pie? How can you tell?

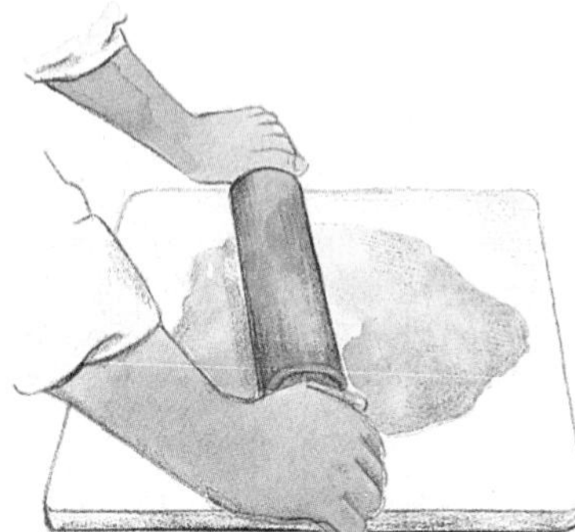

Roll pastry dough from the center outward to form a circle of even thickness.

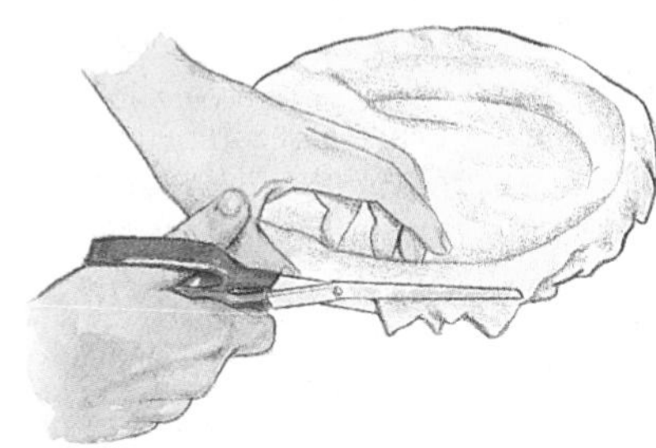

Trim the pastry with kitchen shears.

Fold the pastry so that you can transfer it to the pan without stretching or tearing it.

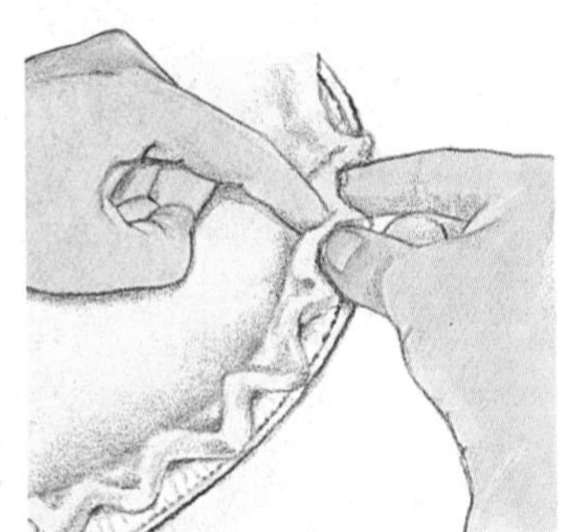

Finish the edge of the crust in some way. Making a fluted edge is shown here.

- *Pies (text pages 582-585)*

VISUAL LEARNING ***Using the Illustration*** Have groups of students work together to prepare a progressive demonstration for the class on one of the following: (1) rolling pastry dough, (2) patching cracks and tears in pastry dough, (3) placing pastry dough in pan and trimming edges, and (4) fluting the edge. After each demonstration, have all students practice the techniques. Discuss why following these techniques is important for a successful pie crust.

Brochures or Posters

Have students prepare brochures or posters titled "Tips for a Top-Notch Pie Crust." Encourage them to use a computer for brochure development. Have students display their brochures or posters. L1

Contest Activity

Have students take part in a pie naming contest. Note that this activity can be done in one of two ways: (1) Give students three minutes to write down as many types of pies as possible. (2) Using numbered photos of pies, have students try to identify the types of pies shown.

Reinforcing Key Skills

Present the following problem to student groups. Allow time for them to discuss and compare their responses.

Management—You have been asked to make four one-crust pies for a large holiday meal. Variety will be important, since everyone has different tastes. What's your plan of action? What will your fillings be?

- *Pies (text pages 582-585)*

Display Activity

Display several pie crust mixes and ready-to-use crusts. What are the advantages and disadvantages of these alternatives? Using the Nutrition Facts panels, students are to take part in a class discussion on the healthfulness of each product. How can higher fat crusts be included in a healthful eating plan? Do students consider any of the crusts to be nutrient-dense? Why or why not?

Recipe Analysis

Have students work in small groups to locate pie recipes. Have groups identify the type of pie, as well as any shortcut ingredients or preparation methods suggested in the recipes. Have students suggest ways to modify the recipes to make them lower in fat. L1

Using 

Have interested students practice both techniques for creating decorative crust edges. Ask if anyone has any other interesting ideas for making decorative crust edges. Encourage these students to demonstrate these techniques for the class.

Two-Crust Pie

For a two-crust pie, fold a rolled pastry circle in half (and in half again), and gently place it in a pie pan. Unfold the circle and fit it into the pan without stretching the pastry. Trim the pastry even with the top edge of the pan. Fill it with a sweet or savory mixture. Place another circle of pastry over the filling to form the top crust. Trim it so that ½ inch (1.3 cm) extends over the edge of the pan. Moisten the bottom pastry around the edge with water. Tuck the top pastry under the edge of the bottom pastry and gently pinch the layers together. Make a decorative edge that also seals the top and bottom crusts. Make several slits in the top crust to allow steam to escape during baking.

Q ***I have seen pies with decorative crust edges. How can I learn this technique?***

A It's actually easy and can be done two ways. One is to dip the tines of a fork in flour, and then use the fork to press the pastry crust against the edge of the pan around the entire crust. The second method is to place the index finger of one hand on the inside edge of the crust and the thumb and the index finger of the other hand on the outside edge. Gently push the crust to form a curved shape, repeating this process around the entire edge.

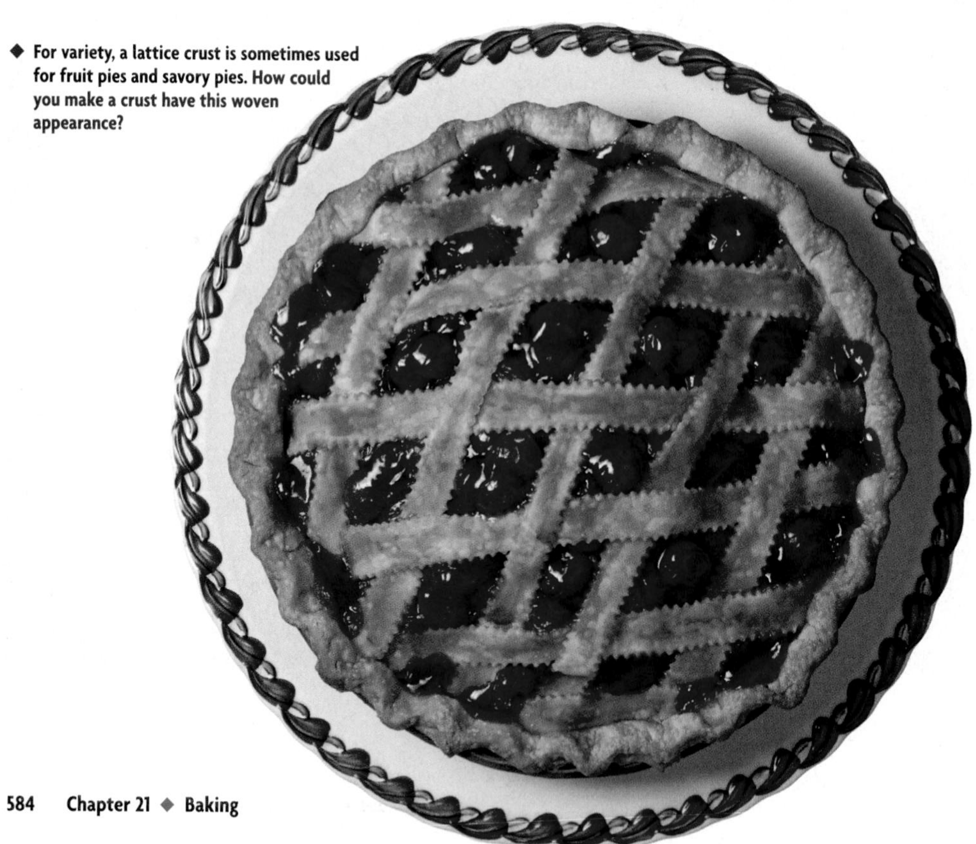

◆ **For variety, a lattice crust is sometimes used for fruit pies and savory pies. How could you make a crust have this woven appearance?**

584 Chapter 21 ◆ Baking

FOOD SCIENCE — Effects of Fats Experiment

Lead students in an experiment that tests the effects of different fats on pastry. Beforehand, ask students to work together to develop a hypothesis, giving concrete reasons for their assumptions.

One-Crust Pie

When making a one-crust pie, roll out one pastry circle for the bottom crust. Put the pastry into the pie pan. Trim it, leaving a ½-inch (1.3-cm) overhang. Pinch the overhang under to form a double thickness along the pan rim. Flute the edge or make a forked edge.

One-crust pies can also be made with crumb crusts. Mix fine crumbs from graham crackers or gingersnaps with melted butter or margarine, and press them into the pan. These crusts, which are usually used with unbaked fillings, are popular because they're easier to make than pastry crusts. They also add flavor and texture to the pie.

Some recipes call for a baked pie shell. The filling is added later. If you bake the pie shell before filling it, pierce the bottom with a fork about every 1 inch (2.5 cm) to prevent the crust from bubbling up while baking.

◆ **Pumpkin pie is an example of a pie that is traditionally made without a top crust. Which others can you name?**

Section 21-4 Review & Activities

1. What are the two basic kinds of cakes? Name two ways they are different and two ways they are alike.
2. What are the differences between cut-out cookies and drop cookies?
3. What should you do if pastry dough tears as you are rolling it?
4. **Analyzing.** Courtney has volunteered to bring cookies to a bake sale tomorrow, but she has little time for baking. What type of cookies would you suggest she bake? Give reasons for your recommendations.
5. **Evaluating.** Why do you think homemade cakes and pies were more common (and perhaps more popular) in years past?
6. **Applying.** Working in small groups, locate several pie recipes in magazines and food advertisements. Write down any shortcut ingredients or preparation methods suggested in the recipes. Make suggestions for modifying the recipes to make them lower in fat.

ASSESS

REVIEW

- Ask students to summarize the main ideas in this section.
- Have students complete the Section Review. (Answers appear below.)

EVALUATION

- Provide a recipe for cookies and have students prepare them. Evaluate procedure and results.
- Have students take the quiz for Section 21-4. (Use the quiz in the *Teacher Resource Guide,* or construct your own with the **Exam***View*® *Test Generator* on the *Effective Instruction CD-ROM.*)

RETEACHING

- Have students deliberately make a tear when rolling out pie crust to practice patching the dough.
- Refer to the *Reteaching Activities* booklet for the Section 21-4 activity sheet.

CLOSE

Lead a discussion on the traditional role of cakes, pies, and cookies as dessert items and ways to reduce the calories and increase nutrition in various desserts.

Answers to Section 21-4 Review & Activities

1. Shortened and foam; differences and likenesses will vary.
2. See pages 581-582.
3. Patch it with another piece of dough.
4. Bar cookies; they're baked all at once, require no additional time to create individual cooking servings since they're baked in a pan, and can be taken to school in the pan.
5. Answers will vary. Many people did much more physical labor, so they could afford the extra calories. Many women didn't work outside the home.
6. Pie recipes and suggestions will vary.

RECIPE FILE

Apple-Bran Bars

This is a bar cookie recipe.

USING THE RECIPE

- Have students read the recipe and discuss each step.
- Review safety and sanitation procedures that apply to this recipe.
- Remind students not to eat cookie dough containing raw eggs, or egg whites.
- Have each lab team fill out a work plan. (See the *Foods Lab Resources* booklet.)
- Have students check off the ingredients and equipment listed on the recipe worksheet and prepare the recipe.
- Have students complete the evaluation and questions on the recipe worksheet.

SEE ALSO...

The *Foods Lab Resources* booklet for the "Apple-Bran Bars" recipe worksheet and other recipe alternatives.

RECIPE FILE

Apple-Bran Bars

Bar cookies are easy to prepare and are fun to eat. Try adding dried cranberries, cherries, or chopped apricots to this recipe.

Customary	*Ingredients*	*Metric*
1 cup	100 percent bran cereal	250 mL
½ cup	Fat-free milk	125 mL
1 cup	All-purpose flour	250 mL
1 tsp.	Baking powder	5 mL
½ tsp.	Ground cinnamon	3 mL
¼ tsp.	Ground nutmeg	1 mL
⅓ cup	Margarine	75 mL
½ cup	Brown sugar, packed	125 mL
2	Egg whites	2
1 cup	Pared, chopped apple	250 mL

Yield: 16 bars
Equipment: 9 × 9 inch (23 × 23 cm) baking pan
Temperature: 350°F (180°C)

Directions

1. Preheat oven.
2. Grease and flour the baking pan.
3. In a large bowl, soak cereal in milk until milk is absorbed.
4. In a separate bowl, mix together flour, baking powder, cinnamon, and nutmeg.
5. In another bowl, beat margarine and sugar until creamy. Add egg whites and beat again until thoroughly combined.
6. Add the dry ingredients to the creamed mixture. Stir well.
7. Stir in apples and the cereal mixture; mix well.
8. Pour mixture into greased baking pan.
9. Bake about 30 minutes or until a wooden pick inserted in the center comes out clean.
10. Cool. Cut into 16 bars and serve.

Nutrition Information

Per serving (approximate–per bar): 92 calories, 2 g protein, 17 g carbohydrate, 2 g fat, trace cholesterol, 106 mg sodium
Good source of: B vitamins, phosphorus

Food for Thought

- What are two other methods you could use to test the bars for doneness?
- How might you adapt this recipe for microwave preparation?

Answers to **Food for Thought**

1. Watch for the sides to pull away from the edges or press gently to see if slight impression remains.
2. Use a microwave-safe pan; cut down some on the liquid ingredients; oven does not have to be preheated; check a microwave cookbook for cooking time; test for doneness by pressing gently instead of using a wooden pick.

Career Wanted

Food Design Consultant

"We eat using all of our senses."

Thomas Biernaski

Education and Training
- Degree in food science, nutrition, or related field
- Experience in food service and design

Qualities
- Creativity
- Problem-solving skills
- Communication skills

Q. Thomas, what does food design consultation involve?

A. Food design is recipe development. When creating a new recipe or changing an older one, a consultant can tell you how the changes will affect taste, texture, and other sensory qualities. I consult for restaurants and food makers, especially when they want to add a line of "lite" or sugar-free foods. I'm also called in to help create authentic ethnic versions of foods, which are becoming more popular.

Q. How do you predict what will work?

A. I have a degree in food science, and I've held more kitchen jobs than I can count. If you're making a fat-free cookie, I can tell you that a certain fat substitute increases baking time, which a commercial baker needs to know to plan the day's production. For a hearty minestrone soup, I know which processing method leaves vegetables firmer.

Q. Do you create any original recipes?

A. Yes, for a Web site that features diabetic recipes. My wife has diabetes, and she's a very willing taste tester.

Related Career Opportunities

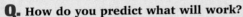

Entry Level
- Baker's assistant
- Salad preparer
- Taste tester

Technical Level
- Dietetic technician
- Test kitchen worker
- Quality assurance technician

Professional Level
- Cookbook editor
- Geriatric nutritionist
- Menu development chef

Making Career Connections

FOOD DESIGN EXPERIENCE. Choose a recipe for a baked item. Develop a version that is lower in fat or sugar, uses no dairy products, or has ethnic appeal. Create nutritional profiles for both recipes with nutrition analysis software. Prepare your recipe and have a class taste testing. Provide survey forms for comments.

Career Wanted

Food Design Consultant

Thinking About the Career

Have students consider all the factors that go into creating and testing recipes, including shopping, kitchen use, food waste, time and resource use.

How specifically would it be helpful to be knowledgeable of nutrients in foods?

What is the difference between a food design consultant and a food stylist?

Career-Building Opportunities

Encourage students to contact cooking schools, or other locations offering culinary courses, in the area to find out about course offerings and costs. Can one class be taken at a time on evenings or weekends while attending high school?

For More Information

For additional information about careers in food design, encourage students to contact:

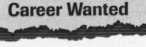

- American Culinary Federation
  10 San Bartola Drive
  St. Augustine, Florida 32086
  www.acfchefs.org
- International Association of Culinary Professionals
  304 West Liberty Street
  Suite 201
  Louisville, KY 40202
  www.iacp.org
- National Restaurant Association
  1200 17th Street NW
  Washington, DC 20036-3097
  www.restaurant.org

REVIEW

- Have students complete the Chapter Review. (Answers appear below.)

EVALUATION

- Evaluate cookies, cakes, and pies prepared by students in the foods lab.
- Have students take the test for Chapter 21. (Use the chapter test in the *Teacher Resource Guide,* or construct your own with the **Exam***View*® *Test Generator* on the *Effective Instruction CD-ROM.*)

ANSWERS

Checking Your Knowledge

1. Pour batters, drop batters, soft doughs, stiff doughs.
2. They add lightness and volume to baked products; by expanding as the baking progresses.
3. Dark pans retain more heat than light pans and can create a thick crust. Glass retains more heat than metal.
4. Products with perishable cream fillings and frostings should be refrigerated. Refrigeration causes other baked goods to get stale more quickly.
5. Muffins, quick loaf breads, biscuits.
6. To avoid overdeveloping the gluten, which would make them tough.
7. Approximately one-third of the total amount of flour.
8. After the first rise; by pushing gently with your fist into the center of the dough.
9. Combine confectioners' sugar and lemon, orange, or pineapple juice and drizzle over cake; sprinkle a small amount of confectioners' sugar over a cake; skip icing and garnish with fresh or frozen fruits.

Chapter 21 Review & Activities

Summary

Section 21-1: Ingredients and Techniques for Baking

- Basic ingredients each play a specific role in baking.
- The strength of gluten determines what texture a baked product will have.
- Recipe directions give the mixing method, size and type of pans, and how to prepare them for baking.
- Conventional and microwave baking produce different results.

Section 21-3: Yeast Breads and Rolls

- Time-saving techniques can speed up yeast bread preparation.
- Yeast bread dough consists of flour, salt, sugar, liquid, fat, and yeast.
- After kneading and rising, the dough can be shaped and baked a number of ways.

Section 21-2: Quick Breads

- Breads, biscuits, and muffins made without yeast are called quick breads.
- They are mixed using the muffin method or the pastry and biscuit method.
- Quick breads can be nutritious, but some are high in fat and calories.

Section 21-4: Cakes, Cookies, and Pies

- Cakes, cookies, and pies are usually high in fat and calories, but can often be made with reduced-fat techniques.
- There are two basic kinds of cakes, shortened cakes and foam cakes.
- Cookies can be shaped in a variety of ways.
- Pies can have sweet or savory fillings, and can be made with one or two crusts.

Working IN THE Lab

1. ***Food Science.*** Demonstrate the action of leavening agents. Dissolve one package of yeast in water. Add both sugar and water to another package of yeast. Combine baking powder with water and baking soda with water. Compare the results of all the samples.
2. ***Foods Lab.*** Prepare yeast dough and freeze it. In the next day or two, allow the dough to thaw and rise in the refrigerator overnight. Bake it the following day. Evaluate the results.

Checking Your Knowledge

1. Name two kinds of each: batters and doughs.
2. What can air, steam, and carbon dioxide do for baked goods? How do they work?
3. What is the difference between using a dark pan for baking and using a light pan? Between using a metal pan and a glass pan?
4. Which baked goods should be refrigerated? Which should not? Why?
5. What are three kinds of quick breads?
6. Why are quick breads mixed only briefly?
7. When making whole-grain yeast dough, how much all-purpose flour should you use in the dough?
8. When and how is dough punched down?
9. What are two examples of low-fat ways to decorate a cake?
10. What are the six basic kinds of cookies?

Thinking Critically

1. **Predicting Consequences.** Jan is baking bread for 45 minutes in a disposable aluminum pan. Because she plans to throw the pan out after using it, she doesn't grease it, as the recipe calls for. What are two problems that using this pan might cause?
2. **Determining Accuracy.** Paula's friend heard that you could substitute applesauce for oil in a muffin recipe to cut down on fat. How can Paula find out whether this is true?

Reinforcing Key Skills

1. **Management.** Your time these days is divided among schoolwork, sports, music lessons, and several other activities. You also have finals coming up next week—just in time for your grandmother's visit. You would like to bake something that is both festive and nutritious to welcome her. What will you make?
2. **Communication.** Celine has just learned that her favorite uncle was diagnosed with heart disease. She is aware of his fondness for cookies. Write the dialogue of the conversation Celine has with her uncle in which she guides him in his food choices.

Making Decisions and Solving Problems

A friend invites you over to make cookies for a party. She says that she likes to bake by just "throwing a bunch of ingredients together." What would you do?

Making Connections

1. **Social Studies.** Use your school or public library to find out how the American colonists (or other groups) baked bread before the invention of the kitchen range.
2. **Math.** Make a bar graph comparing pies made in three different ways—totally from scratch, with a purchased crust and canned filling, and purchased from a bakery. Using different colors for different criteria, rate each type of pie in terms of preparation time, cost, and nutrition (fat, sugar, and calorie content). Place your graph in a location in the classroom near the foods lab.

ANSWERS cont.

10. Bar cookies, drop cookies, cut-out or rolled cookies, molded cookies, pressed cookies, and sliced cookies.

Thinking Critically

1. The bread might stick to the pan; the bread might not rise correctly.
2. Either by speaking with her family and consumer sciences teacher or another expert; by performing an experiment.

Reinforcing Key Skills

1. Answers will vary. Possibilities include selecting a simple but festive cake, such as an angel food cake, and decorating it by topping it with fresh seasonal fruit.
2. Dialogues, which will vary, should indicate that Celine is guiding her uncle to eat fewer cookies (for example, as an occasional treat) and choosing those that are lower in fat and calories.

UNIT 5

Expanding Your Horizons

INTRODUCING UNIT 5

As students enter the classroom, greet them with exotic music and the aroma of foods you have purchased or prepared. Include a variety of the ethnic foods from the various cultures identified in Chapters 22 and 23, and apply some of the artistic touches (garnishes, etc.) discussed in Chapter 24. Invite students to sample the foods. Discuss how food choices and preparation methods reflect both cultural traditions and creativity.

UNIT 5

Expanding

KEY TO ABILITY LEVELS Each section of the text contains skill-building activities. Each activity has been labeled for use with students of various learning styles and abilities.

L1 **Level 1** activities are basic activities and should be within the range of all students.

L2 **Level 2** activities are average activities and should be within the range of students working at average and above-average levels.

L3 **Level 3** activities are challenging activities designed for the ability range of above-average students.

Your Horizons

UNIT 5 PROJECT

Have students with artistic aptitude create a map of the world large enough to cover a fairly large tabletop. The large map is to be used as the foundation of a "Tastes of the Worlds Media Center," to be completed as students work through the chapters of this unit. Encourage students to find as much information as they can about cultural influences on food and food traditions. Information is to have many forms, including snapshots and videotapes of vacations and cookouts, recordings of music of various cultures, and shelf-stable ingredients. All are to be placed on appropriate locations on the large map.

PROJECT FOLLOWUP

At unit's end, invite students to examine their media center. Which areas did they have the most difficulty gathering information and materials for? Why do they think this is?

FCCLA Projects

Focus on Children. Using ethnic foods to teach tolerance and appreciation of differences, students present a lesson to a kindergarten class or children in an aftercare program. An original story or a cooking demonstration is the basis and includes opportunities for children's participation.

Illustrated Talk. Students talk about the foodways of a country or culture. They discuss how customs, cooking methods, and dishes evolved, and explain how the foods or traditions fit into the larger economic and social picture. They show cooking tools and eating utensils, demonstrate their use, and offer food samples.

CHAPTER

22

Foods of the World

Advance Planning Guide ☑

- Purchase ingredients for an ethnic smorgasbord for the unit opener.
- Purchase fruits and vegetables eaten in Latin America.
- Invite a restaurateur, chef, or other guest from the community who prepares homemade tortillas.
- Purchase plantains, either ripe or unripe.
- Bring in pictures of traditional Mexican cooking tools or, ideally, the tools themselves.
- Purchase items for a display of the staple foods of Central America.
- If possible, bring a tajine (the cookware) to class.
- Purchase chickpeas, tahina, and loaves of pita bread.
- Invite a person from Britain to speak to students about the English custom of afternoon tea.
- Obtain ingredients for a multi-course French lunch.
- Create a checklist to distinguish foods of the various regions of Italy.
- Bring to class samples of tofu for a taste test.
- Arrange a field trip to a Chinese restaurant.
- Buy or prepare a *garam masala* according to an Indian recipe.

CHAPTER

22

The world of food is vast and varied. In this chapter, you will learn about different cultures and the contribution each makes to the rich fabric of international food customs and preparation.

MEETING DIVERSE NEEDS

Celebrating Cultural Diversity. If there are students in the class who were born in or have lived in other cultures, ask them to serve as "cultural liaisons" for those cultures during the course of chapter study. These students might wear class-made badges reading "Cultural Liaison for ____," filling in the name of the culture under consideration. These students are to consult with other members of the class who seek firsthand information about the culture in question.

SECTION

22-1

Objectives

After studying this section, you should be able to:

- Describe food choices available in the various regions of Latin America.
- Identify the cultural influences on foods in Latin America.

Look for These Terms

cuisines

maize

Latin America

Over twenty countries in Central and South America make up what is called Latin America. This region of over 300 million people is named because the main languages spoken there—Spanish, French, and Portuguese—are all based on Latin.

The early history of this area is dominated by three native cultures: Aztec, Inca, and Mayan. The Aztecs flourished in Mexico, the Incas in South America, and the Mayans in Central America.

Foods of Latin America

Latin America stretches from Mexico and the islands of the Caribbean to the tip of South America. Because the area is so large, it includes climates and geographical features of all kinds—tropical rain forests, snow-capped mountains, arid deserts, and temperate zones. Foods vary according to the growing conditions. Nevertheless, many similarities exist among the **cuisines**—styles of food preparation and cooking associated with a specific group or culture.

Corn, or **maize**, is the staple grain in much of Latin America. Wheat and rice are also grown in some areas.

◆ **Dry beans, corn products, chili peppers, and avocados are common ingredients in Latin American cooking. What is the staple grain in much of Latin America?**

SECTION

22-1

Latin America

FOCUS

MOTIVATORS

- Ask students to brainstorm foods they associate with Latin America. How many of these foods are fast-food varieties of Mexican food?
- Display fruits and vegetables popular in Latin America. Have students identify the ones with which they are familiar. Identify and provide information about the uses of those that are unfamiliar to students.

VOCABULARY ACTIVITY

Have students note the word *cuisines.* Ask how many know the language the word comes from. What does the word mean? What are some synonyms?

STUDY SKILLS

- **Listening.** Invite a group of volunteers to prepare an oral reading of the section.
- Have students read the section and complete the appropriate part of the Chapter 22 Study Guide in the *Student Workbook*.

Section 22-1 Resources

◆ **Student Workbook,** pp. 163, 166
◆ **Teacher Resource Guide**
Lesson Plan 22-1 Organizer
Section 22-1 Quiz
◆ **Effective Instruction CD-ROM**
Exam*View*® *Test Generator*
PowerPoint® Slide #50
◆ **Transparency Package,** CT-50
◆ **Student Motivation Kit**
Reteaching Activities, p. 100
Enrichment Activities
Foods Lab Resources, pp. 135–136
A Global Foods Tour, pp. 6–16, 19, 20, 28–30, 52–62

TEACH

- *Foods of Latin America (text pages 593-597)*

Discussion Activity

Ask students to describe foods common to Mexican meals, including meals that they have eaten. Discuss other cuisines in which tortillas are widely used.

Demonstration

Invite a restaurateur, chef, or other guest from the community who prepares tortillas from scratch. Have this visitor demonstrate the procedure.

Interviews

Have students speak with adult family or community members with a long-standing appreciation of the foods of Mexico. Students are to learn if and how Mexican food has changed in the United States in the time this person has been a devotee. Urge students to learn whether the types of Mexican foods available in supermarkets have changed and, if so, how. Allow students to share interview summaries. L1

VISUAL LEARNING ***Using the Photograph***

Direct students' attention to the top photo on this page. Ask whether any students have sampled this dish. What other dishes do they know of that are improbable but tasty?

Mexico

Mexico's cuisine developed out of both the native foods and the influence of the Spanish conquerors. Cornmeal, rice, cooked dry beans, and chili peppers are the basics of Mexican cooking. The bland taste of corn and beans provides a contrast to the spicy taste of the various peppers.

The bread of Mexico is the tortilla. You have probably eaten tortillas in tacos, burritos, and similar foods. This flat, pounded bread is usually made from *masa*—dried corn soaked in limewater and ground while wet. In some dishes, masa is made into a dough and cooked by steaming. The best known of such dishes is *tamales,* masa formed into various shapes and often filled with finely chopped chicken and other foods. The bundles are steamed in corn husks or banana leaves.

◆ ***Pollo con mole poblano*** **is a delicious combination of braised chicken in a sauce of chili peppers, nuts, and chocolate. After reading this chapter, identify at least one other dish from another culture that contains an ingredient you would expect to find in a dessert.**

Much of Mexican cuisine is hotly spiced. One dish that often surprises visitors to the country is *pollo con mole poblano,* chicken in a thick, dark sauce of chili peppers and chocolate.

Most Mexican meals include frijoles, cooked dry beans. *Frijoles refritos* are cooked dry beans that are mashed and fried in lard. Popular desserts include *flan,* a sweet baked custard topped with a sauce of caramelized sugar, and preserved guava.

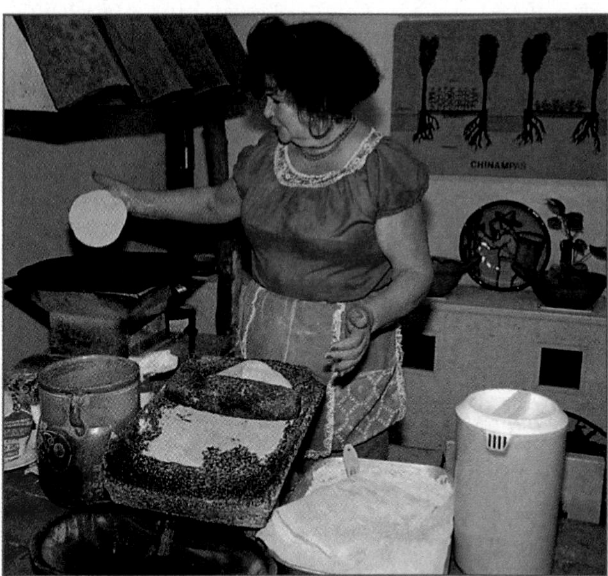

◆ **Following centuries of tradition, this Mexican woman makes tortillas using the traditional tools—a *metate* to hold the dough and a *metlalpil* to roll it. Use a print or online resource to investigate the origin of the Mexican terms in the previous sentence. What does their origin reveal about Mexico's past?**

INFOLINK

For more on baked custard, including general guidelines for preparing this and other egg-based dishes, see Section 18-4.

Technology TIE-IN

Bring to class pictures of traditional Mexican cooking tools such as those shown in the bottom photo on this page or, ideally, the tools themselves. Have students inspect the tools or images, noting the materials. The *molcajete,* a pestle-like bowl in which guacamole was traditionally made, is crafted out of volcanic rock. Ask students to guess the age of these early inventions. Has technology improved, or are these still the tools of choice among Mexican cooks?

Central America

A bridge of seven small countries connects Mexico to South America: Belize, Costa Rica, El Salvador, Guatemala, Honduras, Nicaragua, and Panama. This region is where the Mayan empire flourished. People who live in these countries today are of Mayan, European, African, and mixed descent. The cooking has Mayan and Aztec roots with Spanish and Caribbean influences.

Corn and beans are the staple crops. Bananas, coffee, coconuts, and cacao (the bean from which chocolate is made) are exported to other countries.

Chicken is widely eaten in Central America. It might be prepared with pineapple or in a mixture of ingredients, such as pumpkin seeds, tomatoes, and raisins.

A favorite food is *chayote*, a crisp vegetable with a delicate flavor, which is often sliced and simmered. Costa Ricans mix it with cheese and eggs, whereas cooks in the Dominican Republic fry it with eggs, tomatoes, and hot peppers.

The Caribbean

The tropical islands of the Caribbean Sea are to the south and east of Mexico, between Florida and South America. Caribbean nations include Cuba, Jamaica, Haiti, the Dominican Republic, and Puerto Rico.

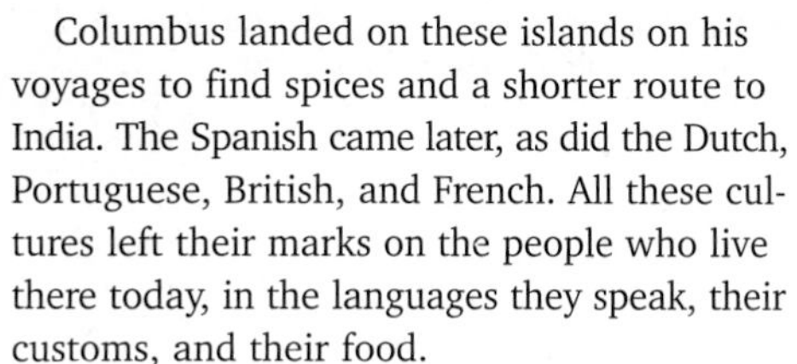

Columbus landed on these islands on his voyages to find spices and a shorter route to India. The Spanish came later, as did the Dutch, Portuguese, British, and French. All these cultures left their marks on the people who live there today, in the languages they speak, their customs, and their food.

Caribbean Cuisine

The staple food is the plantain, a starchy food that looks like a banana but is cooked as a vegetable. It can be roasted, fried, boiled, baked, or combined in dishes with meat and cheese. Abundant fish and shellfish are taken from local waters. Among these are flying fish, conch, shrimp, codfish, clams, grouper, and red snapper. In the warm climate, tropical fruits—including mangoes, bananas, coconuts, papayas, and pineapples—are also plentiful. So are sweet potatoes, pumpkins, and chili peppers.

The dishes of the Caribbean vary from country to country. Some are colorfully named. For example, *Moros y Cristianos* ("Moors and Christians") is a Cuban national dish made with black beans and rice. Jamaican "Saturday Soup" consists of hot peppers (originally from Africa), carrots, turnips, and pumpkin added

◆ **This buffet from the island of Barbados includes beans, rice, plantain, fish, pineapple, and other locally available foods. Which staples of the Barbados table are common to other parts of Latin America?**

- *Foods of Latin America (text pages 593-597)*

Display Activity

Create a display of the staple foods of Central America. Include small samples of corn, beans, bananas, coffee, coconuts, cacao, chicken, and chayote. Ask each student to choose a food and research to find out how it is used in Central American cooking. Have students write a short report of their findings.

Taste Test

Ask a volunteer to read the description of a plantain on this page. Then prepare plantain by roasting, frying, boiling, or baking the fruit. Have students taste the dish. Show students that the raw plantain looks like a banana, but point out that it is cooked like a vegetable.

Name Inquiry

Point out to students that colorful names, such as those mentioned in the text, run the gamut of Caribbean foods, from appetizers to desserts. Have interested students use print or online resources to find out more about these names, which include "Step and Fall Back," a preparation of fish in a pastry crust. Have students share their findings in an oral presentation. L1

Extending Learning

Caribbean Cuisine—Sometimes the names of dishes of a region or culture answer the question "What's in a name?" The name "Saturday Soup" has a clear identification with a day of the week. Students should infer (correctly) that is the day on which this dish is customarily prepared.

Have interested students research other colorfully named foods of Latin America. One possibility is *ropa vijella*, a dish of Mexico, which translates literally as "old clothes." Challenge students to learn the origins of these naming traditions. Allow time for students to share their findings.

- *Foods of Latin America (text pages 593-597)*

Discussion Activity

Ask students to name and describe three foods native to Brazil. Ask: What is the staple food of Peru? Why do people in Argentina eat a lot of beef?

Mapping

Have students draw a map of South America, omitting labels. Instruct students to select three countries beyond those discussed in the textbook. Over the outline shape of each, students are to list typical foods. To complete their maps, students are to create a legend consisting of symbols that identify natural resources of a region and/or European influences, where appropriate. Display completed maps around the classroom for ready reference. L1

Lab Experience

Have students locate and prepare a typical South American recipe that uses plantains, cassavas, bananas, or coconuts. L1

◆ **Black beans are a staple in Brazil. Can you name a popular Brazilian dish made with black beans?**

to beef stock. The cuisine of Haiti, which includes an unusual soup made of bread and pumpkin, reflects both African and French influences.

Islanders use coconut milk and fruit juice to prepare both main dishes and desserts, such as coconut custard. Ice cream made with papaya and other local fruits is also popular.

South America

Twelve nations make up South America, the southern half of the Western Hemisphere: Argentina, Bolivia, Brazil, Chili, Colombia, Ecuador, Guyana, Paraguay, Peru, Surinam, Uruguay, and Venezuela. It also includes French Guiana, a European possession.

As in the rest of Latin America, the population is of native Indian, European, and African ancestry. The climate, culture, people, and growing conditions vary greatly from country to country and from rural area to city.

FOR YOUR HEALTH

Eating What Comes Naturally

Many of the staple foods of Latin America—such as grains, beans, and fresh fruits and vegetables—are rich in nutrients. The popularity of these foods in Latin American cultures is mainly a result of their ready availability.

Following Up

- How might the food customs that originated in the past benefit people now and in the future?

Brazil

Brazil, the largest country in South America, produces great amounts of beef, coffee, and cocoa. The people trace their ethnic roots to native Indians, Portuguese, and Africans. This blend of cultures can be seen in Brazilian food. From West Africa comes *dende,* or palm oil (which gives a bright yellow-orange color to foods), *malagueta* peppers, and coconut milk. From the Portuguese come a love of sausage and the use of kale as a soup ingredient.

Sausage appears in *feijoada,* the national dish of Brazil. Links of the smoked meat are simmered—along with beef short ribs, slices of dried beef, and pork—in a pot of black beans. Side dishes of rice, collard greens, sliced oranges, and manioc flour (a toasted bread crumb-like grain) complete the rib-sticking stew. Brazil's long coastline accounts for the many fish recipes, including *mariscada,* a fish stew consisting of clams, mussels, codfish, shrimp, and crab cooked together with tomatoes and spices.

Reinforcing Key Skills

Present the following problem to student groups. Allow time for them to discuss and compare their responses.

Management—Margot's aunt and uncle come to her family's house every Wednesday for dinner. For this visit, Margot would like to plan something special and cook an authentic South American dinner. The only problem is that her uncle doesn't like spicy food and her aunt is a vegetarian. Help Margot plan her menu.

Peru

Peru is located on the Pacific coast of South America. When the Spanish conqueror Pizarro came to Peru in the sixteenth century, the local people were eating corn, potatoes, squash, beans, cassava, sweet potatoes, peanuts, tomatoes, avocados, and chili peppers. Although these foods are still popular, today Peru is also noted for its fishing industry. The potato remains its staple food. Popular meats include seafood and beef.

Peru was a Spanish colony for almost 300 years. The Spanish influence can be seen in foods such as *gazpacho,* a cold tomato-based soup of Spanish origin. *Ceviche* is a native Peruvian dish in which raw fish is marinated in lime juice. Other foods often eaten in wealthier areas include meat, poultry, vegetables, and grains, which are highly seasoned with onions, garlic, and hot peppers. Rice, potatoes, and bread accompany the main meals.

In poorer areas, meals include potatoes, corn, squash, and soups made of wheat and barley. The foods of those living in jungle areas consist of a variety of fish, small game, fruits, and nuts.

Argentina

South of Brazil, along the eastern coast of South America, lies Argentina. Today most of its inhabitants are of European descent.

Raising beef is one of Argentina's major industries, and as a result, most people eat beef. It is often grilled outdoors and served with spicy sauces. *Puchero* is a meat and vegetable stew. Another widely eaten dish is *empanadas,* turnovers of dough filled with vegetables, meat, fruit, or a combination of the three. Meats are also combined with fruits in local stews such as *carbonada criolla*—beef mixed with peaches.

Section 22-1 Review & Activities

1. What is the staple grain in most of Latin America?

2. What is the most popular type of bread in Mexican cuisine?

3. What cultures have influenced Caribbean food?

4. **Synthesizing.** Choose one of the countries or areas of Latin America covered in the section. Explain the influences of climate or geography on the cuisine of that region.

5. **Comparing and Contrasting.** Divide a sheet of paper into three columns labeled "Brazil," "Argentina," and "Both." In the columns, list unique aspects of the local cuisine for each country as well as features the two countries share.

6. **Applying.** In groups, make lists of the foods described in this section with which you are familiar. What other Latin American foods have you tasted that are not listed in the text? What ingredients appear regularly in the dishes you listed?

ASSESS

REVIEW

- Ask students to summarize the main ideas in this section.
- Have students complete the Section Review. (Answers appear below.)

EVALUATION

- Have students prepare a typical dish from a country in Central or South America.
- Have students take the quiz for Section 22-1. (Use the quiz in the *Teacher Resource Guide,* or construct your own with the **Exam***View*® *Test Generator* on the *Effective Instruction CD-ROM.*)

RETEACHING

- Provide pairs of students with recipes from countries in Central and South America. Partners are to make two lists of recipes—those that give some idea of the variety of foods eaten by the people who live in these countries and those that do not.
- Refer to the *Reteaching Activities* booklet for the Section 22-1 activity sheet.

CLOSE

Lead a discussion on historic and geographic influences on the foods eaten by the people in Central and South America.

Answers to Section 22-1 Review & Activities

1. Maize.
2. The tortilla.
3. Spanish, Dutch, Portuguese, British, French, and African.
4. Answers will vary. One possibility: Brazil's long coastline explains the many fish recipes in the cuisine.
5. Answers will vary.
6. Answers will vary.

RECIPE FILE

Cuban Black Bean Soup

This recipe uses various cutting skills, sautéing, and simmering. You may wish to have students with weaknesses in any of these areas review the relevant portions of Chapters 8 and 9.

USING THE RECIPE

- Have students read the recipe and discuss each step.
- Remind students of the importance of not measuring ingredients carefully.
- Have each lab team fill out a work plan. (See the *Foods Lab Resources* booklet.)
- Have students check off the ingredients and equipment listed on the recipe worksheet and prepare the recipe.
- Have students complete the evaluation and questions on the recipe worksheet.

SEE ALSO...
The *Foods Lab Resources* booklet for the "Cuban Black Bean Soup" recipe worksheet and other recipe alternatives.

RECIPE FILE

Cuban Black Bean Soup

The variations on recipes for this Cuban signature dish are endless. This one has a creamy texture and a sharp citrus bite that makes it irresistible.

Customary	***Ingredients***	***Metric***
1	Medium onion, chopped	1
1	Rib celery, chopped	1
1	Garlic clove, minced	1
1 Tbsp.	Vegetable oil	20 mL
1 cup	Chicken or vegetable broth	250 mL
2 1-lb. cans	Black beans, drained	2 500-g cans
Dash	Cayenne pepper	Dash
1 Tbsp.	Lemon juice	20 mL
	Salt and pepper	

Yield: 4 servings
Equipment: Stock pot or Dutch oven

Directions

1. Sauté onion, celery, and garlic in oil until tender.
2. Add chicken or vegetable broth, black beans, and cayenne pepper.
3. Simmer mixture over medium heat, stirring occasionally, until heated through (about 5 minutes).
4. Carefully purée mixture in small batches in a blender or food processor. Return to stock pot.
5. Stir in lemon juice and simmer until thoroughly heated.
6. Season to taste with salt and pepper and serve hot.

Note: For a chunkier soup, purée only half the mixture before returning to stock pot.

Nutrition Information

Per serving (approximate): 286 calories, 17 g protein, 45 g carbohydrate, 5 g fat, 0 mg cholesterol, 206 mg sodium
Good source of: potassium, iron, zinc, vitamin E, B vitamins, phosphorus

Food for Thought

- Make a list of all the kitchen tools you would need to prepare and cook this soup.
- Discuss how and where in a meal you would serve this soup—for example, as an appetizer or as a main course. What would you serve along with it to make it a well-balanced, authentic Cuban meal?

Answers to **Food for Thought**

1. Answers should include a chef's or utility knife, a cutting board, and a cooking spoon.
2. Answers will vary. The soup might be served as either an appetizer or main course because it provides a protein. Students might recommend serving it with rice to complete the protein and, at the same time, add a serving of grain.

SECTION
22-2

Africa and the Middle East

Although Africa is an ocean away from Latin America, the two continents share some of the same foods and culinary traditions. This is the result of similarities in climate and in exploration and conquest.

Objectives

After studying this section, you should be able to:

- Describe food choices available in Africa south of the Sahara.
- Describe the cuisines of North Africa and the Middle East.
- Identify the cultural and geographical influences on the foods of Africa and the Middle East.

Look for These Terms

berbere
kibbutz

Africa

The Sahara forms a natural east-west dividing line through Africa. It separates the five nations in the north, along the Mediterranean Sea, from the rest of the continent.

The people living south of the Sahara are mainly Africans. Those living north of the Sahara are mostly Arabs, with a culture similar to that of the Middle East.

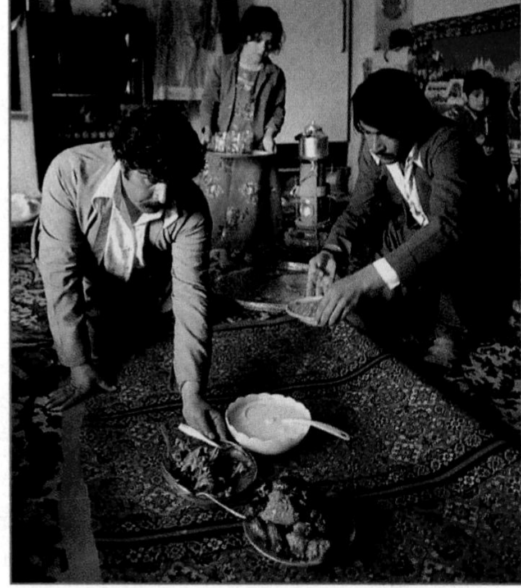

◆ **A family in Afghanistan enjoys the evening meal. Name two differences between the dining customs in the Middle East and those common in the United States.**

Section 22-2 Resources

◆ **Student Workbook,** pp. 163, 167
◆ **Teacher Resource Guide**
Lesson Plan 22-2 Organizer
Section 22-2 Quiz
◆ **Effective Instruction CD-ROM**
Exam*View®* *Test Generator*
PowerPoint® Slide #50
◆ **Transparency Package,** CT-50
◆ **Student Motivation Kit**
Reteaching Activities, p. 101
Enrichment Activities
Foods Lab Resources, pp. 137–138
A Global Foods Tour, pp. 25, 26, 112–136

SECTION
22-2
Africa and the Middle East

FOCUS

MOTIVATORS

- Ask students to recall information about the geography and history of Africa and the Middle East. Ask students to identify possible influences on foods in that part of the world. Ask: What forces contributed to the mixing of cultures? What effect do you think mixing the cultures would have on food traditions of the region?
- Have a volunteer find Africa on a large map of the world. Have another indicate the Middle East. How do these areas compare in size with North America?

VOCABULARY ACTIVITY

Pronounce the terms listed under "Look for These Terms." Have students find the terms and their definitions in the section.

STUDY SKILLS

- **Guided Reading.** Have students look at the headings within Section 22-2 to preview the concepts that will be discussed.
- Have students read the section and complete the appropriate part of the Chapter 22 Study Guide in the *Student Workbook*.

TEACH

- *Africa*
- *Sub-Saharan Africa (text pages 599-601)*

Discussion Activity

Ask students to read pages 599 and 600. Ask a volunteer to explain why food customs in sub-Saharan African countries are more likely to be based on kinship ties than to political boundaries of the countries.

Cultural Influences

Divide the class into two groups, challenging one group to find information on foods that are native to Africa, while the other explores foods that were brought by explorers, traders, and settlers. Allow time to share information. Conclude with a discussion on the effect of these trends on African food customs. L2

Recipe Search Activity

Have students find recipes for preparing yams in a traditional African manner. Are any similar recipes popular in the United States?

Nutritional Analysis

Have students consider the nutritional benefits of using meat as a flavoring ingredient rather than as the main focus of the meal. What foods provide protein in the African diet? L1

Sub-Saharan Africa

The area south of the Sahara is sometimes known as the sub-Saharan region. The concept of society in this region is defined by kinship groups—centuries-old networks of clans and tribes numbering sometimes in the thousands. In the past, these clans often lived together in villages and jointly owned the surrounding farmland. Food traditions are linked more with these social groups than with political boundaries past or present.

Influence of Climate

Most of sub-Saharan Africa has a tropical or subtropical climate. However, there is a wide range of geographical features, including mountains, coastlines, river valleys, tropical rain forests, and desert. Consequently, different foods are raised in these various regions.

In western and central Africa, areas that are hot and humid, the chief crops include plantains, rice, bananas, yams, and cassava. In the grasslands in the east and south, corn, millet, and sorghum are grown. Wheat is grown in many areas, along with foods such as onions, garlic, pumpkins, watermelons, cucumbers, chilies, dates, and figs.

Chickens, cattle, sheep, and goats are raised wherever possible. Small herds of animals have traditionally provided income, as well as food, for small farmers and herders. The eating of meat, however, is usually reserved for special occasions. People living along waterways, such as rivers, lakes, and seas, have an abundant supply of fish.

Influence of Settlers

Over the centuries, food crops introduced from other continents have been incorporated into African cuisines. Coconuts were introduced from Asia in the 1500s. In the same century, corn arrived from the New World. In the 1600s, cassava became an important food source. In the 1700s, peanuts were introduced, possibly from South America.

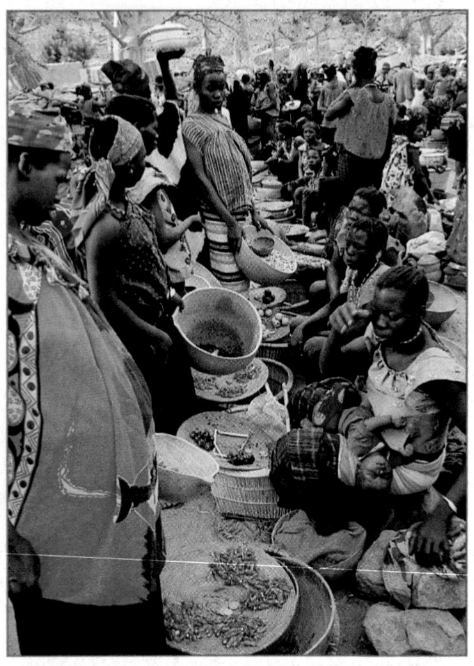

◆ **At this market in the West African nation of Mali, peanuts and yams are among the foods sold. Identify two ways in which yams are prepared and eaten in Africa.**

Yams have remained a staple starch throughout Africa. The traditional way to prepare them is to boil, peel, and slice or pound them until they form a paste, called *fufu.* In West Africa, cooks mash and deep-fry them, make them into croquettes, or slice and bake them. In some areas, cooks make fufu by mashing cassava and plantains.

South Africa was visited and also settled by many waves of Europeans looking for trade routes or escaping persecution. These French, Dutch, British, and German Europeans brought their own food preferences and preparation

HOME & COMMUNITY CONNECTION

Point out to students that true yams, which are native to Africa, are not imported to the United States and that what is eaten here as yams is really sweet potatoes. Have students conduct an exit poll of people leaving a local supermarket to find out how many of them have tasted yams. Consider findings back in class as a bridge to a discussion of how misconceptions and confusions like this get started. What other foods are students aware of that people frequently confuse with other foods?

methods. African cooks modified them with local produce and techniques. *Bredie,* for example, is a stew made with meat or fish, vegetables, onions, and chili peppers.

The African Meal

Most Africans eat one large meal a day, generally in the evening. A typical meal may include a grain such as millet cooked into a porridge or a vegetable such as yams. This is served with a seasoned stew made with vegetables and flavored with meat, poultry, or fish, if available.

The evening meal is always a social occasion. The food may be served in one large bowl, which is set on the ground. People sit around the bowl, using either pieces of bread or their fingers to scoop up the food.

In many areas of Africa, spicy foods are preferred. Cooks make their own seasoning mixes, based on the many kinds of hot chili and spices available. One blend, called **berbere**, is commonly used in Ethiopia in soups and stews. It is a spicy combination of garlic, red and black peppers, salt, coriander, fenugreek, and cardamom. Other spices are added, depending on the cook's preference.

North Africa

The five main countries that make up North Africa are Libya, Egypt, Algeria, Morocco, and Tunisia. The population is clustered along the Mediterranean, in desert oases, or in irrigated parts of Egypt along the Nile. Because of its location along ancient trade routes linking Asia to Europe, this area has been well traveled. Its cuisine reflects the influence of those early travelers. The use of rice as a staple and the variety of produce are two legacies of foreign visitors. Two other staple starches grown in the region and still widely used are wheat and barley.

◆ **The Moroccan dishes shown here are moussaka (top), made of sliced eggplant, seasoned ground beef, and potatoes topped with a special sauce and then baked; hummus (left), a dip made from blended chickpeas lightly seasoned and mixed with sesame sauce; and stuffed Cornish hen el morocco (right), a baked hen stuffed with rice, almonds, raisins, and saffron. What is the name of a sesame seed paste that is popular in this area?**

- *Sub-Saharan Africa*
- *North Africa (text pages 600-602)*

African Meal

After students have read the description of an African meal on this page, challenge students to work in different task groups to learn about and ultimately prepare an authentic African meal. One task group might be in charge of finding recipes, another ingredients, a third details of African dress, a fourth mealtime mood. Invite a representative of the school newspaper to attend and write about the experience. L1

Discussion Activity

Ask students to explain why traditional foods in the countries of North Africa and the Middle East include foods typical of Asia, Europe, and southern Africa.

Map Reading Activity

On a map of Africa, have students locate the areas in North Africa where the population is densely clustered. Discuss reasons other areas are virtually unpopulated.

Extending Learning

North Africa—North Africans enjoy porridge, grilled lamb, meatballs, roasted locust, and mint tea. Poorer individuals eat cereal, legumes, seasonal vegetables, and bread. In Egypt, the poorer segments subsist on even less, making do with a porridge of brown beans, lentils, or rice.

Nomads, who trade goods or perform short-term tasks, live in the desert. Their eating plan centers on camel meat and milk. In an oasis, the date palm is common. Dates have become a symbol of hospitality and are always offered to visitors.

TEACH cont.

- *The Middle East (text pages 602-604)*

Taste Test

Have students sample stuffed vine leaves and couscous. Discuss other dishes commonly found in the countries of North Africa.

Demonstration

Point out to students that the word *tajine* is not only the name of a dish but the vessel in which it is cooked. If you can, bring an actual tajine to class. Have students inspect the vessel, noting in particular the conical shape of the lid. From what students have learned about heat and moist forms of cooking, ask if they can deduce why the cookware has this distinctive shape. (Rising water vapor is trapped and forced down the sloped sides, tenderizing the meat.)

Comparison Activity

Have students review the components of *pollo con mole poblano* on page 594, then compare the dish with *pastilla,* described on this page. In what way are the two dishes similar to each other and different from most dishes students have experienced? What American eating customs are students aware of that might seem odd to visitors from another land? Conclude by asking interested students to investigate unusual regional eating customs in the U.S.

◆ **Tabbouleh (in front) is a refreshing salad from the Middle East made with bulgur and accented with dill. Consult print or online resources to learn what bulgur is.**

North African Cuisine

Although there are some differences among the cuisines of North Africa, all make use of olive oil, chickpeas, fava beans, lentils, lamb, and goat. Dried fruits and nuts play a role in the cuisine, as do chili peppers and cinnamon.

One notable dish of the region is *tajine,* a Moroccan specialty. The dish is a long-cooked stew of lamb, prunes, and almonds, sometimes flavored with cinnamon. Tajine is often served with couscous, a fluffy steamed grain. *Couscous* is also the name of an entire meal featuring the grain and one of several stewed meats or poultry mixed with aromatic vegetables. Another dish that is both savory and sweet is *pastilla,* common in both Morocco and Algeria. This dish, which bears French influences, is a pigeon pie made with phyllo dough, eggs, vegetables, spices, and nuts. The finished dish is sprinkled with sugar.

The Middle East

The Middle East is located just east of North Africa, between Southeast Europe and Southwest Asia. The main countries of the Middle East are Lebanon, Syria, Iran, Iraq, Israel, Jordan, Kuwait, Turkey, and Saudi Arabia. Most people in this area are Arabs. Israel, which is a Jewish nation, is the exception.

Middle Eastern Cuisine

There are many similarities among the foods of the various nations of the Middle East and North Africa. The names and some seasonings may vary, but the basic ingredients and cooking methods are similar.

Fruits include apricots, pomegranates, dates, figs, grapes, and oranges. Vegetables include eggplant, peppers, olives, cucumbers, and tomatoes. Seasonings include parsley, dill, mint, cinnamon, lemon juice, pine nuts, onion, and garlic. *Tahini,* a sesame seed paste, is popular. Lamb is commonly eaten; chicken and fish are also used when available. Chicken is sometimes an ingredient in stews made with lentils, beans, rice, and vegetables. Pork is a food forbidden by religious law throughout this region.

INFOLINK
For more on bulgur and other grains, see Section 17-1.

FOOD SCIENCE

Couscous

Couscous is the cracked endosperm of the wheat kernel. It is one of the most versatile grains. In North Africa, it is used as a cereal, in salads and main dishes, and—in sweetened form—as a dessert. Couscous, which has a nutty flavor, is steamed, generally in a specially made piece of cookware.

In recent years, couscous has become more widely known and used in the United States, but more as a side dish to conventional foods. It can be found in the grain sections of many supermarkets.

Staple Foods

Although rice and barley are eaten, the staple starch of the Middle East is wheat, especially in the form of bulgur. This grain is a featured ingredient in *tabbouleh,* a popular salad that also includes tomatoes, mint, parsley, onions, and olive oil.

Another important staple food is yogurt. Depending on where you are, you might find yogurt made from the milk of cows, goats, camels, or buffalo. In several countries, yogurt is called *leban.* Leban is often mixed with vegetables, especially cucumbers and dates, for a side dish or part of a main dish.

Here are some other dishes commonly found in this area:

- **Kubaybah or kibbi.** A mixture of ground lamb, bulgur, cinnamon, and all-spice.
- **Stuffed vine leaves.** Are filled with a rice and meat mixture and served with a sauce made of yogurt, garlic, and mint.
- **Herrira.** A mutton and vegetable soup. Is eaten often during Ramadan, the month when Muslims fast during daylight hours.
- **Chelo.** Popular especially in Iran, Iraq, and Lebanon. Steamed rice accompanied by a meat or vegetable dish.
- **Koresh.** A stew of meat or poultry with vegetables, fruit, nuts, seasoning, and perhaps cereal. Most Iranians will eat a *chelo koresh* for one meal a day.

Desserts of the Middle East are often fresh, seasonal fruits. The people of the Middle East also enjoy sweet desserts, such as *baklava,* phyllo dough layered with nuts and honey syrup. *Halva* is a candy made of ground sesame seeds and honey.

For a feast, such as a wedding, it is common to roast a whole sheep and serve it with couscous. A salad of tomatoes, peppers, cucumbers, mint, melon, grapes, dates, and figs might be included.

Israel

Israel includes people native to the Middle East along with others from around the world. Consequently, its food customs embrace both Middle Eastern traditions and those of many other countries. Customs also reflect Jewish food traditions and laws, including a prohibition against mixing dairy foods and meat.

Traditional condiments, which find their way into most recipes, include *shatta, zhoug,* and tahini. *Shatta* is a red chili pepper mixture. *Zhoug* is a combination of green chili peppers, parsley, coriander, cumin, garlic, olive oil, and salt and pepper.

Some Israelis live in a **kibbutz** (kee-BOOTS), a communal organization, which raises its own food. Breakfasts at a kibbutz are substantial. They may consist of fresh produce, cold meats, cheese, fish, eggs, condiments, vegetable salads, and hot coffee.

Chicken and lamb are widely used. So are chickpeas, which are enjoyed both in *falafel*—patties of the ground legume seasoned with parsley and fried—and in *hummus b'tahini,* a spread of ground chickpeas, lemon juice, and tahini. Both dishes are served with pita bread, the pocket bread popular throughout much of the Middle East.

- *The Middle East (text pages 602-604)*

Country Food Profiles

Have interested students select one of the countries of the Middle East. Using online or print resources, students are to investigate this country, and then develop a brief profile, noting how the food traditions have been affected by location. Profiles are to be maintained in a classroom resource folder. L1

Research Activity

Have students research the history of Israel and the land that makes up what is now the nation of Israel. Among the questions they are to answer in their research are the following: When did Israel become a state? How has history influenced Israeli culture and food customs?

Lab Experience

Ask students to prepare the recipe for hummus b'tahini in the *Foods Lab Resources* booklet. Invite them to share samples of the spread with classmates, along with triangles of pita bread. Ask students to describe the flavor and texture and to decide if this highly nutritious spread might become a periodic component of their eating plans. L2

Extending Learning

Israel—Israel is considered the Jewish home state among Jews throughout the world. Many of the foods eaten in Israel are largely unknown to Jews elsewhere.

One food that does bond Jews is *gefilte* fish, a dish of eastern European origin. This dish is a poached mixture of ground pike and other white-fleshed fish and may be eaten hot or cold. The name, which is a variant spelling of the German word for "stuffed" or "filled," refers to the early practice of stuffing this mixture into a whole carp, which was then poached.

ASSESS

REVIEW

- Ask students to summarize the main ideas in this section.
- Have students complete the Section Review. (Answers appear below.)

EVALUATION

- Have students write a short essay describing foods available and commonly eaten in Africa and the Middle East.
- Have students take the quiz for Section 22-2. (Use the quiz in the *Teacher Resource Guide,* or construct your own with the **Exam***View*® *Test Generator* on the *Effective Instruction CD-ROM.*)

RETEACHING

- Have partners work with a map of Africa and the Middle East, attaching sticky notes to the places discussed and listing the foods of each.
- Refer to the *Reteaching Activities* booklet for the Section 22-2 activity sheet.

CLOSE

Have students create flow charts or other graphics that highlight the relationship between geography, foods, and food preparation in Africa and the Middle East.

◆ **Hummus b'tahini, a mash of chickpeas, lemon juice, and tahini is a favorite in Israel and other Middle Eastern nations. What nutrients does this dish contain?**

Section 22-2 Review & Activities

1. What are two important food plants that found their way to sub-Saharan Africa from other continents?
2. Identify and describe two North African dishes.
3. Name two staple foods of the Middle East.
4. **Analyzing.** Give an example of how religion influences eating habits in Middle Eastern countries.
5. **Synthesizing.** How does global travel influence the exchange of food customs today? How does this compare with the influence of travel in the past?
6. **Applying.** Find a recipe for making yogurt (using milk and a small amount of cultured yogurt). Prepare a work plan for making some at home or in a foods lab.

Answers to Section 22-2 Review & Activities

1. Any two: Coconuts, corn, cassava, peanuts.
2. Any two: Tajine—a long-cooked stew of lamb, prunes, and almonds; couscous—a fluffy steamed grain topped with stewed meats or poultry and aromatic vegetables; pastilla—pigeon pie made with phyllo dough, eggs, vegetables, spices, nuts, and sugar.
3. Wheat and yogurt.
4. Answers will vary. One possibility: Pork is forbidden by religious law.
5. Answers will vary.
6. Answers will vary.

Recipe File

Couscous Tabbouleh

This refreshing salad combines a staple grain popular in North Africa and flavors of the Middle East.

Customary	Ingredients	Metric
1 cup	Reduced-sodium chicken broth	250 mL
¾ cup	Couscous	175 mL
¼ cup	Lemon juice	50 mL
1 Tbsp.	Olive oil	15 mL
¼ tsp.	Salt	1 mL
¼ tsp.	Pepper	1 mL
½ cup	Peeled, chopped cucumber	125 mL
1	Tomato, chopped	1
½ cup	Chopped green onion	125 mL
½ cup	Chopped fresh parsley	125 mL
¼ cup	Chopped fresh mint	50 mL
	Mint leaves (for garnish)	

Yield: 4 servings, ½ cup each
Equipment: Medium saucepan

Directions

1. In a medium saucepan, bring chicken broth to a boil.
2. Place couscous in a large bowl. Carefully pour hot broth over couscous. Let stand 5 minutes. (All liquid should be absorbed. Drain if necessary.) Cool to room temperature.
3. In a small bowl, whisk together lemon juice, olive oil, salt, and pepper. Set aside.
4. Add cucumber, tomato, green onion, parsley, and mint to couscous.
5. Drizzle lemon juice mixture over couscous. Toss to mix.
6. Serve, garnished with mint leaves, if desired.

Nutrition Information

Per serving (approximate): 183 calories, 4 g protein, 32 g carbohydrate, 4 g fat, 0 mg cholesterol, 339 mg sodium
Good source of: iron, vitamin A, vitamin C, B vitamins

Food for Thought

- Tabbouleh is traditionally prepared with bulgur wheat. Name two other grains you could use to prepare this recipe.
- What pre-preparation tasks could be done while the couscous is cooling to room temperature?

Recipe File

Couscous Tabbouleh

This recipe uses chopping skills, as well as planning skills, in the cooking of the couscous and allowing the couscous to cool.

USING THE RECIPE

- Have students read the recipe and discuss each step.
- Remind students to take extreme care when pouring the hot broth over the couscous.
- Have each lab team fill out a work plan. (See the *Foods Lab Resources* booklet.)
- Have students check off the ingredients and equipment listed on the recipe worksheet and prepare the recipe.
- Have students complete the evaluation and questions on the recipe worksheet.

SEE ALSO. . .
The *Foods Lab Resources* booklet for the "Couscous Tabbouleh" recipe worksheet and other recipe alternatives.

Answers to Food for Thought

1. Answers will vary but should show thoughtful consideration of the nature of the grains used. One possibility would be quinoa, which like couscous is not actually boiled but steeped.
2. The vegetables and herbs could be chopped.

SECTION
22-3
Europe

FOCUS

MOTIVATORS

- On the board, list foods commonly found in Western and Eastern Europe. Ask students to identify those with which they are familiar. Ask if they know the national origin of these dishes.
- Identify the Western and Eastern European countries from which ancestors of the local population migrated to the United States. Ask students to identify any foods associated with these groups that are still popular in the area.

VOCABULARY ACTIVITY

Pronounce the terms listed under "Look for These Terms." Ask for volunteers to find the terms in the section and read aloud their definitions.

STUDY SKILLS

- **Outlining.** Have students read the section and outline it by copying the headers on paper and leaving space after each one. Students are to write a sentence in their own words, summarizing the content under each header.
- Have students read the section and complete the appropriate part of the Chapter 22 Study Guide in the *Student Workbook*.

SECTION 22-3

Objectives

After studying this section, you should be able to:

- Identify foods commonly found in Western and Eastern Europe.
- Identify ways that culture, history, geography, and climate influence European foods.

Look for These Terms

scones
high tea
deglazing
haute cuisine
polenta
antipasto

Europe

The European countries are small, and there is considerable travel among them. They share many food customs and seasoning choices, especially neighboring countries with similar climates. On the other hand, most European countries have had distinctive histories and traditions, which give their foods unique identities.

Western Europe

The cuisines of many world cultures, including our own, trace their roots to countries and regions of Western Europe, which include the British Isles, France, Spain, Portugal, Germany, Austria, Italy, Greece, and Scandinavia.

The British Isles

The British Isles are an island group just off the European continent. The two largest islands are Great Britain—which includes England, Scotland, Wales, and Northern Ireland—and Ireland. The food of this region tends to be hearty and cooked by plain, simple methods. Beef, mutton (meat from older sheep), pork, and fish are favorite foods. Many Britons eat four meals a day: breakfast, lunch, tea, and dinner (or supper).

The habit in our own country of eating hearty breakfasts is a custom inherited from Britain. Today, breakfast in the British Isles still usually includes cereal, eggs, bacon or sausage, broiled tomatoes, toast, and marmalade. Tea is more common in the morning than coffee.

Section 22-3 Resources

◆ **Student Workbook,** pp. 164, 169
◆ **Teacher Resource Guide**
Lesson Plan 22-3 Organizer
Section 22-3 Quiz
◆ **Effective Instruction CD-ROM**
Exam*View*® *Test Generator*
PowerPoint® Slide #50
◆ **Transparency Package,** CT-50
◆ **Student Motivation Kit**
Reteaching Activities, p. 102
Enrichment Activities
Foods Lab Resources, pp. 139–140, 145–146
A Global Foods Tour, pp. 21–23, 63–92
Skills for Making Food Choices, pp. 49–50

◆ Despite differences in culture and customs throughout Europe, some foods and methods of food preparation transcend national boundaries. The shellfish stew shown here is a common sight all along the Mediterranean coast. In a food encyclopedia or similar resource, look up *pizza* and *pissaladiére*. Where did the second dish originate? In what way are the two foods alike?

British Cuisine

Typical lunches and dinners in Britain revolve around meat, including:

- **Roast beef and Yorkshire pudding.** Beef baked in the oven, with a popover-like mixture cooked in the pan drippings. Roast beef is usually served with a horse-radish sauce or mustard.
- **Shepherd's pie.** Leftover ground lamb or beef cooked with onions, garlic, tomatoes, and seasonings. The dish is covered with mashed potatoes and baked.
- **Cornish pasties** (PAS-tees). Popular in the south of England, these baked pastry turnovers—filled with steak, onions, chopped potatoes and carrots—were once carried to work by miners and eaten cold.

The British also enjoy a variety of game—pigeon, quail, pheasant, and deer. Fish is also common to British menus. *Finnan haddie,* a fish dish sometimes eaten for breakfast, is smoked haddock prepared with milk, onion, lemon juice, pepper, and parsley.

Tea

A meal that is uniquely British is four o'clock tea. Tea generally includes bread—either plain or in small finger sandwiches—and a dessert. Crumpets, which are similar to what Americans call English muffins, might also be served. So might **scones**, a tasty variation of baking-powder biscuits. Scones are often served with jam and clotted cream—a thick spread skimmed from rich, whole milk. In Scotland, tea may be served with oatcakes or oatmeal biscuits.

Sometimes, Britons have their tea served with a nonsweet dish that is somewhere between an appetizer and a main course. This meal is called **high tea**. A typical dish served at high tea is *Welsh rabbit* (or *rarebit*), seasoned, melted cheddar cheese on toast. High tea often takes the place of supper.

TEACH

- *Western Europe (text pages 606-612)*

Recipe Search

Have students look for "bubble and squeak" and other recipes typical of Great Britain. Do these recipes give some idea of the variety of foods eaten by the British? 

Guest Speaker

Invite a person from Britain to speak to students about the English custom of afternoon tea, describing how the tea itself is prepared and naming foods beyond those mentioned in the text that are customarily served at high tea. As a followup, students are to prepare their own afternoon (or morning) tea.

Discussion Activity

Discuss dishes commonly served at lunch or dinner in the British Isles, comparing these to ones eaten in the United States. Ask students what they generally eat for the meal known as "tea." Ask volunteers to read about and explain this British custom.

FOOD SCIENCE

Shepherd's Pie

After students have read the bulleted list on this page under the heading "British Cuisine," reveal to them that a recipe for one of the items, shepherd's pie, appears in the *Foods Lab Resources* booklet. Have selected volunteers prepare the recipe, while classmates look on. Students may then sample and comment on the dish. Note that in Britain variations on this theme are made with fish (fish pie). Invite students to share this one-dish meal idea with families and to report back on family reactions.

TEACH cont.

- *Western Europe (text pages 606-612)*

Finding Recipes

Have students look through cookbooks to find at least two French recipes—one crepe recipe and one soup or stew recipe. Ask students whether the recipes found are examples of haute cuisine or cuisine bourgeoise. How can they tell? L1

Comparison Activity

Invite interested students to investigate the origins of cuisine bourgeoise. Have the class as a whole compare this form of cooking with eating trends in early America, where servants first learned that lobster was a tasty food, although one snubbed by the rich.

- So well-loved is cassoulet today among the French, rich and poor, that three different cities in France—Toulouse, Carcasonne, and Castelnaudary—all claim to be the place where the dish originated.
- Leon Gambetta, a 17th-century French noble, holds the distinction of having eaten himself to death by consuming enough cassoulet to feed three hungry adults.

◆ Plum pudding, a Christmas tradition in England, is a dense cake made with raisins, nuts, and flavorings, steamed in cheesecloth. Despite its name, plum pudding is not made with plums. Can you name another food whose name includes an ingredient that is not present?

France

The goal of French cooking is to maximize the flavors of all ingredients in a dish so that no one flavor overpowers another. Much of French cooking is fairly simple—and frugal. The practice of **deglazing** a pan—adding stock or another liquid to a defatted sauté pan to loosen the browned-on particles—got its start in French kitchens. Deglazing is an easy and economical way of making a sauce.

Haute Cuisine

The classic dishes of France are often grouped under the heading **haute cuisine**. Literally "high cooking," this is a method of food preparation that makes use of complicated recipes and techniques, often involving costly ingredients. Originally, great chefs prepared these time-consuming dishes for aristocrats. Food preparation was considered an art. Rich sauces, elegantly decorated dishes, and exotic ingredients characterize haute cuisine. Haute cuisine exists today, usually in expensive restaurants.

Cuisine Bourgeoise

Outside of the aristocracy, a simpler form of cooking developed. *Cuisine bourgeoise* (boor-JWAHZ) is based on hearty, one-dish meals made from fresh ingredients from the local market. Cuisine bourgeoise varies from province to province. Examples include:

- **Ragout.** A flavorful stew made with vegetables and meat, poultry, or fish. It is often named after the region where it originated.
- **Pot-au-feu.** A soupy casserole of less tender cuts of beef, along with sausage and poultry, long-simmered in an earthenware pot with aromatic and root vegetables.
- **Cassoulet.** A hearty blend of white beans, meats, preserved duck, and garlic sausage.
- **Bouillabaisse.** A hearty soup that combines several types of fish and shellfish, tomatoes, and herbs.

◆ Cassoulet is typical French country fare. This rib-sticking dish consists of beans, meats, poultry, and garlic sausage baked together under a breadcrumb topping. What method of cooking do you think is used to make cassoulet?

Reinforcing Key Skills

Present the following problem to student groups. Allow time for them to discuss and compare their responses.

Management—A restaurant offers a fixed-price offering of soup du jour, ragout, salad, and chocolate mousse for $13.99. Ordered separately, the items would cost $2.25, $6.95, $1.99, and $3.95, respectively. Ask students which version of the meal they would be better off ordering. Have them explain their reasoning.

Meals in France

French people rarely eat between meals. A typical breakfast is light, consisting of coffee or hot chocolate and some kind of bread—toast, a croissant, or *brioche,* a round roll made from a rich yeast dough. Lunch or dinner might include an *hors d'oeurve* (appetizer), followed by a light fish course, followed by a main dish and vegetables. Next comes a salad of greens simply dressed with a vinaigrette. A meal concludes with either a sweet dessert or with bread and cheese. Such a menu sounds filling. Portions, however, are kept sensible, and food is eaten slowly.

Spain and Portugal

Spain and Portugal inhabit a peninsula, which provides both countries with thousands of miles of coastline. Many of the dishes of both nations are based on fish and seafood.

Meals in Spain

Breakfast in Spain, as in France, generally consists of coffee or hot chocolate and a bread. The bread might be *churros,* fried strips of dough.

Lunch often consists of a salad, fish, a meat course, and fruit or a light dessert. Supper at home may be a light meal, but at a restaurant, it may be another large meal. Spanish people eat out late, with dinner hour generally starting at 10:30 P.M.

A few dishes are enjoyed throughout the country. These include chicken with garlic, garlic shrimp, *gazpacho* (cold vegetable soup), and *paella*—a combination of saffron-flavored rice, poultry, and shellfish. Another dish of Spain, *tortilla española,* is an omelet made with potatoes, onions, and green peppers. The dish, served in slices at room temperature, is popular in *tapas* bars—restaurants that specialize in small servings of foods ranging from main dish to salad items.

Portuguese Cuisine

Portuguese cooking is similar to Spanish cooking, except that the Portuguese prefer foods with a spicier kick. The cuisine was greatly influenced by travelers to India, South Africa, and South America. Portuguese foods tend to be rich because they contain more cream and butter.

◆ **Tortilla española is one of numerous dishes featured among the selection of tapas in Spain. It is an omelet filled with green peppers, onion, and potato, served at room temperature. Compare the above description with the recipe for frittata in Section 18-3, on page 481. What similarities can you find between the two dishes? What does this reveal about the sharing of food traditions among cultures?**

- *Western Europe (text pages 606-612)*

Eating Plan

Discuss with students the components of a typical French meal. Note that most people in France will either eat a multi-course meal at lunch *or* dinner—not both. Emphasize people there eat few between-meal snacks. Follow up by challenging students to "eat like the French" over a 24-hour period. If class time coincides with lunch, arrange for the large meal to be prepared by students in class. Students are to follow up at home with a sandwich or other light dinner. Have students discuss the experience. L1

Recipes Analysis Activity

Have students study recipes from Spain and Portugal. Have students write a short report of their findings.

VISUAL LEARNING ***Using the Photograph***

Have students study the photograph on this page, noting the name of the dish it depicts. With what other cuisine do students associate the tortilla? In what way is this tortilla different? Similar?

Extending Learning

Spain—Because much of the topography of Spain is mountains, the country is better able to support olive trees (brought by the ancient Romans) and vineyards than dairy farms and cattle ranches. As a result, menus are more likely to center on small animals than on beef, veal, and other meats. Olive oil is used almost exclusively in recipes; butter is rarely called for. Fruit grows well in Spain and is an integral part of most meals. Vegetables—except for tomatoes and peppers—are not often served alone, but they do appear as ingredients in many dishes.

TEACH cont.

- *Western Europe (text pages 606-612)*

Discussion Activity

Ask students to identify breads for which the Germans are famous. What are some other traditional German baked goods?

Social Influences

Have students study the historical relationships between Germany and Austria. Have students explain why the food customs in some parts of Austria are so similar to those of Germany. **L1**

Foreign Language Connection

Have volunteers read aloud and describe each of the foods read about on this page. Ask whether there are students in the class who speak or are studying German as a foreign language. If so, ask these individuals to translate literally the phrase *nürnberger lebkuchen.* As an alternative, reveal to students that phrase translates to "bread cakes typical of the city of Nürnberg." Challenge volunteers to investigate the literal meanings and/or origins of the terms sauerkraut, *streusel-kuchen,* and *Sachertorte* and report their findings back to the class. **L1**

Germany and Austria

Generally speaking, German food tends to be rich and heavy. Sausages abound, with different combinations and seasonings in each region. Familiar favorites include bratwurst and knockwurst.

Veal and pork are the most popular meats. Germans also eat beef and poultry, but fish is not popular.

German Cuisine

Some German dishes are characterized by a blending of fruit, vegetables, and meat to achieve sweet-sour flavors. An example is *sauerbraten,* beef marinated for several days in a sweet-sour sauce, and then simmered in the same sauce. It is served with noodles, dumplings, or boiled potatoes. *Schnitzel,* means "cutlet" in German, usually of veal. In *wienerschnitzel*—or "Viennese cutlet"—the veal is dipped in egg, breaded, and fried.

Germans are noted for their rye and pumpernickel breads as well as *stollen,* yeast bread with raisins and canned fruit. Another favorite is *streusel-kuchen,* a coffee cake topped with a mixture of flour, sugar, butter, nuts, and cinnamon.

German desserts include cakes and cookies. *Marzipan,* a rich candy made of ground almonds and sugar, has its origins in Germany. So does *nürnberger lebkuchen,* which is better known as gingerbread.

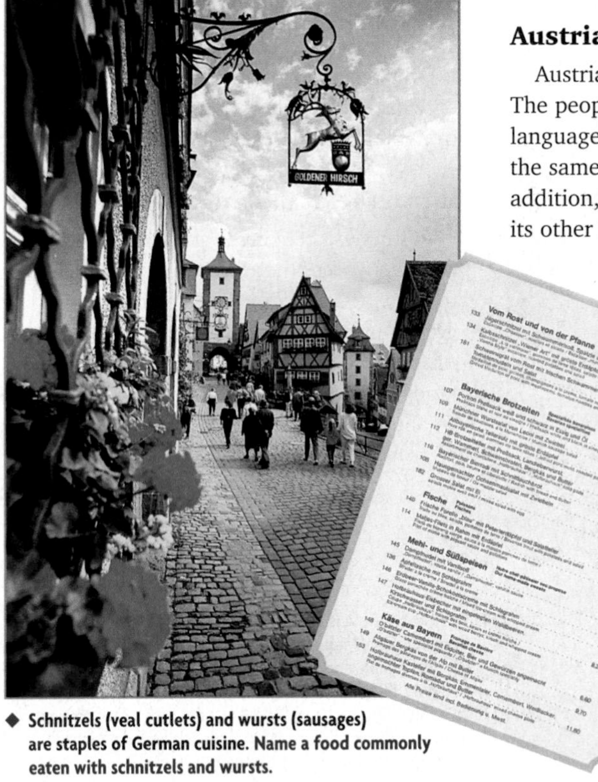

◆ **Schnitzels (veal cutlets) and wursts (sausages) are staples of German cuisine. Name a food commonly eaten with schnitzels and wursts.**

Austrian Cuisine

Austria is a nation south of Germany. The people there share not only a common language with the Germans but also many of the same food customs. Austrian cooking, in addition, bears influences of the cooking of its other Eastern European neighbors.

Austrians are famous for their rich cakes, almost always served *mitt Schlag*—with thick, sweetened whipped cream. *Linzertorte,* a cross between a pie and a cake, has a crust made in part of ground nuts and a sweet jam filling. *Sachertorte,* another famous Austrian dessert, is a rich chocolate cake spread with apricot preserves and a dark chocolate icing.

FOOD SCIENCE

Lactic Acid and Sauerkraut

Sauerkraut is made when cabbage is fermented by bacteria that produce lactic acid. It is the presence of this acid that gives sauerkraut its characteristic tart flavor. Locate a recipe for sauerkraut. Have students prepare a batch of this typical German food. Invite students to taste and record their reactions to some of the freshly pickled cabbage. Save half the batch to be sampled several weeks later. Ask students to compare their reactions to the aged sauerkraut with those of the freshly made product.

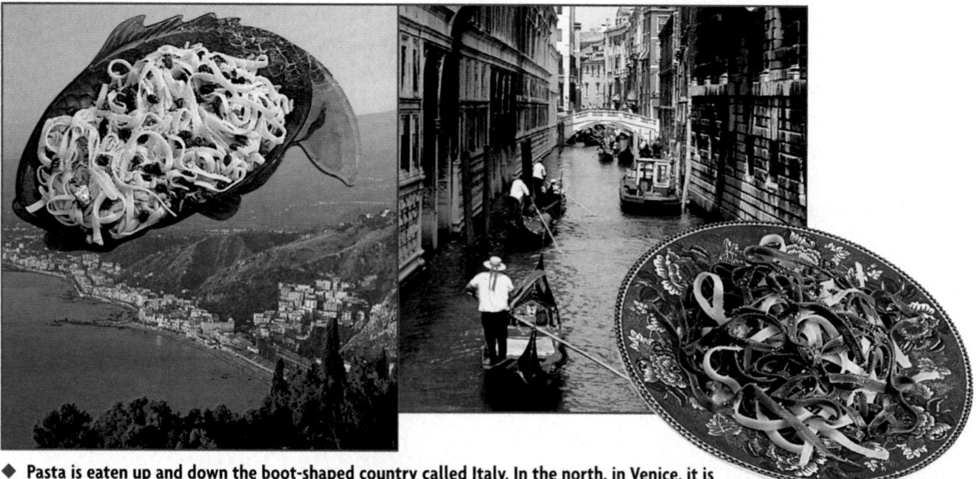

◆ **Pasta is eaten up and down the boot-shaped country called Italy. In the north, in Venice, it is served as "black pasta," deriving its dark color from cuttlefish ink. In the south, in Sicily, it is served with local sardines, pine nuts, and raisins. Look at a map of Italy. Try to explain why seafood plays such a prominent role in the cuisines of this country.**

Italy

Where did pasta come from? A popular explanation is that Marco Polo brought the recipe to Italy from China in the 1300s. Whatever its origins, pasta is the dish most associated with Italy. It is usually eaten, however, as a first course, not as a main course.

Italian Cuisine

In the south of Italy, pasta is often—though not always—served with tomato sauce. On the southern island of Sicily, a local favorite is *pasta con sarde,* made with sardines, raisins, and pine nuts. In some parts of northern Italy, rice is favored over pasta, in both rice balls and *risotto,* short-grained rice simmered carefully in stock. Another grain common in the north is cornmeal, served as **polenta**, cornmeal mush that is sometimes cooled, sliced, and fried.

Along Italy's northwest borders, the cooking is similar to that of France and Germany. Butter is used in place of olive oil. Italians of this region also eat *speck* (SHPEK), a local sausage with a German-sounding name.

Seafood is popular along the coastal areas. In the south, fresh bass is served mariner-style, with tomatoes, onions, and fresh basil.

No Italian meal would be complete without a *contorno* (vegetable course). Served after the main course, a large plate of eggplant, string beans, artichokes, peas, potatoes, or other vegetable is passed around the table.

Salads may begin or end a meal. They are usually served with an oil and vinegar dressing. Salads, pickled vegetables, cheeses, and other appetizers are called **antipasto**, which means "before the meal."

Italy is famous for its cheeses, from the hard parmesan and romano, which must be grated, to *ricotta* (or "recooked" cheese), which is similar to cottage cheese.

Greece

The history of Greece includes a period of nearly 400 years when it was ruled by Turkey. As a result, many Greek dishes, such as vine leaves stuffed with seasoned meat and rice, are similar to foods in the Middle East.

- *Western Europe (text pages 606-612)*

Charting Activity

Invite teams of volunteers to each select a different region of Italy, such as the Veneto, Lombardy, Tuscany, and Sicily. Provide each team with a checklist containing the following: typical foods, type of fat used in cooking, starch most commonly eaten. Have teams combine their findings into a large chart. Use the chart as a bridge to a discussion of what factors might account for these differences.

Border Patrol

Point out to students that political boundaries and cultural boundaries between one nation and another are not always one and the same. Illustrate this point by asking volunteers to research food customs, cultural traits, and place names in the Dolomites, along Italy's northwest border with Germany. Have these students create a game titled "Border Patrol." The game might consist of index cards on which a trait is identified (for example: "The people there commonly have blond hair" or "Little flour or potato dumplings usually accompany roasted and braised meats"). Players are to determine whether the trait is characteristic of northern Italy or its German neighbor. First player to answer 20 questions correctly wins. L2

Extending Learning

Italy

- Fresh fruit is the dessert of choice after most meals. *Biscotti*—cookies whose name translates as "twice cooked"—are also popular.
- On special occasions, special desserts are made and served. These include *pannetone* (a bread-like cake dotted with raisins) and *cannoli* (pastry tubes filled with a ricotta custard).
- *Gelato,* or ice cream, is eaten mostly as a confection but rarely as dessert. *Gelato* may be served either in a cone or in a cup, with or without *panna* (naturally thickened sweet cream).

TEACH cont.

- *Western Europe (text pages 606-612)*

Discussion Activity

On the board, write the following questions for general discussion of this page: Why do many Greek dishes resemble Turkish dishes? What foods are common to most Scandinavian countries? Which are unique to particular countries?

Taste Test

Have students sample several varieties of Scandinavian breads. Ask how these breads are similar to and different from breads students regularly eat. Discuss other foods popular in Scandinavia.

Interview

Invite students who know an individual of Greek or Scandinavian descent to interview that person, if possible recording the interview on video or audio tape. Among the questions interviewers might ask are the following: What foods do you eat that are typical of your culture? Is it difficult while living in the United States to follow the culinary traditions of your country? Allow time for students to share interviews with the class. L1

Greek Cuisine

Greek cooking often makes use of tomatoes, green peppers, garlic, lemon juice, and olive oil. Rice appears in many dishes. *Feta cheese,* made from sheep's or goat's milk and cured in brine, is widely eaten as an appetizer and in salads. It is also used in cooking.

Because of Greece's location on the Mediterranean, Greek cuisine makes use of fish and shellfish. Grilled octopus is eaten, and shrimp are sometimes baked with tomatoes and feta cheese. Lamb is the most popular meat, often served grilled. *Moussaka* is a layered casserole made with seasoned ground lamb and sliced eggplant. A rich white sauce is poured over the mixture before baking.

Northern Europe

Denmark, Norway, Sweden, and Finland make up the Scandinavian countries. Although these countries do not have a lavish cuisine, the people have used the foods available to them creatively and tastefully.

Foods of Scandinavia

Scandinavians rely heavily on fish for food. Dried and salted cod is a staple. Fish may also be fried, poached, or grilled, as well as used in soups and fishballs.

Dairy products are also important to Scandinavian cooks. Each country seems to have a version of thick or sour milk, which may be eaten with sugar. Milk, butter, and cream are essential ingredients in many dishes. Scandinavians also bake an array of rye and white breads.

Because the local growing season is so short, Scandinavian meals rarely include an abundance of fresh fruits and vegetables. Root vegetables such as potatoes, carrots, onions, and rutabagas are used regularly. Fresh berries (lingonberries, raspberries, and strawberries) are often used to accent desserts. *Fruksoppa,* or "fruit soup," is a mixture of dried fruit and tapioca cooked in a sweetened liquid and served cold.

Scandinavian Cuisine

The Swedish *smorgasbord* is perhaps the finest example of a bountiful buffet. Originally, the word meant "sandwich board." Now it is a collection of assorted meats and fish dishes, raw vegetables, salads, and hot dishes.

Smørrebrød are open-faced sandwiches, which the Danes eat daily. Thin slices of buttered bread are topped with pickled herring, cooked pork, raw cucumbers, onion rings, apple slices, mustard, and horseradish. The Danes are also well known for their rich, flaky, buttery pastries with touches of sugar, almonds, or jam.

◆ **Fish is a prominent part of this Swedish smorgasbord. Why is fish so common in Scandinavian cooking?**

Extending Learning

Greek Cuisine—Phyllo pastry, a paper-thin dough that becomes quite crisp when baked, is widely used in Greek cuisines. The pastry is used both in savory dishes, such as *spanakopita* (triangles of phyllo dough filled with seasoned spinach and feta cheese) and *baklava,* the dessert popular in the Middle East.

Phyllo dough is found today in American supermarkets and has a variety of uses beyond those of Greek cooking. When working with it, one must be careful to keep the sheets wrapped in a damp towel, since they dry out rapidly when exposed to air.

Eastern Europe

The countries of Eastern Europe underwent major changes in borders—and even names—in the late twentieth century. For ease in describing culinary history and tradition, general areas will be referred to by their traditional names. The following discussion will include the foods and culture of Russia, Czechoslovakia, Hungary, Bulgaria, Yugoslavia, and Rumania.

Russia

Russia is one of the many countries that once made up the Soviet Union. It covers a vast area, from Eastern Europe to the Pacific Coast in Asia.

Russian Cuisine

Food in Russia differs from region to region, as it does in most countries. National dishes are based mainly on available staple foods. One example is Russian black bread, a dark, heavy, moist bread of rye and wheat, flavored with chocolate, caraway, coffee, and molasses.

Hearty soups are also common. *Schchi* is a soup made from sauerkraut. Other popular soups are made with fresh cabbage and potatoes. *Borscht,* or beet soup, is one of the best-known Russian soups. If available, meat or sausage is added. Most soups either contain sour cream or are served with it.

Fish—including sardines, salted herring, and salmon—are common. Caviar is often served with *blini,* small buckwheat pancakes, and sour cream. Buckwheat is also eaten crushed and cooked as *kasha,* and is served as an accompaniment to meats.

Tea is the most popular beverage. On cold evenings, you might find a gathering of Russians drinking tea and enjoying good conversation.

Other Eastern European Nations

The food in some other nations of Eastern Europe has many similarities to that of Russia and, sometimes, to food of the Middle East. The use of wheat, kasha, and cabbage, for example, is widespread.

Poland. In Poland, the national dish, *bigos,* is a stew of game meat with mushrooms, onions, sauerkraut, sausage, apples, and tomatoes. *Krupnik* is a barley and vegetable soup to which sour cream and dill are added.

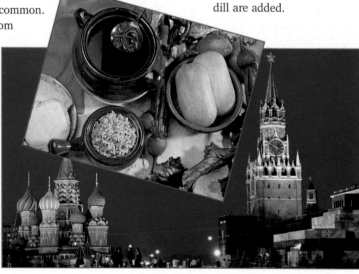

◆ This assortment from the Russian table includes borscht, piroshky, and kasha a la Gouriev. The last of these is a custard-like dessert made with farina and served warm. Which dish pictured is sometimes served cold?

- *Eastern Europe (text pages 613-614)*

Discussion Activity

Ask students to list and describe dishes common to Russian cuisine. Ask: What foods are preferred by other nations of eastern Europe?

Taste Test

Have students taste test cabbage soup, borscht, and black bread. How do the Russian bread and soups differ from those students are most familiar with?

Reasoning Activity

Have students compare the foods eaten in other Eastern European nations with those eaten in Russia and the Middle East. What factors may have contributed to similarities among these foods? To differences?

Reinforcing Key Skills

Present the following problem to student groups. Allow time for them to discuss and compare their responses.

Communication—You overhear two people discussing a restaurant that specializes in eastern European cooking. One of them claims not to like eastern European food because it is so heavy. How might you react if this statement were made to you?

ASSESS

REVIEW

- Ask students to summarize the main ideas in this section.
- Have students complete the Section Review. (Answers appear below.)

EVALUATION

- Have students collaborate on a booklet titled "When in Rome." The booklet is to cover points of etiquette when dining throughout Europe, including what foods to expect in restaurants.
- Have students take the quiz for Section 22-3. (Use the quiz in the *Teacher Resource Guide,* or construct your own with the **Exam***View*® *Test Generator* on the *Effective Instruction CD-ROM.*)

RETEACHING

- Have pairs of students prepare and use flash cards to help each other remember the names and definitions of foods from different countries.
- Refer to the *Reteaching Activities* booklet for the Section 22-3 activity sheet.

CLOSE

Lead a classroom discussion about the foods of Western and Eastern Europe. Ask students which they prefer and why.

Hungary. The Hungarian people enjoy grilled skewered lamb or beef in addition to the dish for which they are most famous, *gulyas* or *goulash*, in our culture. This souplike dish is made with beef, onions, paprika, potatoes, and perhaps garlic, caraway seeds, tomatoes, and honey.

Hungarians also enjoy sauerkraut, pork-stuffed cabbage rolls, strudels, and *dobos torta,* a chocolate-filled sponge cake with many layers, glazed with caramel.

Czechoslovakia. The people of the Czechoslovakia area rely on dumplings as the cornerstone of their meals. Dumplings may be made from a variety of foods and come in many shapes and forms. Pork, beef, and game are common, as are cabbage and sauerkraut with caraway. One of the most famous Czech dishes is *kolacky,* yeast buns filled with fruit, cottage cheese, poppy seeds, or jam.

Yugoslavia. In the region of Yugoslavia, pilafs (seasoned rice dishes) are a favorite, as are cornmeal dishes, vegetables, and pasta. *Sarma,* the national dish, is rolled cabbage or sauerkraut leaves stuffed with a mixture of rice and ground pork. Also popular are thick, dark coffee; baklava; and desserts made with sweet noodles, dumplings, and fried yeast dough.

Romania. Corn is the mainstay of cooking in the area of Romania. Cornmeal mush, the national dish, is served with melted butter, sour cream, or yogurt. Romanian cooks also use peppers in their dishes and are known for their richly flavored stews.

Bulgaria. Grains, vegetables, fruit, nuts, and yogurt are mainstays of Bulgarian cuisine. Fresh vegetables are eaten widely in salads. Fruits, nuts, and herbs grow well in this region. The people prefer fish and lamb to other meats. A favorite dish is *potato musaka,* a casserole of vegetables, meat, potatoes, onions, garlic, tomato, eggs, cream, and grated cheese.

Section 22-3 Review & Activities

1. Name five foods commonly found in the countries of Western Europe.
2. What is the difference between haute cuisine and cuisine bourgeoise?
3. Identify five foods commonly found in Eastern European countries.
4. **Synthesizing.** Choose one of the cultures covered. What factors appear to have influenced food choices and how foods are prepared?
5. **Extending.** Design an international dinner. Choose an appetizer from one country, a main dish from another, a dessert from still another. Select foods that are compatible and varied, and that constitute a balanced, nutritious meal.
6. **Applying.** Choose a European country. Assume you are inviting two teens from that country to dinner with your family. Write a menu showing what you would serve to make these teens feel at home. Give reasons to support your selections.

Answers to Section 22-3 Review & Activities

1. Answers will vary. Be sure students' answers accurately reflect information found in the text.
2. Haute cuisine is complex and time-consuming, calling for expensive ingredients; cuisine bourgeoise is simpler and often involves one-dish meals.
3. Answers, which will vary, might include sour cream, sausage, cabbage, sauerkraut, and dumplings.
4. Answers will vary. Students might mention climate, especially temperature, among the factors for the culture chosen.
5. Answers will vary.
6. Answers will vary.

RECIPE FILE

Scandinavian Marinated Cod

Cod is a staple food in Scandinavia. This recipe might be prepared for a midday meal or a light supper. The cooked cod could also be flaked and used in a salad.

Customary	***Ingredients***	***Metric***
1 lb.	Cod fillets	454 g
¼ cup	Olive oil	50 mL
2 Tbsp.	Lemon juice	30 mL
¼ cup	Finely chopped onion	50 mL
1 tsp.	Salt	5 mL
½ tsp.	Pepper	2-3 mL
2 Tbsp.	Butter or margarine, melted	30 mL
2 Tbsp.	Vegetable oil	30 mL

Yield: 4 servings
Equipment: Shallow baking dish, broiler pan

Directions

1. Wash cod fillets in cold water and pat dry. Place in shallow baking dish.
2. In a small bowl, whisk together olive oil, lemon juice, onion, salt, and pepper.
3. Pour mixture over cod fillets. Let marinade 30 minutes (15 minutes on each side). Drain marinade from fillets and discard.
4. In another small bowl, blend melted butter or margarine with vegetable oil.
5. Preheat broiler.
6. Brush cold broiler grid with 1 tablespoon of the butter and oil mixture.
7. Place cod fillets on broiler pan.
8. Broil fillets 10 minutes per inch of thickness, turning halfway through cooking time.
9. Brush fillets with remaining butter and oil mixture after turning.
10. When done, the fish should flake easily with a fork.
11. Serve immediately.

Nutrition Information

Per serving (approximate): 300 calories, 20 g protein, 1 g carbohydrate, 6 g fat, 49 mg cholesterol, 260 mg sodium
Good source of: potassium, vitamin E, B vitamins, phosphorus

Food for Thought

- What other varieties of fish might you substitute for the cod?
- What other acids, herbs, or spices could be used in the marinade for this recipe?

RECIPE FILE

Scandinavian Marinated Cod

This recipe uses the skills of chopping and fish handling and preparation. Relevant portions of Chapters 8 and 19 might be consulted as needed.

USING THE RECIPE

- Have students read the recipe and discuss each step.
- Review food and kitchen safety procedures that apply to this recipe.
- Caution students to use the proper safety devices, such as potholders, when turning the fish.
- Have each lab team fill out a work plan. (See the *Foods Lab Resources* booklet.)
- Have students check off the ingredients and equipment listed on the recipe worksheet and prepare the recipe.
- Have students complete the evaluation and questions on the recipe worksheet.

SEE ALSO...

The *Foods Lab Resources* booklet for the "Scandinavian Marinated Cod" recipe worksheet and other recipe alternatives.

Answers to **Food for Thought**

1. Answers will vary. Refer students to the information on this subject in Chapter 19.
2. Answers will vary.

SECTION
22-4
Asia and the Pacific

FOCUS

MOTIVATORS

- Locate and identify countries in Asia and the Pacific on a world map. Ask students to identify foods they associate with Asia and the Pacific.
- Have students taste test samples of tofu prepared in different ways. Point out that tofu is made from soybeans. Discuss the nutritive value of tofu and describe other ways it can be prepared.

VOCABULARY ACTIVITY

Have a volunteer pronounce the terms listed under "Look for These Terms," while another finds the terms and their definitions in the section.

STUDY SKILLS

- **Listening.** Invite one or two students to prepare an oral reading of the section.
- Have students read the section and complete the appropriate part of the Chapter 22 Study Guide in the *Student Workbook*.

SECTION 22-4

Asia and the Pacific

"East is East, and West is West," Rudyard Kipling wrote over a century ago. Despite the merging of these two worlds since that time, in some ways, the East has remained separate. One way is in the food customs and traditions.

Objectives

After studying this section, you should be able to:

- Identify foods common to the countries of Asia and the Pacific.
- Point out how culture and climate influence the foods of Asia and the Pacific.

Look for These Terms

soba

garam masala

Asia

For purposes of discussion, the countries of Asia and the Pacific will be treated in four sections. The first will look at the world cultures of Japan, China, and Korea. The second will examine Southeast Asia. The third will cover the Asian subcontinent of India; the fourth, Australia and New Zealand.

Asian World Cultures

Asia is the world's largest continent in both area and population. Traditional Asian cooking emphasizes grains and legumes, and uses an abundance of fresh ingredients. The staple grain is rice, though wheat is widely used in parts of China, India, and Japan. Another staple is soybeans, which are used to make many products, such as soy sauce, tamari, and tofu. Soybean sprouts are used fresh and in cooked dishes.

The basic cooking methods include boiling, steaming, and frying. Main dishes are usually a mixture of fried or steamed vegetables, mixed with a small amount of meat, poultry, or fish. Foods are prepared and cooked in bite-size pieces, which allows them to be picked up with chopsticks. The custom of cutting foods in small pieces started centuries ago when fuel was scarce and expensive; small pieces would cook quickly.

Section 22-4 Resources

◆ **Student Workbook,** pp. 164, 171
◆ **Teacher Resource Guide**
Lesson Plan 22-4 Organizer
Section 22-4 Quiz
Chapter 22 Test
◆ **Effective Instruction CD-ROM**
ExamView® *Test Generator*
PowerPoint® Slide #50
◆ **Transparency Package,** CT-50
◆ **Student Motivation Kit**
Reteaching Activities, p. 103
Enrichment Activities
Foods Lab Resources, pp. 141–144
A Global Foods Tour, pp. 24, 27, 93–111, 137–146

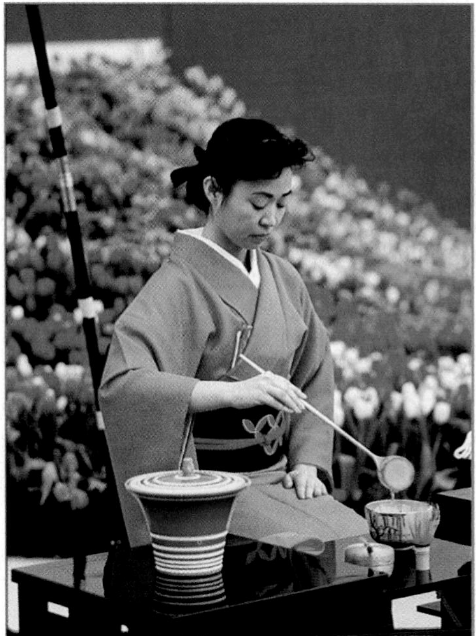

◆ The tea ceremony is a centuries-old Japanese custom. The tea is prepared and served in a ritual of grace and precision. Under what circumstances do you think this ceremony occurs?

Japan

Japanese cuisine features foods that are economical, nutritious, and attractive in appearance. Traditionally, Japanese people have eaten mainly vegetables, seaweed, and fish, as well as some fruit. Popular seafood includes squid and eel.

The Japanese dietary guidelines recommend that a person eat 30 different foods a day. Accordingly, meals usually consist of small amounts of a variety of foods. Fish is consumed both cooked and raw. It is presented the second way as sushi or sashimi, bits of very fresh raw fish combined with vinegared rice. Sushi is additionally wrapped in sheets of *nori,* or pressed seaweed.

Cooked dishes include sukiyaki—a mixture of vegetables and meat cooked quickly in a wok—and tempura—crisp batter-fried vegetables and seafood. **Soba**, buckwheat noodles, are widely eaten for lunches and snacks.

In addition to having a pleasing flavor, Japanese food must also appeal to the eye. Foods and table settings are carefully arranged.

Coastal areas enjoy an abundant variety of seafood. Seaweed is an important ingredient of Asian cooking. It is used in soups, sauces, and main dishes, and is also served as a side dish.

◆ Sushi and sashimi—assorted fish, usually served raw in combination with vinegared rice—are staples of Japan that have gained a following in the United States. What dish of Spain is similar to sushi and sashimi?

TEACH

- *Asia*
- *Asian World Cultures (text pages 616-619)*

Discussion Activity

Ask students to list characteristics common to Japanese foods. Which of these foods have students sampled? What reactions did they have to this cuisine?

Taste Test

Have students taste tempura, the Japanese version of deep-fried vegetables and seafood. The version should be the authentic variety, which is carefully crafted to seal in moisture, while remaining crisp on the exterior. Discuss similarities and differences between tempura and other fried foods students have eaten.

VISUAL LEARNING *Using the Photograph*

Direct students' attention to the bottom photo on this page. Ask a volunteer to read aloud the caption, while others examine the foods shown. Challenge students to answer the caption question. *(Ceviche.)*

Extending Learning

Japan—Note that up through the middle of the twentieth century, Japan was one of the healthiest nations on earth. Add that one likely explanation for this was the emphasis on seafood, which has characterized the eating habits of this island nation for centuries.

Since that time, with the increase in wealth and cultural assimilation with the West, rates of lifestyle disease have quintupled in many cases. Part of the cause is the introduction of beef as a dietary staple and the appearance in large cities of American fast food establishments.

TEACH cont.

- *Asian World Cultures (text pages 616-619)*

Discussion Activity

Ask students to explain how Chinese food ingredients are selected and why. Ask: What is the influence of Chinese philosophy on food preparation?

Field Trip

Take students to a Chinese restaurant for a meal. Arrange in advance for a variety of foods to be served. Have students write a paper describing the Chinese meal pattern and the dishes served.

Student Demonstration

Have students find a recipe for a Chinese dish they have eaten often but have never tried preparing. Examples might include egg drop soup, lo mein, or a stir-fry. Working in a group, students are to prepare the food for the class, demonstrating the steps involved in planning and executing the dish. Allow time for a question-and-answer period after the demonstration. L1

- In China, soup is usually served after the main course.
- Some soups, including red bean soup, are sweetened and served as a dessert.

China

Chinese cuisine dates back thousands of years and goes hand in hand with Chinese philosophy. In this philosophy, the universe is seen as an interplay of opposing forces. Food preparation, therefore, balances opposites. Ingredients are carefully selected and cut into pieces to retain a sense of harmony and symmetry. Whether for a banquet or a simple family meal, the foods blend simplicity and elegance.

◆ **A noodle maker in Hong Kong displays the noodles he has made by swinging the dough in his hands, a traditional Chinese method. What are some of the names by which noodles are known in the cuisines of China?**

A Chinese meal does not have a main dish or a specific serving order of dishes. Instead, many dishes are arranged in the center of the table, the variety depending on the number of diners. Each person is served a bowl of rice, and then helps him- or herself to some of each food. Soup is eaten during the meal or at the end of it—sometimes, sweetened, as dessert—but never at the beginning. Hot tea is always served.

Chinese Cuisine

The foods of China, which vary from region to region, range from spicy to simple and nurturing. From the southern province of Canton comes *congee* (kahn-JEE), a "mother's-milk" dish of rice gruel flavored with meat or poultry. Congee is usually served with fried bread. *Chow fun* is broad noodles stir-fried with strips of meat, onions, and bean sprouts.

Noodle dough is known throughout China. In the northern capital of Beijing, it is made into *lo mein*—thin spaghetti-like strands—and dumplings of all shapes and sizes. The region is also home to a special-occasion dish that is one of the most complicated recipes of any culture. That dish, *Peking duck*, requires several days of preparation, during which the duck is air-dried. The meat and crisp-roasted skin are ultimately presented ceremoniously on separate platters, along with thin pancakes.

First introduced in the United States in the 1960s and 1970s, Szechwan cooking comes from the province of the same name in central China. This area is noted for its extremely hot peppers. Other ingredients that contribute to the zesty, spicy cuisine of this region include fresh ginger and garlic.

Korea

As in much of Asia, rice is also essential in Korea. It is sometimes cooked with barley or millet, which adds nutrients, texture, and flavor to the rice.

Meals usually consist of a soup or stew plus a grilled or stir-fried dish. Fish and fish pastes appear regularly in Korean foods. Garlic, in many forms, is used in meals. In fact, some of the hottest foods in the world can be found in South Korea.

Extending Learning

Chinese Cuisine

- *Thousand year eggs*, a Chinese delicacy, are made by wrapping duck eggs in a special clay for several weeks. The eggs thicken, becoming a vivid green and blue inside. Because they are so rich, half an egg is enough for a single portion.
- Mongolian *hot pot* is a Northern specialty. Similar to a fondue pot, the pot is heated with charcoal and contains broth. Individuals dip small pieces of food into the broth to cook them and then into a sauce before they are eaten. The broth itself is eaten at meal's end.

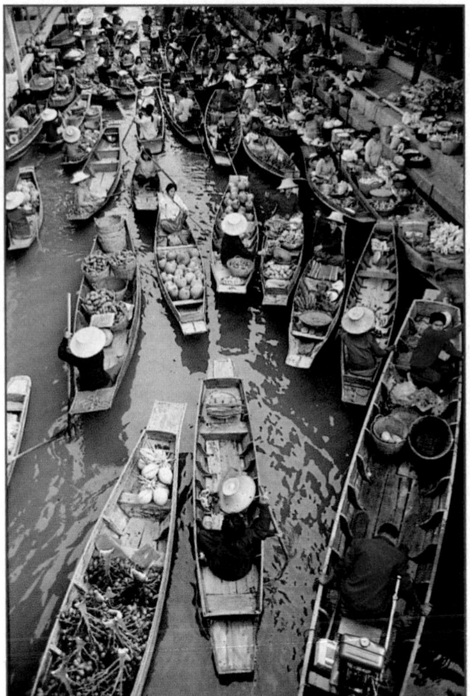

◆ **Like many nations in Southeast Asia, Thailand is a blend of old and new, as this scene at the floating market shows. What can you assume about the geography of Thailand based on this picture?**

Pickles add interest and flavor to Korean dishes. They might be made from almost any foods, such as pumpkins, cabbage, or ginseng. They can be rich in minerals and vitamin C.

Southeast Asia

Southeast Asia includes Myanmar (formerly Burma), Laos, Thailand, Vietnam, Cambodia, and Indonesia. These countries are in the tropics and have a variety of tropical fruits and vegetables, as well as a huge assortment of spices. The cooking reflects the influence of Chinese and European settlers.

Thailand

Coconut milk, the juice from coconuts, is frequently used as a liquid in Thai cooking, from main dishes to desserts. Noodles are a favorite and appear in casseroles and in soups. They are also mixed with sauces made of oysters, black beans, or fish. Then they are topped with chopped peanuts, coconut, and green onions.

Most food combinations in Thailand have four basic flavors—sweet, sour, salty, and spicy. They also meet four texture requirements—soft, chewy, crunchy, and crispy. Popular dishes include *pad Thai,* a mixture of rice noodles, shrimp, peanuts, egg, and bean sprouts. *Satays,* bamboo-skewered lengths of marinated and grilled chicken or beef, are served with a peanut dipping sauce.

Vietnam

Rice and fish are the staple foods in Vietnam. The Vietnamese eat rice every day, by itself and combined with other foods. Rice starch is used to make noodles and dumpling wrappers. Foods are usually seasoned with *nuoc-mam,* a pungent fish sauce.

Fish has always been the main source of protein for the Vietnamese. Fish and other foods are commonly seasoned with fresh ginger, coriander, lemon grass, and sweet basil. Many foods are rolled in lettuce or rice paper wrappers, which are easily dipped into spicy sauces.

◆ **Pad Thai is made with the flat noodles characteristic of Thai cooking. Name another dish common to the Thai table.**

- *Southeast Asia (text pages 619-620)*

Discussion Activity

Ask students to list the countries of Southeast Asia and to describe the general types of food that are grown there.

Documentary

Have interested students work as a group to obtain additional information on one of the cuisines of Southeast Asia and the culture of which the cuisine is a part. The information is to be presented in the form of an actual or mock TV documentary. L1

VISUAL LEARNING *Using the Photograph*

Have students study the top photo on this page. Ask what the photograph shows. (It shows a number of boats gathered together on a waterway to exchange foods and other goods.) Invite interested volunteers to learn more about the "Floating Market of Bangkok." What kinds of goods are sold? How long has the market been in operation? How many boats are there each day?

FOOD SCIENCE Heat Transfer and Food Size

The small size of food pieces used in Asian cooking allows the rapid transfer of heat to the center of each piece. This, in turn, allows the food to cook much faster than would larger pieces of food. Have students stir-fry stalks of celery that have been prepared in the following fashions: grated, diced, sliced, and whole. How much cooking time is needed to enable each piece to reach the translucent stage? What effect does the number of pieces cooked at once have on cooking temperature?

TEACH cont.

- *Southeast Asia*
- *India*
- *Australia and New Zealand (text pages 619-621)*

Separating Fact from Fiction

Ask students to devise a list of ten questions or statements about the cuisines discussed on these pages to use as the basis for a questionnaire. (For example, all Indian food is spicy-hot.) Students are to have at least ten adults fill out the questionnaire. What are the most common misconceptions about foods of this part of the world? **L1**

Comparison Activity

Buy or prepare *garam masala* according to an Indian recipe. Present this spice blend in class side by side with a sample of commercial curry powder. Ask students to examine the two samples in terms of their texture and aroma. Which is the more fragrant of the two? In what ways are they similar? Conclude by allowing students to read the label on the condiment package and to compare it with the recipe for *garam masala*.

Reasoning Activity

Have students read about the geography and history of Australia and New Zealand. What foods are plentiful in these countries? What European countries contributed settlers to Australia and New Zealand? Allow students to share their findings.

◆ **Terraced rice fields like this one in Bali, Indonesia, provide the island nation with an abundant supply of its staple grain.** Explain why so much rice is grown.

The Philippines

The inhabitants of the Philippines are a blend of Chinese, Arab, and Indian people living on 7,000 islands. The culture and food reflect the influences of those who have settled there, including the Spanish and Americans of the last few centuries.

The Chinese introduced foods such as cabbage, noodles, and soy to the Philippines. The Spaniards brought tomatoes, garlic, and peppers.

The staple foods are fish, pork, and rice, which is made into cakes, noodles, and pancakes. Fish sauces are also widely used. The national dish is *adobo,* which is pork marinated and browned in soy sauce, vinegar, garlic, bay leaves, and peppercorns.

Indonesia

Indonesian foods are highly spiced. One of the most popular dishes is *nasi goreng,* a mound of fried rice surrounded by assorted meats, such as beef and shrimp, and vegetables. The diner mixes them to obtain a wide variety of flavor combinations. *Gado gado* is a salad of lettuce, hard-cooked eggs, onions, and bean sprouts, topped with a peanut butter-based dressing.

◆ **This Indian feast includes tandoori chicken, raita, dal, lamb vindaloo, and basmati rice. Describe the role each of these dishes plays in an Indian meal.**

Extending Learning

India

- A typical, middle-class Indian meal is a small serving of a meat, chicken, or fish dish, accompanied by a large plate of rice, several breads, and a number of condiments including chutney (a spicy fruit relish). The poorest people of India subsist almost exclusively on bread and rice.
- The dish known as chicken *shahi korma*—a mild blend of chicken cubes, raisins, almonds, and coconut in a thickened yogurt sauce—is served at weddings.

India

Cooking in India varies from region to region, according to climate and culture. In the northern and central areas, wheat is the staple grain and lamb is the most common meat. In the south, rice is the staple grain and the food is much spicier. Very little, if any, meat is eaten—especially beef, since cows are considered sacred animals. Garlic, cardamom, cumin, coriander, cloves, and other fragrant spices are widely used.

Virtually all Indian recipes begin with an exceedingly complex blend of toasted and ground spices called **garam masala**. Most cooks grind and mix their own spice blends and keep several on hand in jars. Yogurt is used widely.

India boasts a wide variety of meatless main dishes; among these is *chana baji,* sautéed chickpeas and onions liberally flavored with cumin. When poultry and fish are available, they are used sparingly in proportion to other ingredients. The dish *biryani* is a colorful plate piled high with flavorful basmati rice with almonds, raisins, and bits of either lamb, goat, or chicken.

As in Africa, breads are used as edible utensils. *Chapati,* a simple flat wheat bread, is used in some areas to scoop up rice and lentils. Breads are baked in a clay oven, or *tandoor,* which also lends its name to a famous Indian dish—*chicken tandoori.* The dish is made of chicken pieces that have been marinated in a blend of yogurt and garam masala before cooking at high heat in the tandoor.

Australia and New Zealand

The foods in Australia and New Zealand are very similar to those of the cultures who settled the coastal parts of these countries. Among these cultures are the English, the Scottish, and the French.

Menus vary according to location, from the outback of Australia, to the large cities along its coast, to the smaller cities and rural areas of New Zealand. Meals usually feature foods that are locally available. Meat and seafood are plentiful. Many people eat steaks and chops (beef or mutton) for breakfast. New Zealanders enjoy *toheroas,* which resemble clams.

One uniquely Australian dish is *Pavlova,* a rich mixture of meringue, fruit, and cream. Pies and sweet rice dishes are common desserts.

Section 22-4 Review & Activities

1. What is the staple grain throughout much of Asia and the Pacific?
2. What four food flavors are common to the foods of Thailand?
3. Name three foods eaten by the people of India.
4. **Analyzing.** Using what you read in the section, analyze this statement: "The Chinese way of eating relates to the Chinese way of thinking."
5. **Synthesizing.** Describe the role of protein in the eating plans of people in Asia and the Pacific.
6. **Applying.** Plan a meal using foods from an Asian or Pacific country. Look up the calories, grams of protein and fat, and amounts of vitamins A and C found in these foods. Are the foods in this meal a good source of these nutrients?

ASSESS

REVIEW

- Ask students to summarize the main ideas in this section.
- Have students complete the Section Review. (Answers appear below.)

EVALUATION

- Have students write a short story in which a traveler makes stops in the nations of Asia and the Pacific. The story, which may be in diary form, should include descriptions of meals, along with impressions of them.
- Have students take the quiz for Section 22-4. (Use the quiz in the *Teacher Resource Guide,* or construct your own with the **Exam***View*® *Test Generator* on the *Effective Instruction CD-ROM.*)

RETEACHING

- Have students list the place names discussed in the section. They are then to identify two foods for each locale.
- Refer to the *Reteaching Activities* booklet for the Section 22-4 activity sheet.

CLOSE

Ask students to review the foods described in this section and decide which country's foods are most interesting to them. Take a vote to determine which cuisine is most popular.

Answers to Section 22-4 Review & Activities

1. Rice.
2. Sweet, sour, salty, and spicy.
3. Any three: chana baji, biryani, chapati, chicken tandoori.
4. The statement reflects the relationship between Chinese philosophy and cuisine, which dictates that food preparation balance opposites just as the universe does.
5. In most locales, forms of animal protein are eaten in limited amounts with abundant grain; non-animal proteins are common.
6. Answers will vary.

Recipe File

Thai Chicken Satays

This recipe uses the skills of marination and broiling.

USING THE RECIPE

- Have students read the recipe and discuss each step.
- Remind students of the importance of discarding any leftover marinade that came into contact with the raw chicken.
- Have each lab team fill out a work plan. (See the *Foods Lab Resources* booklet.)
- Have students check off the ingredients and equipment listed on the recipe worksheet and prepare the recipe.
- Have students complete the evaluation and questions on the recipe worksheet.

SEE ALSO...

The *Foods Lab Resources* booklet for the "Thai Chicken Satays" recipe worksheet and other recipe alternatives.

Recipe File

Thai Chicken Satays

Satays can be eaten as an appetizer or as a main course served with rice. Traditionally, satays are served with a peanut dipping sauce.

Customary	***Ingredients***	***Metric***
1 lb.	Boneless, skinless chicken breasts	500 g
1 Tbsp.	Lemon juice	15 mL
1 Tbsp.	Lime juice	15 mL
2 Tbsp.	Finely chopped onion	30 mL
1 Tbsp.	Garlic powder	15 mL
½ Tbsp.	Curry powder	8 mL
1 Tbsp.	Sugar	15 mL
½ cup	Coconut milk or plain, nonfat yogurt	125 mL
	Vegetable cooking spray	

Yield: About 4 servings (20 satays, about 5 satays per serving)
Equipment: Bamboo or wooden skewers; broiler pan

Directions

1. Place about 20 bamboo or wooden skewers in water to soak. Set aside.
2. Slice the chicken breast into 1- × 4-inch (2.5 × 10 cm) strips. Place in a medium bowl.
3. In a blender or food processor, blend remaining ingredients until smooth.
4. Reserve ¼ cup mixture and set aside.
5. Pour remaining mixture over chicken strips and marinate 15 minutes.
6. Preheat broiler.
7. Spray the broiler pan with the vegetable cooking spray.
8. Thread each chicken strip onto a skewer and place on cold broiler pan.
9. Broil for about 5 minutes on each side until chicken is golden brown. Brush with reserved marinade while cooking to preserve moistness.
10. Serve hot.

Nutrition Information

Per serving (approximate): 229 calories, 37 g protein, 8 g carbohydrate, 4 g fat, 98 mg cholesterol, 104 mg sodium
Good source of: potassium, magnesium, B vitamins, phosphorus

Food for Thought

- What purpose does the coconut milk or the yogurt serve in the marinade?
- What foods could you serve with this recipe to complete an Asian meal?

Answers to Food for Thought

1. Students should realize that either ingredient will add flavor and that the yogurt will help tenderize the meat since it contains an acid.
2. Students should mention rice, although some might refer to other dishes mentioned in the section, such as *gado gado.*

Career Wanted

Cooperative Extension Agent

"Our motto is 'bring the university to the people.'"

Ed Quintero

Education and Training

- Master's degree in agricultural economics, animal science, or related field
- Practical experience in field

Qualities

- Communication skills
- Problem-solving skills
- Enjoy working with people

Q. Ed, is the CES a service for farmers?

A. Agriculture is our main focus, but the Cooperative Extension Service is a resource for everyone. For instance, we recently helped set up a combination community garden and farmers market in a city neighborhood. Learning to improve nutrition, income, and self-reliance is the kind of teaching that was at the heart of the CES when founded some 90 years ago.

Q. So you're shifting your focus?

A. We still help with the nuts and bolts of farming. Plant pathology—what makes plants sick—is my specialty, but we also have programs to aid farmers with disabilities and to help farmers change from conventional farming to organic. We're seeing more interest in sustainable farming, too.

Q. It sounds like you're changing with the industry.

A. Yes, but some things never change. I was in 4-H as a kid. Now I help with the local club. Although family farms are fewer, much of our work still goes towards strengthening them and the rural community.

Related Career Opportunities

Entry Level
- Teacher aide
- Farm worker
- Nursery worker

Technical Level
- Range technician
- Soil conservation technician

Professional Level
- Family and consumer sciences teacher
- United States park ranger
- Ecologist

Making Career Connections

SERVICE LEARNING. Learn about volunteer opportunities in CES programs at an area university. Choose and apply for a position that meets your skills and interests. Write a report on your experiences. What were your tasks and duties? What did you learn that could help you in a career in this or a related field?

Career Wanted

Cooperative Extension Agent

Thinking About the Career

Prior to assigning the feature, ask students to brainstorm jobs in which the individual looks out for the public welfare. List some of these on the board (for example, police and firefighters). Explain that students are about to learn about a career they may have little awareness of but that, like the police and firefighters, is a profession designed to protect the public.

Career-Building Opportunities

Ask students to find out about one of the other careers listed in "Related Career Opportunities." Students may use online or print resources or may contact a local employment agency. Instruct students to put their findings in the form of a help-wanted ad to be posted on a classroom food career bulletin board.

For More Information

For additional information about careers like a county extension agent, encourage students to contact their County Extension Office, as well as the following resources:

- U.S. Department of Agriculture www.usda.gov
- Institute of Food Science and Engineering Texas A&M University ifse.tamu.edu

REVIEW

- Have students complete the Chapter Review. (Answers appear below.)

EVALUATION

- Divide the class into two teams. Each team should brainstorm questions about Chapter 22. Then allow the teams to take turns asking each other questions. At the end of the questioning period, the team with the most correct answers wins.
- Have students take the test for Chapter 22. (Use the chapter test in the *Teacher Resource Guide,* or construct your own with the **ExamView®** *Test Generator* on the *Effective Instruction CD-ROM.*)

ANSWERS

Checking Your Knowledge

1. A starchy food that looks like a banana but is cooked as a vegetable; it can be roasted, fried, boiled, baked, or combined in dishes with meat and cheese.
2. Any two: Indians, Portuguese, and Africans; *dende* reflects the African influence; sausage and the use of kale as a soup ingredient are Portuguese influences.
3. Coconuts (Asia), corn (the West).
4. Any three: Kubaybah or kibbi—a mixture of ground lamb, bulgur, cinnamon, and all-spice; stuffed vine leaves filled with a rice and meat mixture and served with a sauce made of yogurt, garlic, and mint; herrira—a mutton and vegetable soup; chelo—steamed rice accompanied by a meat or vegetable dish; koresh—a stew of meat or poultry with vegetables, fruit, nuts, seasoning, and perhaps cereal.
5. Zhoug, shatta, and tahini.
6. Any two: Bread (either plain or in small finger sandwiches), crumpets, scones, Welsh rabbit.

Chapter 22 Review & Activities

Summary

Section 22-1: Latin America

- Latin American cooking combines native foods and European influences.
- Corn is the staple grain in most areas.
- Mexican meals include masa, rice, beans, and chili peppers.
- Beef is popular in the countries of South America.

Section 22-2: Africa and the Middle East

- In Africa, staples include yams, cassava, and peanuts.
- Geography, climate, native traditions, religion, and foreign influence have shaped food customs in Africa and the Middle East.
- Some food customs of the Middle East are a part of religious beliefs.

Section 22-3: Europe

- The cooking of the British Isles tends to be plain but hearty.
- French cooking maximizes flavors to enhance one another.
- The foods of Spain and Portugal are based on fish and seafood.
- German cooking tends to be rich and heavy.
- Italian cuisine bears influences of its geographical neighbors.
- Eastern European cooking emphasizes root vegetables, grains, and sour cream.

Section 22-4: Asia and the Pacific

- Rice, seafood, soybeans, and vegetables are the staples of Japanese and Chinese cooking.
- Foods in Korea and Southeast Asia are spicy and include tropical fruits and vegetables.
- Indian cuisine is known for its spicy, often meatless, recipes.
- Australian and New Zealand cuisines have European roots.

Working IN THE Lab

1. ***Foods Lab.*** Choose one popular food of Latin America. Find two recipes for preparing it: one traditional, the other as it is usually prepared in the United States. Prepare and sample both recipes. Tell how they differ in ingredients and flavor. Offer reasons for these differences.
2. ***Demonstration.*** Investigate the traditional ways of serving Japanese and Chinese meals. Then demonstrate these serving methods. Duplicate the foods, serving pieces, and serving styles as closely as possible.

Checking Your Knowledge

1. What is a plantain? How can it be prepared?
2. Name two influences on Brazilian cooking and two foods reflecting these influences.
3. Name two foods introduced to Africa in the sixteenth century and their place of origin.
4. Name and describe three dishes often eaten in the Middle East.
5. Name three traditional condiments used in Israel.
6. Name two foods usually served at British tea.
7. What is the basic philosophy behind the cooking of France?
8. What is a contorno? When in an Italian meal is it served?
9. How is the Chinese cooking of Szechwan province different from that of other regions of the country?
10. What is *nasi goreng*? How is it eaten?

Thinking Critically

1. **Predicting Consequences.** Review the staple foods of the different regions of Latin America as noted in the chapter. For each food, identify one possible health advantage and one disadvantage of the typical way it is eaten in the region.
2. **Comparing and Contrasting.** Using recipe books, Web sites, or other information sources involving food, find examples of bean dishes served in several countries from different continents. How are they similar and different?
3. **Recognizing Values.** As noted in the chapter, Chinese meals reflect the Chinese people's traditional philosophy of life. What philosophies might meals in the United States reflect?

Reinforcing Key Skills

1. **Communication.** Ashley and her family are planning a trip to their ancestral homeland of Kenya, a country in Africa. Ashley has read that certain bacteria and other microorganisms in the foods and drinking water of some regions can cause gastric distress in visitors. What action would you advise Ashley to take to protect her and her family's well-being?
2. **Leadership.** You become friends with an exchange student from Eastern Europe, who tells you she is having trouble adapting to American customs. Think about particular foods and aspects of your eating habits that may be troublesome to someone from your friend's culture. Develop a strategy for helping this person overcome her difficulties.

Making Decisions and Solving Problems

Your new neighbors are a Middle Eastern family. You would like to invite them to dinner. However, you are not familiar with their food customs, their tastes, or any particular foods they may or may not eat.

Making Connections

1. **Social Studies.** Locate information on the controversy surrounding cattle raising in the rain forest regions of South America. What are the arguments of the opposing sides? What are the strengths and weaknesses of these arguments? Which side do you feel has the stronger case, and why? Share your findings with the class in a brief report.
2. **Fine Arts.** Learn more about how Japanese cuisine fits into the wider Japanese philosophy of the arts. How are the Japanese people's ideas about color, balance, and symmetry reflected in their art, music, and dance, as well as their meals? Make a presentation to the class using examples to support your conclusions.

ANSWERS cont.

7. To maximize the flavors of all ingredients in a dish so that no one flavor overpowers another.
8. It is a vegetable course; it is served after the main course.
9. It is spicy, whereas cooking elsewhere in the country is mild.
10. Fried rice surrounded by assorted meats, such as beef and shrimp, and vegetables; the diner mixes them to obtain a wide variety of flavor combinations.

Thinking Critically

1. Corn: Advantage—steamed; disadvantage—none listed. Beans: Advantage—simmered; disadvantage—fried (in frijoles refritos). Plantains: Advantage—roasted, boiled, or baked; disadvantage—fried.
2. Answers will vary. One possibility: South American *feijoada* and French *cassoulet* are similar in that both involve meats and sausages, and both are topped with a bread crumb mixture. Differences include the type of bean—black in *feijoada*, white in *cassoulet*.
3. Answers will vary.

Reinforcing Key Skills

1. Answers, which will vary, might include writing to a local embassy or contacting a local health department for information on this topic.
2. Answers, which will vary, might include learning more about the other person's culture, including similarities to your own, which might be used to help bridge the gap.

CHAPTER

23

Foods of the U.S. and Canada

Advance Planning Guide ☑

- Purchase a serving of *rillettes* from a local French restaurant or, if that is not possible, find a recipe for this rustic food.
- Obtain sheets of poster board.
- Purchase canned chopped clams and/or cod fillets, milk, canned tomatoes, potatoes, and celery for a chowder cookoff.
- Purchase needed ingredients for the Recipe File on page 633.
- Arrange for a historian from a local university or historical society to speak to the class on the settlement of the Southwest and influences of different cultures on foods of the region.
- Bring to class a large map of the United States, or at least the Pacific coast and the Northwest.
- Purchase supplies of sourdough starter.
- Purchase needed ingredients for a typical Tex-Mex meal.

CHAPTER

23

Section 23-1
Regional Foods of the East, Midwest, and South

Section 23-2
Regional Foods of the West and Canada

When you hear the term *American food,* what comes to mind? You may picture hot dogs and ice cream, but hot dogs are actually of German descent and ice cream comes from France and Italy.

What, then, is American food? After reading this chapter, you will know the answer to this question.

MEETING DIVERSE NEEDS

Celebrating Cultural Diversity. If there are students in the class who have lived in another city, state, or country, ask them to form a panel of experts on food from that region. Arrange chairs at the front of the classroom to simulate the stage of a TV talk show. Ask one student to serve as moderator, while the others field questions from the "audience." Have audience members each devise at least two questions to ask.

SECTION
23-1

Regional Foods of the East, Midwest, and South

Objectives

After studying this section, you should be able to:

- List foods common to the East, Midwest, and South.
- Identify cultural and climate influences on the foods of the East, Midwest, and South.

Look for These Terms

pemmican

filé

Are there chili cook-offs where you live? Do local cooks all have their own recipes for clam chowder? Can you walk into any bakery and order a key lime pie?

These foods all have something in common. All are genuine American dishes. Today, any of these foods can be enjoyed throughout the country. However, at one time, each was known only in the region where it originated.

The Foundations of American Cooking

How did regional differences come about? As noted in Chapter 13, the foods common to an area depend partly on geography and climate. The way North America was settled also affected the development of food customs.

The Native Americans developed their own food customs based on locally available foods. Those foods are the foundation of much of American cooking. Later, immigrants from other parts of the world made additional contributions to the foods of America.

INFOLINK

For more information on the effects of geography and other factors on the staple foods of a region, see Section 13-3.

Native American Culture

Some Native Americans relied mainly on hunting, fishing, and gathering berries for meals. Others were skilled farmers and creative cooks.

Section 23-1 Resources

◆ **Student Workbook**, pp. 173, 175
◆ **Teacher Resource Guide**
Lesson Plan 23-1 Organizer
Section 23-1 Quiz
◆ **Effective Instruction CD-ROM**
Exam*View*® *Test Generator*
PowerPoint® Slide #51
◆ **Transparency Package**, CT-51
◆ **Student Motivation Kit**
Reteaching Activities, p. 104
Enrichment Activities
Foods Lab Resources, pp. 147–148
A Global Foods Tour, pp. 17, 31–44
Skills for Making Food Choices, pp. 51–52

SECTION
23-1
Regional Foods of the East, Midwest, and South

FOCUS

MOTIVATORS

- Ask students to imagine that they are moving to another country or another section of this country. Ask: "What food(s) or food habits would you take with you? Why?" Ask them to identify the place they are moving to and list new foods they would expect to find there.
- Ask students who have visited or lived in the East, Midwest, or South to describe the geography, climate, and culture of the area. Discuss how these characteristics have influenced food traditions of the area.

VOCABULARY ACTIVITY

Have a volunteer locate the terms listed under "Look for These Terms." Instruct him or her to pronounce the words aloud, identifying what each is.

STUDY SKILLS

- **Listening.** Invite a group of volunteers to each prepare an oral reading of a page of text from the section, while others follow along silently.
- Have students read the section and complete the appropriate part of the Chapter 23 Study Guide in the *Student Workbook*.

TEACH

- *The Foundations of American Cooking (text pages 627-629)*

Discussion Activity

Discuss with students theories of how the Native Americans reached the United States. (One popular and widely held explanation is that they crossed from Siberia to Alaska on a land bridge over the Bering Strait.) Ask: What may have prompted some of these travelers to continue on down the Pacific coast, while others remained in what is now Alaska? On what basis did these first settlers develop food customs?

Timelines

Have students refer to an American history text to make a timeline of the arrival of various ethnic groups to the United States from 1600 to the present. Display the timeline in class and discuss how each group influenced American cuisine. Refer to the timeline as you study the regions covered in this section. L1

Writing Activity

Invite students to pretend that they are immigrants to North America in the year 1700. Ask them to write an entry in their diary describing the foods and cooking methods of the Native Americans they encountered. Allow time for authors to share their entries aloud, perhaps dressing in period costumes.

◆ **Corn, or maize, was a legacy of the Native Americans to the first European settlers. How many different uses for corn can you name?**

Native Americans were also early pioneers in food technology. They developed a way of cultivating wild maize (corn) so that it would yield a greater amount of food and seed. They also devised methods for storing and preserving foods. One preserved food they made was **pemmican**—dried meat, pounded into a paste with fat and preserved in cakes. Because of its nonperishable properties, pemmican could be stored for long periods of time, making meat available when hunting was scarce. The high fat content, which enabled a little of the food to go a long way, also helped sustain energy.

Native American Staples

Maize was a staple grain for many Native American groups. It was prepared in a variety of ways, some of which are still used today. Native Americans roasted and boiled the corn in the husk. Some removed the kernels and made them into a powder, which was then made into flatbread, mush, corn puddings, and beverages. Sometimes the Native Americans softened the kernels in homemade lye and made hominy, which was cooked with bits of meat.

Regional differences often determined which other foods were available. In coastal areas, seafood was a staple. Native Americans in the South concocted soups and stews from fish and small game. In the Southwest, groups grew beans to use in soups. They also roasted meats over open fires.

Colonial Cooking

In the fifteenth century, immigration from Europe began. Immigrants coming to this continent brought their food customs with them. They tended to settle as groups in areas that reminded them of their homelands. Settling in these clusters helped them preserve their traditions.

Native Americans played an important role in the survival of the first European immigrants to the New World. They introduced the immigrants to the staple foods of various regions and shared food preparation and cooking methods.

◆ **A reenactment of early cooking is shown here. Cooking over an open fire outdoors preceded open hearth cooking indoors, which was the early counterpart to the kitchen stove. What foods were prepared over an open fire and in the open hearth? How are the same dishes cooked today?**

Technology TIE-IN

Underscore the point made in the text that Native Americans were early pioneers in food technology. Refer interested students to sources that detail some of the other culinary achievements of these early settlers. One book to which you might refer students is *Eating in America: A History,* by Waverly Root and Richard de Rochemont. Have students summarize or read aloud key sections.

Gradually, the immigrants began adapting their own recipes to available foods and the cooking and preserving methods that were used in their new homeland. Cultural exchanges also occurred between colonies and immigrant groups. Over time, this process resulted in the unique cooking styles of each region of North America.

The Northeast

Among the first European settlers in the Northeast were the English, Dutch, French, and Germans. Native Americans of the region taught the settlers to use available foods, such as deer, rabbit, wild turkey, and berries. They also taught the immigrants to plant native crops, such as corn, beans, squash, and pumpkins. Corn and dry beans provided carbohydrates and protein to help the immigrants survive in their new homeland.

New England

Because of the extremely cold winters in New England, early settlers cooked hearty foods. From the Native Americans they learned to soak dry beans and then cook them slowly for hours in a kettle over an open fire. The resulting dish, often called *Boston baked beans*, is still a favorite today.

Another New England dish inspired by the Native Americans was *chowder*, a soup made with fish or seafood, which were plentiful along the Atlantic coast. The most famous chowder—clam chowder— is made with milk, butter, onions, and clams. In some areas, cooks use tomatoes instead of milk.

Irish Influence

The Irish came to the Northeast somewhat later than other immigrants. They introduced Irish stew and corned beef with cabbage, known throughout the United States as traditional

◆ **Clam chowder, Boston baked beans, and brown bread are traditional New England dishes. What other local produce do you think appeared on the tables of settlers of the area?**

Irish dishes. Such hearty and filling foods were a trademark of the Irish. These foods used a wide range of vegetables, including cabbage, carrots, and potatoes. Vegetables were combined with eggs, bread crumbs, butter, and spices to make puddings. Irish cooks also used leeks, onions, and garlic to flavor foods.

Pennsylvania Dutch

In the late 1700s, large numbers of Germans arrived in eastern Pennsylvania. They referred to themselves as *Deutsch*, the German word for "German." English-speaking settlers of the area mispronounced the word as "Dutch." The Germans in this area became known as the Pennsylvania Dutch.

These settlers were farmers, which required hard physical labor and large quantities of flavorful, filling food. They continued to prepare familiar foods from their homeland: pork, cabbage or sauerkraut, noodles, and sausage. They also were known for their hearty soups, stews, and homemade breads.

As cooks, the German immigrants were thrifty. They used everything, including the pork scraps, which were formed into a loaf that was cut into slices and fried as *scrapple*. They also enjoyed sweets. They made fruit butters and tasty baked goods. Pies, cakes, rolls, and crumb-topped cakes were shared with the neighbors over mid-morning coffee, or *kaffeeklatsch*.

Extending Learning

Native Americans—Because corn was the primary food source for many Native American groups, maize took on a certain magical quality among some of these peoples. It became the center of many tribal religious beliefs and was depicted in the art of some Southern American Native groups. Planting and harvesting corn became occasions for special rituals and yearly festivals. Ask students in what way these festivals are mirrored by holidays that we celebrate today.

- *The Foundations of American Cooking*
- *The Northeast (text pages 627-629)*

VISUAL LEARNING ***Using the Photograph*** Direct students' attention to the top photo on page 628. Ask for a volunteer to read aloud the caption. Challenge students to come up with as many answers as they can to the question asked. Allow time for students to share their responses.

Bulletin Board Activity

Have students develop a classroom bulletin board of foods eaten by Native Americans. They are to draw or find pictures of these foods. Instruct students to arrange the images in one of several logical formats (for example, by region, by main ingredient, by preservation method).

Taste Test

Although pemmican is difficult to find today, similar food products still exist (one example being potted meat). If there is a French restaurant in your community that has the dish called *rillettes* (ree-ET) on its menu, obtain a serving. If this is not possible, find and prepare a recipe for this rustic peasant dish, which is made by pounding pork and fat into a thick paste, which —like pemmican—can then be stored for a long time, although under refrigeration. Ask students to imagine subsisting on foods like this during periods when hunting was scarce.

TEACH cont.

- *The Northeast*
- *The Midwest*
- *The South*
  (text pages 629-632)

History Review Activity

Ask interested volunteers to review or research the history of the Northeast. In the information they are to provide should be an answer to each of the following questions: Who were the early settlers? What food resources were available to these pioneers? What native crops did Native Americans teach them to plant?

Recipe Analysis

Provide students with recipes for traditional German foods. Ask students to work in groups to analyze the recipes. Ask students to identify recipes that could be used or adapted for use by the early settlers in North America. L2

Comparison Activity

Provide students with sheets of poster board. Invite each of several groups to create a large Venn diagram (two overlapping circles with space to write) that compares and contrasts the eating habits of settlers to the Midwest and the South. Among points of comparison to be reflected in diagrams should be crops grown by settlers to a given region, staple food or foods of a region, and influences on these habits. Finished diagrams are to be displayed as a starting point for discussion.

The Midwest

In the eighteenth century, as the big cities in the East grew crowded, adventurous pioneers set out to explore the "wide-open spaces" farther west. Settlers followed, establishing new homes in the Midwest. During the nineteenth century, newly arrived immigrants from Europe joined this westward movement.

Soon the prairies of the heartland were supporting farms and dairies. Settlers planted familiar crops that grew well in that climate—wheat, corn, other grains, fruits, and vegetables. Farms also produced beef, pork, and poultry. Fish was available from rivers and lakes.

In general, Midwestern menus were hearty and relied on the taste of the foods themselves rather than on seasonings for flavor. The great supply of wheat made home-baked breads, cakes, and pies a way of life. Meat, potatoes, bread, vegetables, and dessert: These foods provided energy for the hard-working pioneers. It was simple fare, simply cooked, and is a part of what is now known as American cooking.

The South

In the eighteenth century, life in the South generally revolved around the plantation and other rural areas. Crops in the South were bountiful because the soil along the lakes, rivers, and deltas was rich and the temperatures were warm. These lakes and rivers, as well as the ocean, provided fish and shellfish. Corn, the staple food, was dried and ground so that it could be used in a variety of recipes, many of which originated with the Native Americans. Included were corn bread, spoon bread, corn pone, fritters, cornmeal batters, and grits. These foods are still served in the South today.

The English were the primary settlers in the area. Food customs, however, were also influenced by the Africans, French, and Spaniards.

African-American Influence

African-American cooks made their mark on Southern food. They incorporated turnip and dandelion greens, black-eyed peas, catfish, fried okra, yams, red beans, rice, and peppers into their cooking.

African Americans developed their own special recipes for foods such as pig's feet and hog jowls. Chitterlings (bits of hog intestine) were fried and dipped into a spicy sauce. Ham hocks (legs) and turnip greens became a popular dish. The backbone of the hog was simmered to make a tasty stew topped with dumplings.

The African Americans had come to appreciate chili peppers, which had been transported to Africa from Latin America. They enjoyed spicy sauces and gravies. They also depended on one-pot cooking. Dishes were cooked in an iron pot and made with a wide variety of foods, including cooking greens.

African-American cooks also combined foods to make new recipes. *Hopping John*, for instance, is a mixture of black-eyed peas and rice. *Hush puppies*, made of cornmeal batter dropped by spoonfuls into hot oil, are often served with fried catfish. According to legend, hush puppies got their name in early days when they were thrown to silence barking dogs around campfires.

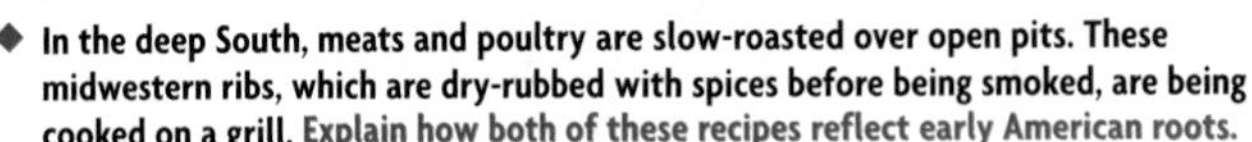

◆ **In the deep South, meats and poultry are slow-roasted over open pits. These midwestern ribs, which are dry-rubbed with spices before being smoked, are being cooked on a grill.** Explain how both of these recipes reflect early American roots.

Extending Learning

New England—Organize two groups of volunteers to participate in a chowder cookoff (or chowderfest, as it is known in some regions). One group is to prepare a white ("New England") version of clam or fish chowder, while the other is to prepare a red version of this soup, using tomatoes. Students may obtain recipes for their chowder from books in the classroom or from online resources. Invite non-participating members of the class to act as judges.

Desserts were sweet and rich, and they included pecan pie, sweet potato pie, and peach cobbler.

Creole Cooking

Creole and Cajun are two specialized kinds of cooking that developed in southern Louisiana. Both feature ingredients such as seafood, pork, rice, peppers, celery, onions, and a variety of herbs and spices. Both are famous for their blending of flavors, which is only natural, because Creole and Cajun cooking each resulted from a blending of cultures.

Creole cooking developed in New Orleans. Many European immigrants settled there, including natives of France, Spain, and Italy. In many families, the meals were prepared by servants. To the European cuisine, these cooks added some of their own food traditions from Africa and the West Indies, as well as ingredients borrowed from Native Americans.

Creole cooking is considered by many to be a more sophisticated style than Cajun. Creole meals are likely to include a variety of separate dishes, each featuring a delicate, subtle blending of flavors. Shrimp, oysters, and crabs appear often. As in classic French cooking, sauces are often based on butter or cream. Creole cooking is sometimes described as a city-style cuisine.

Cajun Cooking

Cajun cooking, in contrast, is a country-style cuisine. The term *Cajun* is derived from *Acadian*. The Acadians were French colonists who had settled in Canada. After they were expelled from Canada by the British, some eventually found their way to the bayous and farmlands of southern Louisiana. The style of cooking that resulted combines French traditions with the locally available foods and the influences of other cultural groups.

One of the key features of Cajun cooking is improvisation. The Cajuns had to learn to

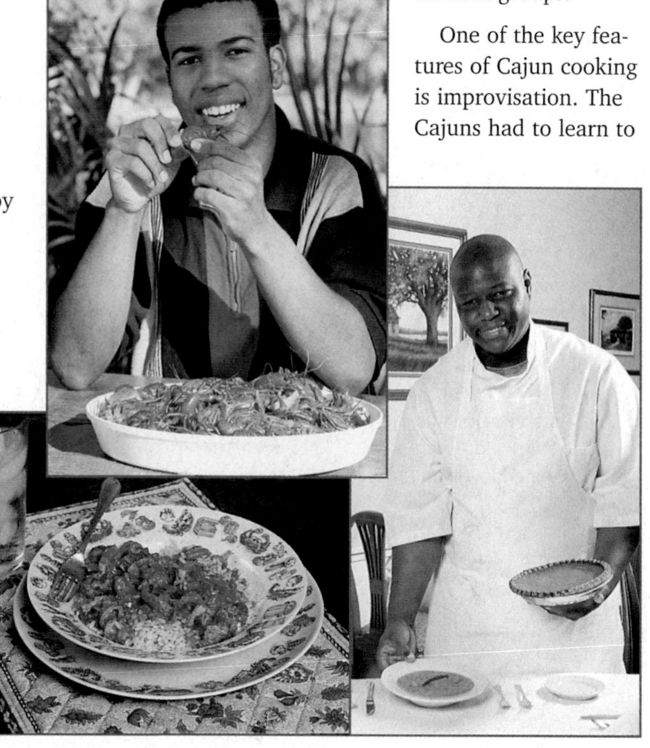

◆ **Many of the dishes for which the coastal South is noted, including peanut soup and sweet potato pie, were inspired by African-American settlers to the area. The rich culinary heritage of Louisiana, influenced both by Cajun and Creole cuisines, includes étouffé, a savory stew of chicken, and shellfish such as crawfish. What other dishes are popular to these regions of the country?**

- ***The Midwest***
- ***The South***
  (text pages 630-632)

Misconception List

Point out to students that many of the foods noted on these pages are shrouded in misconception as to their origins. Point out that at least one Pennsylvania Dutch creation, scrapple, is often thought to be a dish of Philadelphia origin, while pecan pie and cobblers—both perfected by African Americans in the South—are often ascribed to a host of different sources. Invite interested students to compile a list of food misconceptions, including but not limited to the foods mentioned. **L1**

Discussion Activity

Ask students to explain the difference between Creole and Cajun cooking. Ask: What blending of cultures led to the type of cooking we know today as Creole cooking?

Recipe Comparison

Have students compare the ingredients and cooking methods used in recipes for French foods, Creole foods, and Cajun foods. Have them write a report on these similarities and differences. **L1**

Reinforcing Key Skills

Present the following problem to student groups. Allow time for them to discuss and compare their responses.

Management—Plan a menu of southern foods. Investigate resources for ingredients in your community. Obtain prices, and then figure the cost of preparing the meal. Discuss what location has to do with the price and availability of food items. How could people who live outside the South prepare an authentic southern meal, while keeping costs down?

ASSESS

REVIEW

- Ask students to summarize the main ideas in this section.
- Have students complete the Section Review. (Answers appear below.)

EVALUATION

- Have students write a short essay or poem on the development of food customs in the Northeast, Midwest, and South.
  Have students take the quiz for Section 23-1. (Use the quiz in the *Teacher Resource Guide,* or construct your own with the **Exam***View*® *Test Generator* on the *Effective Instruction CD-ROM.*)

RETEACHING

- Have students list five foods typical of the Northeast, the Midwest, and the South. Have them tell which foods appeal to them and why.
- Refer to the *Reteaching Activities* booklet for the Section 23-1 activity sheet.

CLOSE

Refer students to the first motivator that opened this section. Have them choose a new location and revise—or update—their responses.

live off the land, making meals from whatever they could hunt, catch, or grow on their own. Authentic Cajun cooking often includes freshwater fish, crawfish (the Southern term for crayfish), and game such as rabbit, turtle, squirrel, and even alligator. One-dish meals made from whatever foods are on hand are common. Compared with Creole cooking, Cajun foods tend to feature stronger, hotter flavors.

Similarities

Despite these distinctions, Creole and Cajun cuisine have much in common. Many dishes owe their distinctive flavor to a brown roux. In this variation of the French thickening agent, the flour is cooked until it turns a rich, chocolate-brown color. It gives a subtle, dark, roasted flavor to sauces and dishes, such as *étouffé*, a hearty stew of chicken and shellfish. Okra is also commonly used to thicken soups and stews. The use of okra and the method of simmering foods for a long time in iron pots are examples of the African influence on the region's cooking. Still another thickener was borrowed from the Native Americans. They used dried, crushed sassafras leaves to thicken stews and add a delicate flavor. This thickener was called **filé**, or filé powder, by the settlers.

A famous Louisiana dish is *gumbo*, a thick stew that begins with a brown roux. Many variations are possible. A Creole gumbo might include shrimp, crab, and oysters; a Cajun gumbo is more likely to feature ham and crawfish. Vegetables and seasonings are also added. Either okra or filé powder is used as a thickener. Gumbos are simmered slowly for hours, and then served over rice.

For more on the making of a roux and its functions in sauces, see Section 20-3.

Section 23-1 Review & Activities

1. Name two contributions of Native Americans to the growth and development of American food.
2. Name three contributions made by the Africans to the American food culture.
3. What is a brown roux? What two cuisines of Louisiana does it link?
4. **Synthesizing.** What factors do you think encouraged the immigrants to try new foods?
5. **Comparing and Contrasting.** Make a Venn diagram, a chart with two large overlapping circles. Choose any two regional cultures identified in this section, and place their similarities in the overlapping area, their differences in the outer portions of the circles that do not overlap.
6. **Applying.** Plan a dinner meal combining different foods from the South. (You may need to check some recipe books.) Survey a supermarket and gather ingredient prices for the foods in this meal. Which items were most or least expensive? Which were the easiest and most difficult to find? What does location have to do with the price and availability of food items?

Answers to Section 23-1 Review & Activities

1. See page 628.
2. See pages 630-631.
3. A thickener of fat and flour cooked until the flour turns a rich, chocolate-brown color; Creole and Cajun cuisines.
4. Answers will vary. Students should recognize that these people had to try new foods to survive.
5. Answers will vary. Encourage students to be as thorough and accurate as possible.
6. Answers will vary.

Recipe File

Hopping John

Legend in the south has it that eating this dish on New Year's Day brings good luck.

Customary	Ingredients	Metric
1 cup	Chopped onion	250 mL
6 oz.	Ham, cut into 1-inch (2.5 cm) pieces	190 g
2 Tbsp.	Vegetable oil	30 mL
Dash	Ground allspice	Dash
Dash	Cayenne	Dash
1 cup	Instant rice	250 mL
2½ cups	Water	375 mL
4 cups	Canned black-eyed peas, drained and rinsed	1 L
	Salt	
	Pepper	
	Chopped green onion (optional)	

Yield: 4 servings, one cup each
Equipment: 2-quart (2-L) saucepan

Directions

1. Sauté the onion and the ham in vegetable oil until onion is golden and ham is lightly browned.
2. Stir in allspice and cayenne.
3. Add the rice, and toss until coated with the oil.
4. Add the water and bring to a boil. Reduce the heat and simmer for 15 minutes.
5. Add the black-eyed peas and simmer for another 5 minutes.
6. Remove the pan from the heat and cover. Let pan stand, covered, for 5 minutes.
7. Season to taste with salt and pepper.
8. Serve hot, garnished with chopped green onion, if desired.

Nutrition Information

Per serving (approximate): 452 calories, 21 g protein, 55 g carbohydrate, 17 g fat, 30 mg cholesterol, 854 mg sodium
Good source of: potassium, iron, zinc, vitamin E, vitamin C, B vitamins, phosphorus

Food for Thought

- What would you serve with Hopping John to meet one daily serving requirement of vegetables? Of dairy foods?
- How could you reduce the fat in this recipe? How could you reduce the sodium?

Recipe File
Hopping John

This recipe uses the techniques of sautéing and grain (rice) preparation. Prior to assigning the lab, you may suggest students read or review the appropriate text material in Chapters 9 and 18.

Using the Recipe

- Have students read the recipe and discuss each step.
- Remind students to exercise care when using a knife and to make sure that a small piece is cut off any rounded vegetable before it is chopped so that it sits squarely on the cutting board.
- Have each lab team fill out a work plan. (See the *Foods Lab Resources* booklet.)
- Have students check off the ingredients and equipment listed on the recipe worksheet and prepare the recipe.
- Have students complete the evaluation and questions on the recipe worksheet.

SEE ALSO. . .
The *Foods Lab Resources* booklet for the "Hopping John" recipe worksheet and other recipe alternatives.

Answers to Food for Thought

1. Answers will vary but should take into account (1) the fact that this dish provides a complete protein and (2) meal appeal.
2. Fat and sodium could be reduced by eliminating the ham or selecting extra-lean and/or low-sodium ham.

SECTION
23-2
Regional Foods of the West and Canada

FOCUS

MOTIVATORS

- Discuss ways the settlement of the American West differed from the settlement of the rest of the United States. From what countries did early settlers of the American West come?
- Have students turn a sheet of paper sideways and divide it into seven columns with the following headings: Southwest, Pacific Coast and Northwest, Hawaii, Ontario and Western Provinces, Quebec, Atlantic Provinces. Ask students to brainstorm and list as many foods as they can from each region. With which region's foods were students most familiar? Have students retain the lists for future use.

VOCABULARY ACTIVITY

Pronounce the terms listed under "Look for These Terms." Have students find the terms and their definitions in the section.

STUDY SKILLS

- **Guided Reading.** Have students look at the headings within Section 23-2 to preview the concepts that will be discussed.
- Have students read the section and complete the appropriate part of the Chapter 23 Study Guide in the *Student Workbook*.

SECTION
23-2
Regional Foods of the West and Canada

Objectives

After studying this section, you should be able to:

- Identify foods characteristic of the western United States and Canada.
- Describe the cultural influences on foods of the western United States and Canada.

Look for These Terms

sourdough starter

hibachi

Early settlers in the American West brought with them the cuisine of their homelands. In adapting their traditional recipes to the climate and foods available, these early settlers developed foods that are commonly found in these regions today.

The Southwest

Most people associate the Southwest with cowboys and huge cattle ranches. Spaniards introduced cattle to this area in the sixteenth century. By the 1800s, ranches dotted the Texas plains, with large herds of longhorn cattle tended by cowboys.

Influences on Southwestern Food

Long before the Spaniards arrived, Native Americans were raising crops such as corn, beans, pumpkins, squash, and chilies. They also had an abundant supply of fish and wild game as well as berries, nuts, and seeds.

Native Americans and Spaniards influenced the cooking in the region, as did other cultures. These included Mexicans, French, English, and other settlers from the east. Settlers moving westward found rich soil for growing abundant crops.

Cowboy Cuisine

Until the railroads came along in the later 1800s, cowboys represented the only way of getting cattle from ranch to market. These trips frequently covered 1,000 miles (1,600 km) or more.

Because cowboys couldn't go home for meals, a cook traveled with them. Food and essential equipment to cook over a campfire were carried in a chuck wagon.

Section 23-2 Resources

◆ **Student Workbook,** pp. 173, 177
◆ **Teacher Resource Guide**
Lesson Plan 23-2 Organizer
Section 23-2 Quiz
Chapter 23 Test
◆ **Effective Instruction CD-ROM**
Exam*View*® *Test Generator*
PowerPoint® Slide #51
◆ **Transparency Package,** CT-51
◆ **Student Motivation Kit**
Reteaching Activities, p. 105
Enrichment Activities
Foods Lab Resources, pp. 149–150
A Global Foods Tour, pp. 17, 18, 45–51

◆ **Chili con carne is an all-American favorite, but nowhere is it more popular than in the Southwest, where chili "cookoffs" are periodically held.** What different ingredients can be used to vary the taste of chili?

Cowboy cooks prepared simple meals over open fires. Meat was cooked by roasting or stewing in a pot. To save time in the morning, the cook made a biscuit mix the night before, mixing flour, salt, and baking powder in a sack. The next day, he added fat and water, and baked the biscuits over the campfire. For the cowboys, dessert was often biscuits topped with a sweet syrup or "fried" pies. Very strong coffee completed the meal.

Tex-Mex Cuisine

Because Texas had long been a territory under Mexican rule, the Mexican influence on the food remained even after the state won its independence. Beans, corn, tamales, and tacos were as popular as ever—and still are today. The cuisine of Texas, in fact, is often known as Tex-Mex.

As in Mexican cooking, corn continues to be the mainstay of Tex-Mex cooking. Corn products are usually served at every meal. In addition, beans, chili peppers, fresh vegetables, and fruit, sometimes cooked with meats, are included in Southwestern meals.

Two popular Tex-Mex dishes are *nachos*—made by smothering tortilla chips with refried beans, cheese sauce, and chilies—and *fajitas* (fah-HEE-tuhs)—tortillas wrapped around strips of marinated, grilled steak or chicken. They are usually served with grilled onions and sweet peppers, guacamole, refried beans, and salsa.

The seasoning in Tex-Mex cooking can vary from mild to fiery hot, depending on personal preference. One of the most famous Tex-Mex dishes is named for the chili pepper—*chili con carne*. There is a difference of opinion as to where this dish originated, in Texas or Mexico. There's little debate, however, over the popularity of chili, as it is now known—although there is one over whether chili should have

TEACH

- *The Southwest (text pages 634-636)*

Discussion Activity

Lead a discussion among students to explain why a cook traveled with cowboys. What typical early meals were prepared over campfires?

Guest Speaker

Invite a historian from a local university or historical society to pay a visit to the class. The speaker should be an individual who has studied the settlement of the Southwest and who can discuss the influences of different cultures on Southwestern foods. In preparation for the visit, challenge all students to develop at least three good questions to ask.

Recipe Scavenger Hunt

Have students use books in the classroom library, the local public library, and/or the Internet to locate the recipes for the following foods typical of the Southwest and cowboy cuisine: Son-of-a-Gun stew, Mulligan stew, and red-eye gravy. Part of the challenge should be to identify ingredients used in authentic versions of these dishes? L2

- A census conducted in a recent year revealed that there were more Tex-Mex restaurants in New York City than there were in any city in Texas.

Extending Learning

Tex-Mex—Much of the Southwestern cooking that is considered Mexican is actually Tex-Mex.

- Flour tortillas are an American invention.
- The burrito is an American dish with Mexican seasoning.

One of the chief differences between true Mexican dishes and Tex-Mex foods is the presence of meat, which in Mexico was, for a long time, a luxury. With cultural assimilation, the situation in Mexico changed. Most restaurants in northern Mexico now feature Tex-Mex as well as Mexican foods.

TEACH cont.

- *The Pacific Coast (text pages 636-637)*

Barbecue Basics

The term *barbecue* has many interpretations throughout the country and many supposed origins. [One common assertion is that the word derives from a French expression, *barbe au queue* ("beard to tail"), which relates to the way the animal is often cooked—spit-roasted whole.] Have students interview people in their community to learn what the term *barbecue* means to them. Have students gather and chart their findings. L1

Map Study Activity

Bring to class a large map of the United States, or at least the Pacific coast and the Northwest. Review with students the geography of this region. What natural food resources are readily available? How have the great shipping ports of San Francisco, Seattle, and Los Angeles influenced the foods available?

Finding Recipes

Have students find recipes for foods popular on the Pacific coast and in the Northwest, including those associated with Asian cultures and those for fish, seafood, fruits, and vegetables. Discuss and compare these recipes. Is there any overlap in resources used? L1

◆ **San Francisco is the undisputed capital of sourdough bread. Name another culinary claim to fame of the Pacific Coast area.**

beans. Originally, chili was little more than cubed beef cooked in a spicy sauce of red chilies and marjoram. Today, cooks may use ground meat and add pinto beans, tomatoes, onions, cilantro, and spices. Local contests are held yearly from coast to coast to find out who can make the best chili.

Southwestern Barbecue

Another popular form of cooking throughout the Southwest is barbecue. Many people believe that Southerners moving to the Southwest introduced the barbecue. The word *barbecue* may be derived from the Spanish word *barbacoa*, which refers to the grid on which meat is roasted in Latin America. However, records show that meat was barbecued in Virginia as early as the seventeenth century.

Like chili, barbecue recipes vary from cook to cook. Most agree that the meat in a true barbecue should be seasoned only with a "dry rub" of spices. Barbecue sauce is added only at the very end of the roasting.

The Pacific Coast

Early settlers along the Pacific coast and in the Northwest found an abundant food supply. Natural resources such as seafood and game were plentiful. The settlers used simple food preparation methods to bring out the natural flavors of these foods. For example, elk and deer were grilled or roasted. Seafood was steamed, boiled, or grilled.

The coast also had a rich supply of tasty fresh fruits and vegetables. The temperate climate of southern California provided the perfect growing conditions.

Influences on Pacific Coast Food

Great shipping ports developed along the Pacific coast, including San Francisco, Seattle, and Los Angeles. When gold was discovered in California and Alaska, people from Asia

Extending Learning

Pacific Coast Salmon—Remind or point out to students that one of the great anomalies of the food world can be found in the Pacific Northwest, home to Pacific coast salmon. Explain that once a year adult females battle the current of the Columbia River, swimming upstream to lay their eggs. Add that some food lovers insist that Pacific coast salmon is the finest in the world.

flocked to the New World. These Japanese, Chinese, Russian, and Korean immigrants were joined by Mexicans, French, and Canadians.

The immigrants brought their food specialties with them and mingled them with local food customs. For example, *chow mein* is a dish created in California about 100 years ago. It is not an authentic Chinese dish, but an American dish based on Chinese cooking.

Early sailing ships brought food from China, Japan, and the Polynesian islands to America. The influence of Asian cooking is still strong in the Pacific Coast and Northwest regions.

Sourdough Bread

Sourdough bread today is considered one of the classic breads in America. Yet it had humble beginnings in the mid-nineteenth century, during the days of the gold rush. Many early settlers in California and Alaska came looking for gold. Most of the prospectors were poor and relied on bread as their staple. They had no yeast, but made bread with a **sourdough starter**, a mixture of flour, water, and salt on which wild yeast cells grew. The mixture fermented and became a leavening agent.

The prospectors never put all their starter in the bread. A small amount was always left in a crock and then replenished by adding flour and water. In this way, sourdough starter was always on hand, and the prospector was then assured of a food supply. Because they were so dependent on the starter, the prospectors came to be known as sourdoughs.

The Northwest

The northwest corner of the United States was the last part of the U.S. mainland to be settled. Settlers in Oregon and Washington came to these northwestern states by way of the Oregon Trail. Many brought seeds from fruit trees to begin orchards. Fruit orchards, which later became profitable businesses for the settlers, remain a major industry in the Northwest today. Along with raising fruits, such as pears, peaches, and apples, these settlers created delicious dishes from the abundance of fish and seafood. Dungeness crab and coho salmon were often steamed or served with creamy sauces.

Hawaii

The fiftieth state to join the Union, Hawaii has been the midway stopping point for ships traveling the long shipping lanes between Asia and North America.

Hawaiian Cuisine

The original inhabitants of Hawaii were Polynesian, but many other cultures have settled in the chain of islands, bringing their food customs with them. Today, Hawaiian cooking is a blend of Polynesian, Chinese, Japanese, Korean, Filipino, French, English, and Portuguese, as well as mainland American.

The rich soil and warm climate offer a wide variety of tropical fruits, including mango, papaya, pineapple, and bananas. The surrounding waters and inland streams provide a real bounty of flavorful fish.

Other foods were introduced by settlers. The Japanese introduced seaweed, teriyaki sauce for marinating, a new kind of noodle, and many rice and bean products. They also brought the **hibachi**, a small charcoal grill. The Chinese brought rice, soybeans, pork, and Asian vegetables such as Chinese cabbage. These, along with chicken, are the mainstays of Hawaiian cooking.

- ***The Northwest***
- ***Hawaii***
  (text pages 637-638)

Role Play Activity

Invite volunteers with a gift for dramatization and/or public speaking to research the Gold Rush—especially the emotional climate of the era. These students are then to write and stage a one-act play that captures this mood. Encourage these students to show in their drama the effect the discovery of gold in California and Alaska had on the people who settled in these areas.

Discussion Activity

Ask students to describe the use of sourdough starter by prospectors. Can students think of other food, including ones they read about earlier in this chapter, that were influenced by necessity? (Students might mention pemmican.)

Research Activity

On the board, write the phrase *Pacific rim*. Invite volunteers to investigate "Pacific rim" cooking, which was especially popular in the city of San Francisco. Ask students to share their findings, explaining the link between Pacific rim cooking and the foods of Hawaii. (Both are multicultural blends.)

FOOD SCIENCE

Sourdough Starter

Have students research the chemical action that underlies sourdough starter and makes it possible to keep an endless supply by simply adding more flour, water, and salt to a small amount of the starter.

Then provide students with sourdough starter and have them bake bread from it. Give each student a supply of the starter to take home for future use. Survey students at the end of the term to find out who is still using the starter, and how often it is being used.

TEACH cont.

- *The Northwest*
- *Hawaii*
- *Canada*
  (text pages 637-640)

Discussion Activity

Ask students to list the cultures that have had an effect on Hawaiian cooking. Ask what a hibachi is and what culture introduced it to Hawaiian cooking.

Culinary Detectives

Emphasize that meats and fish at a luau are wrapped in leaves before they are cooked in the open pit. Have interested students, working either individually or in pairs, become culinary detectives. Provide each pair with a mystery to unravel. One possible mystery might be the question of other cultures that cook foods in leaves of one kind or another that may have influenced this practice in Hawaii. Have detectives share the results of their cases. L1

Demonstration

Help students obtain references on the preparation of fresh coconut, pineapple, papaya, and mango. Ask for volunteers to demonstrate ways to prepare the tropical fruits for eating. Distribute samples, getting reactions from students—especially those who have never before tasted some or all of these fruits.

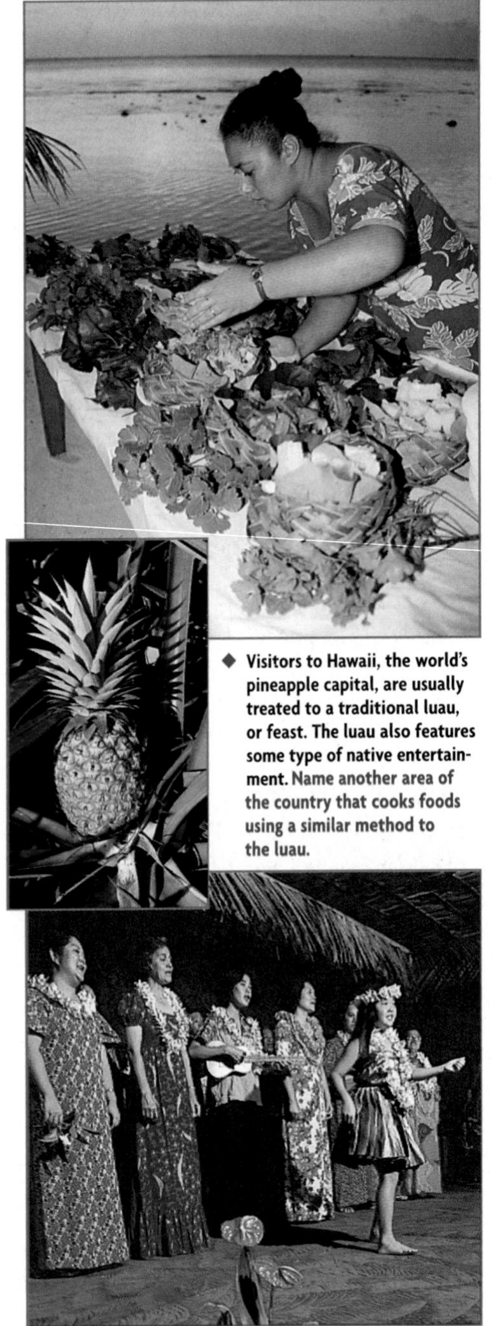

◆ **Visitors to Hawaii, the world's pineapple capital, are usually treated to a traditional luau, or feast. The luau also features some type of native entertainment.** Name another area of the country that cooks foods using a similar method to the luau.

The early Polynesians had no pots and pans, so they invented techniques for preparing food. One was *poi* pounding. They pounded fruits or roots into a bland, sticky paste, which was their staple. Today, poi is made from ground taro root and is often used in cooking or served as a side dish. If allowed to ferment for several days, it develops a more sour flavor. Duck may be steamed in a banana leaf with cabbage, pineapple, and poi. Taro chips, similar to potato chips, are deep-fried, thin slices of taro root.

Another cooking method was the open pit, which became famous as the *luau*, or feast. The luau is a tradition observed on special occasions, such as birthdays, marriages, and other events. Tourists visiting Hawaii are usually treated to a luau, which also features native entertainment.

The highlight of the luau is a pig roasted in an open pit. Fish and other meats are wrapped in leaves and roasted with sweet potatoes and bananas on the hot coals. Besides poi, other Hawaiian dishes that might be served include *lomi lomi salmon*—salted salmon with onions and tomatoes—and *haupia*—a sweet pudding made with arrowroot and coconut milk.

Canada

As in the United States, the foods of Canada reflect the nation's natural resources and rich cultural diversity. The natural resources include wild rice, beef, and more than 150 species of fish and shellfish. Apples and peaches lead fruit production. Just like the United States, Canada is populated by many nationalities that have retained their identities.

Extending Learning

Hawaiian Cooking—Common in Hawaiian cooking, the coconut is actually the seed of the coconut palm. It provides a refreshing beverage and an edible pulp called "coconut meat."

The clear—and bitter-tasting—liquid released by a coconut when it is first cracked open is sometimes erroneously called "coconut milk." True coconut milk is a manufactured product. It is made by grating coconut meat, mixing it with water, then squeezing and straining it to produce a white, sweet juice.

Atlantic Provinces

Newfoundland, New Brunswick, Nova Scotia, and Prince Edward Island make up the Atlantic provinces. The ethnic origins of the people are largely English and French, with some German, Dutch, and Irish as well. Almost half of the people speak both English and French.

Fish and seafood are the most important foods of the region. Fresh fruits and vegetables are grown locally, but the growing season is short because of the long periods of cold weather. Blueberries are an important crop.

Specialty potatoes are raised on Prince Edward Island and in New Brunswick, showing the influence of the Irish who settled the region. Potatoes were used for many things other than food by the early settlers—laundry starch, headache remedies, and bottle corks. They were an important ingredient used to help stretch soups to feed families.

A traditional Saturday night meal in the Atlantic provinces is homemade baked beans and steamed brown bread. Other popular meals include rich pea soup and a special Acadian dish called *râpée pie*, consisting of layers of cooked poultry and puréed potatoes. Another dish, *colcannon*, came from Scotland and Ireland. It is made by mashing together potatoes, turnips, and cabbage.

Quebec

As a result of its cultural and linguistic ties to France and Switzerland, Quebec shows the most European influence of any Canadian province. About one-fourth of the population of Canada resides in Quebec. These French Canadians are proud of their language and heritage. French is spoken almost exclusively in this province.

It is not surprising, then, that the food in Quebec displays a distinct French influence. Common dishes include seafood soups, special cheeses, and French breads and pastries. At the same time, there are foods that are unique to Quebec. Among these is *smoked meat*, beef

◆ **The rich mix of cultures in Canada may be felt in the unmistakably French food of Quebec City in the east and salmon smoking for use in a Native American potlatch in the west.** Read the "Connecting Food and Social Studies" feature in Section 19-4, on page 510, which describes the potlatch.

- *Canada (text pages 638-640)*

Discussion Activity

Compare the countries from which people immigrated to Canada with those who immigrated to the United States. What similarities and differences in food traditions have resulted from these migrations?

Pen Pals to the North

Have students exchange letters or, if the classroom has a computer hooked to the Internet, e-mails with students in different provinces of Canada. Have students ask questions about the geographic and cultural influences, food production, and food traditions. Have students request that the Canadian students send recipes that reflect the food traditions of the area. Have students read the letters they receive to the class. Ask volunteers to test out some of the recipes. L1

DID You Know?

- A food similar to colcannon popular throughout the British Isles has the colorful name "bubble and squeak"—a term that derives from the appearance and sound cabbage and sliced potatoes make when they are sautéed together.

Extending Learning

Quebec—Quebec became a British possession as a result of the Treaty of Paris, which marked the official end of the Seven Years War. This decision had little to do with the sentiments of the inhabitants.

The tension between Canadians of English descent and those of French descent continues even today. Because of this tension, and tension between Quebec and other provinces, a vote was taken in 1992 to determine whether Quebec should secede from Canada. Although the majority felt that Quebec should remain a part of Canada, the people of Quebec remain loyal to their heritage.

TEACH cont.

- *Canada*
- *Cultural Diversity Today (text pages 639-641)*

Discussion Activity

Ask students to explain why the United States and Canada have recently experienced so much growth in their minority populations.

Identifying Contributing Factors

Refer students to the discussion on page 641 of factors that have led to the assimilation of cultures in North America. Observe that there are other factors that contribute to this tendency and that these factors have, in turn, helped people become familiar with foods from all over. Challenge students to identify some of these. (Possible answers include world travel, restaurants, and increased interaction with people from other cultures.) L1

Tradition "Map" Activity

Remind students that concept or word maps are intended to show relationships between thoughts and ideas in graphic terms. Explain that students are about to try their hand at another kind of graphic display—a "tradition map." Students are to write the word *tradition* at the center of a large sheet of paper. They are to write the words *time* and *energy* elsewhere on the page, with arrows pointing at tradition. Ask students to complete their tradition maps by noting the influence of these and other constraints on traditions as we know them.

brisket smoked in a blend of spices and served thinly sliced. *Back bacon*, better known in the United States as Canadian bacon, has far less fat and a milder flavor than streaky bacon.

Quebec produces about 90 percent of Canada's maple syrup. Maple sugar was the only sweetener that early settlers had. Some Canadians still prefer blocks of maple sugar to other sweeteners. One Quebec dessert made with maple sugar is *sugar pie*. *Grand-pères* are dumplings that are served with maple syrup.

A pie made with ground pork, called *tourtière*, is another French Canadian specialty. Ground pork is also a main ingredient in *cretons*, a popular spread made with kidney and lard. The early settlers made *cipate*, a pie made with game meats. Today, however, it is made with chicken, pork, veal, and beef.

Ontario

Ontario is centrally located in Canada, lying to the north of Minnesota, Wisconsin, and Michigan. Over one-third of Canada's population lives in Ontario, making it the most heavily populated province in the country.

Beef, dairy foods, maple syrup, and wild rice are among the chief products of Ontario. Poultry, eggs, fruits, and vegetables are also plentiful. The Canadian flag's maple leaf is a clue to the abundance of maple trees. Syrup drawn from the sap of these trees is used in candy and as a popular sweetener in desserts.

Food customs in Ontario are as varied as the people who live there. Many came from Scotland, Ireland, and England. Shortbread is popular among residents with Scottish ancestors and is a common holiday gift. Swiss Mennonites, who had landed first in Pennsylvania, settled in Ontario in the late 1700s. Immigrants from most European countries, as well as India and the West Indies, came to the province. In addition, more Native Americans live in Ontario than in any other province.

The Western Provinces

To the west of Ontario are the prairie provinces of Manitoba, Saskatchewan, and Alberta. Spacious wheat fields and grazing land for cattle make the traditional foods in these provinces similar to those in the Midwestern United States. Honey and whitefish are also important products. One unique fish that is sold smoked, *Goldeye*, is known as a delicacy in many parts of the world.

In British Columbia, on the North Pacific coast, salmon is a staple. *Loganberries*, a cross between blackberries and raspberries, are also grown in British Columbia. They are a favorite in pies. Vancouver, the largest city in British Columbia, is located just north of Seattle. It has a significant Chinese population and its own Chinatown. Foods from all regions of China can be found there.

The Northwest Territories stretch across northern Canada. Native Americans and Inuit are the primary inhabitants. Until the nineteenth century, most Inuit hunted and fished for food. Seal meat, caribou, trout, and cod were staples. One fish that is unique to northern Canada is *Arctic char*, or *ilkaula*, which is a cross between salmon and trout.

As in the United States, early pioneers in northern Canada relied on sourdough starter for preparing bread. Another early bread product was *bannock*, a flat, round cake. Introduced by immigrants from Scotland and northern England, this unleavened cake was made from oatmeal, rye, or barley meal.

HOME & COMMUNITY CONNECTION

Have students interview older people in their families or community about changes these people perceive in the preserving of traditions relating to food and other aspects of culture. Before proceeding, students should form brainstorming groups and devise meaningful questions to ask respondents. All questions should then be pooled and converted into a questionnaire. After the interviews, encourage a roundtable discussion of the findings. Ask: Should we try to preserve traditions? If so, what steps can we take to do so?

Cultural Diversity Today

In recent decades, the minority populations of the United States and Canada have grown significantly. Millions of immigrants have flocked to North America in search of a better life and have settled in communities across both nations. The traditions of the various cultures have merged and blended, further enriching and diversifying the area.

In addition to immigration, other factors that affect the cultural diversity in North America include:

- **Mobility.** People now move from one region to another more often than in the past. They carry their food traditions along with them.
- **Media.** Through television, magazines, and other sources, people are exposed to various cultures and their traditions.
- **Technology.** As a result of modern transportation and packaging methods, foods from many regions and cultures are available all across the United States and Canada.

For these and other reasons, the food in a specific region today can be as diverse as the people who live there. Many food habits and patterns now reflect the traditions of individual families more than the area in which the families live.

Section 23-2 Review & Activities

1. Briefly describe cowboy and Tex-Mex cuisines.
2. Explain two ways in which the geography of the Pacific Coast and Northwest affected the food supply.
3. Describe the contribution of the Polynesians to Hawaiian cuisine.
4. Identify one Irish influence on the foods of the Atlantic provinces of Canada. Identify two foods that are unique to Quebec.
5. **Analyzing.** Do you think the type of foods people were accustomed to influenced their decision about where to settle? Explain.
6. **Extending.** Purists are people who are resistant to change and insist on sticking with tradition. Which of the foods you learned about in this section do you think would be most likely to have a purist following? Explain your answer.
7. **Applying.** List ten foods that you enjoy eating. Identify the regional or ethnic source of each food.

ASSESS

REVIEW

- Ask students to summarize the main ideas in this section.
- Have students complete the Section Review. (Answers appear below.)

EVALUATION

- Have students create a menu for and prepare a typical Tex-Mex meal that is attractive and nutritious.
- Have students take the quiz for Section 23-2. (Use the quiz in the *Teacher Resource Guide,* or construct your own with the **ExamView®** *Test Generator* on the *Effective Instruction CD-ROM.*)

RETEACHING

- Ask students to work in pairs to prepare a chart of regional foods of the American West.
- Refer to the *Reteaching Activities* booklet for the Section 23-2 activity sheet.

CLOSE

Refer to the lists students prepared for the second motivator for this section. Have students add to their lists new foods they learned about in this section.

Answers to Section 23-2 Review & Activities

1. See pages 634-636.
2. Along the Pacific coast, seafood was plentiful; the temperate climate of southern California allowed fresh fruits and vegetables to be grown.
3. They invented techniques for making poi, fruits or roots pounded into a bland, sticky paste.
4. Potatoes; see pages 639-640.
5. People may have looked for land similar to that of their homeland.
6. Answers will vary. Students might mention chili and barbecue.
7. Answers will vary.

Recipe File

Southwest Guacamole

This recipe makes use of the technique of making fruit and vegetable spreads. Prior to assigning the lab, you may wish to have students review relevant portions of Chapter 16.

USING THE RECIPE

- Have students read the recipe and discuss each step.
- Review kitchen and food safety procedures that apply to the recipe.
- Have each lab team fill out a work plan. (See the *Foods Lab Resources* booklet.)
- Have students check off the ingredients and equipment listed on the recipe worksheet and prepare the recipe.
- Have students complete the evaluation and questions on the recipe worksheet.

SEE ALSO...

The *Foods Lab Resources* booklet for the "Southwest Guacamole" recipe worksheet and other recipe alternatives.

Recipe File

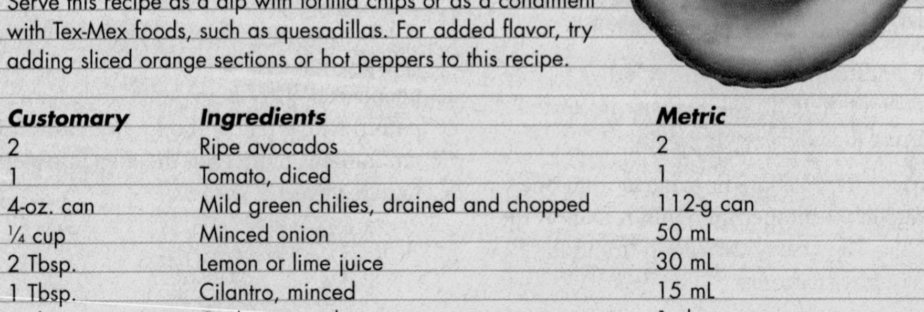

Southwest Guacamole

Serve this recipe as a dip with tortilla chips or as a condiment with Tex-Mex foods, such as quesadillas. For added flavor, try adding sliced orange sections or hot peppers to this recipe.

Customary	***Ingredients***	***Metric***
2	Ripe avocados	2
1	Tomato, diced	1
4-oz. can	Mild green chilies, drained and chopped	112-g can
¼ cup	Minced onion	50 mL
2 Tbsp.	Lemon or lime juice	30 mL
1 Tbsp.	Cilantro, minced	15 mL
1 clove	Garlic, minced	1 clove

Yield: 8 servings, ¼ cup each

Directions

1. Peel and seed the avocados.
2. In a medium bowl, mash the avocados.
3. Stir in tomato, chilies, onion, lemon or lime juice, cilantro, and garlic.
4. Serve at room temperature or chilled.

Note: To store, cover the surface of the guacamole with plastic wrap and refrigerate.

Nutrition Information

Per serving (approximate): 87 calories, 1 g protein, 5 g carbohydrate, 8 g fat, 0 mg cholesterol, 173 mg sodium
Good source of: vitamin A, vitamin C

Food for Thought

- How could this recipe be varied to suit individual tastes?
- What purpose does the lemon or lime juice serve in this recipe?

Answers to Food for Thought

1. Answers will vary. Possibilities include adding more or less spice, cutting down on the degree of tartness from the citrus juice.
2. It helps preserve the color and also adds a refreshing tartness.

Career Wanted

Family & Consumer Sciences Teacher

Education and Training
- Degree in family and consumer sciences
- Certification through state-approved teacher education program

Qualities
- Interest in helping people
- Communication skills
- Leadership
- Flexibility

"In teaching, I help shape the future of society."

Doreen Krebbs

Q. Doreen, why did you become a teacher?

A. First, I enjoy working with young people—they're never boring. Also, teaching family and consumer sciences allows me to cover so many important issues—foods and nutrition, relationships, citizenship. These all deal with life skills, things students need to know regardless of their career or other choices they make.

Q. What surprised you most about being a teacher?

A. I hadn't expected it to be so physically demanding. Just setting up and supervising a foods lab can be taxing. There's a lot of "behind-the-scenes" work that has to be done outside of school and outside of school hours. It's a good thing I teach health and managing stress as part of the course.

Q. What philosophy helps you be an effective teacher?

A. I try to keep things new and fresh. I take advantage of opportunities to learn. I read and travel, and just talk to people in their work. That keeps me up-to-date. It reminds me that there is so much going on in the world to learn about. That's an attitude I want to impart to my students.

Related Career Opportunities

Entry Level
- Child care worker
- Summer camp counselor
- Medical assistant

Technical Level
- Preschool teacher
- Teacher aide

Professional Level
- Consumer advocate
- Career counselor
- Director of human resources

Making Career Connections

TEACHING EXPERIENCE. With your teacher's help, plan a lesson for older children on a topic or concept you've studied in foods and nutrition. Teach the lesson at a school or after-school program. Discuss your experience in class. What insights into teaching did you gain? How is teaching, itself, a learning experience?

Career Wanted

Family & Consumer Sciences Teacher

Thinking About the Career

Have students read the feature, then seek out additional information on a career in this field. You might remind them that a family and consumer sciences teacher is available in the classroom for questions. Depending upon your experience, you might describe for students what it is like to work in a medium-size or large school district versus work in a rural school setting.

Ask students to brainstorm characteristics and traits a person in this line of work should have beyond those noted in the feature.

Career-Building Opportunities

You may wish to explain that certified teachers who have been on the job for several years are eligible for tenure in most school systems. This can lead to higher salary and prestige. It can also be a stepping-stone to a career in school administration.

For More Information

For additional information about a career in family and consumer sciences teaching, encourage students to contact:

- Teacher's Net
  www.teachers.net
- United Federation of Teachers
  260 Park Avenue South
  New York, NY, 10010
  www.uft.org

REVIEW

- Have students complete the Chapter Review. (Answers appear below.)

EVALUATION

- Present a map of the United States and Canada. Have students identify the various regions and describe foods typical of each.
- Have students take the test for Chapter 23. (Use the chapter test in the *Teacher Resource Guide,* or construct your own with the **Exam***View*® *Test Generator* on the *Effective Instruction CD-ROM.*)

ANSWERS

Checking Your Knowledge

1. Roasted, boiled, removed the kernels and made them into a powder (or meal) for baking and frying.
2. In coastal areas, seafood was a staple, with fish usually steamed or cooked over an open fire; in the South, soups and stews were made from fish and small game; in the Southwest, beans were used in soups, and meats were roasted over open fires.
3. The climate, the availability of crops and farmlands on which livestock could be raised, the cooking styles of the settlers themselves.
4. French, Spanish, Italian, African, West Indian, and Native American.
5. Any four: Freshwater fish, crawfish, rabbit, turtle, squirrel, alligator, and okra.
6. To save time in the morning so that everyone could get an early start; it may have originated with Southerners moving to the Southwest, though meat was barbecued in Virginia as early as the seventeenth century.
7. Chinese and American.

Chapter 23 Review & Activities

Summary

Section 23-1: Regional Foods of the East, Midwest, and South

- Some Native Americans were skilled farmers and cooks. They were pioneers in storing and preserving foods.
- They shared the foods and cooking methods with European immigrants, who adapted them to their own lifestyles and cooking traditions.
- British, Dutch, and German groups in the Northeast developed recipes to supply their energy needs.
- Midwestern farmers raised cattle, grains, and vegetables.
- Southern staples were incorporated into new dishes by African Americans living in the South.
- Creole and Cajun cuisines are famous for their distinctively spiced, seafood-based recipes.

Section 23-2: Regional Foods of the West and Canada

- Foods and preparation methods of the American Southwest reflect the influence of Native American and Mexican cultures.
- Along the Pacific coast and in the Northwest, shipping ports brought the influence of Asian cooking to native food supplies.
- Hawaiian cuisine combines many traditions.
- Fish, shellfish, blueberries, and potatoes are plentiful in the Atlantic provinces of Canada.
- The cuisine of Quebec reflects its historical ties to France.
- Food customs in Ontario are as varied as the residents themselves.
- Foods in Canada's Western provinces are similar to foods in the Midwestern United States.

Working IN THE Lab

1. ***Foods Lab.*** Find and prepare an authentic recipe for one of the regional favorites described in this chapter. Compare its basic flavor with that of the food as it is usually prepared today. Describe and give reasons for the similarities and differences you find.
2. ***Foods Lab.*** Combine the preferences and cooking traditions of your lab group to create your own "regional" cuisine. Prepare a meal of these favorite recipes, explaining how each one became part of the group's "heritage."

Checking Your Knowledge

1. Name three ways that Native Americans prepared corn that are still used today.
2. Describe three ways in which regional differences affected the foods and preparation methods of Native Americans.
3. Identify the three influences on the development of Midwestern cooking styles.
4. What cultures are blended in Creole cooking?
5. Name four foods that are often combined in Cajun cooking.
6. Why did cowboy cooks often make a biscuit mix before going to bed at night when on the trail? What is the origin of the barbecue?
7. *Chow mein* reflects a blending of what two cultures?
8. How is sourdough bread made? What is the advantage of this method?
9. Identify two uses of the taro root.
10. Name two foods that are unique to Quebec. Why does the Canadian flag feature a maple leaf?

Thinking Critically

1. **Recognizing Alternatives.** Identify the traditional cooking methods used to prepare the regional foods described in this chapter. Suggest some modern methods that could replace the traditional methods.
2. **Analyzing Behavior.** What personal qualities did immigrants and settlers show by trying new foods and developing new recipes? In what other situations did those qualities help them survive? How might people today benefit from trying new foods?
3. **Predicting Consequences.** How do you think appreciating the food traditions of other cultures affects your attitudes and feelings toward the people of those cultures?
4. **Recognizing Points of View.** Do you think that being served some of their province's traditional dishes would be a problem for some health-conscious Canadians? Choose two of the Canadian specialties and think about how they might be prepared so that they would be more nutritious. Which traditional Canadian food products would be the most healthful?

Reinforcing Key Skills

1. **Management.** Carlita lives in a small town in New England. She has read about the nutrients in poi and would like to prepare it for her family. However, taro root is not available where Carlita lives.
2. **Communication.** Trying the foods of different regions and cultures of America and Canada can be an enriching experience. Imagine you have been asked to create a campaign to make people of the North American continent more aware of their rich and diverse cultural backgrounds. Write, draw, or act out your ideas for heightening awareness.

Making Decisions and Solving Problems

You are spending a few months with friends in the South. You are concerned that many of the foods they prepare—fried chicken and fish, hush puppies, meat gravy—are high in fat and calories. You would like to suggest ways of preparing foods that are more healthful, but retain the flavors and textures your friends enjoy.

Making Connections

1. **Language Arts.** In Willa Cather's *My Antonia*, find a passage related to food, or to the lack of food. What does the scene tell you about meals, food supplies, and preparation methods of people of that time and place? What might the scene tell you about the characters involved?
2. **Social Studies.** Interview people of different cultural backgrounds who live in your community. What are some traditional foods of their ethnic groups? If they originally came from another country or region, how has moving affected their cooking and eating habits? How have their cooking traditions affected the way they prepare common American dishes?

ANSWERS cont.

8. It is made from a sourdough starter, a mixture of flour, water, and salt on which wild yeast cells grow. The mixture ferments and becomes a leavening agent. An advantage is that you can save a small amount of the starter and replenish it by adding flour and water. That way, you always have a head start on making bread.
9. Poi and taro chips.
10. Any two: Smoked meat and back bacon, sugar pie, grand-pères tourtière, cretons, cipate. Because of the abundance of maple trees and maple syrup in Canada.

Thinking Critically

1. Answers will vary.
2. They showed courage, adaptability, and a willingness to try new things. They may have applied these traits to their system of government and to setting up communities. People trying new foods today can lower their levels of cholesterol as well as the fat and sodium in their eating plans.
3. Answers will vary. Understanding the food traditions of a culture helps you better understand the people.
4. Answers will vary. Students should use what they have learned in earlier chapters about health and nutrition to answer the questions.

Reinforcing Key Skills

1. She might research whether this root can be successfully shipped, and, if so, from where and at what cost. Alternatively, she might investigate other foods that have been used by Polynesians of the past to make poi.
2. Answers will vary. Encourage students to be creative.

CHAPTER

24

Special Topics in Food

Advance Planning Guide ☑

- Purchase or obtain all necessary ingredients, materials, or equipment for the following: Section 24-1, 24-2 Motivators; Lab Experience on pages 649, 655, 656, 657, 664, 671; Recipe File on page 659.
- Obtain pictures of meat loaf, au gratin potatoes, baked fish, and applesauce.
- Purchase a variety of bottled waters for a Taste Test on page 655.
- Purchase various brands of tea and/or coffee.
- Gather photos of formal table service.
- Create a bulletin board entitled "Preserving Summer's Harvest—A Time-honored Tradition."
- Gather containers for freezing produce.
- Purchase fruit and ascorbic acid for the Student Demonstrations on page 671.
- Invite a home economist to speak.
- Obtain a pressure canner.
- Purchase foods to dry; obtain a food dehydrator for the Demonstration on page 673.
- Purchase or obtain green beans for Working in the Lab on page 676.

CHAPTER 24

Special Topics in Food

Good friends and good food—the recipe for a great time. Add some creative techniques for food preparation and presentation, and any occasion becomes special.

In this chapter, you will learn ways to give food eye appeal as well as taste appeal.

MEETING DIVERSE NEEDS

Naturalistic Learners. If there are students in the class who enjoy working with plants, ask them to grow a variety of fresh herbs. Have them air-dry or microwave some of the fresh herbs. Ask them to give herb growing tips to students and offer them tastes of the fresh and dried herbs. Have all students compare the taste and cost of these herbs to those sold commercially. What do students conclude?

SECTION 24-1

Creative Techniques

"This cole slaw is great, Uncle Ted!" Alonza remarked. "How did you make it so good?"

"It's a little secret I learned," her uncle said, smiling. "I added a little celery seed."

Like Alonza's uncle, many cooks know that seasonings can wake up the flavor of even basic foods.

Objectives

After studying this section, you should be able to:

- Describe how to use a variety of seasonings.
- Explain how to use your creativity in cooking.
- Describe ways to improve the appearance of foods with garnishes.

Look for These Terms

seasoning blends

julienne

en papillote

garnish

Seasoning Secrets

Seasonings are ingredients that are used in small amounts to flavor foods. They include herbs, spices, and condiments. Seasonings can be helpful for health-conscious people who are limiting their use of salt and fat by providing flavor.

When you begin to experiment with seasonings, use a small amount at first. You can always add more. If you add too much at the beginning, there's little you can do to correct the flavor.

Herbs and Spices

Herbs are the flavorful leaves and stems of soft, succulent plants that grow in the temperate zone. Some familiar examples are basil, oregano, sage, and bay leaf. Herbs are usually sold dry, but increasing numbers are available fresh in many supermarkets.

Spices are usually dried, ground buds, bark, seeds, stems, or roots of aromatic plants and trees. Most grow in tropical countries. Some—whole nutmeg, peppercorns, and cinnamon sticks, for example—are sold whole or in pieces. A few are sold fresh, such as ginger root, which is commonly used in Asian cooking.

SECTION 24-1

Creative Techniques

FOCUS

MOTIVATORS

- Provide small samples of drained, canned white beans to students. Ask students to comment about the eye appeal and flavor. Next, mix the beans with fresh, chopped basil. Discuss the difference in appeal.
- Show students plain mashed potatoes spooned onto a plate. Then show students how to add creativity simply by using a pastry bag. Have students practice making potato designs with the pastry bag.

VOCABULARY ACTIVITY

Pronounce the terms listed under "Look for These Terms." Have students find the terms and their definitions in the section. Ask two student volunteers to research the derivation of the terms *julienne* and *papilotte*.

STUDY SKILLS

- **Outlining.** Have students read the section and outline it by copying the headers on paper and leaving space after each one. Students are to write a sentence in their own words, summarizing the content under each header.
- Have students read the section and complete the appropriate part of the Chapter 24 Study Guide in the *Student Workbook*.

Section 24-1 Resources

◆ **Student Workbook,** pp. 179, 182
◆ **Teacher Resource Guide**
Lesson Plan 24-1 Organizer
Section 24-1 Quiz
◆ **Effective Instruction CD-ROM**
Exam*View*® *Test Generator*

◆ **Student Motivation Kit**
Reteaching Activities, p. 106
Enrichment Activities
Foods Lab Resources, pp. 151–152
Skills for Making Food Choices, pp. 53–54

TEACH

- *Seasoning Secrets (text pages 647-651)*

Lab Experience

Have students test dried herbs in the class foods lab for freshness using the test described under the heading "Buying and Storing Seasonings." What were the results? Ask students if any herbs need to be replaced. Are the herbs being stored correctly? If no, what needs to be changed with their storage? L1

Information Search

Take the class to the library or computer lab. Give students 15 minutes to find out and list the names of as many herbs as they are able. Have a few volunteers compile an alphabetical chart of all students' listed herbs. L1

Cultural Connection

Have students bring to class copies of at least three recipes for dishes associated with a particular culture. In groups, have students compile recipes and develop a cultural flavor chart, listing culture next to common herbs and spices. Moderate a discussion on how these herbs and spices can lend unique flavors to typical "American" dishes. L1

◆ Herbs and spices give many dishes an added dimension. When adding seasonings like these, remember the saying: "Less is more." Explain how the saying applies in this case.

Seasoning Blends

Seasoning blends are convenient combinations of herbs and spices. Most blends are used for specific purposes. For instance, Italian seasonings combine flavors typical in Italian cooking. You can buy blends or mix your own.

Buying and Storing Seasonings

Because herbs and spices are used in such small amounts, consider buying them in bulk. That way, you can buy only the amount you can use in a short time.

Light, air, and heat are the main enemies of herbs and spices. Store them in tightly closed, opaque containers in a cool, dark place. Do not keep them next to the range.

Dried, crushed herbs keep their flavor for about six months. To test dried herbs for freshness, rub a small amount in the palm of your hand with your thumb for about five to ten seconds. If there is little or no aroma, the herb is probably too old to use. It might give food a bitter flavor.

Ground spices keep their flavor for about a year. Whole spices may last as long as three years.

Using Herbs and Spices

Here are some guidelines for using herbs and spices:

- Begin with a few of the more basic herbs and spices. (The chart on pages 649 and 650 shows some of these.) Once you learn how to use these, you can add others.
- Herbs and spices vary in strength and are used in differing amounts. Dried herbs are more potent than fresh herbs. As a rule, you can substitute 1 tablespoon (15 mL) of fresh herbs for 1 teaspoon (5 mL) of dried, crushed herbs.
- When preparing hot foods, add herbs and spices at least 10 minutes before tasting or serving. This allows time for the heat to release the flavor. Do not add herbs more than 45 minutes before serving—they will lose their flavor if overcooked.
- When preparing cold mixtures, add herbs and spices 30 minutes to several hours before serving so that flavors can be released.

Extending Learning

Herbs and Spices—The American Heart Association has developed a salt substitute, "herb shaker blend," composed of herbs and spices. Mix all of the following ingredients together and store in a cool, dark place.

Yield: ¼ cup
1 Tbsp. garlic powder
1 tsp. each dried, ground, or crushed basil, thyme, parsley, savory, mace (or nutmeg), onion powder, black pepper, and sage
½ tsp. cayenne

Q ***How can I dry my own fresh herbs?***

A There are two methods—air-drying and microwaving—both of them easy. To air-dry herbs, first rinse sprigs of herbs and shake off excess water. Tie herbs into bunches, and label them. Hang them in a dry, shady, well-ventilated place. They should dry in about two weeks. To microwave herbs, place the rinsed herbs between several layers of paper toweling. Microwave on 100 percent power, 15 to 30 seconds at a time, until the herbs are dry and can be crumbled.

◆ **Keep in mind that dried herbs and spices go farther than fresh ones. How many tablespoons of dried rosemary would you use in a chicken recipe that called for two tablespoons of fresh rosemary?**

Basic Herbs, Spices, and Seasoning Blends

		Flavor	*Uses*
Herbs	**Basil**	Mild licorice flavor with a hint of mint	Dishes containing tomatoes, meat and poultry, carrots, peas, rice
	Bay leaf	Strong, aromatic, pungent flavor	Braised meat, stews, soups, bean dishes (Use leaf whole; remove before serving.)
	Dill weed	Sharp flavor, similar to that of caraway seeds	Cruciferous vegetables, carrots, green beans, cucumbers, fish, poultry, breads
	Marjoram	Delicate, sweet, spicy flavor with hint of mint	Soups, stews, poultry, stuffings, salads, tomato sauces
	Mint	Strong, refreshing, aromatic flavor	Yogurt dishes, tomato dishes, rice, bulgur, vegetables, lentils, fruits, tea
	Oregano	Strong, clovelike flavor	Italian and Mexican dishes, bean dishes, pork, poultry, salads, green beans

- *Seasoning Secrets (text pages 647-651)*

Lab Experience

In lab groups, have students prepare couscous, according to box directions, to use as a base for tasting herbs. Have them taste at least three different fresh herbs, separately, with the couscous. Ask them to write their own specific descriptions of the flavors of each herb. **L1**

Oral Reports

Assign a different herb or spice to each of several selected interested students. Have each student (1) prepare and present a three-minute report on the history and use of that spice or herb and/or (2) bring to class a copy of one recipe that uses the herb or spice. Create a class herb and spice recipe file. **L1**

Using 

Demonstrate how to air-dry fresh parsley by placing it in a shady, well-ventilated place in the classroom. Have students watch the parsley over a couple of weeks. You may wish to demonstrate as well how to microwave fresh parsley to dry it. Have students crumble the dried parsley.

FOOD SCIENCE

Salt Content of Seasoning Blends

Ask students to conduct a supermarket survey. Have students locate and read the ingredients in seasoning blends. How many of the seasoning blends contain salt? How many list salt as the first ingredient? In class, discuss the implications of this for people who are on low-salt or low-sodium eating plans.

TEACH cont.

- *Seasoning Secrets (text pages 647-651)*

Identification

Ask students to identify "all-purpose" herbs, spices, and blends—those that can be used with a variety of foods. When might it be a good idea to buy these before you buy those that have narrower uses? **L1**

VISUAL LEARNING *Using the Chart*

Discuss the use of the herbs, spices, and blends in the chart on pages 649-650. Then, using recipe resources, students are to find recipes that use herbs, spices, and seasoning blends listed in the chart, adding names of recipes to an additional chart column.

Store Survey

Have students survey a local supermarket to identify the variety of condiments available. They are to include mustard, salsa, ketchup, and other sauces used to introduce a contrasting flavor. Have students compare the Nutrition Facts panels and categorize condiments by nutrients, such as highest to lowest sodium and highest to lowest calories. Discuss uses for each condiment. What might people following restricted eating plans need to know about use of condiments? **L1**

Basic Herbs, Spices, and Seasoning Blends (cont'd)

		Flavor	*Uses*
Herbs (cont'd)	**Rosemary**	Strong, piney flavor	Poultry, lamb, pork, potatoes, breads, bean dishes, pasta sauces, soups
	Sage	Strong, slightly bitter flavor	Poultry, pork, stuffings, potatoes, white beans, chowders
	Thyme	Strong, clovelike flavor	Poultry and stuffings, lamb, dry beans, stews, soups
Spices	**Cinnamon**	Sweet flavor	Meat dishes, desserts, legumes, sweet potatoes, squash
	Cloves	Strong, hot, pungent flavor	Meat dishes, grains, legumes, fruit desserts
	Cumin	Strong, musty flavor	Mexican and Middle Eastern foods, legumes, tomato sauces, soups, rice
	Dry mustard	Hot, sharp, spicy flavor	Meat, poultry, soups, stews, egg dishes, salad dressings
	Ground ginger	Hot, pungent, spicy flavor	Stir-fries, stews, soups, squash, sweet potatoes, grains, legumes, desserts
	Nutmeg	Mild, spicy flavor (best if purchased whole and grated fresh)	Cooked spinach, zucchini, and carrots; sweet potatoes; soups; stews; ground meat; bulgur; fruits; desserts
Seasoning Blends	**Chili powder**	Spicy, hot, pungent flavor	Tex-Mex cooking, chili, stews, soups, barbecue sauces, dishes made with corn
	Curry powder	Pungent, spicy flavor	East Indian cooking, poultry, meats, fish, yogurt dishes, legumes
	Italian seasoning	Blend of basil, marjoram, oregano, rosemary, sage, savory, and thyme	Italian cooking
	Poultry seasoning	Blend of lovage, marjoram, and sage	Any dishes made with poultry, including stuffing

Extending Learning

Saffron—Saffron is an expensive spice. Why is it so costly? Nearly 15,000 tiny stigmas from a small purple crocus are needed to make an ounce of saffron. Each crocus contains just three stigmas, which are hand-picked and dried. This very laborious process seems well-worth the effort after enjoying the taste of paella, bouillabaisse, and other saffron-spiced dishes. Luckily, only small amounts are needed to provide its distinctive flavor, aroma, and deep yellow color.

Condiments

Condiments are liquid or semiliquid accompaniments to food. You can also use them as flavorful seasonings. Condiments vary in flavor—sweet, salty, or spicy. Mustard, salsa, and ketchup are popular condiments. Here are some others:

- **Soy and tamari sauces.** Are made from fermented soybeans. Soy sauce has a sharper, more pungent flavor than tamari. Low-sodium types are available.
- **Hot pepper sauce.** Is made from hot chili peppers. It is measured by drops because it's so strong.
- **Worcestershire sauce** (WOO-stuhr-shuhr). A dark, spicy sauce used in soups, stews, and meat mixtures.

Using Your Creativity

Seasonings make food taste good. What's the secret to making it *look* good? Using your creativity and your "meal appeal" skills—that's the secret. For many people, preparing food is more than just cooking. It's art. A creative cook may plan the appearance of a plate of food much as an artist plans a painting. Think about the colors and shapes of food or how the flavors blend. What would your edible work of art look like?

Creative Touches

You might want to look in a variety of cookbooks for different ways to present food. Here are a few possibilities:

- Swirl whipped potatoes into a fluffy mound by using a pastry bag with a decorative tip similar to those used in cake decorating.
- Cut foods into **julienne**—long, thin strips of food.
- Use a small scoop to mold fruits such as melons into balls.

◆ **Salads like this one can become a feast for the eyes as well as the palate when creative touches are used. Identify the items in this dish that have been julienned.**

- *Using Your Creativity*
- *Garnishes*
  (text pages 651-653)

Creativity

Ask students to bring to class a sample of what they believe represents "food art." Display all the submissions. Conduct a discussion of whether students agree that each item is an example of art and why. Have students suggest ways of using such foods creatively in a meal. L1

Connection Activity

Compare creative cooking with other forms of creativity, such as art or music. Discuss ways creative cooking could be an enjoyable leisure activity.

Poster Project

Have students clip illustrations from magazines that show examples of creative cooking to create a poster display. L1

Discussion Activity

Ask students to define *garnish.* What is the purpose of garnishes? Then, based on many of the garnishes listed in each of the food categories on page 652, moderate a discussion of specific food examples for which each garnish could be used. Have students review recipe resources with pictures for more ideas.

FOOD SCIENCE

Keeping Garnishes Crisp

The crispness of a fresh fruit or vegetable depends on the amount of water in the cells of the food. Water, called "free water" because it is not chemically bound to other molecules in the food, is lost through evaporation and can be restored by soaking the food. Placing many of the garnishes shown on page 653 in ice water helps swell the cells with water, making the garnishes crisp.

TEACH cont.

- *Garnishes (text pages 652-653)*

USING
Safety Check

First, ask students to explain what is meant by cooking *en papillote*; then have a volunteer read aloud the feature. Tell students there is an additional safety consideration with food prepared *en papillote*. That is the need to be careful when opening the parchment paper because of the release of hot steam, which can lead to burns. If possible, demonstrate the sweet potatoes *en papillote* recipe at the bottom of this page.

Demonstration

Demonstrate how to make several of the garnishes described or shown on this or the next page. Note: To help curl carrots, fan celery, and open radish roses, soak them in ice cold water. Ask students to make a list of possible uses for each of these garnishes. Discuss uses.

Student Practice

Set up various garnishing stations in the classroom. Have students practice making the garnishes at each of the stations. Give students guidance when needed. L1

Cooking in parchment paper, or **en papillote** (ehn pah-pee-YOHT), is another method creative cooks use. Fish and tender cuts of meat and poultry are often cooked this way. Place one serving in the center of a square of parchment paper along with other ingredients, such as vegetables, butter, or a sauce. For each serving, fold the paper around the food to form a package. Close the ends tightly, and fold them under so that the package does not leak. Place the packages on a baking sheet and bake in the oven. As the food cooks, the flavors blend. The sealed packages retain the flavor and aroma.

To serve, place each package on a dinner plate. Cut an X in the top of the paper, and peel the paper back. As you read about garnishes, think about ways you might dress up foods served *en papillote*.

Safety Check

Do not use brown paper bags as a substitute for cooking parchment. They are not made to withstand high cooking temperatures and may burn. In addition, chemicals in the paper may be transferred to the food.

Garnishes

Have you ever been served food that had a sprig of parsley on it or next to it? Touches like that are known as garnishes. A **garnish** is any small, colorful bit of food that is used to enhance the appearance and texture of a dish. Garnishes can be used on appetizers, salads, main dishes, vegetables, desserts, and beverages. Presenting foods that are attractive, as well as tasty, helps make mealtime an enjoyable experience.

Keep size in mind when garnishing foods. If a garnish is too large, it may overpower the food. Choose colors and flavors that complement the food the garnish is added to. Here are some ideas for simple garnishes:

- **Soups.** Float a spoonful of yogurt, cucumber slices, a lemon slice, croutons, or chopped parsley or chives on soups.
- **Salads.** Top with green pepper rings, cherry tomatoes, pimiento strips, red onion rings, tomato wedges, pickle fans, radish roses, chopped nuts, or seeds.
- **Meat, poultry, and fish dishes.** Use citrus fruit slices, twists, or wedges; a small bunch of grapes; cranberry sauce; spiced crabapples; currant or mint jelly in lemon baskets; sprigs of parsley or fresh herbs; pineapple slices; or olives.
- **Sandwiches.** Use crisp vegetables—such as scored cucumber slices, carrot curls, celery fans, radish roses—and fruit slices or wedges.
- **Beverages.** Try citrus twists on a skewer, lemon or lime slices slit and slipped onto the edge of a glass, marshmallows or peppermint sticks in cocoa, or fruit slices and whole fruits frozen in an ice ring for punch.

Extending Learning

Cooking en Papillote—To make one serving of sweet potatoes *en papillote*:

- Preheat oven to 425°F (220°C).
- Pare a sweet potato and cut in bite-size chunks.
- Mound in the center of a square of parchment paper.
- Chop one medium apple and spread over sweet potatoes.
- Dot with 1 tsp. (5 mL) butter.
- Sprinkle with ¼ tsp. cinnamon and ¼ tsp. fresh, grated nutmeg.
- Close the package and place on baking sheet.
- Bake for 25 minutes. Serve hot.

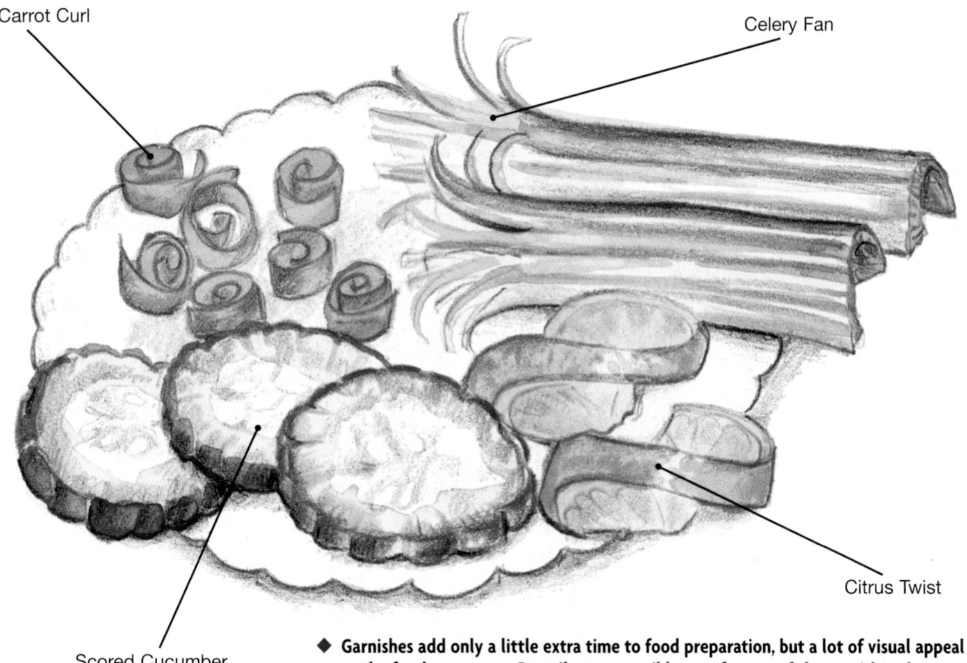

◆ **Garnishes add only a little extra time to food preparation, but a lot of visual appeal to the foods you serve. Describe two possible uses for one of the garnishes shown.**

Section 24-1 Review & Activities

1. When should herbs be added to hot foods? To cold foods?
2. In what way might cooking *en papillote* be said to be both a moist and a dry cooking method? Explain.
3. Name one way to garnish each of the following dishes: tomato soup, tossed salad, roasted whole chicken, tuna sandwich, iced tea. Explain why you would choose each garnish.
4. **Analyzing.** Imagine that you are teaching a food preparation class. What are some cautions you would encourage your students to be aware of when it comes to using herbs and spices?
5. **Synthesizing.** How can seasoning with herbs and spices replace other methods of flavoring food that are higher in fat and sodium?
6. **Applying.** Make a list of herbs and spices used regularly in your home. Create a recipe using some of these herbs and spices. Explain how you would use them, and describe the flavor they would give to the foods.

ASSESS

REVIEW

- Ask students to summarize the main ideas in this section.
- Have students complete the Section Review. (Answers appear below.)

EVALUATION

- Ask students to prepare garnishes to accompany specific foods that you mention.
- Have students take the quiz for Section 24-1. (Use the quiz in the *Teacher Resource Guide,* or construct your own with the **Exam***View*® *Test Generator* on the *Effective Instruction CD-ROM.*)

RETEACHING

- Show students pictures of meat loaf, au gratin potatoes, baked fish, and applesauce. What garnishes could they use with these foods? What herbs and spices might they use?
- Refer to the *Reteaching Activities* booklet for the Section 24-1 activity sheet.

CLOSE

Have students create a list of "ten ways to a better burger." Lists should include herbs, spices, garnishes, or other creative ideas.

Answers to Section 24-1 Review & Activities

1. See bulleted list on page 648.
2. Moist: Food is actually steamed in its packet. Dry: Food is baked in oven.
3. Answers will vary.
4. Answers will vary. Possibilities: Don't overdo it with a single herb or spice, which can overpower the flavor of the main ingredient. Avoid using a seasoning that is not compatible with a certain main ingredient.
5. Answers will vary. The herbs and spices add flavor, so added salt and fat are not necessary.
6. Answers will vary.

SECTION
24-2
Beverages

FOCUS

MOTIVATORS

- Show a videotaped recording of a televised coffee, tea, or hot cocoa advertisement. If the ad is appealing to students, ask them why. Have them note the social importance of beverages.
- Discuss ways in which beverages are related to human needs and desires. Point out that beverages provide water and sometimes other nutrients, but they can also play a part in meeting emotional and social needs.

VOCABULARY ACTIVITY

Pronounce the three terms listed under "Look for These Terms." Have students find the terms and their definitions in the section. Have students determine whether each term is a noun, verb, or adjective.

STUDY SKILLS

- **Guided Reading.** Have students look at the headings within Section 24-2 to preview the concepts that will be discussed.
- Have students read the section and complete the appropriate part of the Chapter 24 Study Guide in the *Student Workbook*.

SECTION
24-2

Objectives

After studying this section, you should be able to:

- Identify various types of beverages.
- Explain how different types of beverages fit into a healthy eating plan.
- Describe procedures for preparing and serving beverages.

Look for These Terms

mulled

infuser

steep

Beverages

As noted in Chapter 2, water is one of the six main nutrients. One of the most enjoyable ways of making sure your body gets the water it needs is by drinking beverages. No meal, in fact, is complete without one.

Nutrients in Beverages

In addition to being a source of water, beverages can provide other essential nutrients. Consider the following:

- Milk supplies protein, calcium, phosphorus, and vitamins D and A. Beverages that are made with milk, such as cocoa and milk shakes, also provide these same nutrients. However, they may have more sugar, fat, and calories.
- Fruit and vegetable juices provide the same vitamins and minerals found in the fruit or vegetable, and in the same amounts, except for fiber. Many types of fruit and vegetable juices are available, including fruit and vegetable juice blends. Some types of juices are fortified with vitamin C, calcium, or other nutrients.

Juices and fruit drinks can be found on store shelves as well as in the refrigerated section. They may be in ready-to-use or concentrated form. Frozen, powdered, and liquid concentrates must be reconstituted before using. Follow the directions on the label.

INFOLINK

For more information on the nutrients in vegetables and fruits, see Section 16-1.

Section 24-2 Resources

◆ **Student Workbook**, pp. 179, 183
◆ **Teacher Resource Guide**
Lesson Plan 24-2 Organizer
Section 24-2 Quiz
◆ **Effective Instruction CD-ROM**
Exam*View*® *Test Generator*
PowerPoint® Slide #52
◆ **Transparency Package**, CT-52
◆ **Student Motivation Kit**
Reteaching Activities, pp. 107–108
Enrichment Activities
Foods Lab Resources, pp. 153–154
Food Science Resources, pp. 36–39

FOR YOUR HEALTH

Real Juice=100%

Despite what you may hear or read in ads and commercials, not all juice products are created equal. Only products labeled "fruit juice" contain 100 percent juice. Other products, such as fruit drinks, may contain large amounts of added sugar. At the same time, some may be fortified with added nutrients. If you want to be sure you're getting the real thing, read the product label carefully.

Following Up

- Find a magazine advertisement for a juice product, or listen for a claim you might hear on TV that mentions "real juice." Find the product in your supermarket and read the label. Does it state that the product contains 100 percent juice? How will this affect you and your family's future purchases?

◆ **Most of the beverages shown here provide essential nutrients, as well as being a source of water. What is missing in fruit and vegetable juices that is found in the actual fruit or vegetable?**

Types of Beverages

Every beverage has water as its common denominator. Some beverages, such as punch and mulled cider, are served on festive occasions. Others, including bottled water, soft drinks, coffee and tea, are enjoyed at any time.

Punch

A punch is generally a mixture of fruit juices and carbonated beverages, such as ginger ale and seltzer, or tea. It is usually served in a punch bowl. Sherbet, ice cream, or fruit may be added. To serve the punch, ladle it from the bowl into small glasses or cups.

If the punch is to be served cold, combine all liquids except the carbonated beverages ahead of time and chill well. Chill the carbonated beverages separately; add them just before serving the punch. If you add them ahead of time, they will go flat.

Fruit is often floated in the bowl as a garnish; the type depends on the fruit flavors in the punch. Another popular garnish is an ice ring; it also helps keep the punch cold. The ice ring is usually made with punch or water. Fruit is placed in the ring mold in a decorative design. You can also freeze fruit in ice cubes.

Punches may also be **mulled**—served hot and flavored with sweet spices, such as cinnamon, nutmeg, or cloves. This is also a popular way of preparing cider.

Bottled Water

What do you reach for when you are thirsty? Although many people reach for plain water, bottled specialty waters have become very popular in the United States. There are many different kinds, such as mineral water, spring water, seltzer water, and club soda. They vary in mineral content. Some are carbonated or have a flavoring added. Check the list of ingredients on the label.

TEACH

- *Nutrients in Beverages*
- *Types of Beverages (text pages 654-658)*

Nutrition Analysis

Have students research the nutrients in beverages. Discuss which beverages are nutrient-dense and those that provide "empty calories." L1

Menu Planning Activity

On the board, write several basic breakfast, lunch, and dinner meals. Ask students to brainstorm beverage suggestions for each meal to make it more nutritionally complete. Ask students why specific beverages are chosen.

FOR YOUR HEALTH

Ask students to bring to class empty containers or food labels for any "fruit juice" beverages; set up a display. Ask students to identify the similarities of the beverages, including nutrients, cost, and packaging.

Taste Test

Have students taste several varieties of bottled water. Discuss reasons bottled water has increased in popularity in recent years. What are the nutritional advantages and disadvantages of bottled waters? Hold an informal debate on these advantages and disadvantages.

Technology TIE-IN

Technology has played a major role in the growing number and types of beverages available to consumers. Ask interested students to research this role of technology. Have them write a research report on their findings, including the projected, anticipated role of technology in future beverage products, and how technology has played and will play a role in the nutrients in beverages.

TEACH cont.

- *Types of Beverages (text pages 655-658)*

Discussion Activity

Hold a Q&A discussion on the differences between regular coffee and decaffeinated coffee. Ask: Why are various coffee grinds available? How can you determine the correct amount of coffee and water to use in an automatic drip coffeemaker?

Research/Writing

Have students research the cultivation, picking, and processing of coffee beans. Alternatively, have students research the different coffee beans available and their countries of origin. Have them write a short report on their findings. **L2**

Lab Experience

Have students prepare several types of coffee using different methods. Include one or more specialty coffees. Compare preparation times, flavors, and nutrients. **L1**

Soft Drinks

Soft drinks represent a multibillion-dollar industry. These carbonated beverages are available with or without caffeine and sugar. These can be part of a healthful eating plan as long as you realize that they are found in the top section of the Food Guide Pyramid and should be used sparingly.

Coffee

Coffee is brewed from ground coffee beans, which are the seeds from trees grown in South and Central America, Asia, and Africa. Ground coffee can be made from just one variety of coffee beans or a blend of several varieties. Gourmet coffee is more expensive because it is made from costlier beans.

Like soda, coffee contains caffeine, a stimulant drug, which can excite the nervous system. Most forms of coffee are also available in decaffeinated (dee-KAFF-in-ay-tuhd) versions.

Instant coffee is brewed coffee that has been dried and ground. It comes as a powder or as freeze-dried crystals, regular or decaffeinated. All you do is add hot water.

Besides regular and gourmet coffee, flavored coffees are also available. Flavors include mocha, vanilla, and assorted spices.

Ground coffee comes in different grinds to suit the brewing method. Buy the grind of coffee recommended for your coffeemaker.

Unopened containers of vacuumed-packed coffee can be stored at room temperature for about a year. Once opened, refrigerate fresh coffee, whether ground or whole beans, in an airtight container. Instant coffee can be kept at room temperature.

Making and Serving Coffee

The most popular appliance for making coffee is the automatic drip coffeemaker. Most automatic drip coffeemakers have four parts—a water reservoir, a basket that holds a filter and the coffee, a carafe that catches the coffee as it brews, and a hot plate that keeps the carafe and coffee warm.

Automatic drip coffeemakers are easy to use. Just put ground coffee into a filter inside the basket, pour cold water into the reservoir, and turn on the controls.

If desired, change the amounts of water and coffee to get the strength of coffee you want. Coffeemakers usually have convenient markings on the carafe or sides of the reservoir so that you can measure the water easily.

Clean the coffee carafe and basket in hot sudsy water after every use. Coffee contains oils that cling to the inside of the carafe and basket. They can give the next carafe of coffee an unpleasant flavor.

Serve coffee piping hot, right after it is made. If coffee is held at a high temperature for too long or reheated, it loses its flavor and aroma.

Coffee can also be served iced. Make double-strength coffee, and pour it over ice cubes.

◆ **The type of coffee to buy depends on the way you plan to brew it. Popular coffeemakers include the automatic drip coffeemaker and the nonautomatic drip model. Instant coffee is also an option. Name some different varieties of coffee.**

FOOD SCIENCE

Methods of Decaffeination

There are two basic methods used to remove the caffeine in coffee beans before they are roasted. In a method sometimes advertised as "water processed," the beans soak in hot water containing a solvent which dissolves the caffeine. The solvent is removed from the water, the beans soak in the water to restore their flavor, and then they are rinsed. "Natural decaffeination" means that ethyl acetate is used as the solvent.

In the Swiss water process method, the beans soak in plain water with no solvent. Charcoal filters are used to remove the caffeine from the water.

Tea

Tea is a beverage made from the leaves of a shrub grown in tropical mountainous areas. Three basic kinds of tea are produced and used worldwide. *Black tea* has a dark, rich color and deep hearty flavor. *Green tea* has a delicate, light green color and a very mild flavor. *Oolong tea* is partly oxidized, so the leaves are partly brown and partly green. Its flavor and color are between those of black and green teas. Tea is sold loose or in tea bags.

Tea contains caffeine, although not as much as coffee. It is also available decaffeinated. The same processes are used to decaffeinate tea and coffee.

In addition to plain tea, you can also buy flavored and instant teas. Flavored tea includes fruit, herb, and spice flavors. Instant tea is brewed tea that has been dried and ground to a powder. It is available plain, flavored, and presweetened.

Herb teas are made from herbs and other plants. They do not contain regular tea and are caffeine-free.

Buy herb teas from reliable sources. Most supermarkets carry the major brands. Avoid teas that make health claims, such as weight-loss teas.

Brewing and Serving Tea

Tea can be brewed in a teapot or right in the cup. An automatic hot tea maker is also available. It works in much the same way as an automatic coffeemaker. It preheats the teapot, brews the tea, and keeps it at serving temperature.

To brew tea yourself, begin by heating fresh, cold water in a teakettle. Bring the water to a rolling boil.

Preheat the teapot or cup by rinsing it with hot water. Then put in the tea or tea bags. As a rule, use 1 teaspoon (5 mL) of tea, or one tea bag, for each serving. To make loose tea easier to use, put it in an **infuser**—a small container with tiny holes that let water in but don't allow the tea leaves to come out. Like tea bags, the infuser is easy to remove at the end of the brewing time.

◆ **The many varieties of tea and herb tea can be purchased loose or in bags. What tea-making utensils are shown here?**

Pour boiling water over the tea. The tea will **steep**, or brew in water just below the boiling point. Follow package directions for brewing time.

Stir the tea before pouring or drinking to be sure it's uniformly strong. If the brewed tea is too strong, add a little hot water. Tea may be served with milk or lemon and sweetener.

To make iced tea, brew as for hot tea but use 50 percent more tea. That allows for melting ice when hot tea is poured into ice-filled-glasses. For six servings, use 9 teaspoons (45 mL) of tea. Steep. Remove tea and pour into ice-filled glasses.

You can use an automatic iced tea maker to prepare iced tea or iced coffee. Instant tea is another option. Just follow the directions on the label.

- *Types of Beverages (text pages 655-658)*

Lab Experience

Have students brew loose and bagged tea correctly and incorrectly. Have students taste the teas and evaluate their differences. L1

Research and Oral Presentation

Have students research the cultivation and processing of tea and herb teas. Alternatively, have students research health benefits associated with drinking tea. Have students share research results in an oral presentation, including at least one visual learning tool. L2

COMPUTER ACTIVITY

Internet Search

Ask students to search the Internet for an answer to this question: How much caffeine consumption is considered "moderate"? Have students share the sources of their information. Compare various responses based on the sources of the information.

FOOD SCIENCE — Effect of Temperature on Solute

Demonstrate to students what happens when a cube of sugar is added to hot tea and to iced tea. Which cube dissolves faster? (Sugar dissolves faster in hot tea.) Point out that in this solution, the tea is the solvent and sugar is the solute. Explain that a solution can hold a greater amount of solute at a higher temperature. Have students test this phenomenon using coffee.

ASSESS

REVIEW

- Ask students to summarize the main ideas in this section.
- Have students complete the Section Review. (Answers appear below.)

EVALUATION

- Have students prepare charts or posters showing the correct way to prepare coffee or tea by various methods.
- Have students take the quiz for Section 24-2. (Use the quiz in the *Teacher Resource Guide,* or construct your own with the **Exam***View*® *Test Generator* on the *Effective Instruction CD-ROM.*)

RETEACHING

- Provide various brands of tea and/or coffee and have students categorize them according to type of tea/coffee, loose or bagged, instant, caffeine or no caffeine.
- Refer to the *Reteaching Activities* booklet for the Section 24-2 activity sheet.

CLOSE

Hold a class beverage debate on "to have caffeine" or "not to have caffeine."

Sources of Caffeine

Beverages containing caffeine can fit into a healthful eating plan as long as they are used in moderation.

Beverage	*Amount of Caffeine (mg)*
Coffee (5-ounce serving)	
brewed	60-180
instant	30-120
decaffeinated, brewed	2-5
decaffeinated, instant	1-5
espresso (2-ounce serving)	40-170
Tea (5-ounce serving)	
brewed	25-110
instant	25-50
iced (12-ounce serving)	65-75
decaffeinated	—
Caffeinated soft drinks (12-ounce serving)	30-60
Cocoa or hot chocolate (5-ounce serving)	2-20

Section 24-2 Review & Activities

1. How do beverages meet the body's need for water?
2. Name two types of fruit or vegetable juices, and identify the nutrients they provide.
3. Why are milk and fruit and vegetable juices more healthful choices than other beverages?
4. **Extending.** Why do you think it is necessary to use double-strength coffee when serving the beverage iced?
5. **Analyzing.** What are the nutritional drawbacks of coffee, tea, and soft drinks? How do these compare with other beverage choices?
6. **Applying.** Look through cookbooks and magazines to find a punch recipe. How might you change the ingredients in this recipe to add more nutrients?

Answers to Section 24-2 Review & Activities

1. Beverages are mostly water; they're considered enjoyable ways to meet water needs.
2. Answers will vary; nutrients provided will depend on which juices are named.
3. They're nutrient-dense, supplying a variety of vitamins and minerals.
4. Answers will vary. As ice melts, it waters down the strength of the coffee.
5. Answers will vary. Drawbacks: caffeine content and low-nutrient contents. Juices and regular milk: no caffeine, nutrient-dense. Water: no caffeine, no calories.
6. Answers will vary. Replace "empty-calorie" liquids with real fruit juices.

Recipe File

Fruit Punch

Fruit punch can be served either chilled or hot. Try heating a cup of this punch in the microwave, adding cloves or a cinnamon stick.

Customary	***Ingredients***	***Metric***
6 oz.	Frozen lemonade concentrate, thawed	177 mL
6 oz.	Frozen orange juice concentrate, thawed	177 mL
32 oz.	Cranberry juice cocktail, chilled	1 L
2 qt.	Ginger ale or lemon-lime soda, chilled	1 L

Yield: 32 servings (approximate)
Equipment: Half-gallon (2-L) pitcher, punch bowl

Directions

1. Combine thawed juice concentrates and cranberry juice cocktail in pitcher.
2. Pour juice mixture into punch bowl.
3. Add ginger ale or lemon-lime soda and stir the mixture gently.
4. Serve chilled, garnished with citrus fruit slices or an ice ring, if desired.

Note: Do not put frozen juice concentrate directly into punch bowl—you may crack the bowl.

Nutrition Information

Per serving (approximate): 49 calories, 0 g protein, 12 g carbohydrate, 0 g fat, 0 mg cholesterol, 6 mg sodium
Good source of: vitamin C

Food for Thought

- How could you serve this punch if you didn't have a punch bowl?
- What liquids and fruits could you use to make an ice ring for the punch?

Recipe File

Fruit Punch

This is a nutritious punch recipe that can be served for special occasions, or any time. Prior to having students prepare the punch, you may want them to consider ingredient substitutions that can be made to vary the flavors.

Using the Recipe

- Have students read the recipe and discuss each step.
- Point out the warning in the recipe that advises students not to put frozen juice concentrate directly into a punch bowl—the bowl may crack.
- Review safety and sanitation procedures that apply to this recipe.
- Have each lab team fill out a work plan. (See the *Foods Lab Resources* booklet.)
- Have students check off the ingredients and equipment listed on the recipe worksheet and prepare the recipe.
- Have students complete the evaluation and questions on the recipe worksheet.

SEE ALSO. . .
The *Foods Lab Resources* booklet for the "Fruit Punch" recipe worksheet and other recipe alternatives.

Answers to Food for Thought

1. Answers will vary. You could use a large mixing bowl or serve the punch from pitchers.
2. Water, punch, or fruit juice; fruits named will vary.

SECTION
24-3
Entertaining

FOCUS

MOTIVATORS

- Ask students to make a list of occasions for entertaining guests. Have students categorize these occasions as formal or informal. What factors help determine whether an occasion will be formal or informal?
- Have students describe orally or in writing the best party they ever attended and explain what made it enjoyable.

VOCABULARY ACTIVITY

Pronounce the three terms listed under "Look for These Terms." Have students find the terms and their definitions in the section. Discuss with students the connection between the noun *reception* and the verb *receive*. Point out that receptions are occasions when hosts receive, or welcome, guests.

STUDY SKILLS

- **Guided Reading.** Have students look at the headings within Section 24-3 to preview the concepts that will be discussed.
- Have students read the section and complete the appropriate part of the Chapter 24 Study Guide in the *Student Workbook*.

SECTION 24-3

Objectives

After studying this section, you should be able to:

- Identify ways to plan for entertaining.
- Develop menus and organize food preparation and cleanup for entertaining.
- Describe different methods of serving food depending on the occasion.

Look for These Terms

modified English service

service plate

reception

Entertaining

"Would you like to come to my house for dinner Friday?" Tamera asked. "My dad's making his special lasagne."

"That would be great," Leslie answered. "Are you sure it'll be OK with your dad?"

"He loves company!" Tamera said. "He told us to invite a friend."

Reasons for Entertaining

Like Tamera's dad, many people enjoy inviting friends into their homes. Entertaining is a way of making people feel welcome and special. Although food is generally served, entertaining involves much more than just preparing a meal.

Entertaining does not have to be elaborate. You can have a successful party with a simple soup-and-salad meal if the atmosphere is right. With planning and organization, entertaining can be as much fun for the person giving the party as it is for the guests.

Planning for Entertaining

When you think about entertaining, what comes to mind? Whether you picture a big family get-together or just having a few friends over for pizza, careful planning goes a long way when you entertain.

Informal and Formal Events

The first step in planning is to identify the type of occasion or event. The type of planning you would do for a casual party, for example, would differ from the planning necessary for a formal sit-down dinner.

Section 24-3 Resources

◆ **Student Workbook,** pp. 180, 184
◆ **Teacher Resource Guide**
Lesson Plan 24-3 Organizer
Section 24-3 Quiz
◆ **Effective Instruction CD-ROM**
Exam*View*® *Test Generator*
PowerPoint® Slide #53
◆ **Transparency Package,** CT-53

◆ **Student Motivation Kit**
Reteaching Activities, p. 109
Enrichment Activities

◆ **Parties are more memorable when both the food and decorations relate to a theme, such as a Mexican fiesta. Think of two other possible themes. List foods and decorations you would choose to go with each.**

Whether the occasion is to be formal or informal also affects the menu and the way you will serve the food. Think about your skills in entertaining. If this is the first party you're giving, it's probably best to start with a simple, informal event.

Themes and Decorations

When Nikki greeted her guests at the door, she was wearing a grass skirt. She placed a *lei* around each person's neck and said, "Aloha!" Construction paper cutouts in the shape of palm trees and pineapples decorated the walls.

As Nikki knows, parties and get-togethers can be more fun when they have a theme. A theme is a specific idea on which the occasion is based. Holidays, birthdays, and graduations provide ready-made themes. For other occasions, be creative! Choose an interest you and your guests share—such as sports or old movies—or go for an ethnic theme, such as a Mexican fiesta. After you have chosen your theme, plan the menu, activities, and decorations to go with it.

What are some simple ways I can decorate a table?

As with other aspects of decorating, let your imagination run free. A potted plant on a place mat, an arrangement of fresh or artificial flowers, a grouping of seashells on a wicker mat are just a few possibilities.

Invitations

As you decide on a list of guests, try to put together a combination of people who are likely to enjoy each other's company and be interesting to one another. Strive for a good blend of listeners and talkers. Whenever possible, avoid inviting people that you know don't get along.

For informal events, you will most likely invite your guests in person or by telephone about one week before the event. Of course, spur-of-the-moment gatherings are fun, too! Just be sure to check with the adults in your home first.

TEACH

- *Reasons for Entertaining*
- *Planning for Entertaining (text pages 660-663)*

Party Ideas

Discuss how a theme helps you plan a party. Then have students think of one theme for a party. Have them draw a table setting or create a decoration that represents the theme. Suggest that they use magazines or other resources for party ideas, if necessary. Include students' ideas in a classroom resource folder for ready reference. L1

Using

Have students brainstorm other table decorations that are inexpensive, yet attractive, for use at formal parties and informal parties. Ask students if they would consider the same types of decorations for both formal and informal occasions. Why or why not?

COMPUTER ACTIVITY

Graphic Design

If the classroom computer has a variety of decorative and practical fonts loaded, ask students with a strong design sense to work as a team to match fonts to party themes. For example, a font that consists of crooked, twisting letters could be used for a "haunted house" theme, while playful balloon characters could serve for a "beach party" theme. Ask students to share type samples and theme ideas with classmates.

Extending Learning

Entertaining—People sometimes hesitate to entertain for many reasons. Some think they do not have the right kind of tableware or their cooking is too plain. People often don't have much time to prepare fancy foods for entertaining. Budgets limit the kind of food that can be served or the number of people who can be invited. Most of these objections can be overcome with a little ingenuity. Have students brainstorm to think of ways to get around the objections stated above.

TEACH cont.

- *Planning for Entertaining (text pages 660-663)*

Poster Project

Have students collect pictures that illustrate party themes. Have students display their pictures on poster board. L1

Display Activity

Have students bring to class a sample invitation, if possible. Create a display of students' and other invitations appropriate for different types of occasions. Have students categorize the invitations as formal or informal.

VISUAL LEARNING ***Using the Illustration***

Direct students' attention to the sample invitation on this page. Have volunteers identify each of the bulleted features noted earlier on the page. Then provide students with specific information for another party. Have them develop an invitation, preferably using a computer, based on the information. Have students share and compare invitations.

Menu Planning

Ask students to find recipes for simple, nutritious hors d'oeuvres or appetizers that guests can nibble on while hosts make last-minute preparations in the kitchen. Encourage students to share recipes. L1

Invitation Specifics

Formal occasions or larger parties require sending written invitations. This will help eliminate any mix-ups about the time and date. Send your invitations ten days to two weeks before the event is to occur.

On your invitation, be sure to include the following specific information:

- The date, location, and time of the event.
- The occasion, if there is one.
- Your name as host.

It is customary for written invitations to include the abbreviation *R.S.V.P.* followed by the host's telephone number. These letters are short for a phrase meaning "please reply." You might also include a date by which guests are to reply so that you can buy the necessary amount of food.

Help us celebrate
Westview High Marching Band's
first place trophy!
Please come to a Pizza Party
Saturday, November 9 at 7 p.m.
417 Ridgeway Road
Hosted by Sheila Wilson and Carlos Morales
R.S.V.P. to Sheila (555-9843)
by November 3

◆ **Invitations need to include certain information. Refer to the list above. Find each of the pieces of information called for.**

If, as an invited guest, you are asked to reply to an invitation, it is your responsibility to follow through on this request. If you can't reach a person by telephone, send a brief note in the mail.

Menus for Entertaining

When planning food for parties and other special occasions, follow the same guidelines as when planning meals. Choose a variety of nutritious foods that appeal to the eye as well as the palate. If you are planning foods for a special theme, try to choose some foods that most of your guests will like. Here are a few guidelines for selecting foods for your menu:

- Find out about special food needs or preferences that your guests might have.
- Keep food choices simple. Choose foods that can be prepared ahead of time with a minimum of last-minute preparation. For example, you might decide to prepare lasagne as the main course and do all the preparation, except for the actual baking, the day before. Add a tossed salad, bread, a beverage, and perhaps some fruit for dessert.
- You might want to make a simple appetizer, such as a dip and crackers or fruit, that your guests can nibble on while you make a few last-minute preparations in the kitchen.

Making a Schedule

You want to have as good a time as your guests. How can you achieve this? The one-word answer is *organization.*

After you've planned your meal or refreshments, identify the tasks you need to accomplish before the event. You might start with a list organized by categories—food shopping and preparation, decorations, setup, and cleanup.

Extending Learning

Party Etiquette—When you receive an invitation to a party, answer it as soon as possible. When you reply, repeat the date and time, in case the invitation had an error.

Arrive on time. Don't arrive early, unless you are helping.

As a guest, offer to help wherever you can. Remove empty soft drink bottles, cans, and/or glasses as they accumulate. If food falls on the floor, pick it up, even if you weren't the person who dropped it. Wipe up spills immediately. Always remember to thank your host.

List the tasks in order, beginning with the one you must do first. Think about ways to accomplish the items on your list efficiently. Some jobs can be done far ahead of the event. Make a special list for things to be done the day of the event. Cross each item off your list as you get it done.

Serving Food

How will you serve the meal? Will it be a sit-down meal or a buffet, informal or formal? The answer depends on the type of event, the number of people eating, the time available for serving and eating, the menu, and your personal preference.

Informal Table Service

Informal table service includes several ways to serve food. The method you choose will depend on your menu and the space that you have for serving.

One popular method of serving is family-style, bringing the food to the table in serving dishes and inviting people to help themselves. If space and tableware are limited, a good option is plate service. This means portioning out food on individual dinner plates that are then served to each person at the table. Plate service eliminates the need for serving dishes and makes cleanup easier.

Regardless of the method of service you select, you will want to set the table properly. In addition to the dinner plate, flatware, and glassware, you may want to add a bread-and-butter plate or a salad bowl above the forks on the left side of the cover.

INFOLINK
For more on the table-setting basics, family service, and plate service, see Section 10-1.

Formal Service

For formal occasions, there are several ways you might handle serving food. If your guest list is limited to eight people (including yourself), you can easily handle serving the meal yourself. For larger groups, you will need help serving the meal so that all your guests are served quickly and efficiently.

For serving small groups yourself, use **modified English service**. This is a method of food service in which dinner plates and the food for the main course are brought to the table in serving dishes and placed in front of the host. If meat is to be carved, this is done by the person hosting. He or she then places the meat and vegetables on a plate and passes it to the right. The first plate is passed down to the person at the end of the table. When all the people on the right have been served, those on the left are served.

Salad is often served on individual plates from the kitchen and placed on the table before the guests are seated. Accompaniments, such as rolls and butter, are usually passed at the table.

Formal service for large groups is very rarely done at home because extra help is needed to serve the meal. This style of service is often used in fine restaurants, at hotels for banquets, and for other formal occasions.

For most formal occasions, the table is set with flatware, glassware, and a service plate for the appetizer course. A **service plate** is a large and beautifully decorated plate used for the first course only. It is removed from the table before the main course is served. Never put food directly on the service plate—serve it in a separate dish and place the dish on the service plate.

- *Serving Food (text pages 662-664)*

Identification Activity

Show students photos, drawings, or sketches of formal table service with approximately three pieces of flatware on each side of the plate. Ask students to identify for what foods each piece of flatware is to be used.

Categorization Activity

Suggest to students several scenarios involving occasions for entertaining. Scenarios should include number of people, type of food, and theme. Students are to categorize each scenario into the most appropriate service category.

Q & A Exchange

Divide the class into random pairs. Have all students devise ten written questions; then exchange papers with partners and attempt to respond to the questions they have received. Possible questions: How would you serve an informal meal for guests? What styles of service might you choose for a formal occasion? What is modified English service? How is a service plate used? Why is buffet service popular? What type of service is used at a reception? L1

Reinforcing Key Skills

Present the following problem to student groups. Allow time for them to discuss and compare their responses.

Leadership—Alexandra and Pete are hosting a party at which you are a guest. You overhear the couple discussing at the last minute a plan to switch from sit-down to buffet service. At mealtime, everything seems disorganized. Flatware isn't available, serving spoons haven't been provided, and a stack of plates sits in the center of the table. Your hosts look unhappy. What can you suggest to salvage the party?

TEACH cont.

- *Serving Food (text pages 663-665)*

Student Demonstration Activity

Have students work in small groups to plan and give demonstrations of the types of service appropriate for entertaining.

Lab Experience

Have students plan and prepare a simple meal in the foods lab and serve it buffet-style, following the guidelines outlined in the text. Discuss the advantages of buffet service and the occasions for which it might be used. Have students list other foods that are good choices for buffet meals. L1

VISUAL LEARNING *Using the Illustration*

Ask students to carefully examine the illustration on page 665. Have a volunteer answer the questions posed in the caption. (Each line starts at the point where plates are stacked and moves from left to right, as you face each side of the table). Ask students to suggest when two serving lines might be useful. On the board, illustrate another reception table. Have students suggest alternative food or beverage choices for each item on the table.

◆ **When preparing foods for a buffet, arrange and garnish them attractively. Be sure to provide appropriate serving utensils where necessary. What are two important things to remember when planning a buffet meal?**

As a rule, formal service includes a number of courses, each served separately on clean plates. Flatware is needed for each course. It is not uncommon to have three pieces of flatware on each side of the plate.

Buffet Service

A buffet is an easy, practical way to entertain if you don't have enough seating space at a dining table. For eating, you can set up card tables or small snack tables. People can also hold plates of food on their laps.

The prepared food is placed in the serving dishes on a large table, on the kitchen counter, or perhaps on several card tables. When setting up the buffet, stack the plates where you want guests to begin to serve themselves. After the plates, place the main dish, followed by vegetables, salad, rolls, and butter. The flatware, rolled up in a napkin, should be the last item your guests pick up.

When planning a buffet meal, choose foods that are easy to serve and that do not have to be cut with a knife. This makes the food easier to eat. Casseroles, stir-fries, sandwiches, and salads are good choices. You may want to serve beverages to your guests after they are seated.

Receptions

Receptions are social gatherings usually held to honor a person or an event, such as a wedding or a graduation. These gatherings are usually formal. Buffet service is most often used, with the food being placed on a large table. The table is covered with a floor-length tablecloth, and an eye-catching centerpiece is placed in the center.

Indicate the starting point of the reception table by where you place the plates. For large groups, divide the table in half lengthwise and offer the same food on both sides of the table. This allows people to move in two lines instead of one.

Extending Learning

Receptions—Special occasions, such as receptions, give many people an excuse for eating foods high in fat, sugar, and calories. However, some people may not be able to eat such foods.

When planning the menu for a reception, consider those who may be on special eating plans. Have at least one finger food that these people can eat. Ideas include: Fresh fruit on skewers, raw vegetables with a tofu or yogurt dip, dry-roasted nuts, lean meats and poultry.

◆ A reception table should be organized for the convenience of both servers and guests. This table is set up to handle two serving lines. What is the starting point for each line? Which direction would each line move?

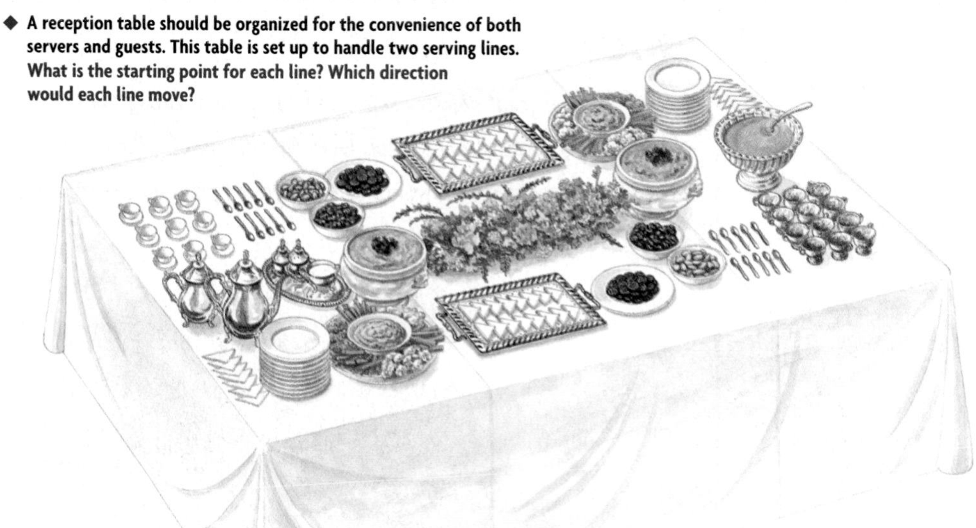

Types of Foods to Serve

Hot beverages, such as coffee and tea, are generally served at one end of the table. A cool beverage—perhaps a fruit punch—is served at the opposite end. Food choices can include finger sandwiches, cheese, crackers, fruit kabobs, or any other foods that you think your guests will enjoy.

Section 24-3 Review & Activities

1. How do formal and informal occasions differ?
2. What are three guidelines that can help when planning a party menu?
3. How should you set up a buffet table for serving food?
4. **Extending.** Suppose you want to host a sit-down dinner but have limited space. Think of a creative way of using the space available to seat your guests.
5. **Synthesizing.** Suppose you are hosting a buffet to celebrate an important event. After identifying the event, name three foods or dishes that you will include. What influences these food choices?
6. **Applying.** Work with several others to list themes that might be appropriate for a teen party. Choose one theme and describe how you would carry it out with invitations, decorations, music, and menu. How would you serve the food?
7. **Applying.** Plan and serve nutritious refreshments for a small group of people. For the occasion, you might choose a club meeting, a before-the-game party, or a friend's or family member's birthday. Follow a simple theme and extend invitations.

ASSESS

REVIEW

- Ask students to summarize the main ideas in this section.
- Have students complete the Section Review. (Answers appear below.)

EVALUATION

- Ask students to identify the different ways food can be served and the various occasions for which each type of service is appropriate.
- Have students take the quiz for Section 24-3. (Use the quiz in the *Teacher Resource Guide,* or construct your own with the **ExamView**® *Test Generator* on the *Effective Instruction CD-ROM.*)

RETEACHING

- Have students plan a party for an occasion of their choice.
- Refer to the *Reteaching Activities* booklet for the Section 24-3 activity sheet.

CLOSE

Develop a class tip guide entitled: "Sixteen Steps to Entertaining Success." Emphasize that the host must plan more than just which foods to serve.

Answers to Section 24-3 Review & Activities

1. Answers may include: reason for event; planning needed; menu; way food is served; invitations.
2. Determine special food needs or preferences; keep food simple; plan an appetizer for eating during final preparations.
3. Stack plates where serving starts. Follow with main dish, vegetable, salad, rolls, butter, flatware in napkin.
4. Ideas are: use counters or kitchen island; sit on pillows around large coffee table; set up card tables.
5. Answers will vary.
6. Answers will vary.
7. Plans will vary.

SECTION

24-4

Outdoor Meals

FOCUS

MOTIVATORS

- Ask students to identify their favorite foods for a picnic or for outdoor cooking.
- Ask students to describe problems they have encountered at picnics or when cooking outdoors. How could these problems have been avoided?

VOCABULARY ACTIVITY

Pronounce the term listed under "Look for This Term." Have students find the term and its definition in the section.

STUDY SKILLS

- **Listening.** Invite a group of volunteers to each prepare an oral reading of a page of text from the section, while others follow along silently. Preparation should include mastering the pronunciation of unfamiliar words and a grasp of essential concepts. At the end of the reading, the students are to list as many key concepts as they can recall.
- Have students read the section and complete the appropriate part of the Chapter 24 Study Guide in the *Student Workbook*.

SECTION

24-4

Objectives

After studying this section, you should be able to:

- Identify ways to cook foods safely outdoors.
- Identify foods suitable for outdoor cooking.
- Describe how to choose and pack picnic foods.

Look for This Term

micro-grill

Outdoor Meals

Outdoors is a great place to share and enjoy food. Eating outdoors can take many forms, from a picnic lunch to a dinner of grilled foods. It can also occur almost anywhere—around a campfire, at the seashore, or right in your own backyard.

Outdoor Cooking

No matter when or where it happens, outdoor cooking uses many of the food preparation skills you have already learned. The most common form of outdoor cooking is grilling, also called barbecuing in some areas.

Grilling

Before grilling, be sure you have the proper tools and understand how to use an outdoor grill safely. The simplest grill is a round, kettle-shaped metal container that holds burning charcoal. It is topped with a wire grate for holding food above the hot coals. There are many other kinds of grills. Some cook with bottled propane gas instead of charcoal.

All grills cook by the same principle. Heat radiates upward and cooks the food held on the grate above. Grilling is a dry-heat method of cooking, similar to broiling. Cooking time depends on the kind and thickness of food and its distance from the heat.

Follow the directions in the owner's manual for using the grill. Methods vary, depending on the kind of grill you have.

Micro-Grilling

Some cooks choose to **micro-grill**. This is a cooking method that combines microwaving and grilling. The food—usually meat or poultry—is partially cooked on a rack in the microwave oven and then finished immediately afterward on the outdoor grill. Juices that collect during

Section 24-4 Resources

◆ **Student Workbook,** pp. 180, 185
◆ **Teacher Resource Guide**
Lesson Plan 24-4 Organizer
Section 24-4 Quiz
◆ **Effective Instruction CD-ROM**
Exam*View*® *Test Generator*
PowerPoint® Slide #54
◆ **Transparency Package,** CT-54
◆ **Student Motivation Kit**
Reteaching Activities, p. 110
Enrichment Activities

the microwave phase are discarded. Micro-grilling allows foods to cook faster and remain moist and juicy. An added advantage of micro-grilling is highlighted in "For Your Health" on page 668.

Accident Prevention

Home is one place where you should feel safe and secure. Yet every year, thousands of people are injured in home accidents. To lessen the risk of accidents involving grilling, follow these guidelines:

- Use fireproof gloves and heavy-duty grilling tools with long handles. The long handles keep your hands away from the intense heat.
- Set the grill on a level surface so that it won't tip over. Keep it away from buildings, shrubs, trash containers, or anything else that could catch fire.
- Use a clean grill. Before storing the grill after each use, remove baked-on grime from the inside and the grate with a hard-bristled brush. Baked-on food and grease can cause flames to flare up when you light the fire.
- Apply enough of the starter fluid (if you use it) before striking the match. Never add more fluid after the coals have been lighted—doing so could cause an explosion.
- Never use kerosene or gasoline as fire starters—they can explode.
- Fat and meat juices dripping on coals can cause flare-ups. If that happens, raise the grate, cover the grill, or use a long-handled tool to spread the coals apart. You can also remove the food from the grate and use a pump-spray bottle filled with water to spray a mist on the flare-up. Then place the food back on the grate. Don't pour water on the burning charcoal.
- When you have finished grilling, let the coals burn out until only ashes are left. Douse the ashes with water; then put them in a metal trash can. Don't dump hot coals or ashes on the ground. They damage the grass and can even start a fire.

Food for Grilling

Grilling is used mainly for tender cuts of meat and poultry. Cook them thoroughly, turning after half the cooking time.

Fish is also easy to grill. Place fillets skin-side down on a lightly oiled rack to keep them from sticking. Grill until the fish flakes easily. You may have to turn thick pieces.

You can grill most fruits and vegetables. Thread small pieces on metal skewers. Brush them lightly with melted butter or margarine, olive oil, or a basting sauce. Place them on the grate. Turn the skewers frequently until the foods are hot and lightly browned.

◆ **In a basic grill, hot coals provide radiant heat that cooks the food above it. Identify three safety precautions you should take when grilling.**

TEACH

- *Outdoor Cooking (text pages 666-667)*

Discussion Activity

Give students the following scenario: You are in charge of selecting and purchasing a grill for your family. Have students list considerations for buying the outdoor grill. Have students explain considerations.

Developing Educational Tools

Ask students to pick one of the accident prevention guidelines and develop a symbol or sign that helps explain the guideline. Encourage students to develop a symbol that, like the most effective ones, can be understood by all people, including young children and those who don't read English. Display students' symbols. L1

Student Demonstration

Ask selected volunteers to bring to class one item associated with grilling, such as fireproof gloves, a few pieces of charcoal, long-handled tools, or a hard-bristled brush. Have students display the items, explaining or demonstrating their safe and proper use. L1

Reinforcing Key Skills

Present the following problems to student groups. Allow time for them to discuss and compare their responses.

Critical Thinking—Have students discuss the factors that might affect a family's decision to buy a gas grill instead of a charcoal grill.

Communication—Your neighbor invites you over for a cook-out. You notice that he is planning to use the platter, which had raw meat on it, to place the cooked meat. What might you say?

TEACH cont.

- *Outdoor Cooking*
- *Picnic Foods (text pages 666-669)*

Finding Recipes

Have students find recipes for outdoor grilling. Discuss how techniques for outdoor grilling differ from the usual techniques. What foods seem to be popular? Which cuts of meat, poultry, and fish are commonly grilled? Discuss unique recipes, such as grilled pizza. L1

FOR YOUR HEALTH

Ask students to extend research on PAHs to all health-related connections to grilling. Have students make a list of, or informally debate, benefits and risks. Students should find that the low-fat benefit of this technique outweighs the risks.

Picnic Brochures

Have students work in groups to create a brochure on picnics, including sections on planning, safety, packing, and cleanup. Have students include a picnic checklist. Encourage students to share copies of the brochure with family and community members. L1

Healthful Picnic Planning

Ask students to write a menu for a healthy picnic, which represents all food groups. Encourage students to share and compare menus. L1

FOR YOUR HEALTH

"No-Deposit" Grilling

Some health experts have voiced concerns about the chemicals deposited on food as it cooks over charcoal. Studies have linked these chemicals—polycyclic aromatic hydrocarbons, or PAHs—to certain kinds of cancer. PAHs are carried in the smoke that rises after the melted fat from meat or poultry hits the heat source.

One precaution that can be taken is microgrilling. This cooking method causes much of the fat to be lost before the meat even reaches the grill.

Another precaution is preventing fat from dripping on the heat source. Trim fat from meat before cooking. Make a drip pan from heavy-duty foil, and place it in the center of the charcoal, under the food on the grate, to catch drippings.

Following Up

- In recent years, a line of smokeless indoor grills has become available. Do research to learn whether these products produce PAHs. Is the flavor of foods cooked on them similar to that of foods prepared on an outdoor grill?

Picnic Foods

Not all food eaten outdoors is cooked there. Some food is cooked or prepared elsewhere and taken to a park, beach, or other recreational area for a picnic.

The food you choose for a picnic might depend on how far you have to travel. Avoid taking hot cooked food unless you know it will be eaten within two hours. For safety, keep hot foods in a separate insulated container.

Cooking foods on a grill at the picnic site is often safer than transporting hot food. Cook raw foods, like hamburgers, or warm up cold cooked foods. For safety, don't partially cook food at home and then finish cooking it at the picnic.

INFOLINK

For more information on keeping food safe to eat, see Section 7-3.
For specific food safety tips when packing a lunch, see Section 20-1.

Packing the Picnic

If you're traveling to the picnic area, make a list of everything you'll need, including food, tableware, and cleanup equipment. Don't forget items such as premoistened cleaning wipes, can and bottle openers, a paring knife, paper towels, trash bags, and extra plastic bags for dirty utensils. As you pack for the picnic, check off each item on your list.

Be sure to follow the same food safety precautions that you would when packing a lunch. Pack nonperishable items in a basket or other container. Use an insulated cooler for perishable food. To keep the food chilled, put ice cubes or reusable frozen gel packs in the cooler. Frozen food, such as boxed frozen juices, will help keep other foods cold.

If you're taking raw meat or poultry to cook at the picnic, pack it in a separate cooler to prevent cross-contamination with ready-to-eat foods.

Extending Learning

Using the Grill Safely

- Keep pets away from the cooking area. They could knock over the grill or work table.
- When you are through grilling, allow the briquettes to cool in the fire bowl. They retain heat for a long time, so don't discard them right away. Don't dump them in a combustible box—it could ignite.
- Don't remove the grid until it is cool. Don't place a hot grid on the ground. Someone could step on it barefoot and suffer serious burns.

◆ A picnic can have almost any kind of food, as long as it is properly packed and kept at a safe temperature. Insulated coolers provide the best way to keep foods cold. Can food be kept cold inside a picnic basket like the one shown here? What types of food would be safe to store in this basket?

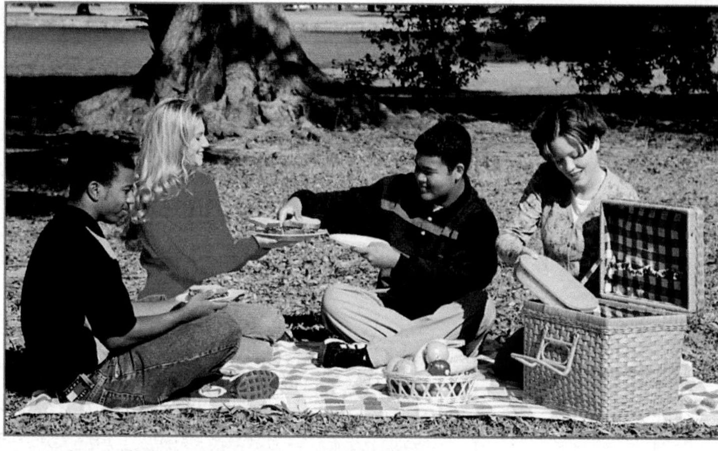

Packing Order

When packing the cooler and picnic basket, put the last item you will need on the bottom and the first one on the top. To pack the cooler, start with the end of the meal. Put the dessert on the bottom (if it's fragile, put it in a crush-resistant plastic container first). Packing food in this order eliminates the need to unpack the whole cooler every time you want something. Don't remove food from the cooler until you need it.

At the picnic site, keep the cooler in a cool, shady spot. Keep the cover on the cooler at all times. Don't leave the cooler in the sun, a hot car, or a car trunk. Even an insulated cooler won't stay cool under such conditions.

Section 24-4 Review & Activities

1. Give four guidelines for safe grilling.

2. Give three safety tips for choosing and preparing picnic foods.

3. After Michelle finished packing for her family's picnic, she remembered she had forgotten to put in the cookies her brother baked. Should she repack completely? Why or why not?

4. Evaluating. What are some health advantages and disadvantages of outdoor cooking?

5. Extending. What effect might local government regulations have on outdoor cooking in your area? Why is following posted regulations important?

6. Applying. Bring to class a favorite recipe for indoor cooking. Explain how it might be modified for preparation on a grill.

ASSESS

REVIEW

- Ask students to summarize the main ideas in this section.
- Have students complete the Section Review. (Answers appear below.)

EVALUATION

- Provide each student with a problem-solving exercise of an unsafe, unhealthful, or inappropriate situation related to grilling or picnicking. Each student needs to solve the problem and present it to the class.
- Have students take the quiz for Section 24-4. (Use the quiz in the *Teacher Resource Guide,* or construct your own with the **Exam***View*® *Test Generator* on the *Effective Instruction CD-ROM.*)

RETEACHING

- Have students prepare posters that illustrate safety rules for using an outdoor grill.
- Refer to the *Reteaching Activities* booklet for the Section 24-4 activity sheet.

CLOSE

Ask students to bring to class four servings of one appropriately packed food item for an indoor or outdoor class picnic. During the picnic, have students discuss the healthfulness and taste of each picnic food.

Answers to Section 24-4 Review & Activities

1. See bulleted list on page 667.
2. See page 668.
3. Although eaten last, a package of cookies might be left on top to prevent crushing them. If container is sturdy, repacking would be okay, if desired.
4. Advantages include: it allows fat to drip off food; dry heat helps preserve some nutrients. Disadvantages: possible PAH formation; safe temperature may be hard to maintain.
5. Might limit times or places for grilling to prevent fires, preserve habitats, protect privacy of people living in area.
6. Answers will vary.

SECTION
24-5
Preserving Food at Home

FOCUS

MOTIVATORS

- Create a bulletin board entitled "Preserving Summer's Harvest—A Time-Honored Tradition." Use historical and modern illustrations and photographs of different methods of food preservation (for example, salting, smoking, drying, storing, canning, and freezing). Discuss the history of food preservation.
- Ask students to describe any of their own experiences with home canning, freezing, and drying. Ask students to list the advantages of preserving foods at home.

VOCABULARY ACTIVITY

Pronounce the terms listed under "Look for These Terms." Have students find the terms and their definitions in the section.

STUDY SKILLS

- **Note Taking.** Have students read the section independently. While they are reading, they are to take notes, in their own words, on important concepts within each section.
- Have students read the section and complete the appropriate part of the Chapter 24 Study Guide in the *Student Workbook*.

SECTION 24-5

Preserving Food at Home

Today, most foods can be purchased in either fresh, canned, frozen, or dried form. In this section, you will learn about advantages and methods of preserving fresh foods at home.

Objectives

After studying this section, you should be able to:

- Identify ways to freeze fruits and vegetables safely while retaining quality and nutrients.
- Explain how to can fruits and vegetables safely at home.
- List the benefits of drying foods at home.

Look for These Terms

dry-packing
blanching
raw-pack
hot-pack
headspace

Advantages of Home Preserving

Preserving foods at home affords several real benefits to families. For many, it's a way to stretch the food budget. For others, it's a way to spend time working together and having fun. People who maintain vegetable gardens have a ready source of foods to preserve.

◆ **When preserving foods, choose high-quality produce for the best results. Identify three methods for preserving foods.**

Section 24-5 Resources

◆ **Student Workbook,** pp. 181, 186
◆ **Teacher Resource Guide**
Lesson Plan 24-5 Organizer
Section 24-5 Quiz
Chapter 24 Test
◆ **Effective Instruction CD-ROM**
Exam*View*® *Test Generator*
◆ **Student Motivation Kit**
Reteaching Activities, pp. 111–112
Enrichment Activities
Food Science Resources, pp. 66–68, 110–112

Methods of Home Preserving

The preserving procedures followed today have been in use in one form or another for generations. They include freezing, canning, and drying. The method you use depends on personal preference and the equipment you have available.

If you don't grow your own food, you may be able to buy seasonal foods at low cost and save money. Farmers often have lower prices for fruits and vegetables that people pick themselves. Stores may have specials on locally grown produce.

Always use ripe, high-quality food. Freezing and canning do not improve the quality of the food. Buy only the amount you can process in the time you have available. Wash the food carefully, and prepare it according to recipe directions, keeping both cleanliness and food safety in mind.

Freezing

You may think that because freezing is so closely associated with technology, it's a modern development. However, its roots lie deep in the past. Primitive people long ago discovered that burying food under ice or snow kept it intact through the cold months.

INFOLINK

For more on procedures for packing and freezing foods, see Section 7-4. For more on enzymatic browning and ways of preventing it, see Section 16-2.

Freezing Fruits

Many fruits can be frozen. However, pears, oranges, and bananas do not freeze well. Applesauce freezes better than apples.

Before freezing any fruit, you need to know whether the fruit undergoes enzymatic browning. If it does not (which is the case with most berries, melons, pineapple, and cherries), simply dry-pack the fruit. **Dry-packing** means placing the prepared fruit on a cookie sheet, leaving space in between the pieces before placing it in the freezer. Once the food pieces are frozen solid, place them in a labeled and dated freezer package.

If you are freezing a fruit that does darken —for example, apples, figs, peaches, nectarines, or plums—use one of these two methods:

- Sprinkle the fruit with a ready-to-use ascorbic acid mixture according to package directions. Then dry-pack.
- Toss the fruits in sugar until they are well coated. Use this method—known as *sugar-packing*—whenever you want sweetened fruits or fruits in syrup to use as a sauce. When fruits defrost, their juices combine with the sugar to form a sweet syrup.

Freezing Vegetables

Before they can be frozen, vegetables require **blanching**, or partial cooking, to kill enzymes. Tomatoes do not need to be blanched. Work with 1 pound (500 g) of vegetables at a time.

To blanch vegetables, place the prepared vegetables in the strainer, and immerse them in boiling water. Allow the water to return to a rolling boil, and begin timing the vegetables. Timing depends on the type of vegetable and the size of the pieces. The larger the pieces, the longer they must blanch. (Follow the time recommended in a blanching chart.)

TEACH

- *Advantages of Home Preserving*
- *Methods of Home Preserving*
- *Freezing (text pages 670-672)*

Display Activity

Display appropriate containers for freezing fruits and vegetables. Point out that it is false economy to skimp on containers and wrappings. Show various types of labels and emphasize the importance of good labeling.

Student Demonstrations

Discuss procedures for freezing fruits. Point out that pears, oranges, and bananas do not freeze well. In lab groups, students are to plan, and then demonstrate to the rest of the class, how to prepare fruits, using dry-pack plain, dry-pack with ascorbic acid, and sugar-packed methods. L1

Lab Experience

Ask students to describe the blanching process. Then divide the class into lab groups. Have them blanch batches of vegetables, leaving some unblanched. Ask them to pack, label, and freeze each. Have students compare the two types of frozen vegetables one week later. Help students recognize that blanched vegetables retain their nutrients, color, flavor, and texture far longer than vegetables that have not been blanched. L1

Extending Learning

Freezer Packaging—Here are some guidelines for choosing packaging materials and containers for freezing:

- They should withstand freezer temperatures. Some materials, such as waxed paper and cellophane, will crack. Some glass jars and brittle plastics will crack when frozen.
- Packaging should suit the food.
- Packaging should be strong. Packages are often shifted in the freezer. This can tear or crack weak materials.
- Empty cottage cheese and margarine tubs are not heavy enough for freezer storage. However, they can be used to hold freezer bags.

TEACH cont.

- *Canning Produce (text pages 672-673)*

Discussion Activity

Have students write responses to the following: Name foods that are processed using water-bath canning. Explain the difference between raw-pack and hot-pack foods. Discuss students' responses to these and other pertinent questions.

Demonstration

Demonstrate the hot-pack method and the raw-pack method of packing food in jars. Have students make a list of foods for which each of the methods is recommended.

Guest Speaker

Invite a Cooperative Extension or other home economist to speak to the class on canning and other preservation methods. Ask the speaker to explain to students why recommendations for home canning change periodically. Have students be prepared to ask the speaker questions.

Demonstration

Show students a pressure canner. Have students examine it and become familiar with the various parts.

When the time is up, remove the strainer of vegetables and plunge them in the ice water until completely cooled. Add ice cubes as needed to keep the water ice-cold. Drain the vegetables on the clean, dry towels and pat dry. Pack them into containers and freeze.

You can also blanch vegetables in a microwave oven. Use the same method as used for microwaving vegetables. Blanching times are generally similar to those for top-of-the-range blanching.

Canning Produce

Canning methods have changed in recent years to prevent serious foodborne illness. A reliable source of information is your local cooperative extension service.

Before canning, be sure you have up-to-date recipes, instructions, and equipment. Follow the recipe directions; don't take shortcuts or change recipes.

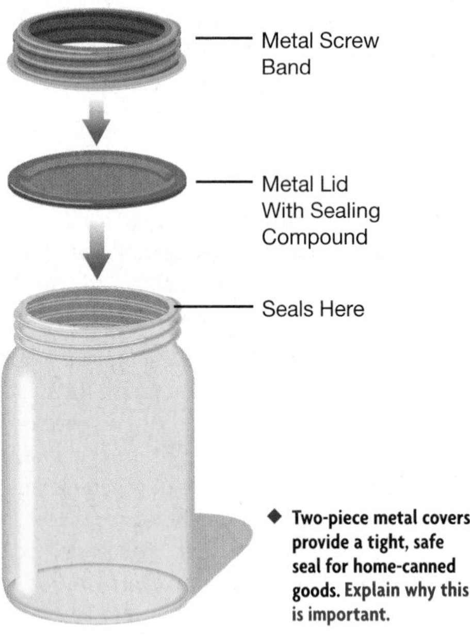

◆ **Two-piece metal covers provide a tight, safe seal for home-canned goods. Explain why this is important.**

Note that in many canning recipes, sugar and salt are used as preservatives. If you want low-sugar or low-sodium foods, look for those types of recipes.

Jars and Lids

Use only jars made for home canning. Be sure they are in perfect condition. Discard any that have cracks or chips that might keep the lids from sealing tightly.

Use two-piece metal covers, which combine a flat lid with a screw band. The lid is used only once. The band may be reused. Follow the manufacturer's directions for preparing the covers. Do not use one-piece covers that seal with separate rubber rings, such as glass or metal with a porcelain lining. They do not seal properly.

If filled jars are to be heated more than 10 minutes, you do not need to sterilize them before packing the food. Others should be sterilized. Follow the recipe directions.

Processing the Food

Just as in commercial food processing, food that you plan to can at home needs to be heated to stop enzyme activity and kill harmful microorganisms. There are two different heating methods. *Water-bath canning* is used for high-acid foods, such as fruits and most tomatoes. The natural acid protects the food against the growth of harmful microorganisms once the food has been canned.

Low-acid foods, such as vegetables, require *pressure canning* to be safe. A pressure canner is like a pressure cooker, only larger. It heats food under pressure to temperatures above the boiling point to kill harmful microorganisms.

FOOD SCIENCE

Maximum Freezer Storage Times

Some people think you can put food in the freezer and preserve it forever. This is not so. Have students research maximum storage times for frozen fruits and vegetables. Using the information, have students create a chart for the most commonly frozen fruits and vegetables.

Packing Methods

There are several methods you can use to pack the jars for processing. To **raw-pack** jars, place the raw foods into the jars and then pour in hot syrup, water, or juice. To **hot-pack** foods, heat the food in liquid first; then pack it into the jars.

When packing jars, leave about ½ to 1 inch (1.3 to 2.5 cm) headspace for food to expand. **Headspace** is the space between the top of the food and the rim of the jar. Run a spatula between the food and the jar to remove air bubbles. Wipe the jar top clean. Apply the covers. Screw the metal band on tightly by hand.

Processing Methods

Process the jars by using one of the recommended processing methods. Do not process canned food in conventional or microwave ovens.

- **Fruits.** After raw-packing or hot-packing fruits into jars, process the jars in boiling water in a water-bath canner for the time directed on the recipe. The canner is a large, covered pot with a rack to hold the jars.
- **Jams and fruit spreads.** Fill the jars with the prepared jam or fruit spread and apply the two-part covers. Process the jars in boiling water in a water-bath canner for the time specified in the recipe. Do not seal jars with paraffin—it does not make a tight seal.
- **Vegetables.** After raw-packing or hot-packing the jars with vegetables, process the jars in a pressure canner.

After processing, let the jars cool on a rack or clean dish towel away from drafts until completely cool, usually about 12 hours.

Check the covers to be sure they have sealed. Press the center of the cover, or tap it with a spoon. The cover should stay down and give a clear, ringing sound when tapped. If the jar has not sealed, reprocess or remove the food and refrigerate or freeze it.

Store home-canned foods in a clean, cool, dry place. Before tasting or using home-canned vegetables, boil them for 10 to 15 minutes to be certain that any harmful microorganisms are destroyed.

◆ **A pressure canner heats foods to temperatures higher than 212°F (100°C). For which types of vegetables is pressure canning used?**

Safety Check

A pressure canner contains a rack to hold jars, a steam-tight cover, a safety release valve, and a pressure gauge that measures accurate pressure during processing. To prevent accidents when using a pressure canner:

- *Carefully* read the manufacturer's directions.
- Process foods at the pressure indicated in the instructions for each type of food.
- Be sure the cover of the canner is fastened securely.

When the processing time is over, remove the pressure canner from the heat and allow it to cool until the pressure gauge returns to zero. Open the safety release. If no steam escapes, the pressure is down and the canner can be opened safely. *Failure to follow these instructions could result in serious injury.*

- *Canning Produce*
- *Drying Food*
  (text pages 672-674)

Demonstration

Demonstrate how to prepare foods for drying and then dry several types of foods using a food dehydrator. Have students taste the dried foods and discuss the results.

Store Survey

Have students visit a supermarket and make a list of the dried foods available. Which ones can be eaten as they are? Which need to be reconstituted? How can they be used within a healthful eating plan? L1

Cost Comparison

Have students compare the features and cost of several food dehydrators. Ask them to determine whether a food dehydrator could help a family save money on food. Under what circumstances? L1

USING Safety Check

If possible, obtain a pressure canner. Have students identify the name of each part and a safety tip related to each part.

Extending Learning

Drying Foods—Early American explorers often traveled alone, on foot, and needed a food supply that was easy to carry and required little, if any, preparation. They relied heavily on dried foods, especially beef jerky, developed by the Native Americans.

Legend has it that jerky was originally developed by the Indians in Peru. Lean beef was sliced ¼ inch thick and preserved with salt or brine for about 12 hours. Then it was dried in the sun and tied into convenient bundles. Its Native American name, "charqui," eventually was pronounced as "jerky."

ASSESS

REVIEW

- Ask students to summarize the main ideas in this section.
- Have students complete the Section Review. (Answers appear below.)

EVALUATION

- Have students list the steps for freezing, canning, and drying foods.
- Have students take the quiz for Section 24-5. (Use the quiz in the *Teacher Resource Guide,* or construct your own with the **Exam***View*® *Test Generator* on the *Effective Instruction CD-ROM.*)

RETEACHING

- Ask students to explain how drying helps keep food from spoiling.
- Refer to the *Reteaching Activities* booklet for the Section 24-5 activity sheet.

CLOSE

Lead a discussion about the advantages and disadvantages of preserving your own food. List them on the board, encouraging at least one point from each student.

Drying Food

The easiest way to dry food at home is with a food dehydrator. Most food dehydrators have a 24-hour timer and an adjustable thermostat that allows you to dry foods between 90°F and 155°F (32°C and 69°C). Follow the manufacturer's directions for drying times and temperatures.

Foods such as fruits and vegetables, granola, and beef jerky can be dried easily at home. By taking advantage of low prices on seasonal fruits and vegetables, you can save money, too.

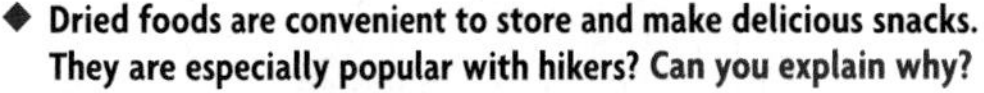

◆ **Dried foods are convenient to store and make delicious snacks. They are especially popular with hikers? Can you explain why?**

Section 24-5 Review & Activities

1. Anita bought a large amount of different fruits inexpensively at a food warehouse. Her plan is to freeze the fruits. How can she determine which fruits are high in natural acid?
2. Briefly explain why and how vegetables are blanched.
3. Give four guidelines for using a pressure canner safely.
4. **Analyzing.** Why do you think preserving food at home has remained popular even with today's busy lifestyles?
5. **Synthesizing.** Respond to this question: "Why bother to can food at home when you can easily buy foods in cans?"
6. **Applying.** Brainstorm a list of all the frozen, canned, and dried products your family uses regularly. Identify those that you might preserve at home. Why might it be impractical or unwise to preserve the others at home?

Answers to Section 24-5 Review & Activities

1. Foods high in natural acid will not undergo enzymatic browning quickly.
2. Vegetables are blanched to kill enzymes. See pages 671-672.
3. See the "Safety Check" on page 673.
4. Answers will vary. Once preserved, foods become convenient choices. Also, home-preserved foods may not contain added sugars, salt, or other preservatives that health-conscious consumers try to moderate.
5. Answers will vary.
6. Answers will vary.

Career Wanted

Pastry Chef

Education and Training
- Degree from culinary arts school
- On-the-job training/internship

Qualities
- Creativity
- Attention to detail
- Management skills
- Communication skills

"Pastries are the show-offs of the dinner table."
Orlando Diaz

Q. Orlando, do pastries take hours to make?

A. Yes, about four hours from start to finish. We make our own puff pastry, cook our custard fillings, and pipe the trim. These steps can't be rushed—and it is work. We often have four commercial ovens going at once.

Q. How much of the work do you do yourself?

A. Assistants do the routine jobs, like measuring ingredients and mixing dough. They're learning, as I did, and working up to more complex tasks. Besides creating pastries, I manage the kitchen, plan the dessert menu, order supplies, and pre-price recipes.

Q. Does mass-producing pastries stifle your creativity?

A. It is limiting, but I have techniques and tools to add a personal touch. I can make my own stencils and molds, for instance. Catering events lets me get fancier, like airbrushing a design or making special marzipan decorations. With creative decoration and presentation, I'm able to "wow" the diner. That adds to the diner's enjoyment as well as mine.

Related Career Opportunities

Entry Level
- Short-order cook
- Food batchmaker
- Line cook

Technical Level
- Sauce chef
- Baker
- Food stylist

Professional Level
- Executive chef
- Research and development chef
- Culinary educator

Making Career Connections

JOB SHADOWING. Arrange to shadow a pastry chef or someone in a similar position. What baked goods were prepared? What baking skills and knowledge that you've learned were demonstrated? What new information did you learn? Did any problems arise? If so, how were they handled? Report on your experience.

Career Wanted

Pastry Chef

Thinking About the Career

Have students think about what pastries they might make as a pastry chef.

Ask students to cut out (or draw) pictures of pastries they would consider "art."

Ask students to consider the differences between a career as a sous chef and a career as a pastry chef.

Career-Building Opportunities

Students interested in a career as a pastry chef may practice baking in their own home kitchens or seek experience as a baker in a restaurant, cafeteria, or catering business.

For More Information

For additional information about culinary careers, encourage students to contact:

- American Culinary Federation
  10 San Bartola Drive
  St. Augustine, Florida 32086
  www.acfchefs.org
- International Association of Culinary Professionals
  304 West Liberty Street
  Suite 201, Louisville, KY 40202
  www.iacp.org
- National Restaurant Association
  1200 17th Street NW
  Washington, D.C. 20036-3097
  www.restaurant.org

REVIEW

- Have students complete the Chapter Review. (Answers appear below.)

EVALUATION

- Have students write a short essay discussing the topics covered in this chapter.
- Have students take the test for Chapter 24. (Use the chapter test in the *Teacher Resource Guide,* or construct your own with the **Exam***View*® *Test Generator* on the *Effective Instruction CD-ROM.*)

ANSWERS

Checking Your Knowledge

1. Herbs are the leaves and stems of soft, succulent plants that grow in temperate zones. Spices are usually dried, ground buds, bark, seeds, stems, or roots of aromatic tropical plants and trees.
2. The bags are not made to withstand high cooking temperatures and may burn; chemicals in the paper may transfer to food.
3. Any three: protein, calcium, phosphorus, vitamin D, vitamin A.
4. The water reservoir, the basket that holds a filter and the coffee, the carafe, and the hot plate.
5. Start with a list organized by categories, list the tasks in order, make a special list for things to be done the day before and the day of the event, cross each item off the list as it is accomplished.
6. Dinner plates and the food for the main course are brought to the table in serving dishes and placed in front of the host or hostess. The host carves the meat, places the meat and vegetables on a plate, and passes it to the right. When all the people on the right have been served, the plates are passed down the left side of the table.

Chapter 24 Review & Activities

Summary

Section 24-1: Creative Techniques

- You can add flavors to foods with seasonings such as herbs, spices, and condiments.
- Cooking foods *en papillote,* in a sealed parchment paper package, allows the flavor of several foods to blend.
- Garnishes are colorful bits of food that complement a dish's appearance and texture.

Section 24-2: Beverages

- Beverages help you meet your body's requirement for one of the six main nutrients—water.
- Milk and pure fruit juice are high in other nutrients, including calcium and vitamins.
- Coffee and tea come in several varieties and are easy to prepare.

Section 24-3: Entertaining

- Good planning helps make any occasion, whether formal or informal, a success.
- When you plan, consider the theme, decorations, invitations, and menu.
- Options for serving the food include modified English service, formal service, and buffet service.
- Receptions are usually formal gatherings at which buffet service is used.

Section 24-4: Outdoor Meals

- Safety is especially important when planning and preparing outdoor meals.
- Pack foods with care, and follow rules for safe grilling.
- Meats, fish, fruits, and vegetables can all be grilled successfully.

Section 24-5: Preserving Food at Home

- When freezing fruits and vegetables, take steps to stop enzyme activity.
- To can safely, use up-to-date recipes and equipment, and follow recipe directions exactly.
- Some foods can be dried at home with a food dehydrator.

Checking Your Knowledge

1. What is the difference between herbs and spices?
2. Give two reasons for not using brown paper bags for cooking foods *en papillote.*
3. Identify three nutrients found in milk.
4. Identify the four main parts of an automatic drip coffeemaker.
5. Give four suggestions for making a schedule of things to do when organizing a party.
6. Describe modified English service.
7. Explain how to handle grill flare-ups.
8. Give two guidelines for packing chilled food in a cooler.
9. Describe two differences between the dry-pack plain and sugar-pack methods of freezing fruits.
10. Briefly describe how to prepare raw-packed and hot-packed jars for processing.

Working IN THE Lab

1. ***Foods Lab.*** Create your own herb or spice blend. Experiment with different combinations and proportions of seasonings. Prepare a recipe using your blend.
2. ***Food Science.*** Blanch and freeze a batch of green beans. Freeze another batch without blanching. After one week, thaw the packages and compare the appearance and texture of the beans. Cook the beans, and compare their taste. How do you explain your findings?

Thinking Critically

1. **Recognizing Points of View.** Aldo watched as his sister sprinkled dried oregano into the stew she was cooking. "Wouldn't that dish turn out better if you used the fresh herb?" he said. His sister replied that dried herbs have "their place in the kitchen." Based on what you learned in the chapter, explain what Aldo's sister may have meant.
2. **Comparing and Contrasting.** The Morabitos are shopping for a backyard grill. Charcoal grills are much less expensive than gas grills, but the store is running a clearance sale and has marked down the gas grills significantly. Make a list of the factors the Morabitos need to consider in order to make an informed decision.

Reinforcing Key Skills

1. **Communication.** Reggie is timid about cooking. He follows recipes to the letter, not changing a single ingredient or amount, and in general expresses the attitude that "I'm just not creative." How could you encourage Reggie to explore his creativity in cooking?
2. **Management.** At Luisa's dinner party, some of the guests do not seem to be enjoying themselves. They aren't eating much, they are hardly speaking, and they generally seem uncomfortable. Before you could advise Luisa on steps to take to improve the situation, what additional information would you need to have?

Making Decisions and Solving Problems

You have several items to pack in your cooler for a picnic for yourself and three family members: a large container of ham salad, a loaf of bread, a six-pack of soda, a block of cheese, a chocolate cake, and ice for the drinks. As you pack, however, you realize that there is not enough room in the cooler for everything.

Making Connections

1. **Social Studies.** Choose five different herbs or spices, and find out where they are commonly grown. Make a display using a world map. Identify the herb or spice, the region in which it is produced, and the geographic conditions that help it grow there.
2. **Science.** Find more information about one of the chemical processes involved in preserving food at home, such as oxidation, the action of enzymes, or dehydration. If possible, set up an experiment or other demonstration to illustrate the principles involved.

ANSWERS cont.

7. Raise the grate, cover the grill, or use a long-handled tool to spread the coals apart; remove the food from the grate and spray a mist of water on the flare-up using a pump-spray bottle.
8. Put the last item you will need on the bottom and the first one on top; at the picnic site, keep the cooler in a cool, shady spot.
9. Dry-pack plain does not contain sugar; in the dry-pack plain method, the food must be frozen before it is put into its container, but sugar-packed fruits are frozen in their containers.
10. *Raw-packed:* place raw foods into the jars, and then pour in hot syrup, water, or juice. *Hot-packed:* heat the food in liquid before putting it into the jars; then pack heated food into the jars.

Thinking Critically

1. Answers will vary. Aldo's sister may have meant that dried herbs are useful for some dishes; dried herbs can be an alternative to fresh herbs.
2. Answers will vary. Students may mention such factors as convenience, ease of fire starting, and cost.

Reinforcing Key Skills

1. Answers will vary. You may suggest that Reggie start experimenting slowly with creativity, one ingredient at a time. For instance, he might add a small amount of one dried herb to a basic dish or he might substitute one favorite fruit or vegetable for another, such as substituting red peppers or green peppers in a stir-fry.
2. Answer will vary. Additional information may include the type of party, if there's a theme, type of food being served, and if all people in the group get along.

CHAPTER

25

Careers in Food and Nutrition

Advance Planning Guide ☑

- Create a bulletin board illustrating a variety of food and nutrition careers.
- Plan a field trip to a food service setting for employee observation. As an alternative, invite food and nutrition professionals to class for a panel discussion.
- Obtain a cookie recipe; modify one ingredient; purchase necessary ingredients for the Test Kitchen Experience on page 682.
- Invite a dietitian to speak to the class.
- Invite a school counselor to speak to the class.
- Obtain two different job application forms.
- Invite a quick-service restaurant manager to speak to the class.

CHAPTER

25

Carrie had always enjoyed preparing food for her family and friends. When she entered high school, she thought she might like to become a chef or a baker. After a few foods and nutrition courses, she discovered her opportunities in the food area were even more varied. In this chapter, you will learn, as Carrie did, about the many career possibilities in this exciting, growing field.

MEETING DIVERSE NEEDS

Interpersonal Learners. If there are students in the class who enjoy working in groups, ask them to produce two or three different, 10-minute, instructional skits for the class. The skits are to demonstrate appropriate interview scenarios for two or three specific food-related careers. Have the students dress professionally and bring all appropriate materials for the "interviews."

SECTION
25-1

Career Opportunities

When you were a young child, a question you probably heard often was, "What do you want to be when you grow up?" Now that you are on the threshold of adulthood, it is the time to consider seriously the question of a career.

Objectives

After studying this section, you should be able to:

- Identify some career opportunities in food and nutrition.
- Describe the training and education needed for various careers.

Look for These Terms

career
entry-level job
entrepreneur
franchise

Thinking About Careers

A **career** is a profession or a life's work within a certain field. It usually begins with an **entry-level job**, a job that requires little or no experience. These jobs often lead to better-paying jobs with more responsibility.

Employees will advance in their careers by mastering the skills needed for their jobs and showing they are qualified to take on new responsibilities. Many seek additional education or training throughout their lives to further their careers.

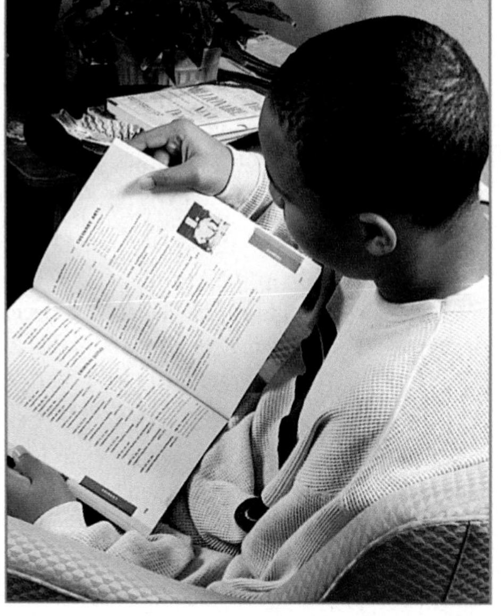

◆ **An interest in food now could turn into a career someday. Identify questions you could ask yourself to determine what kind of career to pursue.**

SECTION
25-1
Career Opportunities

FOCUS

MOTIVATORS

- Create a bulletin board illustrating a variety of food and nutrition careers. Discuss the jobs involved in each area.
- Discuss how high school courses might help a person get an entry-level job or even lead to a career.

VOCABULARY ACTIVITY

Pronounce the terms listed under "Look for These Terms." Have students find the terms and their definitions in the section. Point out that the word *entrepreneur* and the word *enterprise* both come from the same French word, *entreprendre,* meaning "to undertake."

STUDY SKILLS

- **Guided Reading.** Have students look at the headings within Section 25-1 to preview the concepts that will be discussed.
- Have students read the section and complete the appropriate part of the Chapter 25 Study Guide in the *Student Workbook*.

Section 25-1 Resources

◆ **Student Workbook,** pp. 187, 189
◆ **Teacher Resource Guide**
Lesson Plan 25-1 Organizer
Section 25-1 Quiz
◆ **Effective Instruction CD-ROM**
Exam*View*® *Test Generator*
PowerPoint® Slide #55
◆ **Transparency Package,** CT-55

◆ **Student Motivation Kit**
Reteaching Activities, pp. 113–114
Enrichment Activities
Skills for Making Food Choices, pp. 55–56

TEACH

- *Thinking About Careers*
- *Food-Related Careers (text pages 679-684)*

Discussion Activity

Divide the class into two groups. Give each group one of the following to use for a Q&A discussion: (1) Why do educational requirements vary? (2) What is the advantage of getting higher education? Reconvene the class as a whole to discuss and share group reactions.

Using 

Ask students to write a short essay based on their Q&A responses. In their essays, ask them to conclude with specific careers that seem to match their responses to the Q&A. Suggest that students save their essays for their own future reference.

Career Search

Divide the class into small groups. Provide each group with one specific food service career beyond the positions covered in the "Career Wanted" features at the end of text chapters. Have them research the job—personal traits, education, and other requirements. Have each group develop a fact sheet about the job. All fact sheets are to be compiled into a classroom resource. L1

Q ***What's the best way to identify careers I might enjoy and do well in?***

A Start by asking yourself questions. What classes and activities do you enjoy? Why do you like them? What are your skills and talents? Do any point toward a specific career you might enjoy? Working in community service or at a part-time job will also give you valuable information about yourself, your abilities, and your preferences.

Food-Related Careers

A recent study on job growth for the coming years predicted great expansion in service industries, including those pertaining to food and nutrition. The job outlook for this field is bright. Consider these trends:

- More people are eating out.
- Consumers are more interested in the relationship between food and health.
- The growing world population and other global factors make efficient production and use of high-quality food more important than ever.

Food Service

The food service industry includes all aspects of preparing and serving food for the public. It is expected to create more new jobs than any other retail industry in the next decade.

Jobs in food service can vary from serving food to developing recipes to merchandising food products. These jobs are usually available in every part of the country. If you like to travel, you might consider food service jobs with cruise lines or airlines, or jobs in other countries.

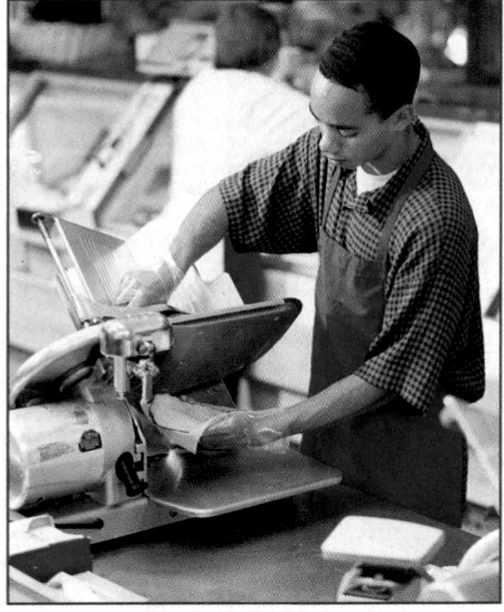

◆ **Many entry-level jobs are available in the food service industry. List characteristics that can help a person move up the ladder to higher-paying jobs.**

Educational Background

Educational requirements in food service vary, depending on the job you want. Part-time, entry-level jobs are often a good start. Food preparation classes in high school can also provide a valuable foundation. For more training, consider vocational schools, junior or community colleges, and four-year colleges and universities. Many companies offer on-the-job training to help employees advance.

Personal Qualifications

Food service jobs require certain personal traits. Employees must enjoy and be able to work successfully with people. They must be willing to do their share as part of a team. Producing quality food on a schedule can

Reinforcing Key Skills

Present the following problem to student groups. Allow time for them to discuss and compare their responses.

Communication—One of Gil's classmates, Richard, just began a part-time job in the kitchen at a local restaurant. Gil overhears Richard telling a friend that he is now thinking about pursuing a career in food service because he is convinced that running a restaurant requires little more than greeting customers as they arrive. If you were Gil, what advice might you have for Richard?

Q How can I get the career I really want?

A The career of your dreams may seem out of reach, but it probably isn't if you do some planning. How do you begin? Start by setting goals, both long-term and short-term. The career you want is a long-term goal because it takes time to get there. By breaking your long-term goal down into shorter ones, it becomes more manageable and more achievable. Short-term goals are smaller and less intimidating. You reach them sooner on the way toward larger goals. As part of a career plan, your short-term goals could include working part-time in a job that gives you career-linked experience. Other short-term goals include doing volunteer work in the field and taking a related class. Researching the field could be a goal, as could visiting a job site. Education and training can also be on your goal list. Eventually, you might set your sights on an entry-level position. All of these steps can be part of the plan that gets you moving toward your dream.

mean hard work and long hours. Good health, enthusiasm, ambition, and a sense of humor are essential. So are good work habits, such as punctuality and the ability to follow directions and accept criticism.

Job Advancement

Brent started working in a restaurant bussing tables. Through hard work and study, he moved up to the position of assistant manager. His goal now is to become a manager.

As a rule, more education and training allow you to start in a higher position. Food service offers many different career directions to take.

Family and Consumer Sciences

Family and consumer sciences—called home economics, human ecology, or family studies at some universities—involves using knowledge and skills to solve problems and make decisions about the home and family. Professionals with degrees in food and nutrition have many career options in addition to food service. These include teaching, communication, and research and development.

Teaching

Family and consumer sciences specialists teach in schools, colleges, and universities. They teach classes ranging from nutrition to ethnic foods. Nutritionists may work for county or regional extension services, teaching consumers about food preparation and related topics. They are also needed by other government agencies and health organizations to teach consumers how to make wise food choices.

Communication

This area involves communicating information to the public through television, magazines, books, and newspapers. People with strong communication skills are needed to help write speeches, articles, and advertisements about food products and services. Food stylists create attractive arrangements of foods for photographs. Employers include food producers, manufacturers, government agencies, and trade associations.

- *Food-Related Careers (text pages 680-684)*

Student Speaker Activity

Ask students who have worked, or currently work, in food service to describe their experiences. What opportunities do entry-level food service workers have to advance? What effect does education have on their chance to be promoted? Encourage all students to ask questions.

Field Trip

Visit a restaurant, cafeteria, hotel, or institution to observe what employees in the different areas of food service do. After the field trip, have students write about their experience. Have them conclude with a paragraph on why they would or would not consider a career in food service. As an alternative to the field trip, invite people who work in food and nutrition careers to discuss their work, education, and training.

Small Group Discussion Activity

Have students work in small groups to find out what family and consumer sciences specialists do in teaching, communications, and research and development, and what training is required in each field.

Technology TIE-IN

The first food industry in the United States was born with the arrival in colonial times of "way houses," which provided not only a meal but sleeping accommodations for weary travelers. The kitchens of early way houses were not without their tools of the restaurant trade. Among these was a very small iron grid at the end of a long handle. This device was used to make toast—one piece at a time. Salt had the form of a cone from which crystals were hand-grated. Sugar, when available, had the same form.

- *Food-Related Careers (text pages 680-684)*

Test Kitchen Experience

Tell students they are going to be food scientists for a new cookie company. Explain that the foods lab is to be their test kitchen. Provide lab groups with a basic cookie recipe, with too much of one ingredient, such as sugar. Have students prepare the recipe and evaluate the product. Does it meet quality standards for the "company"? Can they detect the problem? L2

Guest Speaker

Invite a dietitian to speak to the class about career opportunities in dietetics. Ask students to develop at least one question each to potentially ask the dietitian. Examples include: Where do dietitians work? What are their specialties?

Recruitment

Have students pick one food-related career that sounds interesting—and ideally one that they may be interested in pursuing. Have each of them prepare a recruitment poster to promote that profession and educate other students about the requirements and other background information. L1

Research and Development

Food researchers help develop new products and appliances in test kitchens or research laboratories. They may work for universities, food producers, appliance manufacturers, or the government.

Jobs in family and consumer sciences require at least a bachelor's degree. Some, such as teaching, research, and management, may require higher degrees. Study and experience in related fields also helps. Specialists in communications, for example, might have a background in journalism or public relations.

Food Science

Food science is the study of the physical, chemical, and microbiological makeup of food. Food scientists develop food products and new ways to process and package them. They also test foods and beverages for quality and purity to be sure they meet company standards and federal food regulations.

Food scientists are generally employed by the food processing industry. They may work in laboratories, in test kitchens, or on the production line. The many careers in food science include basic research, product development, quality control, and sales.

Food scientists need at least a bachelor's degree with a major in food science, food engineering, or food technology. Higher degrees are needed for research and managerial jobs.

Dietetics

A dietitian is a professional trained in the principles of food and nutrition. Dietitians may work for large institutions such as hospitals, health maintenance organizations, company cafeterias, and food service companies. They help develop special diets and counsel groups or individuals in making wise food choices.

◆ **A college education can lead to a rewarding career as a food scientist. What are some of the tasks a food scientist does?**

Technology TIE-IN Explain to students that the Internet has made finding a dietitian easy. Ask one student to visit The American Dietetic Association's (ADA) web site at www.eatright.org. Have the student find the names of three area dietitians using the site's dietitian referral system. Note that this technological advance is good advertising for career dietitians. Invite students to find out what other food-related careers have specialized web sites and referral services. Findings are to be filed in a classroom resource center for easy reference.

Dietitians must have a bachelor's degree in food and nutrition. They must then serve a one-year internship at an approved institution. A registered dietitian (RD) must pass the Registration Examination for Dietitians. Some community colleges offer two-year programs for dietetic technicians, who work as assistants to dietitians.

Food Production, Processing, and Marketing

As noted in Chapter 13, a vast network of people is involved in producing food and getting it to the marketplace. Career opportunities vary from hydroponic farming to supermarket management.

Training and education also vary, but a combination of experience and formal education is best. Farmers, for example, need to know how to do the everyday work on the farm itself but can also benefit from studies in related topics, such as soil conservation and plant and animal genetics. A bakery owner must have experience in preparing the food as well as knowledge about business management, marketing techniques, and tax laws.

INFOLINK
For more on hydroponic farming and other food technologies, see Section 13-1.

Entrepreneurship

Many people dream of owning their own businesses. A person who runs his or her own business is called an **entrepreneur** (AHN-truh-pruh-NOOR). Successful entrepreneurs share certain personal qualities. They are willing to work hard and take risks. They can make sound decisions, are well organized, and understand the basic business management practices. Opportunities for entrepreneurs in food and nutrition include catering, running a snack shop, providing home delivery from restaurants or supermarkets, providing nutritional consultation, and preparing and selling food.

◆ **Owning a business takes hard work, but the results are worthwhile. Entrepreneurs feel the special satisfaction of building their own success. Respond to the statement: "Entrepreneurs contribute to the strength and growth of their communities."**

Franchises

Entrepreneurs sometimes invest in a **franchise**, an individually owned and operated branch of a business with an established name and guidelines. Some fast-food restaurants are franchises. Not all franchises are reliable, however, so potential owners should investigate carefully before buying. Also, the fact that the business is a franchise cannot guarantee success. It's up to the individual businessperson to provide the skills and commitment needed to succeed.

- *Food-Related Careers (text pages 680-684)*

Research

Have students research local career opportunities in food production, processing, and marketing. Resources may include the telephone directory, local business and industry directories, the Chamber of Commerce, interviews, and the Internet. L2

Interviews

Have students interview local food and nutrition entrepreneurs. Among questions which students might ask are the following: Was your business a part of a franchise? If so, what assistance was provided by the franchiser? Ask students to give brief presentations summarizing their interviews. L1

Letter Writing

Have students write a letter or send an e-mail to one of the sources listed on page 684 for more information about food and nutrition careers. Additionally, have students print pertinent career information from these sources' web sites. L1

Extending Learning

Franchises—A franchise is actually a license to conduct a business enterprise in the name of an established corporation or, in some cases, the government. The franchisee usually pays an initial fee and a percentage of gross receipts to the franchiser in exchange for the privilege of marketing a well-known product or service. In corporate franchises, the franchiser usually helps the franchisee with merchandising and advertising.

ASSESS

REVIEW

- Ask students to summarize the main ideas in this section.
- Have students complete the Section Review. (Answers appear below.)

EVALUATION

- Have students write a short essay describing the various careers available in food and nutrition.
- Have students take the quiz for Section 25-1. (Use the quiz in the *Teacher Resource Guide,* or construct your own with the **Exam***View*® *Test Generator* on the *Effective Instruction CD-ROM.*)

RETEACHING

- Have students make a chart of the various occupations and the educational requirements for each.
- Refer to the *Reteaching Activities* booklet for the Section 25-1 activity sheet.

CLOSE

Lead a discussion about the importance of education in the appropriate field so that you can advance in your career. As a class, have students suggest one important key for each letter of "EDUCATION," such as "E" for enriched knowledge and "D" for developing skills.

Sources of Food and Nutrition Career Information

American Association of Family and Consumer Sciences
1555 King Street
Alexandria, VA 22314

The Institute of Food Technologists
525 West Van Buren, Suite 1000
Chicago, IL 60607

The American Dietetic Association
216 W. Jackson Boulevard, Suite 800
Chicago, IL 60606-6995

U.S. Department of Agriculture
14th Street and Independence Avenue, SW
Washington, DC 20250

Small Business Administration
409 3rd Street, SW
Washington, DC 20416

Section 25-1 Review & Activities

1. List four types of education or training for a career in food service.
2. Name three food and nutrition career options other than food service.
3. Briefly describe the educational and training requirements for registered dietitians.
4. **Applying.** Suppose you wanted to be an executive chef. List short-term and long-term goals that could lead to this career. What jobs might gradually build up to a position as an executive chef?
5. **Synthesizing.** What social and cultural trends have contributed to the increased need for workers in food and nutrition?
6. **Extending.** Take a survey in class to see how much interest students have in becoming entrepreneurs. Use a scale of 1-5, with 1 as no interest and 5 as very high interest. Discuss the reasons for the results.
7. **Applying.** Describe how the skills you've gained by studying nutrition could be used in the following careers: chef; dietitian; foods writer; social worker; and restaurant owner.
8. **Applying.** Choose a food that you like. List as many workers as you can that are involved in producing, processing, and distributing that food.
9. **Extending.** Choose a food-related career of interest to you. Work with your teacher or counselor to plan and carry out an experience that will provide you with information about this career. The experience could be based on job shadowing, service learning, or a site visit with interviews. Find out how what you have studied in this course is used in the career.

Answers to Section 25-1 Review & Activities

1. See page 680.
2. See pages 681-683.
3. See page 683.
4. Goals and jobs may include: food science courses in school; entry-level job in restaurant; culinary school; work as baker in supermarket or sauce chef in large hotel kitchen.
5. Answers may include: greater awareness of diet's impact on health; rise in cases of diet-related diseases; greater use of convenience foods.
6. Answers will vary.
7. Answers will vary.
8. Answers will vary.
9. Experiences will vary.

SECTION 25-2

The Successful Worker

The careers of your future will have high impact on your life. Not only will you enjoy the benefits and pride of earning a paycheck, but you will also feel the satisfaction of work well done. Although success on any job is measured in many ways, employers share certain expectations of people. If you learn and practice these skills now, they'll be polished and ready for use in the years ahead.

Objectives

After studying this section, you should be able to:

- Identify qualities of successful workers.
- Describe the steps in applying for a job.
- Give guidelines for job interviews.
- Explain how to handle leaving a job.

Look for These Terms

networking
resumé
references
interview

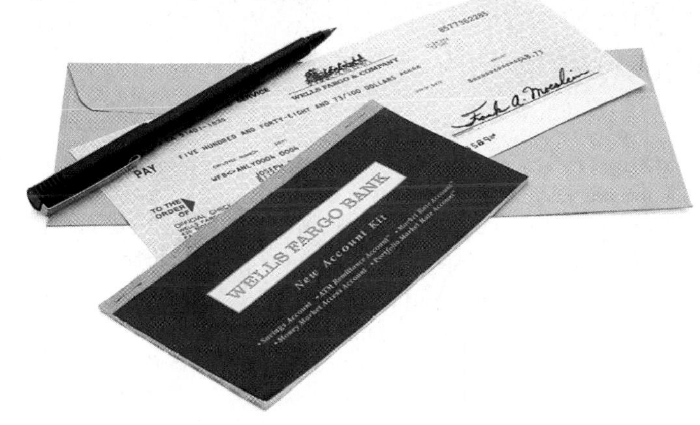

Preparing for Work

What are the qualities employers look for? Recent surveys have identified certain qualities and skills. You can develop many of them while still in school.

- **Communication skills.** These include writing, reading, speaking, and listening. Employees often write reports. They must read and understand company bulletins and guidelines. They must also listen carefully to instructions they receive and to customer requests.
- **Computer skills.** Most jobs involve the use of a computer in some way. In many restaurants, for instance, servers use computers to send customer food orders to the kitchen.
- **Critical thinking and problem solving skills.** Employees who can analyze situations and suggest solutions to problems are valued by their employers.
- **Positive attitude.** Employees must be enthusiastic about their work and interested in what they do.
- **Math skills.** Even though computers and calculators are widely used, employees must understand basic math. They may have to make change, keep a time schedule, or solve math-related problems.
- **Teamwork and self-responsibility.** Employees must be willing to do their share, and more if necessary. They must work well with others to achieve common goals.

Section 25-2 Resources

◆ **Student Workbook,** pp. 188, 191
◆ **Teacher Resource Guide**
Lesson Plan 25-2 Organizer
Section 25-2 Quiz
Chapter 25 Test
◆ **Effective Instruction CD-ROM**
Exam *View® Test Generator*
PowerPoint® Slide #56
◆ **Transparency Package,** CT-56
◆ **Student Motivation Kit**
Reteaching Activities, p. 115
Enrichment Activities

SECTION 25-2

The Successful Worker

FOCUS

MOTIVATORS

- Ask students who work to describe how they found their jobs. How many had to fill out an application form? How many had a job interview? What did they learn that would help them do better next time?
- Ask students to list qualities they have that will help them be successful workers. Ask several volunteers to share their lists with the class.

VOCABULARY ACTIVITY

Pronounce the terms listed under "Look for These Terms." Have students find the terms and their definitions in the section. Ask a volunteer to look up *network* in the dictionary and read aloud some of its definitions. Ask students what these definitions have in common.

STUDY SKILLS

- **Outlining.** Have students read the section and outline it by copying the headers on paper and leaving space after each one. Students are to write a sentence in their own words, summarizing the content under each header.
- Have students read the section and complete the appropriate part of the Chapter 25 Study Guide in the *Student Workbook*.

TEACH

- *Preparing for Work (text pages 685-689)*

List Development

Assign each student one of the seven qualities/skills listed on pages 685-686. Have each student develop a list of "10 ways that (quality/skill) can help me be a successful worker." Have students share lists. L2

Group Discussion Activity

Divide the class into small groups. Assign each group one of the following topics: volunteer work, school projects, social activities, part-time jobs. Ask students to consider how each activity would help them develop qualities needed for job success. Have each group share a summary of its group's discussion with the class.

Guest Speaker

Invite a school counselor to discuss the job placement assistance programs offered by the school. If time allows, have every student ask the school counselor one pertinent job-related question.

◆ **Learning to communicate effectively—for example, by speaking to adults who can help you with career decisions—is an important aspect of preparing for the future. Name three other skills that can help you become a successful member of the workforce someday.**

- ◆ **Ability to learn.** New technology will continue to cause rapid changes in the workplace. This means learning new skills will be a lifelong process for employees.

Develop good learning and work habits while you are still in school. Volunteer work, school projects, and social activities can provide opportunities to develop essential skills.

Looking for a Job

As a student, right now you may be looking for only a part-time job. Even so, the experience of finding and keeping a job will be valuable to you personally as well as professionally.

There are many ways to find a job. Check your school employment or counseling office. Read the newspaper want ads and community bulletin boards. You can also contact employers directly and ask if they currently have any job openings.

Another idea helpful in job hunting is **networking**. This means making connections with people who can provide information about job openings. When Anton began exploring careers in food science, his network included his food science teacher, a nutritionist at a county extension office, and the writer of a foods column in the local newspaper. Remember, however, that other people can only help you find a job. Getting the job and keeping it are up to you.

Applying for a Job

Your next step is to apply for a specific job. This usually involves completing a job application form or letter of application and, sometimes, submitting your resumé and personal references.

A Job Application

A job application form requires basic personal information, such as your age and home address, and information about your education and experience. Remember to print your answers in ink, answering all questions as accurately as possible.

A letter of application serves the same purpose as an application form. However, you have a choice of what information to include. Include basic personal information plus any other helpful facts about yourself. As with the application form, focus on those things that will demonstrate your suitability for the job you are seeking. For example, being editor of the school yearbook shows that you can work well with other people and delegate authority. Earning good grades in food science courses indicates your knowledge of foods and any related fields.

Reinforcing Key Skills

Present the following problems to student groups. Allow time for them to discuss and compare their responses.

Critical Thinking—Why is it so important to follow directions exactly when answering want ads?

Leadership—A new mall opened just a few blocks away from your home. It has many stores that you are excited to have nearby. You'd like to work part-time at one of the stores, but there's no sign indicating that any need help. What action can you take?

A Resumé

For some jobs, you may need to submit a **resumé** (REH-zoo-may). This is a written summary of your experience, skills, and achievements that are related to the job you seek. A chronological resumé lists jobs and experiences in *reverse order*. That is, the list begins with the most recent experience and ends with the earliest. A functional resumé describes your skills and accomplishments as they relate to the job you are seeking.

Although a resumé is more detailed than a letter of application, it should be brief—not more than one page—and contain only relevant information. If you have no previous work experience, don't mention it. Focus instead on those activities that show your skills and abilities.

References

When applying for a job, you may be asked for **references**—people who know you well and can give information about your previous work or your character. A teacher or former work supervisor might be a good reference. Be sure to ask the people you wish to use as references for their permission for you to do so. You will need their names, addresses, and phone numbers.

Employers are prohibited by law from asking, in person or on application forms, for certain information, such as your race, gender, religion, or marital status. They may not ask questions about some aspects of your personal life or about your past.

An application form, letter of application, and resumé all demonstrate your ability to communicate in writing. All three should be carefully thought out and neatly written or typed. Be sure the grammar and punctuation are correct. Remember that this will be your potential employer's first—and possibly only—impression of you as a worker. Make it a positive one.

Ginny Arnold
800 Southwest Street
Anytown, US 11111
Home Phone: (000)000-0000

OBJECTIVE: Kitchen helper, part-time.

QUALIFICATIONS:
- Received high grades in food preparation class.
- Have ability to organize work.
- Know how to use a computer.
- Would like to become a chef.

EXPERIENCE:
- Help with Friday night suppers at church.
- Organized successful pancake breakfast for parents, sponsored by the FHA/HERO Club.
- Worked at the Community Center soup kitchen, helping with meals for homeless.

EDUCATION:
- Junior at Anytown High School.
- Currently taking advanced food preparation class.

◆ **A well-written resumé is brief, but provides the information that employers need in order to consider you for the job. What kind of job is the writer of this resumé seeking?**

Working Papers

When applying for work, you may also be asked to furnish working papers. These are the documents and certificates needed for employment. Your school counselor can tell you how to obtain these important items, which include:

- ◆ **Social Security number.** Lifelong identification number allowing you to receive Social Security payments when you retire or if you are disabled. You may already have a number. If not, you can get one at the nearest Social Security office.

- *Preparing for Work (text pages 685-689)*

Want Ad Analysis

Have students collect "Help Wanted" ads from national and local newspapers, including papers with Web sites. What jobs are available in the area of food and nutrition? Ask students to look through the ads in search of jobs that look attractive and accessible for a young applicant. How many listings request a written reply? How many ask you to apply in person? By phone? L1

Form Completion Activity

Provide students with two different job application forms. Have them fill out the forms neatly and completely.

Developing a Resumé

Have students develop a resumé showing past experience, skills, and achievements that would help them get an entry-level food service job. Suggest that they create their resumé using chronological or functional formats. The illustration on this page can be a guide. Encourage students to enter their resumé on a computer, so that they can easily update it, as needed, and have it readily available when a job-opening arises.

Extending Learning

Tips for Writing a Resumé

- Do not include references, unless you are asked for them.
- Do not include previous salary or wages.
- Do not include personal information that is not related to the job.
- Avoid subjective statements using "I." Just stick with facts.
- Be honest. Don't exaggerate qualifications.
- Avoid using "I" when listing qualifications.
- Keep it brief. Concise statements are much more effective than lengthy sentences.

- *Preparing for Work (text pages 685-689)*

Educational Material Development

Ask students to develop a brochure or other educational tool that suggests strategies for successfully getting and keeping a job. **L1**

Guest Speaker

Invite the manager of a quick-service restaurant to speak to the class. Ask the guest to explain the preparation, appearance, social skills, body language, etc., that make a job applicant successful. Encourage the guest to relate pertinent anecdotes. What are the most serious mistakes people make when they interview for a job? Have the manager interview a volunteer in front of the class and evaluate the interview.

Practice Interviews

Have students work in groups of three to conduct practice job interviews for an entry-level food service job. Ask students to come to class dressed as they would for the interview. Have one student interview another. Have the third student evaluate the interviewee's performance. Have students rotate until all have been interviewed. **L1**

- **Work permit.** Required of students in some states.
- **Health certificates.** Necessary in some areas for working with food.

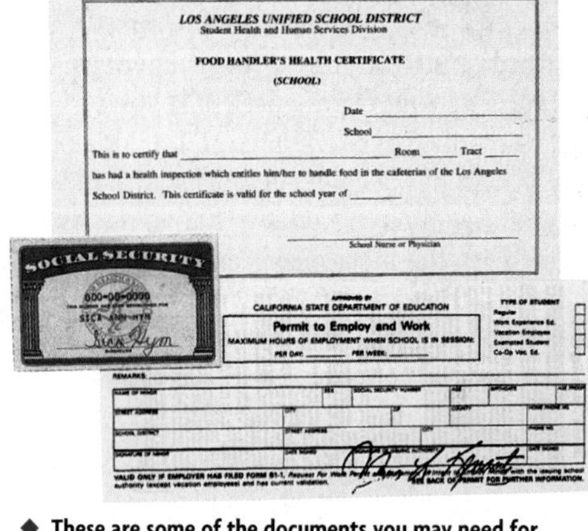

LOS ANGELES UNIFIED SCHOOL DISTRICT
Student Health and Human Services Division

FOOD HANDLER'S HEALTH CERTIFICATE
(SCHOOL)

Date ____
School ____

This is to certify that ____ Room ____ Tract ____ has had a health inspection which entitles him/her to handle food in the cafeterias of the Los Angeles School District. This certificate is valid for the school year of ____

School Nurse or Physician

SOCIAL SECURITY

CALIFORNIA STATE DEPARTMENT OF EDUCATION
Permit to Employ and Work

◆ **These are some of the documents you may need for employment. You may already have a Social Security number. Speak with the school counselor about where to obtain these and other necessary work documents. Record the agency names and addresses you are given in your Wellness Journal.**

Interviewing for a Job

If the employer thinks you might be a good prospect for employment, you will be called for an **interview**. This is a meeting with an employer during which both the employer and applicant get more information and perhaps reach a conclusion regarding the job.

The impression you make at the interview should continue the one you began in your application. You want to show that you are enthusiastic, qualified, and willing to work hard. You convey this by being on time, neatly groomed, and polite.

Interview Behavior

Although interviews can be stressful, try to relax. Let the interviewer direct the conversation. Show your interest in the job and familiarity with the company. Explain how you can help the company, and be prepared to answer questions such as, "What are your strengths and weaknesses?" Remember to phrase your answers in ways that will emphasize your abilities and qualifications. Ask questions about the nature of the job, but don't focus on money or benefits yet.

At the end of the interview, thank the interviewer and repeat your interest in the job. If you are not told whether you are being offered the job, ask when you may call to find out about the decision.

◆ **It is natural to feel a little nervous when going to a job interview. Think of the interview as an opportunity to visit a workplace, learn more about an interesting job, and meet new people. Describe how you should behave on an interview.**

Extending Learning

About Interviewing for a Job

- Most hiring decisions are made at the first interview. First impressions are important.
- Do not chew gum during the interview.
- As part of the interview, you may be asked to take some tests.
- After the interview, evaluate it. How did you perform? Did you answer the questions well? Did you get all the information you need? Were you dressed appropriately? Did you close the interview effectively? What can you do to improve?

After the Interview

When you get home, write the interviewer a note of thanks, again expressing your interest in the job. If you are offered the job, you have completed one step in reaching your career goals. Now you must work to continue making progress toward those goals.

If you don't get the job, you may politely ask why. Whatever the reason, use the interview as a learning experience.

On the Job

Once you have found a job, it is up to you to keep it. These tips can help you:

- ◆ Arrive on time and dress appropriately.
- ◆ Follow company rules, such as those about taking breaks and eating on the job.
- ◆ Pay attention when receiving instruction or training.
- ◆ Don't be afraid to ask questions about your responsibilities.
- ◆ Accept criticism and suggestions without resentment.
- ◆ Admit your mistakes and learn from them.
- ◆ Take pride in your work. Remember that even small jobs can make a big difference.

TAP-ping Your Strengths

According to a popular saying, "You get only one chance to make a first impression." To make a positive impression in a job interview, remember the *TAP* strategy:

- **(T)horoughness.** Learn all you can about the company, including the job you are applying for. Make up an interview packet. Include your resumé (if needed), a good pen, and a small notebook.
- **(A)ppearance.** Dress neatly. Avoid jeans, excessive makeup, and excessive jewelry. Go to the interview alone. Don't bring family members or friends.
- **(P)unctuality.** Be sure to arrive on time. Write down the time and place of the interview. Be sure you know how to get there and how long the trip will take.

Following Up

- Suppose you have a job interview at a restaurant. Assess your appearance, including your hair length, neatness, and cleanliness; your fingernail length and cleanliness; and any facial rings or tattoos. What changes, if any, would you make?

Working Ethically

Job success also depends on ethics. Ethics are moral principles and values that guide people's actions. With high ethical standards, people are honest. They make decisions at home, school, and work according to what is right. People who behave ethically do not steal, cheat, or lie. They show respect for others and their property.

In the workplace ethical behavior means certain things. It means that employees work hard and do their best. They do not steal money, equipment, or supplies, including software, from an employer or coworkers. They communicate truthfully to customers and on expense reports. They don't read or listen to private communications.

An employee who is unethical risks loss of job and reputation, and possibly even legal charges. Behaving ethically is a far better choice, because it earns admiration, reward, and a clear conscience.

- *On the Job (text pages 689-690)*

Writing

Ask students to write a short essay on how people in their age group can balance the demands of school, work, and family life. Within their essays, have them include the importance of good stress management skills. L1

FOR YOUR HEALTH

Ask one student pair to perform a skit of a poor interview, and another pair to perform a skit of a good interview. Have all students evaluate each skit interview using the *TAP* strategy.

Critical Thinking Activity

Ask students to identify good and poor ways to leave a job. What steps should you take to leave the job on good terms? What should you do if you are fired? Encourage lively class discussion.

Community Connection

Have students develop a list of opportunities for volunteer work in their community that could give them valuable job-related experience. Suggest that students share their findings. L1

Reinforcing Key Skills

Present the following problems to student groups. Allow time for them to discuss and compare their responses.

Leadership—Your younger brother has taken a summer job. After a week, he begins to go to work dressed sloppily and is often late. When confronted, he replies that it's "just a summer job." How do you respond?

Management—You've just been promoted to weekend assistant manager at a quick-service restaurant. You need to train new employees on how to help customers happy.

ASSESS

REVIEW

- Ask students to summarize the main ideas in this section.
- Have students complete the Section Review. (Answers appear below.)

EVALUATION

- Have students fill out a job application correctly and completely.
- Have students take the quiz for Section 25-2. (Use the quiz in the *Teacher Resource Guide,* or construct your own with the **Exam***View*® *Test Generator* on the *Effective Instruction CD-ROM.*)

RETEACHING

- Ask students to write a brief letter asking for a job interview. Discuss what they should say in the letter.
- Refer to the *Reteaching Activities* booklet for the Section 25-2 activity sheet.

CLOSE

Create a verse entitled: "Take this Job and Love It."

Leaving Your Job

When you end a job, try to leave with a good impression. Give at least two weeks notice in a brief but polite letter of resignation. You can mention your reasons for leaving, but avoid a negative tone. Offer thanks for the opportunities you've had. As your last day approaches, continue to do your best work. Leaving with a good impression counts if you decide to use the employer as a reference in the future.

If you are fired, find out why, and learn from the experience. Think about how you can improve your job performance the next time.

When you interview for a job, be honest about why you left your previous job. If you were fired, briefly explain the situation and your plans for preventing it from happening again. Employers are more willing to give a second chance to someone who seems eager to improve and change. When looking for the right employee, an employer values a positive attitude and commitment as well as skills.

◆ **A letter of resignation should be worded carefully. What might happen if you are very critical and angry toward your employer in your letter?**

Section 25-2 Review & Activities

1. Name six qualifications of a successful worker.
2. How are a job application form and a letter of application similar? How do they differ?
3. Give five suggestions for interviewing successfully.
4. How much notice should you give an employer before leaving a job?
5. **Extending.** Mount five newspaper job listings on paper. Beside each one, list qualities and skills that successful workers need for the job. Give specific examples and reasons for your selections.
6. **Applying.** Write one of the following letters: (a) letter of application for a job; (b) letter of resignation.
7. **Applying.** Demonstrate effective verbal communication skills by working with others to plan and present a skit based on one of the following situations: (a) someone is interviewing for a food-related job; (b) a job trainee makes several mistakes; (c) an employee gives a supervisor verbal notice of quitting.

Answers to Section 25-2 Review & Activities

1. Any six: communication; computer skills; critical thinking and problem solving; positive attitude; math; teamwork and self-responsibility; ability to learn.
2. Both tell about you, your education, and experience; both should focus on useful facts. Letter lets you choose what facts to include.
3. See pages 688-689.
4. At least two weeks.
5. Answers will vary.
6. Letters will vary.
7. Skits will vary.

Career Wanted

Restaurant Sales Representative

"My success depends on my customers' success."

Charles Maysch

Education and Training
- Degree in business or related field
- Corporate training program
- Knowledge of food service industry

Qualities
- Communication skills
- Outgoing personality
- Flexibility

Q. What aspect of sales are you involved in, Charles?

A. I represent a restaurant supplies manufacturer. We make and sell everything restaurants need to operate, from small wares to large equipment—from soup ladles to pizza ovens. We even have a staff of kitchen designers.

Q. Your job involves responsibility. Do you need a degree?

A. I have an associate's degree in management, which stressed accounting and computer skills. Also, my company has a training program to help sales reps understand the different products. If I were starting now, though, I'd get a bachelor's degree.

Q. So experience and personality count as much as technical knowledge?

A. I think so. Making sales takes persistence and belief in what you sell. That comes from knowing your product and your client well, so you can honestly say, "This is what I sell, and this is why you need it." You act almost as a consultant. Your client should be able to trust your judgment.

Related Career Opportunities

Entry Level
- Bus person
- Sales associate
- Product promoter

Technical Level
- Purchasing clerk
- Assistant copywriter

Professional Level
- Accounts director
- Promotion manager
- Market analyst

Making Career Connections

SELLING EXPERIENCE. Choose a food that you enjoy, or a useful item related to food or nutrition. If needed, research the item's special features and how it is made. Who would be most interested in the item? Plan a sales presentation for the product, aimed at a target audience. Give your presentation to the class.

Career Wanted

Restaurant Sales Representative

Thinking About the Career

Have students consider why it's important to be self-motivated for this career. Ask students to debate whether they think sales experience or restaurant/food knowledge is more critical to success in this line of work. Have students make a list of changes they may expect in the restaurant business in the next 20 years.

Career-Building Opportunities

Have interested students arrange, as a group, to visit a food service supply company.

For More Information

For additional information about careers in restaurant sales, encourage students to contact:

- International Council on Hotel, Restaurant, and Institutional Education (CHRIE)
  2613 North Parham Rd., 2nd Floor
  Richmond, VA 23294
  www.chrie.org
- National Restaurant Association
  1200 17th Street NW
  Washington, D.C. 20036-3097
  www.restaurant.org

REVIEW

- Have students complete the Chapter Review. (Answers appear below.)

EVALUATION

- Ask students to prepare a written plan for looking for a potential job for the upcoming summer. Where would they look, how would they get any required experience, and how would they apply?
- Have students take the test for Chapter 25. (Use the chapter test in the *Teacher Resource Guide,* or construct your own with the **Exam***View*® *Test Generator* on the *Effective Instruction CD-ROM.*)

ANSWERS

Checking Your Knowledge

1. More people eating out, consumers are more interested in the relationship between food and health, and the growing world population and other global factors.
2. Any six: communication skills, computer skills, critical thinking and problem solving, positive attitude, math skills, teamwork and self-responsibility, and ability to learn.
3. Answers can vary. Teaching: (any two) teach nutrition/foods classes in schools, colleges, universities; work for county regional extension services, government agencies, and/or health organization. Communications: (any two) food stylists; write speeches, articles, or advertisements about food products/services.
4. At least a bachelor's degree with a major in food science, food engineering, or food technology.
5. A person who runs his or her own business.
6. Not all franchises are reliable; it's not guaranteed to succeed.

Chapter 25 Review & Activities

Summary

Section 25-1: Career Opportunities

- Career opportunities in food and nutrition are growing and varied.
- Food service jobs include all those needed to prepare and serve food for the public. Food and consumer science specialists are needed to inform consumers about food, food choices, and related topics. Food scientists develop new foods and test foods for safety and quality. Dietitians help develop special diets for individuals or large groups. Many opportunities exist in food production, processing, and marketing.
- The food industry offers many options for entrepreneurs.
- The training and education needed for these careers varies.

Section 25-2: The Successful Worker

- Successful workers share certain qualities. They can communicate well, solve problems, and learn new things. They have a positive attitude and work well with others.
- Applying for a job may involve filling out an application form, writing a letter of application, and/or submitting a resumé.
- Interviews can be successful if you are relaxed, display a positive attitude, and show an interest in the job and a willingness to learn.
- Even deciding to leave a job or being fired can be a learning experience.

Working IN THE Lab

1. ***Computer Lab.*** Design and print a form that might be used by an entrepreneur in the food industry, such as an inventory report or an employee schedule.

2. ***Foods Lab.*** Suppose you are a dietitian working in an institution. Think of the special diets that might be needed by people in that setting. Create one such diet, and prepare one of your recipes.

3. ***Demonstration.*** Working in pairs, demonstrate how to successfully interview for a job. Have the rest of the class identify the positive points of the interview.

Checking Your Knowledge

1. Give three reasons for the expected job growth in food and nutrition.

2. Name six personal traits needed to succeed in food service.

3. Identify two career options for family and consumer scientists in teaching and two in communications.

4. What degrees and majors are needed to become a food scientist?

5. What is an entrepreneur?

6. Identify two risks of investing in a franchise.

7. Identify three instances when employees need good communication skills.

8. What is networking?

9. Give three tips for preparing for an interview.

10. Give four tips for being a valuable employee.

Review & Activities Chapter 25

Thinking Critically

1. Recognizing Stereotypes. You have accepted a summer job bussing tables in a local restaurant. You share your news with a friend, who comments that he thinks it's an unimportant, dead-end job. How do you respond?

2. Comparing and Contrasting. How might the training and communication skills needed by a family and consumer sciences teacher be similar to those needed by a family and consumer sciences professional in research and development? How might they differ?

3. Predicting Consequences. Paul and José work for the same catering firm. Lately, Paul has begun to grumble a lot about his responsibilities and often shows up late for work, asking José to cover for him. Paul's poor work habits are affecting his working relationship with José. What are some possible negative long-term consequences to the business if Paul's slacking off continues?

Reinforcing Key Skills

1. Directed Thinking. Jared has worked as a counselor at the same summer camp for three years in a row and has worked in a fast-food restaurant part-time. He has maintained a low B average through his school years. He has always been weak in math but strong in language arts. When applying for a job as a waiter in an exclusive French restaurant, what personal resources can Jared mention that will make him a candidate worth considering for the position?

2. Communication. Amanda, a high school student, is checking the help wanted ads for summer jobs. She has always enjoyed baking and would like to learn more about it, with an eye toward a possible career in this field one day. Most of the ads state that applicants must have prior job experience. Do you think Amanda should abandon her goal? If not, what would you advise her to do?

Making Decisions and Solving Problems

You have been working for almost a year as a cook in a fast-food restaurant, hoping to work your way up the career ladder. However, others who have been working at the restaurant less time than you have are being promoted ahead of you.

Making Connections

1. Economics. Interview at least two local entrepreneurs about the economic aspects of their businesses. What economic factors encouraged them to start their businesses? What social and economic trends affect their business decisions? What role do their businesses play in the local or national economy? Do they feel the economy is a good one now for starting a business? If so, what kind? Write a transcript or a summary of your interview, including an explanation of what you learned from it.

2. Social Studies. Trace the history of child labor and child labor laws in this country. At what jobs and under what conditions have children worked in the past? How have attitudes toward child labor changed over time? What circumstances led to the enactment of child labor laws? How do these laws protect children in the workplace? Are there any disadvantages to these laws? Share your findings in a short report to the class.

ANSWERS cont.

7. Write reports; read and understand company bulletins and guidelines; listen carefully to instructions received or to customer requests.
8. Making connections with people who can provide information about job openings.
9. Answers will vary. Prepare a resumé, have available references, find out about the company.
10. Answers will vary. (See bulleted list on page 689.)

Thinking Critically

1. Answers will vary. It's my first step of many towards a successful food-related career; I'll gain valuable experience.
2. Similar: Bachelor's degree. Differ: Those in research/development may require higher degrees; those in communication may have journalism or public relations backgrounds.
3. Answers will vary. Potential to lose clientele due to inability to produce high-quality food/work.

Reinforcing Key Skills

1. Answers will vary. Dedication, ability to work with others, restaurant experience, and communication/language skills.
2. Answers will vary. Advise her to bake for friends and family; take pictures of her baked products. Volunteer, if possible. Apply for jobs, and keep applying.

Glossary

A

aerobic (uh-ROH-buhk) exercise. Vigorous activity in which oxygen is continuously taken in for a period of at least 20 minutes. Activities including walking, jogging, bicycling, etc. (Section 5-3)

AIs. Stands for "Adequate Intake." Approximate nutrient measures set when an RDA cannot be established. (Section 2-1)

albumen (al-BYOO-muhn). A thick, clear fluid inside an egg; also known as egg white. (Section 18-3)

al dente (ahl DEN-tay). Term meaning firm to the bite, often referring to cooked pasta. (Section 17-2)

amino (uh-MEE-noh) acids. Chains of chemical building blocks from which proteins are made. (Section 2-2)

anabolic steroids (AN-uh-bahl-ik STEHR-oydz). Prescription medicines used to help build muscle strength in patients with chronic diseases. When used illegally, dangerous side effects can occur. (Section 5-4)

anaerobic (AN-uh-ROH-buhk) exercise. Exercise, which builds flexibility and endurance, involving intense bursts of activity in which the muscles work so hard that they produce energy without using oxygen. (Section 5-3)

analogues (AN-uh-logs). Foods made from a vegetable protein and processed to resemble animal foods. (Section 15-1)

annual percentage rate (APR). The yearly cost of a loan. (Section 14-1)

anorexia nervosa (an-uh-REK-see-yuh ner-VOH-suh). A type of eating disorder that involves an irresistible urge to lose weight through self-starvation. (Section 6-3)

antioxidants. Substances that protect body cells and the immune system from harmful chemicals in the air, certain foods, and tobacco smoke. (Section 2-4)

antipasto. Italian for "before the meal"; referring to appetizers. (Section 22-3)

appetite. A desire to eat. (Section 4-2)

aquaculture. A method of growing fish or seafood in enclosed areas of water. (Section 13-1)

arcing. Electrical sparks produced when metal is used in a microwave oven; can damage the oven or start a fire. (Section 9-4)

aromatic vegetables. Vegetables that add flavor to soups and other recipes; includes onions, garlic, celery, and green peppers. (Section 20-3)

assembly directions. The step-by-step procedure that explains how to put the ingredients in a recipe together. (Section 8-1)

au jus. Serving food with the pan drippings from which the fat has been skimmed. (Section 20-3)

B

bakeware. Equipment for cooking food in an oven. (Section 9-1)

basal metabolism (BAY-suhl muh-TAB-uh-lih-zuhm). Minimum amount of energy required to maintain the life processes in a living organism. (Section 2-5)

base. A foundation of greens for a salad. (Section 20-2)

behavior modification. Making gradual, permanent changes in your eating and activity habits. (Section 5-2)

berbere. A spicy combination of garlic, red and black peppers, salt, coriander, fenugreek, and cardamom. (Section 22-2)

bias. A tendency to be swayed toward a particular conclusion. (Section 3-3)

binder. A liquid that holds the other ingredients of a casserole together. (Section 20-4)

binge eating disorder. A type of eating disorder involving a lack of control while eating huge quantities of food at one time. (Section 6-3)

blanching. Partial cooking of food, usually vegetables, to kill enzymes. (Section 24-5)

body. Main part of the salad. (Section 20-2)

body mass index (BMI). Uses a ratio of weight and height. (Section 5-1)

bouillon (BOOL-yon). A simple, clear soup without solid ingredients. (Section 20-3)

bran. The edible, outer protective layers of a seed. (Section 17-1)

budget. Plan for managing money in order to cover the costs of life's necessities. (Section 11-3)

bulimia nervosa (byoo-LIM-ee-yuh ner-VOH-suh). A type of eating disorder that involves episodes of binge eating followed by purging. (Section 6-3)

bulk foods. Shelf-stable foods that are sold loose in covered bins or barrels. (Section 12-3)

C

calorie. The amount of energy needed to raise the temperature of 1 kilogram of water 1 degree Celsius. (Section 2-1)

carbohydrates (kar-boh-HY-drayts). Nutrients that are the body's main source of energy. (Section 2-1)

career. A profession or a life's work within a certain field. (Section 25-1)

certified nurse midwife. An advanced practice nurse who, in addition to providing prenatal care, specializes in the delivery of healthy babies. (Section 6-1)

chalazae (kuh-LAH-zuh). Twisted, cordlike strands of albumen which anchor the yolk in the center of the egg. (Section 18-3)

chlorophyll (KLOR-uh-fil). The chemical compound that plants use to turn the sun's energy into food. (Section 16-3)

cholesterol (kuh-LES-tuhr-ol). A fatlike substance present in all body cells that is needed for many essential body processes. (Section 2-3)

club sandwich. A sandwich made with three slices of toasted bread and filled with chicken or turkey breast, bacon, tomato, lettuce, and mayonnaise. (Section 20-1)

coagulate. To become firm. (Section 18-3)

code dating. A series of numbers or letters that indicate where and when the product was packaged. (Section 12-2)

colostrum (kuh-LAH-strum). A special form of thick, yellowish milk that is produced three days after birth and is rich in nutrients and antibodies. (Section 6-1)

comparison shop. Compare prices and characteristics of similar or like items to determine which offers the best value. (Section 12-3)

complete proteins. Proteins that supply all nine essential amino acids. (Section 2-2)

conduction. Heat transfer by direct contact. (Section 9-2)

conservation. Concern about and action taken to ensure the preservation of the environment. (Section 7-5)

contaminants. Harmful substances that accidentally get into food as it moves from the farm to the table. (Section 13-2)

continuous cleaning. An oven that has special rough interior walls that absorb spills and splatters. (Section 14-2)

convection. Transfer of heat by the movement of air or liquid. (Section 9-2)

convection current. A circular flow of air or liquid resulting from uneven heating. (Section 9-2)

cookware. Equipment for cooking food on top of the range. (Section 9-1)

cover. The arrangement of a place setting for one person. (Section 10-1)

CPR. Stands for cardiopulmonary resuscitation (KARD-ee-oh-PUL-muh-nayr-ee ree-SUS-uh-TAY-shun), a technique used to revive a person whose breathing and heartbeat have stopped. (Section 7-2)

credit. Money you borrow from a lender. (Section 14-1)

critical thinking. Examination of printed and spoken language in order to gain insights into meanings and interpretations. (Section 1-5).

cross-contamination. Letting microorganisms from one food get into another. (Section 7-3)

cruciferous (kroo-SIH-fur-uhs) **vegetables.** Vegetables in the cabbage family. (Section 16-1)

crustaceans. Shellfish that have long bodies with jointed limbs, covered with a shell; includes crabs, crayfish, lobsters, and shrimp. (Section 19-4)

cuisine. Styles of food preparation and cooking associated with a specific group or culture. (Section 22-1)

culture. The shared customs, traditions, and beliefs of a large group of people which defines a group's unique identity. (Section 1-2)

cultured. Fermented by a harmless bacteria added after pasteurization. (Section 18-1)

cut. A particular edible part of meat, poultry, or fish. (Section 19-1)

cut in. To mix solid fat and flour using a pastry blender or two knives and a cutting motion. (Section 21-2)

D

Daily Value (DV). A specific nutrition reference amount recommended by health experts. (Section 12-2)

deglazing. Adding stock or another liquid to a defatted sauté pan to loosen the browned-on particles. (Section 22-3)

dehydration (dee-hy-DRAY-shun). Lack of adequate fluids in the body. (Section 5-4)

desired yield. Number of servings you need. (Section 8-3)

developing nations. Countries that are not yet industrialized or are just beginning to become so. (Section 13-3)

diabetes. A condition in which the body cannot control blood sugar levels. (Section 6-2)

dietary fiber. A mixture of plant materials that is not broken down in the digestive system; necessary for good health. (Section 2-1)

dietary supplements. Nutrients taken in addition to foods eaten. (Section 6-2)

digestion. Process of breaking down food into usable nutrients. (Section 2-5)

doneness. Having cooked food long enough for the necessary changes to take place so that a cut tastes good and is safe to eat. (Section 19-5)

dovetail. To fit different tasks together smoothly. (Section 8-5)

DRIs. Stands for "Dietary Reference Intakes"; A series of standards for assessing nutrient needs among people of different age and gender groups. (Section 2-1)

drop biscuits. Biscuits made by dropping dough from a spoon. (Section 21-2)

dry heat cooking. Cooking food uncovered without added liquid or fat. (Section 9-3)

dry-packing. Leaving spaces between the pieces of food before placing it in the freezer. (Section 24-5)

E

eating disorder. An extreme, unhealthful behavior related to food, eating, and weight. (Section 6-3)

eating patterns. Food customs and habits, including when, what, and how much people eat. (Section 4-1)

electrolytes (ee-LEK-troh-lyts). Specific major minerals that work together to maintain the body's fluid balance; includes sodium, potassium, and chloride. (Section 2-4)

emulsion. An evenly blended mixture of two liquids that do not normally stay mixed. (Section 20-2)

endosperm. Food supply, made of protein, for a seed's embryo. (Section 17-1)

EnergyGuide label. Label on a large appliance that gives consumers information about estimated yearly energy costs. (Section 14-1)

en papillote (ehn pah-pee-YOHT). Cooking foods in parchment paper. (Section 24-1)

enrichment. A process in which some nutrients lost as a result of processing are added back to the product. (Section 17-1)

entrée (AHN-tray). The term used for main dishes on many restaurant menus. (Section 4-3)

entrepreneur (AHN-truh-pruh-NOOR). A person who runs his or her own business. (Section 25-1)

entry-level job. A job that requires little or no experience. (Section 25-1)

enzymatic (EN-zih-mat-ik) **browning.** Discoloration of fruits which results when the fruit is exposed to air. (Section 16-2)

equivalent. The same amount expressed in different ways by using different units of measure. (Section 8-2)

ergonomics. The study of ways to make tools and equipment easier and more comfortable to use. (Section 1-4)

esophagus (ih-SOFF-uh-gus). A long tube connecting the mouth to the stomach. (Section 2-5)

ethnic group. A cultural group based on common heritage. (Section 1-3)

extender. A food ingredient that helps thicken a dish. (Section 20-4)

F

fad diets. Popular weight-loss methods that ignore sound nutrition principles. (Section 5-2)

famine. Food shortages that continue for months or years, frequently resulting in starvation. (Section 13-3)

fats. A nutrient that provides a concentrated source of energy. (Section 2-1)

fat-soluble vitamins. Vitamins that are absorbed and transported by fat; includes vitamins A, D, E, and K. (Section 2-4)

fetus (FEE-tus). An unborn baby. (Section 6-1)

filé. Dried, crushed sassafras leaves used to thicken stews and add a delicate flavor. (Section 23-1)

finance charge. The total amount a person is charged for borrowing money; includes interest plus any service charges or insurance premiums. (Section 14-1)

foam cakes. Cakes that are leavened with beaten egg whites, which give them a light texture. (Section 21-4)

folding. A technique used to gently mix delicate ingredients. (Section 8-4)

food additives. Chemicals added to food to preserve freshness or enhance color and flavor. (Section 13-2)

food allergy. An abnormal, physical response to certain foods by the body's immune system. (Section 6-2)

food cooperatives. Food distribution organizations mutually owned and operated by a group of people. (Section 12-1)

Food Guide Pyramid. A pyramid-shaped food grouping system that is designed to help you choose a variety of foods in moderate amounts. (Section 3-2)

food safety. Following practices that help prevent foodborne illness and keep food safe to eat. (Section 7-3)

food science. The scientific study of food and its preparation. (Section 1-4)

food tolerance. A physical reaction to food not involving the immune system. (Section 6-2)

formed product. A food made from an inexpensive food source processed to resemble a more expensive one. (Section 15-1)

fortification. A process of adding 10 percent or more of the Daily Value for a specific nutrient to a product by the manufacturer. (Section 17-1)

franchise. An individually owned and operated branch of a business with an established name and guidelines. (Section 25-1)

freezer burn. A condition that results when food is improperly packaged or stored in the freezer too long; food dries out and loses flavor and texture. (Section 7-4)

frying. Cooking food in oil or melted fat. (Section 9-3)

G

garam masala. A complex blend of toasted and ground spices that most Indian recipes begin with. (Section 22-4)

garnish. Any small, colorful bit of food that is used to enhance the appearance and texture of a dish. (Section 24-1)

generic. Items produced without a commercial or store brand name which are less expensive and have a plain label. (Section 12-3)

genetic engineering. A method of enhancing specific natural tendencies of plants and animals. (Section 13-2)

germ. A tiny embryo in a seed that will grow into a new plant. (Section 17-1)

giblets (JIB-luhts). Edible poultry organs such as the liver, gizzard, and heart. (Section 19-3)

glucose (GLOO-kohs). The body's basic fuel supply. (Section 2-5)

gluten (GLOO-ten). A protein that affects the texture of a baking product. (Section 21-1)

glycogen (GLY-kuh-juhn). A storage form of glucose that is stored in the liver and the muscles. (Section 2-5)

gratuity (grah-TOO-uh-tee). Extra money given to a server in appreciation of good service; also known as a tip. (Section 10-2)

grazing. An eating pattern in which people eat five or more small meals throughout the day. (Section 4-1)

grounding. A method of minimizing the risk of electrical shock by providing a path for current to travel back through the electrical system. (Section 14-3)

H

haute cuisine. Literally means "high cooking"; a method of food preparation that makes use of complicated recipes and techniques. (Section 22-3)

HDL. Stands for "high-density lipoprotein"; a chemical that picks up excess cholesterol and takes it back to the liver, keeping it from causing harm. (Section 2-3)

headspace. In canning, the space between the top of the food and the rim of the jar. (Section 24-5)

heating units. Energy sources in ranges used to heat foods. (Section 9-1)

Heimlich maneuver. Technique used to rescue victims of choking. (Section 7-2)

herbal remedies. Nonstandardized products containing herbs known to have medicinal-like qualities. (Section 6-2)

hibachi. A small charcoal grill. (Section 23-2)

high tea. A meal when tea is served with a nonsweet dish that is somewhere between an appetizer and a main course; originated in England. (Section 22-3)

HIV/AIDS. A disorder that interferes with the immune system's ability to combat disease-causing pathogens. (Section 6-2)

home-meal replacement. A term used by the food service industry that refers to take-out or carry-out meals. (Section 4-3)

homogenization. The process whereby fat is broken down and evenly distributed in milk. (Section 18-1)

hot-pack. A method of filling jars for canning. The food is first heated in liquids and then packed into jars. (Section 24-5)

hot spot. An area of concentrated heat. (Section 9-4)

hydrogenation (hy-DRAH-juh-NAY-shun). A process in which missing hydrogen atoms are added to an unsaturated fat to make it firmer in texture. (Section 2-3)

hydroponic (high-druh-PAH-nik) farming. Using nutrient-enriched water to grow plants without soil. (Section 13-1)

I

impulse buying. Buying items you didn't plan to purchase and don't really need because it seems appealing at the time. (Section 12-1)

incomplete proteins. Proteins lacking one or more essential amino acids; foods from plant sources provide incomplete proteins. (Section 2-2)

industrialized nations. Countries that rely on a sophisticated, organized food industry to supply their citizens with food. Also called "developed countries." (Section 13-3)

infuser. A small container with tiny holes that let water in but don't allow tea leaves to come out. (Section 24-2)

insoluble fiber. A type of fiber that will not dissolve in water but will absorb water; helps move waste through the digestive system. (Section 2-2)

interest. The amount of money a lender charges as a fee for the loan; equals a specific percentage of the amount borrowed. (Section 14-1)

interview. A meeting with a potential employer in which both the employer and applicant get more information and perhaps reach a conclusion regarding the job. (Section 25-2)

inventory. Ongoing record of the food stored in the freezer. (Section 7-4)

irradiation. Process of exposing food to gamma rays to increase its shell life and kill harmful microorganisms. (Section 13-2)

island. A freestanding unit, often in the center of a kitchen. (Section 14-3)

J K L

julienne. Long, thin strips of food. (Section 24-1)

kibbutz (kee-BOOTS). An Israeli communal organization that raises its own food. (Section 22-2)

knead. To work dough with your hands to thoroughly mix ingredients and develop gluten. (Section 21-1)

lacto-ovo vegetarians. People who eat foods from plant sources, dairy products, and eggs. (Section 4-4)

lacto vegetarians. People who eat dairy products in addition to foods from plant sources. (Section 4-4)

LDL. Stands for "low-density lipoprotein"; a chemical that takes cholesterol from the liver to wherever it is needed in the body. (Section 2-3)

leavening agent. A substance that triggers a chemical action causing a baked product to rise. (Section 21-1)

legumes. Plants whose seeds grow in pods that split along both sides when ripe; includes dry beans and peas, lentils, and peanuts. (Section 17-3)

life span. Constant progression from one stage of development to the next. Stages include prenatal period, infancy, childhood, adolescence, and adulthood. (Section 6-1)

life-span design. A design approach in which living space is adapted to the needs of people of various ages and degrees of physical ability. (Section 14-3)

lifestyle. A person's typical way of life, which includes how you spend your time and what is important to you. (Section 1-2)

lifestyle activities. Forms of physical activity that are a normal part of your daily routine or recreation that promote good health throughout a lifetime. (Section 5-3)

lifestyle diseases. Illnesses that relate to how a person lives and the choices he or she makes. Examples include high blood pressure, heart disease, stroke, diabetes, and certain kinds of cancer. (Section 3-1)

M

maize. Corn; a staple crop in many countries. (Section 22-1)

major appliance. A large device that gets its energy from electricity or gas. (Section 7-1)

major minerals. Minerals needed in relatively large amounts. (Section 2-4)

malnutrition. Serious health problems caused by poor nutrition over a prolonged period of time. (Section 2-1)

management. Specific techniques that help you use resources wisely. (Section 1-5)

manufactured food. A product developed to serve as a substitute for another food. (Section 15-1)

marbling. Small white flecks of internal fat that may appear within the muscle tissue of meat. (Section 19-1)

marinades (MAR-uh-nayds). Flavorful liquids in which food is steeped. (Section 19-5)

marinating. A method of tenderizing and adding flavor to foods before you cook them by steeping the foods in a liquid. (Section 19-5)

mature fruits. Fruits that have reached their full size and color. (Section 16-1)

meal appeal. Characteristics that make a meal appetizing and enjoyable. (Section 11-1)

media. A multitude of communication sources, including television, radio, movies, newspapers, magazines, advertisements, and the Internet. (Section 2-1)

medical nutrition therapy. An assessment of the nutritional status of a patient with a condition. (Section 6-2)

megadose (MEH-guh-dohs). An extra-large amount of a supplement thought to prevent or cure diseases. (Section 6-2)

meringue (muhr-ANG). A foam made of beaten egg whites and sugar. (Section 18-4).

micro-grill. A cooking method that combines microwaving and grilling. (Section 24-4)

microorganisms. Tiny living creatures, such as bacteria, visible only through a microscope. (Section 7-3)

minerals. Nonliving substances that help the body work properly and may become part of body tissues. (Section 2-1)

moderation. Avoiding extremes, such as eating adequate amounts of a variety of foods. (Section 3-1)

modified English service. A method of food service in which dinner plates and the food for the main course are brought to the table in serving dishes and placed in front of the host. (Section 24-3)

moist heat cooking. Method in which food is cooked in hot liquid, steam, or a combination of both. (Section 9-3)

mollusks. Shellfish with soft bodies that are covered by at least one shell such as clams, mussels, oysters, scallops, and squid. (Section 19-4)

monounsaturated (MAH-no-un-SAT-chur-ay-ted) **fatty acids.** Fats that appear to lower LDL cholesterol levels and may help raise levels of HDL. (Section 2-3)

mulled. Beverages that are served hot and flavored with sweet spices. (Section 24-2)

N

net weight. The weight of the food itself, not including the packaging. (Section 12-2)

networking. Making connections with people who can provide information about job openings. (Section 25-2)

nutrient deficiency. A nutrient shortage. (Section 2-1)

nutrient-dense. Describes foods that are low or moderate in calories yet rich in important nutrients. (Section 3-2)

nutrients. Chemicals from food that your body uses to carry out its functions. (Section 1-1)

nutrition. The study of nutrients and how they are used by the body. (Section 1-1)

O

obese (oh-BEESE). A term that means having excess body fat. (Section 5-1)

obstetrician (ob-stuh-TRISH-un). A physician who specializes in pregnancy. (Section 6-1)

open dating. A practice in which a date is stamped directly on the product for the benefit of the consumer, such as a "sell by" or expiration date. (Section 12-2)

osteoporosis (AH-stee-oh-puh-ROH-sis). A condition in which bones lose their minerals and become porous, making them weak and fragile. (Section 2-4)

over-the-counter drugs. Drugs that can be obtained without a prescription. (Section 5-2)

overweight. Weighing more than 10 percent over the standard weight for one's height. (Section 5-2)

ovo vegetarians. People who eat eggs in addition to foods from plant sources. (Section 4-4)

oxidation (AHKS-ih-day-shuhn). A process in which fuel is combined with oxygen to produce energy. (Section 2-5)

P

pare. To cut a very thin layer of peel or outer coating of a food. (Section 8-4)

pasteurized. A heat treatment that kills enzymes and harmful bacteria. (Section 18-1)

pediatrician. A physician who cares for infants and children. (Section 6-1)

pemmican. Dried meat, pounded into a paste with fat and preserved in cakes. (Section 23-1)

peninsula. An extension of a countertop. (Section 14-3)

peristalsis (PEHR-uh-STAHL-suhs). A series of wavelike movements that force food into the stomach. (Section 2-5)

place setting. Pieces of tableware used by one person to eat a meal. (Section 10-1)

phytochemical. A disease-fighting nutrient found in plant foods. (Section 2-4)

poaching. Simmering whole foods in a small amount of liquid until done. (Section 9-3)

polarized plugs. Electrical plugs made with one plug wider than the other and designed to fit in the outlet in only one way as a safety measure. (Section 7-2)

polenta. A cornmeal mush that is sometimes cooled, sliced, and fried. (Section 22-3)

polyunsaturated (Pah-lee-un-SAT-chur-ay-ted) **fatty acids.** Fats that seem to help lower cholesterol levels. (Section 2-3)

preheating. Turning the oven on about 10 minutes before using it so that it will be at the desired temperature when the food is placed inside. (Section 9-3)

pre-preparation. Refers to tasks done before assembling the actual recipe. (Section 8-5)

principal. The amount of money that is borrowed from a lender. (Section 14-1)

proteins. Nutrients that help build, repair, and maintain body tissues; also a source of energy. (Section 2-1)

psychological (sy-kuh-LAH-jih-kul). Having to do with the mind and emotions. (Section 1-1)

purée. To make food smooth and thick by putting it through a strainer, blender, or food processor. (Section 8-4)

Q

quiche (KEESH). A pie with a custard filling that contains foods such as chopped vegetables, cheese, and chopped cooked meat. (Section 18-4)

quick-mix method. A bread-making method that combines active dry yeast with the dry ingredients. (Section 21-3)

R

radiation. A heat transfer method that uses infrared rays to strike and warm an object. (Section 9-2)

raw-pack. In canning, placing the raw foods into jars and then pouring in hot syrup, liquid, or juice. (Section 24-5)

RDAs. Stands for "Recommended Daily Allowances"; the amount of a nutrient needed by 98 percent of the people in a given age and gender group. (Section 2-1).

rebate. A partial refund from the manufacturer of a purchased good. (Section 12-1)

recall. The immediate removal of a product from store shelves and the notification of the public through the media by the government or the manufacturer. (Section 13-2)

receptions. Social gatherings usually held to honor a person or an event. (Section 24-3)

recipe. A set of directions for preparing a food or beverage. (Section 8-1)

reconstitute. To add back the liquid in a food that was removed in processing. (Section 15-2)

recycling. The treating of waste so that it can be reused; an awareness of such practices. (Section 7-5)

references. People who know you well and can give you information about your previous work or your character. (Section 25-2)

refined sugars. Sugars that are extracted from plants and used as a sweetener. (Section 2-2)

reservation. An arrangement made ahead of time for a table at a restaurant. (Section 10-2)

resource. An object and quality that can help you reach a goal; includes time, money, skills, knowledge, and equipment. (Section 1-2)

resumé (REH-zoo-may). A written summary of your experience, skills, and achievements that are related to the job you seek. (Section 25-2)

retail cuts. The smaller cuts of meat from wholesale cuts found in the supermarket. (Section 19-2)

ripe fruits. Fruits that are tender and have a pleasant aroma and fully developed flavor. (Section 16-1)

ripened cheese. Aged cheese that is made from curds to which ripening agents—bacteria, mold, yeast, or a combination of these—have been added. (Section 18-1)

rolled biscuits. Biscuits made by rolling out dough to an even thickness and cutting it. (Section 21-2)

roux (ROO). A blending of equal parts of flour and fat. (Section 20-3)

S

saturated (SAT-chur-ay-ted) **fatty acids.** Fats that appear to raise the LDL cholesterol in the blood stream. (Section 2-3)

sauté (saw-TAY). To brown or cook foods in a skillet with a small amount of fat. (Section 9-3)

scalded milk. Milk that is heated to just below the boiling point. (Section 18-2)

scones. A variation of baking-powder biscuits; popular in parts of Britain. (Section 22-3)

score. To make shallow, straight cuts in the surface of a food. (Section 8-4)

seasoning blends. Convenient combinations of herbs and spices; examples are chili powder and Italian seasoning. (Section 24-1)

self-cleaning. An oven with a special cleaning cycle using high heat to burn off food stains. (Section 14-2)

serrated. Refers to a knife with sawtooth notches along the edge of its blade. (Section 8-4)

service contract. Repair and maintenance insurance purchased to cover a product for a specific length of time. (Section 14-1)

service plate. A large, decorative plate used for the first course of a formal meal. (Section 24-3)

serving pieces. Platters, large bowls, and other tableware used for serving food. (Section 10-1)

sharpening steel. A long, steel rod on a handle used to help keep knives sharp. (Section 8-4)

shelf life. The length of time food can be stored and still retain its quality. (Section 7-4)

shelf-stable. Foods that will last for weeks or even months at room temperatures below 85°F (29°C). (Section 7-4)

shirred eggs. Baked eggs. (Section 18-3)

skinfold calipers. A device that pinches the skin to measure body fat. (Section 5-1)

shortened cakes. Cakes usually made with a solid fat. (Section 21-4)

small appliance. A small electrical household device used to perform simple tasks such as mixing, chopping, and cooking. (Section 7-1)

smoking point. A temperature at which fat begins to smoke and break down chemically. (Section 9-3)

soba. Buckwheat noodles. (Section 22-4)

soluble fiber. Dietary fiber that dissolves in water; may help lower blood cholesterol levels. (Section 2-2)

soufflé (soo-FLAY). A dish made by folding stiffly beaten egg whites into a sauce or batter, and then baking the mixture in a deep casserole until it puffs up. (Section 18-4)

sourdough starter. A mixture of flour, water, and salt on which wild yeast cells grow. (Section 23-2)

spores. Cells that will develop into bacteria if conditions are right. (Section 7-3)

standing time. Period during which heat build-up in a microwaved food completes its cooking. (Section 9-4)

staple foods. Foods that make up a region's basic food supply. (Section 13-3)

staples. Items used on a regular basis such as flour and honey. (Section 12-1)

steep. To brew in water just before the boiling point. (Section 24-2)

stewing. To cover small pieces of food with liquid, then simmer until done. (Section 9-3)

stock. A clear, thin liquid made by simmering water flavored with the bones of meat, poultry, or fish, plus aromatic vegetables and seasonings. (Section 20-3)

store brands. Brands specially produced for the store; also called "private labels." (Section 12-3)

stress. Physical or mental tension triggered by an event or situation in your life. (Section 6-2)

study design. The approach used by researchers to investigate a claim. (Section 3-3)

subsistence farming. Practice of maintaining a small plot of land on which a family grows its own food. (Section 13-3)

sustainable farming. The cutting back on, or elimination of, chemicals in farming. (Section 13-1)

T

table etiquette. Courtesy shown by good manners at a meal. (Section 10-2)

tableware. Includes any items used for serving and eating foods. (Section 10-1)

task lighting. Bright, shadow-free light over specific work areas. (Section 14-3)

technology. The practical application of scientific knowledge. (Section 1-2)

texture. Way food feels when you chew it. (Section 11-1)

tolerance levels. Maximum safe levels for certain chemicals in the human body. (Section 13-2)

toxins. Poisons produced by bacteria. (Section 7-3)

trace minerals. Minerals needed in very small amounts. (Section 2-4)

tuber. A large underground stem that stores nutrients. (Section 16-1)

U

underweight. Weighing 10 percent or more below the standard weight for one's height. (Section 5-2)

unit price. An item's price per ounce, quart, pound, or other unit of measurement. (Section 12-3)

unripened cheese. Cheese made from curds that have not been aged. (Section 18-1)

UPC. Universal Product Code. A bar code on food labels and other products; it carries coded information that can be read by a scanner. (Section 12-2)

utensils. Tools or containers used for specific tasks in food preparation. Examples include measuring cups, peelers, and cookware. (Section 7-1)

V

vacuum bottle. A glass or metal bottle with a vacuum space between the outer container and the inner liner; used to keep food hot. (Section 20-1)

variety meats. Edible animal organs. (Section 19-2)

vegans (VEE-guns or VEH-juns). Also known as pure vegetarians. People who eat only food from plant sources, such as grain products, dry beans and peas, fruits, vegetables, nuts, and seeds. (Section 4-4)

vegetarians. People who do not eat meat, poultry, or fish; some do not eat dairy foods or eggs. (Section 4-4)

versatility. Capability of being adapted to many uses. (Section 11-2)

vitamins. Chemicals in food that help regulate many vital body processes and aid other nutrients in doing their jobs. (Section 2-1)

volume. The amount of three-dimensional space something takes up. (Section 8-2)

W

waist-to-hip ratio. A measure of how fat is distributed in the body. (Section 5-1)

warranty. Manufacturer's written guarantee that a product will perform as advertised; it will repair or replace the product that does not perform properly. (Section 14-1)

water-soluble vitamins. Vitamins that dissolve in water and pass easily into the bloodstream in the process of digestion; include B vitamins and vitamin C. (Section 2-4)

watts. Units by which electrical power is measured. (Section 9-4)

wellness. A philosophy that encourages people to take responsibility for their own physical, emotional, and mental health. (Section 1-1)

whisk. A balloon-shaped device made of wire loops held together by a handle which is used for mixing, stirring, beating, and whipping. (Section 8-4)

white sauce. A milk-based sauce thickened with a starch. (Section 20-3)

whole grain. The entire grain kernel. (Section 17-1)

wholesale cuts. Large cuts of meat for marketing; also called primal cuts. (Section 19-2)

WIC program. Stands for "Women, Infants, and Children"; a government-sponsored program designed to improve the health of low-income pregnant and breast-feeding women, infants, and children up to five years of age. (Section 11-3)

wok. A special bowl-shaped pan used for stir-frying. (Section 9-3)

work center. An area in the kitchen designed for specific tasks; includes equipment needed for the task and adequate storage and work space. (Section 7-1)

work flow. Recurring patterns of activities and repetitive tasks associated with any type of job routine. (Section 14-3)

work plan. A list of all the tasks required to complete a recipe and an estimate of how long each task will take. (Section 8-5)

X Y Z

yield. Number of servings or the amount a recipe makes. (Section 8-1)

Appendix A

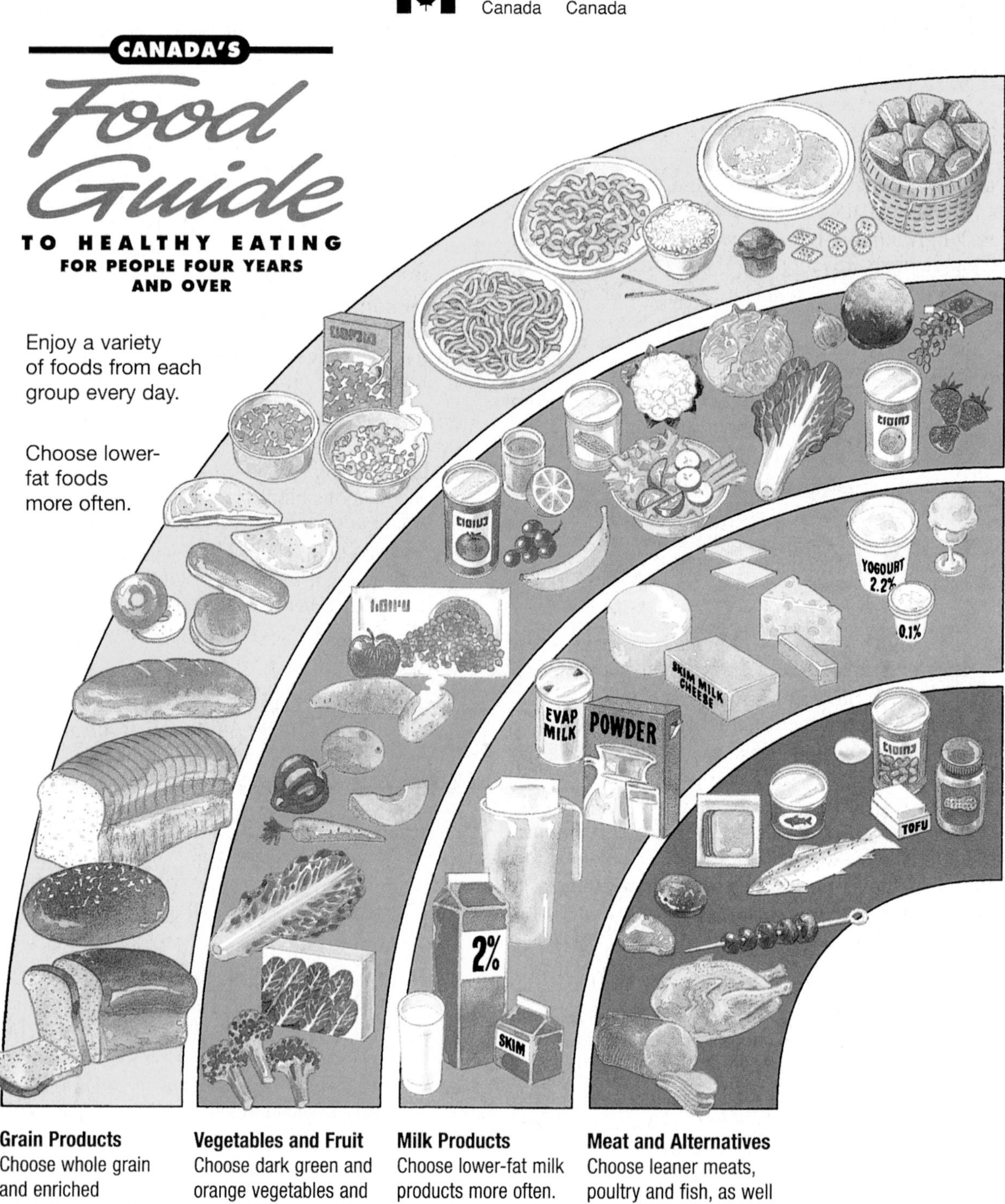

Health Canada
Santé Canada
CANADA'S
Food Guide
TO HEALTHY EATING
FOR PEOPLE FOUR YEARS AND OVER
Enjoy a variety of foods from each group every day.
Choose lower-fat foods more often.
YOGOURT 2.2%
0.1%
SKIM MILK CHEESE
EVAP MILK
POWDER
2%
SKIM
TOFU
Grain Products
Choose whole grain and enriched products more often.
Vegetables and Fruit
Choose dark green and orange vegetables and orange fruit more often.
Milk Products
Choose lower-fat milk products more often.
Meat and Alternatives
Choose leaner meats, poultry and fish, as well as dried peas, beans and lentils more often.

Canada

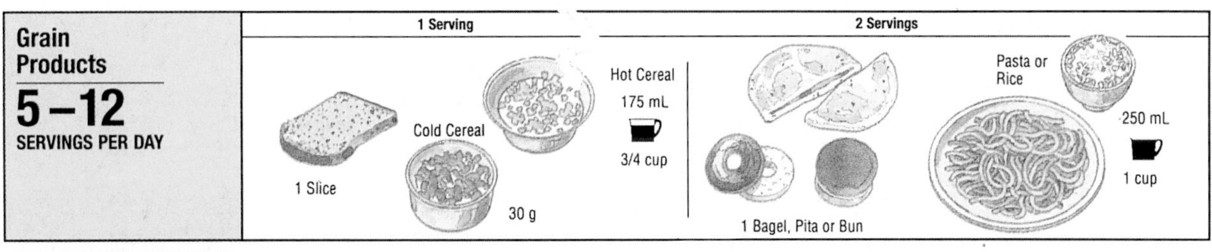

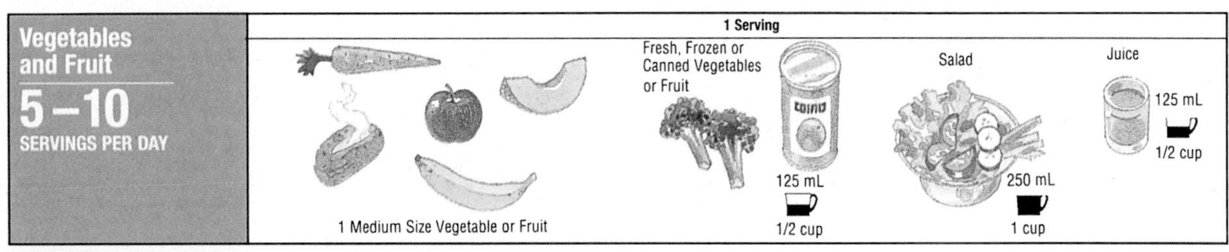

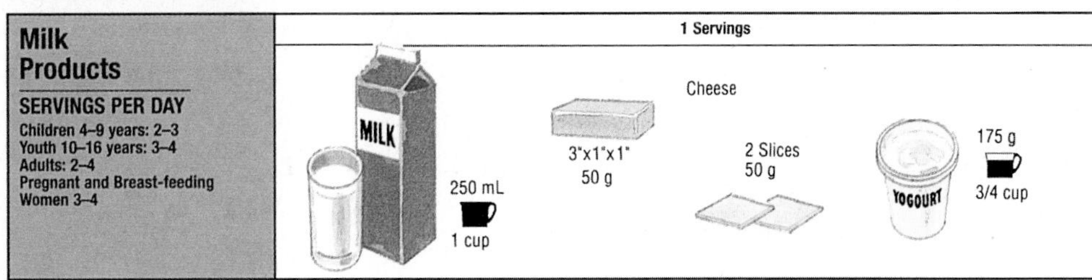

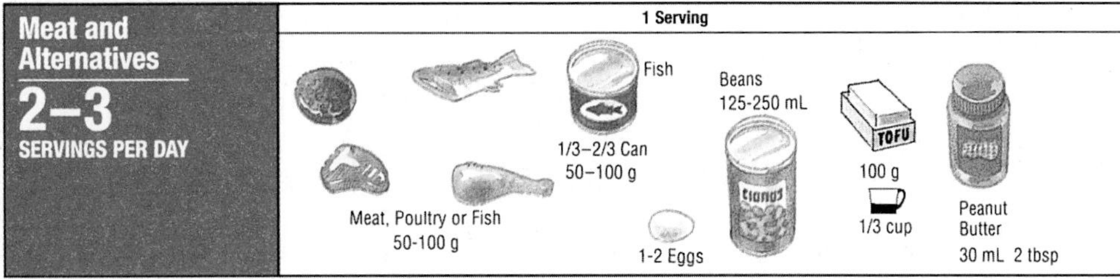

Other Foods

Taste and enjoyment can also come from other foods and beverages that are not part of the 4 food groups. Some of these foods are higher in fat or Calories, so use these foods in moderation.

Different People Need Different Amounts of Food

The amount of food you need every day from the 4 food groups and other foods depends on your age, body size, activity level, whether you are male or female and if you are pregnant or breast-feeding. That's why the Food Guide gives a lower and higher number of servings for each food group. For example, young children can choose the lower number of servings, while male teenagers can go to the higher number. Most other people can choose servings somewhere in between.

Enjoy eating well, being active and feeling good about yourself. That's VITALIT

Cat. No. H39-252/1992E ISBN 0-662-19648-1

Appendix B: Nutritive Value of Foods

Item No.	Food Description	Approximate Measure	Weight	Food energy	Protein	Fat	Cholesterol	Calcium	Iron	Sodium	Vitamin A value*	Vitamin C
				Nutrients in Indicated Quantity								
			Grams	Calories	Grams	Grams	Milligrams	Milligrams	Milligrams	Milligrams	Retinol equivalents	Milligrams
	Beverages											
9	Club soda	12 fl oz	355	0	0	0	0	18	Tr	78	0	0
10	Regular cola	12 fl oz	369	160	0	0	0	11	0.2	18	0	0
11	Diet, artificially sweetened cola	12 fl oz	355	Tr	0	0	0	14	0.2	32	0	0
20	Fruit punch drink	6 fl oz	190	85	Tr	0	0	15	0.4	15	2	61
	Dairy Products											
	Natural Cheese:											
32	Cheddar, cut pieces	1 oz	28	115	7	9	30	204	0.2	176	86	0
38	Cottage cheese, lowfat (2%)	1 cup	226	205	31	4	19	155	0.4	918	45	Tr
43	Mozzarella, part skim milk	1 oz	28	80	8	5	15	207	0.1	150	54	0
46	Parmesan, grated	1 tbsp	5	25	2	2	4	69	Tr	93	9	0
52	Pasteurized process American cheese	1 oz	28	105	6	9	27	174	0.1	406	82	0
	Milk, fluid:											
78	Whole (3.3% fat)	1 cup	244	150	8	8	33	291	0.1	120	76	2
79	Lowfat (2%)	1 cup	244	120	8	5	18	297	0.1	122	139	2
83	Nonfat (skim)	1 cup	245	85	8	Tr	4	302	0.1	126	149	2
85	Buttermilk	1 cup	245	100	8	2	9	285	0.1	257	20	2
88	Evaporated skim milk	1 cup	255	200	19	1	9	738	0.7	293	298	3
91	Dried, nonfat, instantized	1 cup	68	245	24	Tr	12	837	0.2	373	483	4
	Milk beverages:											
94	Chocolate milk, lowfat (1%)	1 cup	250	160	8	3	7	287	0.6	152	148	2
105	Shakes, thick: Vanilla	10 oz	283	315	11	9	33	413	0.3	270	79	0
	Milk desserts, frozen:											
	Ice cream, vanilla, regular (about 11% fat):											
107	Hardened	1 cup	133	270	5	14	59	176	0.1	116	133	1
109	Soft serve (frozen custard)	1 cup	173	375	7	23	153	236	0.4	153	199	1
	Ice cream, vanilla, low-fat:											
113	Hardened (about 4% fat)	1 cup	131	185	5	6	18	176	0.2	105	52	1
116	Sherbet (about 2% fat)	1 cup	193	270	2	4	14	103	0.3	88	39	4
	Yogurt, made with lowfat milk:											
117	Fruit-flavored	8 oz	227	230	10	2	10	345	0.2	133	25	1
118	Plain	8 oz	227	145	12	4	14	415	0.2	159	36	2

Eggs												
	Eggs, large (24 oz. per dozen):											
	Cooked:											
124	Fried in margarine	1 egg	46	90	6	7	211	25	0.7	162	114	0
125	Hard-cooked, shell removed	1 egg	50	75	6	5	213	25	0.6	62	84	0
Fats and Oils												
129	Butter (4 sticks per lb) (⅛ stick)	1 tbsp	14	100	Tr	11	31	3	Tr	116	106	0
138	Margarine (⅛ stick)	1 tbsp	14	100	Tr	11	0	4	Tr	132	139	Tr
147	Corn oil	1 cup	218	1,925	0	218	0	0	0.0	0	0	0
	Salad dressings, commercial:											
162	French, Regular	1 tbsp	16	85	Tr	9	0	2	Tr	188	Tr	Tr
163	French, Low calorie	1 tbsp	16	25	Tr	2	0	6	Tr	306	Tr	Tr
Fish and Shellfish												
177	Fish sticks, frozen, reheated, (stock, 4 by 1 by ½ in.)	1 fish stick	28	70	6	3	26	11	0.3	53	5	0
181	Haddock, breaded, fried	3 oz	85	175	17	9	75	34	1.0	123	20	0
182	Halibut, broiled, with butter and lemon juice	3 oz	85	140	20	6	62	14	0.7	103	174	1
195	Tuna, canned, oil pack, chunk light	3 oz	85	165	24	7	55	7	1.6	303	20	0
196	Tuna, canned, water pack, solid white	3 oz	85	135	30	1	48	17	0.6	468	32	0
Fruits and Fruit Juices												
198	Apples, raw, unpeeled, 2¾-in. diam.	1 apple	138	80	Tr	Tr	0	10	0.2	Tr	7	8
202	Apple juice, bottled or canned	1 cup	248	115	Tr	Tr	0	17	0.9	7	Tr	2
204	Applesauce, canned, unsweetened	1 cup	244	105	Tr	Tr	0	7	0.3	5	7	3
215	Bananas, raw, without peel, whole	1 banana	114	105	1	1	0	7	0.4	1	9	10
229	Fruit cocktail, canned, juice pack	1 cup	248	115	1	Tr	0	20	0.5	10	76	7
230	Grapefruit, raw, without peel, 3¾-in. diam.	½ grapefruit	120	40	1	Tr	0	14	0.1	Tr	1	41
233	Grapefruit juice, canned, unsweetened	1 cup	247	95	1	Tr	0	17	0.5	2	2	72
237	Grapes, Thompson Seedless	10 grapes	50	35	Tr	Tr	0	6	0.1	1	4	5
239	Grape juice, canned or bottled	1 cup	253	155	1	Tr	0	23	0.6	8	2	Tr
242	Kiwi fruit, raw, without skin	1 kiwifruit	76	45	1	Tr	0	20	0.3	4	13	74
250	Mangos, raw, without skin and seed	1 mango	207	135	1	1	0	21	0.3	4	806	57
251	Cantaloupe, orange-fleshed, 5-in. diam.	½ melon	267	95	2	1	0	29	0.6	24	861	113
253	Nectarines, raw, without pits	1 nectarine	136	65	1	1	0	7	0.2	Tr	100	7
254	Oranges, raw, whole	1 orange	131	60	1	Tr	0	52	0.1	Tr	27	70
260	Orange juice, frozen concentrate, diluted	1 cup	249	110	2	Tr	0	22	0.2	2	19	97
262	Papayas, raw, ½-in. cubes	1 cup	140	65	1	Tr	0	35	0.3	9	40	92
263	Peaches, raw, whole, 2½-in. diam.	1 peach	87	35	1	Tr	0	4	0.1	Tr	47	6
273	Pears, raw, with skin, cored, Bartlett, 2½-in. diam.	1 pear	166	100	1	1	0	18	0.4	Tr	3	7
283	Pineapple, chunks or tidbits, juice pack	1 cup	250	150	1	Tr	0	35	0.7	3	10	24
287	Plantains, without peel, cooked, boiled, sliced	1 cup	154	180	1	Tr	0	3	0.9	8	140	17
288	Plums, raw, 2⅛-in. diam.	1 plum	66	35	1	Tr	0	3	0.1	Tr	21	6
297	Raisins, seedless, cup, not pressed down	1 cup	145	435	5	1	0	71	3.0	17	1	5

Item No.	Food Description	Approximate Measure	Weight	Food energy	Protein	Fat	Cholesterol	Calcium	Iron	Sodium	Vitamin A value*	Vitamin C
				Nutrients in Indicated Quantity								
			Grams	Calories	Grams	Grams	Milligrams	Milligrams	Milligrams	Milligrams	Retinol equivalents	Milligrams
303	Strawberries, raw, capped, whole	1 cup	149	45	1	1	0	21	0.6	1	4	84
309	Watermelon, 4 by 8 in. wedge	1 piece	482	155	3	2	0	39	0.8	10	176	46
	Grain Products											
311	Bagels, plain or water, enriched	1 bagel	68	200	7	2	0	29	1.8	245	0	0
314	Biscuits, from mix, 2-in. diam.	1 biscuit	28	95	2	3	Tr	58	0.7	262	4	Tr
	Breads:											
319	Cracked-wheat bread (18 per loaf)	1 slice	25	65	2	1	0	16	0.7	106	Tr	Tr
332	Pita bread, enriched, white, 6½-in. diam.	1 pita	60	165	6	1	0	49	1.4	339	0	0
346	White bread, enriched (18 per loaf)	1 slice	25	65	2	1	0	32	0.7	129	Tr	Tr
353	Whole-wheat bread (16 per loaf)	1 slice	28	70	3	1	0	20	1.0	180	Tr	Tr
355	Bread stuffing, dry type, from mix	1 cup	140	500	9	31	0	92	2.2	1,254	273	0
	Breakfast cereals:											
359	Cream of Wheat®, cooked	1 cup	244	140	4	Tr	0	54	10.9	5	0	0
367	Cheerios®	1 oz	28	110	4	2	0	48	4.5	307	375	15
368	Kellogg's® Corn Flakes	1 oz	28	110	2	Tr	0	1	1.8	351	375	15
383	Shredded Wheat	1 oz	28	100	3	1	0	11	1.2	3	0	0
386	Sugar Frosted Flakes, Kellogg's®	1 oz	28	110	1	Tr	0	1	1.8	230	375	15
390	Wheaties®	1 oz	28	100	3	Tr	0	43	4.5	354	375	15
	Cakes prepared from cake mixes:											
394	Angelfood, 1/12 of cake	1 piece	53	125	3	Tr	0	44	0.2	269	0	0
396	Coffeecake, crumb, 1/6 of cake	1 piece	72	230	5	7	47	44	1.2	310	32	Tr
398	Devil's food with chocolate frosting, 1/16 of cake	1 piece	69	235	3	8	37	41	1.4	181	31	Tr
	Cookies, commercial:											
424	Brownies with nuts and frosting	1 brownie	25	100	1	4	14	13	0.6	59	18	Tr
426	Chocolate chip, 2¼-in. diam.	4 cookies	42	180	2	9	5	13	0.8	140	15	Tr
429	Fig bars, square, 1⅝ in. square	4 cookies	56	210	2	4	27	40	1.4	180	6	Tr
430	Oatmeal with raisins, 2⅝-in. diam.	4 cookies	52	245	3	10	2	18	1.1	148	12	0
437	Corn chips	1-oz pkg.	28	155	2	9	0	35	0.5	233	11	1
	Crackers:											
444	Graham, plain, 2½ in. square	2 crackers	14	60	1	1	0	6	0.4	86	0	0
448	Snack-type, standard	1 cracker	3	15	Tr	1	0	3	0.1	30	Tr	0
449	Wheat, thin	4 crackers	8	35	1	1	0	3	0.3	69	Tr	0
	Doughnuts, made with enriched flour:											
456	Cake type, plain, 3¼-in. diam.	1 doughnut	50	210	3	12	20	22	1.0	192	5	Tr
457	Yeast-leavened, glazed, 3¾-in. diam.	1 doughnut	60	235	4	13	21	17	1.4	222	Tr	0

458	English muffins, plain, enriched	1 muffin	57	140	5	1	0	96	1.7	378	0	0
461	Macaroni, enriched, cooked	1 cup	130	190	7	1	0	14	2.1	1	0	0
	Muffins, 2½-in. diam., commercial mix:											
467	Blueberry	1 muffin	45	140	3	5	45	15	0.9	225	11	Tr
468	Bran	1 muffin	45	140	3	4	28	27	1.7	385	14	0
470	Noodles (egg noodles), enriched, cooked	1 cup	160	200	7	2	50	16	2.6	3	34	0
	Pancakes, 4-in. diam.:											
474	Plain, from mix (with enriched flour), egg, milk, and oil added	1 pancake	27	60	2	2	16	36	0.7	160	7	Tr
	Pies, 9-in. diam:											
478	Apple, ⅙ of pie	1 piece	158	405	3	18	0	13	1.6	476	5	2
488	Lemon meringue, ⅙ of pie	1 piece	140	355	5	14	143	20	1.4	395	66	4
494	Pumpkin, ⅙ of pie	1 piece	152	320	6	17	109	78	1.4	325	416	0
	Popcorn, popped:											
497	Air-popped, unsalted	1 cup	8	30	1	Tr	0	1	0.2	Tr	1	0
498	Popped in vegetable oil, salted	1 cup	11	55	1	3	0	3	0.3	86	2	0
499	Sugar syrup coated	1 cup	35	135	2	1	0	2	0.5	Tr	3	0
500	Pretzels, stick, 2¼ in. long	10 pretzels	3	10	Tr	Tr	0	1	0.1	48	0	0
	Rice:											
503	Brown, cooked, served hot	1 cup	195	230	5	1	0	23	1.0	0	0	0
505	White, enriched, cooked, served hot	1 cup	205	225	4	Tr	0	21	1.8	0	0	0
	Rolls, enriched, commercial											
509	Dinner, 2½-in. diam.	1 roll	28	85	2	2	Tr	33	0.8	155	Tr	Tr
510	Frankfurter and hamburger	1 roll	40	115	3	2	Tr	54	1.2	241	Tr	Tr
514	Spaghetti, enriched, cooked	1 cup	130	190	7	1	0	14	2.0	1	0	0
	Legumes, Nuts, and Seeds											
526	Almonds, shelled, whole	1 oz	28	165	6	15	0	75	1.0	3	0	Tr
	Beans, dry, cooked, drained:											
527	Black	1 cup	171	225	15	1	0	47	2.9	1	Tr	0
528	Great Northern	1 cup	180	210	14	1	0	90	4.9	13	0	0
531	Pinto	1 cup	180	265	15	1	0	86	5.4	3	Tr	0
536	Black-eyed peas, dry, cooked (with cooking liquid)	1 cup	250	190	13	1	0	43	3.3	20	3	0
544	Chickpeas, cooked, drained	1 cup	163	270	15	4	0	80	4.9	11	Tr	0
550	Lentils, dry, cooked, with peanuts	1 cup	200	215	16	1	0	50	4.2	26	4	0
553	Mixed nuts, dry roasted, salted	1 oz	28	170	5	15	0	20	1.0	190	Tr	0
555	Peanuts, roasted in oil, salted	1 cup	145	840	39	71	0	125	2.8	626	0	0
557	Peanut butter	1 tbsp	16	95	5	8	0	5	0.3	75	0	0
564	Refried beans, canned	1 cup	290	295	18	3	0	141	5.1	1,228	0	17
	Soy products:											
567	Miso	1 cup	276	470	29	13	0	188	4.7	8,142	11	0
568	Tofu, piece 2½ by 2¾ by 1 in.	1 piece	120	85	9	5	0	108	2.3	8	0	0
569	Sunflower seeds, dry, hulled	1 oz	28	160	6	14	0	33	1.9	1	1	Tr
570	Tahini	1 tbsp	15	90	3	8	0	21	0.7	5	1	1

Item No.	Food Description	Approximate Measure	Weight	Food energy	Protein	Fat	Cholesterol	Calcium	Iron	Sodium	Vitamin A value*	Vitamin C
				Nutrients in Indicated Quantity								
			Grams	Calories	Grams	Grams	Milligrams	Milligrams	Milligrams	Milligrams	Retinol equivalents	Milligrams
	Meat and Meat Products											
	Beef, cooked, braised, or pot roasted:											
575	Chuck blade, lean and fat, piece	3 oz	85	325	22	26	87	11	2.5	53	Tr	0
577	Round, bottom, lean and fat, piece	3 oz	85	220	25	13	81	5	2.8	43	Tr	0
578	Lean only from item 577	2.8 oz	78	175	25	8	75	4	2.7	40	Tr	0
580	Ground beef, regular, broiled, patty	3 oz	85	245	20	18	76	9	2.1	70	Tr	0
585	Round, eye of, lean and fat, roasted	3 oz	85	205	23	12	62	5	1.6	50	Tr	0
587	Sirloin, steak, broiled, lean and fat	3 oz	85	240	23	15	77	9	2.6	53	Tr	0
590	Beef, dried, chipped	2.5 oz	72	145	24	4	46	14	2.3	3,053	Tr	0
	Lamb:											
593	Chops, loin, broiled, lean and fat	2.8 oz	80	235	22	16	78	16	1.4	62	Tr	0
	Pork, cured, cooked:											
599	Bacon, regular	3 slices	19	110	6	9	16	2	0.3	303	0	6
601	Ham, light cure, roasted, lean and fat	3 oz	85	205	18	14	53	6	0.7	1,009	0	0
	Luncheon meat:											
605	Chopped ham (8 slices per 6 oz pkg)	2 slices	42	95	7	7	2`	3	0.3	576	0	8
	Pork, fresh, cooked:											
610	Chop, loin, pan fried, lean and fat	3.1 oz	89	335	21	27	92	4	0.7	64	3	Tr
614	Rib, roasted, lean and fat	3 oz	85	270	21	20	69	9	0.8	37	3	Tr
	Sausages											
618	Bologna, slice (8 per 8-oz pkg)	2 slices	57	180	7	16	31	7	0.9	581	0	12
620	Brown and serve, browned	1 link	13	50	2	5	9	1	0.1	105	0	0
621	Frankfurter cooked (reheated)	1	45	145	5	13	23	5	0.5	504	0	12
	Mixed Dishes and Fast Foods											
	Mixed dishes:											
629	Beef and vegetable stew, home recipe	1 cup	245	220	16	11	71	29	2.9	292	568	17
631	Chicken a la king, home recipe	1 cup	245	470	27	34	221	127	2.5	760	272	12
642	Spaghetti in tomato sauce with cheese, home recipe	1 cup	250	260	9	9	8	80	2.3	955	140	13
	Fast food entrees:											
645	Cheeseburger, regular	1 sandwich	112	300	15	15	44	135	2.3	672	65	1
648	English muffin, egg, cheese, bacon	1 sandwich	138	360	18	18	213	197	3.1	832	160	1
649	Fish sandwich, regular, with cheese	1 sandwich	140	420	16	23	56	132	1.8	667	25	2
651	Hamburger, regular	1 sandwich	98	245	12	11	32	56	2.2	463	14	1
653	Pizza, cheese, ⅛ of 15-in. diam.	1 slice	120	290	15	9	56	220	1.6	699	106	2
654	Roast beef sandwich	1 sandwich	150	345	22	13	55	60	4.0	757	32	2
655	Taco	1 taco	81	195	9	11	21	109	1.2	456	57	1

No.	Food	Measure	Weight									
	Poultry and Poultry Products											
	Chicken:											
	Fried, flesh, with skin and bones:											
656	Breast, ½ breast, batter dipped	4.9 oz	140	365	35	18	119	28	1.8	385	28	0
657	Drumstick, batter dipped	2.5 oz	72	195	16	11	62	12	1.0	194	19	0
	Roasted, flesh only:											
660	Breast, ½ breast	3.0 oz	86	140	27	3	73	13	0.9	64	5	0
662	Stewed, flesh only, light and dark meat	1 cup	140	250	38	9	116	20	1.6	98	21	0
	Turkey, roasted, flesh only:											
665	Dark meat, piece, 2½ by 1⅝ by ¼ in.	4 pieces	85	160	24	6	72	27	2.0	67	0	0
666	Light meat, piece, 4 by 2 by ¼ in.	2 pieces	85	135	25	3	59	16	1.1	54	0	0
667	Chopped or diced	1 cup	140	240	41	7	106	35	2.5	98	0	0
	Soups, Sauces, and Gravies											
	Soups, condensed:											
	Canned, prepared with milk:											
679	Cream of mushroom	1 cup	248	205	6	14	20	179	0.6	1,076	37	2
680	Tomato	1 cup	248	160	6	6	17	159	1.8	932	109	68
	Canned, prepared with water:											
681	Bean with bacon	1 cup	253	170	8	6	3	81	2.0	951	89	2
682	Beef broth, bouillon, consomme	1 cup	240	15	3	1	Tr	14	0.4	782	0	0
684	Chicken noodle	1 cup	241	75	4	2	7	17	0.8	1,106	71	Tr
693	Vegetarian	1 cup	241	70	2	2	0	22	1.1	822	301	1
	Dehydrated, prepared with water:											
697	Onion	1 pkt (6-fl-oz)	184	20	1	Tr	0	9	0.1	635	Tr	Tr
	Sauces, ready to serve:											
703	Barbecue	1 tbsp	16	10	Tr	Tr	0	3	0.1	130	14	1
704	Soy	1 tbsp	18	10	2	0	0	3	0.5	1,029	0	0
	Gravies:											
708	Brown, from dry mix	1 cup	261	80	3	2	2	66	0.2	1,147	0	0
709	Chicken, from dry mix	1 cup	260	85	3	2	3	39	0.3	1,134	0	3
	Sugars and Sweets											
	Candy:											
711	Chocolate, milk, plain	1 oz	28	145	2	9	6	50	0.4	23	10	Tr
712	Chocolate, milk, with almonds	1 oz	28	150	3	10	5	65	0.5	23	8	Tr
717	Fondant, uncoated (mints, other)	1 oz	28	105	Tr	0	0	2	0.1	57	0	0
720	Hard candy	1 oz	28	110	0	0	0	Tr	0.1	7	0	0
723	Custard, baked	1 cup	265	305	14	15	278	297	1.1	209	146	1
724	Gelatin dessert	½ cup	120	70	2	0	0	2	Tr	55	0	0
726	Honey, strained or extracted	1 tbsp	21	65	Tr	0	0	1	0.1	1	0	Tr
727	Jams and preserves	1 tbsp	20	55	Tr	Tr	0	4	0.2	2	Tr	Tr
739	Pudding, vanilla, instant	½ cup	130	150	4	4	15	129	0.1	375	33	1

Item No.	Food Description	Approximate Measure	Weight	Food energy	Protein	Fat	Cholesterol	Calcium	Iron	Sodium	Vitamin A value*	Vitamin C
				Nutrients in Indicated Quantity								
			Grams	Calories	Grams	Grams	Milligrams	Milligrams	Milligrams	Milligrams	Retinol equivalents	Milligrams
	Sugars:											
741	Brown, pressed down	1 cup	220	820	0	0	0	187	4.8	97	0	0
742	White, granulated	1 tbsp	12	45	0	0	0	Tr	Tr	Tr	0	0
745	White, powdered, sifted	1 cup	100	385	0	0	0	1	Tr	2	0	0
	Syrups:											
748	Molasses, cane, blackstrap	2 tbsp	40	85	0	0	0	274	10.1	38	0	0
749	Table syrup (corn and maple)	2 tbsp	42	122	0	0	0	1	Tr	19	0	0
	Vegetables and Vegetable Products											
750	Alfalfa seeds, sprouted, raw	1 cup	33	10	1	Tr	0	11	0.3	2	5	3
	Beans, snap, cooked, drained:											
761	From frozen (cut)	1 cup	135	35	2	Tr	0	61	1.1	18	71	11
	Broccoli:											
771	Raw	1 spear	151	40	4	1	0	72	1.3	41	233	141
772	Cooked	1 spear	180	50	5	1	0	82	2.1	20	254	113
	Cabbage, common varieties:											
778	Raw, coarsely shredded or sliced	1 cup	70	15	1	Tr	0	33	0.4	13	9	33
	Cabbage, Chinese:											
780	Pak-choi, cooked, drained	1 cup	170	20	3	Tr	0	158	1.8	58	437	44
	Carrots:											
784	Whole, 7½ by 1⅛ in.	1 carrot	72	30	1	Tr	0	19	0.4	25	2,025	7
786	Cooked, sliced, drained, from raw	1 cup	156	70	2	Tr	0	48	1.0	103	3,830	4
	Celery, pascal type, raw:											
792	Stalk, large outer, 8 by 1½ in.	1 stalk	40	5	Tr	Tr	0	14	0.2	35	5	3
	Collards, cooked, drained:											
795	From frozen (chopped)	1 cup	170	60	5	1	0	357	1.9	85	1,017	45
	Corn, sweet:											
	Cooked, drained:											
796	From raw, ear 5 by 1¾ in.	1 ear	77	85	3	1	0	2	0.5	13	17	5
798	From frozen kernels	1 cup	165	135	5	Tr	0	3	0.5	8	41	4
	Canned:											
799	Cream style	1 cup	256	185	4	1	0	8	1.0	730	25	12
800	Whole kernel, vacuum pack	1 cup	210	165	5	1	0	11	0.9	571	51	17
801	Cucumber, with peel, slices ⅛ in. thick, 2⅛-in. diam.	6 slices	28	5	Tr	Tr	0	4	0.1	1	1	1
806	Kale, cooked, drained, from raw	1 cup	130	40	2	1	0	94	1.2	30	962	53

	Lettuce, raw:											
813	Crisp head, as iceberg, chopped	1 cup	55	5	1	Tr	0	10	0.3	5	18	2
814	Loose leaf, chopped or shredded	1 cup	56	10	1	Tr	0	38	0.8	5	106	10
830	Peas, green, frozen, cooked, drained	1 cup	160	125	8	Tr	0	38	2.5	139	107	16
832	Peppers, sweet, raw	1 pepper	74	20	1	Tr	0	4	0.9	2	39	95
	Potatoes, cooked:											
834	Baked, with skin	1 potato	202	220	5	Tr	0	20	2.7	16	0	26
	French fried, strip, frozen:											
838	Oven heated	10 strips	50	110	2	4	0	5	0.7	16	0	5
839	Fried in vegetable oil	10 strips	50	160	2	8	0	10	0.4	108	0	5
849	Potato chips	10 chips	20	105	1	7	0	5	0.2	94	0	8
852	Radishes, raw	4 radishes	18	5	Tr	Tr	0	4	0.1	4	Tr	4
	Spinach:											
856	Raw, chopped	1 cup	55	10	2	Tr	0	54	1.5	43	369	15
858	Cooked, drained, from frozen (leaf)	1 cup	190	55	6	Tr	0	277	2.9	163	1,479	23
	Squash, cooked:											
861	Summer, sliced, drained	1 cup	180	35	2	1	0	49	0.6	2	52	10
862	Winter, baked, cubes	1 cup	205	80	2	1	0	29	0.7	2	729	20
863	Sweet potatoes, baked in skin, peeled	1 potato	114	115	2	Tr	0	32	0.5	11	2,488	28
	Tomatoes:											
868	Raw, 2⅗-in. diam.	1 tomato	123	25	1	Tr	0	9	0.6	10	139	22
869	Canned, solids and liquid	1 cup	240	50	2	1	0	62	1.5	391	145	36
870	Tomato juice, canned	1 cup	244	40	2	Tr	0	22	1.4	881	136	45
877	Vegetable juice cocktail, canned	1 cup	242	45	2	Tr	0	27	1.0	883	283	67
	Miscellaneous Items											
885	Catsup	1 cup	273	290	5	1	0	60	2.2	2,845	382	41
894	Mustard, prepared, yellow	1 tsp	5	5	Tr	Tr	0	4	0.1	63	0	Tr
895	Olives, canned, green, medium	4	13	15	Tr	2	0	8	0.2	312	4	0
	Pickles, cucumber:											
901	Dill, medium, whole, 3¾ in.	1 pickle	65	5	Tr	Tr	0	17	0.7	928	7	4
903	Sweet, small, whole, 2½ in. long	1 pickle	15	20	Tr	Tr	0	2	0.2	107	1	1

*1 RE = 3.33 IU from animal foods or 1 mcg retinol.
1 RE = 10 IU from plant foods or 6 mcg beta carotene.
Tr = Trace amount.
Source: USDA Home and Garden Bulletin No. 72, "Nutritive Value of Foods"

NOTE: Nutritive values of most packaged foods may be obtained from the "Nutrition Facts" label on the container.

Index

A

B

C

D

E

F

G

H

N

O

P

Q

R

S

T

U

V

W

Y

Z